BASIC ELECTRICITY FOR ELECTRONICS

Robert Middleton

Milton Goldstein

DEAN AND DIRECTOR OF RESEARCH
AMERICAN INSTITUTE OF ENGINEERING AND TECHNOLOGY
CHICAGO, ILLINOIS

HOLT, RINEHART AND WINSTON, INC.

NEW YORK · CHICAGO · SAN FRANCISCO · TORONTO · LONDON

Library of Congress Catalog Card Number: 66–10519
25704–0116

September, 1966

Printed in the United States of America

PREFACE

ELECTRONICS IS THE FASTEST-GROWING AREA of science and technology. Until recently, it was defined as the formulation of laws governing the flow and control of electrons in vacuum tubes. This definition did not include borderline phenomena, such as conduction by gases in thyratrons, spark gaps, and arcs. Nevertheless, texts often included extensive discussions of gas-tube characteristics and the laws of gaseous conduction. With the advent of the transistor in 1948, solid-state physics entered the picture, and electronics textbooks promptly included extensive treatments of electric-current flow in crystal lattices.

Today, electronics includes numerous specialized branches, such as computers, radio, television, automation control, radar, instrumentation, pure research, servomechanisms, and microelectronics. Nevertheless, all these diversified areas have a common denominator, which can be appropriately termed *basic electricity and electronics.*

The intent of the authors in this book is to present clearly the fundamentals of twentieth-century electricity and electronics. The book is designed for use in a first course in the electricity/electronics sequence, and is intended primarily to fulfill the needs of the beginning technology student.

The book begins with a brief review of the history of electricity, covering the events that led to the concept of the electron. Atomic structure is treated to the extent required by the beginning student. Descriptive relations between various forms of energy are explained early. The topical coverage progresses to the concept of a closed circuit, and the laws governing voltage, current, and power. An analysis of series, parallel, and series-parallel circuitry is followed by a discussion of testing and measuring equipment. The treatment is both descriptive and analytical, supplemented by a presentation of practical considerations to provide a valid perspective.

Magnetic circuits are analyzed with the beginning student in mind. Unlike other texts, the analysis is presented in terms of English units. Conversion tables are provided for metric units. Alternating current, voltage, reactance, and impedance are presented graphically, insofar as possible. The reader will find minimum difficulty in visualizing and solving a-c circuit problems. Various analogies with d-c situations are drawn. Semiconductor circuit analysis is presented graphically, wherever feasible. Basic filter networks are presented with due stress on the vital resistance parameters. Elementary network theorems are applied to those circuit situations which clearly exhibit the strategy and tactics of analysis.

No mathematics other than algebra and trigonometry are required. Considerable attention is given to basic distinctions between pure mathematics and physical situations. Solved problems are introduced at intervals to illustrate methods of attack. Unnecessary labor in computation is avoided by the provision of tables of squares, square roots, conversion factors, and dimensions. A section covering both generalized and specialized slide rules is included in the Appendix. Analytical treatment of nonlinear resistance is restricted to linear approximations, supplemented by examples of graphical solutions. These graphical analyses include piece-wise constructions, to provide an introduction to the elements of the calculus.

This book is a teaching tool. It is respectfully dedicated to junior-college, community-college, and technical-institute students.

ROBERT MIDDLETON
MILTON GOLDSTEIN

Lafayette, California
Chicago, Illinois
January 1966

CONTENTS

1

ELECTRONS AND ELECTRICITY

1.1 HISTORICAL BACKGROUND

It is probable that prehistoric man experienced electricity only in the form of lightning, which he interpreted as a manifestation of divine wrath. Anthropologists assert that man's first million (or possibly three million) years was lived in almost total ignorance of natural laws. Proof that lightning is an electrical phenomenon was first made by Benjamin Franklin. Although a few isolated and arbitrary physical facts were noted in the Rhind papyrus of 2000 B.C., there was no organized science at that time. This papyrus was written by Ahmes, an Egyptian, prior to 1700 B.C., and records facts that were known as early as 3400 B.C. It was translated in 1877 by Eisenlohr, and is on display in the Rhind collection of the British Museum.

The recorded history of electrical science and technology starts in 600 B.C., when the Greek philosopher Thales wrote of the curious attraction which an iron ore, later called lodestone, exerted upon iron. This ore, now termed magnetite, was first discovered at Magnesia, in Asia Minor, from which the word *magnet* is derived. The ancients also discovered that the earth is a weak magnet, and that a lodestone orients itself approximately in a North-and-South direction when suspended by a string, or placed on a float in a vessel of water. The word *lodestone* originally meant "leading stone."

A modern visualization of the earth's magnetic characteristics is seen in Figure 1-1. The ancients observed certain facts of magnetic polarity. They recognized not only that a lodestone orients itself in a North-and-South direction, but that the *same* end of the lodestone always points in the approximate direction of the North Star. The Asians knew that unlike magnetic polarities attract, and that like magnetic polarities repel. They recognized that the north end of a lodestone has opposite magnetic polarity from the earth's North Pole; that is, the north pole of a lodestone is a North-seeking pole. The lodestone's north pole accordingly has South magnetic polarity. The term *North Pole* always refers to the earth's magnetic polarity; however, the term *north pole* is applied to the North-seeking pole of a compass needle.

Magnetite is an iron oxide, Fe_3O_4; it has no inherent magnetic action. Modern physicists believe that lodestone has been magnetized by lightning strokes, or by the magnetism of the earth. The source of the earth's magnetism is still unknown. Scientists have not penetrated the crust of the earth deeply enough to determine what causes terrestrial magnetism. Thus, the visualization of Figure 1-1 has no scientific basis; it is only an "as if" picture of the earth's magnetic properties. We know that the earth's magnetic poles do not remain fixed, either in position or intensity. Over a period of years, the magnetic North and South poles change their

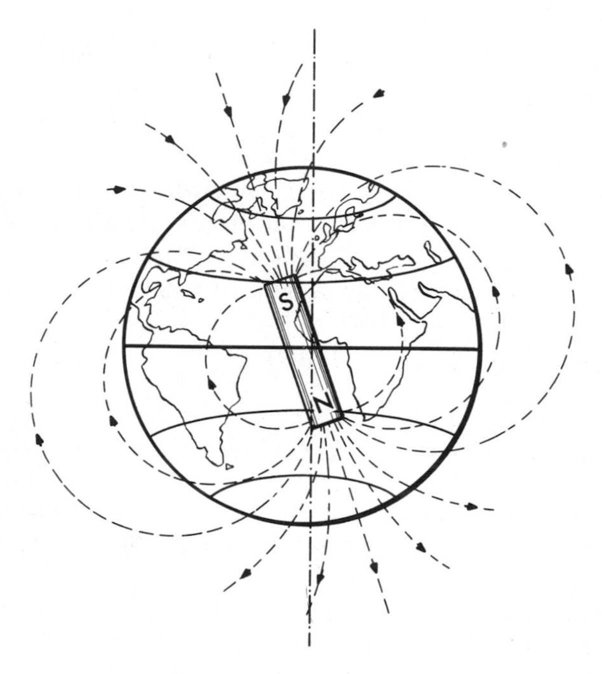

Figure 1-1
An "as if" visualization of the earth's magnetic field.

geographical location. The strength of the earth's magnetic field also varies somewhat.

MAGNETIC AND ELECTRIC "ACTION AT A DISTANCE"

Thales also investigated natural phenomena other than magnetism. He recorded the attraction which amber, when rubbed, exerts upon pieces of straw. The Greek name for amber is "elektron," from which the modern term *electron* is derived. Thales observed some basic principles of electric polarity. He noted that electrified substances could repel or attract one another in different circumstances. The ancients were mystified by both magnetic and electric "action at a distance." This has remained essentially a mystery to this day, although many additional laws of electricity and magnetism have been discovered. "Action at a distance" classically refers to something that happens at one point in space because something else happened at a distant point, with no visible means to relate cause and effect.

In 460 B.C., Democritus asserted that all substances are built up from tiny indivisible particles called "atomos," from which the word *atom* is derived. However, Democritus could give no convincing proof of his theory. The Greeks had no useful concept of chemistry. They believed that there were only four elements: earth, air, fire, and water, which combined in some mysterious manner to form all other substances. Nevertheless, the Greeks handed down the concept of pure science, which is a quest after knowledge for its own sake. They also developed the principles of mathematical reasoning, which is the handmaiden of the exact sciences. Electronics is an exact science because it concerns itself chiefly with mathematical discussions of pertinent phenomena.

As is explained in Appendix I, Greek mathematics was not basically adapted to a description of physical phenomena. The Greeks were geometers first, and arithmeticians last. They failed to conceive of a symbol for zero, a cipher that corresponds to the metaphysical nothing, or naught. Classicists cannot explain why Greek philosophers did not confront the startling fact that nothing is more real than nothing. This deficiency is manifest in Grecian art, no less than in their mathematics. Since arithmetic contributes much more to the exact sciences than geometry, Thales and Democritus were seriously handicapped.

LACK OF PROGRESS DURING THE MEDIEVAL PERIOD IN HISTORY

Following the period of Grecian enlightenment, scientific progress remained virtually at a standstill for more than 2000 years, while new cultures and subcultures slowly evolved. Men have always found it difficult to reject the assumption that all things in nature were created for a purpose as part of a humanly ordered plan. Eventually, William Gilbert, an English physician, succeeded in extending the knowledge gained by Thales. Gilbert exploded the conception that electrical attraction by amber is the same as magnetic attraction by lodestone. He proved by experiment that "the magnetical motions are widely different from the forces of amber." Accordingly, in A.D. 1600, the science of electrostatics was clearly separated from the science of magnetism. Gilbert defined electric polarity. He stipulated that, when glass is rubbed by silk, the glass is *positively* electrified, and the silk is *negatively* electrified.

Modern scientists have compiled the so-called *electric series*, based on Gilbert's work. Table 1-1 lists a number of familiar substances in this order. If one substance is rubbed by a following substance, the first will acquire a positive charge, and the second will acquire a negative charge.

Table 1-1

THE ELECTRIC SERIES

Fur	Glass	Metals	Resin
Wool	Silk	Hard rubber	Sulfur
Quartz	Wood	Sealing-wax	Gun-cotton

For example, if glass is rubbed by wood, the glass becomes positively electrified, and the wood becomes negatively electrified.

UNLIKE POLARITIES ATTRACT; LIKE POLARITIES REPEL

Charles Coulomb, a French physicist, followed up these discoveries. He investigated the *quantitative* relation between the electrostatic forces exerted by two charges at various distances. With the aid of a sensitive balance, Coulomb proved that the force exerted between two charged bodies varies inversely as the square of the distance between them. Other scientists discovered that the electrostatic force varies directly as the product of the two quantities of charge. It was then possible to state a comprehensive law that has become known as Coulomb's law of electrostatic force:

$$f = \frac{Q_1 Q_2}{k d^2} \tag{1.1}$$

Q_1 and Q_2 are the two quantities of electric charge, d is the distance between the charges, f is the force that acts in a straight line joining the two charges, and k is a constant, the value of which depends on the medium in which the two charges are placed. For example, k has a different value when the charges are placed in oil, instead of air. In turn, f will have a different value. The electrostatic force acts equally, as we might expect, on both of the charges.

The value of k is greater for any insulating medium (such as air or oil) than for a vacuum. Thus, the force between two electric charges is less when they are placed in oil, instead of a vacuum. Again, the force is slightly less when the charges are placed in air, instead of a vacuum. We call k the *dielectric coefficient* of an insulating medium; its value is defined as unity in a vacuum. Values of k for familiar dielectrics such as oils, glass, mica, and sulfur fall in the range from 1 to 10. (See Table 1-2.) The value of k for air is approximately 1.0006; this value is so near to 1 that the dielectric coefficient of air is taken as 1 in all practical work.

Up to the time of Coulomb, electricity was known only as stationary charges on substances, or as miniature lightning discharges produced by static machines [see Figure 1-2(a)]. You have probably become familiar with static machines in your physics courses.

(*a*)

Figure 1-2

(*a*) View of a Wimshurst electrostatic generator. (Illustration courtesy Edmund Scientific Co., Barrington, New Jersey. (*b*) An electric eel, generating electricity.

(*Continued on p. 6*)

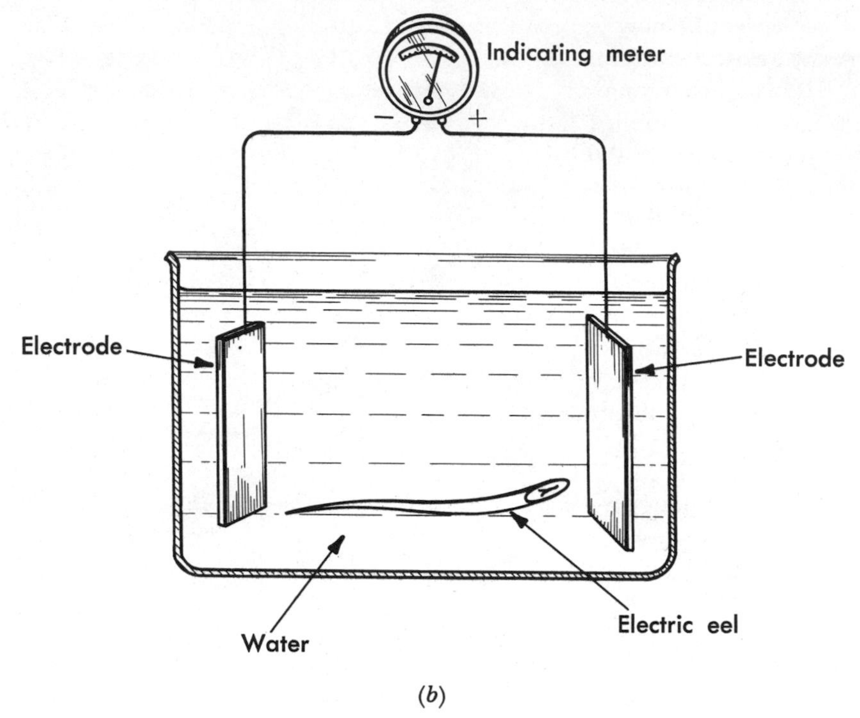

(*b*)

Fig. 1-2 (*Continued*)

Some scientist, whose name has been lost to history, duplicated the experiment of Benjamin Franklin in the biological domain, and demonstrated that an electric eel generates electric currents, as depicted in Figure 1-2(*b*). This type of fish can inflict painful electric shocks.

Two hundred years passed after Gilbert made his basic discoveries in electrostatics before Alessandro Volta developed the *voltaic pile*, which for the first time provided a sustained and steady flow of electric current. Volta used chemical action, instead of mechanical friction, to generate electricity. The term for electric "pressure" or electromotive force, the

Table 1-2

DIELECTRIC COEFFICIENTS

Substance	*Value*	*Substance*	*Value*
Vacuum	1.0	Sulfur	2.2–4.0
Air	1.0006	Mica	6.0–8.0
Paraffin wax	2.0–2.3	Glass	6.6–9.9
Petroleum	2.07	Distilled water	75.0
Hard rubber	2.0–3.1	Alcohol	25.0

volt, honors this pioneer investigator. Thenceforth, progress was rapid. Physicists could now experiment with electricity under controlled and clearly defined conditions.

Electric charges will not flow of their own accord along a wire. Energy must be applied to move them. The amount of energy consumed per unit charge moved is called *electromotive force,* abbreviated emf. It is the *potential difference* between the two points, measured in volts. The *volt* is defined as the potential difference existing between two points when one unit of work is done in moving one unit of electric charge from one point to the other. Note carefully that although the volt is basically a measure of work per unit charge, a very common and often more satisfactory interpretation is that voltage is an electrical pressure that causes electric charges to move. Units of work, charge, and distance are reserved for subsequent discussion.

$$W = q(V_1 - V_2) \tag{1.2}$$

This formula expresses the amount of work done by a quantity of electricity q when it flows from a point at the potential V_1 to another point at the potential V_2. Accordingly, the potential difference or emf between two points is the ratio of work to electrical quantity: $(V_1 - V_2) = W/q$.

ELECTRICITY IS RELATED TO MAGNETISM

In 1820, Hans Christian Oersted discovered that electricity and magnetism are not isolated phenomena, as Gilbert had surmised. Oersted observed that an electric current exerts action at a distance upon a compass needle, as illustrated in Figure 1-3. His experiments proved that electricity *in motion* is an *electromagnetic* phenomenon.

Oersted's work was extended by Andre Marie Ampere, who first constructed an electromagnet (see Figure 1-4), and disclosed the laws relating magnetic polarities to electric polarities. Ampere theorized that

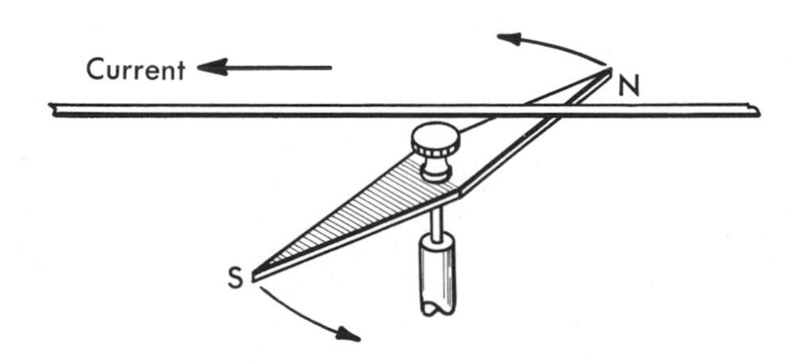

Figure 1-3
Current-carrying wire in the vicinity of a compass needle.

the source of magnetism in lodestones and compass needles might be due to electric currents in atoms, a theory that has been fully verified in recent times. Ampere also proposed the possibility of devising a magnetic telegraph. It is appropriate that the rate of current flow, the *ampere,* has been named after this brilliant investigator.

In 1821, Michael Faraday developed the first electric motor, thus ushering in the modern electrical age. Faraday also discovered that a moving magnet exerts action at a distance upon a wire, and induces electric current in the wire. (See Figure 1-5.) This discovery marked the birth of the electric generator. The unit of capacitance, the *farad,* was named in Faraday's honor.

You may have made the experiment depicted in Figure 1-5 during your physics courses. A galvanometer is a sensitive current indicator,

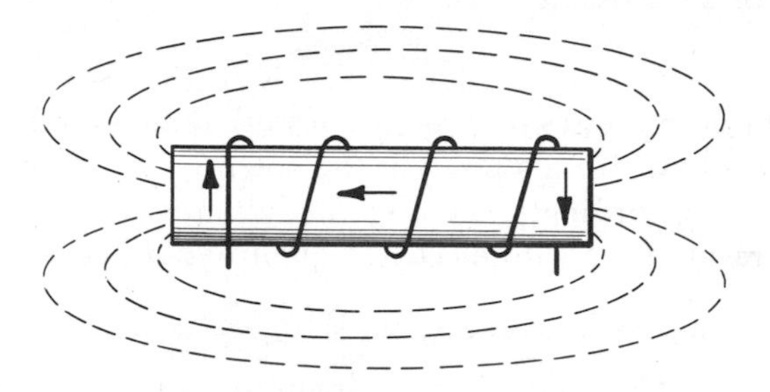

Figure 1-4
Basic straight-bar electromagnet.

which operates on the principle illustrated in Figure 1-3. When the magnet is moved (Figure 1-5), the galvanometer deflects. However, when the magnet is motionless, the galvanometer is not deflected. A lodestone can be used in place of an artificial permanent magnet; also, an electromagnet (Figure 1-4) can be used instead of a lodestone in this experiment. We shall return to detailed analysis of this principle in subsequent chapters.

In Faraday's period, the necessity for mathematical treatment of electrical data was brought into sharp focus. For example, George Simon Ohm published a famous book in 1827, entitled *The Galvanic Chain.* Ohm's researches disclosed the entity of electrical resistance as a basic analytic unit. He related the unit of resistance to the unit of current flow and to the unit of electromotive force. Today, *Ohm's law* is thoroughly familiar to every electrical student. It is highly appropriate that the unit of electrical resistance has been named the *ohm.* Ohm's law is written as follows:

$$I = \frac{E}{R} \tag{1.3}$$

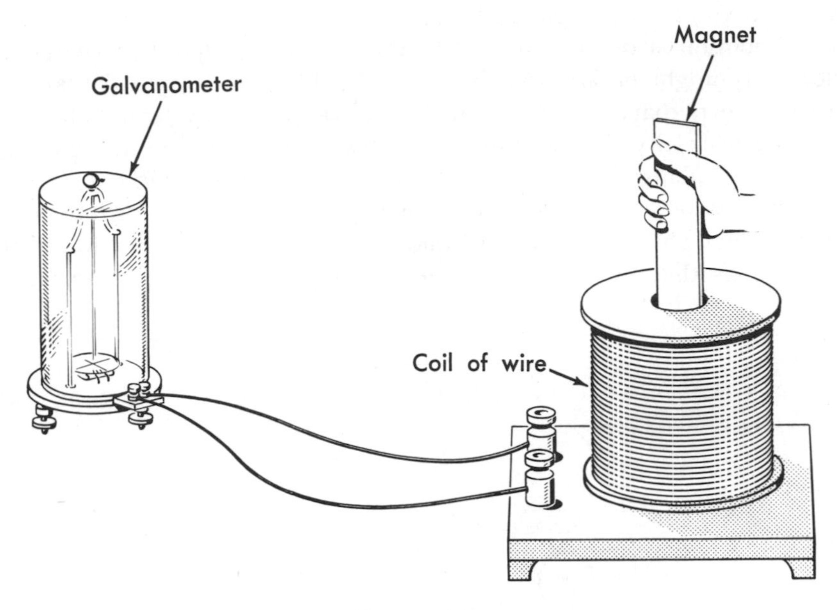

Figure 1-5
A moving magnet, inducing electric current in a wire.

where I equals the current in amperes, E equals the electromotive force in volts, and R equals the resistance in ohms. Note that the symbol I was originally chosen to represent the *intensity* of current flow.

1.2 THE DAWN OF ELECTRONICS

Early workers supposed electricity to be some form of subtle fluid, or perhaps two fluids, corresponding to positive electricity and negative electricity. Benjamin Franklin accepted the fluid hypothesis. Even to this day it is found convenient to compare the flow of electricity in wires with the flow of water in pipes. Although this analogy cannot be pressed too far without leading to absurdities, it is nonetheless quite useful in restricted discussions. But the notion of a "subtle fluid" was exploded in 1896 by the physicist J. J. Thomson. He discovered that the blue streams of light produced by electric current flow in partially evacuated glass tubes were associated with tiny electric charges. These particles of electricity were soon to be called *electrons.*

Researches of the Curies and others concerning the disintegration of radium led to the conclusion that electrons not only flow as electric current, but that electrons are also a fundamental building-block of all substances. By 1908, studies of heat laws placed the atomic theory of matter beyond any reasonable doubt.

Thomson strove to conceive how electrons and positive charges of electricity might be arranged in atoms. In 1907, he suggested that electrons were perhaps distributed within a comparatively large volume of positive electricity. A conception of Thomson's atom is seen in Figure 1-6. This was a plausible hypothesis because positive and negative electricity attract each other, and they must somehow come to equilibrium in an atom. Other physicists, however, conducted experiments which forced the conclusions that the positive charge in an atom is restricted to an extremely small space, and that the electrons must be disposed outside of the positive charge in some manner.

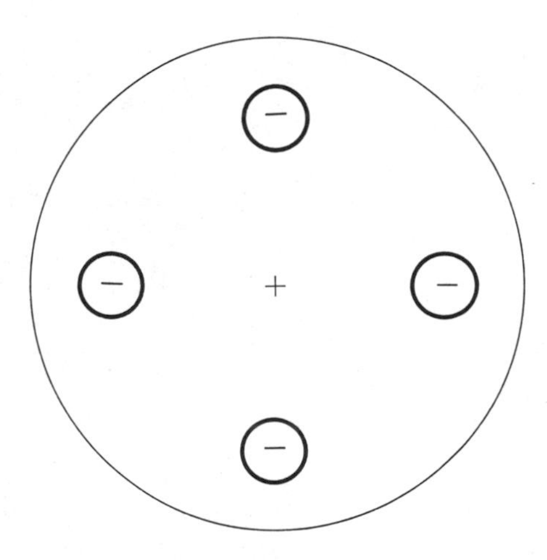

Figure 1-6
Thomson's concept of atomic structure.

It was further discovered that, although the positive charge in a simple atom such as a hydrogen atom is restricted to an extremely small volume, the positive charge nevertheless has a much greater mass than that of an electron. Thus, the hypothesis of "large" and light electrons disposed outside "small" and heavy positive charges presented a serious difficulty. Physicists were confronted with the nagging question of why electrons, presumably at rest in an atom, do not fall into the central positive charge. It was undeniable that, although electrons approach the central positive charge in an atom, some unknown factor was present that imposed a definite limit to the approach distance. What is it that determines the closeness to which an electron can approach the central positive charge?

In this period, astronomy was comparatively far advanced, which understandably led to the proposal that the atom is a miniature solar system, with its electrons moving in orbits as the planets move about the sun. But then, another difficulty was pointed out. For reasons to be explained subsequently, it was recognized that orbiting electrons would be expected to gradually lose their energy of motion, and spiral into the central positive charge (nucleus) of the atom. Radical new concepts were imminent, and new laws of electricity were to appear. In 1913, Niels Bohr broke abruptly with classical electrical theory in his analysis of atomic structure. He boldly asserted that new and unexpected laws hold sway when electric charges are separated by extremely small distances.

Bohr postulated that certain orbits exist near the nucleus in which the classical laws of electricity do *not* apply, and that electrons can move in these orbits without losing their energy of motion and falling into the nucleus. This was a disturbing assertion. Many scientists found it exceedingly difficult to admit that established laws of electricity are abruptly "repealed" at atomic distances. Physicists sought in every possible way to avoid this heretic approach. However, all efforts were fruitless, and the Bohr atom with its new laws of electrical action had to be accepted as a valid description of nature's elementary particles and their behavior. Bohr's theory of atomic structure gradually became elaborated, modified, and cast into more general forms until it retained only an ancestral resemblance to its 1913 context.

1.3 ATOMIC STRUCTURE

It is a fundamental present-day concept that all matter behaves as if it were built up from invisible particles. A *molecule* is a unit of matter. It is the smallest particle of an element or a chemical combination of atoms. The molecule is also the smallest particle of a substance that is capable of retaining chemical identity with the substance in mass. If we take a lump of table salt and divide it again and again, a single molecule of salt would eventually be obtained. A salt molecule is the smallest particle of the substance that retains the chemical identity of salt. If we divide the salt molecule, we obtain two different substances: one sodium and one chlorine atom in elementary form. (Sodium and chlorine are chemical elements.) Electric (electrostatic) forces bind the sodium and chlorine atoms together to form the salt molecule. The forces will be discussed subsequently.

The sodium and chlorine atoms that comprise a salt molecule do not have the characteristics of salt. At room temperature, sodium has the characteristics of a soft metal, while chlorine is a pungent gas. Yet, when sodium and chlorine combine to form salt, the characteristics of a crystal appear. Salt molecules associate in orderly arrays, as depicted in Figure

1-7, to form a crystal. Electrical particles with their binding forces can accordingly form substances with the characteristics of a crystal from other substances that have metallic and gaseous characteristics. At present, there are over 100 known chemical elements from which all matter is built up.

You will recall that an *atom* is the smallest particle of an element that can exist either alone or in combination with similar particles of the

Figure 1-7
A representation of crystal structure. (Illustration courtesy Edmund Scientific Co., Barrington, New Jersey.)

same or of a different element. An atom is the smallest particle of an element that enters into the composition of molecules. For example, a hydrogen atom is the smallest particle of the substance that can exist alone; it is also the smallest particle of the substance that enters into the composition of a water molecule.

SUBATOMIC STRUCTURE

Although atom originally meant *indivisible,* we know today that atoms can be split, and that they are far from being the ultimate particles of matter. Atoms have a *subatomic structure*. Subatomic structure relates to the phenomena occurring inside of atoms or particles smaller than atoms. Many of you have learned that this is a curious and surprising structure compared with the phenomena of everyday experience. The unexpected laws of electricity that apply to subatomic structure are of basic importance in various areas of electronics. For example, we shall learn how a transistor operates in your transistor radio. This understanding entails a basic knowledge of subatomic structure. We shall learn how and why electric current flows through the wires and coils in radio loudspeakers and earphones. Again, this understanding comprises a basic knowledge of subatomic structure.

Electrostatic forces are a fundamental concept in subatomic structure, and also in the operation of many electrical and electronic devices. Have you charged an electroscope in your physics laboratory experiments? The gold-leaf plates diverged because of electrostatic force. Did you watch a television program last night? The picture was "painted" on the screen in part by electrostatic forces. Electrostatic force is a *stress*; it is a force of attraction or repulsion existing in the space surrounding an electric charge or an electrically charged body.

Everyone is familiar with electrostatic forces. When you comb your hair on a dry winter day, tremendously high voltages are generated by friction between comb and hair. Both comb and hair become electrified, or charged with electricity. The same force that attracts small particles to an electrified comb also operates in the submicroscopic domain to bind electric charges, and atoms, together. Note that if you scuffle your feet over a good insulator (such as a rug) when the humidity is low, a potential difference of 10,000 volts or more can be generated between your body and the ground. Figure 1-8 shows the distances that a spark will jump through air at various voltages. The graph states that it requires 27,500 volts per in. to break down an air gap between needle points.

We know that an atom is the smallest particle of matter that can exist as a substance; however, an atom can be divided. For example, a sodium atom can be split by striking it with high-speed particles from a cyclotron (atom smasher). The sodium atom loses its original identity and part of its substance is changed into electrical charges; hence, atoms are built up from tiny particles of electricity. Negative electrons and positive protons are the chief particles of concern in subatomic structure in electronics technology.

Protons are basic particles in subatomic structure. A proton is an elementary particle that is identified with the nucleus of the hydrogen atom. Protons, along with neutrons, are constituents of other atomic nuclei. A proton carries a positive charge that is numerically equal to the charge of an electron. The mass of a proton is equal to 1.672×10^{-24}

gram. This is a very small mass; a gram is equal to 3.527×10^{-2} ounce, avoirdupois. Note that a neutron is an uncharged elementary particle having a mass nearly equal to that of the proton. Neutrons are present in all known atomic nuclei except the hydrogen nucleus.

An *electron* is one of the elementary constituent electrical particles of an atom. It is a charge of negative electricity equal to about 1.602×10^{-19} coulomb. The coulomb unit of electric charge is discussed

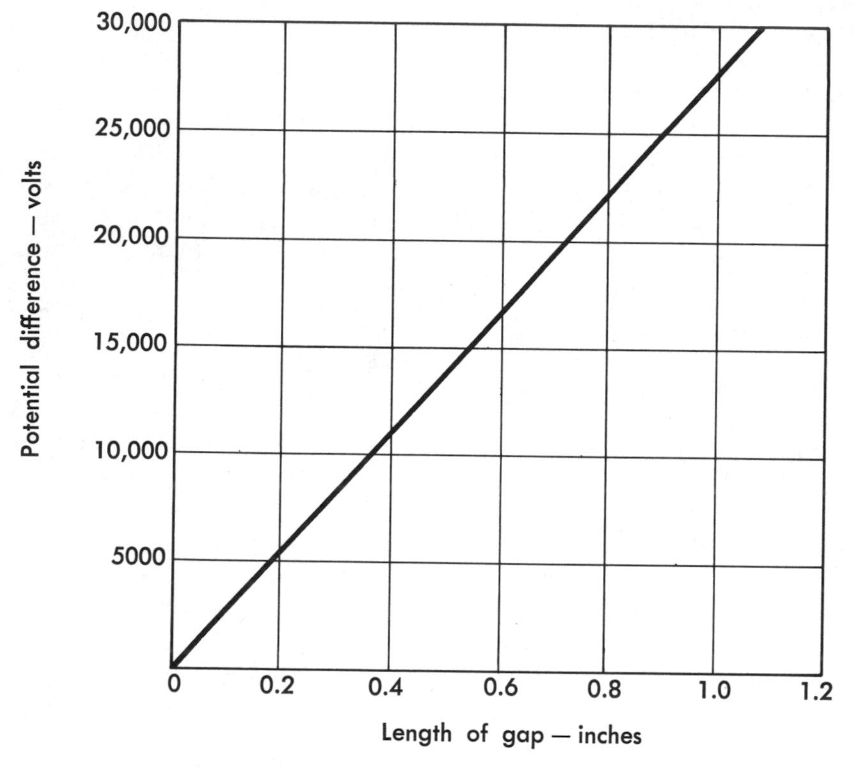

Figure 1-8
Sparking voltages between needle points at normal temperature and air pressure.

in detail subsequently. An electron has a mass when at rest of about 9.107×10^{-28} gram, or 1/1836 that of a neutron. The mass of an electron is sometimes thought to reside wholly as energy in the electrostatic field of the particle, in which case the radius of the electron must be in the order of 10^{-13} cm. One centimeter (cm) is equal to 0.3937 in. An electrostatic field is the portion of space in the neighborhood of a charged body in which the forces due to the charge are detectable.

A small bit of matter contains a vast number of molecules. For example, 1 cu cm of air contains 2.7×10^{19} molecules. An amount of an element equal to its atomic weight in grams contains 6.02×10^{23} atoms. The atomic weight of copper is 63.57. Thus, a small piece of copper contains a vast number of atoms. A piece of copper that weighs 1 gram contains about 9.62×10^{21} atoms. It follows that a small bit of matter contains an enormous number of electrons. For example, 1 gram of water contains 10^{27}, or 1000 trillion, trillion electrons—and note that there are less than 10^{27} drops of water in both the Atlantic and Pacific oceans.

DUALITY IN THE BASIC CONCEPTS OF PHYSICS

The description of an electron as a negatively charged particle is somewhat oversimplified, since physicists have produced convincing evidence that an electron also appears as a *wave* of electromagnetic energy. The idea of an electron is not a simple concept. Until recently, it was maintained that an electron is an ultimate particle or wave of matter. It is believed that an electron cannot exist as a particle and as a wave simul-

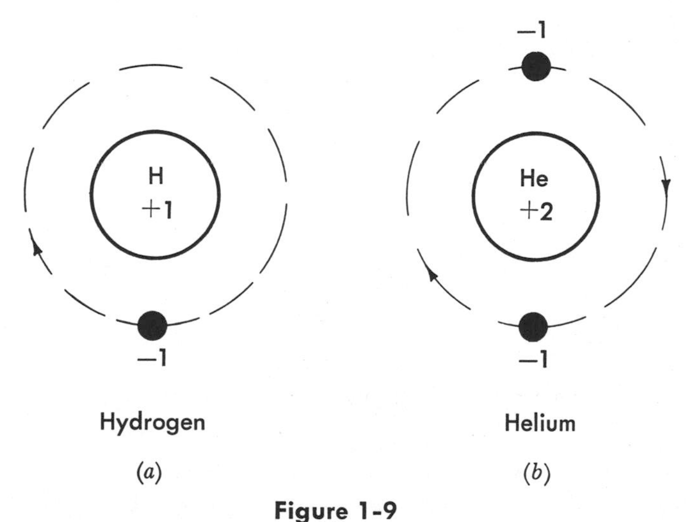

Figure 1-9
Diagrammatic structure of *(a)* the hydrogen atom, and *(b)* the helium atom.

taneously; it may *change* from a particle into a wave, or vice versa. The manner in which this change occurs is not known. Some tentative attempts have been made to find a structure for the electron. However, from the standpoint of electronic technology, an electron is simply regarded as an exceedingly small charge of negative electricity.

Figure 1-9 shows an elementary representation of structure for a hydrogen atom and a helium atom. The negative electrons are depicted as solid dots, and the positive nuclei as open circles. Note that this is only a diagrammatic representation, which does not indicate the relative spacing nor the relative sizes of electrons and nuclei. It has been estimated that if a hydrogen atom were magnified to the size of a 3-ft sphere, the proton would appear about the size of a pinhead. The relative distance of the electron from the proton is approximately the same as the relative distance of the earth from Pluto.

Hence, an atom consists of much "empty space," and can be compared with our solar system in this respect. The hydrogen-atom nucleus is an elementary positive charge: the proton. Since an atom contains equal and opposite charges, the atom as a whole is electrically neutral at

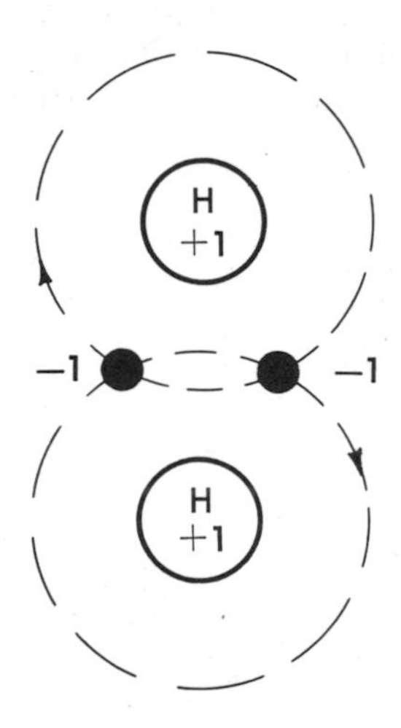

Figure 1-10
A hydrogen molecule comprises two hydrogen atoms.

an appreciable distance. Thus, a hydrogen atom does not drift when placed between two metal plates, one of which is charged positively and the other negatively. But when one hydrogen atom approaches another hydrogen atom very closely, localized electric forces come into play, binding the two atoms into a hydrogen molecule (Figure 1-10).

This formation of a hydrogen molecule H_2 from two hydrogen atoms appears quite puzzling at first. We will find that the orbit of a hydrogen atom is most stable when it is occupied by two electrons. Accordingly, two atoms will "share" their electrons, as depicted in Figure 1-10, to achieve maximum stability. More complex atoms are built up as shown in Figure 1-11. An atom has more than one shell, or orbit systems. Only two electrons can occupy the first shell; after that, a second shell is formed.

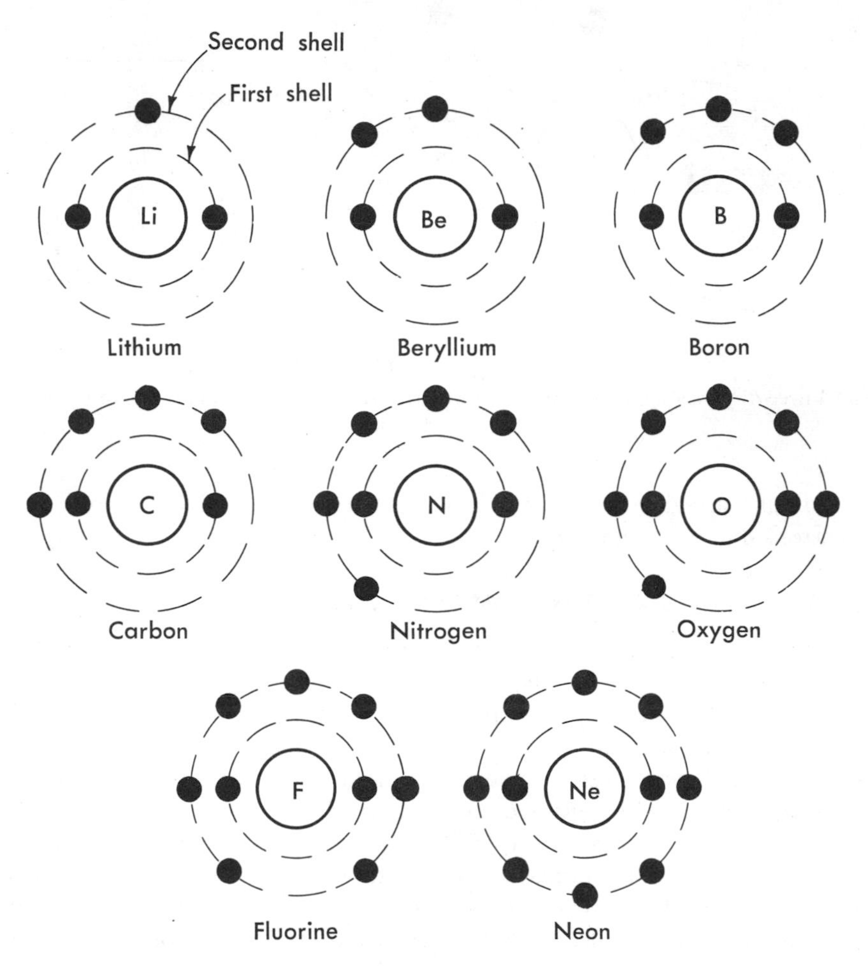

Figure 1-11
Diagrammatic structure of the eight elements following helium.

Thus, the lithium atom has two shells occupied by electrons; its third electron moves in a second-shell orbit. Beryllium has two electrons in its second shell; boron has three electrons in its second shell.

Each of the atoms depicted in Figure 1-11 is electrically neutral at appreciable distances. Note that, like our solar system, atoms actually have a three-dimensional structure, and their electrons move in elliptical instead of circular orbits. Figure 1-12(*a*) illustrates a three-dimensional concept of the lithium atom. However, most electronic principles can be satisfactorily discussed from the standpoint of two-dimensional models.

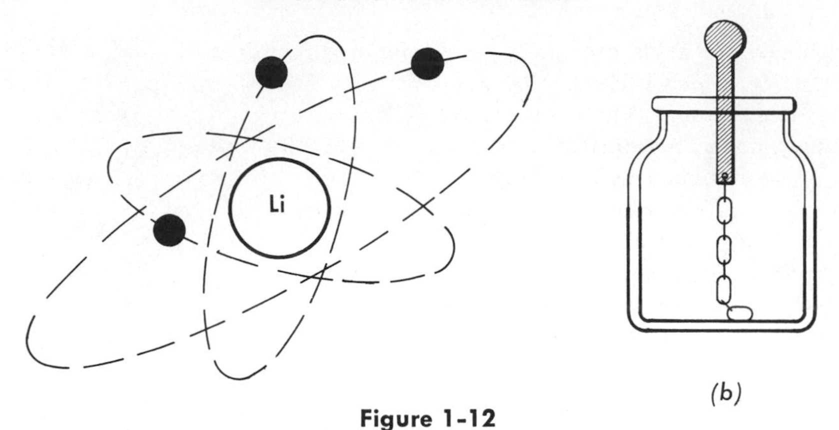

Figure 1-12
(a) Three-dimensional diagrammatic structure of a lithium atom. *(b)* Construction of a Leyden jar.

We often abbreviate our atomic models still more, and indicate only the electrons that move in the outermost shell.

1.4 THE PHYSICS OF ELECTROMOTIVE FORCE

Electromotive force is that which moves, or tends to move, electricity. Electromotive force, or voltage, is conveniently regarded as an attractive or repulsive force. However, as previously noted, voltage is defined physically as a work unit. Electricity, of course, consists of electric charges, such as electrons. Electromotive force is a potential for action at a distance. An electric field exists between charges, which urges an electron, for example, to move from a point of higher potential to a point of lower potential. *Work* is accomplished when the electron is moved. If we ask what an electric field "really is," we can find no satisfactory answer. The space occupied by an electric field is in a modified condition, which can be defined only in terms of charge behavior. Electromotive force is measured in volts, just as water pressure is measured in psi (pounds per square inch).

All electrons have the same charge of electricity, or more precisely, electrons *are* identical charges of electricity. The charge of an electron is commonly denoted by e. We know that an electron is surrounded by an electric field. It is interesting to observe some salient characteristics of electric fields in *capacitors*. You have probably experimented with Leyden jars in your physics courses. The Leyden jar [see Figure 1-12(*b*)] was invented in 1746 by Professor Pieter van Musschenbroek. A Leyden jar is also called a *condenser,* although the term *capacitor* is preferred in modern terminology. The modern term is intended to avoid confusion with a steam condenser, which is an entirely different device. An acquaintance with electric fields can easily be made from consideration of a simple capacitor, which is charged to a chosen voltage by a large number of displaced electrons. Why were the first capacitors designed as Leyden jars? Early workers reasoned that if electricity were a subtle fluid, a capacitor must be designed as a jar to retain the fluid. Much later, experiments proved that electricity will not "spill out" of a capacitor which does not have the form of a jar.

Basically, a capacitor consists of two metallic plates (conductors) separated by an insulator such as air or glass. Figure 1-13 represents a unit capacitor. Its metal plates are separated 0.001 in. Each plate has an area

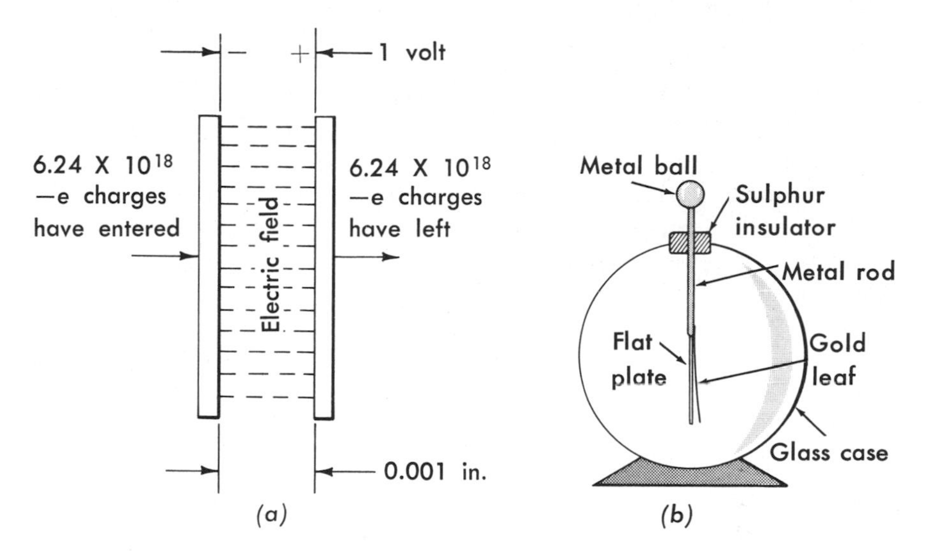

Figure 1-13

(a) Electron charge separation, producing a potential difference between capacitor plates. *(b)* Construction of a gold-leaf electroscope.

of 4.46×10^9 sq in. Such a capacitor will have a capacitance of 1 farad. The formula for calculating capacitance is

$$C = \frac{2.24 \times 10^{-13} kA\,(n\text{-}1)}{d} \tag{1.4}$$

where C is the capacitance in farads, k is the dielectric coefficient of the material between the plates (see Table 1-2), A is the area of one side of one plate in square inches, d is the separation of the plates in inches, and n is the number of plates.

Of course, this particular capacitor could not be practically constructed; its plates are too large. This fact emphasizes the circumstance that the farad is a very large unit of capacitance. Much smaller values of capacitance, measured in millionths or million-millionths of a farad, are commonly used in electronic equipment. However, it is instructive to observe the electrical relations in a unit (1-farad) capacitor. Suppose 6.24×10^{18} electrons are formed to enter one plate of a unit capacitor. Then, the same number of electrons will leave the other plate via the charging circuit (which we must take for granted at this point). One unit of work has been done in separating the unit charges. In turn, there is a potential difference of 1 volt between the two plates.

Since unlike charges attract, there is a force of attraction between the two capacitor plates. This force is a property of the electric field that has been established in the air space between the two plates. The force of attraction is given by the formula

$$F = \frac{AV^2}{k(1504S)^2} \tag{1.5}$$

where F is the attractive force in dynes, A is the area of one plate in square centimeters, V is the potential difference in volts, k is the dielectric coefficient, and S is the distance between the plates in centimeters.

Since a dyne is about 1/980 gram, and there are 454 grams per lb, approximately, the force of attraction between the plates in Figure 1-13(*a*) is about 4400 lb. The flux lines depicted in Figure 1-13 are imaginary threads representing the electric field. By definition, each pair of unit charges produces one line of electric flux when separated by a unit of distance.

Suppose *both* plates in Figure 1-13 to be charged negatively. Since like charges repel, there is a force of repulsion between the two plates. Note that if the *same* number of electrons were forced to enter each plate, there would be no potential *difference* (voltage) between the two plates, although the plates would repel each other. This principle is used in an instrument called the *gold-leaf electroscope* to indicate the presence of high voltage [see Figure 1-13(*b*)].

1.5 ELECTRONS IN MOTION

Electric current is a flow of electrical charges. When a steady current transfers 1 coulomb of electricity past a point over a period of 1 sec, the rate of current flow is 1 amp. A coulomb consists of 6.24×10^{18} electrons; it follows that an electron is a negative charge of 1.6×10^{-19} coulomb. The rate of current flow is stated in coulombs per second, or amperes, just as the rate of water flow is stated in gallons per second. An electric current that flows in one direction and does not change its value is called a *direct current* (d-c). If a current of 160 amps flows past a point for one year, the total weight of the electrons that have passed will be approximately 1 ounce.

Metals are conductors of electric current because a metal contains free electrons that are not bound to the metal atoms. One cu cm of copper contains approximately 8×10^{22} free electrons. Free electrons in a wire can be compared by rough analogy to a pipe filled with marbles. A free electron in a wire moves with comparative ease when a voltage is applied across the two ends of the wire. Electrons flow from the negative end of the wire to the positive end, because like charges repel and unlike charges attract. We recall that, before the electron was discovered, electricity was supposed to be a subtle fluid. It was only possible to guess at the direction of current flow. It was erroneously supposed that electric current flows from the positive end of a wire to the negative end. Benjamin Franklin worked under this misconception. Today, a clear distinction is made between classical (conventional) current flow, and electron flow.

Metals such as copper contain vast numbers of free electrons. Since a copper wire contains so many free electrons, it follows that electron flow in it is ordinarily very slow. For example, if a current of 1 amp flows in ordinary bell wire (diameter about 0.04 in.), the velocity of each free electron is only 0.001 in. per sec, approximately. Suppose that the current flow is increased to the point at which the wire begins to melt; each free electron then has a velocity of about 0.4 in. per sec. This slow velocity of electron flow in wires is not an obvious fact. However, it follows directly from a calculation of the number of free electrons available to carry past a point a flow of 6.24×10^{18} electrons per sec.

On the other hand, it must not be supposed that, when electrons are forced into one end of a long wire, considerable time is required for electrons to start flowing out the other end. (Remember the analogy of water or marbles in a pipe.) Actually, electrons flow out the other end of the wire almost immediately. Thus, the *effective* speed of electrical energy flow in a wire is almost the speed of light, or 186,000 miles per sec. Of course, it is quite a while before an individual electron entering a long wire finally arrives at the far end.

1.6 THE NATURE OF RESISTANCE

At room temperature, free electrons in metals are not *completely* free to move in response to an applied voltage. At ordinary temperatures, each moving electron collides with metal atoms at intervals, and these collisions clearly oppose current flow. The atoms in a metal are bound into fixed positions by interatomic forces. Only free electrons move in response to an applied voltage. The resistance value of a metal depends basically upon its composition. Iron has a higher relative resistance than copper, and manganin (an alloy) has a higher relative resistance than iron. Table 1-3 lists the comparative resistances of some familiar metals.

Table 1-3

COMPARATIVE RESISTANCES OF METALS

Metal	*Resistance Relative to Copper*
Aluminum	1.8
Brass	3.6
Iron	6.0
Lead	15.0
Silver	0.94
Tin	7.8
Zinc	3.6

When electrons collide with atoms in a metal, some of their energy of motion is changed into heat energy. We know that when a nail is flattened by hammer blows, the nail becomes very hot. In this example, mechanical energy is changed into heat energy by collision of the hammer with the nail. Of course, energy is neither created nor destroyed in any case. One form of energy is merely changed into another form of energy. If a certain amount of electrical energy is consumed by a resistance, an equal amount of heat energy must be produced. This basic equivalence is called the *law of conservation of energy.*

The relative resistance of carbon is about 1800 times that of copper. Edison used carbon filaments in his original incandescent lamps. Carbon has a comparatively high resistance because far fewer free electrons are present in carbon than in copper. Resistance serves a useful purpose in a lamp filament, because electric current flow must heat the filament to a white-hot temperature. Otherwise, electrical energy will not be converted in part to light energy. On the other hand, resistance does not serve a useful purpose in the wires that conduct electric current to the lamp. Wire resistance imposes a loss of electrical energy as heat that would otherwise contribute to the production of light by the lamp. The system efficiency is lowered by wire resistance. Hence, copper wires that have comparatively low resistance are commonly used to conduct electricity from one point to another. If iron wires were used, the initial cost would be less, but the efficiency of the system would be comparatively poor.

Wood has about 10^{22} times as much resistance as an equal volume of copper and has comparatively few free electrons. Although wood does conduct a very slight amount of current, this conduction can be disregarded in many practical situations. Hence, wood is often assumed to completely block current flow. Substances that have extremely high resistance are called *insulators.* Thus, wood is usually classified as an insulator. Air is a very good insulator until the applied voltage is sufficiently ıoves 6.24 × 10^{18} electrons from one point to the other, 0.7376 work has been done. Work is equal to force times distance in ıse. *Work is numerically equal to energy.*

ıt is a form of energy. It is the energy of random motion (vibraf the molecules in a substance. Recall that the molecules in a re fixed in their general position. When the resistance element in ric stove is hot, its molecules vibrate more violently than when it Although each molecule maintains a certain average position, it vertheless vibrate about this position. Since the flow of electric results in collisions between free electrons and molecules in the e element, this energy of collision is changed into molecular vibraenergy. In turn, heat is produced. Note that 1 calorie is the amount required to raise the temperature of 1 gram of water 1°C.

hen we look at water in a glass, we see no evidence of molecular on. The surface of the water appears completely quiet—it reflects s if the water were a continuous and motionless substance. But this ely the illusion of unaided eyesight. In the nineteenth century, microscopes were developed; in turn, very small particles in water ısion could be observed. Surprisingly, it was seen that these particles ıot at rest. Instead, they darted about in arbitrary directions. Though icle maintains its average position, it is never at rest in that position. zig-zag motion was discovered by a botanist named Robert Brown, called the *Brownian motion.*

Thus, when the sense of sight is extended by means of a microscope, e direct evidence of the fact that the molecules of substances are not t. Vibrating water molecules are striking the small suspended par. Since the particles are very light, they respond to the random ions by zig-zagging about their average position. Many other lines idence have been discovered that also lead to the conclusion that ıolecules of substances are not at rest. However, the most direct visual nce is the Brownian motion.

We know that a molecule consists of two or more atoms in chemical ination. Atoms, of course, are built up basically from electrons and ons. Electric charges are surrounded by electric fields when the ges are at rest. On the other hand, when electric charges are in mo, they are surrounded by both electric and magnetic fields. If a charge ıddenly forced from a resting position, or its velocity is forced to ıge, the charge is said to undergo an *acceleration*. It is a basic law of ical physics that an accelerated charge must radiate electromagnetic gy into surrounding space.

What is meant by radiation of electromagnetic energy, or waves? s simply means that part of the acceleration energy is changed into tromagnetic field energy, which escapes from the vicinity of the charge

great to produce spark breakdown (Figure 1
voltage is reached, air suddenly becomes a fair

The electrical resistance of a substance c
Thus, in the vicinity of 0°K (−273°C), the re
become zero. When a metal imposes no opposi
called a *superconductor.* The resistance of pu
temperature rises. The increase per degree from
fraction of the resistance at 0°C. This fraction
coefficient of resistance. The relation between re
for a pure metal over *moderate* ranges of temperat

$$R_t = R_0 (1 + \alpha t)$$

where R_t is the resistance at temperature t, R_0 is
is the temperature coefficient of resistance, and t i

Temperature coefficients of resistance for so
listed in Table 1-4.

Table 1-4

TEMPERATURE COEFFICIENTS OF M

Metal	*Temperature C per °C*
Aluminum	0.0043
Copper	0.0040
German silver	0.0004
Iron	0.0062
Manganin	0.00002
Platinum	0.00366

Why is Equation (1.6) applicable only over mod
perature? This is an *empirical* equation, which has b
mental data. However, the fit is not exact. Over a wi
ture, the equation does not fit the data satisfactorily
is included. Over a still wider range of temperature, c
be included. Hence, the equation becomes more cum
in the vicinity of absolute zero, Equation (1.6) is com
(see Appendix I).

1.7 THE RELATIONS BETWEEN ELECTRICITY AND EN

When the electrical charges present in a substance
to make electrical energy available, as in a voltaic cell, w
Work is measured in foot-pounds. If 2 lb are lifted thr
3 ft, 6 ft-lb of work has been done. If 1 volt of emf ap

points r
ft-lb of
either c
He
tions) c
metal a
an elec
is cold.
can ne
curren
resistiv
tional
of hea
W
vibrati
light a
is me
good
susper
were r
a part
This
and is
T
we se
at res
ticles
collis
of ev
the n
evide
com
prot
char
tion
is su
cha
class
ene
Th
ele

and travels out through space at the speed of 186,000 miles per sec. When a molecule is forced to vibrate about its average position, its constituent electrons and protons are accelerated and they radiate electromagnetic waves, which are recognized as heat.

LIGHT WAVES AND HEAT WAVES

Light is also a form of energy radiated as electromagnetic waves. However, light waves have a higher rate of vibration than heat waves. Light waves vibrate about 3^{15} times per sec; heat waves vibrate about 3^{12} times per sec. Figure 1-14 illustrates the various orbits of the Bohr atom in which an electron may revolve about a hydrogen nucleus. Each shell in an atom comprises a group of permissible orbits. It is a fundamental principle of atomic structure that an electron must occupy one of its permissible orbits, but cannot be found between any two orbits. If an electron acquires sufficient energy, it can suddenly be raised from a lower orbit to a higher orbit. But if an electron loses sufficient energy, it can suddenly fall from a higher orbit to a lower orbit.

When an electron has minimum energy, it moves in the first orbit

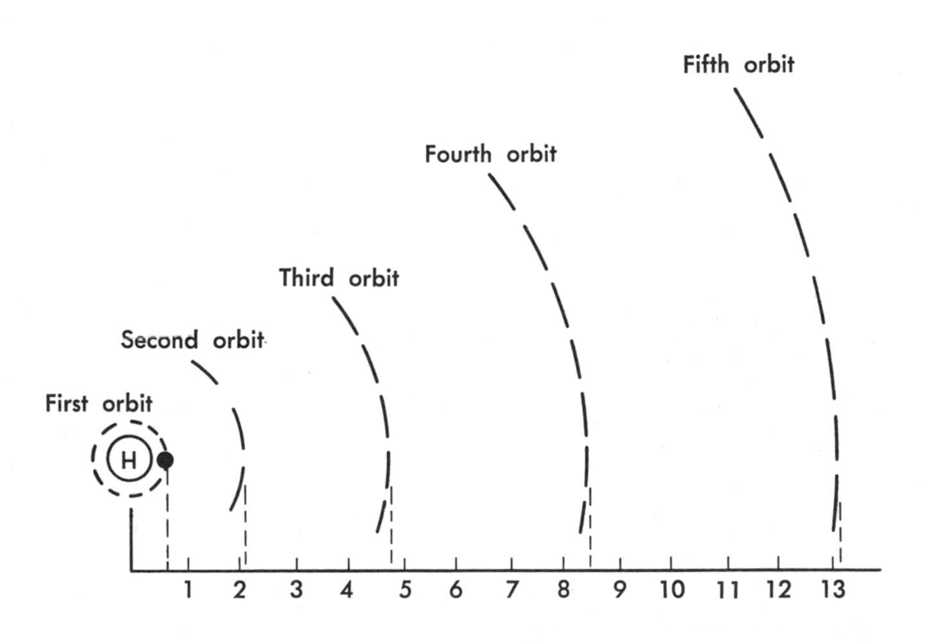

Figure 1-14
Radii of the first five orbits in a Bohr hydrogen atom.

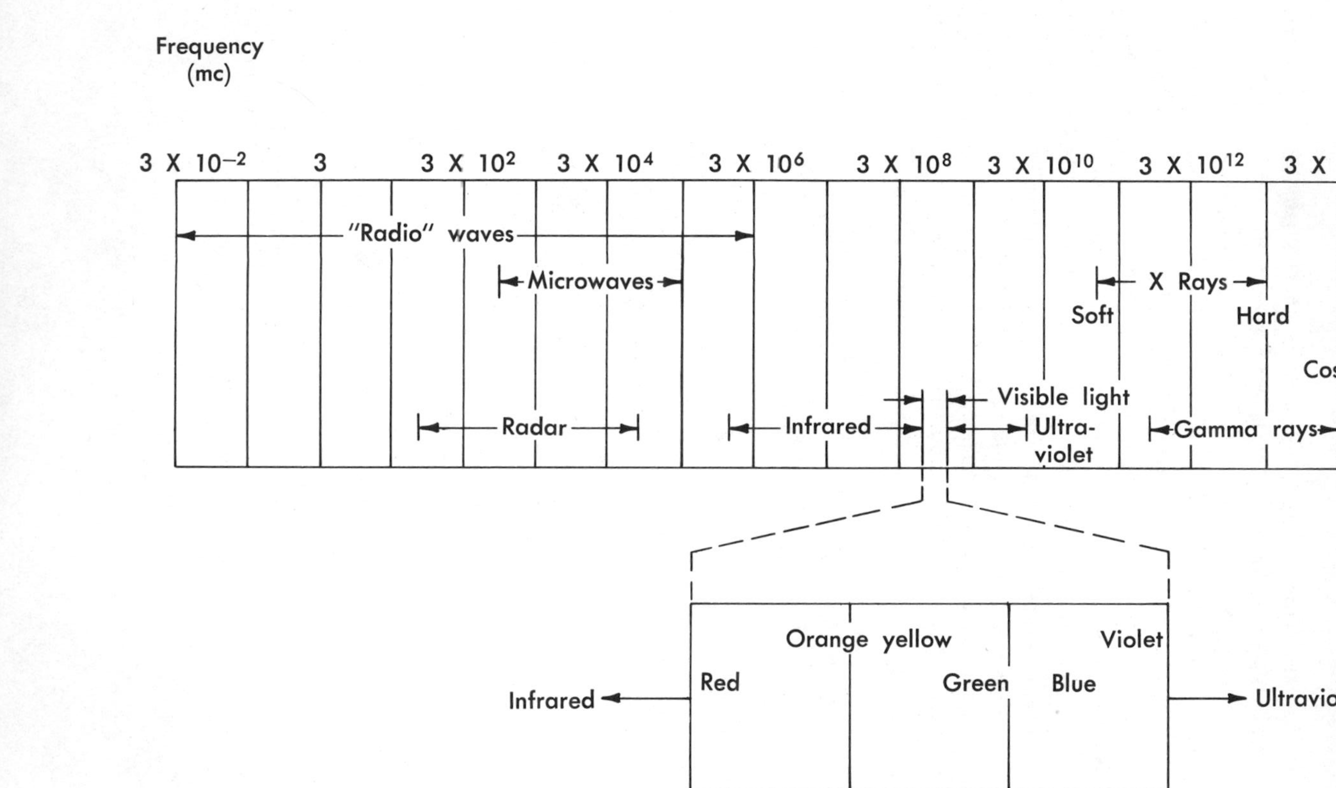

Figure 1-15
An electromagnetic-wave frequency spectrum.

(Figure 1-14). Upon acquiring a definite and sufficient amount of energy, the electron can be suddenly displaced into the second, third, or higher orbit. However, the electron does not remain in a high orbit very long. It will suddenly lose its acquired energy and drop back into a lower orbit. In so doing, the electron radiates its excess energy as an electromagnetic wave.

Radiation resulting from an electron's drop into a lower orbit has a comparatively high rate of vibration, appearing in the form of light. The color of the light depends upon how many orbits the electron has dropped through. It is in this manner that the mechanical energy of collision can be changed into light energy. We know that both heat and light are produced by a lamp filament when electrons collide with molecules. Heat is produced by the vibration of a molecule as a whole. Light is produced by a bound electron dropping from a higher orbit to a lower orbit. Note that only bound electrons move in orbits—free electrons have no orbits, and may occupy any arbitrary point in space.

Figure 1-15 shows a frequency spectrum, which is of basic interest to electronics students. Observe that the visible spectrum is only a small "slice" in the vast range from gamma rays to radio waves. Each frequency corresponds to a certain wavelength. Since electromagnetic radiation travels at a velocity of approximately 300,000,000 meters per sec, the wavelength is evidently equal to $300{,}000{,}000/f$, where f is the frequency of the radiation. For example, a radio broadcast station that transmits on a frequency of 1 mc radiates a wavelength of 300 meters.

GREAT MEN IN THE HISTORY OF SCIENCE

1700 B.C.	Ahmes of Egypt
600 B.C.	Thales of Miletus
460 B.C.	Democritus of Abdera
1540–1603	William Gilbert
1692–1741	Pieter van Musschenbroek
1706–1790	Benjamin Franklin
1736–1806	Charles Coulomb
1745–1827	Alessandro Volta
1775–1836	Andre Marie Ampere
1777–1851	Hans Christian Oersted
1777–1855	Karl Friedrich Gauss
1781–1854	George Simon Ohm
1791–1867	Michael Faraday
1797–1878	Joseph Henry
1804–1891	Wilhelm Eduard Weber
1824–1887	Gustav Robert Kirchhoff
1831–1879	James Clerk Maxwell
1853–1926	Heike Kammerlingh Onnes
1856–1940	J. J. Thomson

1857–1894 Heinrich Hertz
1858–1947 Max Planck
1859–1906 Pierre Curie
1865–1923 Charles Heinrich Steinmetz
1867–1934 Marie Curie
1885–1962 Niels Bohr

Mathematics has been called the handmaiden of the exact sciences. Hence, it is interesting to observe the comparative chronologies of mathematics and physics. Some of the important dates and concepts are listed in Table 1-5. We may be surprised that mathematics was not applied to electrical phenomena for over 3000 years after mathematics was born. Before the first electrical formula was written, arithmetic, algebra, geometry, the decimal system, trigonometry, logarithms, analytic geometry, and

Table 1-5

COMPARATIVE CHRONOLOGY

Mathematics		Physics	
1700 B.C.	Beginnings of arithmetic, algebra, geometry, and the decimal system		
370 B.C.	Irrational numbers recognized		
		550 B.C.	Static electricity and permanent magnetism discussed
400	Development of trigonometry		
876	Discovery of the cipher zero		
1614	Logarithms introduced		
1637	Analytic geometry conceived, and differential calculus proposed		
		1785	Electric quantity defined
		1799	Current electricity produced
		1820	Electromagnetism discovered
		1827	Electric resistance defined
1831	Algebra of complex numbers established	1831	Electromagnetic induction discovered
		1838	Electric capacitance defined
1865	Theory of probability conceived	1865	Existence of electromagnetic radiation predicted
		1887	Electromagnetic radiation discovered
		1896	Atomicity of electricity discovered
		1900	Atomicity of energy discovered
		1913	Atomic orbital quanta established
		1924	Probability laws introduced into atomic physics

the differential calculus were in common use. Pure mathematics is much older than applied mathematics in the field of electricity and electronics.

A new physical concept may or may not find technological application. However, many discoveries in physics are soon followed by technological

Table 1-6

CHRONOLOGY OF BASIC ELECTRICAL AND ELECTRONIC INVENTIONS

Year	Invention
1700 B.C.	Magnetic compass
1600	Electroscope
1671	Static machine
1746	Leyden jar
1799	Voltaic battery
1822	Electric arc
1843	Wheatstone bridge
1844	Electric telegraph
1851	Spark coil
1862	Moving-coil galvanometer
1866	Electric motor and generator
1874	Semiconductor rectifier
1876	Telephone
1879	Electric light
1887	Wireless telegraph
1905	Radio vacuum tube
1948	Transistor

inventions. Table 1-6 lists the dates of some basic electrical and electronic inventions.

1.8 CIRCUIT CONCEPTS

Since electrons must flow continuously in a wire to maintain a steady conversion of energy, a *closed circuit* is required. A closed circuit is basically an unbroken conducting path. A typical closed circuit includes a source of electricity such as a dry cell or battery. The closed circuit might also include an incandescent lamp. Therefore, two conducting wires are required to form this closed circuit, as seen in Figure 1-16. Note that the lamp can *produce* neither current nor voltage. Electrons must be forced through the lamp resistance by the source of emf. We recall that the action of certain chemical solutions on dissimilar metals generates an emf. Thus, a cell or battery is a chemical charge separator. (A battery consists of two or more cells.)

So long as the circuit remains closed in Figure 1-16, as many electrons are entering the positive terminal of the battery as are leaving the negative terminal. Current flow through the resistance of the lamp filament continuously changes electrical energy into heat energy and light energy.

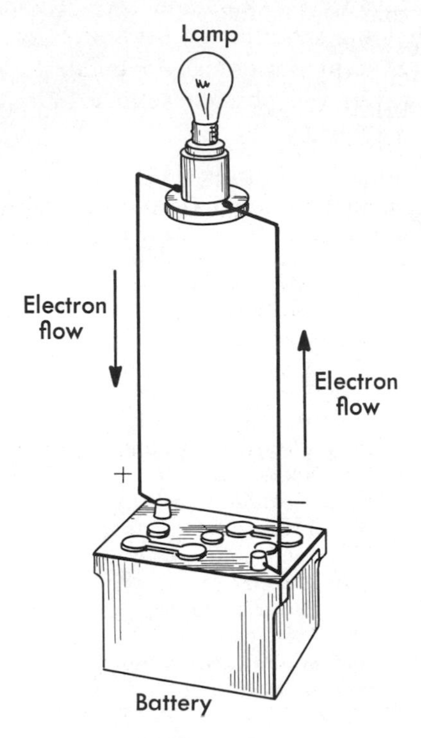

Figure 1-16
An example of a closed circuit.

Note that only current (the stream of free electrons) flows in the closed circuit; voltage does not flow and resistance does not flow. The *same* current value is found at every point in the closed circuit. This is a d-c flow.

Electrons flow through the circuit from the negative terminal of the battery to the positive terminal. It might appear that electrons flow through the battery from its positive terminal to its negative terminal. However, this statement of the situation is not in accordance with the physical facts. From previous discussion, recall that electrons do not flow through a cell or battery as if it were a copper wire. Instead, the battery consumes chemical energy and *separates* electric charges. It separates electrons from atoms and molecules at the expense of chemical energy; by means of chemical reactions, an excess of electrons is maintained at the negative terminal, and a deficiency of electrons is maintained at the positive terminal of the battery. Eventually, of course, all the chemical energy of the battery is used up, and the battery "dies."

If one of the wires in Figure 1-16 is disconnected from the battery, the circuit is then said to be *open,* and current flow stops. No further electrical energy is supplied by the battery to the lamp, and the lamp no longer glows. The consumption of chemical energy in the battery stops. It is evident that a switch can be connected into the circuit, as shown in Figure 1-17. The lamp can then be turned on or off by closing or opening the switch. Let us briefly consider the water analogy of a closed circuit depicted in Figure 1-18. The pump represents a voltage source and conductors correspond to the large pipes. The resistance of a lamp filament corresponds to the small pipe, which imposes substantial hydraulic friction. Current flow in the closed circuit can be measured with the flow

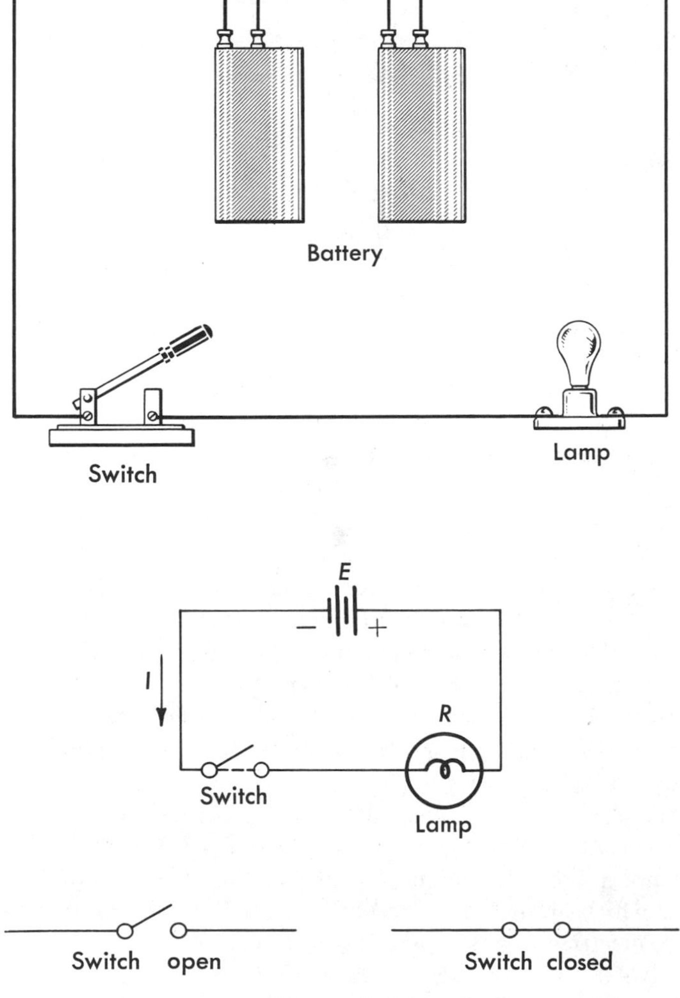

Figure 1-17
A switch connected in series with a circuit.

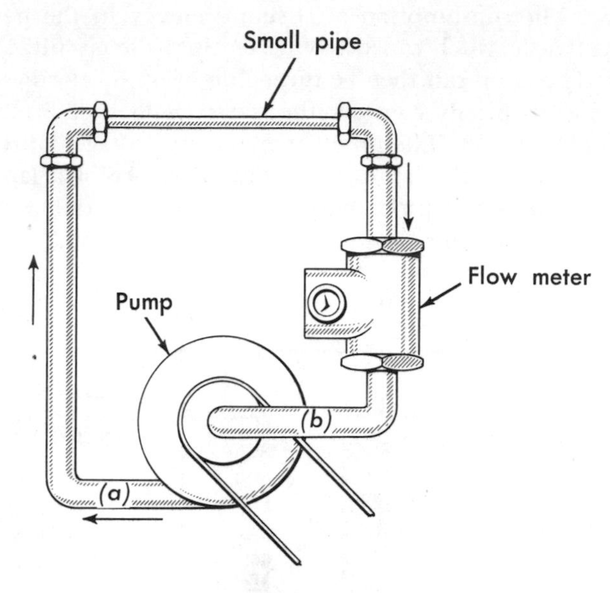

Figure 1-18
A water analogy of a simple closed circuit.

meter. Water pressure drops across the small pipe, and kinetic energy is changed into heat.

Compare the picture diagram with the *schematic* diagram in Figure 1-17. Schematics involve a form of technical shorthand that simplifies circuit presentation. A symbol reduces its corresponding component, such as a battery, lamp, or switch, to its electrical essentials. Similarly, voltage, current, and resistance are abbreviated to the standard symbols E, I, and R, respectively. Recall that E stands for emf, I stands for intensity of current, and R stands for resistance. Thus, it might be specified that the battery consists of two 1.5-volt cells, which together form a battery that supplies 3 volts, that the current flow has an intensity of 0.25 amp, and that the lamp has a resistance of 12 ohms. Because $I = E/R$, specification of any two values fixes the third value; thus, the current flow *must* be 0.25 amp in this example—no other value of current flow is physically possible.

When the switch is closed in Figure 1-17, it might *seem* that there is an open circuit at the battery, because the short and long lines of each cell are not joined. Remember, however, that a cell contains chemical solutions which are not indicated by a symbol. These solutions are a conductor of electricity, which permit the separated charges to flow easily to the positive and negative terminals of the battery. This is a simple example of a situation in which we must read between the lines of a schematic diagram.

SUMMARY OF FUNDAMENTAL CONCEPTS

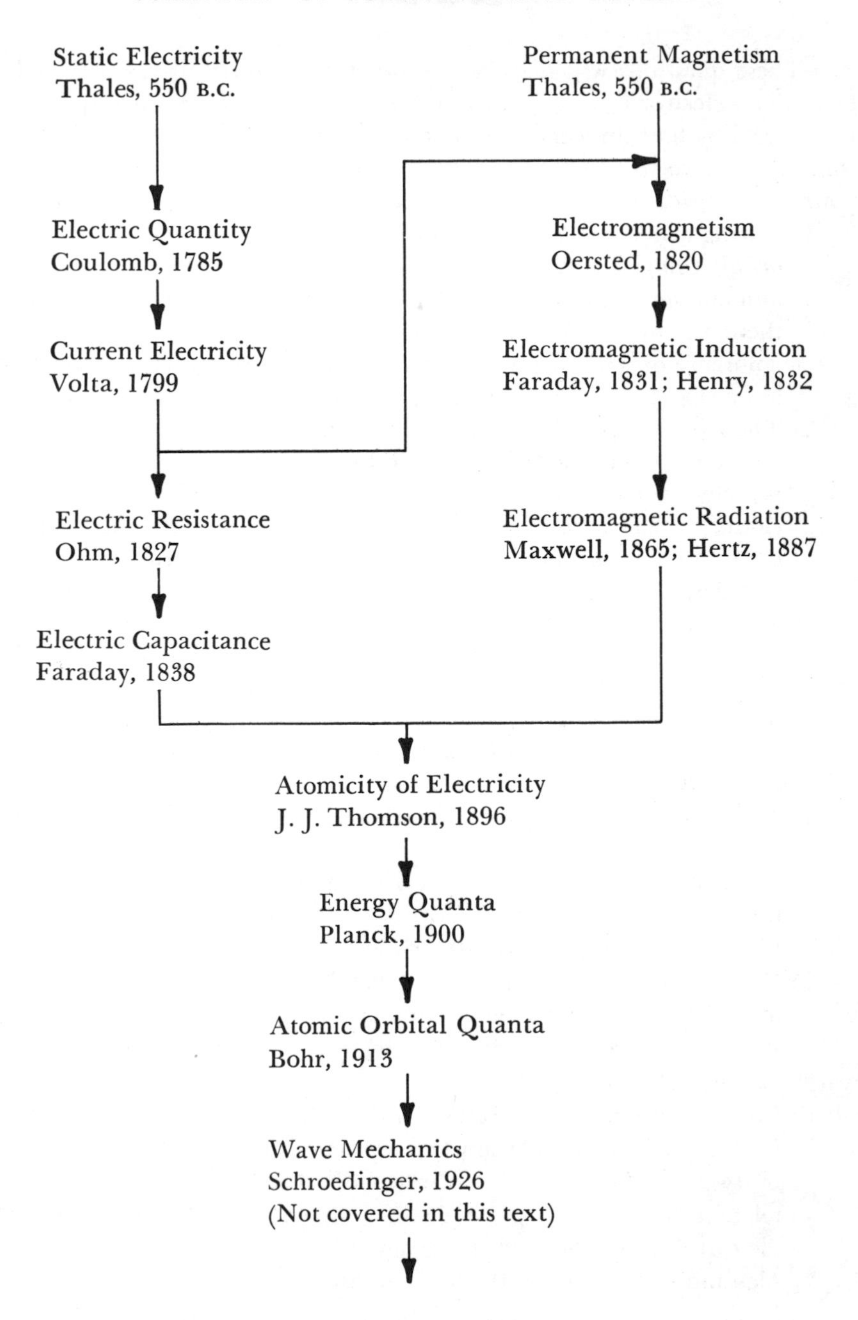
Static Electricity
Thales, 550 B.C.
Permanent Magnetism
Thales, 550 B.C.
Electric Quantity
Coulomb, 1785
Electromagnetism
Oersted, 1820
Current Electricity
Volta, 1799
Electromagnetic Induction
Faraday, 1831; Henry, 1832
Electric Resistance
Ohm, 1827
Electromagnetic Radiation
Maxwell, 1865; Hertz, 1887
Electric Capacitance
Faraday, 1838
Atomicity of Electricity
J. J. Thomson, 1896
Energy Quanta
Planck, 1900
Atomic Orbital Quanta
Bohr, 1913
Wave Mechanics
Schroedinger, 1926
(Not covered in this text)

QUESTIONS

These questions will help you to determine how well you know the facts about electrons and electricity presented in Chapter 1. Each question is followed by four answers; only one answer is correct. Mark the answer that you believe to be correct. After you complete this section, compare your answers with Key at the end of the book.

1) During man's first million years, he proved that:
(*a*) all things in nature were created for a purpose, as part of a humanly ordered plan. (*b*) lightning is an instrument of justice in the moral order of nature. (*c*) prehistoric man lived in almost total ignorance of natural laws. (*d*) all substances are built up from various proportions of earth, air, fire, and water.
2) The Rhind papyrus of 2000 B.C. explains:
(*a*) why a lodestone orients itself in a North-and-South direction. (*b*) why amber attracts pieces of straw after it has been rubbed by cloth. (*c*) that action at a distance is caused by a concentration of the luminiferous ether. (*d*) a few isolated and uncoordinated physical facts.
3) Thales wrote in 600 B.C. concerning:
(*a*) tiny indivisible particles of matter called "atomos." (*b*) the identity of lightning and electricity. (*c*) action at a distance exhibited by lodestone upon iron, and by rubbed amber upon pieces of straw. (*d*) the difference between "the magnetical motions and the forces of amber."
4) The chief contribution of the classical Greek civilization to the science of physics was:
(*a*) the principles of mathematical reasoning. (*b*) proof of the atomic theory. (*c*) that everything which moves is in some sense alive. (*d*) the trisection of any angle.
5) William Gilbert (1540–1603) discovered:
(*a*) the dielectric coefficients of insulating substances. (*b*) the Leyden jar. (*c*) that earth, air, fire, and water are not chemical elements. (*d*) the electric series.
6) Charles Coulomb (1736–1806) discovered:
(*a*) the quantitative relation between the electrostatic forces exerted by two electric charges at various distances. (*b*) the quantitative relation between voltage, current, and resistance. (*c*) the source of the earth's magnetism. (*d*) the magnetic current.
7) Alessandro Volta (1745–1827) developed:
(*a*) the first static machine. (*b*) the first electric battery. (*c*) the first dynamo-electric machine. (*d*) the magnetic compass.

8) Andre Marie Ampere (1775–1836) constructed:
(*a*) the first capacitor. (*b*) the first ammeter. (*c*) the first permanent magnet. (*d*) the first electromagnet.
9) Michael Faraday (1791–1867) discovered:
(*a*) the heat of capacitance. (*b*) that a moving magnet exerts action at a distance upon a wire and induces an electric current in the wire. (*c*) that lightning is a form of electricity. (*d*) that twice as much current flows through a resistance when twice as much voltage is applied.
10) Niels Bohr in 1913 produced evidence that:
(*a*) new and unexpected laws of electricity hold sway when electric charges are separated by extremely small distances. (*b*) electrons are distributed within a comparatively large volume of positive electricity. (*c*) electrons are both particles and waves. (*d*) the law of conservation of energy does not apply to electrons.

PROBLEMS

1) Two unit charges separated by a unit distance in a vacuum repel each other with a unit force f. When these same charges are separated by the same distance and placed in oil, which has a dielectric coefficient of 2, what is the force of repulsion?
2) The same charges noted in Problem 1 are placed in pure alcohol. What is the force of repulsion?
3) A certain quantity of electricity does one unit of work when it flows from a point of zero potential to a point of potential V. How much work does this same quantity of electricity do when it flows from a point of potential V to a point of potential $3\ V$?
4) If the quantity of electricity in Problem 3 is halved, how much work does it do in flowing from a point of zero potential to a point of potential $V/2$?
5) Ohm's law states that $I = E/R$. If 10 volts cause a current of 2 amps to flow through a resistance, what is the value of the resistance?
6) If a current of 3 amps flows through a resistance of 5 ohms, what voltage is present across the terminals of the resistance?
7) How many electrons are there in 1 ounce of water?
8) If two needle points are separated ½ in., how much voltage must be applied to produce a spark?
9) Two metal plates, each of which has an area 4.46×10^9 sq in., are separated 0.001 in. and placed in oil, which has a dielectric coefficient of 2. What is the capacitance of this capacitor in farads?

10) What is the force of attraction between the capacitor plates in Problem 9 when the capacitor is charged to a potential of 1 volt?
11) How many free electrons are there in a copper cube that measures 0.0000001 cm along its edge?
12) A current of 1 amp flows in a copper wire that has a diameter of ¼ in. What is the approximate velocity of each free electron?
13) If a current of 1 amp flows in a long copper wire when 1 volt is applied to the ends of the wire, how much current will flow if the copper wire is replaced by an iron wire of the same length and diameter?
14) If the experiment of Problem 13 is performed at 20°C initially, how much current will flow in the iron wire if the experiment is repeated at a temperature of 120°C?
15) If 6 volts emf applied between two points moves 1 coulomb between the two points, how many foot-pounds of work have been done?
16) An electromagnetic field is radiated by an accelerated charge, and the field travels through space for 0.001 sec. How far has the field traveled?
17) An electron rests temporarily in the second orbit of a hydrogen atom. How far is the electron from the nucleus?
18) A battery supplies 10 amps to an electric circuit. Calculate the number of electrons leaving the negative terminal of the battery per second.

2

LAWS OF VOLTAGE, CURRENT, AND POWER

2.1 PRIMARY STANDARD OF VOLTAGE

Our most basic references of physical values are called *primary standards.* For example, the Weston cell (Figure 2-1) is the official standard of emf, specified by the National Bureau of Standards. Other electrical sources, or voltmeters, that have been calibrated against a primary standard are called *secondary standards. Calibration* is the procedure of checking indication accuracy, or measuring a value with respect to a reference value. For example, a typical general-purpose voltmeter is illustrated in Figure 2-2. Its indication accuracy can be checked against the emf supplied by a Weston cell. If there should be a slight error in indication, it can be noted on a calibration chart or tabulation. Hence, the voltmeter becomes a secondary standard. This terminology implies that an experimental error may be present, although it might be very small (see Appendix I for further discussion). The Weston cell is named after Edward Weston, who suggested and assisted in the development of this primary standard.

The official standard of emf is called the Weston *normal* cell, and has the construction depicted in Figure 2-3. A *saturated* cadmium-sulfate solution is used as the electrolyte. At 20°C, the Weston normal cell gen-

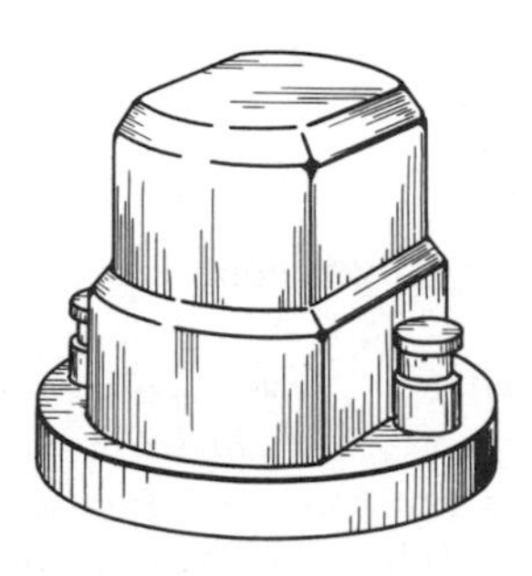

Figure 2-1
Sketch of a Weston cell.

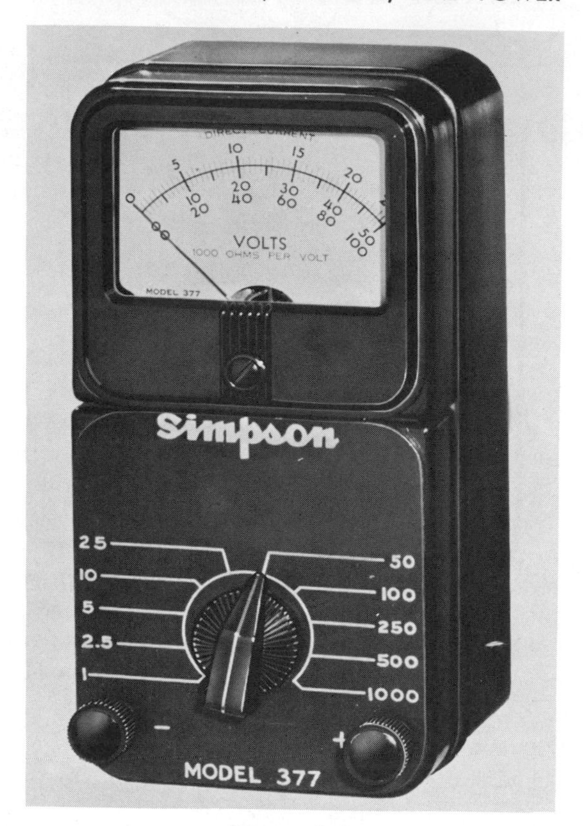

Figure 2-2
A typical general-purpose voltmeter. (Courtesy of Simpson Electric Co.)

erates an emf of 1.0183 volts, which is found to agree with similar cells to a few parts in 100,000. Its emf changes slightly with temperature. Hence, when used at a temperature other than 20°C, the cell's emf is calculated according to the formula:

$$E_t = 1.0183\ [1 - 0.0000406\ (t - 20) - 0.00000095\ (t - 20)^2]\ \text{volts} \qquad \textbf{(2.1)}$$

where E_t is the emf at the changed temperature and t is the temperature of the cell in °C.

We must remember that a Weston cell generates its rated emf only at 20°C. Equation (2.1) is an *empirical* formula, which has been "fitted" to experimental data. It is not intended for use other than over a moderate range of temperature. The second term may be neglected for small temperature changes. A discussion of how empirical formulas are derived is reviewed in Appendix I.

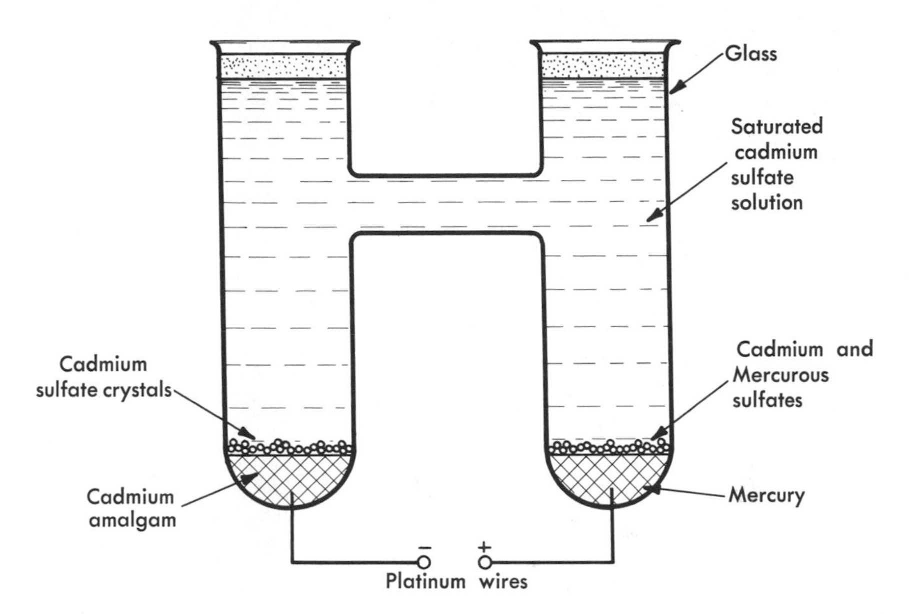

Figure 2-3
Plan of a Weston normal cell.

The essential feature of a cell is that it is comprised of two conductors and an electrolyte; the latter acts chemically on one of the conductors more than on the other. Although many of these cells are interesting (such as the classical and formerly popular Edison cell), only a few have any practical value as primary or secondary standards of emf. The familiar dry cell, invented by Georges Leclanché (1839–1882), lacks the stability of the Weston cell. Hence, a dry cell is a poor standard of emf. The original Voltaic cell consisted of a plate of copper separated from a plate of zinc by moistened paper. Later, the copper and zinc plates were immersed in a sulfuric-acid solution. However, a Voltaic cell lacks the stability of a Weston cell, and is unsuitable as a standard of emf.

A somewhat similar standard of emf is called the *unsaturated* Weston cell. Its accuracy is not quite as great as that of a saturated cell; however, the use of an unsaturated cadmium-sulfate solution results in practically no temperature coefficient. The emf of a new unsaturated cell falls in the range from 1.0185 to 1.0190 volts. Most of the Weston cells used in school laboratories are unsaturated.

Standard cells are not designed to supply current flow. When appreciable current is drawn from a standard cell, its emf decreases. This decrease is caused by chemical reactions in the cell, termed *polarization* processes. Of course, a slight current drain is unavoidable before the calibrating equipment is precisely adjusted. Fortunately, the effects of polarization disappear after a polarized cell is permitted to stand on open circuit for a suitable length of time. An unsaturated cell should not be required to supply more than 0.0001 amp at any time.

Because of this current limitation, most calibration procedures are arranged to compare the emf of a standard cell against an adjustable source of emf with no current flow. When two equal voltages oppose each other, as depicted in Figure 2-4, there is no net voltage present to cause

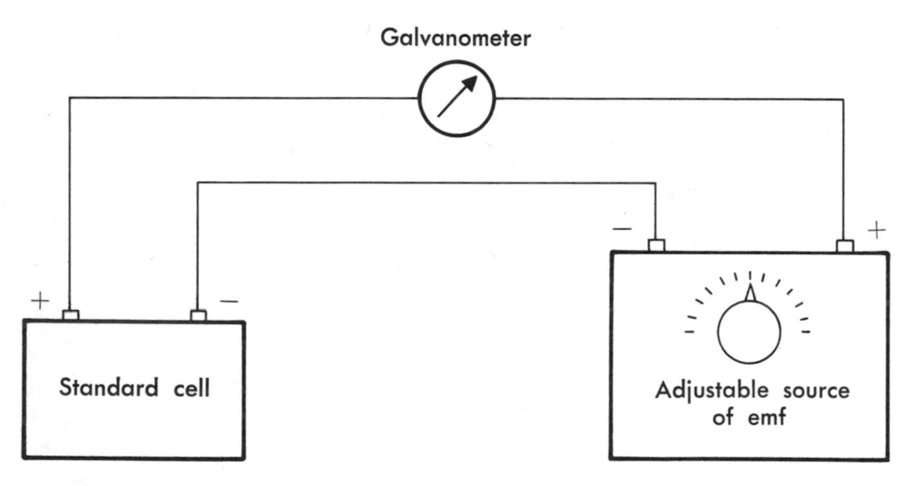

Figure 2-4
Basic calibrating arrangement.

electron flow in the wires. The galvanometer (a sensitive current indicator) will read zero. In turn, the adjustable source of emf is calibrated, and becomes a secondary standard. A few calibration procedures are used on occasion that do require a slight current drain from the standard cell. These are arranged to demand less than 0.0000075 amp. Decrease of emf supplied by a standard cell is negligible at this slight current flow.

We recall that a galvanometer is a sensitive current indicator. Thus, although a flashlight bulb could be used to indicate current flow instead of a galvanometer in Figure 2-4, the bulb will serve this purpose poorly. A comparatively large current flow is required to produce a visible glow in a flashlight bulb. On the other hand, a sensitive galvanometer can indicate the flow of 10^{-12} amp. A small flashlight bulb does not glow visibly until the current rises to about 0.15 amp. The design and operation of a galvanometer are explained in Chapter 18.

2.2 THE ELECTRON-VOLT

Another basic unit called the *electron-volt* is widely used in stating the energies of electrons and other charged particles. The electron-volt must not be confused with the volt unit. If an electron is accelerated through a potential of 1 volt, its kinetic energy increases by 1 electron-volt. One electron-volt is equal to 1.6×10^{-19} joule. One joule of work is equal to 0.7378 ft-lb. We are often concerned with the velocity of an electron which falls through a given potential. If the initial velocity of

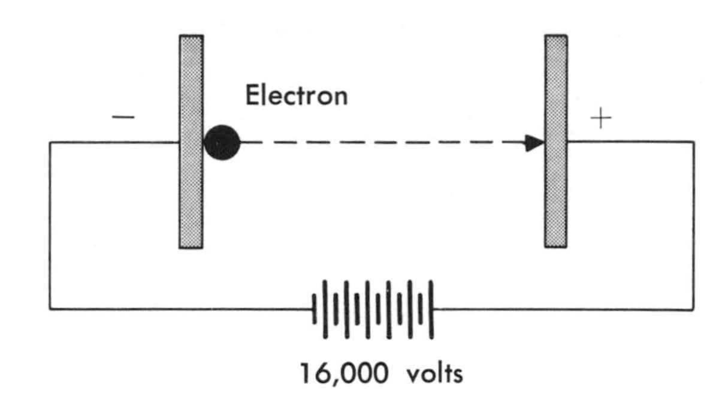

Figure 2-5
An electron is accelerated in free fall through an electric field.

the electron is zero, and it falls through a potential of V volts, its final velocity is

$$v = 5.93 \times 10^5 \sqrt{V} \tag{2.2}$$

where v is the final velocity of the electron in meters per second, and V is the potential difference in volts.

For example, if an electron falls through 16,000 volts, as depicted in Figure 2-5, its final velocity will be 7.5×10^7 meters per sec. A meter is equal to 39.37 in. The electron attains a velocity of approximately one-fourth the speed of light at the end of its fall. It then has 16,000 electron-volts of energy. From a previous discussion, it follows that this is an energy of 2.56×10^{-15} joule. In terms of the erg, 1 electron-volt (1 ev) is equal to 1.6×10^{-12} erg. One million electron-volts (Mev) is called 1 *mega-electron volt.* In modern nuclear experiments, particle energies are often stated in billions of electron-volts (Bev). Note that the mass of an electron increases as its velocity increases. This is called the *Einstein correction,* and is negligible until the velocity becomes a substantial fraction of the velocity of light. If an electron could be accelerated to the velocity of light, its mass would become infinite. It is accepted as a general principle of physics that no particle or object can travel faster than the velocity of light. You will have an opportunity to learn more about this topic in your advanced physics courses.

2.3 PRIMARY STANDARD OF CURRENT

Let us consider the primary standard of current flow. Most of us are aware of the principle of electroplating. Suppose that it is desired to copper-plate a metal object. The basic arrangement is seen in Figure 2-6. If the electrodes were placed in pure distilled water, current would not flow (chemically pure water is a good insulator). However, a salt solution is a good conductor. Thus, the copper-sulfate solution, called an *electrolyte,* depicted in Figure 2-6 is a good conductor. When an electric current is

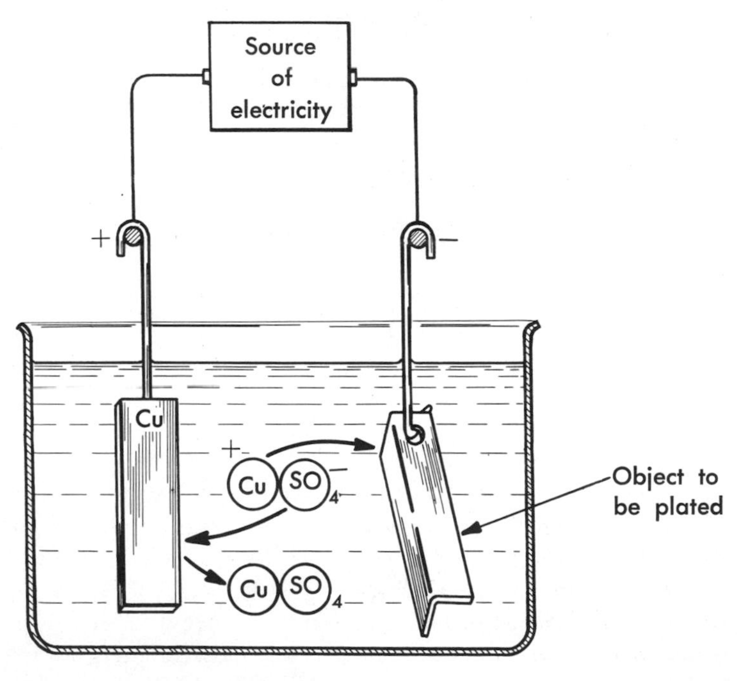

Figure 2-6
Illustration of the electroplating principle.

passed through an electrolyte, chemical decomposition occurs. This process is called *electrolysis.* Electrolysis was discovered in 1800 by William Nicholson and Anthony Carlisle.

The tank shown in Figure 2-6 contains a solution of copper sulfate. Each molecule of copper sulfate comprises one atom of copper (Cu), one atom of sulfur (S), and four atoms of oxygen (O_4). In water solution, each copper-sulfate molecule splits up into two ions (charged particles). Thus, an ion has an electric charge. The SO_4 ion is charged negatively; it has two extra electrons. These two extra electrons are obtained from the copper atom. Hence, the copper ion has two electrons less than normal and is charged positively.

Unlike charges attract. Accordingly, the positive Cu ions drift to the negative electrode (object to be plated). Each ion acquires two electrons from the negative electrode. Meanwhile, the SO_4 ions drift to the positive electrode. Each SO_4 ion relinquishes two electrons to the positive electrode. As the ionic charge is thus neutralized, the ion combines with one atom of copper. Thereby, one molecule of copper sulfate is formed. Copper returns to the solution in the form of copper sulfate as fast as it is taken from solution by the negative electrode. Hence, the concentration of the solution does not change. The electroplating action can continue until the Cu electrode is completely consumed.

Note that current flow occurs in Figure 2-6 both from negative to positive and from positive to negative electrodes. Both positive and negative charge carriers are present. Thus, current flow in an electrolyte differs from current flow in a wire. In a subsequent discussion, we will find that there are solids in which both positive and negative charge carriers are present. In these solids, current flow differs from that in an electrolyte. We will also find that conduction in gases entails the presence of both positive and negative charge carriers.

THE COULOMETER

The basic electroplating principle depicted in Figure 2-6 is used in primary standards of current flow. Electroplating was discovered in 1802 by Brugnatelli. A current standard is called a *coulometer,* or *voltameter;* coulometer is preferred in modern terminology. Some types of current standards utilize a copper salt; others use a silver salt. By international agreement, the ampere is defined as a current flow depositing 0.001118 gram of silver per sec in a coulometer which is operated under specified standard conditions. Silver nitrate is used in the primary current standard specified by international electrical congresses. The solution is about 15 percent silver nitrate by weight, and the immersed area of the *anode* (positive electrode) is approximately 50 cm^2 per amp. The anode is fabricated from pure silver. The negative electrode is called the *cathode*. The terms anode and cathode were coined by Faraday about 1830.

$$I = \frac{M}{0.001118t} \tag{2.3}$$

where I is the current in amperes, M is the weight of deposited silver in grams, 0.00118 is the electrochemical equivalent of silver, and t is the time in seconds that the current flows.

Although the process of electroplating was discovered by Brugnatelli, its mathematical analysis was the product of Faraday's genius. Faraday's two laws of electrolysis state:

1. The mass of a substance liberated at an electrode is directly proportional to the current value, and to the time that the current flows.
2. The mass of a substance liberated at an electrode is proportional to its chemical equivalent weight.

Thus, Faraday's first law states that the amount of metal which is liberated is directly proportional to the quantity (coulombs) of electricity that passes. This law is expressed by the equation

$$M = KIt \tag{2.4}$$

where M is the number of grams liberated, I is the current flow in amps, t is the time of current flow in seconds, and K is a constant, called the *electrochemical equivalent* of the substance.

Therefore, the electrochemical equivalent of a substance is the number of grams of that substance liberated by a current flow of 1 amp for 1 sec. Table 2-1 notes the electrochemical equivalents of several common elements.

Faraday's second law states that if the *same* current flows through different electrolytic cells containing, for example, a solution of sulfuric acid (H_2SO_4), a solution of silver nitrate ($AgNO_3$), and a solution of

Table 2-1

ELECTROCHEMICAL EQUIVALENTS

Element	*Atomic weight*	*Valency*	*Chemical equivalent*	*Electrochemical equivalent*
Chlorine	35.46	1	35.46	0.0003675
Copper	63.57	2	31.78	0.0003294
Hydrogen	1.008	1	1.0008	0.00001046
Iron++	55.84	2	27.92	0.0002893
Iron+++	55.84	3	18.61	0.0001929
Oxygen	16.00	2	8.00	0.00008291
Silver	107.88	1	107.88	0.0011180
Zinc	65.37	2	32.68	0.0003387

copper sulfate ($CuSO_4$), 8 parts by weight of oxygen will be liberated at the anode of each cell. 1.008 parts by weight of hydrogen will be liberated at the cathode of the first cell, 107.9 parts by weight of silver at the cathode of the second cell, and 31.8 parts by weight of copper will be liberated at the cathode of the third cell.

We see that the chemical equivalent value is equal to the atomic weight of the element divided by its valency. Since iron has two valencies, it has two chemical equivalents corresponding to the ferrous ion and to the ferric ion. The values for chemical equivalents tell us the parts by weight that will be liberated by a reference current flow. If we know the electrochemical equivalent for any one element, we can then calculate the electrochemical equivalents of all other elements from their atomic weights and valencies. The electrochemical equivalent for silver has been measured with highest accuracy. Hence, the electrochemical equivalents for the other elements are calculated with respect to silver.

2.4 RESISTANCE IS A VOLTAGE/CURRENT RATIO

We know that resistance is in opposition to current flow. However, to measure a resistance value, the voltage/current ratio must be determined. That is, resistance is defined as the ratio of voltage to current; and is called a *derived* unit. It follows that primary standards of voltage and current define the unit of resistance. If 1 amp flows through a resistance when 1 volt is applied, the resistance value is 1 ohm. Again, if 2 amps flow through a resistance when 2 volts are applied, its resistance value is 1 ohm. Thus, we can write

$$\text{Resistance} = \frac{\text{volts}}{\text{amperes}} = \text{ohms}$$

$$R = \frac{E}{I} \tag{2.5}$$

Observe that this is merely a rearrangement of Ohm's law. Although there is no primary standard of resistance, it has been found convenient to establish an international standard of resistance. Availability of a resistance standard simplifies many laboratory procedures. Nevertheless, the international standard lacks the significance of a primary standard. The international ohm is defined as the resistance of a mercury column which has a length of 106.3 cm and a mass of 14.4521 grams; the mercury column has a constant cross-sectional area of 1 sq millimeter at the temperature of melting ice. (One millimeter is 0.001 meter.)

When electric current flows through resistance, heat is generated. Incandescent lamps and electric stoves are prime examples. Thus, a flow of 1 amp through a resistance of 1 ohm for 1 sec generates 0.24 calorie of heat. Recall that the calorie is a basic heat unit. One calorie raises the temperature of 1 gram of water 1°C. If considerable current flows through a resistor, enough heat will be generated to burn your finger when you touch the resistor. Still greater current flow will burn up the resistor. Heat is radiated from the resistor as electromagnetic waves into surrounding space. Heat is also conducted from the resistor by its connecting wires. The wires also radiate electromagnetic waves (thermal energy). Note that good conductors of electricity are also good conductors of heat.

2.5 APPLICATION OF OHM'S LAW

Ohm's law states that $I = E/R$. To apply the law, we must know the values of two variables; the value of the third variable can then be calculated. Hence, we find it necessary to measure voltage, current, and resistance values in electric circuits. Routine measurements are made with voltmeters, ammeters, and ohmmeters. A voltmeter was illustrated in Figure 2-2, the appearance of a typical ammeter is seen in Figure 2-7, and an ohmmeter is illustrated in Figure 2-8. These three instruments are often combined in a volt-ohm-milliammeter (VOM), as shown in Figure 2-9. (One milliampere is 0.001 amp.) Details of instrument design and operation are explained subsequently.

Figure 2-7
A laboratory-type ammeter. (Courtesy of Simpson Electric Co.)

Figure 2-8
A general-purpose ohmmeter. (Courtesy of Simpson Electric Co.)

It follows from Ohm's law that if *any* two of the basic electrical units can be measured, the third can be calculated. In other words, $I = E/R$, $E = IR$, and $R = E/I$. We will find certain forms of resistance in electronic equipment that cannot be measured with an ohmmeter.

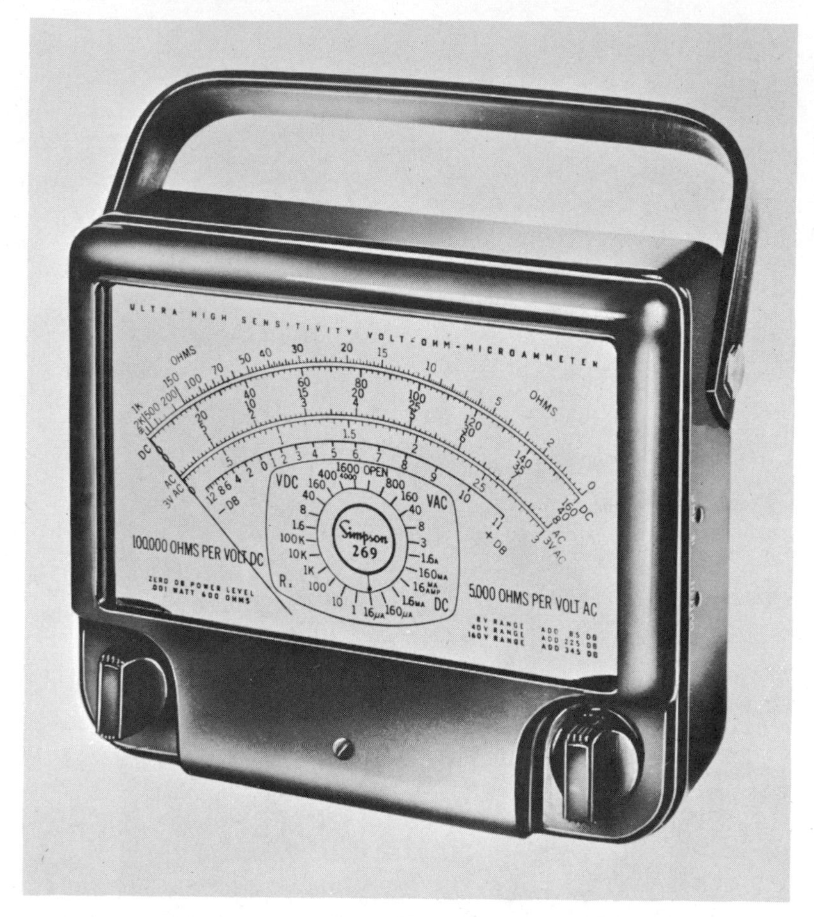

Figure 2-9
A typical volt-ohm-milliammeter. (Courtesy of Simpson Electric Co.)

Nevertheless, we can measure the current flow through the resistance, and the voltage across it in such situations. The resistance value can then be calculated easily from Ohm's law.

We will find circuits in which it is inconvenient to measure the current flow. However, it may be easy to measure the voltage across a known resistance, through which the current flows. Then the current flow can be easily calculated from Ohm's law. Evidently, Ohm's law is the keystone of all electrical analyses. Next, let us consider another restatement of Ohm's law. Conductance is the reciprocal of resistance:

$$G = \frac{1}{R} = \frac{I}{E} \tag{2.6}$$

The unit of conductance is the *mho* ("ohm" spelled backward), and is represented by the symbol G. A resistance of 1 ohm has a conductance of 1 mho. As resistance expresses opposition to current flow, conductance expresses permissiveness to current flow. The foregoing equation can be rearranged in the forms: $I = EG$, and $E = I/G$.

It is evident that circuit action can be described and calculated either in terms of resistance or conductance. You will find that certain circuit configurations can be analyzed more easily in terms of resistances; other configurations are simplified by expression in terms of conductances. The mathematical tools we choose in various situations should be those that minimize the time and effort entailed. Some of us tend to feel that it is easier to visualize circuit action in terms of resistances, rather than conductances. This may have semantic significance, or it may be a result of traditional exposition in which we become familiar with resistance before we learn about conductance.

The Greek letter omega (Ω) is commonly used as a symbol for ohm or ohms. Thus, one ohm may be written 1 Ω. However, no symbol has been formally assigned to the mho (although ℧ has been used by individual authors). Hence, the words mho and mhos must always be spelled out. For example, 0.5 Ω = 2 mhos. The symbol for resistance, or the word for conductance, is often implied but not expressed. For example, the statement that $G = 5$ is read: "The conductance is 5 mhos." Similarly, $R = 100$ is read: "The resistance is 100 ohms."

"SMALL" AND "LARGE" CURRENTS AND VOLTAGES

Brief consideration of Ohm's law discloses that a large current does not necessarily flow in a circuit when a large voltage is applied. If the resistance is extremely high, the application of high voltage results in little current flow. Moreover, in the special case in which the resistance is infinite, zero current flows although the applied voltage might be extremely great. On the other hand, a low voltage applied to a circuit will cause a large current flow if the resistance is quite small (conductance very large). Suppose that you apply 10,000 volts across a 100,000,000-ohm resistor; the current flow is small: $I = E/R = 10{,}000/100{,}000{,}000 = 0.0001$ amp. On the other hand, if you apply 0.1 volt across 100,000 mhos, the current flow is very large: $I = EG = 0.1 \times 100{,}000 = 10{,}000$ amps.

Whether a given voltage is regarded as "high" or "low" must depend upon the field in which you are working. A so-called high voltage in a transistorized radio-receiver circuit would be deemed extremely low in a public-utility distribution system. We recall that prehistoric man experienced electricity only in the form of lightning. The impressive character of a lightning stroke is associated with voltages and currents that are very large, by almost any standard of comparison. For example, the voltage represented by a lightning stroke will range from 2,000,000 to 20,000,000 volts. Lightning currents range from 30,000 amps to 160,000 amps.

What is the resistance of the air path of a lightning stroke? If the stroke comprises 10,000,000 volts and 100,000 amps, Ohm's law tells us that the resistance of the discharge path is equal to 10,000,000/100,000 or 100 ohms. Air has this comparatively low resistance value only when it is ionized by high voltage, which tears electrons from the gas molecules to form charged particles.

An extremely low resistance (extremely high conductance) corresponds to a *short-circuit*. You may have discovered from unfortunate experience with an automobile electrical system that when a battery is short-circuited, it soon "dies." A very large current (by automotive standards) is drawn from the battery through the short-circuit. Soon, the potential energy of the battery chemicals is depleted. On the other hand, an extremely high resistance (extremely low conductance), corresponds to an open circuit. In theory, an open circuit has infinite resistance. But in practice, an open circuit does not have quite an infinite resistance; an extremely small current will flow in response to an applied voltage. For example, you may have charged an electroscope in your physics courses and observed the gradual discharge as the electroscope stood on open circuit for some time.

The lowest known resistance values occur in the phenomenon of superconductivity, noted in Chapter 1. Although a superconducting metal is often said to have zero resistance, this is not strictly true. However, its resistance is very low, indeed. Kammerlingh Onnes of Leyden determined that a typical superconducting metal has less than one-billionth of its resistance value at 0°C. Thus, if a lead ring is cooled to −265.7° or lower, it becomes a superconductor. When an electric current is established in the lead ring, the current continues to flow for days, although no voltage is applied. Eventually, the extremely small resistance of the ring consumes the kinetic energy of the moving electrons, and the current gradually decreases to zero. We recognize also that the moving electrons are accelerated toward the center of the ring, and must accordingly radiate a definite though very slight amount of energy. Superconductivity has some practical applications, as in electronic computers.

We know that a direct current (d-c) is a steady flow of electrons or other charged particles in one direction. It is helpful to analyze d-c situations first, because they are comparatively easy to understand. After the foundations of electrical theory have been established, we will find out how Ohm's law can be extended to the analysis of electric currents which reverse their direction of flow at uniform or nonuniform intervals. A current that reverses its direction of flow is called an *alternating current* (a-c). It must not be supposed that all electric currents can be classified as d-c or a-c currents. For example, consider a simple circuit comprising a battery, lamp, and switch. If you energize the circuit for an instant by closing the switch and then immediately opening the switch, a *pulse* of current flows. The pulse current is a d-c flow, and does not reverse its direction of flow. Hence, it is not an a-c current. However, the pulse is not a *steady* flow of current. Therefore, it is not a true direct current. How shall we classify this type of current flow? The answer to this and other particular types of current flow will be developed in following chapters.

2.6 UNITS OF WORK AND POWER

You have probably become familiar with the mechanical units of work and power in your physics courses. We know that resistance causes the generation of heat in response to current flow. In turn, there is a certain amount of electrical power consumption. Power can be measured in various ways; for example, it can be measured with a wattmeter, such as illustrated in Figure 2-10. Power values can also be calculated from voltage and current measurements with a voltmeter and ammeter. They can also be calculated from voltage and resistance measurements, or from current and resistance measurements. If we multiply the number of volts across a resistance by the number of amperes flowing through the resist-

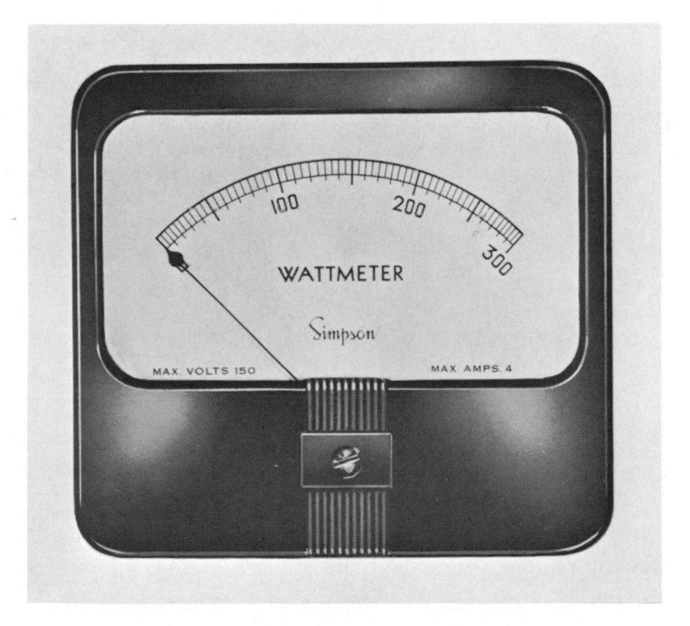

Figure 2-10
A panel-type wattmeter. (Courtesy of Simpson Electric Co.)

ance, the product is the power rate in *watts*. This electrical unit is named after James Watt, who pioneered the Industrial Revolution. In the example cited, it is important to note that the watt is the *rate* of doing work.

If work is done at a certain rate for a chosen length of time, a corresponding amount of energy will have been *consumed*. Thus, this power quantity, or power consumption, is measured in watt-seconds; it is the power rate multiplied by time. We multiply volts times amperes times the number of seconds that the current has flowed to obtain the power quantity in watt-seconds. Similarly, we multiply volts times amperes times hours to obtain the power quantity in watt-hours. Everyone is somewhat familiar with watt-hours. The electric company installs a watt-hour meter in your home, office, or factory. This meter records the amount of energy which your lamps and appliances have consumed during a month—the meter indicates watt-hours. The following equations are almost as basic and important as Ohm's law

$$\text{Power rate} = W = EI \tag{2.7}$$

where W is in watts, E is in volts, and I is in amperes.

$$\text{Power quantity} = W = EIt \tag{2.8}$$

where W is in watt-seconds, E is in volts, I is in amperes, and t is in seconds (or where W is in watt-hours, E is in volts, I is in amperes, and t is in hours).

Students are sometimes confused by use of the symbol W for both power rate and power quantity. It is essential to ask whether W represents volts times amperes, or whether it represents volts times amperes, multiplied by the time that the current has flowed. To draw an analogy, if you drive an automobile 50 miles per hour, this is a statement of rate of travel; it does not state how far you have traveled. But if you drive an automobile 50 miles an hour for 10 hours, you have traveled $50 \times 10 = 500$ miles. EIt equals work, or energy.

HORSEPOWER RATING OF ELECTRICAL MACHINERY

Horsepower is the rate of doing work. When 550 lb are raised vertically at the rate of 1 ft per sec, work is being done at the rate of 1 horsepower; or, 1 horsepower denotes work being done at the rate of 550 ft-lb per sec. Note that the *horsepower-hour* is the *amount* of work performed, or energy consumed, by working at the rate of 1 horsepower for 1 hour. There are 3600 sec in 1 hour; hence, a horsepower-hour is equal to 1,980,000 ft-lb of work. Again, if work is done at the rate of 1 horsepower for 1 min, 33,000 ft-lb of work will be accomplished. As most of us have learned, electric motors are commonly rated in terms of horsepower.

Suppose a washing machine has a ¼-horsepower motor. Disregarding any frictional and heat losses, the motor consumes ¼ horsepower of energy per sec at full load. One horsepower is equal to 746 watts; hence, this motor will consume power at the rate of 186.5 watts. In turn, the current rate is approximately 1.6 amps at 117 volts; $186.5/117 = 1.59 +$ amps. If this ¼-horsepower motor operates at full load for 20 min (1200 sec), it will consume $186.5 \times 1200 = 223{,}800$ watt-sec of energy. Since there are 3600 sec in an hour, your watt-hour meter will register approximately 62.2 watt-hours at the end of 20 min.

Let us consider the number of watt-hours in a lightning stroke. If the discharge has an average value of 10,000,000 volts and 50,000 amps for 50×10^{-6} sec, its power quantity is equal to 25,000,000 watt-sec. This quantity is equal to approximately 7000 watt-hours. Hence, the electrical energy in a lightning stroke could operate a ¼-horsepower motor at full load for approximately 37 hours.

Power can be calculated as the product of voltage and current, as explained previously; however, it can also be calculated from voltage and resistance values. Sometimes the latter is more convenient in practical situations. Since $W = EI$, and $I = E/R$, we can substitute E/R for I in the power formula and obtain

$$W = \frac{E^2}{R} \tag{2.9}$$

This formula states that if we measure the voltage E across a resistance R, we can calculate the power rate in watts. Power rates can also be calculated in terms of current and resistance values. Since $W = EI$ and $E = IR$, it is evident that

$$W = I^2R \tag{2.10}$$

Accordingly, if we measure the current flow through a resistor, we can calculate the power rate from current and resistance values. To demonstrate the equivalence of the three power formulas noted above, consider the circuit shown in Figure 2-11. The lamp has a resistance of 12 ohms. According to Ohm's law, the lamp will draw 0.25 amp at 3 volts. What is its power rate?

$$W = \frac{E^2}{R} = I^2R = EI = \frac{9}{12} = 0.0625 \times 12 = 3 \times 0.25 = 0.75 \text{ watt}$$

We obtain the same answer, 0.75 watt, no matter which of the three power-rate formulas is used. Our choice of formula is simply a matter of expediency in particular situations. If it is difficult to measure resistance, for example, we will use voltage and current measurements to calculate the power rate. Or, if it is not convenient to measure current, we can calculate the power rate from measured voltage and resistance values. In branch-circuit problems, current and resistance may be the known values, from which we can calculate the power rate.

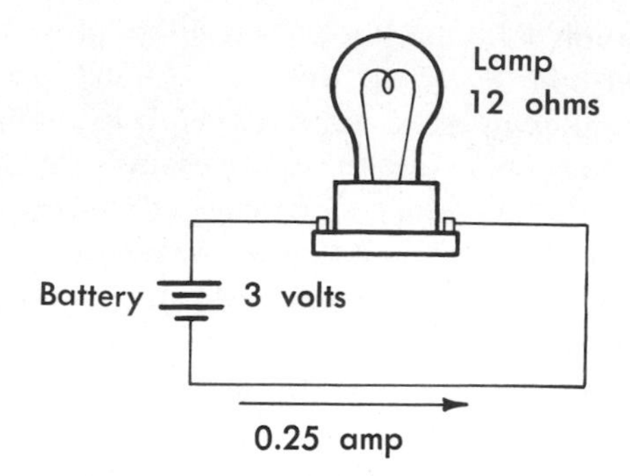

Figure 2-11
The power consumed by the lamp can be measured three different ways.

Of course, a wattmeter, as illustrated in Figure 2-10, can be connected into a circuit to measure the power rate directly. A wattmeter has the functions of both a voltmeter and an ammeter. It is constructed so that the pointer deflection is proportional to the rate of power consumption. However, if a wattmeter is not permanently wired into a circuit, we often find it more convenient to make voltage, current, or resistance measurements, and to calculate the rate of power consumption.

Lamps, motors, and resistors always have *power ratings.* What does this mean? We find that the power rating of a lamp corresponds to the amount of light it generates, in addition to specifying its rate of power consumption. Thus, a 100-watt lamp generates the same amount of light as two 50-watt lamps. Tungsten-filament lamps have a filament temperature of about 2200°C at rated voltage. A lamp consumes its rated power at rated voltage. Thus, a lamp rated at 100 watts and 117 volts will consume 100 watt-sec per sec if 117 volts are applied. However, keep in mind that much of this power consumption appears as heat; that is, a tungsten-filament lamp is not a highly efficient generator of light.

UNIT OF LUMINOUS INTENSITY

Luminous intensity is measured in *standard candles.* This unit is based on the luminous intensity provided by an ordinary wax candle. The luminous intensity of conventional filament lamps is approximately 1 candle for each watt of power rating. For example, a 60-watt lamp operated at rated voltage has a luminous intensity of approximately 60 candles. If you apply over-voltage to the 60-watt lamp, it will have a luminous intensity in excess of 60 candles, but the life of the lamp will be shortened. A substantial over-voltage will result in prompt burnout.

If you apply under-voltage to the lamp, however, its luminous intensity will be lessened, and its life will be increased.

The power rating of an electric motor is specified in two ways. For example, a 1/4-horsepower motor will develop this amount of mechanical power under full load. The motor is also rated for current demand at rated voltage under full load. All motors consume somewhat more electrical power than they deliver in mechanical power; therefore, they are not 100 percent efficient. If a motor is operated at more than its rated voltage, it will develop more than its rated mechanical power. However, the motor will overheat and may be damaged. On the other hand, if the motor is operated at less than its rated voltage, it will not develop its rated mechanical power. It is likely to "stall" under full rated mechanical load.

A power rating for a resistor states the maximum power which the resistor can safely dissipate at a specified ambient temperature and condition of ventilation. A 1-watt resistor that has a resistance value of 1000 ohms should not be operated with more than 31.6 volts across its terminals ($W = E^2/R$). Thus, the resistor dissipates approximately 1 watt of heat under this operating condition. For example, if you apply 100 volts across this resistor, it would overheat excessively and would probably be damaged. Normal ventilation is essential; thus, if the resistor is confined in a small insulating box (which dissipates heat slowly), the resistor will overheat although operated within its power rating.

Note that the rated resistance value of a resistor changes as its temperature increases. All metals have a positive temperature coefficient of resistance. Recall that manganin wire has a small temperature coefficient. Nevertheless, manganin-wire resistors increase in resistance value slightly as the operating temperature is increased. By way of comparison, a lamp filament may have about ten times more resistance when incandescent than when a very small current flows. Composition resistors increase in resistance value when heated. If overheated, a composition resistor does not return to its rated resistance value. Instead, its "cold" resistance remains abnormally high. Accordingly, a composition resistor is damaged in this manner by overload. If greatly overloaded, the resistor will char and burn out.

However, it must not be supposed that *all* resistors increase in resistance value when heated. When the resistance material is heated, it expands. This fact is employed in special constructions that cause the resistor to decrease in resistance value when heated. Such resistors have a negative temperature coefficient of resistance. They are used in many radio and television receivers, for example. We shall learn also that there are certain elements called *semiconductors* that have a negative temperature coefficient of resistance. This topic is reserved for subsequent discussion.

When we know the power rating of a lamp, for example, we can calculate how much it will cost to operate. If you operate five 100-watt lamps for 10 hours, the lamps will consume 5000 watt-hours of electrical energy. In turn, suppose your electric company charges 4 cents per 1000 watt-hours. It will cost 20 cents to operate the lamps for 10 hours. The cost of operation for an electric stove or a washing machine can be calculated in the same manner.

2.7 SURVEY OF PRACTICAL DECIMAL UNITS

Just as weights can be measured in ounces or tons, instead of pounds, electrical quantities can be measured in multiple or submultiple units. It is more convenient to measure the weight of an ordinary business letter in ounces than in fractions of a pound. It is preferred to measure the weight of a truck in tons instead of ounces or pounds. Similarly, the National Bureau of Standards recognizes multiple and submultiple units for the volt, ampere, ohm, mho, and watt. Standard prefixes for the basic electrical units have been assigned by the International Committee on Weights and Measures, listed in Table 2-2.

Table 2-2

METRIC PREFIXES

Multiple	*Prefix*	*Abbreviation*	*Multiple*	*Prefix*	*Abbreviation*
10	deka-	D	10^{-1}	deci-	d
10^2	hecto-	H	10^{-2}	centi-	c
10^3	kilo-	K	10^{-3}	milli-	m
10^4	myria-	My	10^{-4}	—	—
10^6	mega-	M	10^{-6}	micro-	μ
10^9	giga-	G	10^{-9}	nano-	n
10^{12}	tera-	T	10^{-12}	pico-	p

Electrical instruments may be calibrated in volts, amperes, or ohms, as previously noted. Low-range voltmeters may be calibrated in millivolts, as illustrated in Figure 2-12. Low-voltage sources are sometimes calibrated in microvolts with a microvolt attenuator (Figure 2-13). Small-current meters (Figure 2-14) are calibrated in milliamperes or microamperes. Low-range ohmmeters are calibrated in milliohms, as seen in Figure 2-15. Most sound-level meters are calibrated in decibels (Figure 2-16). The bel unit is discussed in Chapter 19. Figure 2-17 illustrates a conventional radio tube tester which indicates conductance values in micromhos.

The picture tube in an ordinary color-television receiver may be rated for operation at 25,000 volts. This figure is often stated as 25 kilovolts, abbreviated 25 kv. Many resistors in electronic circuitry have high

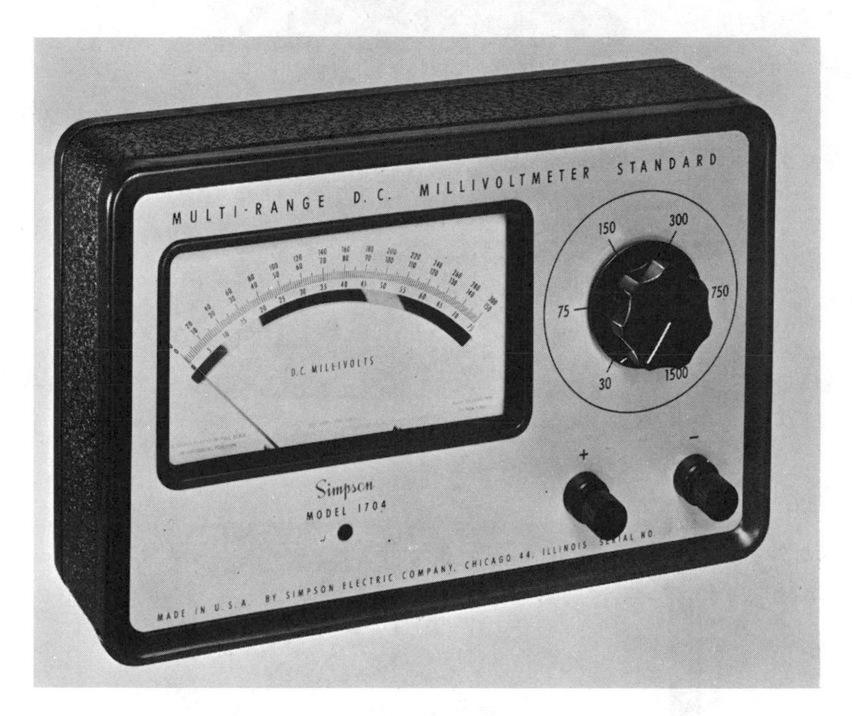

Figure 2-12
A low-range voltmeter, calibrated in millivolts. (Courtesy of Simpson Electric Co.)

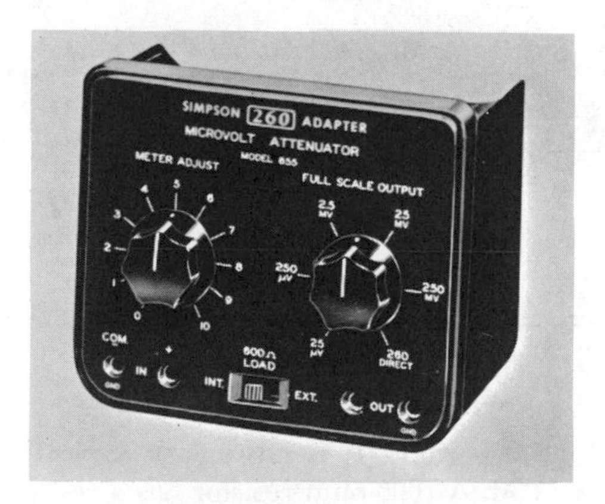

Figure 2-13
A microvolt attenuator. (Courtesy of Simpson Electric Co.)

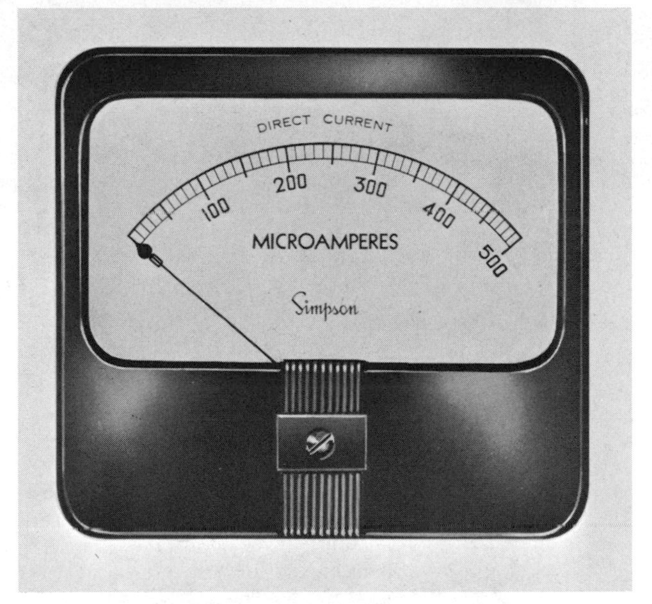

Figure 2-14
Small-current meters, calibrated in milliamperes or microamperes. (Courtesy of Simpson Electric Co.)

values, such as 1,000,000 ohms. It is customary to write this value as 1 megohm, 1 meg, or 1 M. A 1000-ohm resistor has a resistance of 1 kilohm or 1 K. If your electric company charges 4 cents per 1000 watt-hours, this is a rate of 4 cents per kilowatt-hour, or 4 cents per Kwh. Submultiple units of power are encountered in electronic equipment. For example, the power input from an antenna to an ordinary radio receiver might be 0.000001 watt, 1 microwatt, or 1 μw.

It is interesting to note that a signal input of 10^{-11} watt will produce a picture on the screen of a good television receiver. A sound wave of minimum audibility has a power of about 10^{-16} watt per sq cm. A light

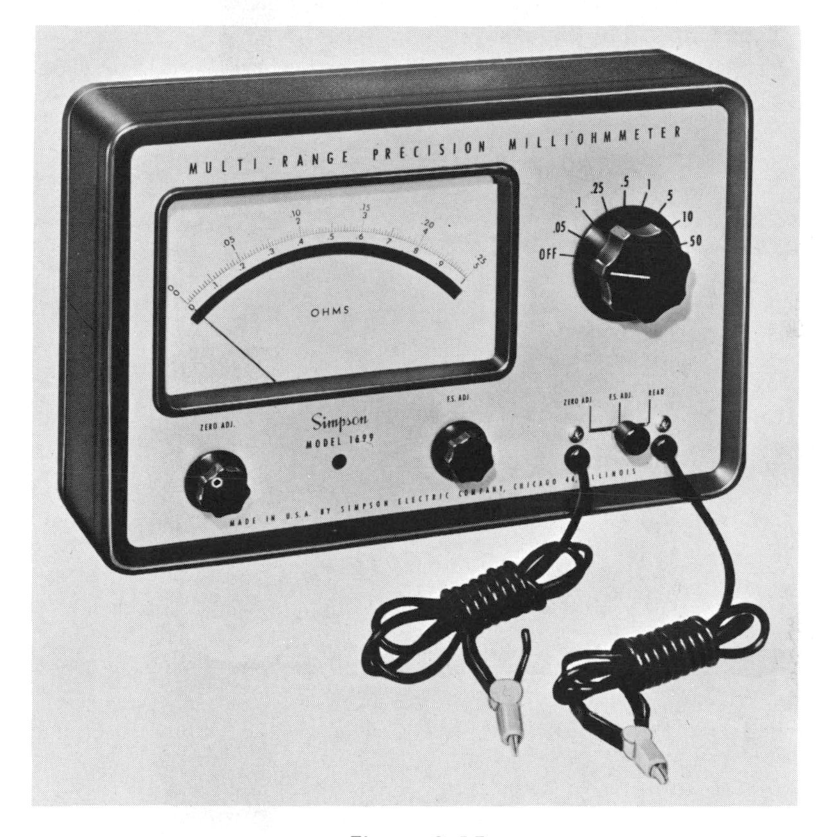

Figure 2-15
Low-range ohmmeter, calibrated in milliohms. (Courtesy of Simpson Electric Co.)

source of minimum visibility has a power of approximately 10^{-15} watt per sq cm. Note the "pico-" prefix in Table 2-2. "Pico-" is symbolized by "p" and denotes 10^{-12} of the basic unit. This is a comparatively recent submultiple assignment that is coming into common use. Formerly, "10^{-12}" was symbolized by "$\mu\mu$," and you will often encounter this symbolization. "Pico-" is also written as "micro-micro-" or "mm-" in older notation.

Multiple and submultiple units are easy to use, because they have a decimal relation to one another. These units are related to each other by some power of 10. Hence, conversion from a basic unit to a multiple or submultiple unit requires only that the decimal point be shifted appropriately. Thus, if 1 ma flows in a circuit, we shift the decimal point three places to the left to obtain 0.001 amp for use in Ohm's law calculations with volt and ohm units. On the other hand, if a calculation should yield an answer of 0.001 amp, we can shift the decimal point three places to the right and state the answer as 1 ma. Evidently, Ohm's law can be employed with multiple or submultiple units throughout. For example,

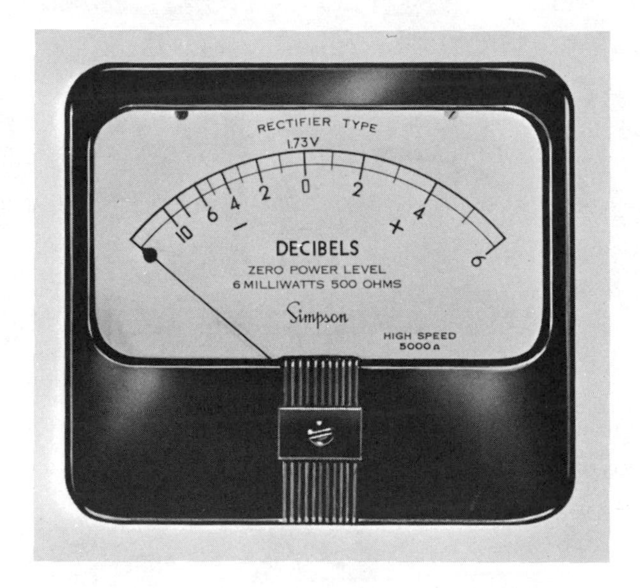

Figure 2-16
A sound-level meter, calibrated in decibels. (Courtesy of Simpson Electric Co.)

1 ma = 1 mv/1 mΩ. It is only necessary that we be consistent throughout in the use of multiple or submultiple units in equations.

DIMENSIONS OF PHYSICAL UNITS

Finally, let us observe the *dimensions* of various units. In your physics courses, you learned that work is equal to force multiplied by distance. Work is equal to energy, and therefore energy is equal to force multiplied by distance. Power is the rate of energy consumption; or, power is equal to energy divided by time. Velocity is equal to distance divided by time, and acceleration is equal to distance divided by time squared. It might seem like belaboring the obvious to review the dimensions of work, energy, power, velocity, and acceleration. However, these simple facts will now be extended into the list of electrical units which we have learned. We also find that voltage, current, and resistance have dimensions.

Analysis of equations in mechanics is made conveniently in terms of force F, length L, and time T. These same dimensions are also convenient for analysis of equations in electricity, provided we also utilize charge Q.

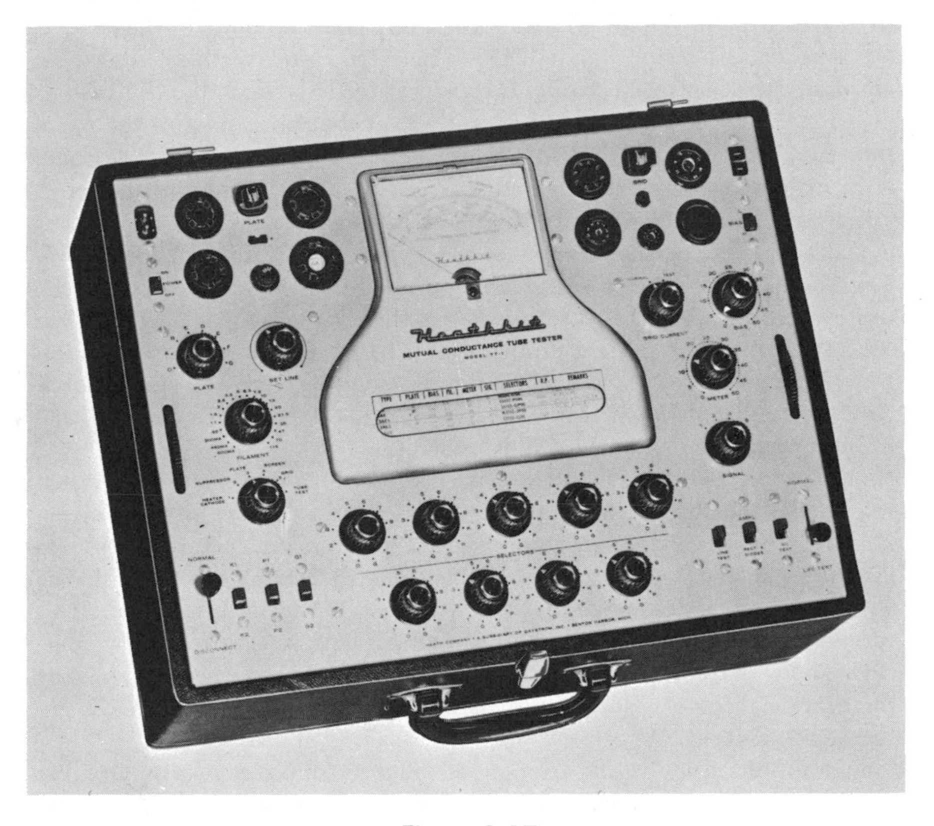

Figure 2-17
A tube tester which indicates conductance values in micromhos. (Courtesy of Heath Co.)

Current has the dimensions of charge divided by time, because we learned that current is measured in terms of charge which flows past a point in one unit of time. We learned also that voltage is a unit of work, and is equal to the work done in separating unit charges by unit distance. Hence, it is evident that voltage has the dimensions of FL/Q. Referring to resistance, we know that $R = E/I$. In turn, $R = (FLQ^{-1})/(QT^{-1})$, or $R = FLT/Q^2$ in terms of dimensions. Since resistivity is resistance per unit length, it follows directly that resistivity is equal FL^2T/Q^2 in terms of dimensions. Of course, energy must be equal to FL, and power must be equal to FL/T, just as in the familiar mechanical system. Referring to capacitance, we note that $Q = CE$, or $C = Q/E$. Accordingly, $C = Q/(FLQ^{-1})$, or Q^2/LF in terms of dimensions.

What is the practical use of dimensions? We know very well that oranges multiplied by oranges yields oranges—the product is never equal to apples. Again, we know that force multiplied by length yields FL—the product is never equal to L/T. Therefore, after we have solved an algebraic problem in mechanics, we can proceed to check the dimensions on both sides of the equation. Unless we find that both sides of the equation contain the *same* dimensions, it follows that we have made some error in our algebra. Then, we must check our solution to find the error.

Recall that voltage multiplied by current yields power—the product is never equal to resistance. But it is easy to make a mistake in algebra. For example, suppose we have written $R = EI$. A dimensional check quickly exposes the error, because R has the dimensions of FLT/Q^2. On the other hand, EI has the dimensions FL/T. Therefore, the equation $R = EI$ is wrong. This is such a simple example that the dimensional check seems unnecessary. However, when we come to involved calculations, dimensional checks are indispensable.

There is another valuable aspect to the basic dimensions. When we observe the chapter summary, we are reminded of the physical meaning of current, voltage, resistance, and capacitance. It is quite easy to visualize current as charge divided by time. It is also easy to visualize voltage as force times length divided by charge. However, it is very difficult to visualize resistance as force multiplied by length, multiplied by time, divided by charge squared. In fact, we would probably never know the physical meaning of resistance unless we had learned how to make dimensional analyses.

It should not disturb us that we find it difficult to visualize the physical meaning of units such as resistance and capacitance. Many concepts in electricity are far from obvious. The important consideration is to know *how to track down the physical meaning* of concepts which are not obvious. As students of electricity, it is important for us to know the basic dimensions.

2.8 EXPERIMENTAL PROCEDURES AND PRECAUTIONS

Almost everyone is familiar with the fact that the human body is a conductor of electricity. Many of us have received accidental shocks from improper handling of electrical equipment. For example, you may have received a severe shock from touching a spark plug in an automobile when the engine was running. You may also have received a shock from touching a defective floor lamp or vacuum cleaner. Household appliances rarely become defective in such manner that the user can be shocked, but such defects do occur on occasion. For example, the continued use of badly frayed power cords can lead to an accidental shock.

Although the human body is a conductor of electricity, it has a comparatively high resistance compared with metals. You can measure the resistance to current flow through your hands and arms by grasping the test clips of an ohmmeter. If your fingers are dry, you might measure a resistance of 100,000 ohms. No shock is felt when this test is made, because the current flow from the ohmmeter is very small. A typical ohmmeter applies approximately 7 volts to your fingers in this test. If your fingers are damp, you might measure a resistance of 10,000 ohms. The current flow then follows from Ohm's law: $I = E/R = 7/10{,}000 = 0.7$ ma.

Since the current flow through your arms and body is very small in this test, no shock is perceived. On the other hand, a higher voltage, such as 25 volts, causes sufficient current flow through your arms to give you a quite perceptible shock (particularly if your fingers are damp). Note that a 117-volt source causes a comparatively large current flow through body resistance often resulting in serious shock. The current flow that occurs when you contact a source of electricity depends not only upon dryness or dampness of your fingers, but also upon the area of contact surface and the firmness of contact. For example, if you grasp a pair of ohmmeter test clips tightly, the meter indicates a lower resistance than when you grasp the clips loosely.

It is the amount of power dissipated in the circuit through your body that determines the severity of a shock. Since electric power is dissipated as heat in a resistance, shocks often produce severe burns at the point or area of contact. If a baby pokes his finger into an open electric-light socket, he receives a cruel shock, and his finger is burned. Electric current produces abnormal nerve and muscle response. Current flow through the heart region is particularly dangerous. Unfortunately, substantial current flow through the hands and arms "freezes" the victim to the source of electricity, and he cannot let go. If he is in suitable position, the "frozen" victim may collapse, so that the contact is broken by his fall. When current flow is substantial, the shock victim thinks that he is screaming, but actually he utters no sound.

Good practice dictates that electricity be turned off in any circuit which operates at more than 25 volts before any exposed terminal or wire is touched. Electricians who must occasionally work with "live" circuits that operate at substantial voltages wear insulating gloves. They also endeavor to work with one hand only, to avoid the possibility of completing a circuit through arms and body. It is good practice to stand on an insulating sheet, such as a rubber mat, when working with live circuits. As seen in Figure 2-18, one side of a 117-volt line is customarily connected to ground. If an electrician stands on a damp floor and touches the live wire with a bare hand or finger, a circuit is completed through his body, and he may receive a severe shock.

Newspapers have reported accidental deaths from defective radio receivers. For example, one victim was seated in a bathtub (connected to ground) and was killed when he reached out to tune a defective radio receiver. The defect caused the live 117-volt line to make electrical connection with the metal construction of the tuning knob. When a person's body makes contact with water over a considerable area, his body resistance becomes quite low. A current flow less than 1 ma through the body

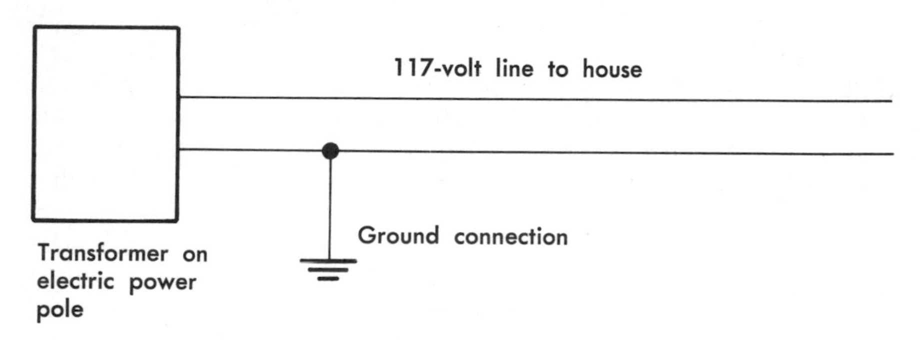

Figure 2-18
One side of the 117-volt line is grounded.

is imperceptible. On the other hand, a current flow of 10 ma produces a serious shock. A current flow of 100 ma is often fatal.

Although contact across a 117-volt line can kill a person, a 10,000-volt source in a television cannot kill anyone in normal health. A person who is subject to heart attacks, however, can be killed by a minor shock through the chest region. The 10,000-volt lead connected to a television picture tube gives a normal person only an unpleasant "bite." This perhaps surprising fact results from the comparatively small current being supplied by a picture-tube circuit. That is, a 117-volt power line is a high-current source. It can supply as much current as permitted by the circuit resistance. However, a 10,000-volt source in a television receiver is a small-current source. It can supply less than 1 ma, even when connected to a low-resistance load. The nature and characteristics of high-current and low-current sources are explained in following chapters.

Beginners sometimes suppose that a dry cell could be dangerous because it can supply many amperes of current. On the contrary, a dry cell is not dangerous because it applies only 1.5 volts to a circuit through the body. It can force only a very small current through a body resistance of 10,000 ohms. However, note that if you touch your tongue to one terminal of a dry cell, and touch the other terminal with your finger, you will experience a small shock and a bad taste at the tip of your tongue. The nerve endings in the membrane of the tongue are very sensitive, which accounts for electric shock at 1.5 volts. Electrolysis in the tongue membrane causes chemical reactions that produce the bad taste. Before the galvanometer was invented, scientists had no other method than the sense of taste to detect the presence of feeble electric currents.

A 12-volt automobile battery can supply hundreds of amperes to a low-resistance circuit. But because 12 volts can force only a very small current through a body resistance of perhaps 10,000 ohms, the storage battery is not dangerous. By way of comparison, a spark plug in an automobile engine operates at 20,000 to 30,000 volts. The spark-plug circuit is a sufficiently high current source that you will receive a severe shock if you accidentally touch a live spark-plug terminal. Individuals differ in their response to pain. Thus, an occasional auto mechanic with a high pain threshold may "show off" by short-circuiting the spark-plug system in an automobile through his hands and arms, thereby "killing" the engine. However, such stunts can be fatal.

Your laboratory experiments are designed to eliminate all possibility of shock, provided that you follow your instructor's directions. Do not take anything for granted; you are not permitted even one mistake. If in doubt, ask your instructor before proceeding with the experiment. Remember that any source of electricity operating at more than 25 volts is a possible source of substantial shock. The ABC of good practice is Always Be Careful.

SUMMARY OF FUNDAMENTAL CONCEPTS

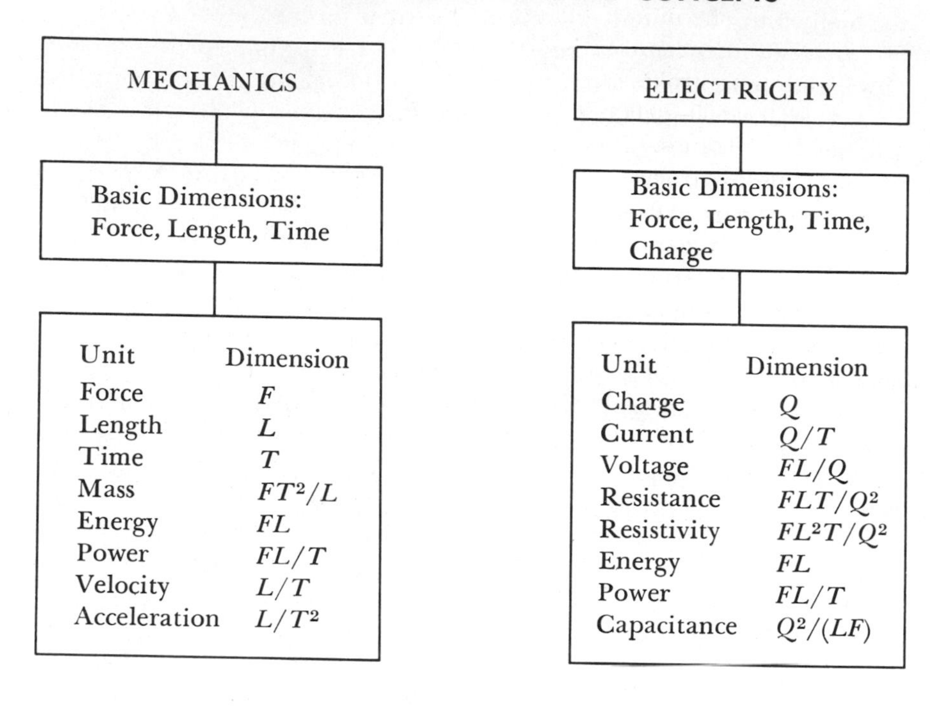

MECHANICS
Basic Dimensions:
Force, Length, Time
Unit Dimension
Force F
Length L
Time T
Mass FT²/L
Energy FL
Power FL/T
Velocity L/T
Acceleration L/T²
ELECTRICITY
Basic Dimensions:
Force, Length, Time,
Charge
Unit Dimension
Charge Q
Current Q/T
Voltage FL/Q
Resistance FLT/Q²
Resistivity FL²T/Q²
Energy FL
Power FL/T
Capacitance Q²/(LF)

QUESTIONS

1) The emf of a Weston normal cell is:
(*a*) approximately 1.5 volts. (*b*) 6 volts. (*c*) 1.0183 volts. (*d*) 117 amps.
2) The electron-volt is:
(*a*) equal to the practical volt unit. (*b*) the energy acquired by an electron when it is accelerated through a potential difference of 1 volt. (*c*) the effective voltage of an electron traveling at the speed of light. (*d*) The induced voltage of an electron traveling at the speed of light.
3) A primary standard of current flow utilizes the principle of:
(*a*) the ammeter. (*b*) the voltmeter. (*c*) the ohmmeter. (*d*) electroplating.
4) Resistance is defined as:
(*a*) a voltage/current ratio. (*b*) the rate at which electrons are slowed down by electrolysis. (*c*) the work done by unit voltage flowing through unit resistance. (*d*) the energy acquired by 1 volt through a current difference of 1 amp.

5) One unit of conductance is defined as:
(*a*) the reciprocal of unit resistance. (*b*) one unit of voltage multiplied by one unit of current. (*c*) the conduction of a Weston normal cell. (*d*) the reciprocal of unit current.
6) Lightning strokes range in voltage from:
(*a*) 2,000,000–20,000,000 volts. (*b*) 200,000–2,000,000 volts. (*c*) 1000–1,000,000 ohms. (*d*) zero–117 volts.
7) Lightning strokes range in current from:
(*a*) 2,000,000–20,000,000 amps. (*b*) 200,000–2,000,000 ohms. (*c*) 1000–1,000,000 electron-volts. (*d*) 30,000–160,000 amps.
8) Superconduction means that a metal has been cooled to a sufficiently low temperature that:
(*a*) all free electrons fall into the nuclei of the metal atoms. (*b*) current flow occurs from negative to positive. (*c*) the resistance of the metal is practically zero. (*d*) the conductance of the metal is practically zero.
9) The power quantity in watt-seconds is given by:
(*a*) $I = E/R$. (*b*) $W = EI$. (*c*) $W = EIt$. (*d*) $W = I^2R$.
10) A 100-watt lamp operated at rated voltage generates a luminous intensity of:
(*a*) approximately 100 volts. (*b*) approximately 100 amps. (*c*) approximately 100 candles. (*d*) approximately 100 light-years.

PROBLEMS

1) What is the emf of a Weston normal cell at 30°C?
2) An electron falls through a potential of 10,000 volts in a television picture tube. With what velocity does the electron strike the screen?
3) In Problem 2, how many foot-pounds of work are required to give the electron its final velocity?
4) An unknown current is maintained constant as it flows through a coulometer. At the end of 1800 sec, 2.0124 grams of silver are deposited. What is the current value?
5) A current of 1 amp flows through a mercury column which has a length of 106.3 cm and a mass of 14.451 grams; the mercury column has a constant cross-section of 1 sq millimeter at the temperature of melting ice. How much heat does the current flow generate per second?
6) If a switch has a resistance of 0.001 ohm when closed, what is the conductance of the switch?
7) An ideal motor consumes 2238 watts of electrical energy at full load.

Calculate the number of horsepower which the motor develops as mechanical energy.

8) Five lamps draw a total current of 5 amps from a 117-volt line. What is the total rate of power expenditure?
9) The five lamps in Problem 8 are operated for 8 hours. What is the quantity of power which has been consumed?
10) A 117-volt line supplies 100 watts of power to an appliance. What is the resistance of the appliance?
11) A lightning stroke has an average value of 15,000,000 volts, with an average current of 55,000 amps; the discharge takes place over a time interval of 60×10^{-6} sec. Calculate the number of watt-hours of power quantity in the stroke.
12) If 5 amps flow at 117 volts through a wattmeter, what value of power is indicated on the scale?
13) Three 50-watt lamps are operated at their rated voltage of 117 volts. How many candles of luminous intensity do they provide, approximately?
14) If a capacitor has a capacitance of 1000 picofarads, what is its capacitance in microfarads?
15) What is the frequency in megacycles of a 60-cycle voltage?
16) Calculate the emf of a 1.5-volt dry cell in millivolts.
17) An incoming radio wave has a potential of 10,000 microvolts. How much power does it develop in a 100-ohm resistor?
18) If a current of 1 milliamp flows through a resistance of 1 milliohm, what is the voltage value across the resistor?

3

CONDUCTORS, SEMICONDUCTORS, AND INSULATORS

3.1 DEFINITION OF A CONDUCTOR

Electrical conductors are substances that have comparatively low *resistivity*. What does this statement imply? Comparative resistances of various metals were noted in Chapter 1. By definition, the resistivity of a substance is the resistance of a cube with edges 1 cm in length. Table 3-1 lists the resistivities of several metals at 0°C.

Table 3-1

RESISTIVITIES OF SEVERAL METALS

Metal	*Resistivity in Ω/cm^3*
Silver	1.5×10^{-6}
Copper	1.7×10^{-6}
Aluminum	3×10^{-6}
Platinum	8.9×10^{-6}
Iron	10.5×10^{-6}
German silver	20×10^{-6}
Manganin	42×10^{-6}
Mercury	94×10^{-6}

The resistance value of a conductor varies directly as its length (assuming a constant cross-sectional area), inversely as its cross-sectional area, and directly as its resistivity. Resistivity is sometimes called *specific resistance*. Of the metals listed in Table 3-1, note that silver is the best conductor, followed by copper, and then by aluminum. The resistivity of a metal varies considerably with the physical processing which it has received. For example, temper, hardness, and crystalline structure affect a metal's resistivity. Accordingly, different samples of the same metal often have quite different resistivities.

Resistivities of conductors have no sharply defined upper limit, but are continuous into the class of semiconductors. Similarly, semiconductors have a wide range of resistivity with no sharply defined upper limit, but are continuous into the class of insulators. Table 3-2 lists the resistivities of several substances that clearly fall into classification as conductors, semiconductors, and insulators.

Table 3-2

COMPARATIVE RESISTIVITIES OF SUBSTANCES

Material	*Resistivity in Ω/cm³*	*Classification*
Silver	1.5×10^{-6}	Conductor
Aluminum	3×10^{-6}	Conductor
Pure germanium	55	Semiconductor
Pure silicon	55,000	Semiconductor
Mica	10^{12}	Insulator
Polyethylene	10^{15}	Insulator

From preceding discussion, it is evident that the resistance of a conductor may be written:

$$R = \rho \frac{L}{A} \tag{3.1}$$

where R is the resistance in ohms, ρ is the resistivity of the substance, A is the uniform cross-sectional area of the substance, and L is the length of the conductor.

You have probably learned in your physics courses that all solid inorganic substances, except glass, have a crystalline structure. That is, the atoms in a crystal are not distributed at random, but are arranged in orderly arrays. A molten metal crystallizes into a solid metal by sharing electrons of adjacent atoms. Each metal atom achieves stability in its solid state by aligning itself with adjacent atoms so that its outer shell is completed by electron sharing. Electron sharing involves forces that bind atoms together in a crystal lattice. The forces resulting from electron sharing are called *covalent* forces.

We recall that hydrogen and helium atoms have the basic structure depicted in Figure 3-1. Note that hydrogen is an active chemical element, but helium is an inactive element. Helium is a noble gas that is exceedingly reluctant to enter into chemical reactions. This difference occurs because the hydrogen atom does not have a filled shell (it has only one electron orbiting around its nucleus). Helium, however, has a filled shell, with two electrons orbiting around its nucleus. This is the condition of stability in the first shell of an atom. We recall that a third electron cannot be introduced into the first shell.

At ordinary temperatures, hydrogen atoms form diatomic molecules, as depicted in Figure 3-2. Electrons are *shared* when two H atoms form an H_2 molecule. Thus, the formation of hydrogen molecules is not a chemical reaction. One atom does not capture an electron from the other atom; the electrons are shared at appreciable distance. The binding force between atoms in a hydrogen molecule is called a *covalent force.* On the

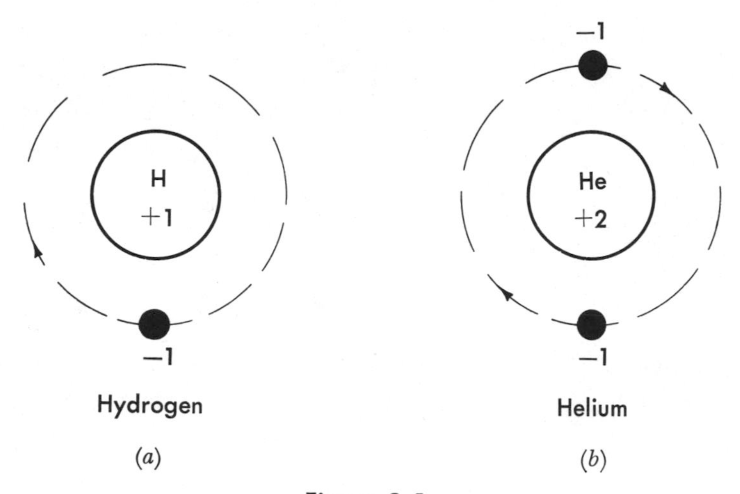

Figure 3-1
Structural representation of *(a)* the hydrogen atom, and *(b)* the helium atom.

other hand, the forces that bind hydrogen and oxygen atoms together into a molecule are called *ionic forces* (see Figure 3-3). When two atoms of hydrogen combine with an atom of oxygen to form a molecule of water, the oxygen atom captures an electron from each hydrogen atom.

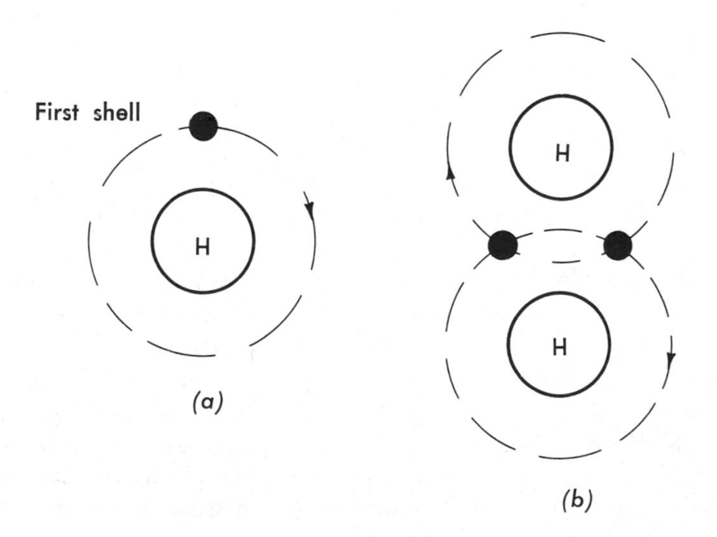

Figure 3-2
(a) Hydrogen atom. *(b)* Hydrogen molecule.

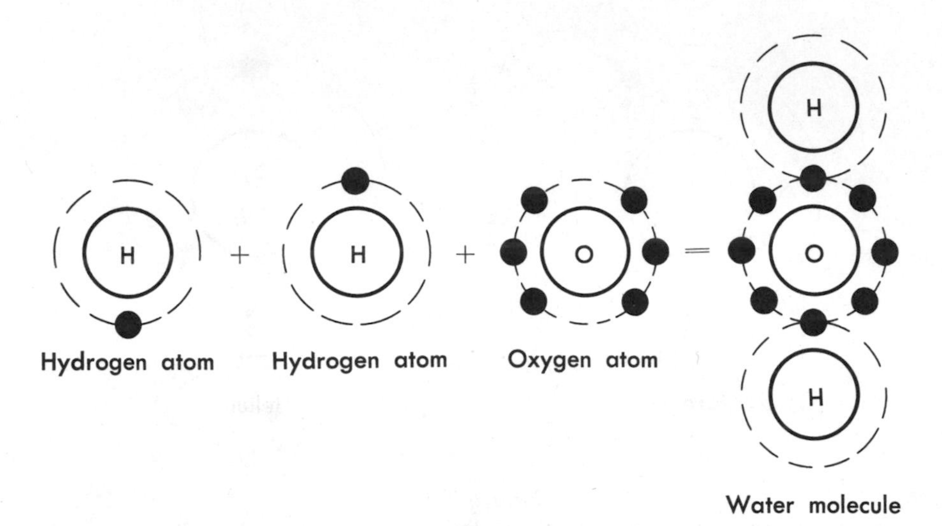

Figure 3-3
The formation of H_2O.

FORMATION OF IONIC BONDS

The basis for establishing ionic bonds in the formation of a water molecule is seen in Figure 3-4. Starting with lithium, a second shell appears because the first shell is filled by two electrons. In the neon atom the second shell is filled by eight electrons. The second shell can accommodate eight electrons, although the first shell can accommodate only two electrons. Note that the oxygen atom has six electrons in its second shell. Accordingly, the oxygen atom achieves maximum stability by capturing electrons from two hydrogen atoms, as we saw in Figure 3-3. Electron capture represents a chemical reaction; consequently, ionic bonds are stronger than covalent bonds.

A transfer of electrons takes place when an ionic bond is formed. On the other hand, an actual transfer does not occur when a covalent bond is formed. Instead, the electrons of one atom associate with adjacent atoms at an appreciable distance, and the electrons are said to be shared. We recall that a hydrogen atom has more than one possible orbit for its electron, as shown in Figure 3-5. This is true of all atoms. The orbit or energy level that is occupied at a given moment is determined by the electron's energy. Hence, the various orbits in a shell are often called *energy levels*.

When the electron in Figure 3-5 has its lowest possible energy, it

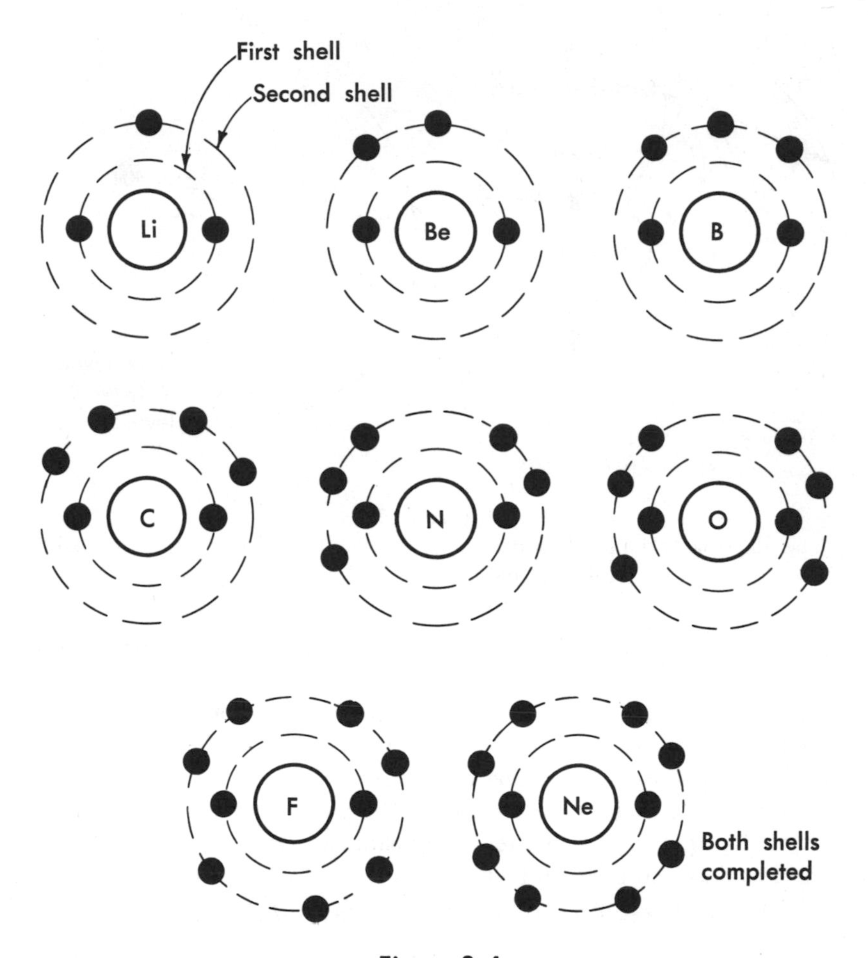

Figure 3-4
Representation of atomic shells for the elements from lithium through neon.

occupies the first orbit, or first *quantum level.* When it absorbs 1 quantum of energy, it suddenly jumps to the second orbit or quantum level. We recall that an electron cannot be found between orbits. This fact implies that an electron can acquire energy only in discrete amounts called *quanta.* If an electron is moving in the second orbit, and suddenly loses a quantum of energy, the electron jumps back to the first orbit. As it does so, the energy quantum is radiated as an electromagnetic wave.

A quantum of energy does not always have the same value. Its value is proportional to the frequency of the radiated electromagnetic wave:

$$E = h\nu \tag{3.2}$$

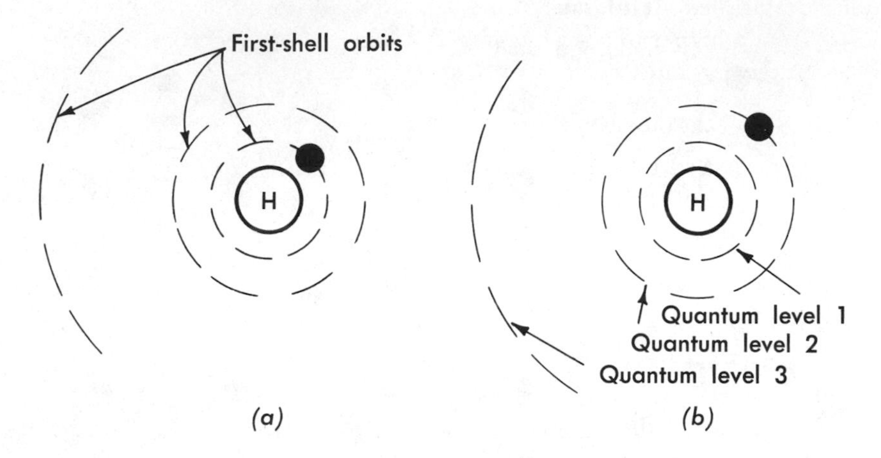

Figure 3-5
(a) The electron is depicted in its first orbit. *(b)* The electron has jumped into its second orbit.

where E is the energy of the quantum in ergs, h is Planck's constant, and ν is the frequency in cycles per sec.

The *erg* is a unit of energy or work that is done when 1 dyne operates through a distance of 1 cm. The *dyne* is a unit of force that will accelerate 1 gram 1 cm per sec per sec. Planck's constant has a value of 6.5×10^{-27} erg-sec. It is clear that we must speak of the *atomicity of energy*, just as we speak of the atomicity of matter. We visualize energy interchange by an electron as depicted in Figure 3-6. If an electron is in its first orbit, it cannot absorb surrounding electromagnetic energy unless the frequency of the

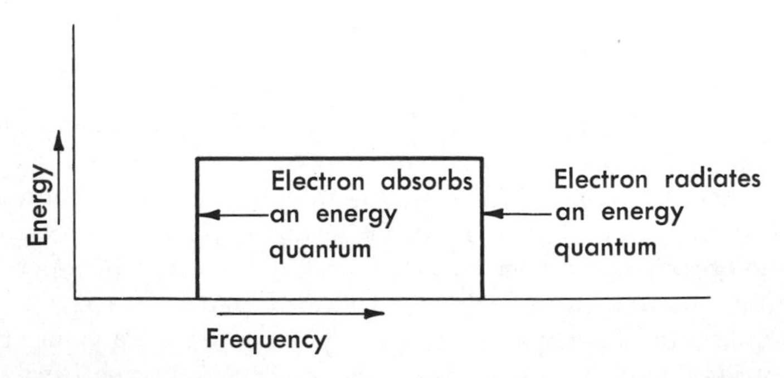

Figure 3-6
An orbiting electron absorbs or radiates energy in discrete quanta.

electromagnetic wave is sufficiently high. Otherwise stated, Equation (3.2) must be satisfied. It follows, similarly, that when the orbiting electron drops from a higher to a lower orbit, the frequency of its radiated electromagnetic energy must satisfy Equation (3.2).

RELATION OF ELECTROSTATIC AND CENTRIPETAL FORCES

Bohr equated the centripetal force of the electron in its orbit to the attractive force of the charged particles, stated by Coulomb's law:

$$\frac{mv^2}{r} = \frac{e^2}{r^2} \tag{3.3}$$

where e is the charge on the electron or proton, m is the mass of the electron, v is the speed of the electron in its orbit, and r is the radius of the orbit.

The energy of the electron in any given orbit can be calculated from the formula:

$$E_p = -\frac{2\pi^2 me^4}{p^2h^2} \tag{3.4}$$

where p is a whole number such as 1, 2, 3, and so forth.

A negative sign is used in Equation (3.4) merely to indicate that the electron has more energy in a higher orbit. This additional energy might come from a collision with a rapidly moving free electron. Or, it might come from a *photon* of light energy. A photon is a quantum of energy in the form of radiation. When an electron is in a low orbit, the holding influence of the nucleus is comparatively large. Thus, a relatively large amount of energy is required for the electron to break loose and become free of the nucleus. Outer-orbit electrons are said to be "stronger" than inner-orbit electrons for this reason. Thus, outer-orbit electrons are of chief concern in chemical reactions and crystal structure. The outer orbit in which these *valence* electrons move is within the *valence band,* or *valence shell.*

When one atom is close to another, associated by covalent bonds in a crystal, the number of permissible orbits is greatly increased. In fact, when copper atoms, for example, crystallize from a melt, so many permissible orbits are established in the atomic shells that it is preferred to speak of them as *energy bands.* Copper has approximately 8×10^{22} free electrons per cu cm. Figure 3-7 depicts how an atom in a crystal may have a valence band and a conduction band separated by a forbidden region. The *conduction band* is defined as a range of states in the energy spectrum of a solid in which electrons move freely from one atom to the next. A *valence band* is defined as a range of energy states in which lie the energies of the valence electrons which bind the crystal together. The electrons in the valence band of a copper crystal are not free to move from one atom to the next in a formal sense, as explained below.

The covalent forces that bind the atoms together in a crystal stem from electrons in the valence band. If an electron happens to absorb sufficient energy, it will jump through the forbidden region (Figure 3-7) into

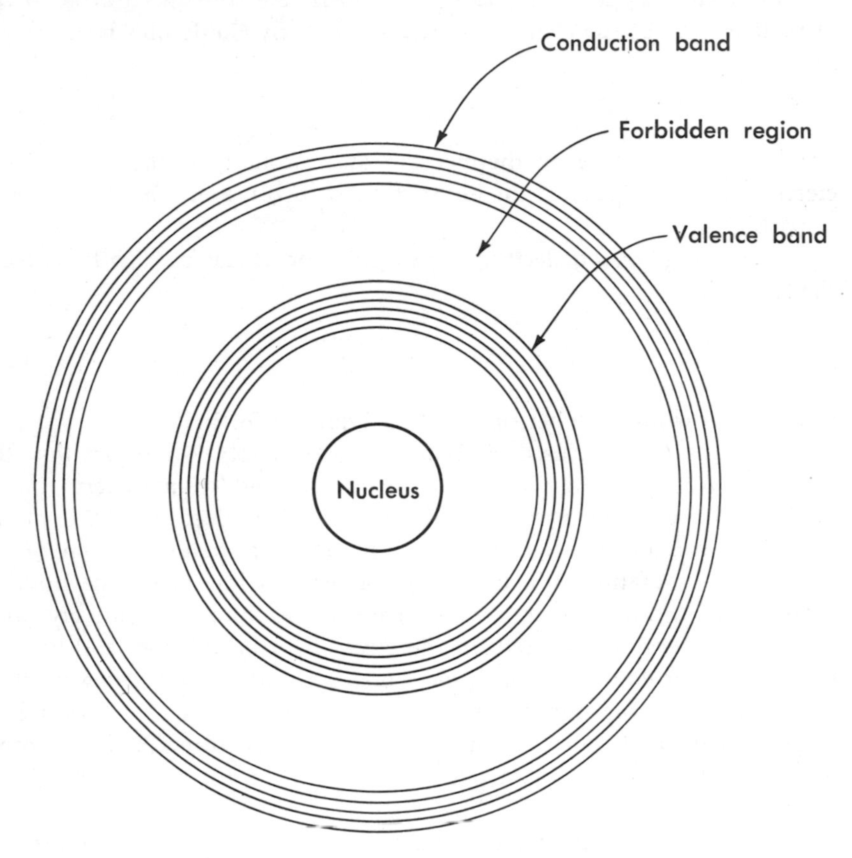

Figure 3-7
Each band comprises a multiplicity of permissible orbits.

the conduction band. There are no permissible orbits in the forbidden region. An electron in the conduction band can jump into the conduction band of an adjacent atom more readily than it can jump back into the valence band. However, if an electron in the conduction band radiates sufficient energy, it will fall back into the valence band.

A representation of the energy bands for two different metallic crystals is shown in Figure 3-8. A poor conductor has energy bands that are separated by a small forbidden region. On the other hand, a good conductor has overlapping energy bands. Thus, in a copper crystal, there is no physical distinction between its conduction and valence bands. Note that electrons in the valence band of a poor conductor must absorb sufficient energy to jump through the forbidden region into the conduction band. According to the laws of probability, comparatively few electrons will have sufficient energy at a given time to make the jump. However, electrons in the valence band of a good conductor are free to enter the conduction band without waiting to absorb energy.

The distinction between good and poor conductors is not sharply defined. Is tap water a good conductor? The practical answer to this question depends upon circumstances. Tap water is a poor conductor if tubes

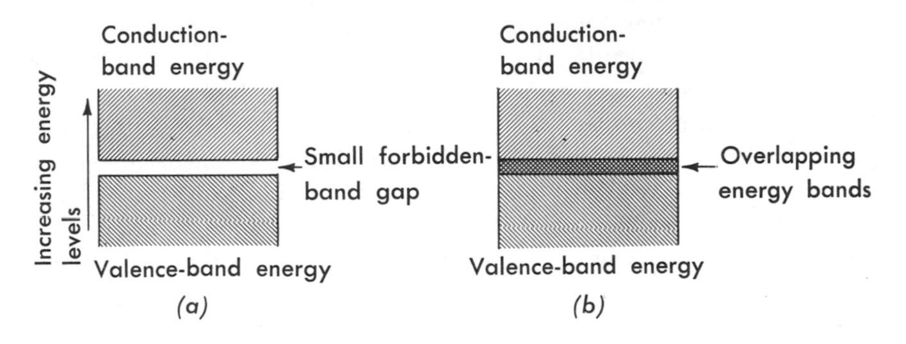

Figure 3-8
Energy bands for two different metallic substances. *(a)* A poor conductor. *(b)* A good conductor.

of water are compared to copper wires in a battery-and-lamp circuit. On the other hand, tap water is a good conductor if you are seated in a bathtub and accidentally touch a "hot" appliance which is 117 volts above ground.

3.2 CONDUCTOR EFFICIENCY, MATERIALS, AND MECHANICAL PROPERTIES

We know that the efficiency of any electrical device is its output/input power ratio. The efficiency of a wiring system, for example, depends upon its resistance. Copper is ordinarily used in wire or bar form to conduct electricity from one point to another because it has comparatively low resistivity. Although silver has a lower resistivity than most varieties of copper, silver is comparatively expensive. Hence, silver is used as a conductor in electronic equipment only when cost is a minor consideration, or when some other characteristic such as minimum tendency to oxidize is a prime requirement.

The efficiency of a conductor decreases with rise in temperature. We recall that copper has a positive temperature coefficient—its resistivity increases as the temperature increases. Consider a copper conductor that has a resistance of 10 ohms at 0°C. Suppose that current flow in the conductor is sufficient to raise its temperature to 100°C. Its resistance then increases to 14 ohms. In other words, the resistance of copper varies 40 percent from the freezing point to the boiling point of water.

Mention has been made of the relation between resistivity and treatment of a metal during fabrication. For example, pure annealed copper has a resistivity of 1.69×10^{-6} ohm/cm^3 at 20°C; on the other hand, hard-drawn copper has a resistivity of 1.77×10^{-6} ohm/cm^3. The hard-drawn variety of copper accordingly has approximately 4.7 percent higher resistance than pure annealed copper. The electrical efficiency of a conductor also depends upon whether the metal is pure or is alloyed with another metal. For example, pure aluminum has a resistivity of 2.63×10^{-6} ohm/cm^3 at 0°C; but aluminum bronze, consisting of 94 parts aluminum and 6 parts copper, has a resistivity of 3.1×10^{-6} ohm/cm^3. Observe that alloying the aluminum with the comparatively low-resistivity copper actually increases the resistivity of the aluminum.

Electric wires are usually manufactured from a commercial grade of copper which is not chemically pure. In turn, its resistivity is slightly higher than pure (and comparatively expensive) copper. Some copper wires are coated or tinned with solder during fabrication to facilitate soldered connections. Various copper wires are stranded to provide flexibility and to lessen the possibility of breaking from repeated bending. For example, the power cords for radio receivers are made from a number of small copper wires grouped together as a single conductor. Any copper wire will harden, "crystallize," and break when flexed repeatedly. However, stranded wire is mechanically superior in this respect. Conducting wires that carry many hundreds of amperes, as in switchboard equipment, are formed from heavy copper bars called *bus-bars*.

The resistivity of commercial-grade aluminum is approximately 1.6 times that of copper. However, since aluminum has only 30 percent the density of copper, it has less resistance per pound than copper, for equal lengths. For conductors with equal resistance per foot, aluminum wire must have a larger cross-sectional area than copper. Aluminum has less mechanical strength and its melting point is lower than that of copper. It is comparatively difficult to make soldered connections to aluminum. However, aluminum bus-bars are used in some applications because its larger cross-section provides more heat-radiating surface than copper.

3.3 AWG (B&S) GAGE DIAMETERS

Most conducting wires used in electronic equipment have comparatively small diameters. Hence, it is convenient to measure wire diameters in thousandths of an inch. One thousandth of an inch is called a *mil.* For example, if a wire has a diameter of 0.005 in., its diameter is expressed as 5 mils. The cross-sectional area of a circular conductor is commonly stated in *circular mils.* If a wire has a diameter of 1 mil, its cross-sectional area is 1 circular mil. The abbreviation "m" stands for mils, and the abbreviation "cm" stands for circular mils. [Note that the context of a discussion will indicate whether "cm" represents circular mils or centimeters.]

The relation between mils and circular mils is shown by the following:

$$\text{cm} = \text{m}^2 \tag{3.5}$$

We square the diameter expressed in mils to find the cross-sectional area in circular mils. Suppose that a wire has a cross-sectional area of 25 cm; its diameter is evidently the square root of 25, or 5 m. This, of course, is a diameter of 0.005 in.

The cross-sectional area of a rectangular conductor, such as a bus-bar, is usually expressed in a unit of area called a square mil (sq m). One sq m is the area of a square that has sides 1 mil in length. Thus, the cross-sectional area of a rectangular conductor in square mils is found by multiplying its width by its thickness expressed in mils. Evidently, there are as many circular mils in a square mil as the area of a circular mil is contained in the area of a square mil:

$$1.2732 \text{ cm} = 1 \text{ sq m} \tag{3.6}$$

Sizes of wires are customarily expressed in numbers according to the Brown & Sharpe (B&S) gage, which has been more recently termed the American wire gage (AWG). Table 3-3 lists a series of gage numbers with corresponding diameters for standard annealed copper wire.

3.4 CONDUCTION AND INSULATION BY SWITCHES AND FUSES

We have seen how switches are used to open or close an electric circuit. A switch has very low resistance and is a *conductor* when closed. On the other hand, a switch has extremely high resistance and is an *insulator* when open. To realize an open circuit in practice, the switch contacts must be spaced sufficiently apart at the open position so that sustained arcing cannot occur. Spark-over voltages for various separations of needle points were discussed in Chapter 1. A *spark* is defined as the light with an extremely short duration that accompanies a sudden disruptive electric discharge in air or some similar medium. An *arc* is defined as a sustained luminous glow that is formed in air or some similar medium when sufficiently heated by an electric discharge.

All switches spark to some extent when they are opened. Interruption of a small current produces a spark that may be invisible. The air path between contacts is not heated sufficiently to maintain ionization, and an

Table 3-3

CIRCULAR OF THE BUREAU OF STANDARDS
WORKING TABLE, STANDARD ANNEALED COPPER WIRE
American Wire Gage (B&S), English Units

Gage No.	Diameter in mils	Cross Section: Circular mils	Cross Section: Square inches	Ohms per 1000 Feet: 25° C (= 77°F)	Ohms per 1000 Feet: 65° C (= 149°F)	Pounds per 1000 feet
0000	460.0	212,000.0	0.166	0.0500	0.0577	641.0
000	410.0	168,000.0	0.132	0.0630	0.0727	508.0
00	365.0	133,000.0	0.105	0.0795	0.0917	403.0
0	325.0	106,000.0	0.0829	0.100	0.116	319.0
1	289.0	83,700.0	0.0657	0.126	0.146	253.0
2	258.0	66,400.0	0.0521	0.159	0.184	201.0
3	229.0	52,600.0	0.0413	0.201	0.232	159.0
4	204.0	41,700.0	0.0328	0.253	0.292	126.0
5	182.0	33,100.0	0.0260	0.319	0.369	100.0
6	162.0	26,300.0	0.0206	0.403	0.465	79.5
7	144.0	20,800.0	0.0164	0.508	0.586	63.0
8	128.0	16,500.0	0.0130	0.641	0.739	50.0
9	114.0	13,100.0	0.0103	0.808	0.932	39.6
10	102.0	10,400.0	0.00815	1.02	1.18	31.4
11	91.0	8230.0	0.00647	1.28	1.48	24.9
12	81.0	6530.0	0.00513	1.62	1.87	19.8
13	72.0	5180.0	0.00407	2.04	2.36	15.7
14	64.0	4110.0	0.00323	2.58	2.97	12.4
15	57.0	3260.0	0.00256	3.25	3.75	9.86
16	51.0	2580.0	0.00203	4.09	4.73	7.82
17	45.0	2050.0	0.00161	5.16	5.96	6.20
18	40.0	1620.0	0.00128	6.51	7.51	4.92
19	36.0	1290.0	0.00101	8.21	9.48	3.90
20	32.0	1020.0	0.000802	10.4	11.9	3.09
21	28.5	810.0	0.000636	13.1	15.1	2.45
22	25.3	642.0	0.000505	16.5	19.0	1.94
23	22.6	509.0	0.000400	20.8	24.0	1.54
24	20.1	404.0	0.000317	26.2	30.2	1.22
25	17.9	320.0	0.000252	33.0	38.1	0.970
26	15.9	254.0	0.000200	41.6	48.0	0.769
27	14.2	202.0	0.000158	52.5	60.6	0.610
28	12.6	160.0	0.000126	66.2	76.4	0.484
29	11.3	127.0	0.0000995	83.4	96.3	0.384
30	10.0	101.0	0.0000789	105.0	121.0	0.304

Table 3-3 (Continued)

		Cross Section		Ohms per 1000 Feet		
Gage No.	Diameter in mils	Circular mils	Square inches	25° C (= 77°F)	65° C (= 149°F)	Pounds per 1000 feet
31	8.9	79.7	0.0000626	133.0	153.0	0.241
32	8.0	63.2	0.0000495	167.0	193.0	0.191
33	7.1	50.1	0.0000394	211.0	243.0	0.152
34	6.3	39.8	0.0000312	266.0	307.0	0.120
35	5.6	31.5	0.0000248	335.0	387.0	0.0954
36	5.0	25.0	0.0000196	423.0	488.0	0.0757
37	4.5	19.8	0.0000156	533.0	616.0	0.0600
38	4.0	15.7	0.0000123	673.0	776.0	0.0476
39	3.5	12.5	0.0000098	848.0	979.0	0.0377
40	3.1	9.9	0.0000078	1070.0	1230.0	0.0299

arc is not established. Interruption of a fairly strong current produces an impressive spark. However, if the air path between contacts is not heated excessively, an arc will not be established. If the voltage between the contacts exceeds a certain critical value, and a very heavy current is interrupted, the air path between contacts is heated sufficiently to maintain an arc. When an arc is established, the switch is opened mechanically but not electrically. An arc is a low-resistance path for current flow. Switches that must open a very heavy current flow are specially designed to extinguish the resulting arc. For example, compressed air may be automatically blown between the contacts to cool the arc and suppress ionization of the gas molecules.

Some basic small-current types of switches are illustrated in Figure 3-9. Switch contacts, of course, must be sufficiently heavy to carry rated current flow without appreciable heating. In other words, the switch must have a very low resistance when closed. We can perceive that when switch contacts are opened, the amount of heat produced by the spark will be minimized if the contacts are separated quickly. The total amount of heat generated is a function of current squared, resistance of the ionized air, and time. The time of spark duration can be minimized by spring-loading the switch to separate the contacts very quickly. For example, the push-button, flush-type, snap-type surface, and toggle-type flush switches shown in Figure 3-9 are spring-loaded. Contacts have longer life when the heat generated by sparking is minimized.

FUSE FUNCTION

Many electronic circuits contain fuses. Figure 3-10 shows a simple circuit having a fuse, battery, lamp, and switch. A fuse protects circuit components from damage in case of an accidental short-circuit which would draw excessive current. For example, suppose the lamp in Figure

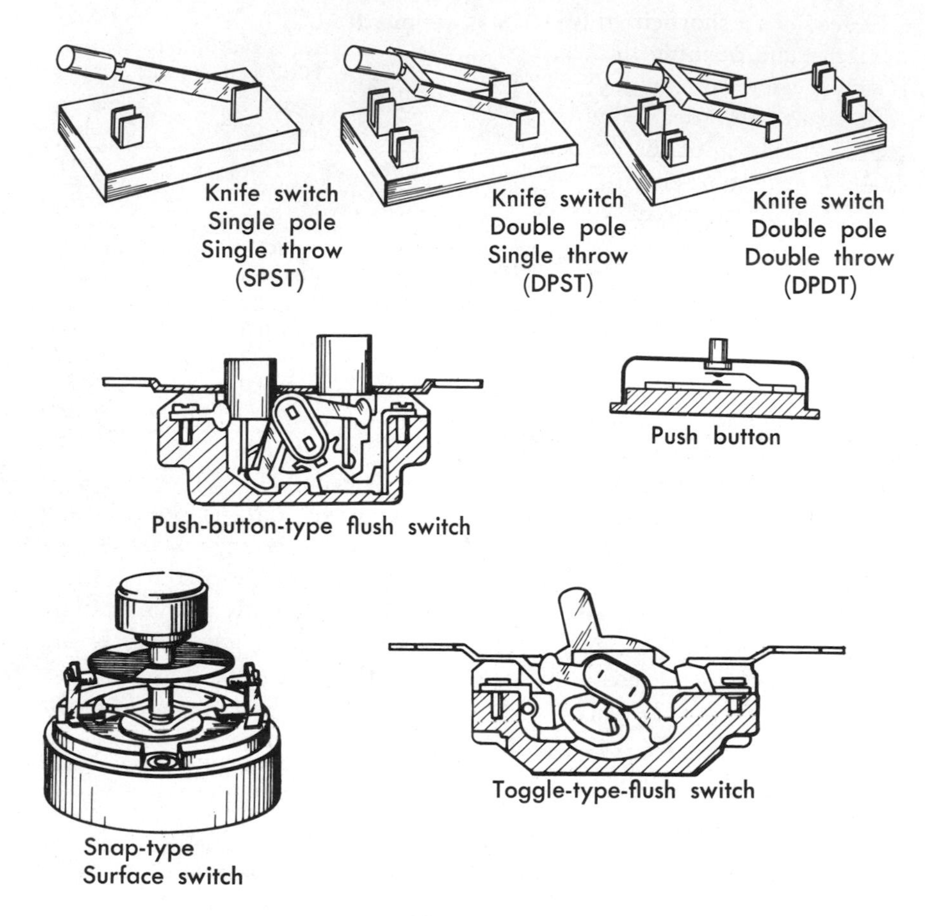

Figure 3-9
Typical construction of basic switches.

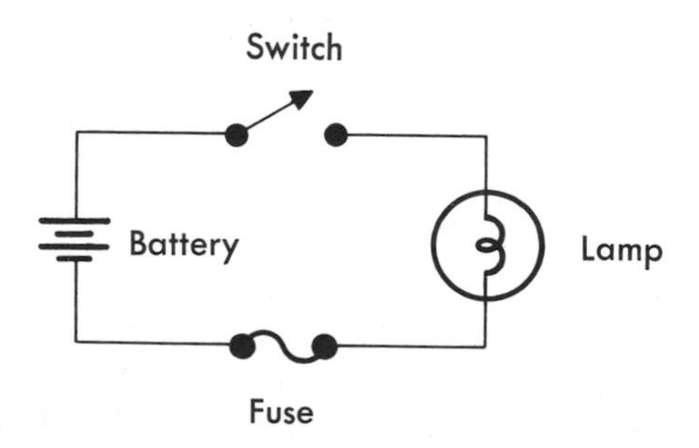

Figure 3-10
A fuse is an automatic protective switch.

3-10 develops a short-circuit. Excessive current begins to flow, melting the fuse wire and opening the circuit as if the switch were opened manually. If a fuse were not included in the circuit, a short-circuited lamp would soon result in a "dead" battery. In some situations, a short-circuit causes excessive heating of the conductors and starts a fire if no fuse is utilized. Of course, a short-circuit must be cleared and the burned-out fuse replaced before the circuit can resume operation.

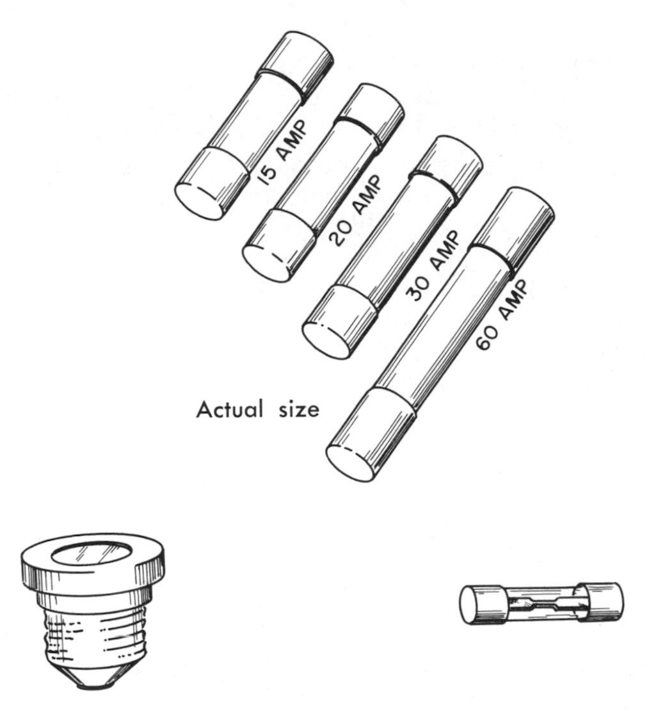

Figure 3-11
Appearance of typical fuses.

Typical fuses are illustrated in Figure 3-11. The fuse wire or ribbon is usually fabricated from aluminum, tin-plated copper, or nickel. The resistance of a fuse is quite low, although not as low as that of a closed switch. Fuses are rated for maximum current values from 0.002 to many hundred amps. It is evident that the thinner the wire or ribbon in a fuse, the smaller its current rating will be. Various special types of fuses are used in electronic devices and equipment described subsequently. Since a fuse, like a switch, must not arc over when it opens, the fuse has a maximum voltage rating in addition to its maximum current rating. This voltage rating states the maximum voltage which can be permitted to exist across the fuse terminals after it blows.

3.5 DEFINITION OF A SEMICONDUCTOR

We have learned that all substances can be arbitrarily classified into three chief categories: conductors, semiconductors, and insulators. This classification is made on the basis of chosen resistivity limits. Most semiconductors are manufactured from germanium or silicon, alloyed with traces of other elements. Germanium has lower resistivity than silicon and is generally utilized in low-power applications. Silicon is preferred in the design of high-power semiconductor devices because it can withstand higher operating temperatures. Germanium and silicon must be highly purified to achieve desired characteristics in electronic applications. This requirement has introduced new concepts of chemical purity and rests upon comparatively new techniques of crystal growth.

We recall that the conductivity (1/resistivity) of a substance is directly proportional to the number of free (loosely bound) electrons in the substance. Thus, good conductors such as copper have an extremely large number of free electrons. On the other hand, good insulators, such as air, have very few free electrons. Chemically pure germanium has a resistivity of about 60 ohms/cm^3. Chemically pure silicon has a much higher resistivity of approximately 60,000 ohms/cm^3. However, germanium or silicon crystals used in semiconductor devices are alloyed with traces of other chemical elements that lower the resistivity of the crystal to approximately 2 ohms/cm^3 at room temperature.

3.6 FIRST PRINCIPLES OF SEMICONDUCTION

Ideal semiconductor materials have a perfectly uniform crystal structure, except when intentionally modified to obtain desired electrical characteristics. Let us see how a crystal lattice is formed. Figure 3-12 shows a Bohr model of the germanium atom. It has four valence electrons. Only valence electrons are of concern in formation of a crystal lattice. Hence, the germanium atom may be treated in simplified form, as depicted in Figure 3-13. A crystal lattice is formed by sharing valence electrons with adjacent atoms. The atoms are not fixed in position when germanium is in the molten state. However, when the melt is cooled, crystallization occurs and each atom is held in a fixed position by covalent forces.

Thus, a germanium atom finds stability in a crystal by positioning itself with respect to adjacent atoms so that its outer shell is completed by electron sharing. We recall that electron sharing involves covalent bonds. A covalent bond for a hydrogen molecule is sometimes represented as in Figure 3-14. The diagram implies that electrons associate with adja-

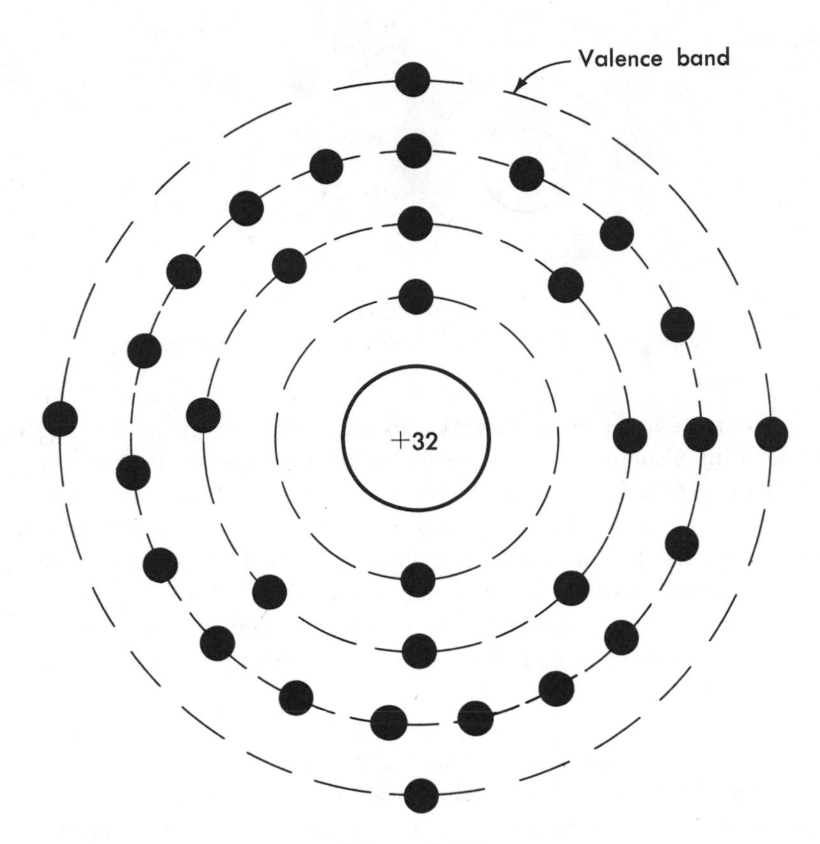

Figure 3-12
A Bohr model of the germanium atom.

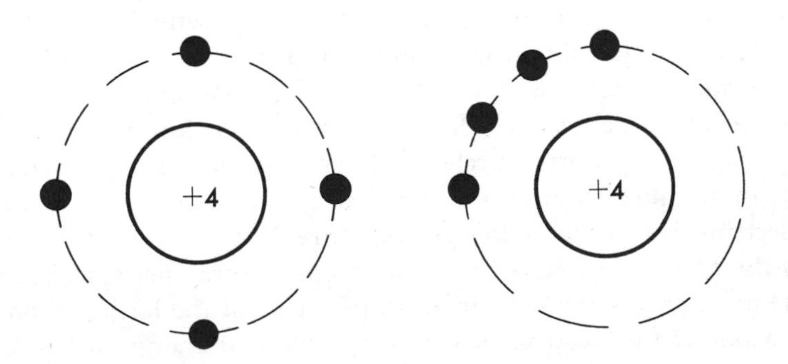

Figure 3-13
Simplified representations of the germanium atom.

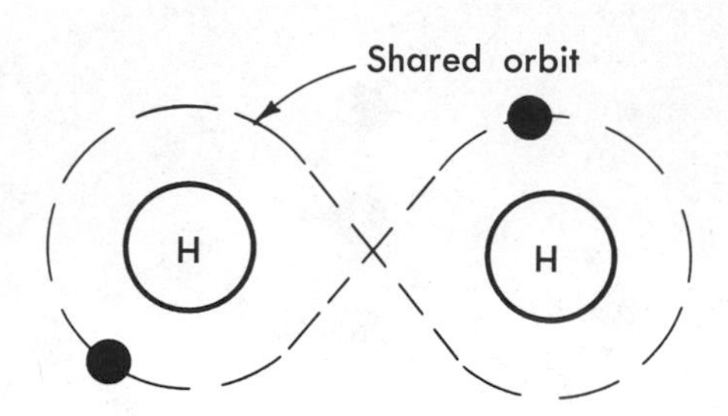

Figure 3-14
Conception of a covalent bond for a hydrogen molecule.

cent atoms at a distance—there is no capture of electrons by adjacent atoms. This visualization can be extended to a germanium crystal, depicted in Figure 3-15. Valence electrons are shared by adjacent atoms that are spaced 2.8×10^{-8} cm from one another. Note that Figure 3-15 can also represent a silicon crystal lattice, because the silicon atom also contains four electrons in its outer shell. Since all the electrons are bonded by covalent forces, there are no free electrons available to provide current flow. Hence, an ideal germanium or silicon crystal is a perfect insulator.

However, so-called chemically pure germanium or silicon crystals do conduct a small amount of current for they contain very slight traces of impurities. Moreover, the covalent forces are discontinuous at the crystal surfaces, as shown in Figure 3-15. Therefore, the physics of crystal surfaces are different from physics of the bulk substance. Crystal surfaces are suitably treated (passivated) to minimize leakage currents. Bulk properties are better understood and are subject to better control than surface properties in the present state of the art.

A germanium crystal lattice can also be represented as Figure 3-16. This diagram is equivalent to that shown in Figure 3-15. Note that Figure 3-16 can also represent a silicon lattice. A germanium crystal contains 4.52×10^{22} atoms per cu cm. The arrows in the diagram indicate covalent forces or bonds; the dotted circles represent positions in the valence shell which are not filled by electrons. An ideal germanium or silicon crystal is a perfect insulator only at low temperature. When the crystal is heated (as by the ambient air in a room), its atoms absorb thermal energy and vibrate more or less about their mean positions in the lattice. From time to time, one of the electrons will acquire sufficient energy to break away from its parent atom, and move through the crystal. This energy level is called the *ionization energy* level.

The probability law determines the average number of electrons which will acquire ionization energy at a given temperature. Figure 3-17 illustrates how a hydrogen atom becomes ionized. Originally, the electron was orbiting about the nucleus. But when sufficient energy is absorbed

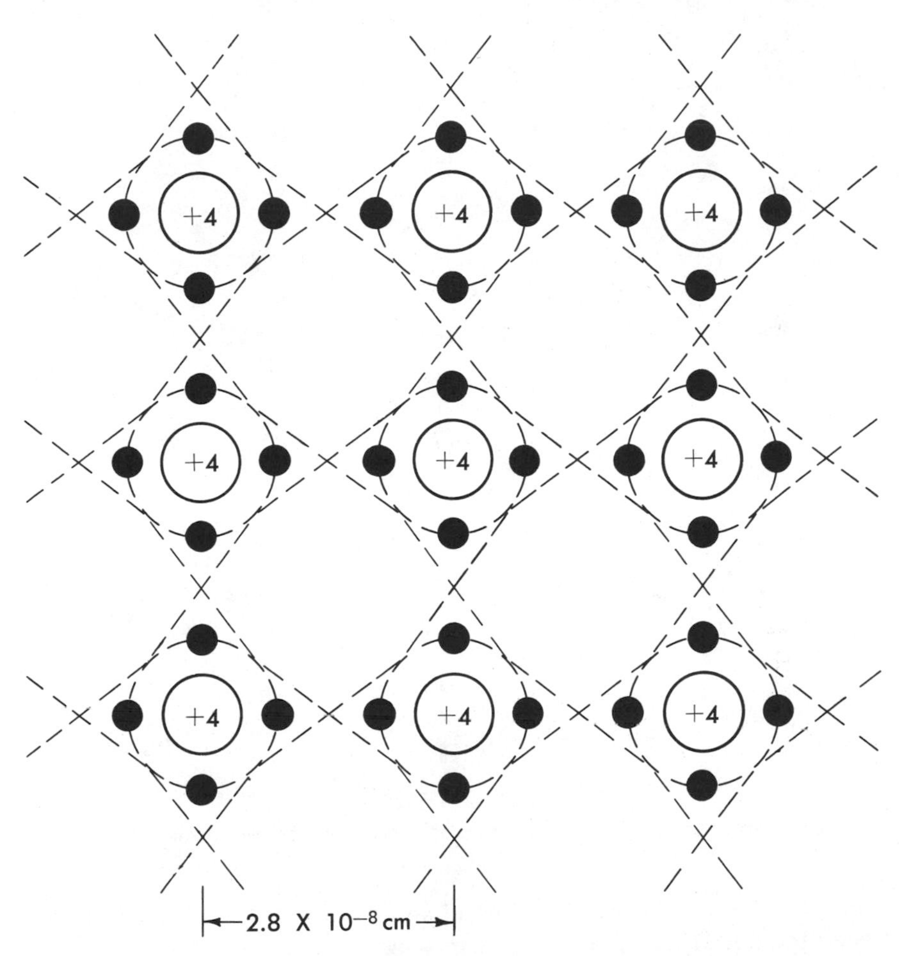

Figure 3-15
Representation of germanium crystal lattice structure.

by the electron, it is ejected from the attractive field of the nucleus. In turn, the nucleus is left as a positive charge. This positive charge is called an *ion*. The word ion is derived from the Greek language, and means wanderer. After an atom in a crystal lattice has lost an electron, it may

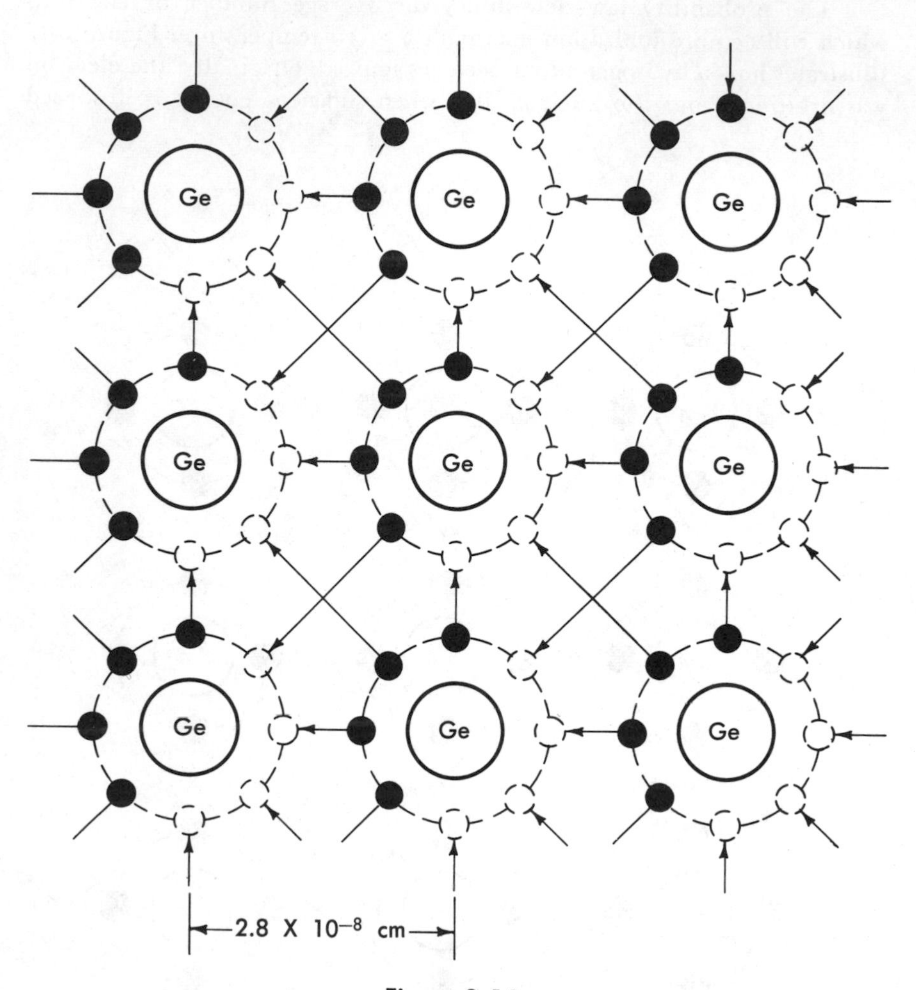

Figure 3-16
Lattice forces indicated in a diagrammatic structure of the germanium crystal.

then acquire an electron from an adjacent atom. When a given electron acquires ionization energy, a covalent bond is broken and leaves a positive charge in its stead.

HOLES IN SEMICONDUCTORS

This positive charge is an *electron deficiency*. Figure 3-18 illustrates how the broken covalent bond leaves an irregularity in the lattice structure. An electron deficiency can move in the crystal just as a free electron. Hence, the electron deficiency is often regarded as equivalent to a particle with a positive charge. The positive particle is called a *hole.* Whenever a free electron is generated by breaking a covalent bond, a hole is simultaneously generated. We call this process the *thermal generation of electron-hole pairs.* Free electrons travel in the conduction band, but holes travel in the valence band; that is, a free electron has a higher energy level than a hole.

It is evident from Figure 3-18 that a hole travels to the negative electrode, while a free electron travels to the positive electrode. When a hole reaches the negative electrode, it acquires an electron and is thereby neutralized. This process is called *recombination.* When a free electron reaches the positive electrode, it enters the electrode. There is also a steady electron flow in the external circuit that is equal to the electron

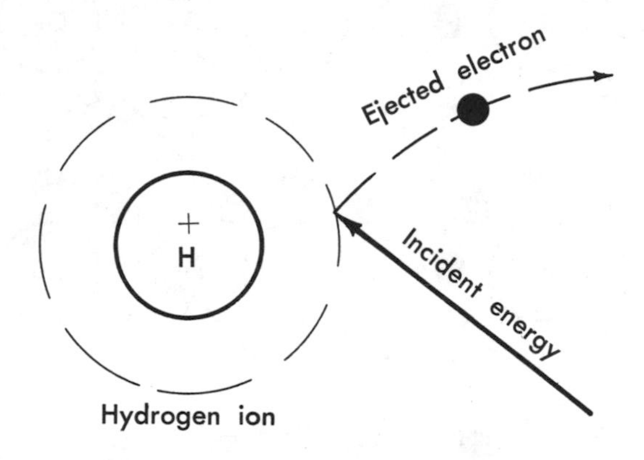

Figure 3-17
Formation of a hydrogen ion.

and hole currents in the crystal. Electron current is separated from hole current by the forbidden region as depicted in Figure 3-19. On first acquaintance, the hole concept seems somewhat artificial. The question is often asked why an electron deficiency in the valence band should be discussed as if it were a positive particle. The answer is that unless the positive-particle viewpoint is accepted, we cannot explain the electrical characteristics of germanium and silicon. Details are reserved for subsequent discussion.

As seen in Figure 3-20, a free electron zig-zags about in a crystal, but its average velocity is zero in the absence of an externally applied electric field. Similarly, a hole zig-zags about in a crystal. When an external electric field is applied, as depicted in Figure 3-18, the average velocity of free electrons and holes is no longer zero. Instead, electrons drift toward the

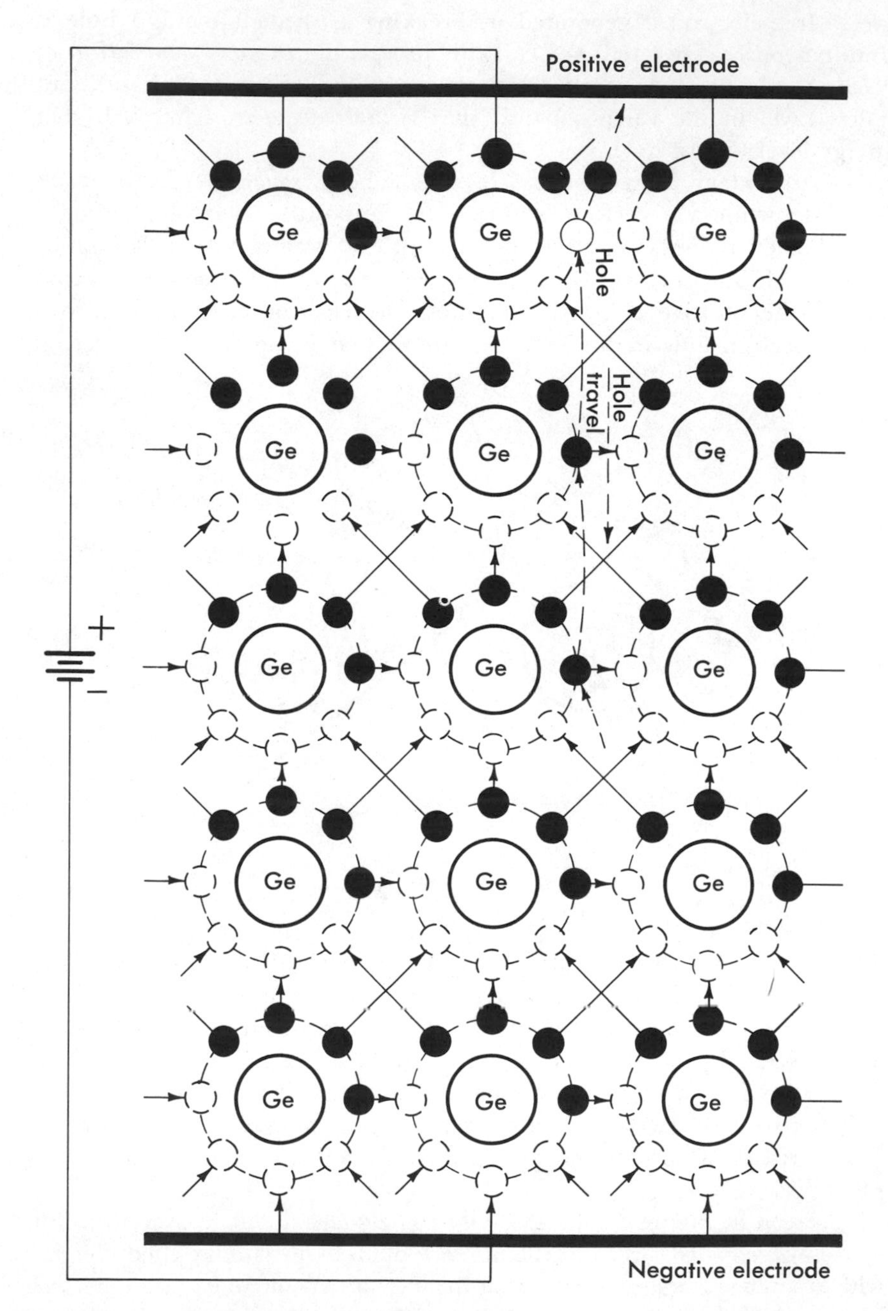

Figure 3-18
Conception of a hole in the lattice structure.

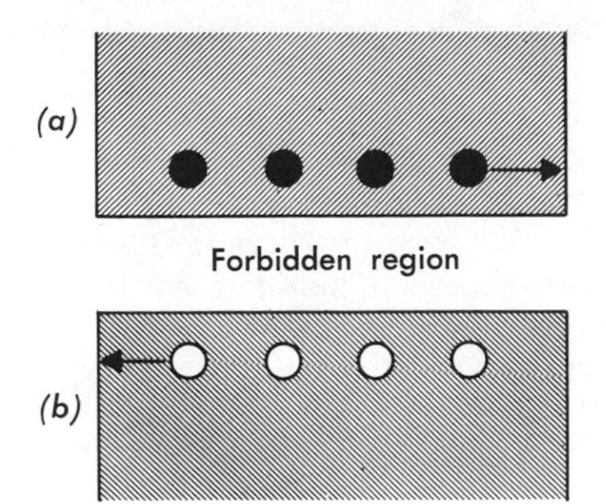

Figure 3-19
(a) The conduction band. *(b)* The valence band.

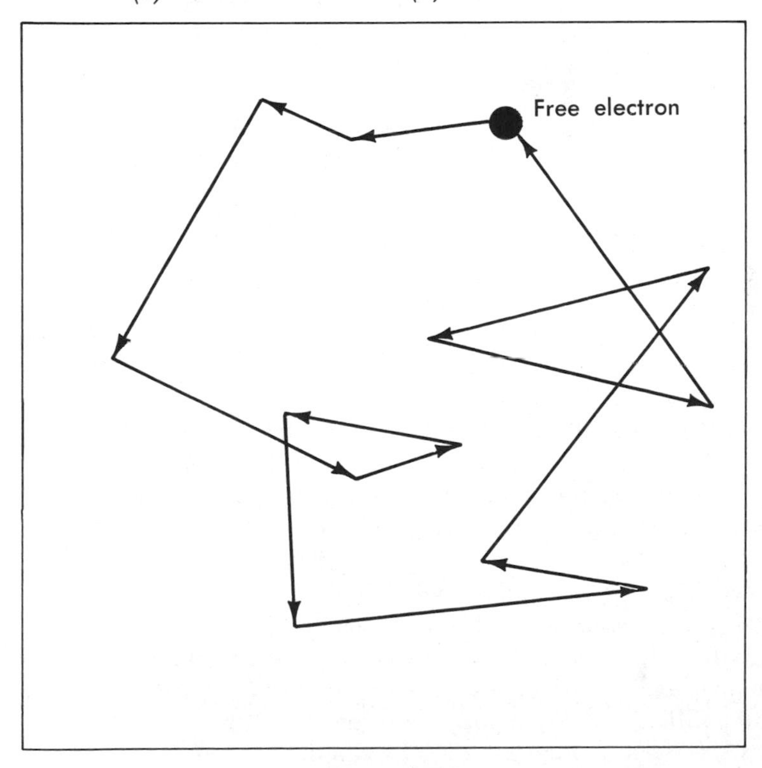

Figure 3-20
The average velocity of a free electron is zero.

positive electrode and holes drift toward the negative electrode. The velocity with which an electron or hole drifts in a unit electric field is called its *mobility*. The mobility of a free electron is greater than the mobility of a hole. At room temperature, the mobility of a free electron is 3000 cm/sec per volt/cm; the mobility of a hole is 1700 cm/sec per volt/cm. A volt/cm is established by 1 volt across 1 cm.

If a battery is connected across a germanium crystal, as shown in Figure 3-21, the current that flows is called a *saturation current*. Both holes and electrons contribute to current flow. The saturation current in an ideally pure crystal is constant, and does not increase with increased voltage. In other words, saturation current flow does *not* obey Ohm's law. A pure germanium crystal at room temperature has about 2.5×10^{13} free

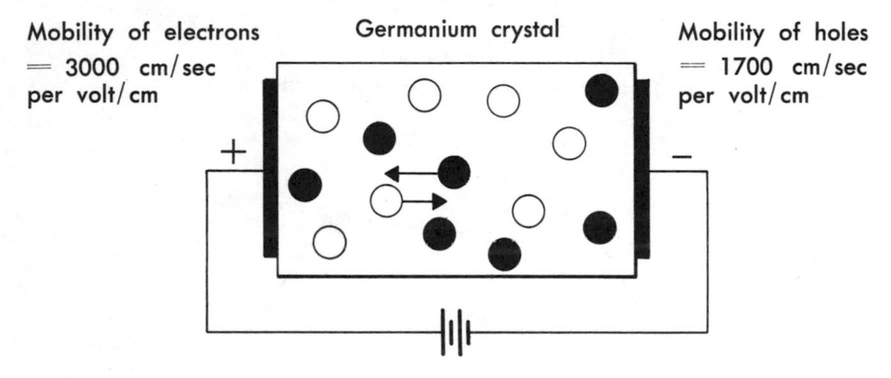

Figure 3-21
Equal numbers of free electrons and holes are produced by thermal generation of electron-hole pairs.

electrons and 2.5×10^{13} holes per cm^3. The total number of charge carriers is 5×10^{13}; it is not changed by the applied voltage. The number of charge carriers depends solely on the temperature of the crystal. In turn, saturation current is determined entirely by the mobilities of the charge carriers.

Free electrons and holes have a limited *lifetime*. If a free electron collides with a hole, the electron deficiency is filled; both the hole and the electron then cease to exist as charge carriers. This is a process of recombination. The lifetime of a charge carrier is typically from 1 microsec to 1 millisec. As the temperature rises, the number of charge carriers increases, as seen in Figure 3-22. The conductivity of a crystal is directly proportional to the number of charge carriers present; hence, conductivity increases with temperature. Remember that the current flow through a

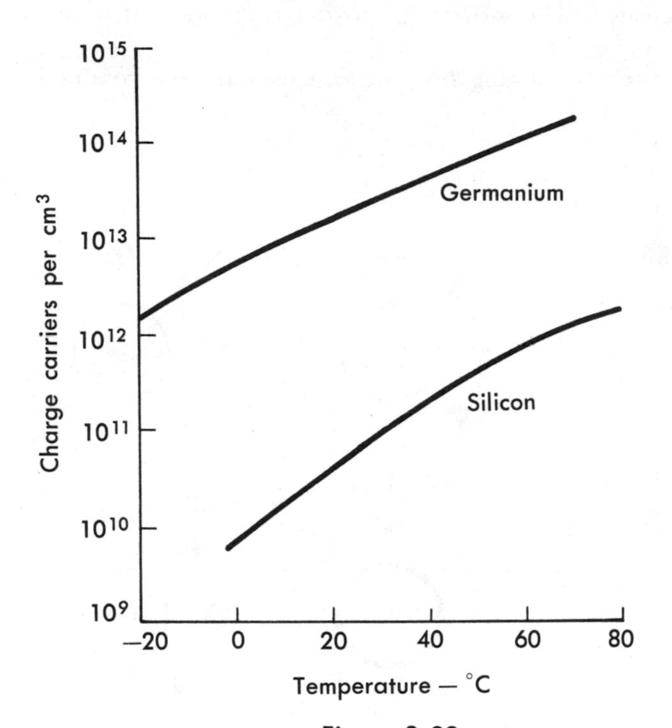

Figure 3-22
Charge carriers per cm^3 for pure germanium and pure silicon.

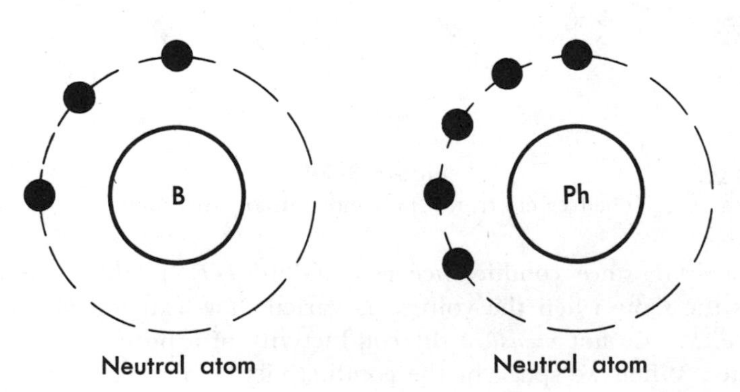

Figure 3-23
Outer shells of boron and phosphorous atoms.

pure (intrinsic) semiconductor crystal does *not* increase when the applied voltage is increased. The saturation current is constant at a given temperature.

You are probably asking how we can measure the conductivity of

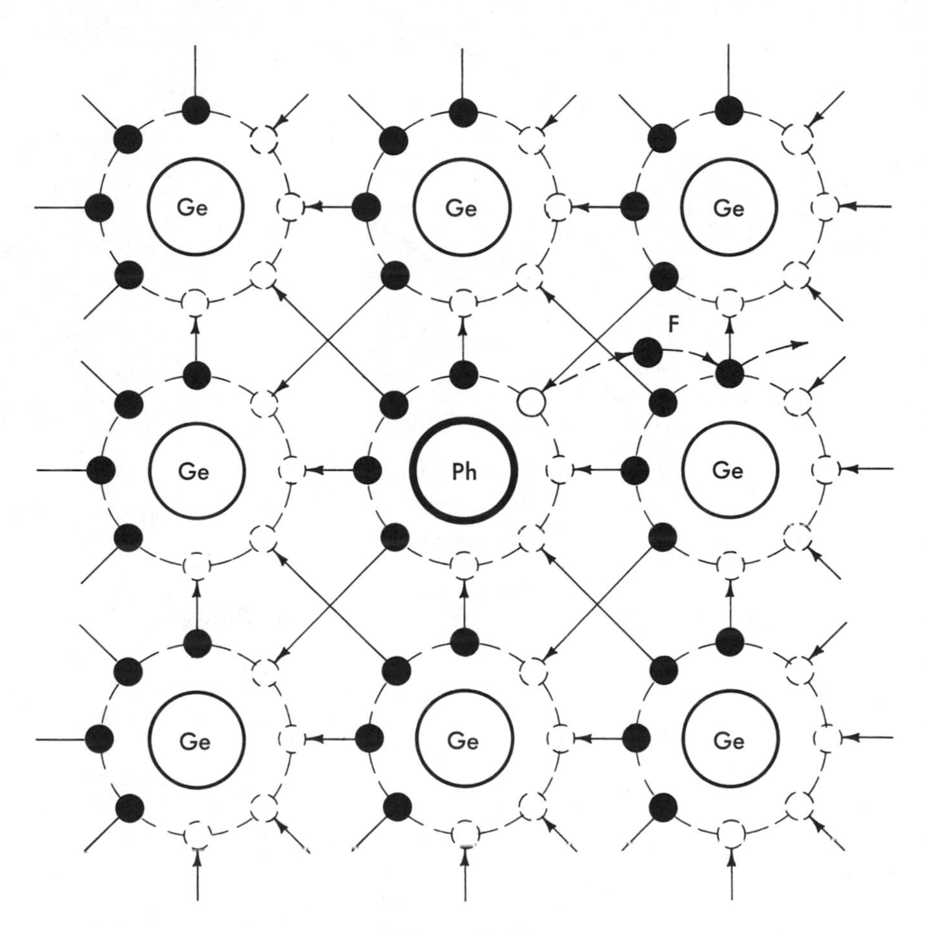

Figure 3-24
The free electron *F* may move in any direction.

a pure crystal, since conductance is equal to I/E. If the current flow remains the same when the voltage is varied, how can we measure conductance? We do not *measure* the conductivity of a pure crystal with an ohmmeter. When we speak of the conductivity of a pure crystal, we are actually *defining* a special concept of conductance which cannot be measured by applying a voltage and observing the corresponding current flow. Insofar as pure semiconductor crystals are concerned, we define this special concept of conductivity by the formula:

$$\text{Conductivity} = e(n\mu_n + p\mu_p) \tag{3.7}$$

where e is the charge of the electron (or hole), n is the concentration of electrons per cc, μ_n is the mobility of the electrons, p is the concentration of holes per cc, and μ_p is the mobility of the holes.

Thus, at room temperature, Equation (3.7) states that the resistivity of pure germanium is approximately 47 ohms/cm³. (Resistivity is equal to the reciprocal of conductivity.) Here, "ohms" has a special meaning.

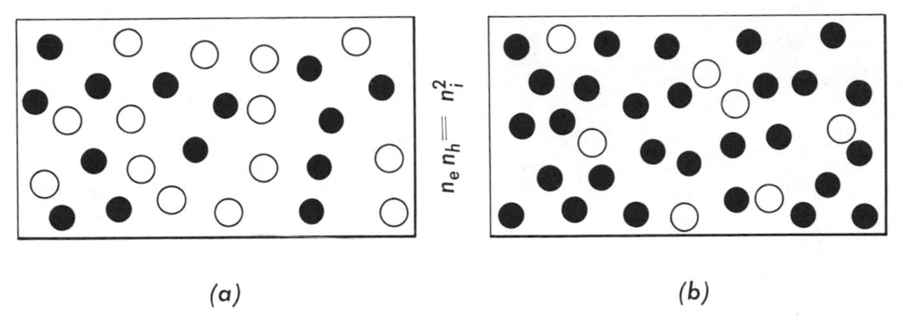

Figure 3-25

A donor element reduces the number of holes in a lattice. *(a)* Intrinsic germanium. There is an equal number of electrons and holes. *(b)* N-type germanium. There are fewer number of holes.

We cannot substitute 47 into Ohm's law. In other words, "ohms" are defined by Equation (3.7) as a function of charge multiplied by mobility.

DONOR AND ACCEPTOR ATOMS

The conductivity of an intrinsic semiconductor can be increased by alloying the germanium or silicon with traces of other elements which are termed *impurities.* When an impurity is present in the crystal lattice, the semiconductor is said to be "doped." Some impurities are *donors,* such as arsenic or phosphorous; a donor atom "donates" an extra free electron to the crystal lattice. As shown in Figure 3-23, donor atoms such as phosphorous have five valence electrons. On the other hand, certain other impurities are *acceptors,* such as aluminum or boron; an acceptor atom "accepts" an electron from the crystal lattice to produce a hole. Figure 3-23 shows that acceptor atoms such as boron have three valence electrons.

Donor atoms, which have five valence electrons, take the place of germanium (or silicon) atoms in the crystal lattice, as shown in Figure

3-24. Only four of the five valence electrons can form covalent bonds with adjacent germanium atoms. Hence, the fifth electron is released as a free electron and moves randomly through the lattice. In turn, the donor atom is left with a positive charge—it becomes a positive ion. However, the

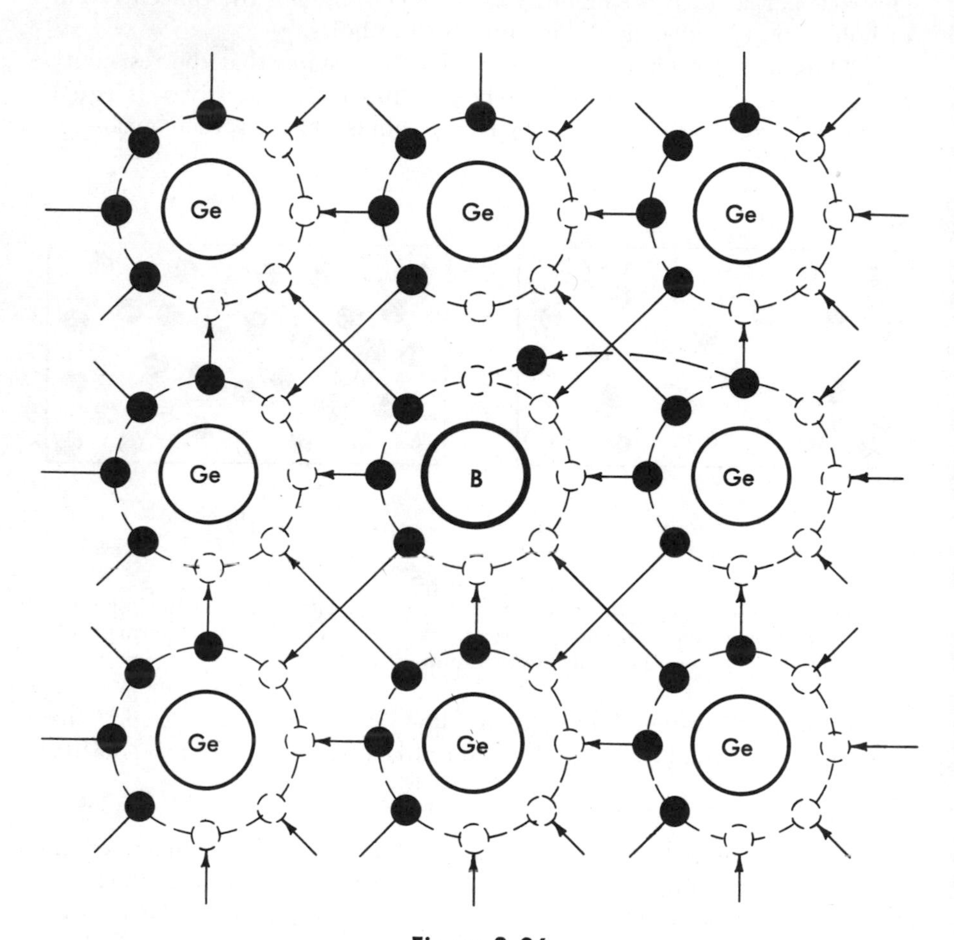

Figure 3-26
Representation of lattice structure for *P*-type germanium.

donor atom remains fixed in its position due to the covalent lattice forces. Such crystals as depicted in Figure 3-24 have an excess of negative charge carriers, and are called *N*-type semiconductors. Only a very small amount of donor substance is used. For example, germanium, which contains 4.52×10^{22} atoms per cm^3, may be doped with 3.5×10^{14} donor atoms per cm^3 to form *N*-type germanium.

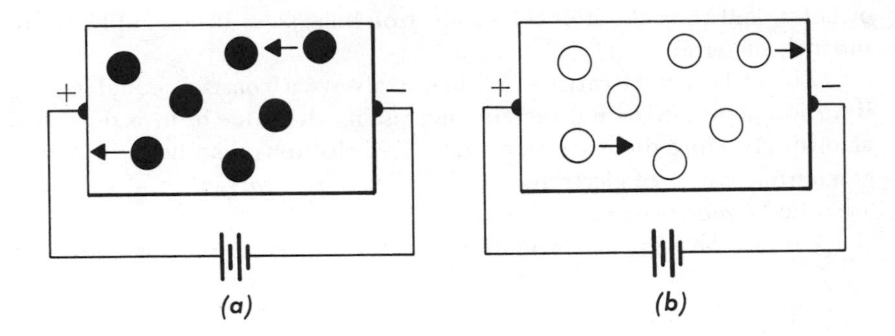

Figure 3-27
(*a*) Germanium crystal doped with phosphorous. (*b*) Germanium crystal doped with boron.

As diagramed in Figure 3-25, the number of holes in a semiconductor is reduced when it is doped with donor atoms. This situation is apparent, and is described quantitatively by the principle of space-charge neutrality. The total number of holes in the semiconductor is determined by the total number of donor atoms in the crystal:

$$n_e n_h = n_i^2 \tag{3.8}$$

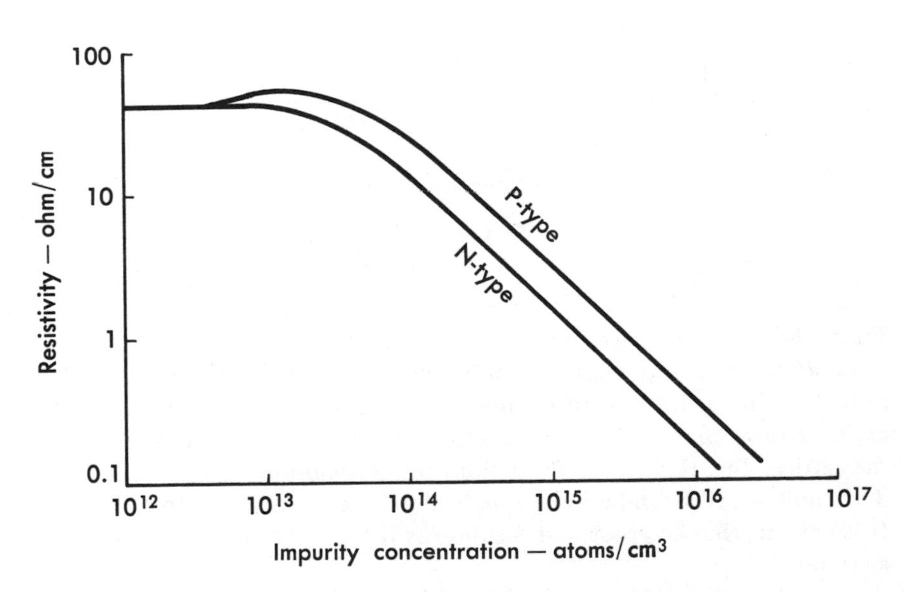

Figure 3-28
Resistivity versus impurity concentration for germanium at 25°C.

where n_e is the number of free electrons in the crystal, n_h is the number of holes, and n_i is the number of electron-hole pairs in a sample of the intrinsic material.

Thus, the charge-carrier product is always a constant equal to n_i^2; if we add donor atoms and thereby increase n_e, the value of n_h is decreased accordingly. Since there are many more free electrons than holes in *N*-type germanium, the free electrons are called *majority carriers*, and the holes are called *minority carriers.*

Let us consider the formation of *P*-type germanium, as shown in

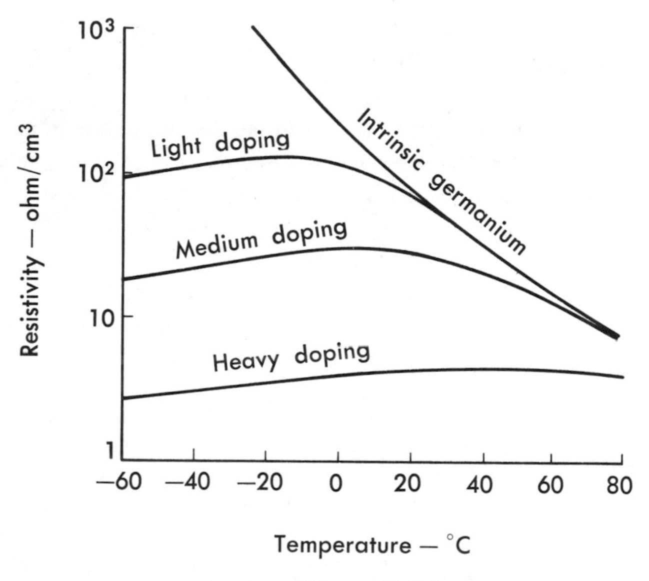

Figure 3-29
Resistivity of doped germanium. (*N*-type) versus temperature.

Figure 3-26. A boron acceptor atom is present in the lattice. Since boron has only three valence electrons, only three covalent bonds can be formed, although the lattice structure calls for four. Hence, the boron atom can easily acquire an electron from an adjoining germanium atom to complete the lattice. But this leaves the adjoining germanium atom with a hole. This hole travels randomly through the lattice just as a free electron. It is evident that acceptor atoms suppress the number of free electrons in a crystal.

N-type semiconductors conduct chiefly by electron flow, and *P*-type semiconductors conduct chiefly by hole flow, as shown in Figure 3-27. We know that impurities reduce the resistivity of a semiconductor. The resistivity varies with the impurity concentration as seen in Figure 3-28. Resistivity depends in part on the mobility of charge carriers. Accordingly, the resistivity of *N*-type material is less than the resistivity of *P*-type material.

The resistivity of doped semiconductors varies with temperature, as would be expected. Figure 3-29 shows typical resistivity variations of *N*-type germanium. At high temperatures, the resistivity of any doped semiconductor becomes practically the same as that of intrinsic material at the same temperature. The reason for this equality is that very large numbers of electron-hole pairs are generated at high temperatures. There are so many electron-hole pairs generated at 80°C, for example, that the n_i^2 term in Equation (3.8) becomes very large and the electrical effect of doping is virtually masked.

3.7 DEFINITION OF AN INSULATOR

Electrical insulators are substances that have comparatively high resistivity. In terms of energy band levels, an insulator has a large forbidden-band gap, as depicted in Figure 3-30. Insulators are used as dielectrics

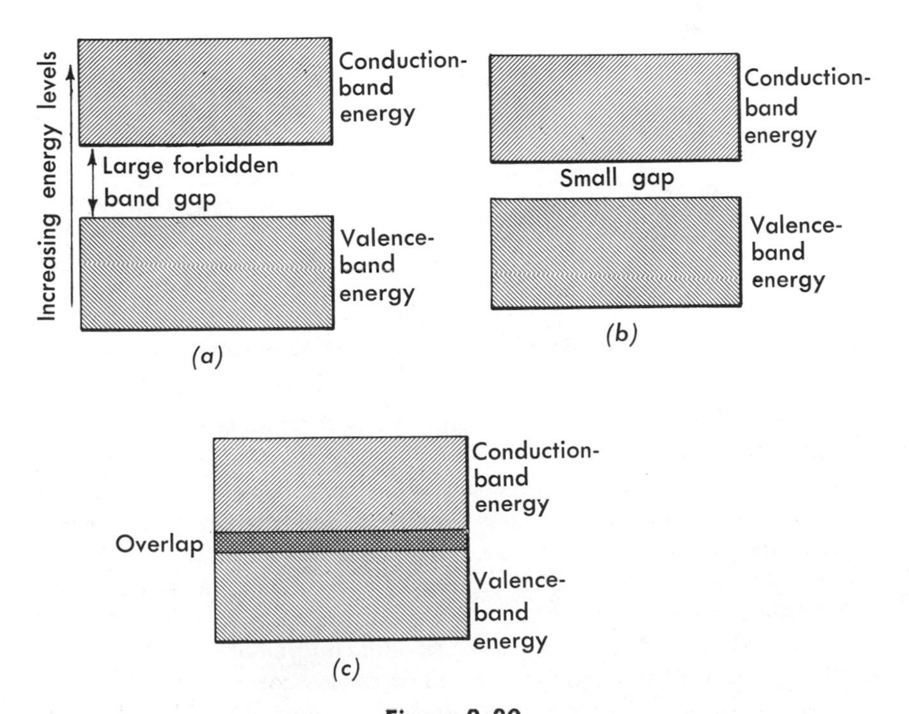

Figure 3-30
Energy band levels for *(a)* insulator; *(b)* semiconductor; *(c)* conductor.

between capacitor plates, as previously noted. These dielectrics may be air, mica, paper, a chemically deposited film, and so forth. Insulators also serve to prevent conduction or short-circuits between wires, metal parts of electrical components, and to prevent spark-over or arcing in high-voltage equipment. Figure 3-31 illustrates various commercial forms of insulators.

Conducting wires are insulated in most applications. Rubber is more widely used to insulate power-carrying wires than any other substance;

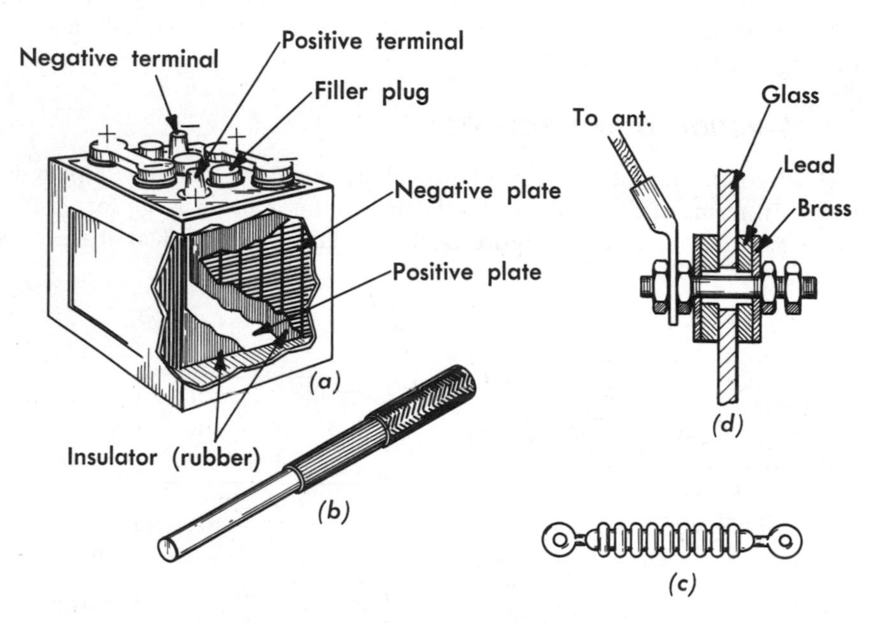

Figure 3-31
Typical insulators used in electronic equipment.

it is a good insulator, is very tough, and is comparatively inexpensive. Rubber-covered wire (type *R*) is commonly used in domestic and factory wiring systems. However, rubber-insulated wire is not suitable for use above 120°F. Rubber deteriorates rapidly at high temperatures, becomes brittle, and breaks apart. Hence, insulation for wires that operate at temperatures in excess of 120°F is usually made from varnished cambric or asbestos.

Cords that conduct power to electronic equipment or appliances are called lamp cord, reinforced cord, hard-service cord, and heater cord. Stranded wires are wrapped with thread to prevent any broken strands from puncturing the outer insulation. Lamp cord comprises two conductors, with thread wrapping covered with rubber, and finally with an outer cotton braid. The two insulated conductors are twisted together beneath the braid. Lamp cord will withstand moderately hard usage, but must not be subjected to dampness.

Reinforced cord (type *P*) is somewhat similar to lamp cord. However, it also has a rubber jacket over the twisted conductors. The jacket is then covered with cotton or silk braid. Reinforced cord can withstand harder service than ordinary lamp cord, but must be kept dry. When severe treatment and dampness are anticipated, hard-service cords (type *S* or *SJ*) are commonly used. Hard-service cords have rubber-covered conductors, which are twisted together and then jacketed with a special high-grade rubber compound. Type *S* cord has thicker insulation than type *SJ*. Though rugged and moisture-resistant, these cords are limited to temperatures below 120°F.

Heater cord is used at high temperatures. The conductors are individually insulated with a 1/64-in. rubber covering, which is jacketed with asbestos. The asbestos is usually protected by cotton braid. Special cords include a copper braid under the cotton braid. This copper braiding is grounded to provide additional safety to the user should the insulation become damaged. If a conductor makes contact with the copper braid in a defective cord, a circuit fuse will often blow; however, the user is protected against possibility of shock.

3.8 SURVEY OF DIELECTRIC STRENGTHS

Any insulator will break down and conduct electricity when stressed by a sufficiently high voltage. Dielectric strengths of insulating materials are accordingly of concern in practical work. The dielectric strength of

Table 3-4

DIELECTRIC STRENGTHS OF INSULATORS

Material	*Breakdown Voltage (volts per mil)*
Air	20, approximately
Bakelite	500
Fiber	200
Formica	450
Window glass	200–250
Lucite	480–500
Paper	1250, approximately
Porcelain	40–500
Hard rubber	450

an insulator is the minimum value of electric field intensity required to rupture the material. Dielectric strengths are usually measured in kilovolts per centimeter of dielectric thickness between the points of applied voltage. The disruptive voltage is the voltage required to break down the dielectric. In the case of air, we sometimes use the terms dielectric strength and disruptive voltage synonymously.

Dielectric strength is dependent upon temperature, mechanical compression, humidity, and purity of the substance. Surface conditions such as scratches may affect dielectric strength. Table 3-4 lists disruptive (breakdown) voltages for a number of common dielectrics at room temperature.

3.9 ANALYSIS OF INSULATION DEFECTS

No insulator is perfect; nevertheless, good insulators have extremely high resistance under normal conditions. After insulation breaks down, its resistance decreases, often to a very low value. Hence, resistance measurements are often used to analyze insulation defects. An ohmmeter is occasionally useful. On the other hand, insulation defects may not appear until substantial voltage is applied. Special ohmmeters operating at high voltage, such as 500–10,000 volts, are utilized for definitive tests. The construction and operation of electrical measuring instruments are explained in following chapters.

When insulation breaks down in electrical or electronic equipment, it often burns and chars. Pungent odors may assist in localizing the defect. Visual inspection will sometimes reveal broken-down insulation. Whenever you troubleshoot an insulation defect, remember that power should first be turned off to avoid possibility of shock. After the defect has been cleared, operation of the equipment will not resume if a fuse has been blown. Remember to turn off the power before replacing a blown fuse. Finally, do not ever defeat the purpose of a fuse by short-circuiting the fuse-holder, because a future insulation defect could cause fire damage.

Many of us have experienced the inconvenience of a "dead" storage battery in an automobile due to an insulation defect. The short-circuit permits heavy current flow and depletes the battery rapidly. Sometimes an insulation defect is *intermittent*. This means that the conductors short-circuit erratically. For example, mechanical vibration might cause momentary short-circuits, resulting in transient engine failure and flickering lights.

SUMMARY OF FUNDAMENTAL CONCEPTS

	Conductors	Semiconductors (Pure)	Insulators
Structure	Crystalline	Crystalline	Crystalline (except the glasses)
Resistance characteristic	Obeys Ohm's law at ordinary temperatures	Does not obey Ohm's law	
Resistivity	Low at ordinary temperatures	Moderate at room temperature	Very high
Resistivity at absolute zero	Zero (many conductors)	Infinite	
Charge carriers	Electrons	Electrons and holes	
Forbidden region	None	Narrow	Wide
Surface effects	None at ordinary frequencies	May be dominant unless passivated	May be dominant unless suitably treated
Temperature coefficient of resistance	Positive	Negative	

QUESTIONS

1) The resistivity of a conductor is defined as:
(*a*) its resistance at −273°C. (*b*) its resistance at room temperature. (*c*) its resistance compared with that of pure copper. (*d*) the resistance of a cube of the conductor with edges 1 cm in length at 0°C.

2) A typical conductor has a resistivity of:
   (*a*) 100 ohms per cm^3. (*b*) 10^{12} ohms per cm^3. (*c*) 1 ohm per cm^3. (*d*) 2×10^{-6} ohm per cm^3.
3) The following substance has a crystalline structure:
   (*a*) copper. (*b*) glass. (*c*) water. (*d*) air.
4) Atoms in a hydrogen molecule are bonded together by:
   (*a*) ionic forces. (*b*) gravitational forces. (*c*) covalent forces. (*d*) the Cariolis effect.
5) A transfer of electrons takes place when:
   (*a*) a crystal lattice is formed. (*b*) when a water molecule is formed. (*c*) when molten copper solidifies. (*d*) when ice melts.
6) The energy of a quantum is:
   (*a*) equal to Planck's constant. (*b*) equal to the frequency of a radiated electromagetic wave. (*c*) equal to the frequency multiplied by its electron-volts. (*d*) equal to the frequency multiplied by Planck's constant.
7) Valence electrons move in:
   (*a*) the forbidden band. (*b*) the valence band. (*c*) the nucleus. (*d*) the gravitational shell of the nucleus.
8) Germanium has lower resistivity than:
   (*a*) silver. (*b*) iron. (*c*) silicon. (*d*) copper.
9) When a covalent bond is broken:
   (*a*) the crystal shatters. (*b*) a positive ion is left in the crystal lattice. (*c*) a negative ion is left in the crystal lattice. (*d*) a molecule is formed.
10) The lifetime of a hole is:
   (*a*) infinite. (*b*) zero. (*c*) from 1 millisec to 1 microsec. (*d*) equal to Planck's constant multiplied by the speed of light.

PROBLEMS

1) A bar of copper has a cross-sectional area of 1 sq cm and is 1 mile long. What is its resistance?
2) A wire has a diameter of 10 mils. What is its cross-sectional area in circular mils?
3) If a No. 30 B&S gage copper wire is 1000 ft long, and has a current of 100 milliamps flowing through it, what is the rate of heat dissipation from the wire?
4) It is desired to make up a flexible cable from six smaller wires that will have the same resistance as a single No. 10 B&S gage copper wire. What gage will you specify for each of the six smaller wires?

5) Aluminum wire is to be used in an application for which a No. 16 B&S gage copper wire is satisfactory. What diameter must the aluminum wire have to give the same resistance?
6) If a No. 14 B&S gage copper wire is the smallest size which may be utilized in an application at 0°C, what is the smallest size which may be used in the same application at 100°C?
7) A No. 8 B&S gage copper wire is interrupted by a switch which has a copper blade of rectangular cross-section. How many square mils of cross-sectional area must the blade have to provide the same current capability as the wire?
8) When 5 volts is applied across a block of intrinsic germanium at a certain temperature, the current flow is 11 microamps. The applied voltage is increased to 10 volts. What is the current flow?
9) If the intrinsic germanium in Problem 8 is heated to a temperature at which the current flow doubles for the same applied voltage, how many more charge carriers are present?
10) A block of intrinsic germanium has 5×10^{13} charge pairs at a certain temperature. Another block of the same size has been doped with 1.79×10^{13} donor atoms per cm^3. How many holes are present in the doped germanium block?
11) A sample of intrinsic germanium is ½ cm in length. Another sample that has the same cross-section is 1 cm in length. Five volts are applied across the ends of each sample. What is the difference in saturation currents?
12) A block of intrinsic germanium with 5×10^{13} charge carriers has been doped with 3.5×10^{14} donor atoms, and 3.5×10^{14} acceptor atoms. We know that $n_e h_h = n_i^2$. How will this doping situation change the resistivity of the intrinsic germanium?
13) If a capacitor that has an air dielectric between its plates will withstand 500 volts, how much more voltage may be applied if bakelite is substituted for the air dielectric?
14) If a fuse operates in a 5000-volt circuit, what is the minimum permissible spacing between its terminals? [Hint: Refer to the discussion of sparking distances between needle points in Chapter 1.]

4

SERIES CIRCUIT ANALYSIS

4.1 THE SERIES LAW

Electronic equipment makes wide use of series circuits. Components in a series circuit are connected end-to-end in one complete path, as illustrated in Figure 4-1. In this example, two dry cells are connected in series-aiding to form a battery. The positive terminal of one cell is connected to the negative terminal of the other cell. Each cell has an emf of 1.5 volts; the battery, therefore, has an emf of 3 volts. This voltage source is connected by conducting wires to the two lamps that consume the electrical energy supplied by the battery. Note that the two lamps are connected in series. Since there is only one path for current flow through the lamps, the *same* current must flow through each lamp. This is an example of the *series law,* which states that the current is the same at any point in a series circuit.

Though the series law is simple, it is not entirely obvious. Thus, it might be supposed that some of the current is somehow "used up" in passage through the first lamp, so that less current is available to flow through the second lamp. Of course, this is not so. We can demonstrate the validity of the series law by connecting three ammeters into the circuit, as shown in Figure 4-2. The three ammeters will read the same current value. Therefore, the same current is flowing in each of the conducting wires in the series circuit. Note that the ammeters are connected in series with the circuit. An ammeter is always connected into a circuit as a series component.

4.2 TOTAL RESISTANCE IN A CIRCUIT

An incandescent lamp is a resistance from the standpoint of circuit analysis. Accordingly, two lamps connected in series with a battery may be represented as two resistances connected in series with the battery, as seen in Figure 4-3. If the two lamps are of the same type, their resistances are equal. In this case, $R_1 = R_2$. On the other hand, if the two lamps are not of the same type, their resistances will be different; hence R_1 is not equal to R_2. But in either instance, it is evident that an equivalent circuit can be drawn as in Figure 4-4(*b*), in which R_1 and R_2 are combined into a single resistance.

This single resistance has a value equal to $R_1 + R_2$; it represents the total resistance in the circuit. Analysis starts with knowledge of the total

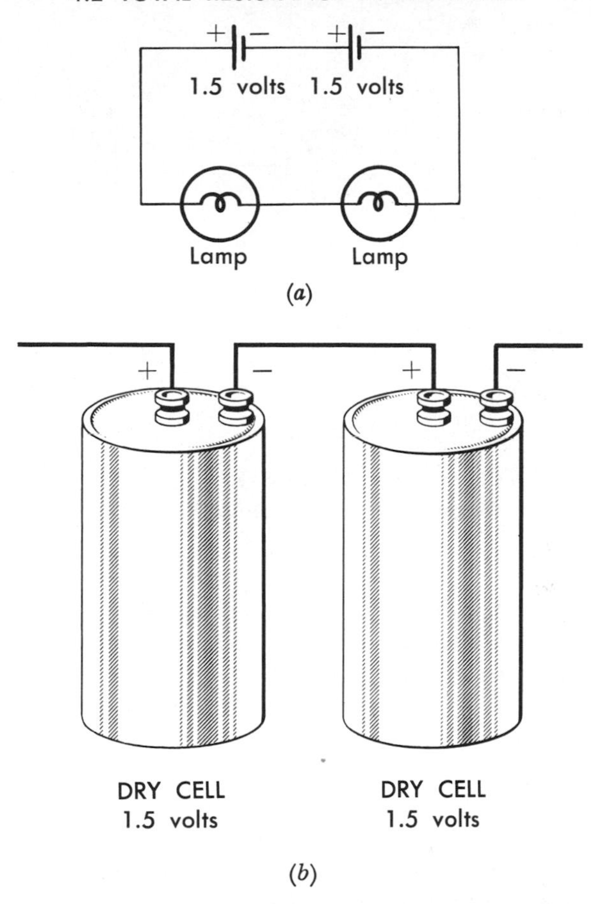

(c)

Figure 4-1

(a) Two dry cells and two lamps connected in series. *(b)* Picture diagram of series-aiding dry-cell connections. *(c)* Photograph of the arrangement depicted in *(a)*.

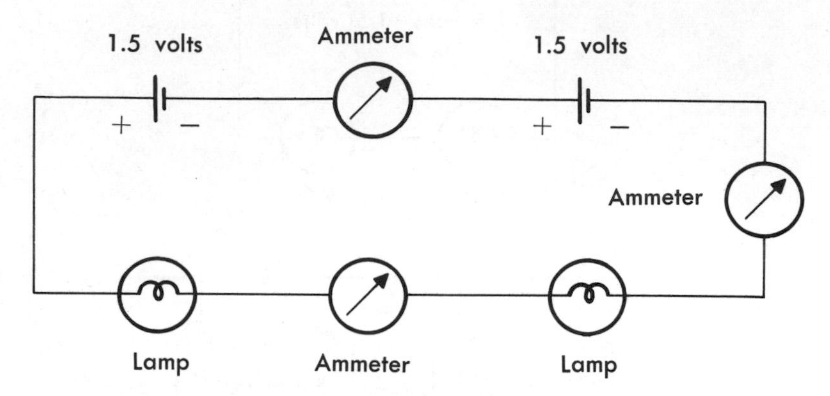

Figure 4-2
Demonstration of the series law.

resistance value and the battery voltage. For example, let $E = 6$ in Figure 4-4. Assume that both lamps are of the same type. If the current flow is 0.25 amp, what is the resistance of each lamp? This problem asks us to solve for the values of R_1 and R_2 in Figure 4-4(*a*). In this example, $R_1 = R_2$. Hence, the total resistance R_T has a value of $2R_1$, or $2R_2$.

The value of R_T follows from Ohm's law: $R_T = E/I = 6/0.25 = 24$ ohms. Since $2R_1 = 24$ ohms, $R_1 = 12$ ohms. Similarly, $R_2 = 12$ ohms. The values for $E = 6$ volts and $I = 0.25$ amp are measured with a voltmeter and an ammeter as shown in Figure 4-5. Note carefully that the ammeter is connected in *series* with the circuit, and that the voltmeter is connected *across* the battery. A voltmeter has a very high resistance and draws very

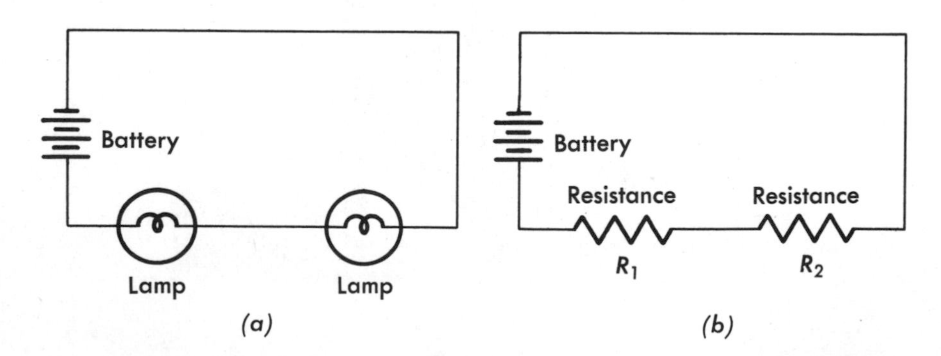

Figure 4-3
(*a*) Schematic representation of a lamp circuit. (*b*) Equivalent electrical circuit.

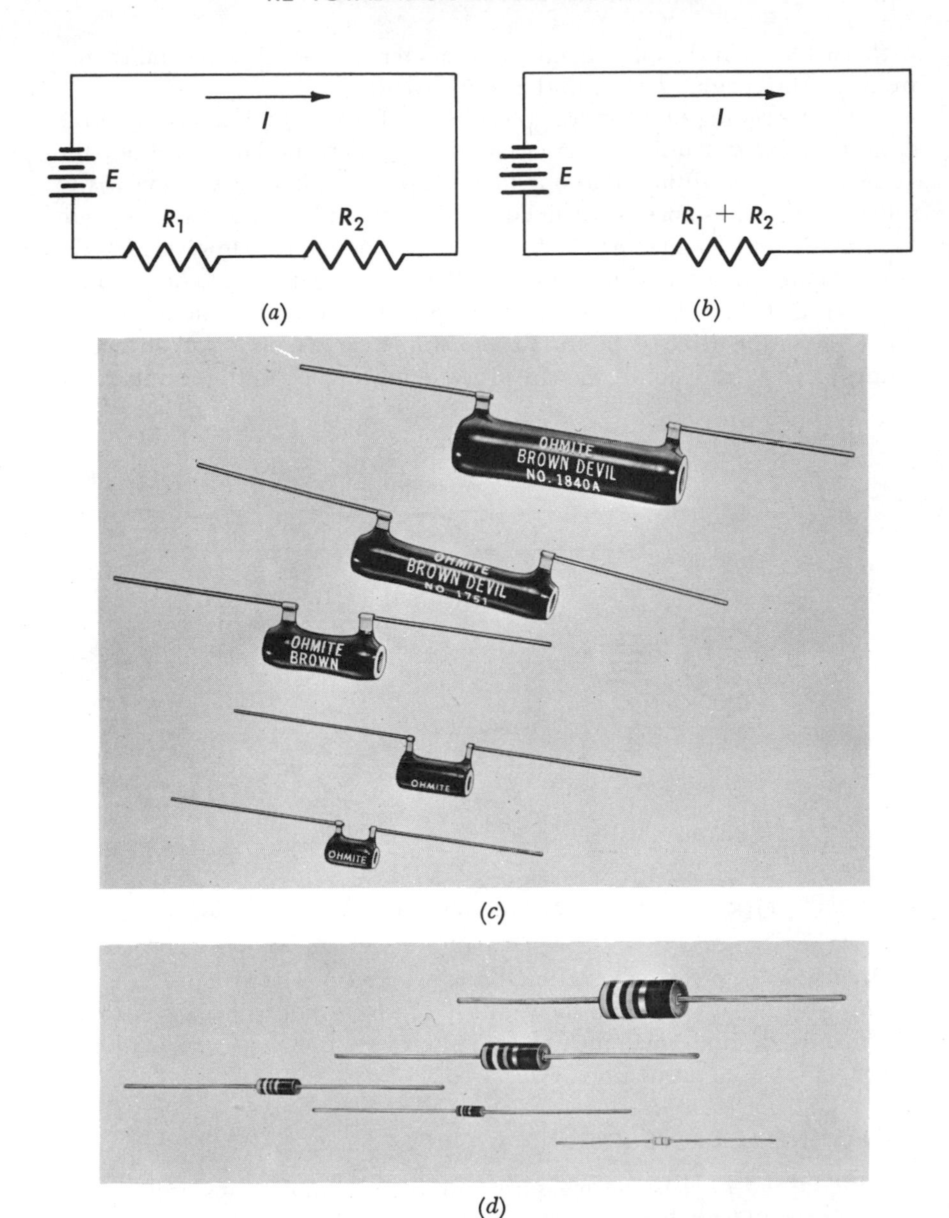

(d)

Figure 4-4

(a) The total circuit resistance is equal to $R_1 + R_2$. *(b)* The total circuit resistance is represented as a single resistance. *(c)* Appearance of wire-round vitreous enameled wire-lead resistors. From top to bottom, resistor power ratings are: 20, 12, 8, 5.25, and 3 watts. (Courtesy of Ohmite Manufacturing Company, Skokie, Illinois. *(d)* Appearance of typical composition resistors. Power ratings are 0.1, 0.25, 0.5, 1, and 2 watts, respectively. (Courtesy of Ohmite Manufacturing Company, Skokie, Illinois.)

little current. On the other hand, an ammeter has very low resistance and indicates the current flowing in the lamp circuit.

The foregoing problem was very simple, because both lamps were the same type. Next, consider a series circuit in which the lamps are not the same type. We shall find that one more step is required in the analysis to solve for the resistance of each lamp. For example, let $E = 6$ volts in Figure 4-5, and let the current be 0.25 amp, as before. However, let the lamps be different types; R_1 is not equal to R_2 (Figure 4-4). The problem requires us to find the values of R_1 and R_2. It is clear that the total resistance R_T is the same as in the first example, or 24 ohms, according to Ohm's law. At this point, we can proceed no farther until we introduce

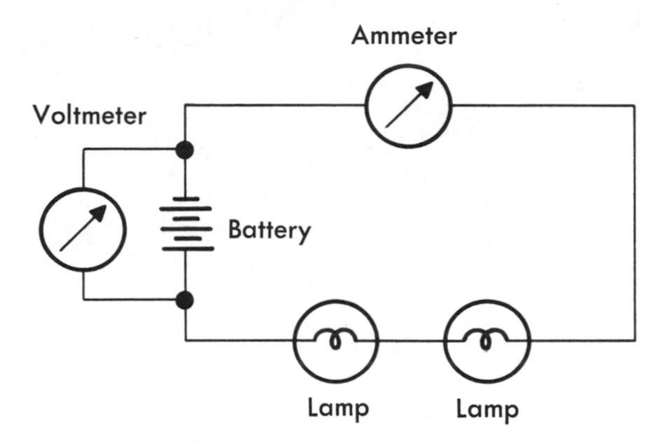

Figure 4-5
Measurement of voltage and current in a series circuit.

another term into the formulation. Since we do not know the ratio of R_1 to R_2, we cannot determine how much of the total resistance is to be assigned to R_1, and how much to R_2. Therefore, our next step is to consider the potential drops around the circuit.

4.3 POTENTIAL DROPS AROUND A CIRCUIT

Figure 4-6 depicts the measurement of potential drops around the series circuit. The voltmeter across the battery indicates 6 volts. Note that the voltage across R_1 is 2 volts, and the voltage across R_2 is 4 volts. Current flow through each resistance is 0.25 amp. Ohm's law applies to *each portion* of the circuit, as well as to the complete circuit. In other words, the voltage across each resistance is equal to IR. We can write $R_1 = 2/0.25 = 8$ ohms. Similarly, $R_2 = 4/0.25 = 16$ ohms. Solution of the problem is thus permitted by measurement of the voltage drops across R_1 and R_2.

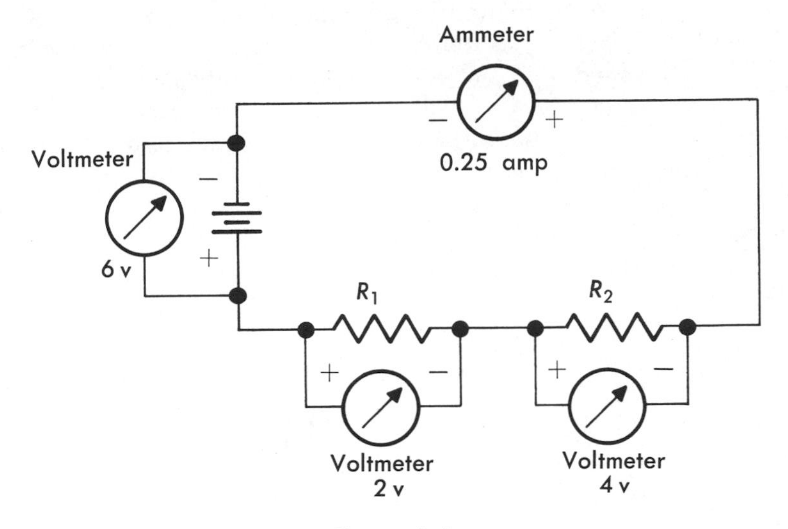

Figure 4-6
An example of potential drops around a series circuit.

In practice, three voltmeters are not required, as depicted in Figure 4-6. It is likely that you would use one voltmeter and make three separate measurements. Moreover, the resistance values of R_1 and R_2 can be determined without measuring the battery voltage. The essential data are the current flow, the voltage drop across R_1, and the voltage drop across R_2. This method of circuit analysis can be easily extended to a circuit having three lamps, or any number of lamps connected in series. It also applies to resistive components other than lamps; for example, the circuit might consist of radio tube heaters connected in series.

4.4 POLARITY REFERENCES

Polarity considerations in series circuits are sometimes puzzling to the beginner. Unless a fixed reference point is chosen, it is quite possible to become confused. Consider the polarity designations in Figure 4-7. All voltmeters and ammeters have polarity markings. For example, the VOM illustrated in Figure 4-8 has positive and negative terminals designated for measurement of voltage and current. In many cases, a red-colored test lead will indicate the positive terminal of a meter; a black-colored test lead will indicate the negative terminal. Meters must be connected into a circuit in such manner that electrons flow from the negative to the positive terminal of the instrument. Otherwise, the pointer will deflect off-scale to the left.

Thus, an ammeter (or milliammeter) indicates the direction of electron flow in a circuit, as well as the amount of current. A voltmeter indicates battery polarity as well as battery voltage. If the voltmeter connections are reversed in Figure 4-7, the pointer will deflect off-scale to the left. Now, let us refer back to Figure 4-6. The voltmeters connected across R_1 and R_2 indicate the polarities of the voltage drops across the resistors, as well as the amount of each voltage drop. Note that the right-hand end of each resistor is negative; the left-hand end of each resistor is positive. This polarity statement refers only to each resistor considered by itself.

A polarity statement with reference to R_1 has no meaning with reference to R_2. For example, the right-hand end of R_1 is negative with respect to the left-hand end of R_1; the same is true for R_2. However, the right-hand end of R_1 is *not* negative with respect to the left-hand end of R_2. Obviously, if we connect a voltmeter from the right-hand end of R_1 to the left-hand end of R_2, the voltmeter will read zero.

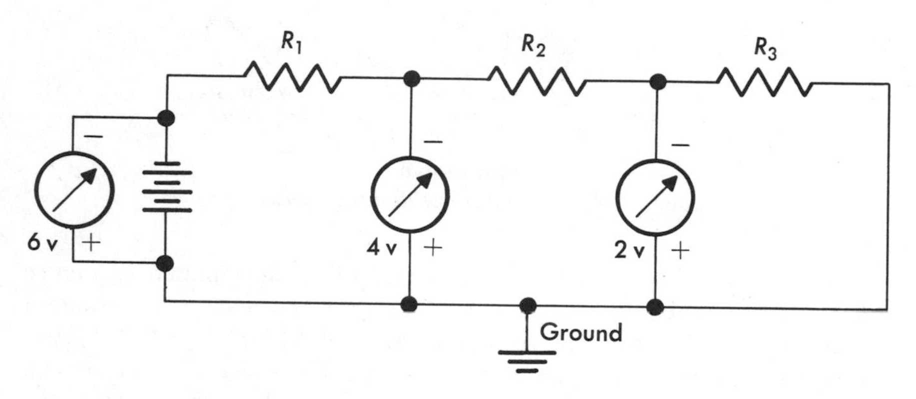

Figure 4-7
Voltages may be measured with reference to a common point in a circuit.

To say that the right-hand end of R_1 is negative with respect to the left-hand end of R_2 has no meaning, because we have shifted our reference in making the statement. That is, we start with reference to R_1, and falsely attribute the same reference to R_2. When we fix our attention on one component in the circuit, we can speak of its polarity in response to direction of current flow. This polarity determination suffices insofar as instrument connections are concerned. On the other hand, we must not suppose that such polarity determinations imply a voltage drop between the two ends of the wire which connects R_1 to R_2.

GROUND TERMINOLOGY

In electronic equipment, one point in a circuit is often selected as a reference point, called the *ground* or *zero-volt* point. In such circuits (see Figure 4-7), it is common practice to measure all circuit voltages with respect to ground. In this example, the positive terminal of each voltmeter is connected to ground. Hence, all voltages in this circuit are negative with respect to ground. The three voltmeters in Figure 4-7 indicate that there is a 2-volt drop across each resistor. Thus, $6 - 4 = 2$, $4 - 2 = 2$, and $2 - 0 = 2$. Therefore, it follows that all three resistors have the same

Figure 4-8

Positive and negative terminals are designated for measurement of voltage and current. (Courtesy of Simpson Electric Co.)

value: $R_1 = R_2 = R_3$. However, we cannot determine this ohmic value unless we measure the current flow.

The left-hand end of each resistor is negative with respect to its right-hand end; the right-hand end is positive with respect to its left-hand end. However, observe in Figure 4-7 that the left-hand end of each resistor is 2 volts *more* negative than the right-hand end of the same resistor. Next, consider the configuration shown in Figure 4-9. In this series circuit, three voltages are negative with respect to ground, and one voltage is positive with respect to ground. The voltage drops across R_1, R_2, and R_3 are negative with respect to ground. On the other hand, the voltage drop across R_4 is positive with respect to ground. Note that if the ground point were shifted to the positive battery terminal, the voltage drops across all four

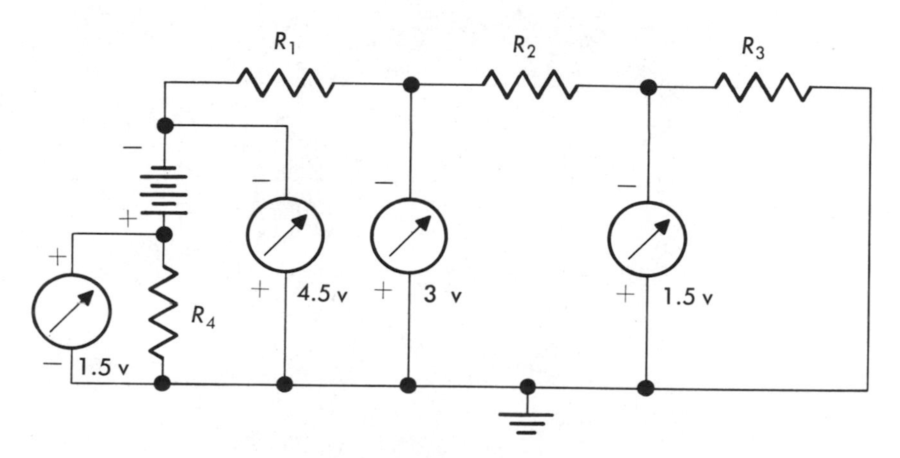

Figure 4-9
An example of positive and negative voltages with respect to ground.

resistors would be negative with respect to ground. It is evident that a ground connection may be made at any point in a series circuit. The choice is made on the basis of desired voltage polarities with respect to ground.

In Figure 4-9, the voltage drop across each resistor is 1.5 volts. It follows from the series law and Ohm's law that all four resistances are the same value. This resistance value cannot be found, however, without making a current measurement. What is the battery voltage in this circuit? The battery voltage is equal to the difference between the readings of the two voltmeters connected at the battery terminals. Hence, the battery voltage is equal to 1.5 volts minus −4.5 volts, or 6 volts. Note that subtraction of a negative voltage from a positive voltage entails addition of the two voltages.

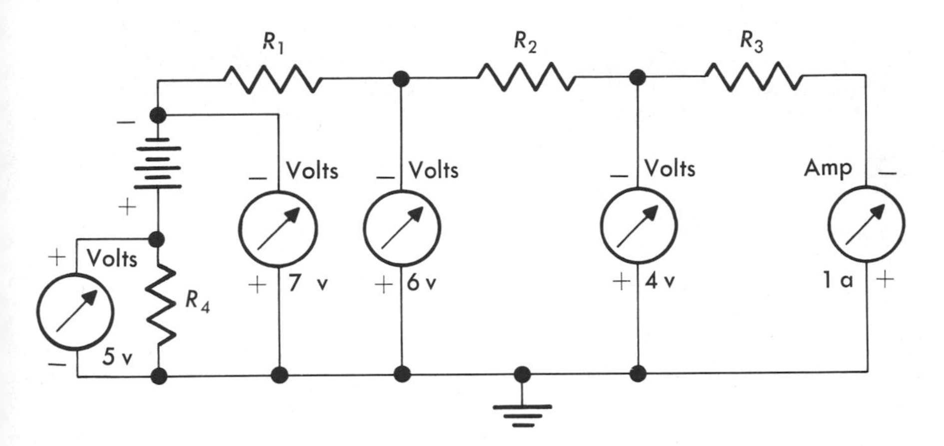

Figure 4-10
The four resistance values are calculated from associated voltage and current readings.

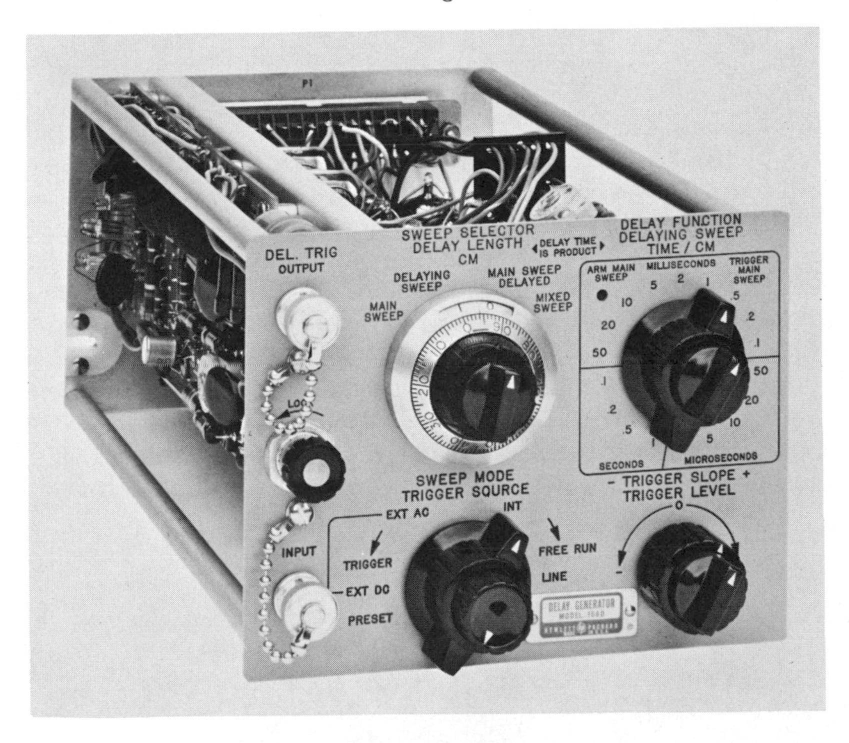

Figure 4-11
The metal framework of the electronic unit is called a chassis. (Courtesy of Hewlett-Packard Co.)

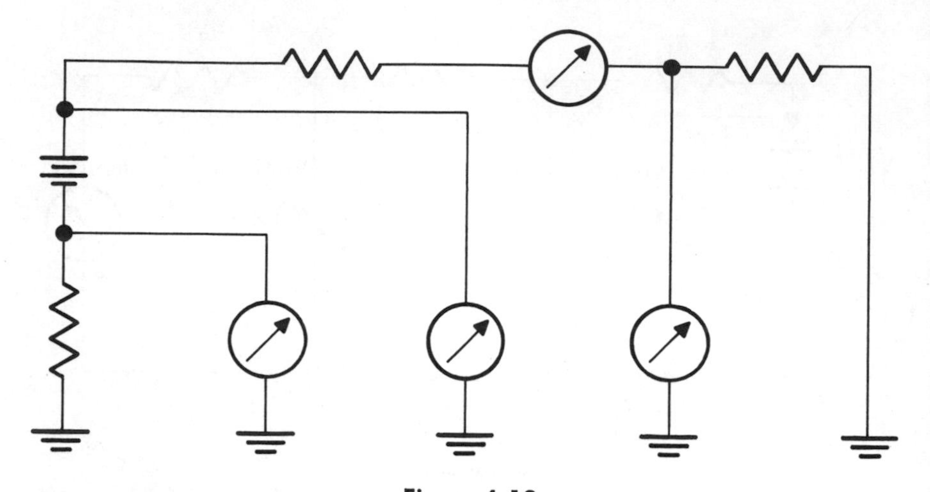

Figure 4-12
The five ground symbols indicate a common electrical connection.

Consider the analysis of a series circuit that comprises four resistances having different values, as seen in Figure 4-10. The battery voltage is evidently 12 volts. The ammeter indicates a current flow of 1 amp. Since Ohm's law applies to each individual resistor, it is seen that $R_1 = 1$ ohm, $R_2 = 2$ ohms, $R_3 = 4$ ohms, and $R_4 = 5$ ohms. The total circuit resistance is 12 ohms. Note that a ground connection may be a physical connection to earth in some cases. For example, a ground connection might be made to a water pipe, which runs down to and is buried in the ground. On the other hand, the ground symbol in the schematic diagram for an electronic circuit often represents a metal chassis, as illustrated in Figure 4-11.

In either case, the ground symbol represents the circuit point to which all voltages are referred. Ground symbols often appear repeatedly in a circuit diagram, as seen in Figure 4-12. All of the ground symbols refer to a common ground. In other words, we regard each ground symbol in

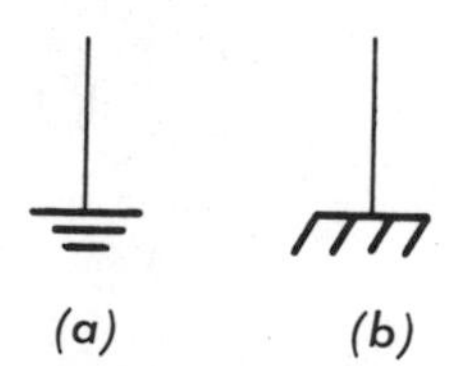

Figure 4-13
(a) Standard symbol for an earth ground. *(b)* Standard symbol for a chassis ground.

Figure 4-12 as if it were connected by a conducting wire to its adjoining ground symbols.

According to established standards, a chassis ground should be indicated by another symbol, shown in Figure 4-13. Historically, the earth-ground symbol was in use long before it was supplemented by the chassis-ground symbol. Understandably, many engineers and technicians have continued to use the earth-ground symbol in a generalized manner. It is helpful, nevertheless, to distinguish between chassis grounds and earth grounds, because a chassis ground sometimes operates at a potential above earth ground. An earth ground, such as a connection to a water pipe buried in the soil, necessarily establishes a zero-volt ground.

4.5 KIRCHHOFF'S VOLTAGE LAW

Kirchhoff's voltage law, established in 1847, has the same basic importance as the series law and Ohm's law in analysis of series circuits. A knowledge of Kirchhoff's law also facilitates analysis of more complex circuits. There are some circuits that cannot be solved without invoking Kirchhoff's voltage law. Previous discussion of series circuit analysis has introduced us to this law, which states that:

$$E = \Sigma e \qquad (4.1)$$

where E is the source voltage and Σe is the sum of the voltage drops around the circuit.

An example of this statement is seen in Figure 4-14. A battery drives current through a series circuit that has four resistances; it also has a terminal voltage E. Voltage drops across R_1, R_2, R_3, and R_4 are e_1, e_2, e_3, and e_4, respectively. Kirchhoff's voltage law states that $E = e_1 + e_2 + e_3 + e_4$. It is evident that this equation can be rewritten: $E - e_1 - e_2 - e_3 - e_4 = 0$. In this form, the equation states that the sum of the voltages around a circuit is equal to zero. If there is a switch in the circuit, and the switch is open (current is zero), Kirchhoff's law still applies, because the source voltage is equal to the voltage across the switch. The validity of Kirchhoff's law follows directly from the series law and Ohm's law. This proof is left as an exercise for the student.

Thus far, we have considered series circuits with only one voltage source. However, circuits are frequently encountered in practice that have more than one voltage source. For example, consider a basic storage-battery charging circuit, as utilized in an automobile or service station. Figure 4-15 shows a series circuit in which generator voltage forces current to flow through a storage battery. In this example, the generator is an 8-volt source; the storage battery is a 6-volt source. These two voltages are opposed, inasmuch as the sources are connected negative-to-negative

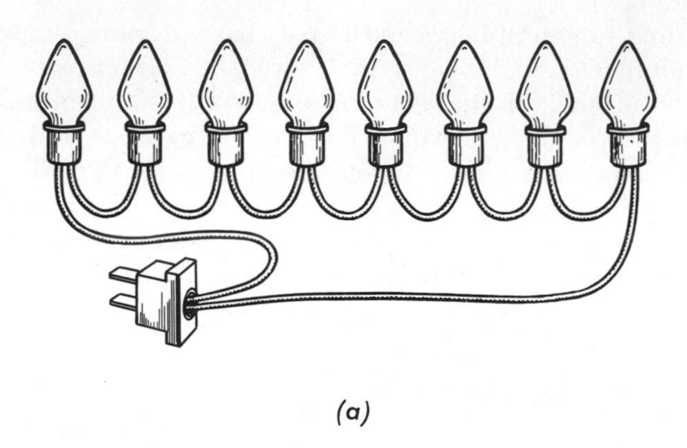

(a)

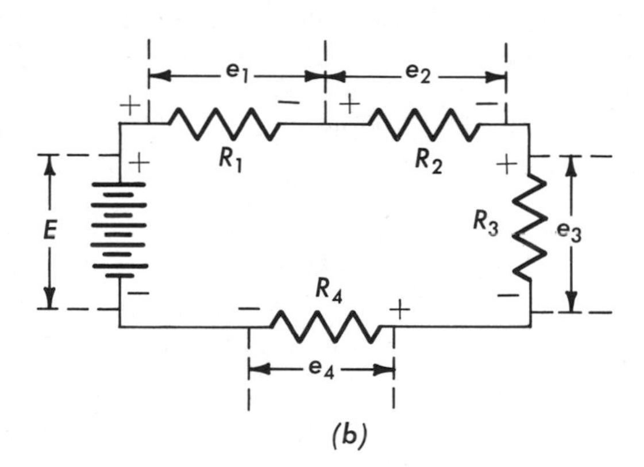

(b)

Figure 4-14

(*a*) Typical series string of electric light bulbs. (*b*) Kirchhoff's law applied to a series circuit.

and positive-to-positive. Since the generator applies 2 volts more than the battery does to the circuit, electron flow occurs in the direction shown in Figure 4-15. Hence, a reverse current flows through the storage battery.

Let us write Kirchhoff's law for this circuit. If we proceed from E_g in a clockwise direction around the circuit, we write

$$E_g - E_r - E_b = 0 \tag{4.2}$$

Since we regarded E_g as a positive voltage, we assigned negative polarity to E_r and E_b. Note that E_b has the same significance in the equation as the voltage drop across a resistor. We can rewrite Equation (4.2) in the form: $E_g - E_b = E_r$. This equation states that the two voltage sources

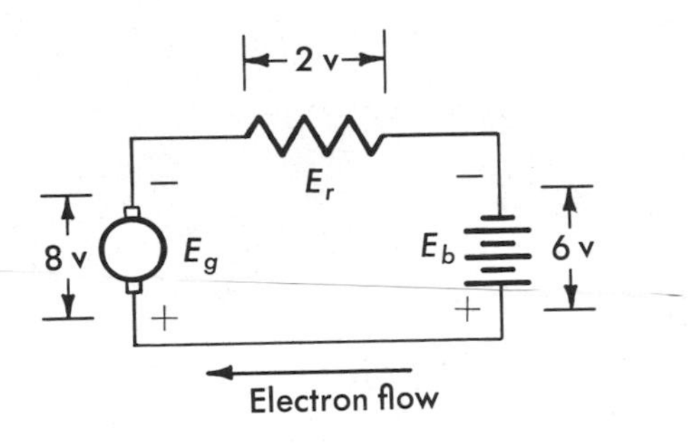

Figure 4-15
A storage-battery charging circuit ($R = 2\ \Omega$).

oppose each other, and that their difference is equal to the voltage drop across the resistor.

Detailed discussion of dry cells, storage cells, and generators is not given in this chapter; however, several basic facts are briefly noted. Cells change chemical energy into electrical energy. They are classified as either primary cells or secondary (storage) cells. A cell contains two conducting plates of different materials that are immersed in an electrolyte. After a primary cell has "run down," it must be discarded or new electrolyte (and possibly electrodes) supplied. On the other hand, a secondary cell can be recharged after it has run down by forcing a current to flow through it in the opposite direction to that of discharge. A generator is a machine that changes mechanical energy into electrical energy. It consists basically of a number of conductors on an iron core which rotates in a magnetic field.

Consider the current flow (charging current) in the circuit of Figure 4-15. In effect, a 2-volt source drives current through the 2-ohm resistance. Hence, the charging current will be 1 amp. Suppose the generator stops; the current flow then reverses in direction and the storage battery discharges at a rate of 3 amps. To prevent battery discharge when an automobile engine stops, an automatic switch is included in the charging circuit. The switch is operated by current flow through an electromagnet. Whenever the generator develops sufficient voltage, the switch is closed by the electromagnet. However, when the generator voltage ceases, the switch is opened by spring action.

4.6 ANALYSIS BY RESISTANCE PROPORTIONS

We have seen that the voltage drops around a series circuit can often be calculated without considering current flow. When we are concerned only with voltage distribution, it saves time to disregard current calcula-

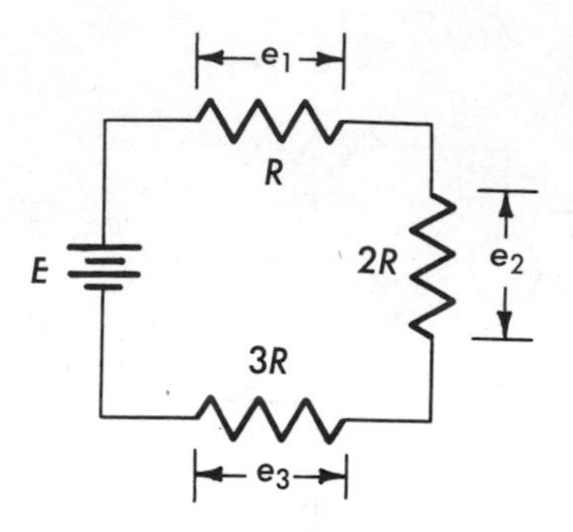

Figure 4-16
The voltage drops are in the ratio of individual resistance values to the total circuit resistance value.

tions. For example, resistance values are not specified in Figure 4-16. It is stated only that the resistance values are in the proportion of 1, 2, and 3. It follows that the voltage drops e_1, e_2, and e_3 will also be in the proportions of 1, 2, and 3. In other words, $e_2 = 2e_1$, and $e_3 = 3e_1$. Suppose that E is assigned a value of 6 volts in Figure 4-16. What are the values of e_1, e_2, and e_3? Note that the total resistance of the circuit is $6R$. Evi-

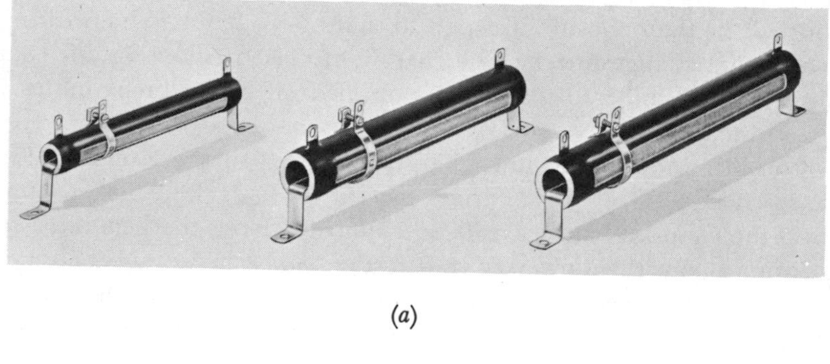

(*a*)

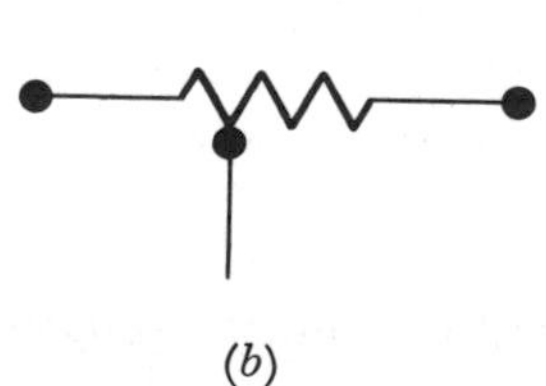

(*b*)

Figure 4-17
(*a*) Appearance of typical tapped resistors. (*b*) Symbolic representation. (Courtesy of Ohmite Manufacturing Company, Skokie, Illinois.)

dently, R will drop $E/6$, or 1 volt; $2R$ will drop $2E/6$, or 2 volts; $3R$ will drop $3E/6$, or 3 volts, and so forth.

Separate resistors are depicted in Figure 4-16. However, electronic equipment often makes use of *tapped resistors.* A tap may be fixed, or it may be adjustable. One or more taps may be provided. A tapped resistor is often called a *bleeder resistor,* which operates as a *voltage divider.* Figure 4-17(*a*) illustrates adjustable tapped resistors that have wire-wound construction. A bleeder resistor is connected across a voltage source. In turn, an intermediate voltage value is provided by the tap. If the tap band is loosened, moved to another point on the bleeder, and again secured, a changed value of intermediate voltage is provided. Figure 4-17(*b*) shows the symbolic representation for a tapped resistor.

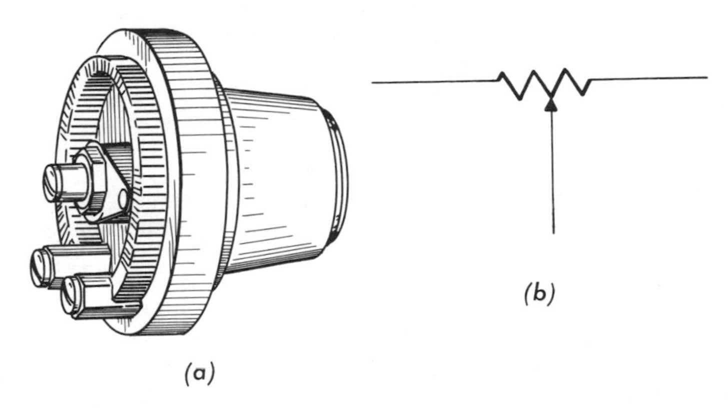

Figure 4-18

(*a*) Appearance of an adjustable tapped resistor. (Courtesy of Ohmite Manufacturing Company, Skokie, Illinois.) (*b*) Symbolic representation.

Another type of tapped-resistor construction is sometimes utilized in electronic equipment. Figure 4-18(*a*) depicts a resistor with a tap in the form of a slider which can be moved manually by rotation of a control knob. This resistor has wire-wound construction. Its symbolic representation is seen in Figure 4-18(*b*). Note that if connection is made to one end of the resistance, and to the slider arm, the component is called a *rheostat.* On the other hand, if connection is made to both ends of the resistance, and to the slider arm, the component is called a *potentiometer.* However, this technical distinction is sometimes disregarded, and a rheostat may be called a potentiometer. Adjustable resistances (tapped resistances) often have carbon resistive elements instead of wire-wound elements [see Figure 4-19(*a*)]. Symbolic representation [Figure 4-19(*b*)] is the same as for wire-wound units.

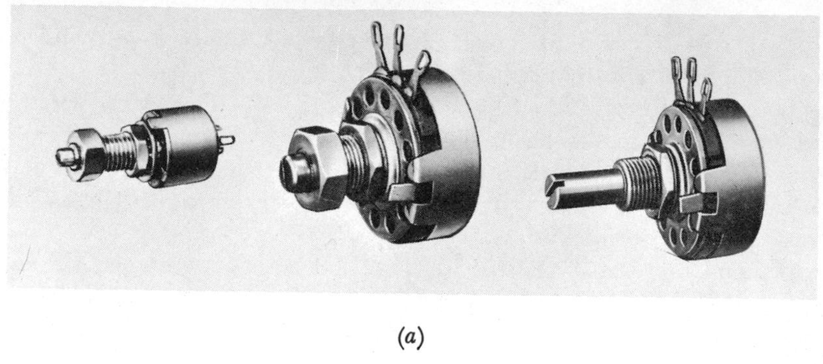

(a)

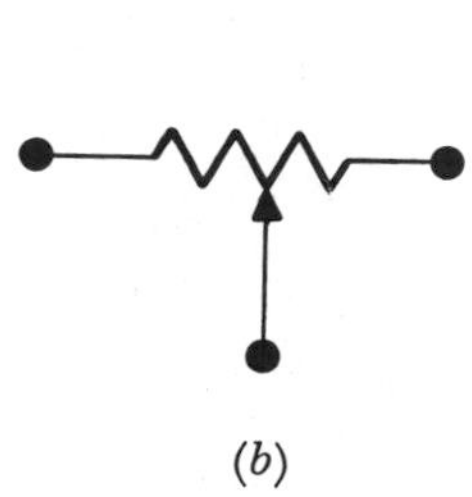

(b)

Figure 4-19
(a) Appearance of carbon potentiometers. (Courtesy of Ohmite Manufacturing Company, Skokie, Illinois.) *(b)* Symbolic representation.

The tapped-resistor construction illustrated in Figure 4-19 is in extremely wide use. Potentiometers may have tubular construction, but commonly utilize a circular resistance element. A metal slider contacts the resistance element and can be moved by rotating a central shaft. Thus, a potentiometer is a variable type of integrated series circuit. Certain types of potentiometers have one or more taps along the resistance element, in addition to the variable slider. Many of the operating controls in radio, high-fidelity, and television receivers are potentiometers.

4.7 SOURCE RESISTANCE

It has been assumed in foregoing discussion that a cell or battery is a source of electrical energy which has negligible *internal resistance.* This assumption is justified only when the cell or battery supplies comparatively little current to its external circuit. If a battery is aged and "weak," the assumption of negligible internal resistance may not be valid even for small current demands. Figure 4-20 shows a series circuit that clearly demonstrates the change in terminal voltage of a battery under no-load and load conditions. If R has a comparatively low value, so that appreciable current is drawn when the switch is closed, we observe that the current demand causes a reduction in the voltmeter reading.

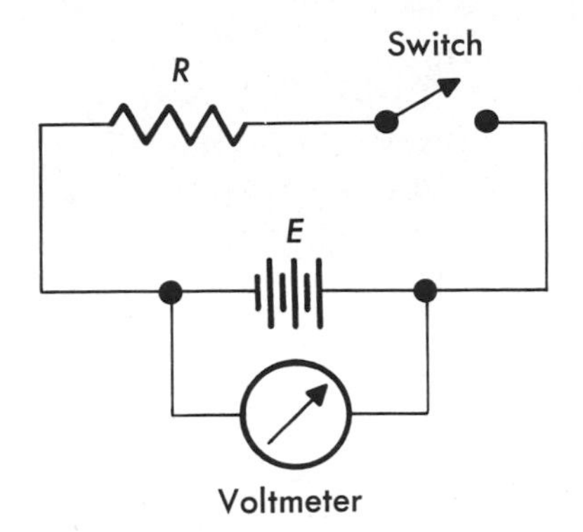

Figure 4-20
The value of E decreases when the switch is closed.

A cell or battery has a certain emf that is established by its chemical characteristics. This emf is constant whether the switch is open or closed in Figure 4-20. However, the internal resistance of the battery is not zero. Consequently, when current is drained from the battery, an IR drop appears across the battery's internal resistance. In turn, the terminal voltage of the battery measures less under load. Its terminal voltage is the difference between its emf and the drop across the battery's internal resistance. Hence, when the current demand is substantial, the diagram in Figure 4-20 must be elaborated as shown in Figure 4-21.

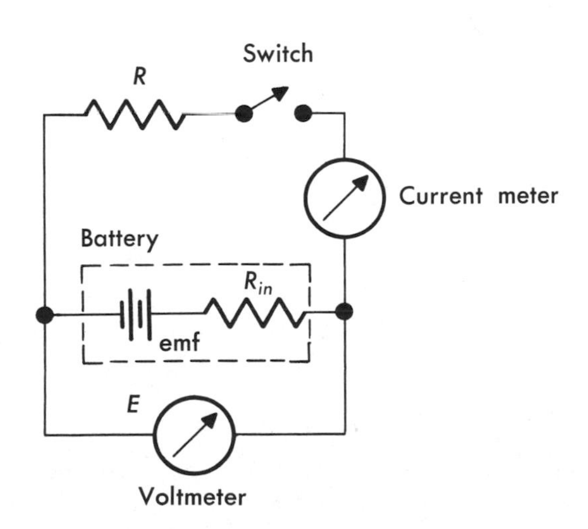

Figure 4-21
R_{in} represents the internal resistance of the battery.

Thus, the complete series circuit includes the internal resistance of the battery, designated as R_{in} in Figure 4-21. From a practical standpoint, the voltmeter indicates the battery's emf when the switch is open. The terminal voltage may be considered equal to the emf in this case, because most voltmeters draw a very slight current; consequently, the IR drop across R_{in} is negligible. However, when the switch is closed, and substantial current is drawn by load resistance R, the voltmeter reading decreases. We can calculate the value of R_{in} from the two voltmeter readings and the current-meter reading.

For example, suppose that the voltmeter reads 1.5 volts on open circuit (switch open). If the voltmeter is a high-resistance instrument, we can assume that the battery's emf is 1.5 volts. With the switch closed, the voltmeter might read 1.3 volts; this is the terminal voltage of the battery under load. The current meter might indicate that 2 amps are being drawn. Hence, the voltage drop across R_{in} is equal to 1.5 − 1.3 volts, or 0.2 volt, in accordance with Kirchhoff's law. Ohm's law states that resistance is a voltage/current ratio; accordingly, $R_{in} = 0.2/2 = 0.1$ ohm. In general form,

$$R_{in} = \frac{E_{oc} - E_{cc}}{I} \tag{4.3}$$

where E_{oc} is the battery's terminal voltage on open circuit, E_{cc} is its voltage on closed circuit, and I is the current flow on closed circuit.

INTERNAL RESISTANCE VALUE IS NOT A CONSTANT

It might be supposed that R_{in} is constant; however, this is not so. To demonstrate this fact, the foregoing test can be repeated for a lower value of R in Figure 4-21. You will find that R_{in} increases in value when more current is demanded from the battery. Furthermore, R_{in} gradually increases over a period of time while constant current is being drawn from the battery. The value of R_{in} is also temperature-dependent. If the battery is permitted to recuperate on open circuit, the value of R_{in} will return almost to its original value. Note that as a battery ages, its internal resistance gradually increases and its recuperation becomes less complete. After a long period of service, the value of R_{in} becomes so large that a battery is no longer useful. A dry cell must then be replaced, or a storage cell must be recharged.

Chemicals utilized in dry cells are not perfectly pure. As a cell ages, progressive side reactions become cumulative. Because of this, the emf of the cell does not remain quite constant, as in theory. The emf decreases slightly as the internal resistance increases substantially. These characteristics become of concern in design of electronic equipment which requires compensation for changes in emf and internal resistance of the source voltage.

A typical battery tester is illustrated in Figure 4-22. It is basically a voltmeter with various load resistors that are switched into the test

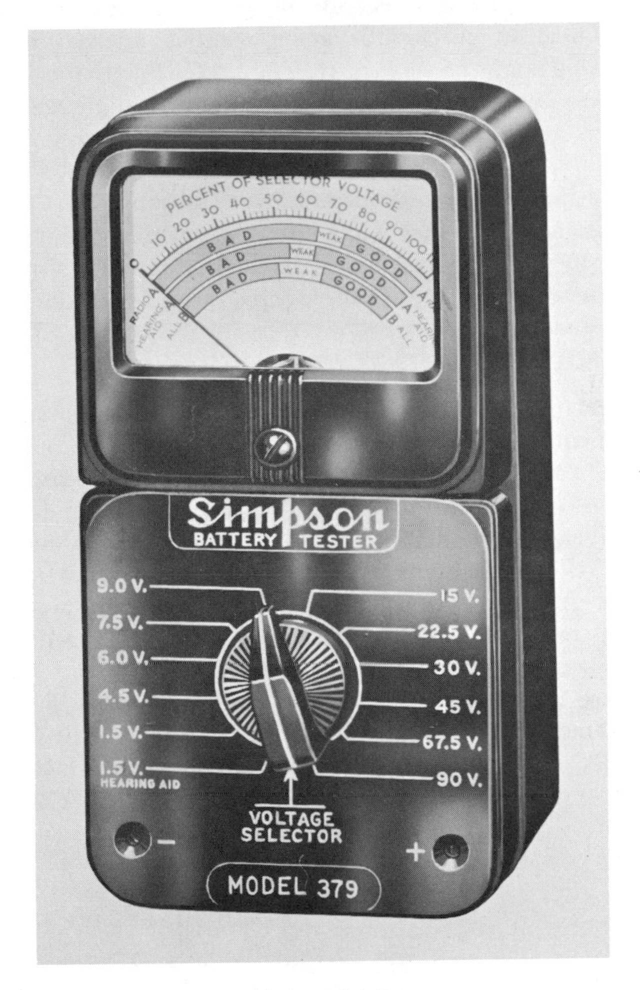

Figure 4-22
A typical battery tester. (Courtesy of Simpson Electric Co.)

circuit on various positions of the selector knob. Accordingly, the terminal voltage of a battery is measured under suitable load conditions. To simplify instrument use, the scale is provided with colored sectors for "bad" and "good" indication. This is called a *go, no-go* type of test. Three "good-bad" scales are provided in this particular instrument for checking radio

A, hearing-aid, and radio *B* battery types. A somewhat higher internal resistance is tolerable for radio *B* batteries than for hearing-aid batteries, or for radio *A* batteries. The differences between these three battery types, and their applications, are explained subsequently.

All sources of electrical energy have more or less internal (source) resistance. Thus, an automobile generator has internal resistance, although its value might be very small. The power line that energizes lamps and appliances in your home is a source of electrical energy which has a small internal resistance. A static machine generates very high voltages which may jump a gap of 1 in. or more. However, the internal resistance of a static machine is very high; the machine can supply very little current. If appreciable current is demanded from a static machine, most of the generated voltage is dropped across its high internal resistance. Consequently, the terminal voltage of the machine falls to a very low value.

4.8 TOTAL POWER AND ITS COMPONENTS

Power relations are of basic importance in the design and operation of electronic equipment. It is often desired, for example, to deliver maximum power from a generator to a load. Thus, it is desired to deliver maximum power from an amplifier to a speaker in a hi-fi installation. Again, consider the storage battery and starter motor in an automobile. The battery is sometimes required to deliver maximum power to the starter motor. A starter motor presents a certain load resistance to the battery while it cranks the engine. What value of resistive load will develop maximum power from the battery?

In Figure 4-23, the current value is evidently $I = E/(R + R_{\text{in}})$. The power consumed by R is given by $W = VI = I^2R$; load voltage $V = E - IR_{\text{in}}$. We know that V must decrease when I increases. Conse-

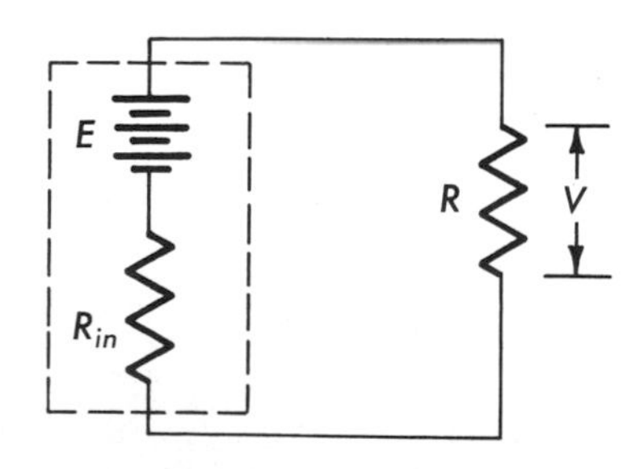

Figure 4-23
Maximum power is to be consumed by *R*; only the value of *R* can be changed.

quently, the power consumed by R must be expressed in terms of V and I; or, $W = I(E - IR_{in}) = EI - I^2R_{in}$. This is a quadratic equation, in which we wish to find the value of I for which W is maximum.

Let us dispose of certain common fallacies at the outset. We might suppose that maximum power would be developed when current flow is greatest. But $W = I^2R$, and R must be zero to obtain greatest current flow; in turn, W is zero. Obviously, maximum power is not consumed by R when the current is maximum. Again, we might suppose that maximum power would be developed when the voltage across R is greatest. However, V is maximum when R is infinite. If R is infinite, no current flows, and W is zero. Maximum power is not consumed by R when the voltage across R is greatest. Therefore, let us return to the quadratic equation previously derived which states the power consumed by R:

$$W = -R_{in}I^2 + EI \tag{4.4}$$

It is helpful to briefly review the solution of the general quadratic equation:

$$y = ax^2 + bx + c \tag{4.5}$$

You will recall from your algebra courses that the solution of the general quadratic equation is expressed by the *quadratic formula*:

$$x = \frac{-b \pm \sqrt{b^2 - 4ac}}{2a} \tag{4.6}$$

ROOTS OF THE QUADRATIC EQUATION

This quadratic formula gives the values of x for which y will be zero; it gives the *roots* of the equation. We shall find that the roots are related to the value of x for which y is maximum. To visualize determination of the maximum value, let us plot the graph of a quadratic equation with numerical values assigned to a, b, and c:

$$y = -x^2 + 10x - 16 \tag{4.7}$$

This plot is shown in Figure 4-24. The graph has x intercepts at $x = 2$ and at $x = 8$. Halfway between these two root values, at $x = 5$, the graph rises to its maximum value of $y = 9$. If the maximum value of y is calculated, it is found to occur at the value of x given by

$$x = \frac{-b}{2a} \tag{4.8}$$

Thus, to continue the foregoing example, the maximum value of y occurs when $x = -10/-2 = 5$. In turn, the maximum value of y is found by substituting $x = 5$ in Equation (4.7), yielding $y = 9$.

Now, let us apply this principle to Equation (4.4). The c term is zero,

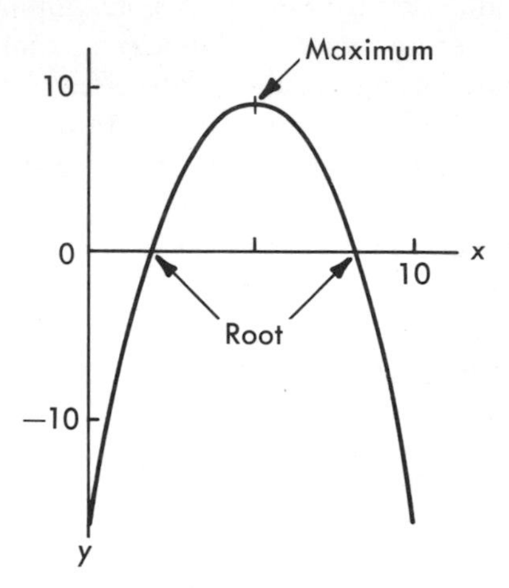

Figure 4-24
Graph of $y = -x^2 + 10x - 16$.

and the equation is simpler in this respect than the general quadratic equation. Evidently, $a = -R_{in}$, and $b = E$. The value of W will be maximum when $I = -b/2a$, or $I = E/2R_{in}$. This result states that the current flow which develops maximum power in the load depends upon the internal resistance of the battery.

The current flow, of course, depends also on the load value R. What is this load value when maximum power is developed? The current flow (Figure 4-23) is given by

$$I = \frac{E}{R + R_{in}}$$

Hence, we can write

$$\frac{E}{2R_{in}} = \frac{E}{R + R_{in}}$$

This expression reduces to

$$R = R_{in} \tag{4.9}$$

MAXIMUM POWER TRANSFER

In other words, maximum power is developed by the load resistance R in Figure 4-23 when the load resistance is equal to the battery's internal resistance. The variation of load power versus R/R_{in} is seen in Figure 4-25.

Note that the power in the load does not drop greatly as the ratio of R/R_{in} is changed from 0.8 to 1.2. However, if the load has a widely different value from the internal resistance, the load power is substantially decreased.

It is evident that when maximum power is delivered to the load, half of the total power is consumed in the load resistance, and the other half of the power is consumed in the internal resistance. The output/input power, or efficiency, is 50 percent when maximum power is transferred.

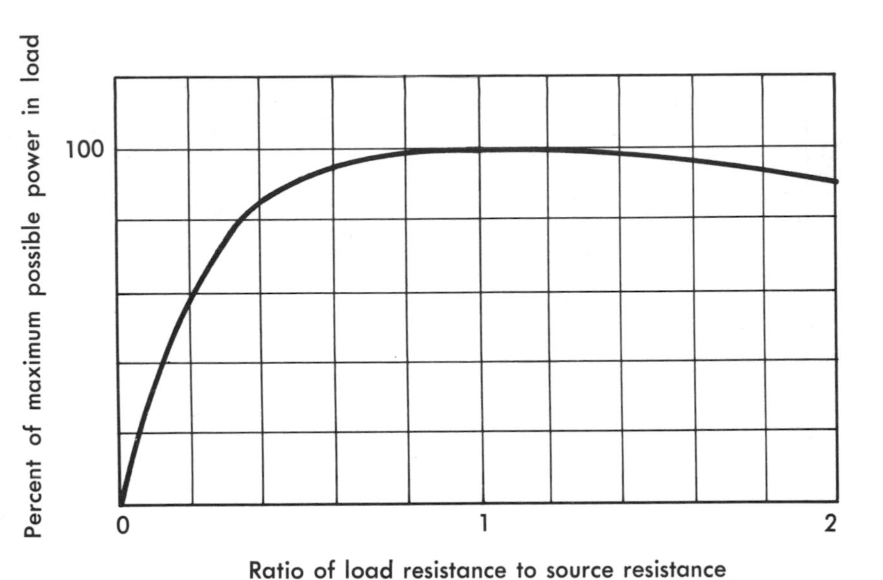

Figure 4-25
Variation of load power versus load resistance.

Efficiency rises as the value of the load resistance is increased, as seen in Figure 4-26. Thus, the value of R in Figure 4-23 can be adjusted either for maximum power transfer or for high efficiency. However, we cannot obtain *both* high efficiency and maximum power transfer.

You will find some electronic systems that are designed for maximum power transfer. For example, when a high-fidelity amplifier is connected to a speaker, the speaker resistance is usually adjusted for maximum power output. In this situation, maximum power is a major consideration, while efficiency is a minor consideration. On the other hand, the power supply (source of d-c energy) in the same amplifier utilizes only a tiny fraction of the available power from the 117-volt line. Accordingly, efficiency is a major consideration and maximum power transfer does not enter the design problem. High power-supply efficiency minimizes the cost of amplifier operation.

We know that metals increase in resistivity as their temperature rises. When a wire-wound resistor, for example, is operated within its rated power dissipation, it does not become heated sufficiently to change its resistance value appreciably. The voltage versus current graph for the

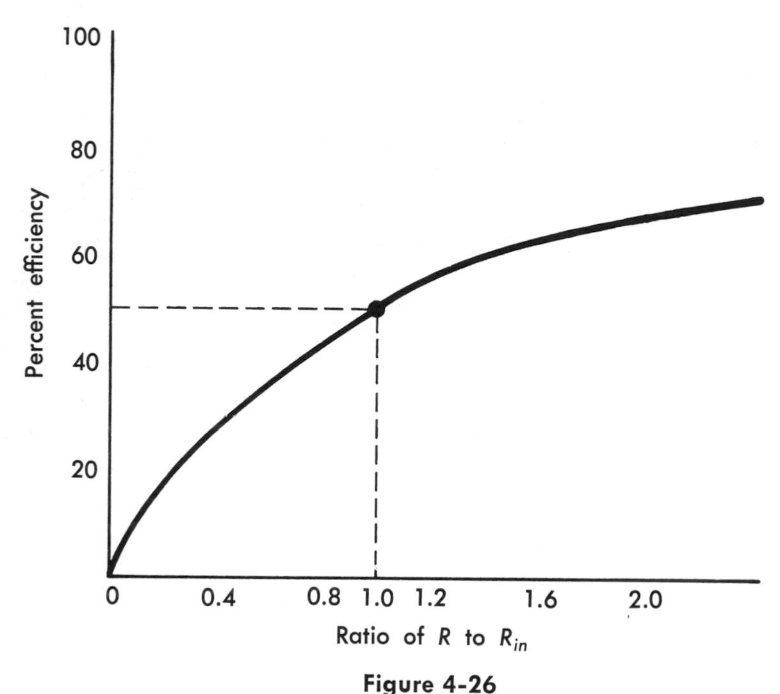

Figure 4-26
The efficiency value rises as the load resistance value is increased.

wire-wound resistor plots as a straight line (see Figure 4-27). Of course, if the resistor were operated at excessive power dissipation, it would become overheated and its resistance value would be increased noticeably. If greatly overheated, the resistor would burn out and become open-circuited.

You will recall that an electric-light bulb operates normally with a very hot filament. Hence, its resistance is much higher at 120 volts, for example, compared with its resistance at 3 volts, or at 10 volts (see Figure 4-28). Its voltage versus current graph plots as a curve, because its resistance increases as the applied voltage is increased. The "hot" resistance of a light bulb may be from 10 to 15 times greater than its "cold" resistance, depending upon the particular metal used in fabrication of the filament.

Since an ohmmeter applies only 2 or 3 volts to the resistance under test, an ohmmeter will indicate the cold resistance of a light bulb such

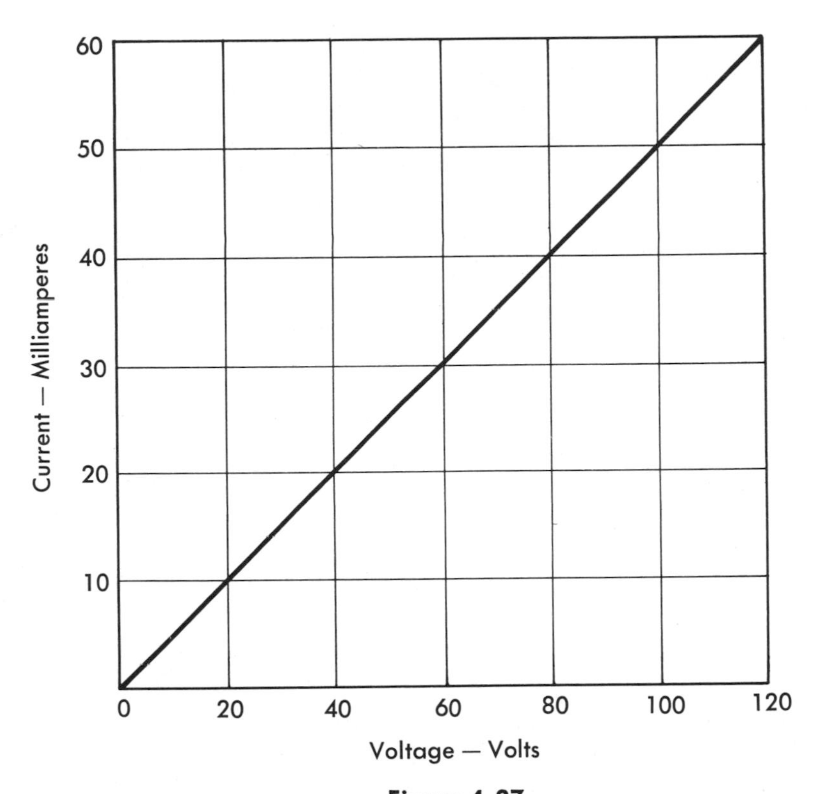

Figure 4-27
Voltage versus current graph for a resistor operated well within its maximum power rating.

as represented in Figure 4-28. On the other hand, if you measure the current drawn by the bulb at 120 volts with an ammeter, Ohm's law will yield the hot resistance value, which is, of course, much greater than the cold resistance value. Note that the resistance value at any point on the graph in either Figure 4-27 or Figure 4-28 is given by Ohm's law when the corresponding voltage and current values are substituted in the equation: $R = E/I$.

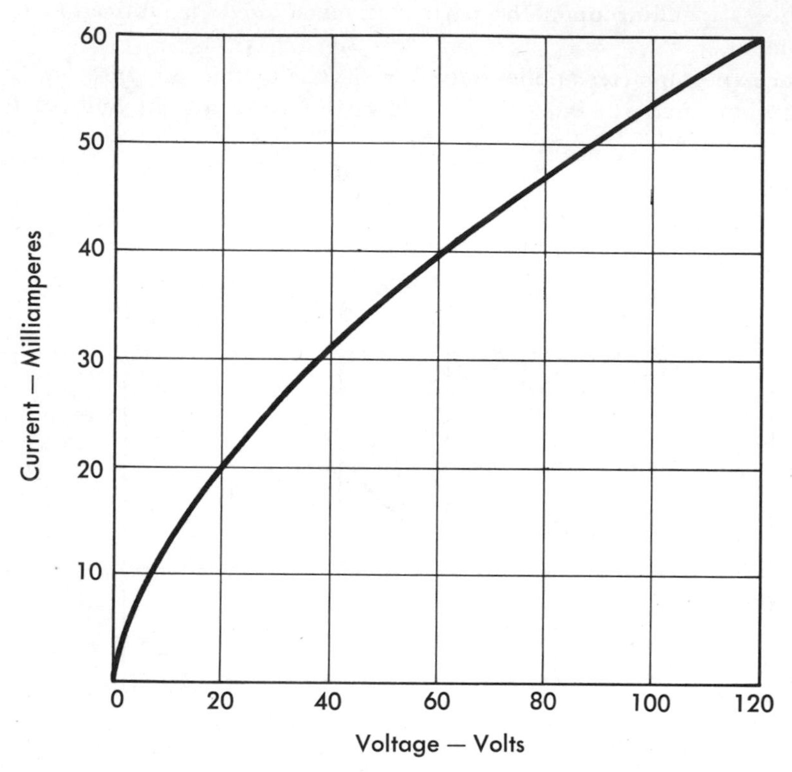

Figure 4-28
Voltage versus current graph for a 120-volt light bulb.

A CONCEPT OF NEGATIVE RESISTANCE

Ohm's law applies to a complete series circuit, or to any part of the series circuit, but how does it apply to the battery? Let us analyze the circuit depicted in Figure 4-29. Ohm's law applies to the resistor, $I = E/R$.

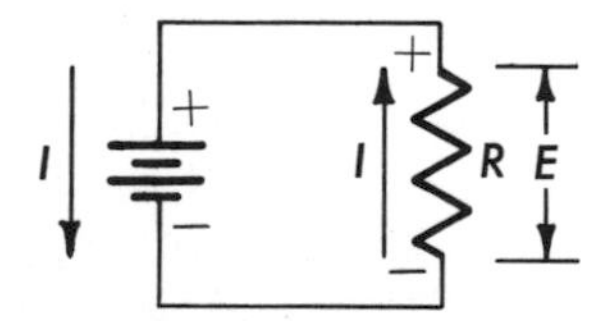

Figure 4-29
Ohm's law applies to the battery, as well as to the resistor.

Note carefully that R is positive because current flow occurs from the negative to the positive end of the resistor. Whenever electrons flow through a positive resistance, we will find that the point of entry becomes negative with respect to the point of exit.

Let us now turn our attention to the battery in Figure 4-29. Ohm's law applies to the battery. However, we observe that the current enters the positive terminal of the battery, and leaves the negative terminal. This situation is exactly opposite to that of R. Hence, the battery represents a *negative* resistance. We now write

$$I = \frac{E}{-R} \tag{4.10}$$

This is the most basic example of negative resistance. The battery is equivalent to a negative resistance because current flow occurs from the

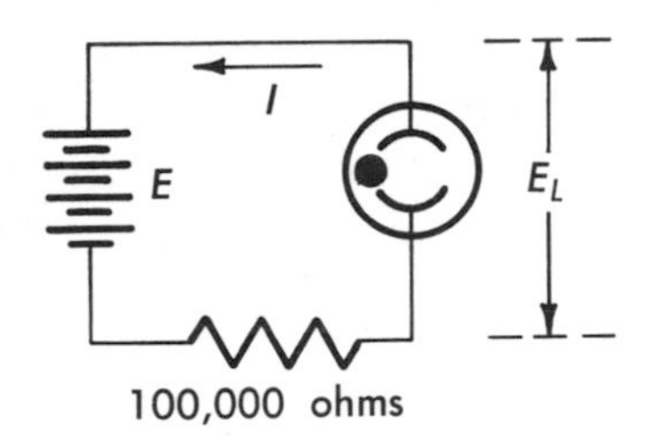

Figure 4-30
The resistance of the neon lamp is the ratio of its terminal voltage to the current flowing through it.

positive to the negative end of the battery. In other words, a negative resistance is a *source* of electricity; it is source of *power*. On the other hand, a positive resistance is a *sink*. It uses up electricity by converting the electrical power into heat. We shall encounter negative resistance again in subsequent chapters.

We recall that resistance is a voltage/current ratio. Let us observe how the resistance of a neon lamp is determined as an E/I ratio. Figure 4-30 shows a common series-circuit configuration for a neon lamp. Typical values for I and E_L are 0.4 ma and 55 volts. (The source voltage E in this example is 95 volts.) The resistance of the neon lamp is equal to E_L/I, or 137,500 ohms. But if you disconnect the neon lamp from the circuit, and check its resistance with an ohmmeter, you will obtain a reading of infinity. The reason for this surprising observation is that an ohmmeter applies perhaps 7 volts across the neon lamp. This low voltage is insufficient to ionize the neon gas in the lamp. Hence, the gas is a good insulator, and its measured resistance is in accordance with Ohm's law: $R = 7/0 = \infty$.

4.9 ANALYSIS OF CIRCUIT DEFECTS

Many circuit defects are caused by poor contacts. For example, when a terminal connection to a battery becomes loose, the contact may develop high resistance or open completely. A high contact resistance is equivalent to increasing the battery's internal resistance. Power consumed in contact resistance is wasted power. If the contact opens completely, we know that no current will flow in the circuit. Connections to storage-battery terminals may become corroded. Although the connection is mechanically tight, the corrosion film between the contact surfaces acts as a resistance, or sometimes as an open circuit.

A simple test can be made with a voltmeter to check for contact trouble. For example, if the electrical system of an automobile is "dead," the trouble could be caused by a film of corrosion at one of the storage-battery terminals. To check the connection, press one test prod of a voltmeter against the battery post; press the other test prod against the cable clamp. With the car lights turned "on," observe the voltmeter reading. If the battery contact is open, the voltmeter will indicate the battery voltage. On the other hand, if the trouble is elsewhere, the voltmeter will indicate zero.

It is quicker and easier to check for poor contacts in this manner than to loosen and inspect the suspected contacts. If you locate a defective connection to a storage battery, for example, remove the cable clamp and clean the contact surfaces of the clamp and battery post. Then, replace the cable clamp and tighten it securely. This will eliminate the fault. Of course, it is possible that two or more defective contacts might occur simultaneously in a circuit. In such case, the voltmeter test discussed above is not applicable. However, experience proves that when contact trouble occurs, there is a high probability that only one connection has failed.

Suppose the connection to the storage battery does not open completely, but imposes appreciable resistance in the circuit. The automobile lights may glow dimly in this case. The foregoing voltmeter test is useful to check suspected connections. When the test prods of the meter are pressed against the cable clamp and battery post, and the car lights are turned on, a poor contact is indicated by a reading on the voltmeter. For example, the voltmeter might read 5 volts, instead of zero. If the battery terminal voltage is 12 volts, it is evident that 5 volts are dropped across the contact resistance, leaving only 7 volts to energize the circuit. The contact surfaces must be cleaned to clear the fault.

Occasionally, a contact becomes intermittent. Thus, the car lights might flicker on and off as the defective connection is jarred by vibration. Intermittent contacts can usually be localized by flexing the wires in the electrical system while an assistant watches the lights. Solder joints are sometimes defective. These are called *cold-solder* joints. The defective connection is due to insufficient heating of the solder; the contact surfaces are not truly bonded, though a casual inspection may not disclose the defect. Flex the wires at suspected solder joints, to see whether intermittent operation results. When a cold-solder joint is discovered, re-heat the connection with a soldering iron or gun. Make certain that the solder flows properly between the contact surfaces and bonds them firmly.

Metallic surfaces must be clean if they are to bond properly with molten solder. A suitable flux is also required. Resin fluxes are preferred because they do not corrode copper or brass. On the other hand, acid soldering fluxes are usually avoided because they attack these metals. Some metals require special types of solders and fluxes. However, the vast majority of solder contacts made in electrical and electronic equipment involve copper, brass, or tin-plated surfaces. These can be bonded satisfactorily with commercial solders and resin flux. You will have an opportunity to learn the practical aspects of soldering techniques in your shop or laboratory experiments.

SUMMARY OF FUNDAMENTAL CONCEPTS

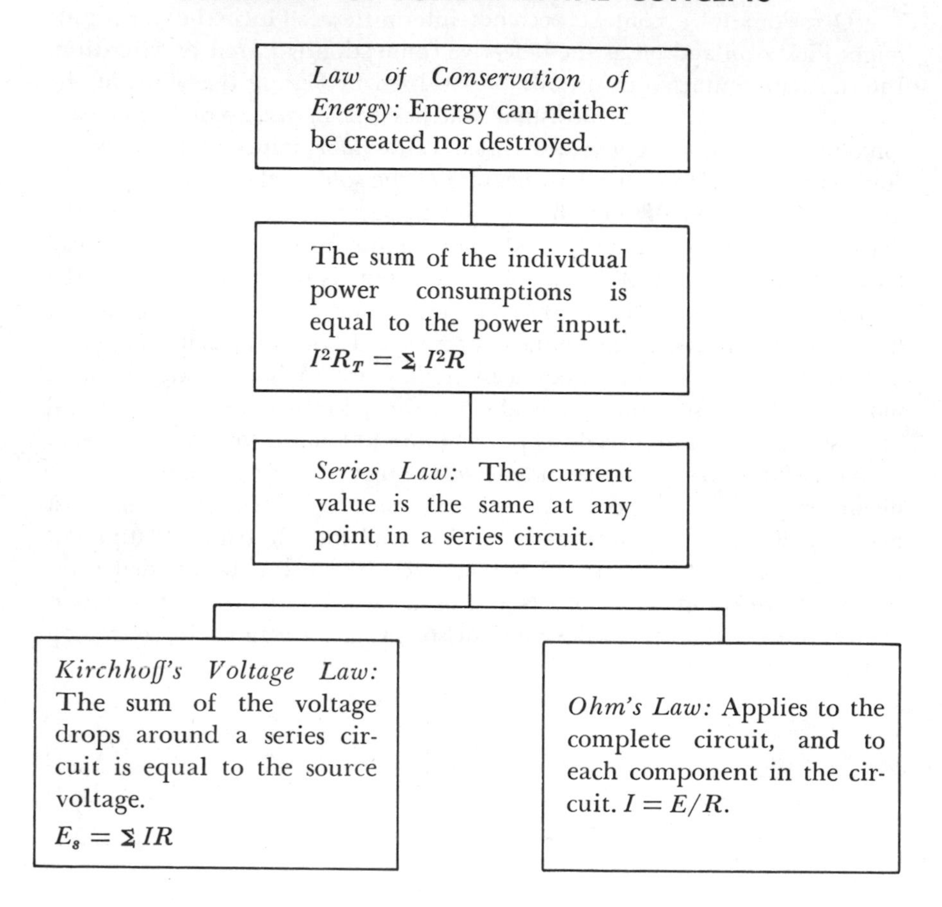

Law of Conservation of Energy: Energy can neither be created nor destroyed.
The sum of the individual power consumptions is equal to the power input. $I^2R_T = \Sigma I^2R$
Series Law: The current value is the same at any point in a series circuit.
Kirchhoff's Voltage Law: The sum of the voltage drops around a series circuit is equal to the source voltage. $E_s = \Sigma IR$
Ohm's Law: Applies to the complete circuit, and to each component in the circuit. $I = E/R$.

Notes: R_T equals the total resistance of the series circuit. R equals an individual resistance in the series circuit. Σ is the symbol for summation. E_s equals the source voltage.

QUESTIONS

1) If two dry cells are connected in series-aiding to form a battery: (*a*) the positive terminal of one cell is connected to the positive terminal of the other cell. (*b*) the positive terminal of one cell is

connected to the negative terminal of the other cell. Then, the remaining positive and negative terminals are connected to each other. (*c*) the positive terminals of both cells are connected to each other, and the negative terminals are connected to each other. (*d*) the positive terminal of one cell is connected to the negative terminal of the other cell.

2) The series law states that:
(*a*) when current passes through a resistance, some of the current is used up. (*b*) the current is the same at any point in a series circuit. (*c*) an excessively high resistance value reverses the polarity of the voltage drop. (*d*) an excessively high resistance value reverses the direction of current flow.

3) A voltmeter must be connected into a circuit in such manner that:
(*a*) the total current in the series circuit flows through the voltmeter. (*b*) the voltage drop to be measured is applied to the voltmeter terminals. (*c*) electrons flow through the instrument from its positive terminal to its negative terminal. (*d*) the voltage flows through the instrument in the same direction as the current.

4) If a voltmeter is connected to a circuit with its test leads reversed:
(*a*) the pointer deflects off-scale to the left. (*b*) incorrect voltage values are indicated in proportion to the resistance of the test leads. (*c*) the source voltage becomes short-circuited. (*d*) the source voltage becomes open-circuited.

5) Kirchhoff's voltage law states that:
(*a*) any source voltage is equal to the sum of the current drops around a complete circuit. (*b*) a source voltage is equal to the product of the voltage drops around a complete circuit. (*c*) the source voltage is equal to the sum of the voltage drops around a complete circuit. (*d*) any voltage drop is equal to the source voltage divided by the source resistance.

6) Voltage dividers consist of:
(*a*) a tapped resistor, or equivalent series resistors. (*b*) two batteries with an external source resistance. (*c*) the voltage drop across a resistance divided by the source resistance. (*d*) the source resistance divided by the voltage drop across each series resistance.

7) To measure the source resistance of a battery:
(*a*) connect an ohmmeter across the terminals of the battery. (*b*) connect a voltmeter across the terminals of the battery. (*c*) connect an ammeter across the terminals of the battery. (*d*) measure the terminal voltage of the battery; then connect a resistance across the battery and observe the decrease in voltage. The source resistance is then equal to the decrease in voltage divided by the current flow through the resistance.

8) If a voltage source has an internal resistance R, maximum power is developed in a load resistance R_L when:
(*a*) R_L has a value which provides maximum current flow. (*b*) R_L has a value that provides maximum voltage across the load. (*c*) R_L has a value equal to R. (*d*) R_L has a value that provides maximum efficiency.

9) When maximum power is delivered to the load in Question 8, the system operates:
(*a*) at maximum efficiency. (*b*) at zero efficiency. (*c*) at 50 percent efficiency. (*d*) at an efficiency that is equal to the open-circuit terminal voltage of the source, divided by the decrease in terminal voltage when the source is short-circuited.

10) The quadratic formula gives:
(*a*) the solution of the general quadratic equation. (*b*) an equivalent square that corresponds to the area of a chosen circle. (*c*) an equivalent circle that corresponds to the area of a chosen square. (*d*) the difference between the area of a quadrangle and an equivalent circle.

PROBLEMS

1) A battery is connected to a 1-ohm resistor. The connecting leads have a resistance of 0.6 ohm. The battery has an internal resistance of 0.5 ohm. What is the total series resistance in this circuit?
2) When a voltmeter is connected to a dry cell, the meter indicates 1.5 volts. A 10-ohm resistor is also connected to the terminals of the dry cell. If the meter now indicates 0.75 volt, what is the internal resistance of the dry cell?
3) Two resistors are connected in series. When 6 volts are applied to the series combination, one resistor dissipates 2 watts and the other resistor dissipates 4 watts. What is the current value, and the value of each resistance?
4) A wattmeter indicates that a battery supplies maximum power to a resistor when the resistor has a value of 1 ohm. What is the internal resistance of the battery?
5) An ammeter connected in a series circuit indicates a current flow of 1 amp. When a voltmeter is connected across the ammeter terminals, a voltage drop of 0.25 volt is measured. What is the internal resistance of the ammeter?
6) If a voltmeter and microammeter are connected in series with a 1.5-volt dry cell, the voltmeter indicates 1.44 volts, and the microammeter

indicates 30 microamps. What is the internal resistance of the voltmeter? What is the internal resistance of the microammeter?

7) When an electric-light bulb is connected to a 1.5-volt dry cell, a current of 75 ma flows. On the other hand, when the bulb is connected to a 117-volt line, a current of 0.585 amp flows. How much does the filament increase in resistance value when connected to the 117-volt source?

8) If a tapped resistor is connected across a 6-volt source, a wattmeter indicates a power consumption of 3 watts. A voltmeter indicates a drop of 2 volts from the tap to one end of the resistor. What is the total value of the resistance, and what is the resistance value on either side of the tap?

9) A resistor which has an unknown resistance value is connected in series with a 2-ohm resistance and a 6-volt source. A voltmeter connected across the 2-ohm resistance indicates a voltage drop of 2 volts. What is the resistance value of the unknown?

10) Fusible resistors are used in series with the line for protection against overload in some television receivers. If a receiver draws 1.22 amps and there is a drop of 9.16 volts across the fusible resistor, what is the resistance value of the fusible resistor?

11) A defective switch becomes hot when a current flow of 10 amps is present. If a voltmeter connected across the switch indicates a drop of 10 volts, what is the contact resistance of the switch? How much power is dissipated in the contact resistance?

12) A 6-volt electric-light bulb rated at 12 watts is used as a fuse in an electronic device. What is the approximate value of its "cold" resistance?

13) When a 60-watt electric-light bulb is switched into a 117-volt line, what is the approximate value of initial current flow? What is the current value after the filament attains normal operating temperature?

14) Three 2-volt cells are connected in series to form a storage battery. When the battery supplies 33 amps, its terminal voltage drops to 5 volts. Assuming that each cell has the same value of internal resistance, what is the internal resistance of each cell?

15) It is desired to charge a 6-volt storage battery at a ¼-amp rate from a 117-volt d-c source. What value of resistance must be used in series with the battery? How much power will the resistor dissipate?

16) Six 12-volt 4-watt lamps are connected in a series string. What value of series resistance must be included with the string to operate the lamps at normal brightness from a 117-volt line?

5

PARALLEL CIRCUIT ANALYSIS

5.1 VOLTAGE AND CURRENT DISTRIBUTION

Parallel circuits are widely used in electronic equipment. We will find that the voltage and current distribution in a parallel circuit is quite different from the distribution in a series circuit. For example, Figure 5-1 depicts two lamps connected in parallel across a battery. Observe that the terminal voltage of the battery is applied across each lamp. The voltage is the *same* across each lamp, regardless of current flow. Each lamp draws current in accordance with its filament resistance.

As seen in Figure 5-2, the total current I_T supplied by the battery has two paths. Part of the total current flows through resistance R_2; the remainder flows through resistance R_1. Hence, the total current I_T is the sum of the branch currents I_1 and I_2. The branch-current values are stated by Ohm's law:

$$I_1 = \frac{E}{R_1} \tag{5.1}$$

$$I_2 = \frac{E}{R_2} \tag{5.2}$$

$$I_T = \frac{E}{R_T} \tag{5.3}$$

where R_T is the combined resistance of R_1 and R_2. R_T is called the total or net resistance of the parallel circuit.

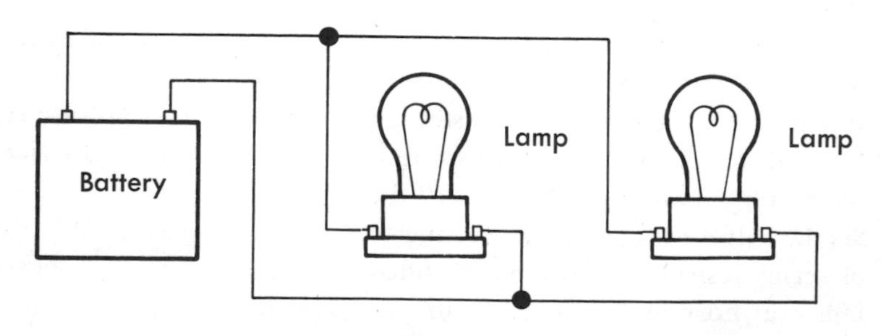

Figure 5-1
A typical parallel circuit.

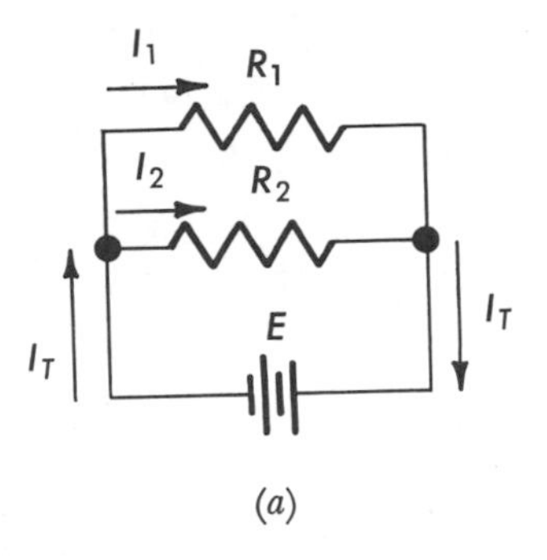

(a)

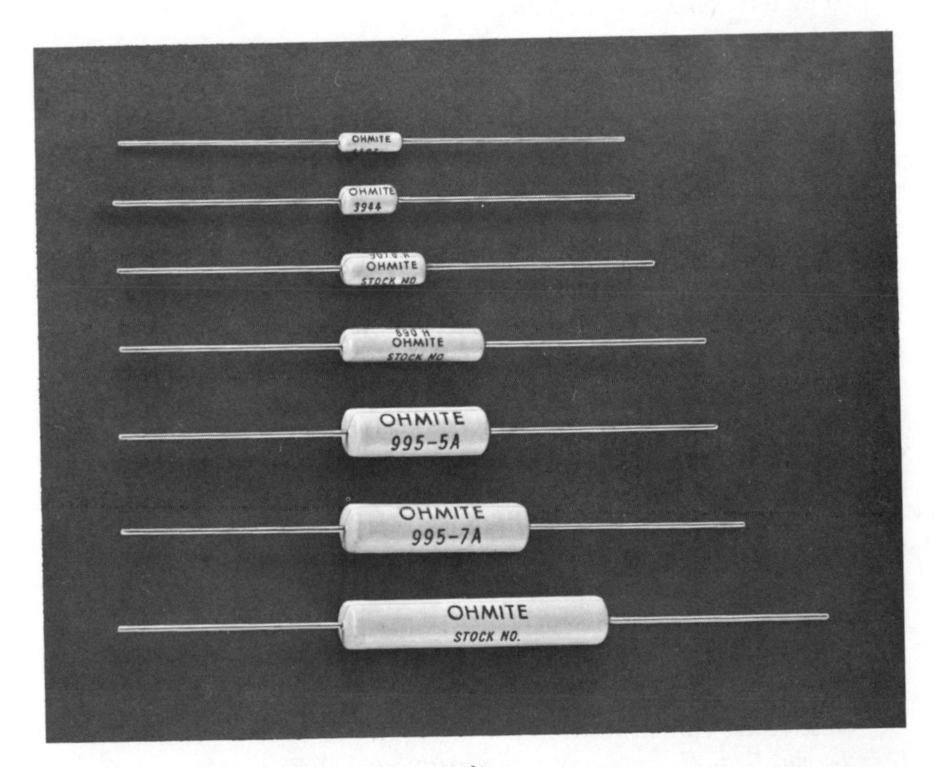

(b)

Figure 5-2

(a) The total current I_T is equal to the sum of the branch currents I_1 and I_2. (b) Wire-wound molded vitreous enameled resistors, with axial leads. Power ratings are 1.5, 2.25, 3.25, 6.5, 9, and 11 watts, respectively. (Courtesy of Ohmite Manufacturing Company, Skokie, Illinois.)

What is the value of R_T? We know that

$$I_T = I_1 + I_2 \tag{5.4}$$

If we substitute Equations (5.1), (5.2), and (5.3) into Equation (5.4), we obtain

$$\frac{E}{R_T} = \frac{E}{R_1} + \frac{E}{R_2} \tag{5.5}$$

Since E cancels out in these three terms, the relation of the resistance values is

$$\frac{1}{R_T} = \frac{1}{R_1} + \frac{1}{R_2} \tag{5.6}$$

If we solve for R_T, we find that

$$R_T = \frac{R_1 R_2}{R_1 + R_2} \tag{5.7}$$

Now, let us observe Equation (5.6). We recall that conductance $G = 1/R$. Therefore, we write

$$G_T = G_1 + G_2 \tag{5.8}$$

Equation (5.8) is simpler than Equation (5.6). Accordingly, we will find it easier to analyze many parallel circuits in terms of conductance, instead of resistance. This approach is based on the fact that the voltage is the same across every branch of a parallel circuit. On the other hand, we recall that the current is the same at any point in a series circuit.

Parallel circuits are utilized in electrical systems which require that the same voltage be applied across each component. For example, consider a house-wiring system. You may wish to operate a half-dozen 117-volt lamps, a refrigerator, a television receiver, and a washing machine from the power line. Each of these components requires 117 volts. The power line supplies 117 volts. Hence, each component must be connected across the line. In turn, the house wiring system is a parallel circuit.

5.2 DETERMINATION OF BRANCH CURRENTS

Observe the current distribution in Figure 5-2. If $R_1 = R_2$, evidently $I_1 = I_2$, and $I_T = 2I_1 = 2I_2$. However, suppose that R_1 is not equal to R_2. If $R_1 = 2R_2$, it follows from Ohm's law that $I_1 = 0.5I_2$, and $I_T = 1.5I_1$. We learned in Chapter 4 that two resistances connected in series can be replaced by a single resistance that has a value equal to the sum of the individual resistances. We then obtained an equivalent circuit that drew the same current from the source as the series circuit. Similarly, we can draw an equivalent circuit for the two resistances R_1 and R_2 in the parallel circuit of Figure 5-2. It is clear that R_1 and R_2 can be replaced by a single resistor having a value of $R_1R_2/(R_1 + R_2)$, and that this single resistor will draw the same current I_T from the source as the parallel circuit.

It has been noted that practical parallel circuits often contain numerous branches. For example, the parallel circuit shown in Figure 5-3 contains four branches. The total current I_T is equal to the sum of the four branch currents. What is the total resistance of this circuit? According to Ohm's law, we can write $R_T = 117/I_T$. The four resistances can be replaced by a single resistance that has a value of R_T, and the same current I_T will be drawn from the 117-volt line.

Again, consider a problem in which I_T is not given; if the problem states only the values of R_1, R_2, R_3, and R_4 in Figure 5-3, how shall we calculate the value of R_T? There are various ways in which R_T can be

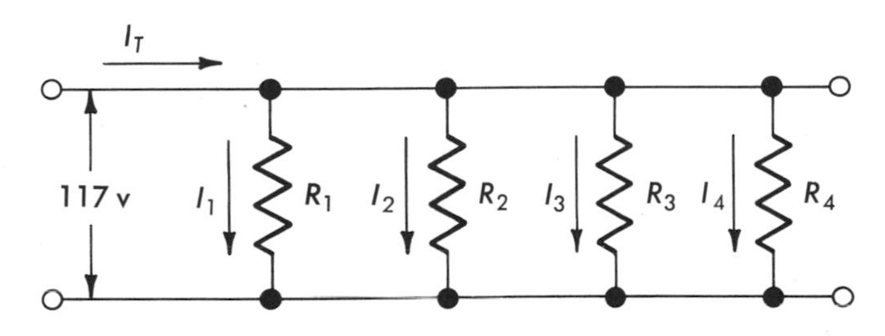

Figure 5-3
A parallel circuit with four branches.

found, and these methods illustrate basic means of circuit analysis. First, observe that we can replace any pair of resistances in Figure 5-3 by a single equivalent resistance. For example, we can replace R_1 and R_2 with a single resistance having a value of $R_1R_2/(R_1 + R_2)$. Next, we can replace R_3 and R_4 with a single resistance having a value of $R_3R_4/(R_3 + R_4)$. Finally, we can combine the two equivalent resistances and replace them with a single resistance that has a value of

$$R_T = \frac{[R_1R_2/(R_1 + R_2)]\,[R_3R_4/(R_3 + R_4)]}{[R_1R_2/(R_1 + R_2)] + [R_3R_4/(R_3 + R_4)]} \tag{5.9}$$

Of course, we could perform this network reduction by taking another choice of pairs; for example, R_1 and R_3 could be replaced by an equivalent resistance, and R_2 and R_4 could be replaced by an equivalent resistance. Finally, these two equivalent resistances could be replaced by their equivalent, and the result would be R_T as before. Again, R_1 and R_4 could be combined, then R_2 and R_3, and R_T would follow. In any case, an equation of the type illustrated by Equation (5.9) is not particularly simple, and it is desirable to find a simpler expression, if possible.

Accordingly, let us perform a network reduction for Figure 5-3 in terms of conductances. We know that $G_1 = 1/R_1$, $G_2 = 1/R_2$, and so forth. Hence, the equivalent conductance of this circuit is written

$$G_T = G_1 + G_2 + G_3 + G_4 \tag{5.10}$$

Since $G_T = 1/R_T$, we divide G_T into 1 to find R_T. It is evidently much easier to analyze the circuit of Figure 5-3 in terms of conductances. If we wish to express the equivalent value in ohms, we simply take the reciprocal of the total conductance. The current drawn by each branch in Figure 5-3 is equal to EG. Thus, $I_1 = 117G_1$, $I_2 = 117G_2$, and so forth. Note in passing that the schematic symbol for conductance is the same as for resistance. Although beginners often prefer to work with resistance values instead of conductance values in parallel-circuit analysis, this procedure is not advised. Much more labor is required in calculation when conductance values are not used. After we become familiar with conductance calculations, parallel circuits can be solved as easily as series circuits.

It might be wondered whether Equation (5.9) could be written in some other form which would provide the convenience of a conductance equation without the use of conductance values. Although the resistance equation can be rewritten, the desired convenience of calculation is not realized. For example, we can express Equation (5.9) in the form

$$R_T = \frac{R_1R_2R_3R_4}{R_1R_2R_3 + R_2R_3R_4 + R_1R_2R_4 + R_1R_3R_4} \tag{5.11}$$

However, Equation (5.11) is about as formidable as Equation (5.9). Neither provides the convenience of Equation (5.10). Hence, the student is well advised to become familiar with conductance analyses.

5.3 KIRCHHOFF'S CURRENT LAW

Kirchhoff's current law is as basic in parallel-circuit analysis as Kirchhoff's voltage law in series-circuit analysis. This current law states that *the algebraic sum of the currents at any junction of conductors is equal to zero.* The foundation for Kirchhoff's current law has been laid in previous discussion of parallel-circuit analysis. Consider the currents depicted in Figure 5-4. Currents I_1 and I_2 have different algebraic signs—note that I_1 is flowing toward the junction, while I_2 is flowing away from the junction. Similarly, currents I_1 and I_3 have different algebraic signs. If we call I_1 positive, then we must call I_2 and I_3 negative. From foregoing discussions, it is clear that $I_1 - I_2 - I_3 = 0$.

Another way of expressing this fact is to state that there is just as

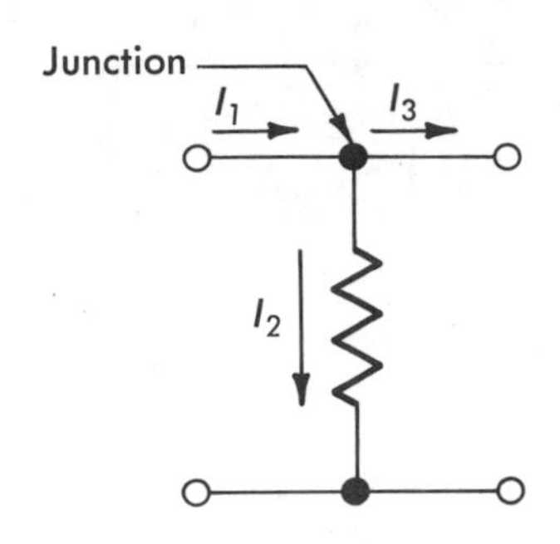

Figure 5-4
The algebraic sum of the currents at the junction is zero.

much current flowing away from a junction as there is flowing into the junction. Let us see how Kirchhoff's current law is used to solve a simple parallel circuit. In the circuit of Figure 5-5, a battery supplies 0.5 amp to two resistors of 30 ohms and 20 ohms, connected in parallel. The battery voltage and the two branch currents are to be calculated. First, write Kirchhoff's current law for the circuit: $I_T = I_1 + I_2$.

Next, apply Kirchhoff's voltage law. This law states that the sum of the voltages around any closed circuit is equal to zero. When we go around the closed circuit *ABEF* in Figure 5-5, we write $E - 30I_1 = 0$, or $I_1 = E/30$. When we go around the closed circuit *ACDF*, we write $E - 20I_2 = 0$, or $I_2 = E/20$. Since $I_T - I_1 - I_2 = 0$, substitution yields $0.5 - E/30 - E/20 = 0$. We solve for E and obtain 6 volts. In turn, $I_1 = 0.2$ amp, and $I_2 = 0.3$ amp.

Circuits may appear superficially different when simply rearranged. For example, the circuit shown in Figure 5-6 is merely a rearrangement of Figure 5-5. It appears to be different because the 30-ohm resistor is drawn on the left-hand side of the battery in Figure 5-6. Exactly the same circuit is depicted in both of the diagrams. If Kirchhoff's laws are applied to the arrangement shown in Figure 5-6, it will be found that $E = 6$, $I_1 = 0.2$, and $I_2 = 0.3$, as before. This calculation is left as an exercise for the reader.

5.4 CURRENT SOURCES IN PARALLEL

When excessive current is demanded from a battery, generator, or other source of electricity, the source is said to be overloaded. The terminal voltage of an overloaded battery decreases substantially and the battery soon dies. For example, a flashlight battery will not operate an automobile electrical system. Small batteries, however, can be connected

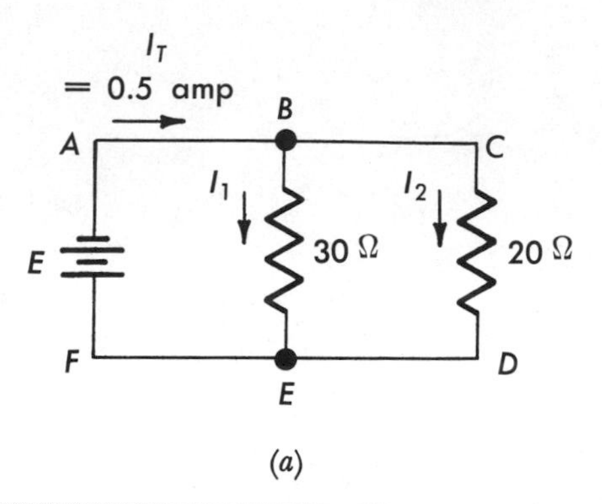

(a)

(b)

Figure 5-5

(a) The values of E, I_1, and I_2 are to be calculated. (b) One potentiometer with a 2-watt power rating. Right: two ganged potentiometers. The potentiometers may be connected in parallel to provide a 4-watt power rating.

in parallel to avoid overload. Any desired amount of current can be drawn from a sufficient number of paralleled batteries.

In many applications, a cell with an emf of 1.5 volts is considered dead when its terminal voltage decreases to about 0.8 volt. Figure 5-7

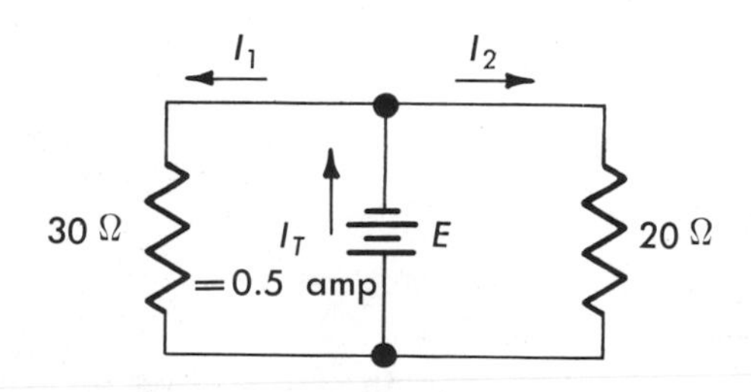

Figure 5-6

A rearrangement of the circuit shown in Figure 5-5.

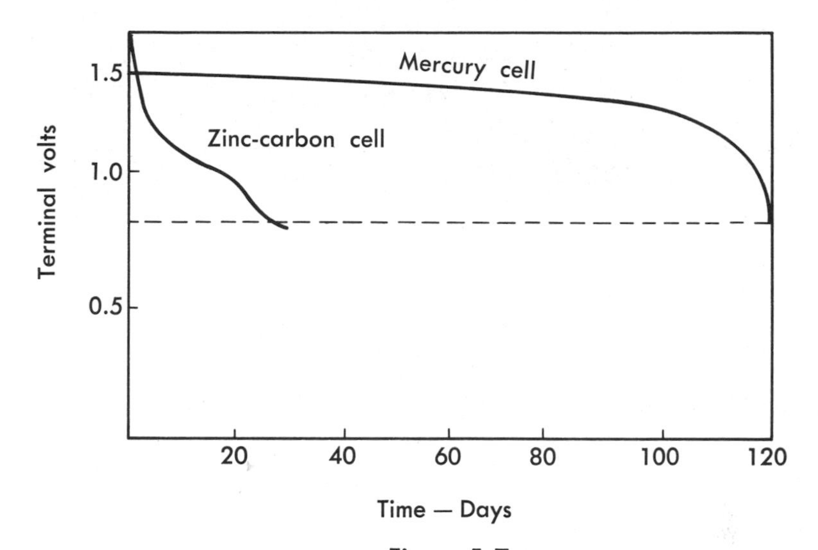

Figure 5-7
Comparative decline of terminal-voltage values for two types of batteries.

illustrates the decline of terminal voltage for a "1.5-volt" zinc-carbon cell discharged into a 60-ohm load for 8 hours each day. The cell is dead at the end of 4 weeks. On the other hand, a 1.35-volt mercury cell of the same physical size discharged into a 60-ohm load for 8 hours each day maintains a terminal voltage above 0.8 volt for about 4 months. The mercury cell has a greater *current capacity* than the zinc-carbon cell.

Suppose you wish to obtain approximately the same current capacity from zinc-carbon cells as from a mercury cell. This can be accomplished by connecting a battery of four zinc-carbon cells in parallel, as seen in Figure 5-8. Since each cell has the same terminal voltage, no current flows in the circuit. If you connect a resistor across the battery, each cell supplies one-quarter of the total current demand. Otherwise stated, a battery of parallel-connected cells is not overloaded by a current drain which would overload a single cell.

A conventional storage battery consists basically of lead plates immersed in sulfuric acid. Each pair of plates forms a cell that provides an emf of approximately 2 volts. A single pair of plates does not have sufficiently high current capacity for most applications. Hence, familiar storage batteries (see Figure 5-9) contain numerous pairs of plates, connected in parallel. Any desired current capacity may be realized by providing a sufficient number of parallel connected plates.

Power houses may be subjected to varying current demands. When the demand exceeds the current capacity of a single generator, additional

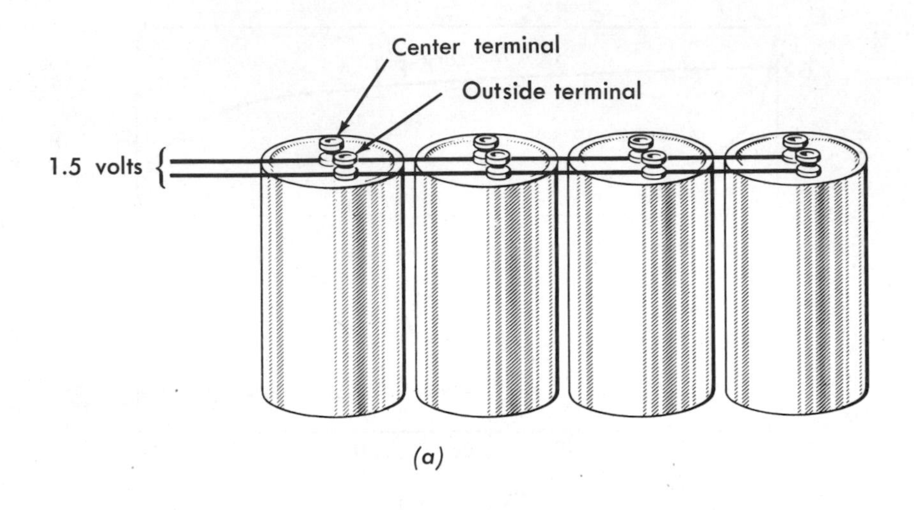

(a)

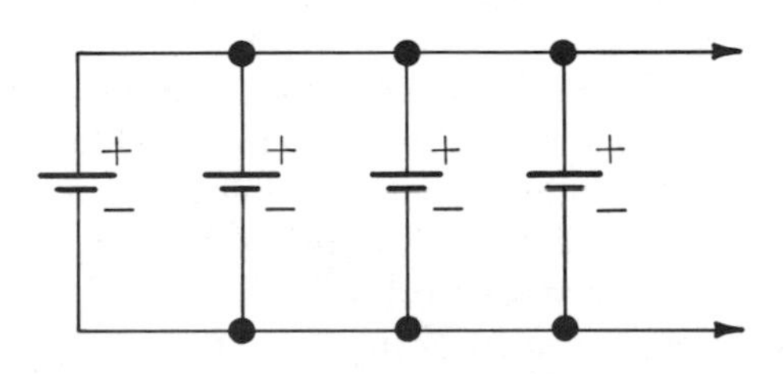

Figure 5-8
Four parallel-connected cells have approximately four times the current capability of one cell.

generators may be connected in parallel, as depicted in Figure 5-10. Each generator develops the same terminal voltage. Hence, there is no current flow in the generator circuit. If a generator should be overloaded, its terminal voltage will decrease. Moreover, the generator will overheat and may be damaged. Consequently, it is necessary to operate a generator within its rated current capacity.

Cells and batteries are fabricated in many sizes. Thus, a flashlight cell has smaller dimensions than a door-bell (No. 6) dry cell. The basic construction of a dry cell is shown in Figure 5-11. From previous discussion, it is evident that a large cell is *equivalent* to a number of small cells connected in parallel. Current capacity is determined by electrode area; it makes no basic difference whether a certain electrode area is realized in a single large cell, or from smaller cells connected in parallel.

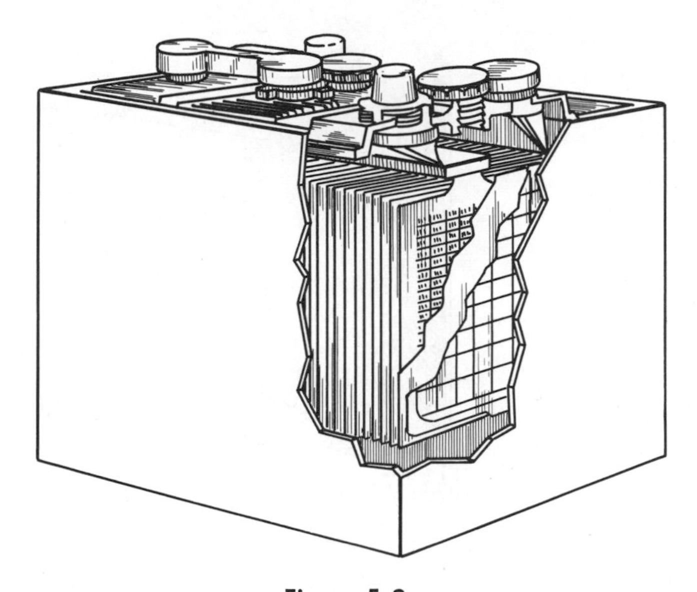

Figure 5-9
A conventional storage battery contains numerous parallel-connected plates.

CONNECTION OF CELLS IN PARALLEL

Of course, two cells that have different emf's must not be connected in parallel. In such case, the cell with the lower emf will discharge the other cell. For example, a zinc-carbon dry cell has a nominal emf of 1.5 volts, but a mercury cell has a nominal emf of 1.35 volts. If a dry cell were connected in parallel with a mercury cell, there would be a potential difference of 0.15 volt between the two cells. In turn, this 0.15 volt will drive a circulating current in reverse through the mercury cell. The value of the circulating current is limited only by the internal resistances of the cells.

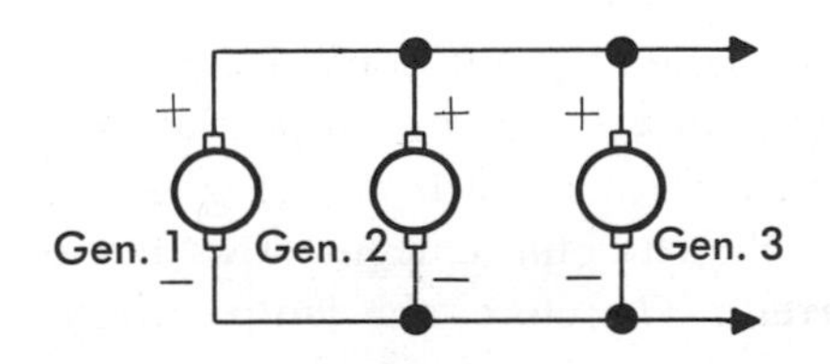

Figure 5-10
Generators can be operated in parallel to provide more current capability than a single generator.

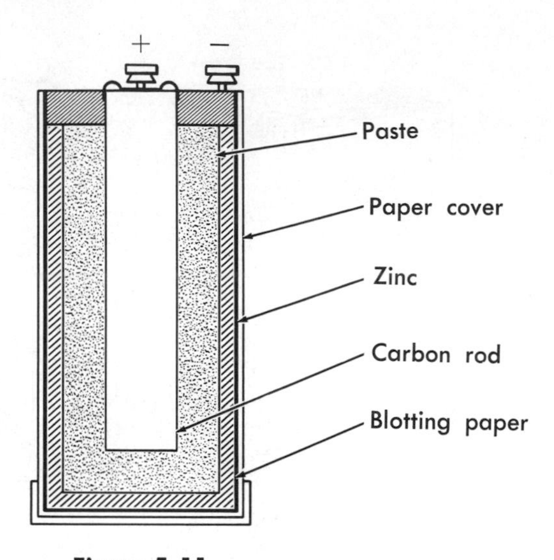

Figure 5-11
Basic construction of a dry cell.

When a flashlight-type dry cell was connected in parallel with a flashlight-type mercury cell, a circulating current of 50 ma was measured. Since $R = E/I$, the total internal resistance of the cells was $R_{\text{in}} = 0.15/0.05 = 3$ ohms. The circulating current gradually decreased in value as the zinc-carbon cell discharged. Since the emf of a cell remains practically the same over its useful life span, it is evident that a mercury cell will eventually discharge a zinc-carbon cell completely in the parallel configuration.

However, we have seen that when a storage battery is charged by a generator, the generator provides a terminal voltage slightly higher than that of the battery. This is an example of unequal voltage sources connected in parallel. In this case, a circulating current is desired in order to charge the storage battery. Accordingly, suppose that the storage battery in an automobile is being charged, and the lights are also switched on (Figure 5-12). Does the lamp current come from the battery, from the generator, or from both voltage sources? Inspection of the circuit reveals that all the lamp current must come from the generator. The battery is being charged; hence, the charging current flows in reverse direction to that of the lamp current. Therefore, the lamp current comes from the generator.

The total current in Figure 5-12 is the sum of the battery charging current and the lamp current. Kirchhoff's current law for this circuit is

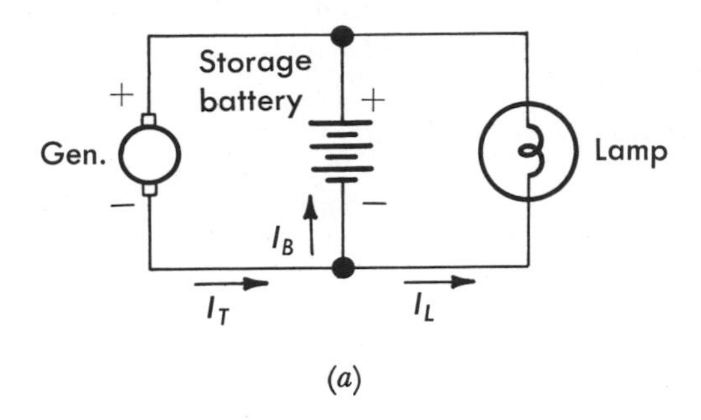

(a)

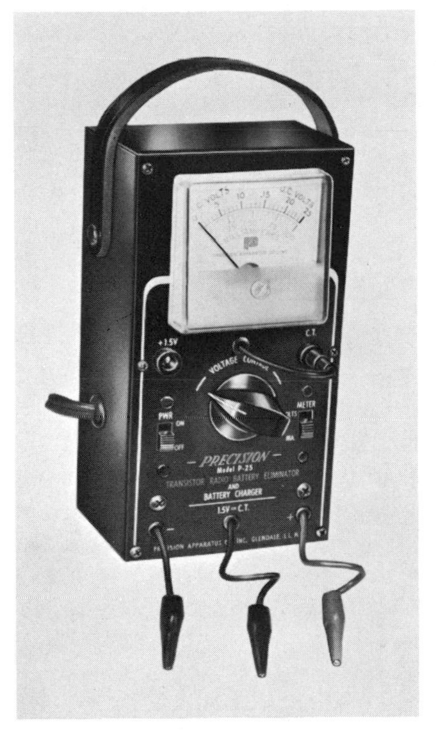

(b)

Figure 5-12
(a) The generator charges the storage battery and also supplies the current demand of the lamp. *(b)* A small storage-battery charger. (Courtesy of Precision Apparatus Co.)

written: $I_T = I_B + I_L$. Thus, parallel circuits with reverse current through one of the voltage sources are analyzed in the same basic manner as simple parallel configurations. Current I_B is equal to the difference between the generator voltage and the storage-battery voltage, divided by the internal resistance of the storage battery. Current I_L is equal to the generator voltage divided by the resistance of the lamp.

5.5 BRANCH POWER AND TOTAL POWER

The power consumed in each branch of a parallel circuit must come from the current source. Thus, the total power supplied by a battery (Figure 5-13) is equal to the sum of the powers in the branches. Note that

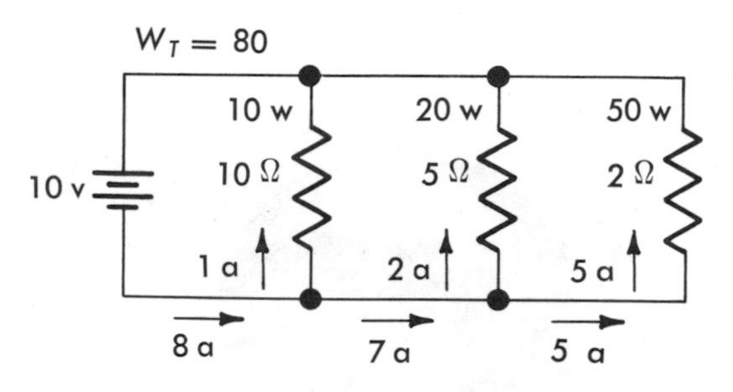

Figure 5-13
The total power supplied by the battery is equal to the sum of the power consumptions in the branches.

the power consumed in each branch is inversely proportional to the resistance of the branch. The 5-ohm resistance consumes twice as much power as the 10-ohm resistance; the power consumed in each branch is directly proportional to its conductance. The 10-ohm branch has a conductance of 0.1 mho, and the 5-ohm branch has a conductance of 0.2 mho; the 0.2-mho branch consumes twice as much power as the 0.1-mho branch.

Observe the parallel circuit depicted in Figure 5-14. The 6-volt generator supplies 5 amps of reverse current to the storage battery, and 2 amps

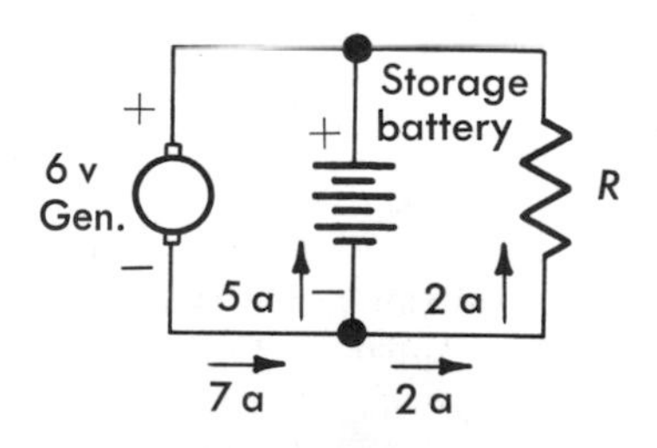

Figure 5-14
Both the storage battery and the resistance R consume power.

to the resistance R. It is evident that the generator supplies power to both branches of the circuit. The storage battery draws 5 amps at 6 volts; hence, it consumes 30 watts. The resistor R draws 2 amps at 6 volts; it consumes 12 watts. In turn, the generator supplies 42 watts to the circuit.

The power consumed by resistor R is dissipated as heat. On the other hand, the power consumed by the storage battery is changed chiefly into chemical energy; a small amount of the total power consumed by the battery is changed into heat. The chemical energy that is thus "stored" in the battery can be utilized subsequently. For example, if the generator is disconnected from the parallel circuit in Figure 5-14, current will continue to flow through the resistor R; this current is now supplied by the storage battery.

A storage battery is commonly rated with respect to the maximum current it can supply for an 8-hour period, and this current value is called its *normal rate of discharge*. For example, if a battery can supply 10 amps for 8 hours, it is rated as an 80 amp-hour battery. If we assume that the average value of the battery's terminal voltage over this period is 5.7 volts, the approximate power supplied by the battery during 8 hours is equal to 456 watt-hours. This is less than 1 horsepower-hour; recall that a horsepower-hour is equal to 746 watt-hours.

EFFICIENCY CALCULATIONS

The efficiency of a storage battery is less than 100 percent. We cannot obtain as much power on discharge as was consumed on charge. Conventional storage batteries will deliver about 85 percent as many ampere-hours as were consumed on charge. Accordingly, approximately 15 percent of the discharge current is dissipated as heat in the internal resistance of the battery. When fully charged, a typical storage battery has a very low internal resistance of approximately 0.0025 ohm. As the battery discharges, its internal resistance increases. For example, if a battery is discharged at a rate of 10 amps for 8 hours, and at the end of 8 hours its terminal voltage has decreased from 6.75 volts to 5.6 volts, its internal resistance has increased by 0.115 ohm. It follows that a battery dissipates less of its power as heat in its internal resistance when the battery is fully charged.

To obtain electrical power from the generator in Figure 5-14, mechanical power must be supplied. In the case of an automobile electrical system, this power is taken from the car engine. The efficiency of a generator is less than 100 percent. It consumes somewhat more mechanical power than the electrical power which it supplies. The difference between these two power values is dissipated as heat in the generator. The total efficiency of the system depicted in Figure 5-14 is the product of the individual efficiencies. For example, suppose that the generator is 85 percent efficient. This means that 85 percent of the mechanical power consumed appears as electrical power. If the battery stores 85 percent of the electrical power, the total efficiency on the charge cycle is 0.85 × 0.85, or approximately 72 percent. Next, if the battery delivers 85 percent of its stored power, the total efficiency on the discharge cycle is 0.72 × 0.85, or approximately 61 percent.

5.6 EQUIVALENT-CIRCUIT CONCEPTS

An equivalent circuit is a simplified arrangement that has the same electrical characteristics as the original circuit. Equivalent circuits simplify analysis, but do not serve the original application. For example, consider the parallel circuit shown in Figure 5-14. The storage battery draws 5 amps at 6 volts. Hence, we can draw an equivalent circuit in which the battery is replaced by a 1.2-ohm resistance, as depicted in

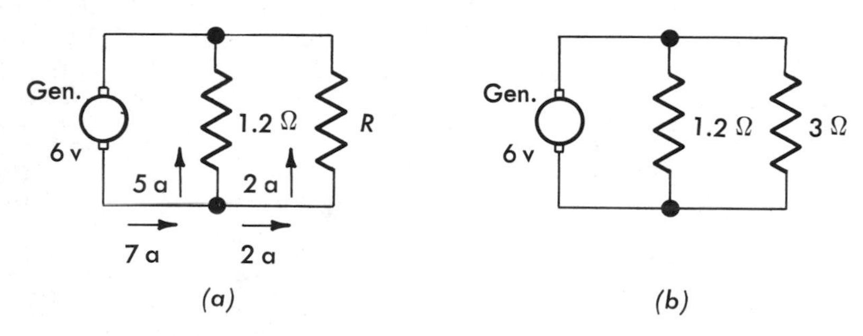

Figure 5-15
(a) An equivalent circuit for the configuration of Figure 5-14. *(b)* Another equivalent circuit for the same system.

Figure 5-15(*a*). Voltages and currents in the system are unchanged. The equivalent circuit facilitates understanding of circuit action, but obviously does not serve the original application.

Figure 5-15(*a*) can be redrawn as in (*b*), which eliminates the currents and assigns *R* its value of 3 ohms. This circuit facilitates visualization of electrical essentials when redrawn as the equivalent circuit in Figure 5-16. Here, the generator has been represented as a battery, to which a single resistor has been connected. This resistor represents the total circuit resistance that is present in Figure 5-14. We often think of equivalent circuits during analysis of a configuration, even if we do not draw the equivalent circuits explicitly.

We observe that Figure 5-16 is a *series* circuit, which is equivalent to

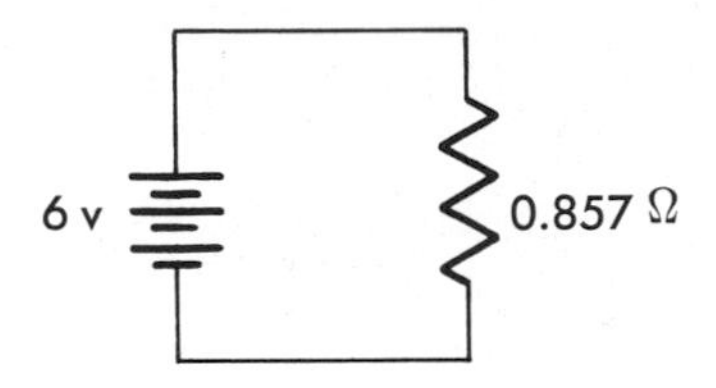

Figure 5-16
An equivalent circuit for the configuration of Figure 5-15(*b*).

the *parallel* circuit in Figure 5-14. A battery connected in series with a resistor is equivalent to a generator, battery, and resistor connected in parallel. Any parallel circuit has an equivalent series circuit. As we eventually proceed to analyze more complex electrical systems, we will find that this basic principle provides great analytical facility. Restrictions are inevitable in consideration of equivalent circuits. For example, the equivalent circuit in Figure 5-16 is subject to the restriction that the storage battery in Figure 5-14 is operating on its charge cycle. Another equivalent circuit is required when the storage battery is operating on its discharge cycle.

Another type of restriction on an equivalent circuit is illustrated in Figure 5-17. Here, a tungsten lamp rated at 300 watts and 120 volts is connected to a voltage source E. It might be supposed that the lamp could be replaced by a resistance in an equivalent circuit, and this is true. However, the value of the resistance in the equivalent circuit depends upon the value selected for E. Tungsten has a positive temperature coefficient of resistance. When the filament consumes 300 watts at 120 volts, it operates at a very high temperature. On the other hand, when 1 volt is applied to the filament, it operates practically at room temperature. The filament resistance is 15.5 times as great at 120 volts than at 1 volt. Conse-

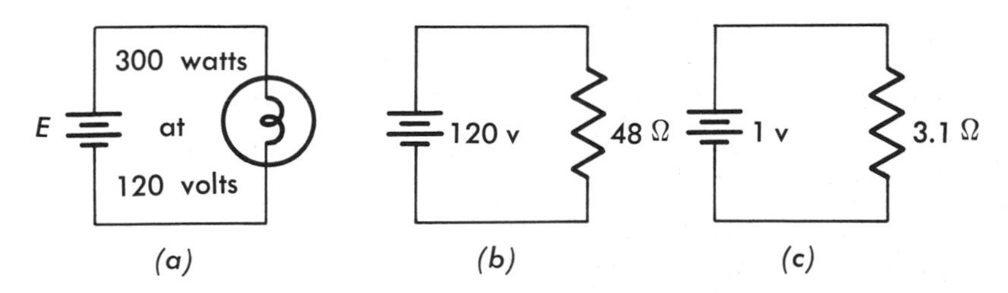

Figure 5-17
(*a*) A tungsten lamp connected to a voltage source. (*b*) Equivalent circuit when $E = 120$ volts. (*c*) Equivalent circuit when $E = 1$ volt.

quently, the filament is represented by a 48-ohm resistor when $E = 120$ volts. On the other hand, when $E = 1$ volt, the filament is represented by a 3.1-ohm resistor.

The *hot resistance* of the filament is 48 ohms, and its *cold resistance* is 3.1 ohms; hence, a tungsten filament is a nonlinear resistance. Over limited ranges of voltage, it can be regarded practically as a linear resistance. But over a wide voltage range, serious error is encountered if we assume that the filament is a linear resistance. When the circuit in Figure 5-17(*a*) is first closed, a comparatively large current flows; it is as if a 3.1-ohm resistance were connected across the 120-volt source. The filament temperature rises rapidly, and at the conclusion of this brief transient period, its resistance increases from 3.1 ohms to 48 ohms.

Conventional ohmmeters apply less than 1.5 volts to a lamp under test. Consequently, an ohmmeter measurement of filament resistance in a 120-volt lamp indicates the cold resistance of the filament. To measure its hot resistance, you must apply 120 volts to the lamp, and measure the current flow. Then, the hot resistance is given by $R = 120/I$. At intermediate values of voltage, you will measure resistance values between 3.1 ohms and 48 ohms. The corresponding voltage and current values plot as a curve on graph paper.

5.7 ANALYSIS OF CIRCUIT DEFECTS

An open circuit is comparable to opening a switch. If a poor contact opens a circuit, current flow stops. Either the total current or a branch current might be stopped. For example, consider the configuration shown in Figure 5-13. When the circuit is intact, the battery supplies 8 amps to the circuit. When a defective battery contact interrupts current flow, the current demand falls to zero. On the other hand, a defective contact to the 2-ohm resistor merely results in decrease of current demand, from 8 amps to 3 amps. It is for this basic reason that technicians often measure the total current demand of a defective electronic device; if the current demand is subnormal, it is possible that an open branch circuit is present.

Consider the effect of a short-circuit across the terminals of any resistor in Figure 5-13. The battery is then connected to a circuit that has negligible resistance. Accordingly, the current demand is limited only by the battery's internal resistance. If a dry battery is used in the circuit, this heavy current demand will soon ruin the battery. But suppose a storage battery is used in the circuit. We recall that a fully charged storage battery has a very low internal resistance. Hence, an extremely large current can be supplied to the external circuit. Although the external circuit has practically negligible resistance, it becomes significant

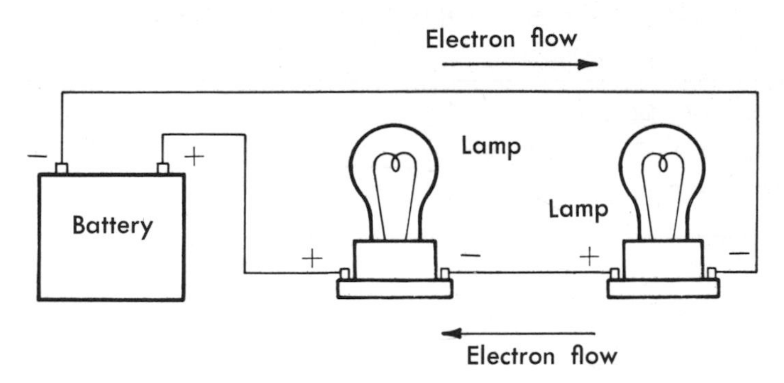

Figure 5-18
Series circuit comprising a battery and two lamps.

when the battery's internal resistance is extremely low. We will expect that the I^2R power which must be dissipated by the short-circuit will burn up the conductors.

When two lamps are connected in parallel, as in Figure 5-1, one lamp may burn out and the other will remain lighted. On the other hand, when two lamps are connected in series, as shown in Figure 5-18, both lamps "go out" when one lamp burns out. Hence, it is easier and quicker to troubleshoot the parallel circuit than the series circuit. You may have previously discovered the convenience of parallel-connected strings of Christmas-tree lights.

SUMMARY OF FUNDAMENTAL CONCEPTS

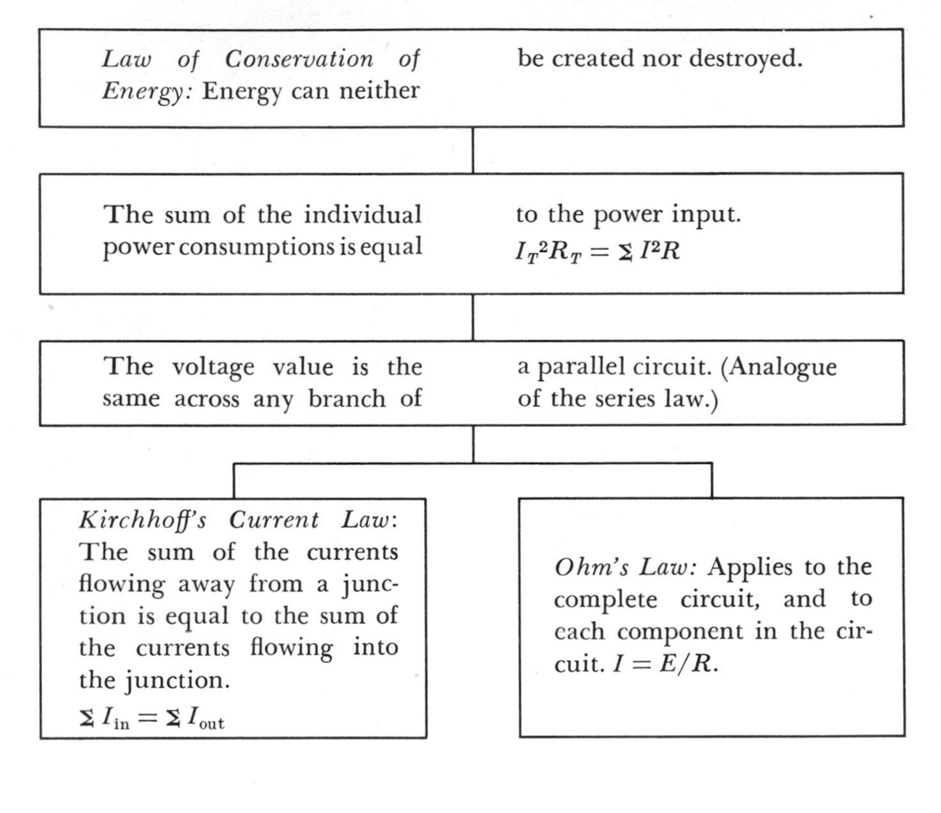

Law of Conservation of Energy: Energy can neither be created nor destroyed.
The sum of the individual power consumptions is equal to the power input. $I_T^2 R_T = \Sigma I^2 R$
The voltage value is the same across any branch of a parallel circuit. (Analogue of the series law.)
Kirchhoff's Current Law: The sum of the currents flowing away from a junction is equal to the sum of the currents flowing into the junction. $\Sigma I_{in} = \Sigma I_{out}$
Ohm's Law: Applies to the complete circuit, and to each component in the circuit. $I = E/R$.

Notes: I_T equals the total current in the parallel circuit. R_T equals the total resistance of the parallel circuit. I equals an individual current in the parallel circuit. R equals an individual resistance in the parallel circuit. I_{in} equals an individual current flowing into a junction. I_{out} equals an individual current flowing away from a junction. Σ is the symbol for summation.

QUESTIONS

1) To find the total current flow in a parallel circuit:
(*a*) calculate the sum of the branch currents. (*b*) calculate the difference between the branch currents. (*c*) add the individual resistance values, and apply Ohm's law to find the total current flow. (*d*) sub-

tract the source voltage from the sum of the branch voltages, and divide by the total equivalent resistance value.

2) Conductance is the measure of:
(*a*) the ease with which current flows through a component or circuit. (*b*) comparative directions of different conductors. (*c*) the ease with which voltage flows through a parallel circuit. (*d*) the ratio E/I.

3) To determine the total conductance in a parallel configuration:
(*a*) calculate the product of the individual conductances, and divide by their sum. (*b*) calculate the sum of the individual conductances. (*c*) multiply the diameter of the conductor by its total length. (*d*) take the reciprocal of the sum of the individual conductances.

4) Kirchhoff's current law states:
(*a*) the current is the same at any point in the circuit. (*b*) current is equal to voltage divided by resistance. (*c*) the sum of the current drops is equal to the total current. (*d*) the algebraic sum of the currents at any junction of conductors is equal to zero.

5) Dry cells or storage cells are connected in parallel to:
(*a*) provide increased current capability. (*b*) increase the source voltage. (*c*) reduce the effective load resistance. (*d*) reduce the effective load conductance.

6) If a dry cell is connected in parallel with a storage cell:
(*a*) the dry cell will soon "die." (*b*) the storage cell will soon die. (*c*) both cells will soon die. (*d*) there is no circulating current flow.

7) The power consumed in each branch of a parallel circuit is:
(*a*) equal to the power consumed by its adjoining branch. (*b*) directly proportional to the resistance of the branch. (*c*) directly proportional to the conductance of the branch. (*d*) equal to the source voltage multiplied by the total current.

8) Every parallel circuit has:
(*a*) an equivalent open circuit. (*b*) an equivalent short-circuit. (*c*) an equivalent series circuit. (*d*) an equivalent quadratic circuit.

9) When a dry cell is short-circuited:
(*a*) an infinite current flows. (*b*) the voltage drop across the short-circuit is equal to the terminal voltage of the battery. (*c*) a current flow occurs that is equal to the resistance of the short-circuit divided by the applied voltage. (*d*) the current flow is equal to the internal resistance of the battery divided by its emf.

10) Conventional ohmmeters apply:
(*a*) approximately 117 volts to the circuit under test. (*b*) no voltage to the circuit under test. (*c*) zero conductance to the circuit under test. (*d*) a comparatively small voltage, such as 1.5 volts, to the circuit under test.

PROBLEMS

1) Four 10-watt 6-volt electric-light bulbs are connected in parallel and energized from a 6-volt source. What is the total current flow?
2) Two 10-watt 6-volt electric-light bulbs, two 5-watt 6-volt bulbs, and a 36-watt 6-volt radio are connected in parallel and energized from a 6-volt source. What is the total current flow?
3) A ¼ horsepower 117-volt motor and three 60-watt 117-volt lamps are operated in parallel from a 117-volt line. Assuming that the motor is operating at full load and is 100 percent efficient, what is the total current flow?
4) Three dry cells are connected in parallel. Each cell has an internal resistance of 0.1 ohm. What is the effective source resistance?
5) If a storage battery has an internal conductance of 500 mhos, what is the value of its internal resistance?
6) Two 300-watt 117-volt lamps are connected in parallel. The parallel combination is energized from a 1.5-volt source. What is the approximate value of the current flow?
7) Two dry cells are connected in parallel, and supply current to a 3-ohm load resistor. Both cells have an emf of 1.5 volts. However, the internal resistance of one cell is 0.1 ohm, and the internal resistance of the other cell is 0.05 ohm. What is the value of the total current flow? What is the value of current supplied by each cell?
8) Two 60-watt 117-volt lamps are paralleled across a 117-volt line. One of the lamp sockets develops a defect which establishes an arc in series with the filament. The resistance of the arc is 13 ohms. What is the value of the total current flow?
9) A 3-volt 0.75-watt bulb is connected in parallel with a 117-volt 60-watt bulb. The parallel combination is energized from a 3-volt source. What is the approximate value of the total current flow?
10) A technician intends to wire one hundred 117-volt 10-watt lamps in parallel for an electric display sign. He makes an error and wires all the lamps in series. When 117 volts are applied to the circuit, what is the approximate value of the total current flow?
11) Two ¼-horsepower 117-volt motors are operated in parallel from a 117-volt line. One motor operates at full load, and the other motor operates at no load. Assuming that both motors are 100 percent efficient, what is the value of the total current flow?
12) In Problem 11, one motor is operated at full load and the other motor is operated at half load. What is the value of the total current flow?

13) Two identical resistors connected in parallel consume a total power of 6 watts when energized by a certain voltage source. If the two resistors are connected in series and energized by the same voltage source, how much total power do they consume?
14) Three 1.5-volt 0.575-watt bulbs are connected in parallel. Their resistance is measured with an ohmmeter which applies 1.5 volts across the parallel combination. What resistance value is indicated by the ohmmeter?
15) Two 0.25-volt 0.025-watt special-purpose bulbs are connected in parallel. Their resistance is measured with an ohmmeter that applies 3 volts across the parallel combination. What resistance value is indicated by the ohmmeter? [Hint: The test voltage is excessive.]

6

SERIES-PARALLEL CIRCUITRY

6.1 BASIC SERIES-PARALLEL CONFIGURATIONS

Series-parallel circuits (also known as compound circuits), fall into a large number of categories, classifications, and varieties. Only the most basic configurations can be considered in this chapter. Two introductory networks are depicted in Figure 6-1. Source voltage and resistances are specified. Hence, we first ask what the total current flow may be in Figure 6-1(*a*). Our approach is to combine R_2 and R_3 into an equivalent resistance, and then to combine this equivalent resistance with R_1. Ohm's law states the total current. We multiply this total current by R_1 to find the voltage drop across R_1. Kirchhoff's voltage law, in turn, states the voltage drop across R_2 and R_3. This voltage drop determines the current values through R_2 and R_3. Note that we could also determine current values through R_2 and R_3 by applying Kirchhoff's current law, with respect to the ratio of R_2 to R_3.

It is easier to solve a network such as shown in Figure 6-1(*b*). Source voltage and resistances are specified. Note that the source voltage is applied directly across R_1; hence, Ohm's law states the current flow through R_1. When R_2 and R_3 are combined, Ohm's law states the current flow through these resistors. In turn, the voltage drops across R_2 and R_3 are easily computed; the total current is the sum of the branch currents.

Let us look at a simple series-parallel circuit in a conventional radio receiver. Figure 6-2 shows a configuration for five vacuum-tube heaters and a pilot lamp. The tubes are designated V_1, V_2, and so forth; the pilot lamp is designated M in accordance with customary practice. A vacuum-

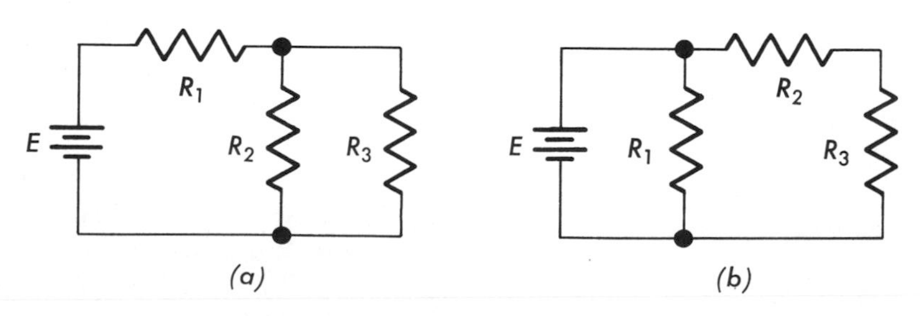

Figure 6-1

(*a*) An elementary series-parallel circuit. (*b*) Another basic series-parallel circuit.

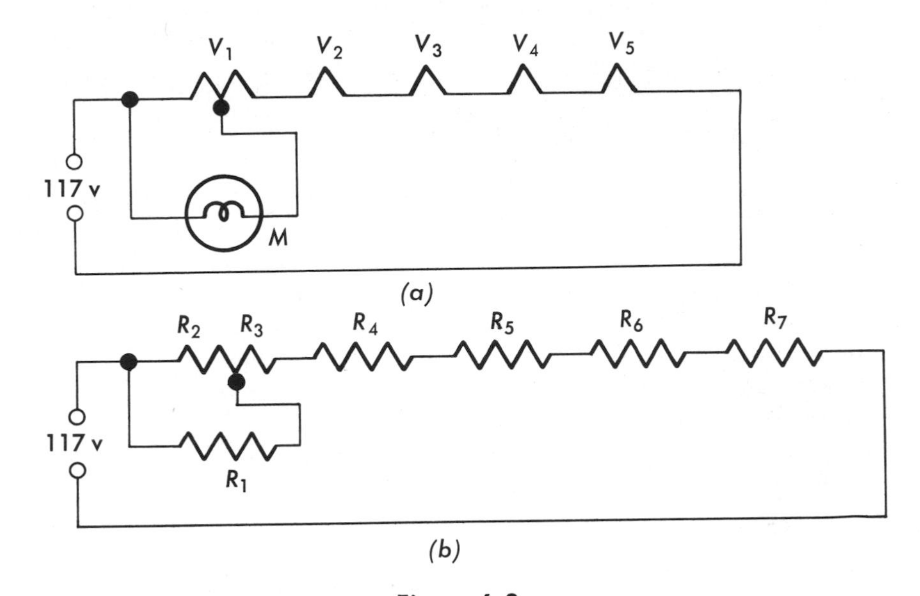

Figure 6-2
(a) A series-parallel circuit that comprises five radio-tube heaters and a pilot lamp. *(b)* Equivalent circuit for *(a)*.

tube heater is a form of filament. Hence, it can be represented as a resistor, just as the filament of an electric lamp can be represented as a resistor. Tube V_1 in Figure 6-2(a) has a tapped filament. A tapped filament can be represented by a tapped resistor; hence, the equivalent circuit for (a) can be drawn as seen in (b).

Compare the network in Figure 6-2(b) with the circuit in Figure 6-1(a). Note that R_1 in Figure 6-1(a) corresponds to $R_3 + R_4 + R_5 + R_6 + R_7$ in Figure 6-2(b). Similarly, R_2 and R_3 in Figure 6-1(a) correspond to R_1 and R_2 in Figure 6-2(b). We recognize the basic similarity of the configurations in Figure 6-2(a) and Figure 6-1(a), despite their superficial differences. Resistors R_2 and R_3 in Figure 6-1(a) are called a *bank*. Similarly, resistors R_1 and R_2 in Figure 6-2(b) comprise a bank. Resistors R_3, R_4, R_5, R_6, and R_7 in Figure 6-2(b) are called a *series string*, or simply a *string*. Thus, two or more resistors connected in *parallel* are called a *bank*; two or more resistors connected in *series* are called a *string*.

It follows from previous discussion that banks and strings connected in various series and parallel arrangements are called series-parallel circuits, configurations, or networks. The terms *circuit, configuration,* and *network* are general, and apply to series, parallel, or series-parallel arrangements. These three general terms are entirely equivalent, and are used interchangeably. However, there is a tendency to apply the term "circuit" to simple arrangements, and to apply the term "configuration" or "network" to elaborate arrangements.

6.2 PRINCIPLES OF NETWORK REDUCTION

The foundation for attack of series-parallel configurations has been laid in the foregoing section. Parallel circuitry is generally reduced to equivalent series circuitry. Equivalent series circuits are combined with the series strings in the configuration. You will find that there is no single rule of attack for all series-parallel configurations, and you must evaluate each problem individually. After you have evaluated a series-parallel problem appropriately, the solution will emerge step-by-step with application of Ohm's law, the series law, Kirchhoff's voltage law, and Kirchhoff's current law.

Consider the series-parallel arrangement shown in Figure 6-3(*a*). A 19-ohm resistor is tapped, with 10 ohms on one side and 9 ohms on the other side. The 10-ohm portion is connected in parallel with a 90-ohm resistor. Hence, this bank has a resistance of 9 ohms. It follows that the total circuit resistance is equal to $9 + 9 + 6 + 12 = 36$ ohms, and the equivalent series circuit is drawn as seen in Figure 6-3(*b*). The battery will supply ⅓ amp to the circuit. In turn, the voltage drop across the 12-ohm resistor [Figure 6-3(*a*)] is 4 volts; the drop across the 6-ohm resistor is 2 volts; the drop across the 9-ohm resistor is 3 volts. Accordingly, the drop across the bank is $12 - 9 = 3$ volts. Current flow through the 90-ohm resistor will be $3/90 = 1/30$ amp; current flow through the 10-ohm resistor will be $3/10$ amp.

Now consider the series-parallel configuration shown in Figure 6-4(*a*). If you connect an ohmmeter between terminals *A* and *B*, what resistance value will the ohmmeter indicate? In this type of problem, start from the far end of the network and reduce it in steps. R_6 and R_7 combine to form an equivalent 9-ohm resistance, as depicted in Figure 6-4(*b*). In turn, the 9-ohm resistance combines with R_3 and R_5 to form an equivalent 9-ohm resistance, as seen in Figure 6-5(*a*). Finally, the 9-ohm resistance combines with R_2 and R_4 to form an equivalent 9-ohm resistance; this 9-ohm resistance combines with R_1 to form an equivalent 90-ohm resistance, as depicted in Figure 6-5(*b*). Hence, the resistance measured between terminals *A* and *B* in Figure 6-4(*a*) will be 90 ohms.

CONCEPT OF CHARACTERISTIC RESISTANCE

This is perhaps a surprising sequence of resistance values. We observe that the equivalent shunt resistance found in each step was 9 ohms. We also observe that the terminal resistance between *A* and *B* is equal to R_7,

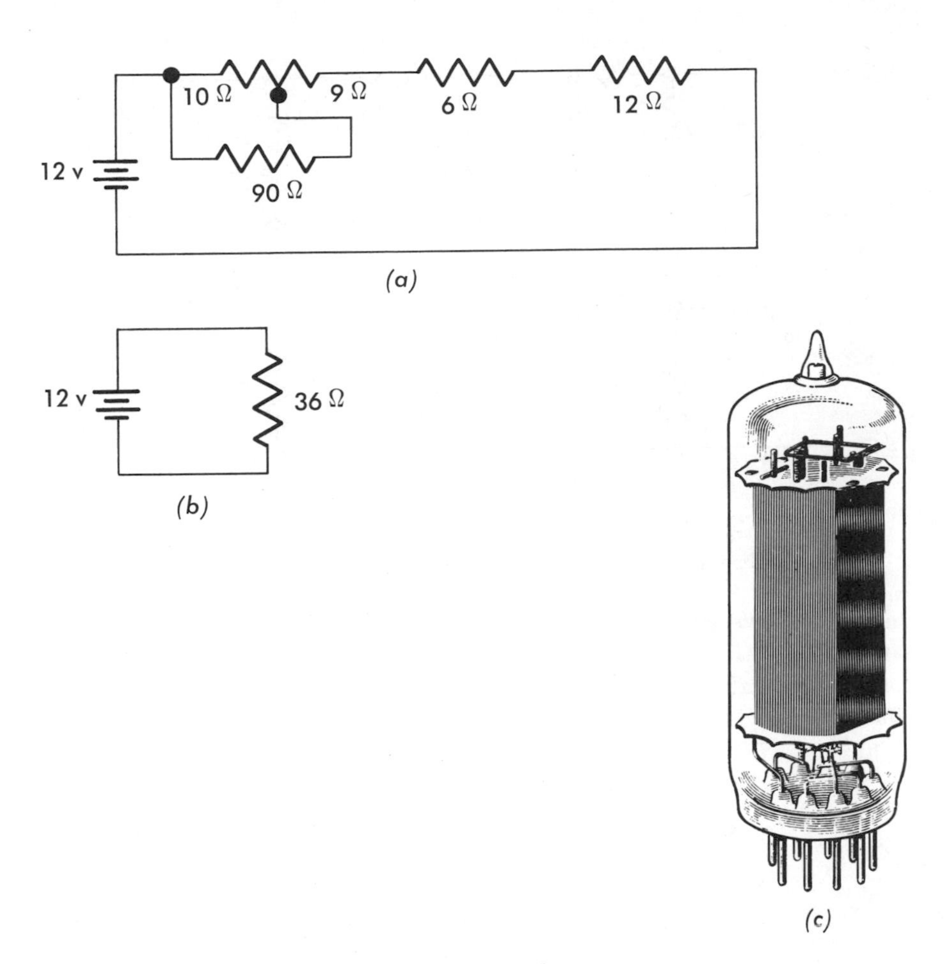

Figure 6-3
(a) A series-parallel circuit. *(b)* Equivalent series circuit. *(c)* A typical vacuum tube.

the final resistance in this circuit. What conclusions are we to draw? First of all, it makes *no difference how many times the 81-ohm and 10-ohm L* section is repeated. You might connect 10,000 *L* sections in sequence, for example; if you shunt a 90-ohm resistance across the far end of this extremely long sequence, the input terminal resistance will obviously still be 90 ohms, as the three *L* sections in Figure 6-4(*a*).

At first, this seems like an impossible situation—although many *L* sections are added, the input resistance does not change. Let us see why this is so. When *L* sections are connected in sequence, as in Figure 6-4(*a*), the resulting network is called a *ladder*. Moreover, if all the series

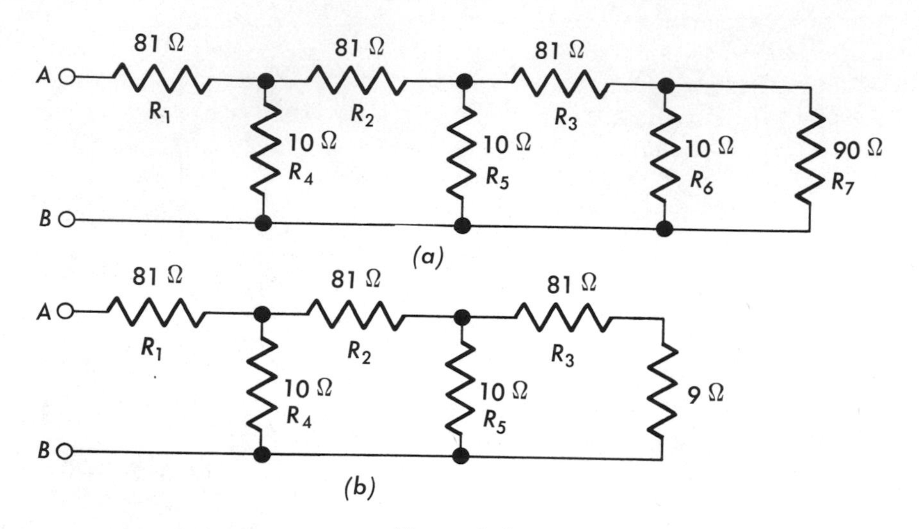

Figure 6-4
(a) A ladder type of series-parallel network. *(b)* First network reduction.

resistances have the same value, and all the shunt resistances have the same value, as in Figure 6-4(*a*), the network is a *uniform* ladder. It can be easily proved that a uniform ladder has a certain resistance, called its *characteristic resistance.*

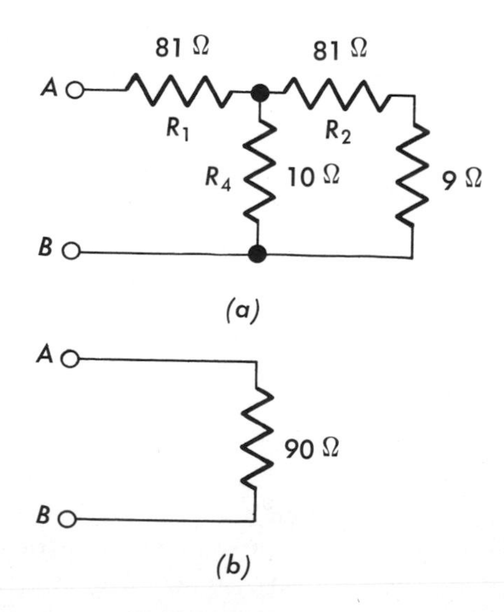

Figure 6-5
(a) Second network reduction. *(b)* Final network reduction.

The characteristic resistance of a uniform ladder is the resistance value which, when shunted across the final L section, causes the input resistance to have the same value as the characteristic resistance. Evidently, the characteristic resistance of the uniform ladder in Figure 6-4(a) is 90 ohms. Let us prove that every uniform ladder has a certain characteristic resistance, and derive this characteristic resistance in terms of series and shunt resistances. We perceive that if some other value were selected for the series resistors in Figure 6-4(a), it would be readily possible to determine a new value for R_7 which would provide the *same* value for the shunt resistance in each step of network reduction.

With this understanding, let us state the problem in general terms, as shown in Figure 6-6. The algebraic values R_1 and R_2 are assigned to the L section. We do not know what value of terminating shunt resistance will provide an equal input resistance R_{in}, but since these resistance values are defined as equal, we specify this condition by assigning the

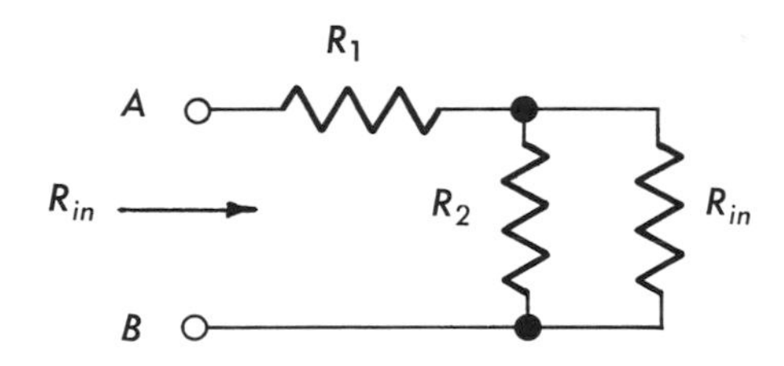

Figure 6-6
The characteristic resistance value can be calculated.

algebraic value R_{in} to the terminating shunt resistance. Let us proceed to solve for R_{in}.

First, combine the two shunt resistances R_2 and R_{in} (Figure 6-6); the equivalent resistance of this parallel bank is

$$\frac{R_2 R_{in}}{R_2 + R_{in}} \tag{6.1}$$

Add this equivalent resistance to R_1 (Figure 6-6) to find the resistance between terminals A and B

$$\frac{R_2 R_{in}}{R_2 + R_{in}} + R_1 \tag{6.2}$$

However, the resistance between terminals A and B is equal to R_{in}; therefore,

$$R_{in} = \frac{R_2 R_{in}}{R_2 + R_{in}} + R_1 \tag{6.3}$$

This equation can evidently be written in standard quadratic form:

$$R_{in}^2 - R_1 R_{in} - R_1 R_2 = 0 \tag{6.4}$$

and, when we solve for R_{in}, we find that

$$R_{in} = \frac{R_1 \pm \sqrt{R_1^2 + 4R_1 R_2}}{2} \tag{6.5}$$

In other words, an L section always has two values of terminating shunt resistance which will make the input resistance equal to the value of the terminating shunt resistance. This is a very interesting analytical result. Let us go back to Figure 6-4 and check this result.

According to our numerical analysis of the configuration in Figure 6-4(*a*), the 90-ohm terminating resistance appears repeated at the input terminals A and B. We also concluded that it makes no difference how many uniform L sections are included. Hence, if we substitute $R_1 = 81$, and $R_2 = 10$ into Equation (6.5), we anticipate that R_{in} will be 90 ohms. Let us see if this is so.

$$R_{in} = \frac{81 \pm \sqrt{6561 + 3240}}{2} \tag{6.6}$$

$$R_{in} = 90 \text{ ohms, or } -9 \text{ ohms} \tag{6.7}$$

We are reassured that the algebraic derivation was correct, because it checks with the independent numerical calculation of 90 ohms. But what about the alternative answer of −9 ohms? Sometimes a negative answer of this type is nonphysical in an algebraic analysis. In such a case, it is simply rejected. At other times it will have a physical interpretation. In this particular situation, the answer of −9 ohms does indeed have a physical interpretation. It states that a negative resistance of 9 ohms connected across R_2 in Figure 6-6 will cause the input resistance to have a value of −9 ohms.

INTERPRETATION OF THE NEGATIVE-RESISTANCE SOLUTION

This leads us up to the question of negative resistance. We recall that resistance is a voltage/current ratio. When we write $I = E/R$, this equation states that if the resistance is positive, application of more voltage will cause more current to flow. However, when we write $I = E/(-R)$, this equation states that application of more voltage will cause less current to flow. It is easier to see this fact if we rewrite Ohm's law in the form $-I = E/R$. Negative current simply means *reverse* current, or *less* positive current. Therefore, when the resistance is negative, application of more voltage causes less positive current to flow.

There are many components that have a negative resistance characteristic, and serve vital functions in electronic equipment. For example, the tunnel diode illustrated in Figure 6-7 has a negative-resistance characteristic. Tunnel diodes and circuit actions that result from the presence of negative resistance are discussed in detail subsequently.

The concept of infinity is met often not only in mathematics, but also in electronics. For example, the analysis of an infinite uniform ladder

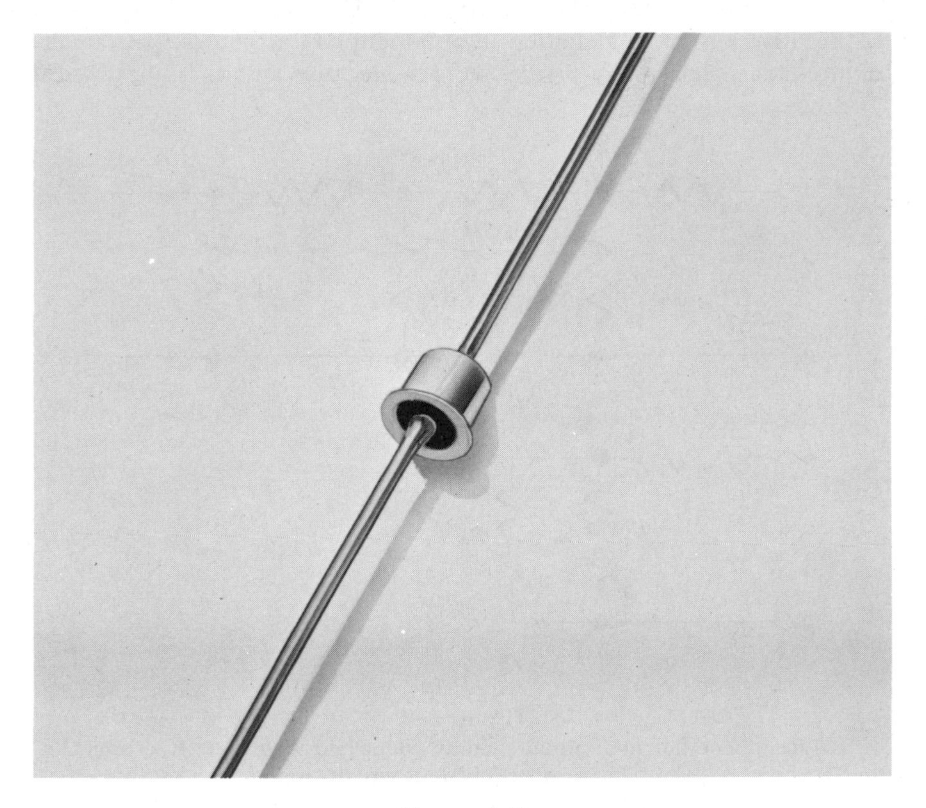

Figure 6-7
A tunnel diode is a semiconductor device which exhibits negative resistance. (Courtesy of Semiconductor Products Division, General Electric Company.)

is fundamental in circuit theory. The infinite uniform ladder is simply an infinite sequence of L sections, as depicted in Figure 6-8. Infinity, of course, is not a number. Infinity is larger than any assigned number, no matter how large. To start, we do not know the resistance value between terminals A and B in Figure 6-8(a). Accordingly, let us call this value R_0. Now, if we disconnect the first L section, the input resistance to the second L section will still be equal to R_0. This conclusion is inescapable, because $\infty - 1 = \infty$. In fact, we could disconnect the first thousand sections from the infinite ladder, and the input resistance to the 1001st L section would still be equal to R_0.

Hence, let us form an equivalent circuit as shown in Figure 6-8(*b*). We disconnect the first L section and terminate it with the input resistance of the disconnected infinite ladder, equal to R_0. We recognize the fact that we have simply repeated the configuration analyzed in Figure 6-6. The answer was derived as formula (6.5). However, note carefully that the negative answer in Equation (6.5) is nonphysical with respect to the infinite ladder depicted in Figure 6-8. The negative answer is nonphysical

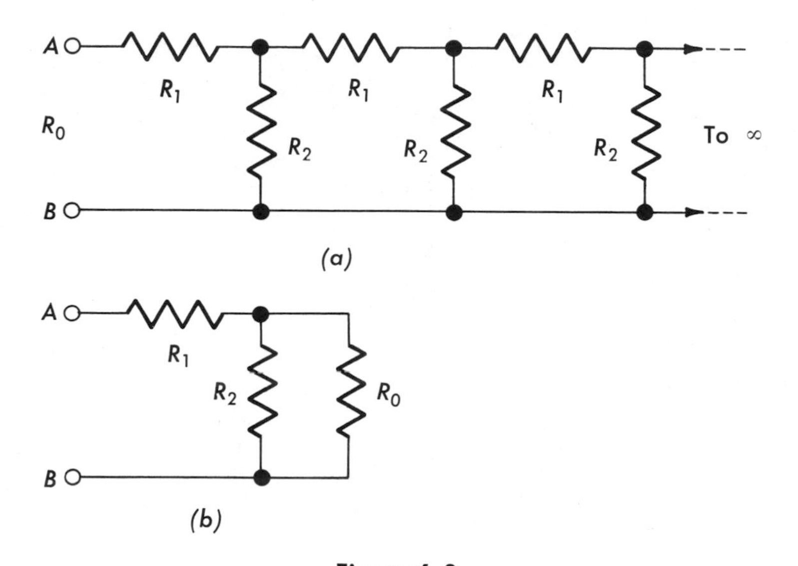

Figure 6-8
(*a*) Representation of an infinite ladder comprised of uniform L sections.
(*b*) An equivalent circuit.

because our infinite ladder is defined as an infinite sequence of positive resistances only.

Let us pause to consolidate our gains. Suppose we start constructing an infinite uniform ladder of L sections as depicted in Figure 6-8(*a*). The first section has an input resistance of $R_1 + R_2$. When the second L section is connected, the input resistance becomes less. Next, when the third L section is connected, the input resistance becomes still less, but the *amount* of decrease is also less. By the time that we have connected 1000 L sections, addition of a 1001st section decreases the input resistance by an *extremely small amount*. The input resistance is approaching a *limit*; this limit will be equal to R_0 when the ladder is infinitely long. Although the existence of the limit can be proven mathematically, the proof is complex and will not be derived in these pages.

Let us turn now to solution of the series-parallel network presented in Figure 6-9. The known values are $I_2 = 0.3$ amp through R_2, $R_1 = 38.1$ ohms, the total resistance $R_T = 39$ ohms, and the source voltage $E = 117$ volts. We shall calculate the total current flow I_T, the resistance of R_2, voltage V_1 across R_1, current I_3 through R_3, the resistance of R_3, and the voltage V_P across the bank. Ohm's law yields $I_T = 117/39 = 3$ amps. Next, $V_1 = I_T R_1 = 3 \times 38.1 = 114.3$ volts. Kirchhoff's voltage law states that $V_P = 117 - 114.3 = 2.7$ volts. Evidently, $R_2 = 2.7/0.3 = 9$ ohms. Kirchhoff's current law states that $I_3 = I_T - I_2 = 3 - 0.3 = 2.7$ amps. The resistance of R_3 is equal to V_P/I_3, or $2.7/2.7 = 1$ ohm.

We must evaluate the knowns to determine what unknowns can be calculated. When our number of knowns is increased, we can calculate other unknowns. Finally, values are found for all unknown voltages, currents, and resistances. In any circuit problem, the known values must be both necessary and sufficient. It is not necessary to state the sum of V_1 and V_P in Figure 6-9, for example, because the source voltage E is already known. To state the sum of V_1 and V_P would be redundant; however, it is necessary that either E or the sum of V_1 and V_P be stated. It is sufficient that the noted values in Figure 6-9 be given. The data are insufficient if any one of these values be omitted—the problem would not have a solution.

THE RESISTANCE BRIDGE

The bridge circuit shown in Figure 6-10 is an important type of series-parallel circuit. Current from the source E divides into I_1 and I_2 through series-connected resistances R_1 and R_4, and R_2 and R_3. Galvanometer G

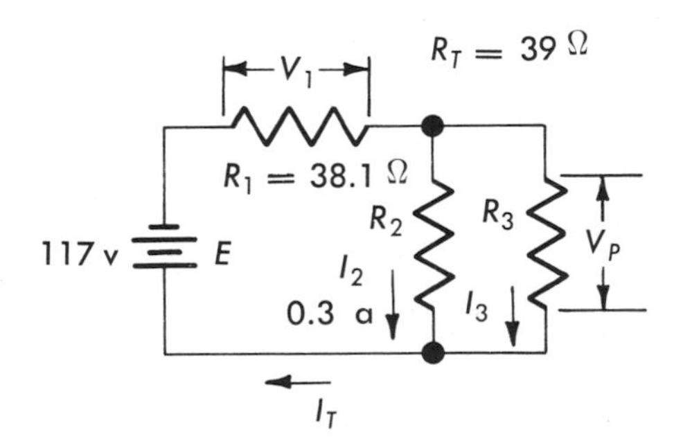

Figure 6-9

Several basic electrical laws are applied in the solution of this series-parallel circuit problem.

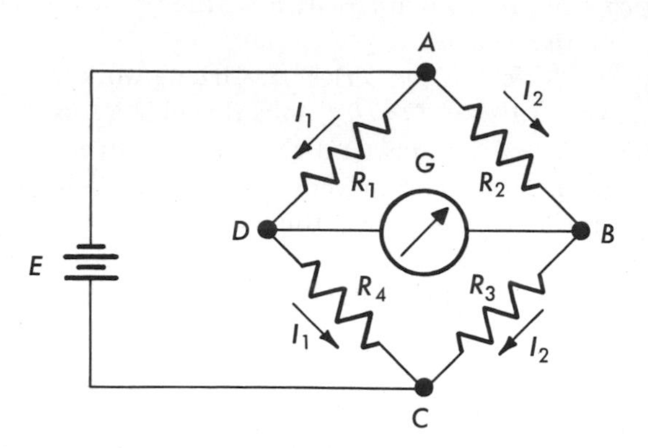

Figure 6-10
A basic bridge circuit which finds application in many electronic instruments and devices.

is connected between points B and D, to indicate whether a potential difference exists between these two points. Observe that R_1 and R_4 form a voltage divider; similarly, R_2 and R_3 form a voltage divider. Suppose that R_1 and R_4 have equal values; then the voltage at D is equal to $E/2$. Again, if R_2 and R_3 have equal values, the voltage at B is equal to $E/2$. Since the voltages at B and D are equal, and are both negative with respect to C, there is zero potential difference between B and D; the galvanometer reads zero.

When the galvanometer reads zero, the bridge is said to be *balanced*. This means that $I_1R_1/I_1R_4 = I_2R_2/I_2R_3$. Since currents I_1 and I_2 cancel out, we can simply write

$$\frac{R_1}{R_4} = \frac{R_2}{R_3} \tag{6.8}$$

Equation (6.8) states that the resistances may have any values, provided the *ratio* of R_1 to R_4 is the same as the *ratio* of R_2 to R_3. For example, R_1 might be 10 ohms and R_4 might be 100 ohms. This is a ratio of 1 to 10. Then, if R_2 is 1000 ohms, R_3 must evidently have a value of 10,000 ohms to maintain a ratio of 1 to 10, and thereby balance the bridge.

A resistance bridge is used to measure resistance values, and is called a *Wheatstone bridge* in this application (see Figure 6-11). We wish to measure the value of a resistor R_x. Two of the bridge arms comprise 20-K resistances. A calibrated variable resistor (rheostat) will be used to indicate the resistance of R_x. Evidently, when the bridge is balanced by suitable adjustment of R_c, we can write

$$\frac{20{,}000}{20{,}000} = \frac{R_c}{R_x} \tag{6.9}$$

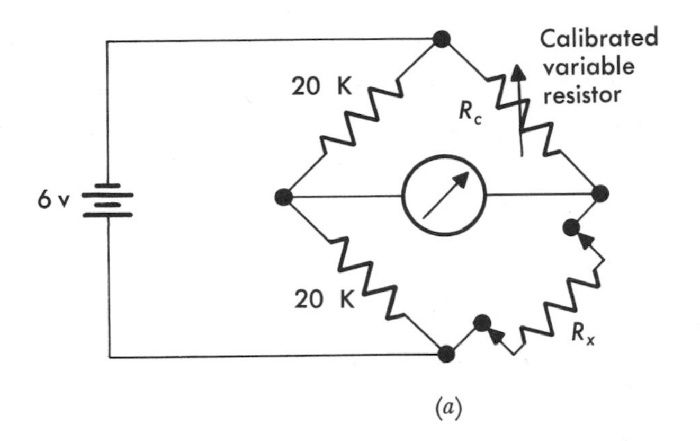

(*a*)

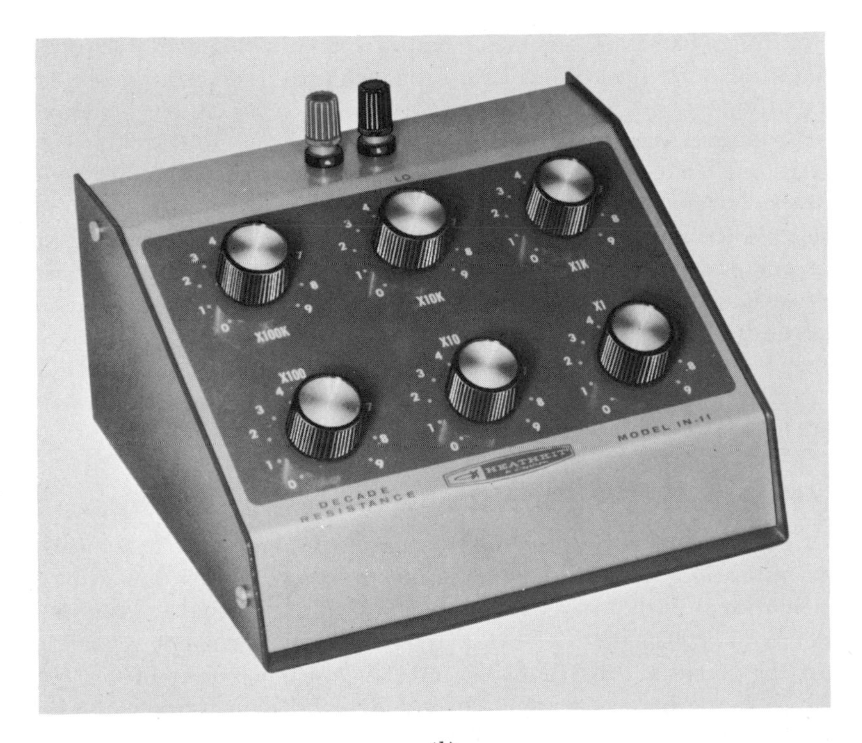

(*b*)

Figure 6-11

(*a*) A simple Wheatstone bridge configuration which can be used to measure the value of the unknown resistance R_x. (*b*) A decade resistance is sometimes used instead of a calibrated variable resistor in a Wheatstone bridge. The decade is adjustable from 1 ohm to 199,999 ohms. (Courtesy of Heath Company.)

Since we wish to find the value of R_x, we will solve Equation (6.9) for R_x:

$$R_x = R_c \tag{6.10}$$

As R_c is adjusted, the galvanometer will swing to the right or left of its zero indication. In other words, an *unbalanced voltage* (or current) might be either positive or negative. When R_c is adjusted to make the galvanometer read exactly zero, the galvanometer is said to be *nulled,* and the bridge has been balanced. We then read the value of R_x from the calibrated scale of R_c.

A Wheatstone bridge provides the most accurate method of measuring resistance values. It is more accurate than an ohmmeter. The bridge method is most accurate because the galvanometer is not calibrated; only the zero indication point is of interest. The zero point can be determined with an extremely high degree of accuracy because it is unaffected by temperature or any drift in electrical characteristics of the galvanometer. On the other hand, an ohmmeter employs a galvanometer with a calibrated scale. Scale readings will vary somewhat over substantial ranges of temperature, and any drift in electrical characteristics of the galvanometer will introduce error into the scale indication.

Although a 6-volt source is depicted in Figure 6-11, this value is arbitrary. A Wheatstone bridge operates with almost any value of source voltage. As the source voltage is increased, the sensitivity of the null indication increases, and the null setting can be determined more precisely. Excessive source voltages must not be used; otherwise, the power dissipation ratings of the bridge resistors will be exceeded. An overheated resistor is likely to change in value. Gross overheating results in resistor burn-out. Practical Wheatstone bridges incorporate many refinements not shown in Figure 6-11. These considerations must be deferred, however.

6.3 ANALYSIS OF SOURCE RESISTANCE

We know that all sources of electricity have internal resistance. In some applications, this internal resistance can be neglected. For example, a conventional fully charged storage battery might have an internal resistance of 0.0025 ohm. If the battery supplies a current demand of 1 amp, the potential drop across the internal resistance is only 0.0025 volt. However, if the battery supplies current demand of 300 amps, the drop across the internal resistance becomes 0.75 volt. If the battery is not fully charged, its internal resistance will be considerably greater; for example, 2 volts will be dropped across the internal resistance in a certain condition of charge.

It follows that any parallel circuit must be regarded as a series-parallel circuit when comparatively great current demand is made upon the source.

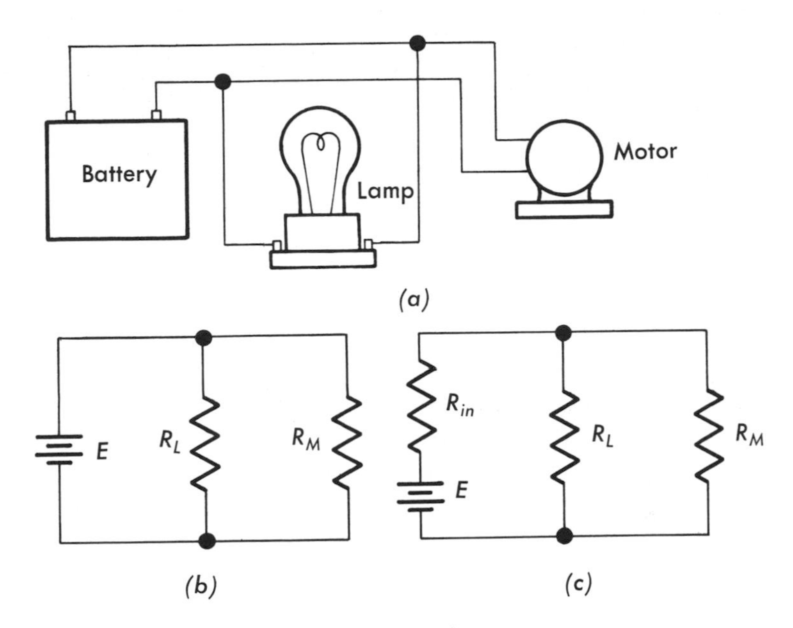

Figure 6-12

(a) The storage battery supplies current to a lamp and to a motor. *(b)* An equivalent circuit for a light load. *(c)* An equivalent circuit for a heavy load.

Consider the arrangement shown in Figure 6-12(*a*). The lamp imposes a comparatively small load on the storage battery. If the motor operates a blower fan, it also imposes a comparatively small load on the battery. The equivalent circuit can be drawn for all practical purposes as seen in Figure 6-12(*b*). On the other hand, suppose that a starter motor is represented in (*a*). The motor imposes a severe load upon the battery while cranking the car engine. Hence, the equivalent circuit must now be drawn in practice

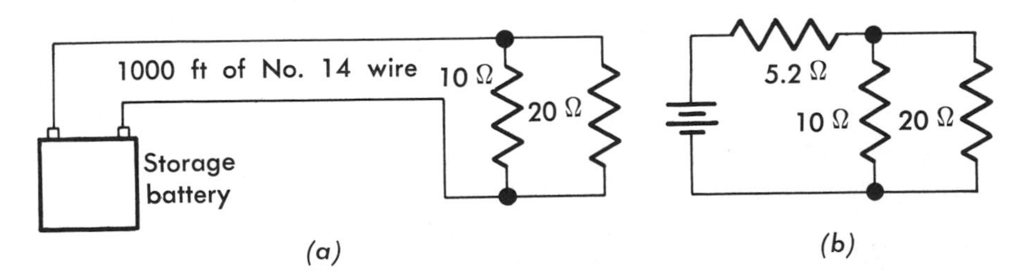

Figure 6-13

(a) The line resistance may be regarded as a source resistance. *(b)* An equivalent circuit.

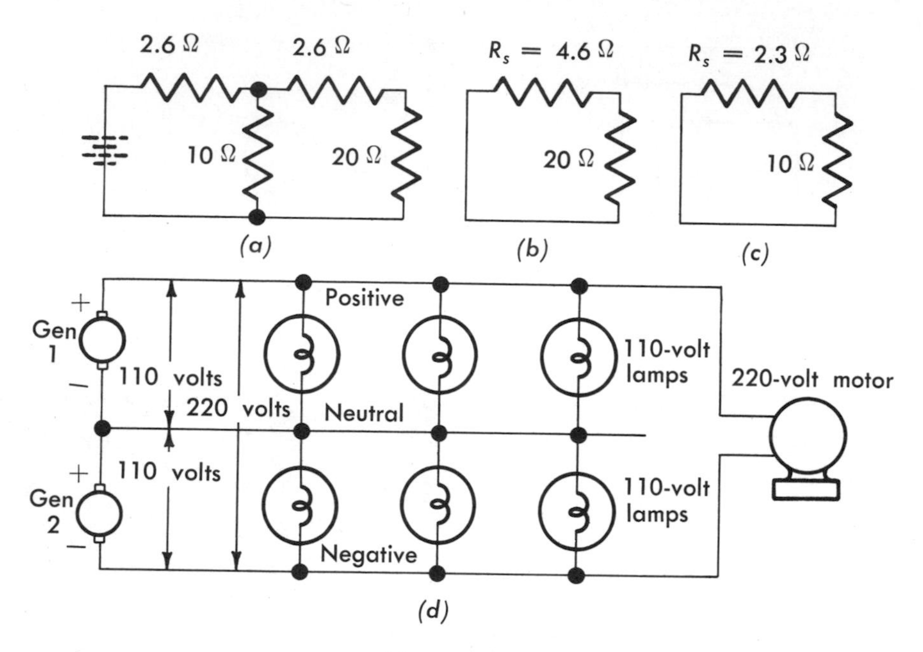

Figure 6-14

(a) An equivalent circuit for loads spaced apart along the line. *(b)* The 20-ohm load "sees" a source resistance of approximately 4.6 ohms. *(c)* The 10-ohm load "sees" a source resistance of approximately 2.3 ohms. *(d)* Six 110-volt lamps and a 220-volt motor connected into a three-wire system. *(e)* The neutral wire could be omitted, if the load is perfectly balanced. *(f)* Current I_N flows in the neutral line when the load is unbalanced.

(Continued on facing page.)

as shown in (*b*). It is because of the voltage drop across R_{in} that the lamp decreases in brightness while the engine is being cranked.

Source resistance often includes the resistance of the conductors between the battery and the load. Whenever appreciable voltage drop occurs along the conductors, we must include the conductor resistance with the internal resistance of the battery. If the conductor resistance is very large compared to the battery's internal resistance, we can neglect the internal resistance. For example, suppose a storage battery supplies current through a 1000-foot line of No. 14 copper wire, as depicted in Figure 6-13(*a*). The wire has a resistance of approximately 2.6 ohms per thousand ft, or 5.2 ohms for the complete circuit. This conductor resistance is very much greater than the internal resistance of the storage battery. Hence, the equivalent circuit can be drawn for all practical purposes as shown in Figure 6-13(*b*). The effective source resistance is the conductor resistance.

Evidently, the source resistance will differ for spaced loads along a

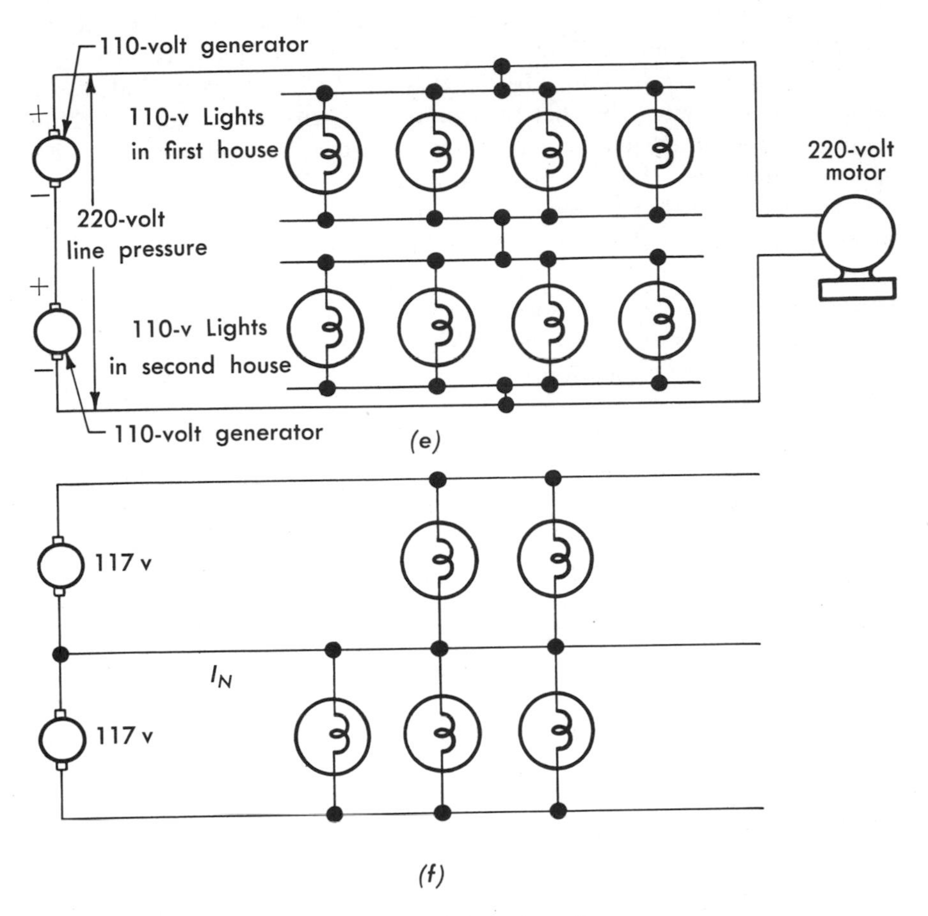

Fig. 6-14 (*Continued*)

line. For example, suppose that the 10-ohm load in Figure 6-13(*a*) is not connected at the far end of the line, but halfway along or 500 feet from the battery. It is clear that the equivalent circuit must now be drawn as shown in Figure 6-14(*a*). It is less obvious what values of source resistance will be "seen" by each load. Consider the 20-ohm load; it first sees a 2.6-ohm series source resistance. To this source resistance is added 10 ohms and 2.6 ohms in parallel. (The battery is neglected since its internal resistance is negligible.) Thus, the 20-ohm load sees a total source resistance of approximately 4.6 ohms, as depicted in Figure 6-14(*b*).

Next, consider the 10-ohm load. It sees a 2.6-ohm source resistance connected in parallel with 22.6 ohms. Accordingly, the 10-ohm load sees a source resistance of approximately 2.3 ohms, as depicted in Figure 6-14(*c*).

This example demonstrates that each of the loads in Figure 6-14(*a*) lowers the source resistance seen by the other load. Of course, each of the loads also reduces the terminal voltage applied to the other load. We say that a system with source resistance becomes "stiffer" when heavily loaded; or, we say that the system has better *regulation* when heavily loaded. This implies that when the load current varies, the terminal voltage across the load will change less if the average load is comparatively heavy.

You will find that voltage sources in electronic equipment are sometimes "bled" with a shunt resistance simply to provide a comparatively heavy load. In turn, the voltage regulation of the source is improved. The bleeder current makes the source stiffer. A disadvantage of a simple bleeder resistance is the power loss which it entails. This is the price which is paid for improved regulation.

THREE-WIRE DISTRIBUTION SYSTEM

Another important example of series-parallel circuitry is the three-wire distribution system used by power companies. It is sometimes called the Edison three-wire system, because it was developed by Thomas Edison. He employed two 110-volt d-c generators connected in series to supply 220 volts across the outer wires, and 110 volts between the center or *neutral* wire and each outer wire, as depicted in Figure 6-14(*d*). Note that power companies now supply a-c power exclusively; however, the basic principle remains the same. We know that when two generators (or other sources of electricity) are connected in series-aiding, their terminal voltages add.

What is the advantage of the three-wire system? We find that it is more economical when substantial power must be supplied. A three-wire system provides 110 volts for lamps, which demand comparatively little current, and 220 volts for motors (or electric stoves) which demand comparatively heavy current. Only three wires are required to supply two different voltages. Note in Figure 6-14(*d*) that the 110-volt lamps actually operate on 220 volts; as long as the system is balanced, there is no current flow in the neutral wire. Because the 110-volt lamps operate in series from the outer wires, only half as much current drain is taken from the 220-volt line, as compared with a 110-volt line. In turn, smaller line wires can be used, saving more than 50 percent of the wire cost.

Since no current can flow in the neutral wire, if the loads are perfectly balanced, it is possible in theory to omit the neutral wire, as depicted in Figure 6-14(*e*). In practice, however, the load will seldom be exactly balanced. A simple example is seen in Figure 6-14(*f*). If the lamps are all rated at 117 volts and 200 watts, each lamp demands 200/117 amps. Accordingly, the neutral line necessarily supplies 200/117 amps to the third lamp in the lower group. However, suppose the neutral line was omitted. Then, because the total resistance of the upper group of lamps is greater than the total resistance of the lower group, more than 117 volts would be applied across the upper group, and less than 117 volts would be applied across the lower group. In turn, the upper group of lamps would burn too brightly, and the lower group would burn too dimly. Hence, practical situations require the use of a neutral line.

6.4 COMPONENT POWER RATINGS

We have seen that resistors are rated for maximum power dissipation. Lamps have power ratings for specified terminal voltages. It follows from the discussion on source resistance that conductors must often be regarded as resistive components in electrical systems. Conductors also have power ratings, which are stated in terms of current-carrying capacity. Current flow through a conductor generates heat. Its temperature rises until the heat is radiated as fast as it is produced. The temperature equilibrium is attained at some point because the *radiation* of all substances *increases* with temperature. In the basic ideal case, radiation increases as the *fourth power* of the absolute temperature:

$$W = kT^4 \tag{6.11}$$

where W is the radiated power, k is a constant, and T is the absolute temperature. The absolute temperature is equal to °C + 273.2.

Excessive current flow in a conductor results in sufficiently high temperature to damage the insulation, or to melt the conductor. Thus, conductors used in house and shop wiring systems are rated for maximum current-carrying capacity in the National Electric Code, listed in Table 6-1.

When a long line is installed, a comparatively large current capacity is often selected to avoid excessive voltage drop across the line. Feeders

Table 6-1

CURRENT-CARRYING CAPACITIES OF COPPER WIRES

Size of wire	*Rubber insulation*	*Varnished cambric*	*Other insulation*
18	3 amps	—	6 amps
16	6	—	10
14	15	18	20
12	20	25	30
10	25	30	35
8	35	40	50
6	50	60	70
5	55	65	80
4	70	85	90
3	80	95	100

that supply power to lamps are chosen to maintain a voltage drop of less than 3 percent from input to output; this is necessary to realize reasonable efficiency. For example, a voltage drop of 10 percent would cause a tungsten lamp to radiate 30 percent less light, although its power consumption is reduced only 19 percent. On the other hand, if the load comprises motors or electric heaters, a line drop of 10 percent would be acceptable.

You may have wondered why electric power is supplied from power houses at surprisingly high voltages. This is done to economize in construction; the lines are long, and it is desirable to use the minimum weight of copper. Simple calculations will show that *if the power-line voltage is doubled, only one-fourth as much weight in copper is required for a given power loss in the line.* Hence, electric power is conducted to the load at high voltage; the voltage is then converted to a lower value for utilization by the load. We shall see that this conversion is accomplished at high efficiency by suitable devices which are explained subsequently.

6.5 TOTAL POWER DISSIPATION

Consider the power values in the series-parallel network shown in Figure 6-15. The 2-ohm resistance consumes 2 watts; the 7-ohm resistance consumes 7 watts; the 90-ohm resistance consumes 0.9 watt; the 10-ohm resistance consumes 8.1 watts. This is a total power consumption of 18 watts. The battery supplies $18 \times 1 = 18$ watts to the circuit. Total circuit resistance is 18 ohms; $I_T^2R_T = 18$ watts. Accordingly, we can add the individual power consumptions together, or we can multiply the square of the total current by the total resistance to find the total power consumption. Again, we can multiply the source emf by the total current to find the total power consumption.

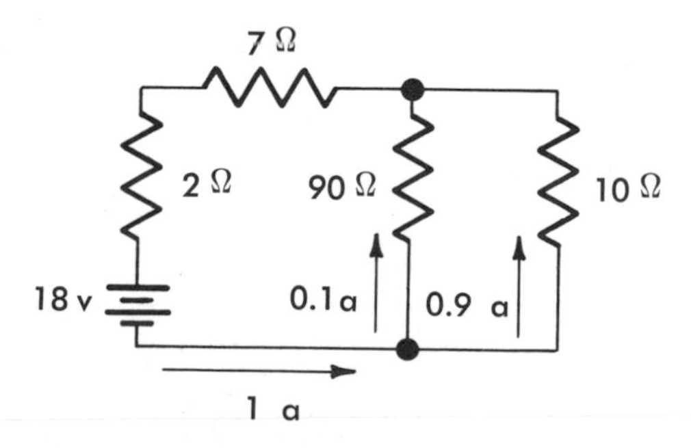

Figure 6-15
A series-parallel circuit for which the total power consumption is to be calculated.

6.6 CIRCUIT EFFICIENCY

What is the efficiency of the circuit depicted in Figure 6-15? This answer will depend upon which of the resistances represent loads. Suppose that the 2-ohm resistance is the battery's internal resistance; it does not consume useful power. Again, suppose that the 7-ohm resistance is line resistance; it does not consume useful power. But if the 90-ohm and 10-ohm resistances represent electrical appliances, their power consumption is useful. In this case, the power efficiency is equal to $9/18 = 0.5$ or 50 percent.

In another example, if the 10-ohm resistance is used as a bleeder, only the 90-ohm resistance represents a useful load. Here, the power efficiency becomes $0.9/18 = 0.05$, or 5 percent.

6.7 ANALYSIS OF CIRCUIT DEFECTS

We have learned that circuit defects often occur as short-circuits or open-circuited components. If a battery terminal in Figure 6-15 becomes open, no current is supplied to the circuit. On the other hand, if the 10-ohm resistor should burn out, its circuit is open but current continues to flow. The voltage across the 90-ohm resistance will increase from 9 volts to approximately 16.4 volts. Suppose that the 10-ohm resistance becomes short-circuited. The voltage across the 90-ohm resistance then falls to zero. A 2-amp current flows through the 7-ohm and 2-ohm resistances.

Accordingly, localization of faults in series-parallel circuits can be made on the basis of voltage measurements. Normal operating voltages are generally specified in electronic and electrical circuitry. When trouble occurs, we start by making voltage measurements at various circuit points. The measured voltages are compared with the specified operating voltages. Discrepancies are evaluated in terms of circuit analysis. In turn, the incorrect voltage readings guide us to the defective component.

SUMMARY OF FUNDAMENTAL CONCEPTS

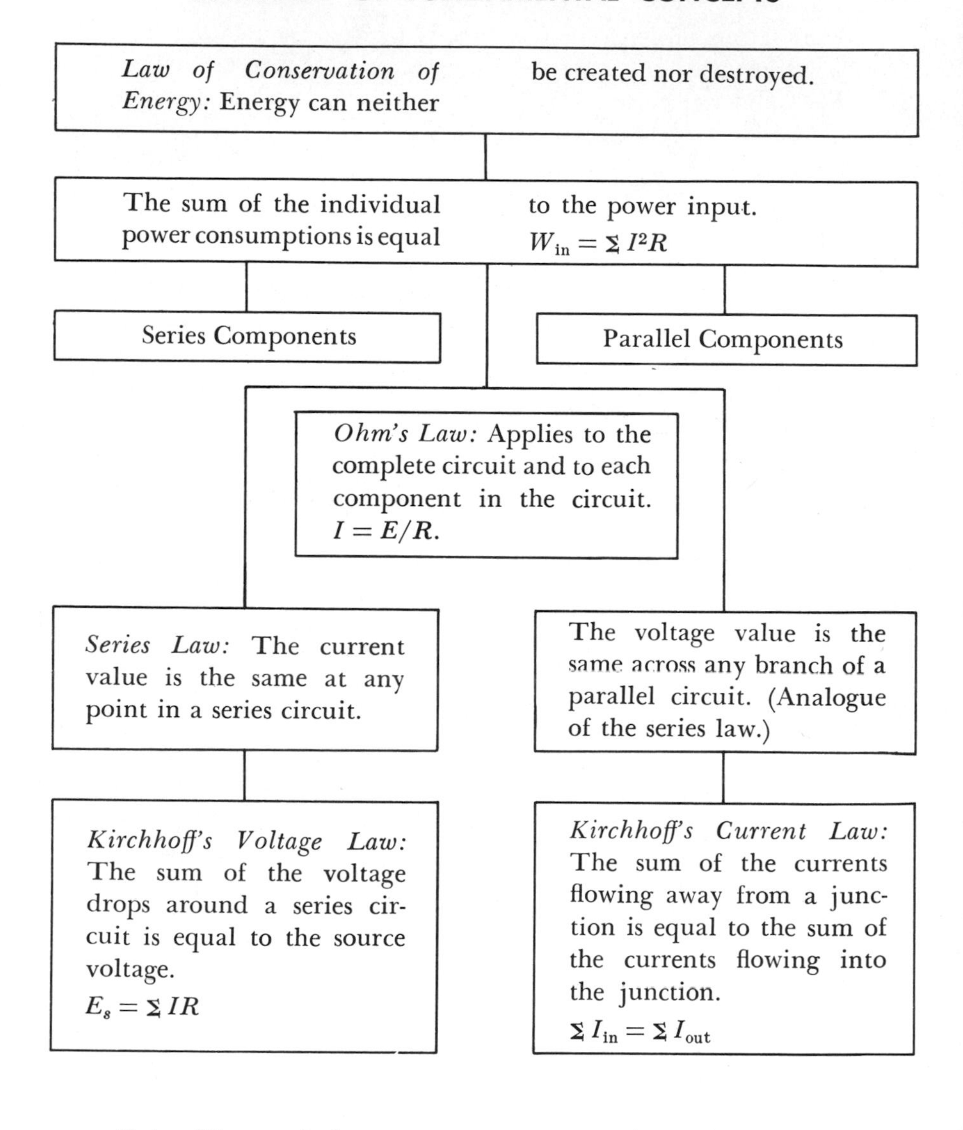

Law of Conservation of Energy: Energy can neither be created nor destroyed.
The sum of the individual power consumptions is equal to the power input. $W_{in} = \Sigma I^2R$
Series Components
Parallel Components
Ohm's Law: Applies to the complete circuit and to each component in the circuit. $I = E/R$.
Series Law: The current value is the same at any point in a series circuit.
The voltage value is the same across any branch of a parallel circuit. (Analogue of the series law.)
Kirchhoff's Voltage Law: The sum of the voltage drops around a series circuit is equal to the source voltage.
$E_s = \Sigma IR$
Kirchhoff's Current Law: The sum of the currents flowing away from a junction is equal to the sum of the currents flowing into the junction.
$\Sigma I_{in} = \Sigma I_{out}$

Notes: W_{in} equals the power input. I equals an individual current. R equals an individual resistance through which the individual current flows. E_s equals the source voltage. I_{in} equals an individual current flowing into a junction. I_{out} equals an individual current flowing away from a junction.

QUESTIONS

1) Two or more resistors connected in parallel are often called:
(*a*) an assembly. (*b*) a complex. (*c*) a bank. (*d*) a string.
2) Two or more resistors connected in series are often called:
(*a*) a chain. (*b*) an array. (*c*) a column. (*d*) a string.
3) Analysis of series-parallel circuits often requires that a bank be reduced to:
(*a*) an equivalent voltage source. (*b*) an equivalent series circuit. (*c*) an equivalent parallel circuit. (*d*) an equivalent current source.
4) An *L* section is the same as:
(*a*) a series resistance connected to a shunt resistance. (*b*) a bank. (*c*) a string. (*d*) the branch current multiplied by the source resistance.
5) A ladder consists of:
a) two or more strings connected in parallel. (*b*) two or more banks connected in parallel. (*c*) two or more branches connected in series. (*d*) two or more *L* sections connected in series.
6) The term *negative resistance* implies that:
(*a*) the current doubles when the voltage is doubled. (*b*) the voltage doubles when the current is doubled. (*c*) the current is halved when the voltage is doubled. (*d*) The voltage is halved when the current is halved.
7) A resistance bridge comprises:
(*a*) an ohmmeter connected across a load resistor. (*b*) two series resistors connected in parallel with two other series resistors. (*c*) two series resistors connected in parallel with another resistor. (*d*) two parallel resistors connected in series with another resistor.
8) If a voltage source has significant internal resistance, a parallel circuit to which the source is connected must be analyzed as:
(*a*) a series-parallel circuit. (*b*) a resistance ladder. (*c*) an open circuit. (*d*) a negative resistance.
9) If a line has significant resistance, a parallel circuit to which the line is connected must be analyzed as:
(*a*) a bank. (*b*) a string. (*c*) a series-parallel circuit. (*d*) a resistance ladder.
10) The total power dissipation in a series-parallel circuit is equal to:
(*a*) the bank power minus the string power. (*b*) the string power minus the bank power. (*c*) the string power plus the product of the branch powers divided by their sum. (*d*) the sum of all the individual power dissipation values.

PROBLEMS

1) Refer to Figure 6-1(*a*). In this circuit, let $R_1 = 350$ ohms, $R_2 = 500$ ohms, and $R_3 = 900$ ohms. If the voltage drop across R_3 measures 90 volts, what is the value of E?
2) Refer to Figure 6-1(*b*). Let $R_1 = 100$ ohms, $R_2 = 200$ ohms, and $R_3 = 300$ ohms. If the voltage across R_3 measures 30 volts, what is the value of E?
3) Refer to Figure 6-6. Let $R_1 = 8100$ ohms and $R_2 = 1000$ ohms. What is the value of R_{in}?
4) Refer to Figure 6-9. If all values are as specified, except that $E = 39$ volts, calculate I_T, R_2, V_1, I_3, R_3, and V_P.
5) How much power is supplied by the battery in Problem 4?
6) How much power is dissipated by R_1, by R_2, and by R_3 in Problem 4?
7) If R_2 should become open-circuited (Problem 4), what is the increase in V_P?
8) Refer to Figure 6-10. If $R_1 = 10$ ohms, $R_4 = 50$ ohms, $R_2 = 25$ ohms, and the galvanometer indicates zero, what is the value of R_3?
9) What current does the battery supply in Problem 8?
10) Which resistor dissipates the most power in Problem 8? Which resistor dissipates the least power?
11) If each resistor in Problem 8 is rated for a maximum power dissipation of ¼ watt, what is the maximum voltage that may be applied to the bridge?
12) Refer to Figure 6-11. If the calibrated variable resistor has a maximum power rating of 2 watts, what is the minimum value of R_x that may be measured?
13) Refer to Figure 6-13(*a*). If the storage battery has a terminal voltage of 12 volts, how much voltage is applied across the parallel combination? If the No. 14 wire is replaced by No. 30 wire, how much voltage will be applied across the parallel combination?
14) How much power is dissipated in the No. 30 wire in Problem 13? How much power is consumed by the parallel-combination load?
15) What is the efficiency of the system in Problem 14 when No. 14 wire is used? What is the efficiency when No. 30 wire is used?

7

PRINCIPLES OF MAGNETISM

7.1 MAGNETISM AND ACTION AT A DISTANCE

Magnetism is a property of the molecules of certain substances, such as iron, which exerts force upon various substances at a distance. If different metals, for example, are brought near a source of magnetism, certain metals are found to be attracted strongly. Iron, nickel, and cobalt are among the metals that are strongly attracted to a source of magnetism. This characteristic of magnetism is widely known, and many laymen suppose that there are no other characteristics of magnetism; however, this supposition is soon dispelled when one starts to delve into magnetic phenomena.

It might be supposed that a magnet exerts no force upon a piece of aluminum. This belief stems from the weak attraction of aluminum by a source of magnetism. If an aluminum object is brought near a pole of a very strong magnet, it is found that a force of attraction indeed exists. Aluminum, chromium, and manganese are typical metals that are attracted weakly. Hence, we classify iron, nickel, and cobalt as *ferromagnetic* substances; this term implies that such metals are strongly attracted by a magnet. On the other hand, we classify aluminum, chromium, and manganese as *paramagnetic* substances; when used in this sense, paramagnetic implies that such metals are weakly attracted by a magnet. However, we find that the term paramagnetic is also used in a generic sense; in this particular context it implies that the substance is attracted by a magnet, although the attractive force might be very strong or very weak.

It is perhaps surprising to discover that there is a class of substances that is not attracted by a magnet, but is repelled weakly. Copper, silver, and bismuth are feebly repelled when brought near the pole of a strong magnet. This class of substances is termed *diamagnetic*. Both paramagnetism and diamagnetism are properties of the molecules in various substances. These properties will seem less mysterious as we proceed with our analysis of magnetism.

When substances having strong magnetic activity are heated above a certain temperature, called the *Curie point,* they change into feebly magnetic substances. For example, when iron is heated to 785°C, it ceases to be ferromagnetic, though it remains slightly magnetic. The Curie point for lodestone is 535°C. We have seen that magnets such as lodestones are classed as *permanent magnets.* On the other hand, it was noted in Chapter 1 that a bar of soft iron becomes a magnet when electric current flows in a wire around the bar. The soft iron remains a magnet only while the current flows. As soon as the current stops, the soft iron loses nearly all of its magnetism. This type of magnet is called an *electromagnet.* If we make the same experiment with a bar of hard steel, we find that the bar retains most of its magnetism after the current flow stops. The bar has become a permanent magnet.

The only known entity that is neither attracted nor repelled by a magnet is empty space, or a *vacuum.* It is perhaps surprising to learn that air is attracted by a magnet, although it must be noted that this attraction is extremely weak. The magnetic force that is exerted in any case is inversely proportional to the *permeability* of a substance. Since a vacuum is the dividing medium between paramagnetic and diamagnetic substances, a vacuum has a permeability of unity (1). Air has a slightly greater permeability than a vacuum; it has a permeability of 1.0000004. Any substance that has a permeability greater than unity is paramagnetic; any substance that has a permeability less than unity is diamagnetic.

METHODS OF MAGNETIZATION

Because a bar of hard steel retains magnetism, we say that it has high *retentivity.* By comparison, soft iron has very low retentivity. It has long been known that substances that have high retentivity can be magnetized by four chief methods:

1. A lodestone or other permanent magnet can be brought into contact with the high-retentivity substance; or, the substance can be stroked by the source of magnetism. It is thereby formed into a permanent magnet.

2. If you pound a high-retentivity substance with a hammer while the substance is placed in the direction of the earth's magnetic field, it becomes a permanent magnet.

3. A high-retentivity substance can be heated and subsequently cooled while it is placed in the direction of the earth's magnetic field. The substance is thereby formed into a permanent magnet.

4. You can pass electric current through a wire around a high-retentivity substance, and it will become a permanent magnet, as noted previously.

A permanent magnet is conventionally represented as seen in Figure 7-1. We recall Coulomb's law, which states that the force, acting between two charged bodies, is directly proportional to the product of the charges and inversely proportional to the square of the distance between them. A similar law states the force between two magnetic poles:

$$F = \frac{m_1 m_2}{\mu d^2} \tag{7.1}$$

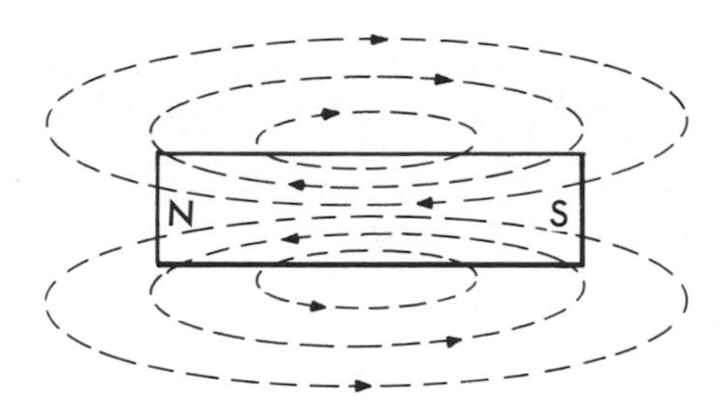

Figure 7-1
Conventional representation of the magnetic field for a bar-type permanent magnet.

where m_1 and m_2 are the magnetic pole strengths, d is the distance between the poles, and μ is the permeability of the medium between the poles.

Since the permeability of air is practically 1, μ can be disregarded whenever a magnet is surrounded by air (μ is equal to 1.0000004 for air). To conveniently visualize Equation (7.1), it is customary to say that a magnet contains and is enveloped by a magnetic *field*. This field is represented by the curved lines in Figure 7-1. The complete system of lines is called the magnetic *flux*, represented by the symbol ϕ. An individual line is called a *line of magnetic induction*, or simply a line of force. Each line represents one flux unit. The number of lines per unit of the cross-sectional area is called the *flux density*, represented by the symbol B. Note that lines of magnetic flux are said to pass through a magnet from its south pole to its north pole. The lines leave the magnet at its north pole and re-enter at its south pole. Each line is continuous and cannot be broken.

Observe how the lines of force spread out in Figure 7-1. It is considered that each line repels its neighbors. A line can expand or contract. For example, if a permanent magnet is demagnetized, as by heating, the lines of force contract to a point and disappear. If a piece of iron is placed near a permanent magnet, the lines of force change shape and become distorted. However, each distorted loop remains a closed figure. Magnetic lines of force can be brought nearer together or farther apart, but they can never cross. The lines will pass through any substance; hence, there is no known insulator for magnetic lines of force.

A demonstration that bolsters the assumption of magnetic flux lines is seen in Figure 7-2. If you place a sheet of cardboard over a bar magnet and sprinkle iron filings over the cardboard, the filings arrange themselves in a manner that suggests a conventionalized flux field. The pattern becomes more distinct if you tap the cardboard gently as the filings are sprinkled. When two magnetic fields aid each other, the flux field appears

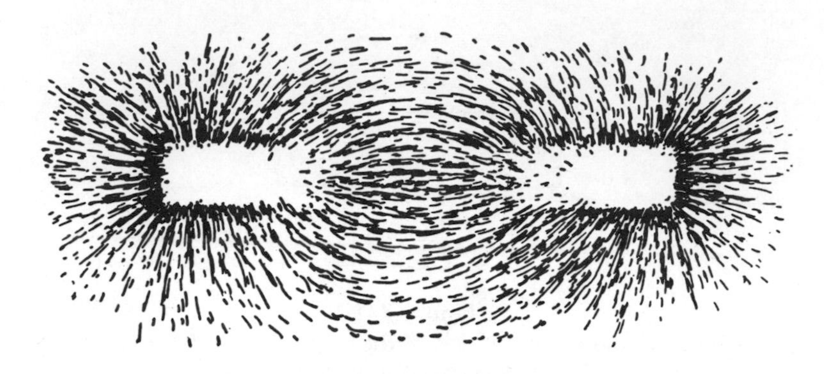

Figure 7-2
A pattern formed by iron filings suggests the assumption of magnetic flux lines.

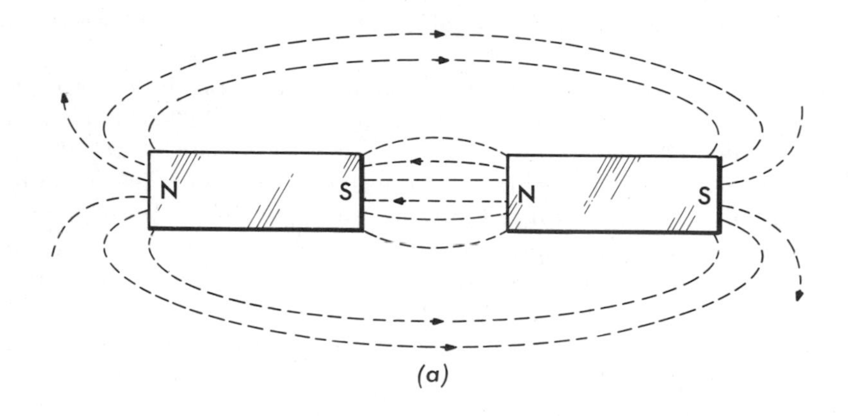

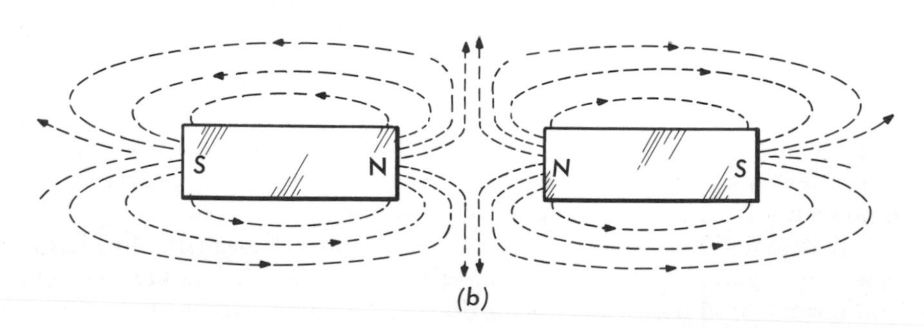

Figure 7-3
(*a*) Magnetic fields aiding. (*b*) Magnetic fields opposing.

as depicted in Figure 7-3(*a*). However, when two fields oppose, the flux field appears as in Figure 7-3(*b*). Note that the magnets attract each other when their fields aid, but repel each other when their fields oppose.

7.2 THE DIPOLE PRINCIPLE

Single magnetic poles do not exist. A north pole is always associated with a south pole. This means that if you cut or break a permanent magnet into two or more pieces, each piece will have a north and a south pole. If you cut a bar magnet exactly in half, for example, the smaller magnets will each have one-half the strength of the original magnet. But if you cut only a small section off the north pole of a bar magnet, the small section will have much less field strength than the larger section. A magnetic substance is visualized in Figure 7-4(*a*). It is considered to consist of a very large number of elementary bar magnets disposed at random. In this state, the substance has no external magnetic field. When the substance is magnetized, the elementary magnets line up with one another, and establish north and south poles associated with an external magnetic field.

What is the physical basis of the elementary dipoles depicted in Figure 7-4? This is explained by *Weber's theory*, which states that each atom is a magnet with a north and a south pole. We recall that electrons revolve in orbits about the nucleus of an atom. Compare this concept with the construction of an electromagnet (Figure 7-5). When current flows in the wire around the soft iron bar, an external magnetic field is established.

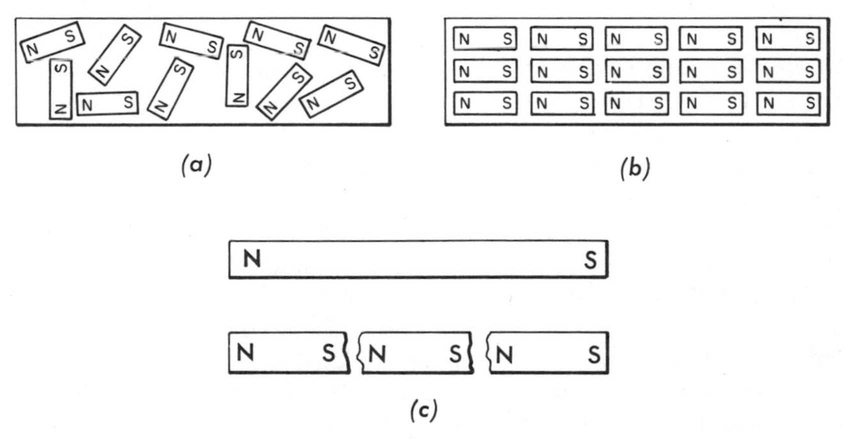

Figure 7-4
(*a*) Elementary dipoles distributed at random. (*b*) Elementary dipoles lined up.

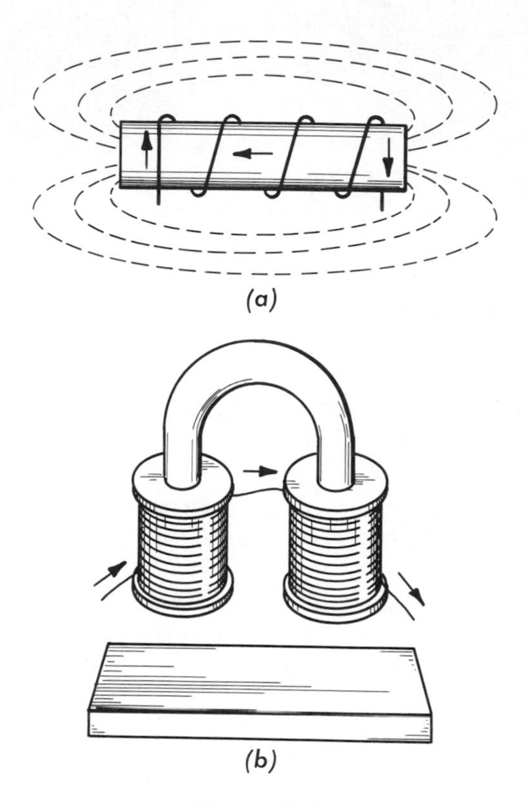

Figure 7-5
(a) Basic construction of an electromagnet. *(b)* Simple horseshoe electromagnet with soft-iron armature.

An electric current consists of electrons in motion. Hence, it is evident that an electron, revolving in an orbit about the nucleus of an atom, must establish a magnetic field.

There is no magnetism without moving electric charges (electric current). In strongly magnetic substances, it is believed that the electrons orbit about the nucleus of each atom in the same general direction. In weakly magnetic substances, however, we consider that roughly one-half of the electrons orbit about the nucleus of each atom in one direction, and that the remainder of the electrons orbit in the opposite direction. This is the physical basis for the dipoles depicted in Figure 7-4.

It is easy to see how the atomic dipoles line up in a paramagnetic substance when it is magnetized. On the other hand, how are we to visualize the behavior of atomic dipoles in a diamagnetic substance, when it is being repelled by a magnetic field? Theory hypothesizes that atomic dipoles in a diamagnetic substance line up in *opposition* to the applied magnetic field. This is possible due to the *gyroscopic* characteristic of rotating electrons. Without going into the theory of gyroscopes, let us merely note that this action opposes magnetization in all substances. However, gyroscopic action in iron, for example, is not the dominant factor in the lining up of atomic dipoles. Yet, gyroscopic action in copper is a dominant factor causing the average line-up of the atomic dipoles to oppose the magnetizing field. Hence, copper is weakly repelled by a strong magnetic field.

Since the atomic dipoles reorient themselves when a substance is magnetized, it is not surprising to find that an iron bar changes slightly in length when placed in a magnetic field. When partially magnetized, it increases very slightly in length. As the bar is more strongly magnetized,

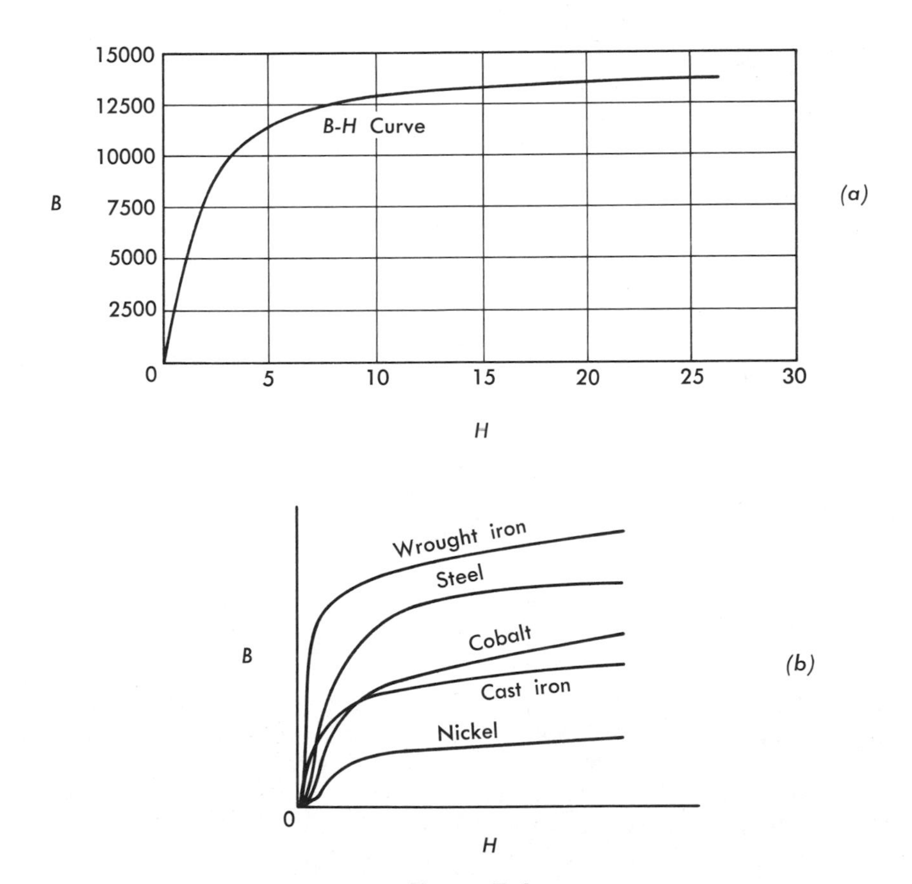

Figure 7-6
(a) A typical *B-H* curve for iron. *(b)* Comparative *B-H* curves.

it returns to its original length. Finally, when it is very strongly magnetized, it becomes very slightly shorter than originally. This change in length with magnetization is called *magnetostriction.* There is a limit to the amount of magnetism which a substance can acquire. When the current flow is increased in an electromagnet, its field strength increases as seen in Figure 7-6. As its field strength approaches an upper limit, the core material is said to become *saturated.*

7.3 FLUX DENSITY VERSUS MAGNETIZING FORCE

Let us analyze the *B-H* curve depicted in Figure 7-6. First, we recall that a wire is surrounded by a magnetic field while it conducts electric

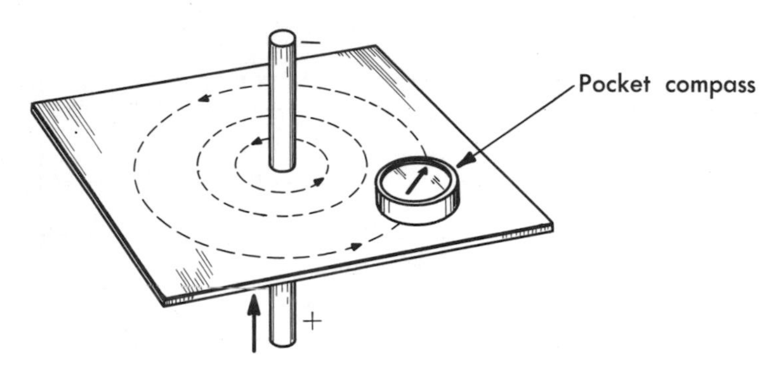

Figure 7-7
Lines of magnetic flux encircle a current-carrying conductor.

current. If you explore the space around a current-carrying conductor with an ordinary compass, you will observe that the compass indicates the presence of a magnetic field. The lines of magnetic induction are found to encircle the conductor. Note that the current flow through the conductor in Figure 7-7 is indicated opposite to electron flow. In other words, the current is shown flowing from positive to negative. This is the direction of *conventional current flow.*

You will often encounter such representations of conventional current flow. This would seem to be unnecessary, since we know that electrons always flow from negative to positive. However, this convention has a historical background. Before the electron was discovered, scientists had to guess at the direction of current flow in a wire. Benjamin Franklin, for example, supposed that current flowed from positive to negative terminals of a wire. Hence, a vast literature accumulated in which conventional current flow was assumed. After discovery of the electron, this convention

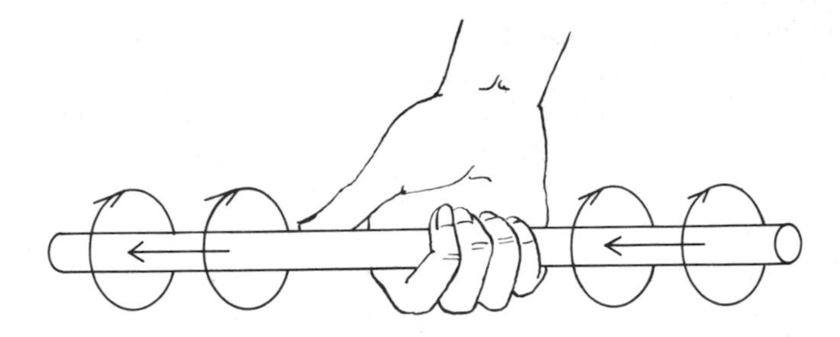

Figure 7-8
The right-hand thumb rule for conventional current flow.

persisted in many areas of electrical theory. In fact, it still persists to some extent today, particularly in the literature of electromagnetism.

There need be no confusion in the reader's mind, if he clearly determines at the outset of a discussion whether conventional current flow or electron flow has been assumed. Observe the right-hand thumb rule depicted in Figure 7-8. Conventional current flow is assumed. If your thumb points in the direction of conventional current flow, your fingers indicate

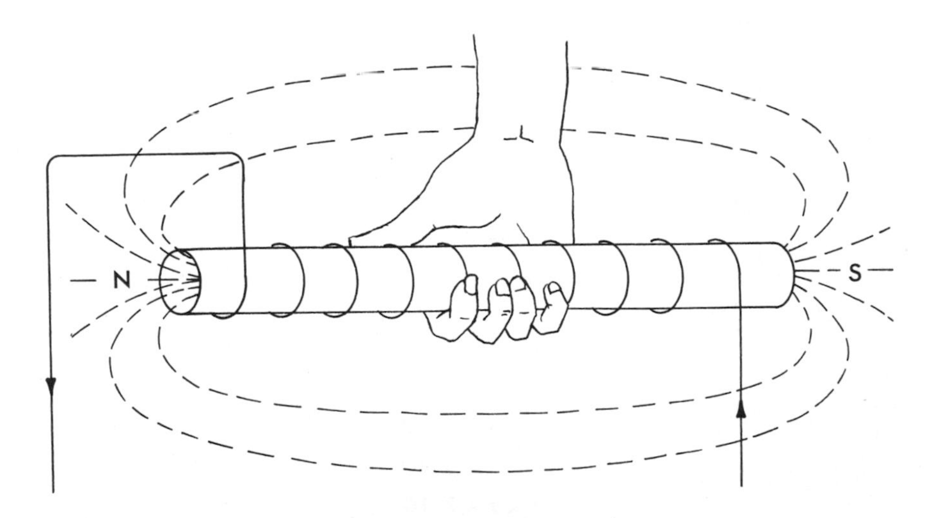

Figure 7-9
The right-hand rule for an electromagnetic assumes conventional current flow.

the direction of the flux lines. If you assume electron flow in the wire, you would then have to use a left-hand thumb rule to determine the direction of the magnetic flux lines.

Note the right-hand rule for an electromagnet, shown in Figure 7-9. Conventional current flow is assumed. If your fingers indicate the direction of conventional current flow in the coil, your thumb then points to the north pole of the electromagnet. If you should assume electron flow in the wire, you would then have to use a left-hand rule to determine the north pole of the electromagnet.

Although current flow in a single wire deflects a compass needle as shown in Figure 7-7, the magnetic field is comparatively weak. On the other hand, if the wire is formed into a loop, as depicted in Figure 7-10, the flux lines are no longer circular. They become more crowded as they pass through the loop of wire; outside of the loop, the flux lines become less crowded. For this reason, the magnetic field intensity is greater inside the wire loop than it is outside. This simply means that there are more

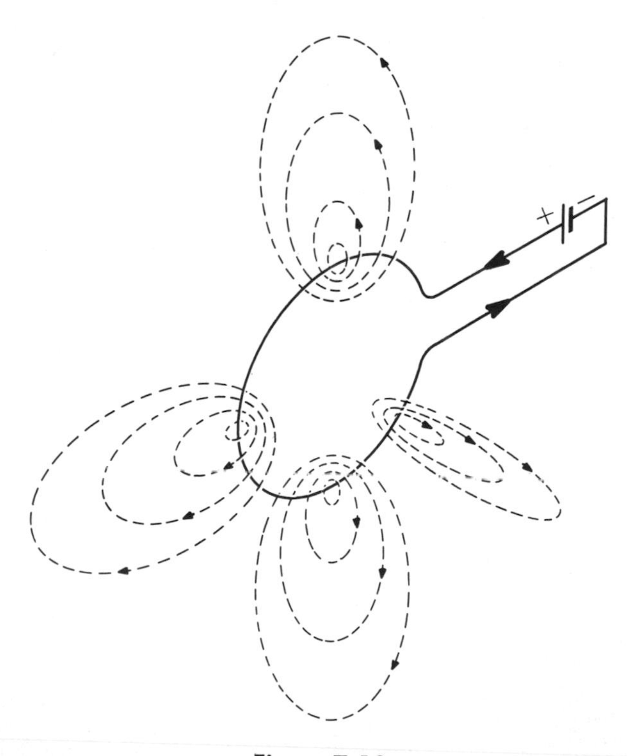

Figure 7-10
Magnetic flux-line distribution for a circular conductor with conventional current flow.

flux lines per unit of cross-sectional area where they are crowded together inside the loop.

When the electrical circuit consists of a number of turns of wire, as depicted in Figure 7-9, the magnetic field intensity is multiplied by the number of turns. Observe that the magnetic field produced by current flow in a coil of wire has the same pattern as the magnetic field of a permanent bar magnet, or lodestone. We learned that the permeability of iron is much greater than the permeability of air. Hence, it comes as no surprise to find that the magnetic field intensity is greatly increased if you insert an iron core into a current-carrying coil. If you insert a copper core into a current-carrying coil, however, the magnetic field intensity is not increased; instead, it is very slightly decreased below the magnetic field intensity of an air-core coil.

AIR CANNOT BE MAGNETICALLY SATURATED

In theory, there is no limit to the magnetic field intensity that can be produced by an air-core electromagnet. That is, if you increase the current flow through the coil, the magnetic field intensity increases in direct proportion. Of course, we know that excessive current flow will burn out a coil. However, if a coil is water-cooled, much more current can be passed through the coil and much stronger magnetic fields produced. Note carefully that air does not saturate at high magnetic field intensities. In this respect, air is basically different from iron.

An air-core coil can be constructed which is quite long compared to its diameter. If the coil has 1 turn per cm of length, and the current flow is 1 amp, the magnetic field intensity *inside* the coil is given by

$$H = \frac{NI}{L} \tag{7.2}$$

where H is the magnetic field intensity in *ampere-turns per meter*, N is the number of turns in the coil, I is the number of amperes current flow, and L is the length of the coil expressed in meters.

Note that Equation (7.2) does not contain the diameter of the coil; the magnetic field intensity inside of the coil does not depend upon its diameter. The field intensity H is the force that produces magnetic flux in each unit length of the space inside the coil; or, H is the *magnetomotive force* per unit length of the coil. The *total* magnetomotive force developed by a coil is expressed by

$$MMF = NI \tag{7.3}$$

where the MMF is defined as the number of ampere-turns. One amp flowing in 1 turn gives 1 amp-turn; 2 amps flowing in 1 turn gives 2 amp-turns.

We know now that if we insert an iron bar into the air-core coil, the number of lines of magnetic induction is greatly increased. In other words, the flux density (number of lines per unit cross-section of the core) is much greater for an iron core than for an air core, with the same number of ampere-turns. We say that when the iron core is placed in the coil, the *reluctance* is less inside the coil. A lower reluctance permits the magnetomotive force to produce many more flux lines. This is just another way of stating that the permeability of iron is greater than the permeability of air.

Thus, we can express the amount of magnetic flux per unit cross-section of the core by the equation

$$\frac{\phi}{A} = H\mu \tag{7.4}$$

where ϕ is the number of flux lines in the core, A is the cross-sectional area of the core in square meters, H is the number of ampere-turns per meter of coil length, and μ is the permeability of the core material with respect to air.

Since the number of flux lines per unit cross-sectional area is equal to B, we may also write

$$B = H\mu \tag{7.5}$$

IRON IS SUBJECT TO MAGNETIC SATURATION

Permeability is analogous to electric conductivity. Note that we found that a lamp filament does not have a constant conductivity; its conductivity becomes less as the current flow is substantially increased. In much the same way, we find that the permeability of iron depends upon the number of flux lines passing through the iron. Recall that an iron core saturates according to the graph in Figure 7-6. This curve is merely typical. Different samples of iron will have different *B-H* curves. When an iron core is completely saturated, its permeability becomes unity, or the same as the permeability of air. Thus, you can remove a completely saturated iron core from an electromagnet and B will be unchanged.

The form of a *B H* curve shows how μ changes with H. Suppose we check the value $H = 5$ in Figure 7-6. When H is equal to 5, we know that an air-core coil will have a magnetic field intensity of 5 amp-turns per meter, and that B will be equal to 5 lines per sq meter in accordance with Equation (7.5). Next, let us place an iron core in the coil. H remains the same; but, according to the graph in Figure 7-6, B then becomes 11,250 lines per sq meter. To put it another way, this iron core has a permeability of 11,250/5 or 2250 when H is equal to 5. Now let us increase H to 25 (Figure 7-6). The same iron core has a permeability of 13,750/25 or 550 when H is equal to 25. It is obvious that when we increase H to complete saturation, the permeability of the iron core will decrease down to unity.

The shape of a *B-H* curve depends upon whether we use steel, cast iron, or wrought iron for the core material. It also depends upon the chemical purity of the iron. Permeability depends upon the heat treatment that has been used in fabricating the core material. Various alloys have greater permeability than iron. For example, Alnico is an alloy of aluminum, nickel, iron, cobalt, copper, and titanium. This alloy is used to make strong permanent magnets. The permeability of any iron or magnetic alloy also depends to some extent upon whether the core material has any *residual magnetism.*

7.4 HYSTERESIS AND B-H CURVES

Before an iron core is magnetized, it has no magnetic field. When it is first magnetized, the flux density increases along the curve *ab* in Figure 7-11. If you decrease the current in the coil of the electromagnet, the flux

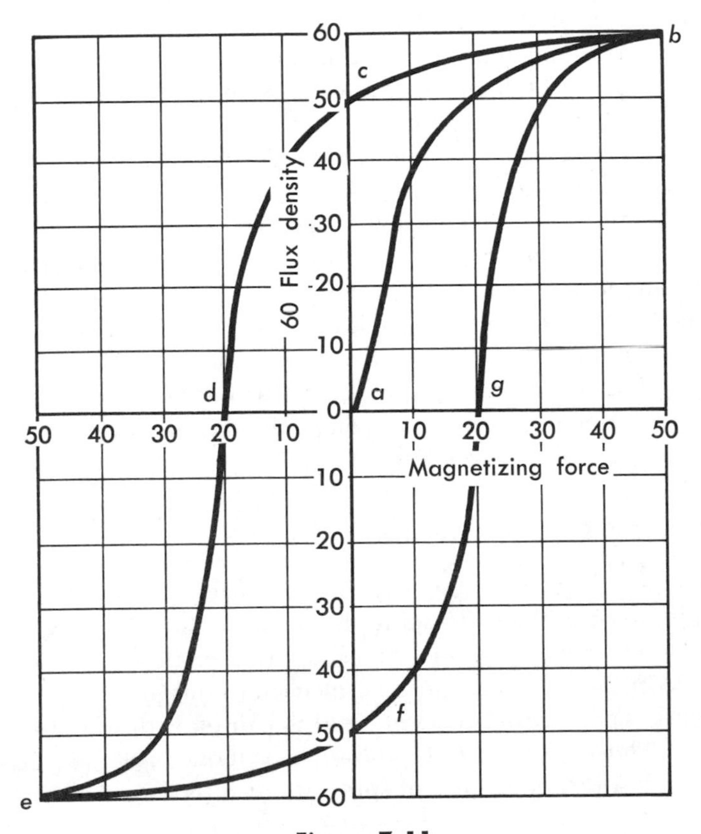

Figure 7-11
A typical hysteresis loop.

density does *not* decrease along the curve *ba*. Instead, the flux density decreases less rapidly along the curve *bc*. The magnetomotive force is zero when you reach point *c*, but note that the flux density is 50,000 lines per unit area. This flux, which remains in the iron core after the current in the coil is reduced to zero, is called *residual magnetism*.

What is the physical basis of residual magnetism? Reorientation of the atomic dipoles is opposed by a form of friction in the core material, causing heat to be generated. This friction also prevents the iron atoms from returning to their initial positions after the magnetomotive force has been reduced back to zero. Consequently, the iron remains magnetized to some extent. At point *d* in Figure 7-11, the residual magnetism has been reduced to zero; this requires a *reversal* of the magnetomotive force to a value of 20 amp-turns.

As this magnetomotive force is further increased, the flux density builds up along curve *de*. For equal but opposite magnetomotive forces, we see that the flux density is the same at points *e* and *b*. If the coil current is again reduced to zero, the flux density will decrease along curve *ef* and again reaches 50,000 lines per unit area at zero current flow. To bring the flux to zero, you must apply a magnetomotive force *ag*; the flux density then decreases along the curve *fg*. Note that this is again a magnetomotive force of 20 amp-turns.

Application of further magnetomotive force increases the flux density along curve *gb*, and the *hysteresis loop* is then closed. This hysteresis loop encloses an area that is bounded by the path *bcdefgb*. Once you have established residual magnetism in an iron core, the path of operation is always around the hysteresis loop. To get back on curve *ab*, you must completely demagnetize the core; this could be done by violent jarring of the core material. Note that the *area* of the hysteresis loop bounded by the path *bcdefgb* is proportional to the heat that has been generated in the core by work done in traversing the loop. In other words, the area of the hysteresis loop defines the *core loss*.

7.5 MAGNETIC CORE MATERIALS

Magnetism is basically an electronic characteristic. An electron spins on its axis, much as the earth spins on its axis. A spinning electron is an elementary permanent magnet that has a strength equal to 1 Bohr *magneton*. In most substances, these elementary magnets largely nullify one another. The electrons in atoms tend to pair off with spins in opposite directions. Thus, an atom can exhibit an external magnetic field only when there is a preponderance of spins in one direction. This is the case when an atom has an odd number of electrons, and also when a group of electrons do not pair off in opposite directions, but all spin in the same direction.

Figure 7-12 depicts the structure of an iron atom. The third shell comprises a *subshell,* in which most of the electrons spin in the same direction. Note that five of the six electrons in the subshell spin in the same direction; only one electron spins in the opposite direction. Thus, the subshell has a net magnetism of 4 Bohr magnetons. Magnetons must be aligned in aiding orientation; otherwise, an external field will not be

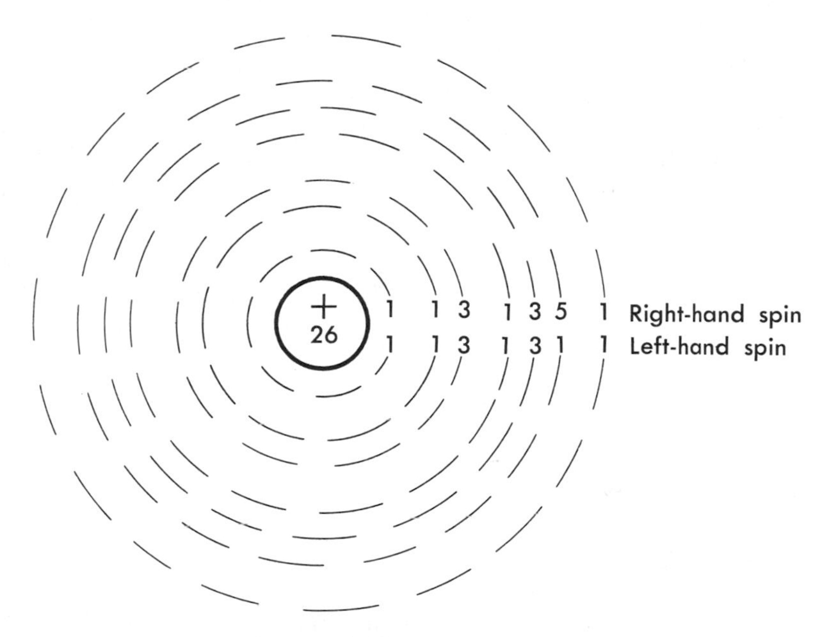

Figure 7-12
An iron atom has 26 orbiting electrons.

produced by the electrons which are spinning in the same direction. Their axes of spin tend to be reoriented from one moment to the next by the thermal vibrations of the iron atoms in the crystal lattice.

Ferromagnetic substances have an electron orienting force which is greater than the disorienting forces of thermal agitation. When atoms in a crystal are spaced within certain limits of distance, an interatomic mechanical force called the *exchange force* is sufficiently great to overcome the disordering thermal forces and thereby line up the axes of electron spin. We recall that when iron is heated to a certain temperature (1420°F), it is no longer ferromagnetic.

MAGNETIC DOMAINS

A ferromagnetic substance must be magnetized before it becomes a magnet. For example, a lodestone is not a magnet when it is first formed from its elements. After a lodestone has been subjected to a magnetic field from a lightning stroke, or after it has been mechanically jarred in the earth's magnetic field, the lodestone becomes a magnet. Hence, ferromagnetic substances do not become magnets spontaneously in consequence of atomic and crystal structure. It has been shown experimentally that there are structural units in a ferromagnetic crystal, called *domains*. Such domains are depicted in Figure 7-13.

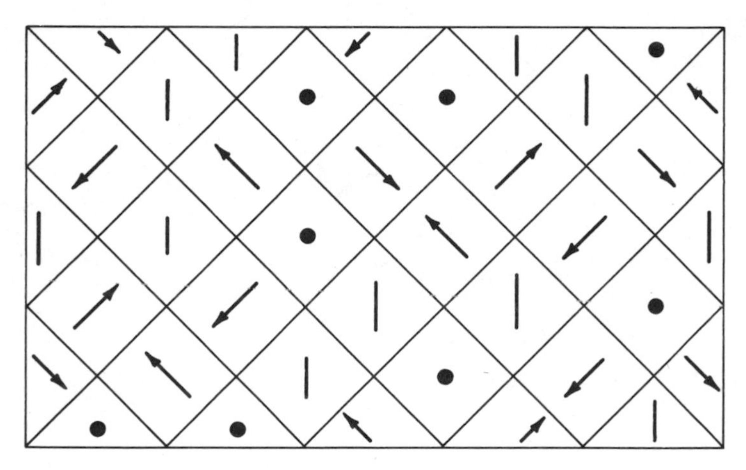

Figure 7-13
Diagrammatic representation of domains in a ferromagnetic crystal.

Domains are subcrystalline particles that consist of approximately 10^{15} atoms. A domain has a volume of approximately 10^{-9} cu cm; the shape is irregular and varies considerably from one part of the crystal lattice to another. The domains in iron and other ferromagnetic substances are oriented at random when the crystal is first formed. An external magnetic field must be applied to line up the domains in the same direction. We recall that iron filings sprinkled over a permanent magnet form a pattern that depicts the magnetic field. In similar fashion, when extremely small particles of iron oxide are deposited on a ferromagnetic substance, they form patterns that depict the domains of the substance.

Scientists have found that domains are separated by "walls" that are simply transition regions in which magneton orientation changes gradually from one domain to the next. When an external magnetic field is applied, the magneton orientation in domains and walls is shifted in accordance with the direction of the applied field. The question may be asked why ferromagnetic crystals form with their domains originally oriented in random directions. The answer is that crystal structures obey a law, called the *principle of least energy*. Stated otherwise, natural forces come to equilibrium in a state requiring the least energy; this is the condition of maximum *stability*.

Physical analysis has proved that an iron crystal, for example, obeys the principle of least energy and achieves maximum stability by forming the structural units called domains. We know that an iron bar increases in length very slightly when it is partially magnetized, and that work must be done (energy expended) to overcome the opposition of magnetostriction. Consequently, a partially magnetized condition is not a condition of least energy and maximum stability. It is for this same basic reason that a permanent magnet gradually loses its magnetism, although the loss may occur at a very slow rate.

Let us consider the modern powder magnets. Powder magnets are fabricated from extremely small particles approximately one-millionth of an inch in diameter. These particles form single domains because they are smaller than the wall thickness between domains in an iron crystal, for example. When domains are formed without walls, a much stronger external field must be applied to orient the magnetons of a domain in the same direction. But this opposition is also a factor in the formation of a powerful permanent magnet.

However, the strongest permanent magnets are alloys in which the fine particles are formed automatically as the alloy crystallizes out of molten solution. When an alloy is made of suitable amounts of iron, cobalt, nickel, aluminum, and copper, extremely small domains are formed. These domains are separated by thin films in which the crystal composition differs.

Ferrites are oxides of iron and other metals that have useful magnetic properties. Ferrites provide powerful magnets and they also have unusually high electrical resistivity. We shall find in the following chapters that high resistivity is needed in various applications to minimize a certain type of core loss. The resistivity of ferrites is over a million times greater than any other known magnetic material. Ferrite magnets are fabricated by grinding the oxides to an extremely fine powder, which is then pressed into a desired shape and heated to a very high temperature.

7.6 AGING OF PERMANENT MAGNETS; AIR GAPS AND KEEPERS

We recall that a permanent magnet tends to gradually lose its strength. Some ferromagnetic substances lose their magnetism at an extremely slow rate, and are preferred for the fabrication of high-quality

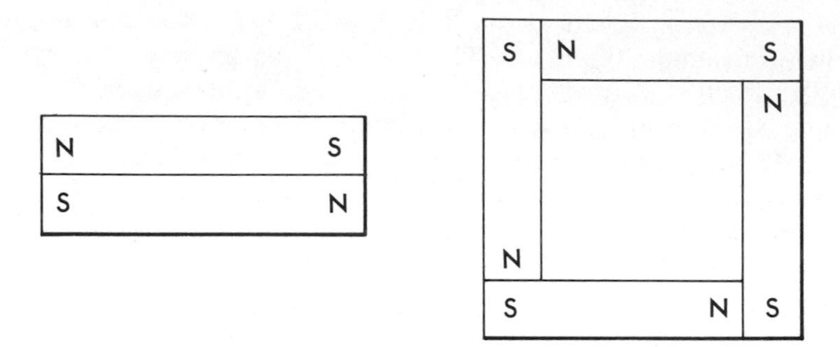

Figure 7-14
Two ways in which bar magnets can be grouped to minimize their external fields.

permanent magnets. Even the best permanent magnets must be artificially aged to minimize the rate of deterioration. This entails initial magnetization to saturation. Next, a certain fraction of the magnetic field strength is sacrificed by suitable treatment. For example, the permanent magnet may be placed in a liquid and boiled at a suitable temperature for a specified length of time. The magnet is then said to be *aged*.

Although an aged permanent magnet has maximum stability, care must still be taken to avoid subjecting the magnet to mechanical shock or excessive vibration. Obviously, when a number of permanent magnets are stored, they should be arranged so that the field of one magnet does not tend to demagnetize its neighbor. All permanent magnets have air gaps from which the flux spreads out into surrounding space. A bar magnet has a maximum air gap. If bar magnets are packed as shown in Figure 7-14,

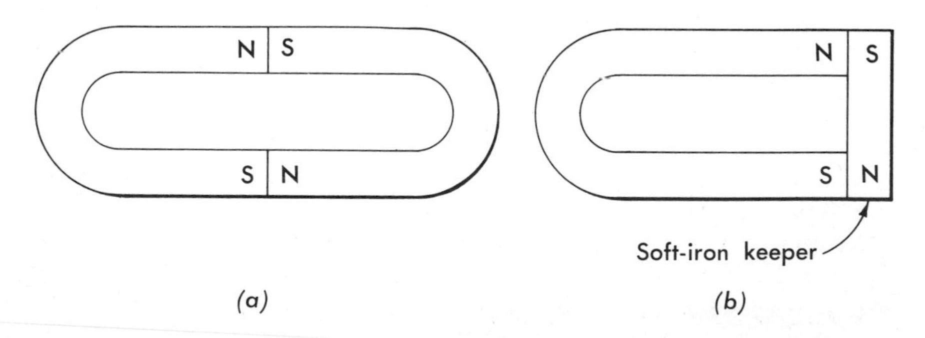

Figure 7-15
(a) Arrangement to minimize the external field. *(b)* A soft-iron keeper minimizes the external field.

the external field is minimized. Hence, each assembly has very little tendency to demagnetize a neighbor assembly. Note that if two magnets were placed with *like* poles together, they would tend to demagnetize each other.

Horseshoe magnets can be arranged as shown in Figure 7-15(*a*). This is basically the same method as depicted in Figure 7-14. In these arrangements, the air gap is effectively reduced to zero, because iron has a much higher permeability than air. Another common method of minimizing the

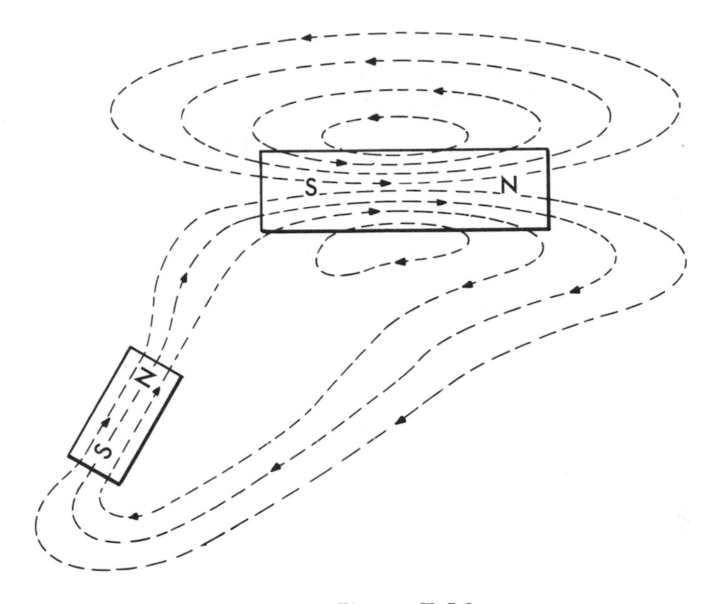

Figure 7-16
A small piece of soft iron, magnetized by induction in the field of a permanent magnet.

external field of a horseshoe magnet is seen in Figure 7-15(*b*). Here, a soft-iron *keeper* is placed across the poles of the permanent magnet. The keeper becomes magnetized by *induction* and remains a magnet as long as it is placed across the poles of the permanent magnet. Since the keeper has much higher permeability than air, it is evident that the external field of the permanent magnet will be concentrated through the keeper.

Let us consider magnetic induction in somewhat greater detail. Figure 7-16 depicts a small piece of soft iron which is placed near a permanent magnet. Note how the magnet flux lines are distorted. The soft iron has much greater permeability than air. Hence, the flux lines tend to concentrate through the piece of soft iron. In so doing, the soft iron becomes a magnet with poles as indicated. The piece of soft iron has been magnetized by magnetic induction. It will remain a magnet as long as it is left in the field of the permanent magnet.

7.7 MAGNET APPLICATION NOTES

Permanent magnets are used in electrical meters, as seen in Figure 7-17. The magnet has the general shape of a horseshoe. A circular air gap is seen between the pole pieces. In this air gap, the meter movement (explained in Chapter 18) is assembled. Permanent magnets are also used

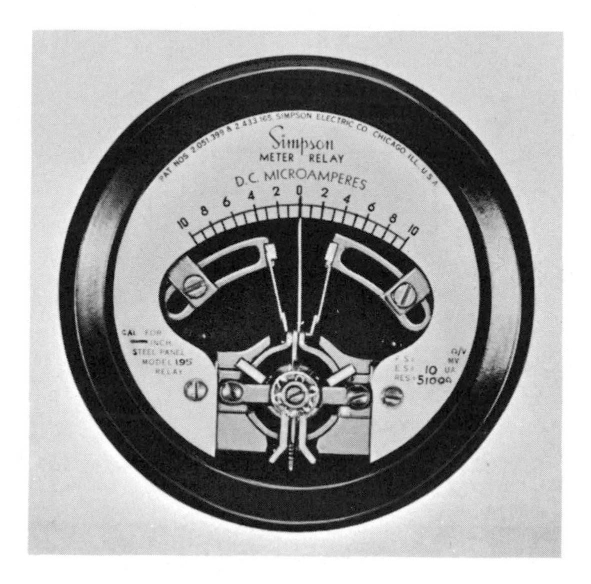

Figure 7-17
Permanent magnets are used in electrical meters. (Courtesy of Simpson Electric Co.)

in telephone receivers. Figure 7-18 shows diagrammatic representations of two basic and historic types of telephone receivers. The earliest receiver, invented by Alexander Graham Bell, employed a bar type of permanent magnet. Later, horseshoe permanent magnets were utilized.

Electromagnets are also used in telephone receivers. Soft-iron cores are mounted on the poles of the permanent magnet, as seen in Figure 7-18. A coil of wire is wound around the soft-iron core. When electric current passes through the wire, the core becomes magnetized; its magnetic field will either aid or oppose the permanent-magnet field depending upon the direction of current flow. Details of telephone-receiver operation are reserved for subsequent discussion. A classical example of electromagnet application is found in the telegraph sounder, depicted diagrammatically in Figure 7-19. When electric current from the line passes through the

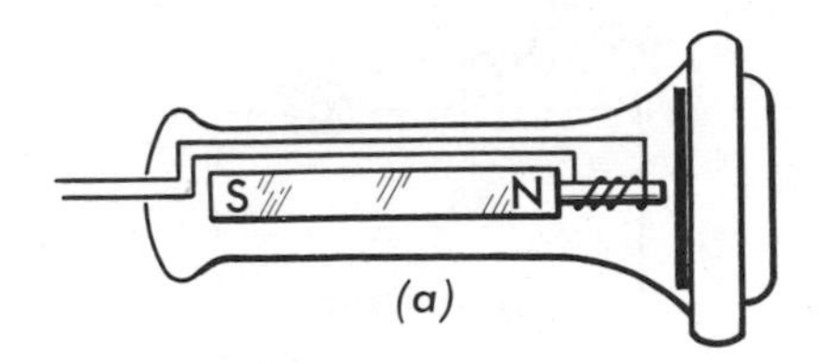

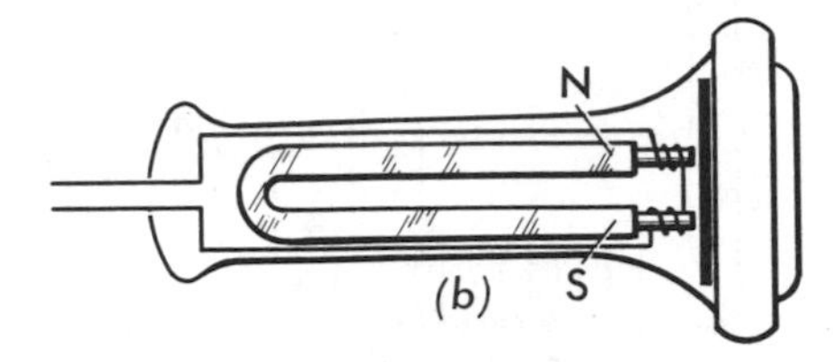

Figure 7-18

(a) Dr. Bell's original telephone receiver utilized a bar-type permanent magnet. *(b)* A later version utilized a horseshoe-type permanent magnet.

electromagnet, the armature is attracted downward. The lever clicks as it strikes the adjustable stops. Communication is obtained by transmission of standardized click sequences called dots and dashes, formalized in the Morse code.

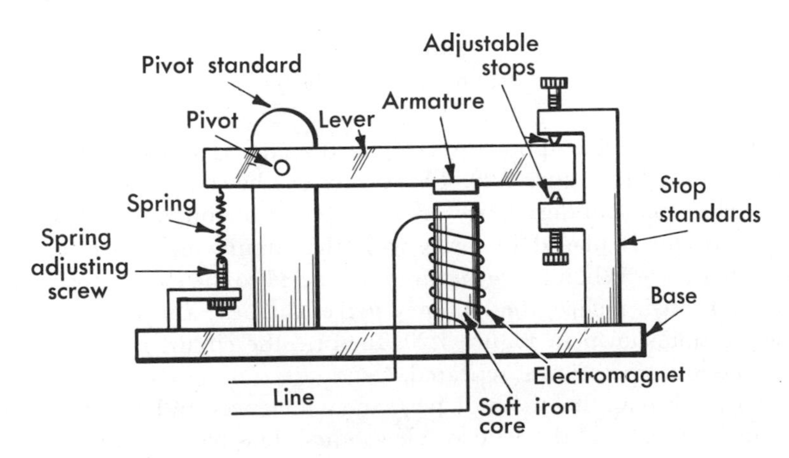

Figure 7-19

Diagrammatic rendering of a telegraph sounder.

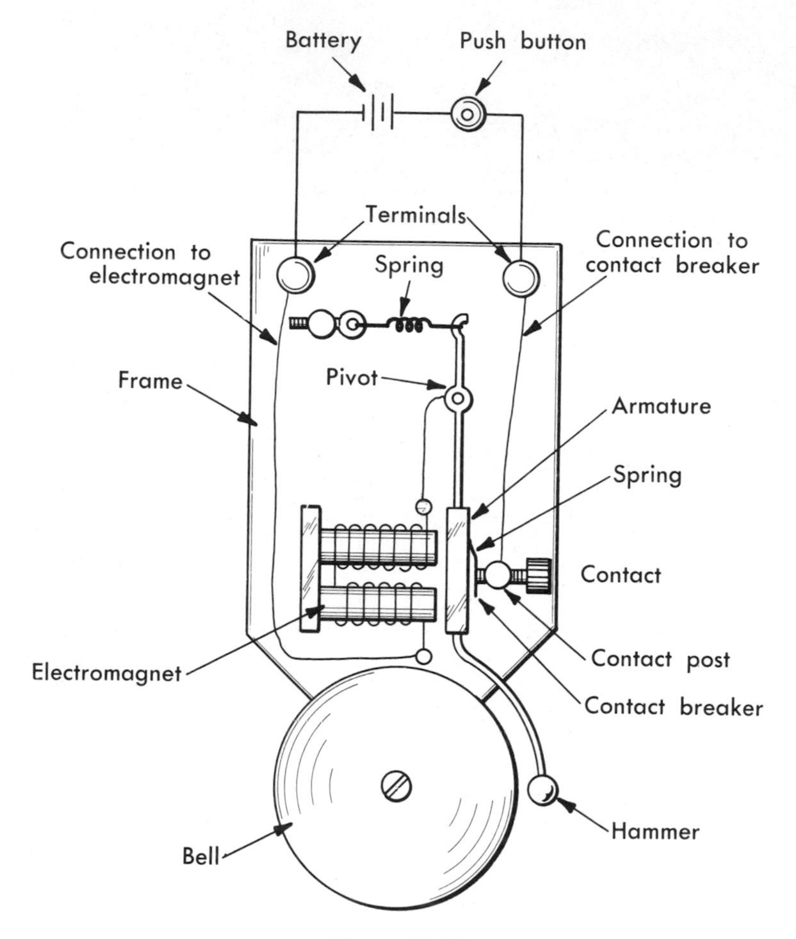

Figure 7-20
Plan of an electric bell.

Another common application of electromagnets is found in electric bells, as depicted in Figure 7-20. This device can be compared in principle with a telegraph sounder; however, it differs in an important respect. A contact breaker is placed in series with the circuit, and operates as an automatic switch. When the armature is attracted to the electromagnet, the circuit is opened. Hence, the hammer strikes the bell, and then falls back to the position shown in Figure 7-20. In turn, the circuit is closed again, and the cycle of operation is repeated.

Many other applications of permanent magnets and electromagnets are found throughout the field of electronics. The basic applications are explained and illustrated throughout the following chapters.

SUMMARY OF FUNDAMENTAL CONCEPTS

Magnetism: A class of physical phenomena that includes attraction for iron by a lodestone or magnet, and that is believed to be inseparably associated with moving charges of electricity; magnetism is characterized by fields of force in which both magnets and electric currents experience mechanical forces.

Ferromagnetic Substances: A class of substances characterized by abnormally high magnetic permeability, a limiting saturation point, and appreciable residual magnetism and hysteresis.

Paramagnetic Substances: A class of magnetizable substances characterized by a small but positive ratio of magnetization to magnetizing force that varies slightly with magnetizing force.

Diamagnetic Substances: A class of substances characterized by a magnetic permeability less than that of a vacuum.

Principle of Least Energy: A law which states that natural forces come to equilibrium in a manner that requires the least energy; in turn ferromagnetic crystals form domains that are oriented in random directions.

Dipole Principle: An assertion that magnetic monopoles or magnetic charges do not exist; that a magnetic north pole is inseparably associated with a magnetic south pole.

Curie Point: The temperature at which there is a transition between ferromagnetic and paramagnetic characteristics, particularly of soft iron.

QUESTIONS

1) Ferromagnetic substances are:
(*a*) good insulators. (*b*) the same as diamagnetic substances. (*c*) strongly attracted by a magnet. (*d*) repelled by a magnet.
2) Paramagnetic substances are:
(*a*) weakly attracted by a magnet. (*b*) the same as superconducting substances. (*c*) the same as semiconducting substances. (*d*) repelled by a magnet.
3) Diamagnetic substances are:
(*a*) magnetic monopoles. (*b*) alloys of ferromagnetic substances and lodestone. (*c*) produced by heating iron above the Curie point. (*d*) weakly repelled by a magnet.
4) Permeability is a measure of:
(*a*) the conductivity of a substance for magnetic lines of force. (*b*) the resistance of a metal. (*c*) the sum of the voltage drops around a magnet. (*d*) the number of electrons in the valence band.
5) The force that acts between two magnetic poles is:
(*a*) equal to the earth's magnetic field. (*b*) directly proportional to the product of the pole strengths and inversely proportional to the distance between them. (*c*) equal to the magnetic field intensity multiplied by the permeability. (*d*) directly proportional to the product of the pole strengths and inversely proportional to the square of the distance between them.
6) A line of magnetic force:
(*a*) passes through a magnet from its north pole to its south pole. (*b*) leaves the south pole of a magnet and re-enters at its north pole. (*c*) is reflected by iron and refracted by air. (*d*) passes through a magnet from its south pole to its north pole.
7) Weber's theory states that:
(*a*) an iron bar becomes longer when it is magnetized. (*b*) an iron bar becomes shorter when it is magnetized. (*c*) each atom is a magnet with a north and a south pole. (*d*) an iron bar becomes saturated at the Curie point.
8) The magnetic field intensity inside a coil depends upon:
(*a*) the diameter of the coil. (*b*) the dielectric coefficient of the core. (*c*) the length of the coil, number of turns, and current value. (*d*) the diameter of the coil, dielectric coefficient of the core, total number of turns, and the voltage flowing in the coil.
9) To find the number of flux lines per unit cross-sectional area:
(*a*) multiply the number of ampere-turns per unit length by the

permeability. (*b*) multiply the number of volt-turns by the diameter of the coil, and divide by the permeability. (*c*) multiply the number of ampere-turns per unit length by the conductivity. (*d*) multiply the number of ampere-turns per unit length by the reluctivity.

10) Domains are defined as:
(*a*) covalent bonds in a ferromagnetic crystal. (*b*) ionic bonds in a ferromagnetic crystal. (*c*) structural units in a ferromagnetic crystal. (*d*) conduction bands in a ferromagnetic crystal.

PROBLEMS

1) A pair of magnetic poles attract each other with a force of 3 dynes. The distance between the poles is doubled. What is the force of attraction at the increased separation?
2) A pair of magnetic poles attract each other with a force of 3 dynes. One pole is then tripled in strength. What is the force of attraction with the increased pole strength?
3) A pair of magnetic poles in an evacuated container repel each other with a force of 5 dynes. Air is then admitted to the container. What is the force of repulsion with air present between the poles?
4) An air-core coil is wound with 100 turns which occupy a coil length of 0.1 meter. If 1 amp flows through the coil, what is its magnetic field intensity?
5) In Problem 4, the coil is modified by winding with two layers, so that the coil length becomes 0.05 meter. If 1 amp flows through the coil, what is its magnetic field intensity?
6) What is the value of the magnetomotive force in Problem 4?
7) What is the value of the magnetomotive force in Problem 5?
8) An air-core coil has a diameter of 0.1 meter, and is wound with 100 turns that occupy a coil length of 0.1 meter. If 10 amps flow through the coil, what is the amount of magnetic flux per unit cross-section of the coil?
9) In Problem 8, an iron core is utilized instead of an air core. The iron core has a permeability of 2000. What is the amount of magnetic flux per unit cross-section of the coil with the iron core present?
10) What is the value of the magnetomotive force in Problem 9?
11) An iron core is used instead of an air core in Problem 8. However, the core has a very small diameter, and is completely saturated under the condition of operation. What is the amount of magnetic flux per unit cross-section of the coil?
12) A somewhat larger iron core is used instead of an air core in Prob-

lem 8. When 1 amp flows through the coil, the permeability of the core is 2000. However, when 10 amps flow through the coil, the permeability decreases to 500. What is the value of the magnetomotive force for a current flow of 1 amp? What is the value of the magnetomotive force for a current flow of 10 amps?

13) An electromagnet dissipates 1 watt of energy in the form of core loss when it is turned on and off at uniform intervals for one-half hour. Another type of iron is then substituted for the original core. This type of iron differs only in the fact that its hysteresis loop has twice the area of the original. When operated in the same manner as before, how many watt-hours of energy will be dissipated at the end of one-half hour?

14) An iron-core coil has a diameter of 0.05 meter, and is wound with 100 turns that occupy a coil length of 0.1 meter. The current flow is 1 amp. The iron core is heated to a temperature of 1450°F. What is the amount of magnetic flux per unit cross-section of the coil?

8

THE MAGNETIC CIRCUIT

8.1 CONCEPT OF THE MAGNETIC CIRCUIT

The idea of a magnetic circuit is based on the principles of an electric circuit. We are familiar with Ohm's law, $I = E/R$. This equation states that the current in an electric circuit doubles if the applied voltage is doubled. When current flows through a coil, we learned that a magnetic field is established. The path of the magnetic flux lines traverses a *magnetic circuit.* For example, Figure 8-1 shows a coil wound on an iron core. If you pass electric current through the coil, magnetic energy is stored in the iron core. Note that the iron core is the magnetic circuit. Any magnetic circuit obeys a law that is analogous to Ohm's law.

First, we perceive that there is a magnetic force or "pressure" that does work and sets up magnetic flux in the iron core. Recall that this force is called magnetomotive force, or mmf. The mmf applied to a magnetic circuit can be compared with electromotive force (emf) in an electric circuit. Magnetic flux in the iron core can be compared with current in an electric circuit. The current in an electric circuit does not build up to infinity because it is opposed by resistance. Similarly, flux in a magnetic circuit does not build up to infinity because it is opposed by a magnetic "resistance," called *reluctance.*

Now, let us compare Ohm's law for an electric circuit with the corresponding law for a magnetic circuit.

In an electric circuit,

$$\text{Current} = \frac{\text{emf}}{\text{Resistance}} \tag{8.1}$$

In a magnetic circuit,

$$\text{Flux} = \frac{\text{mmf}}{\text{Reluctance}} \tag{8.2}$$

Equation (8.2) states that if the mmf is doubled, the flux is doubled. Note that volts, amperes, and ohms in an electric circuit correspond to ampere-turns, magnetic lines, and rels in a magnetic circuit. The ampere-turn is the unit of mmf. If 1 amp flows in a one-turn coil, one unit of mmf is applied to the magnetic circuit. Again, if 2 amps flow in a one-turn coil, two units of mmf are applied to the magnetic circuit. Thus, the ampere-turn is analogous to the volt.

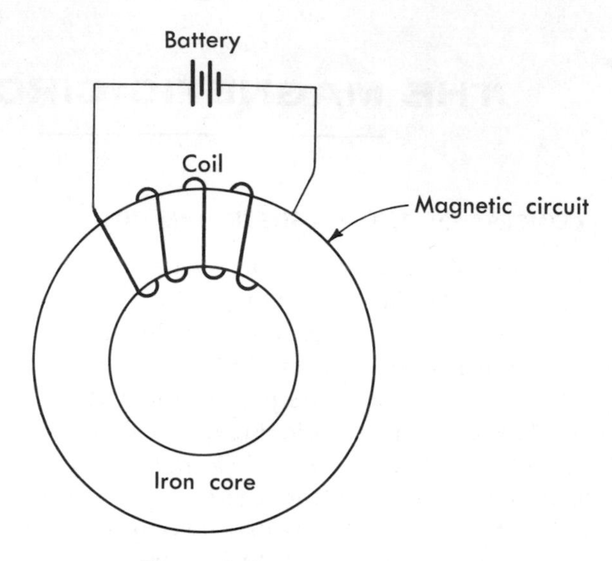

Figure 8-1
The iron core is the magnetic circuit.

The magnetic line (also called a flux line) is the unit of magnetic field intensity. An iron core with two flux lines has twice as much magnetic field intensity as a core with one flux line. Hence, the flux line is analogous to the ampere, the unit of current intensity. Equation (8.2) states that 1 amp-turn of mmf will establish one line of flux in a magnetic circuit that has a reluctance of 1 rel. Thus, the rel is analogous to the ohm. These basic facts are illustrated in Figure 8-2.

There are several systems of units used in various areas of electrical theory. Practical workers prefer to use a unit of reluctance, called the rel, and defined by Equation (8.2). However, physicists and engineers generally use other units. We will first review magnetic circuits from the standpoint of the practical worker. Later in this chapter, we will briefly review the various systems of units and relate them to our practical units. This is a functional development that makes magnetic circuits easier to understand.

THE UNIT OF RELUCTANCE

We know that iron has a low reluctance compared with air. A volume of air 1 in. sq and 3.19 in. long has a reluctance of 1 rel. If we double the length of this air column (6.38 in. long by 1 in. sq), its reluctance becomes 2 rels. Let us compare the reluctance of air with the reluctance of iron. If an iron core is 1 in. sq, a typical length of 475 ft will have a

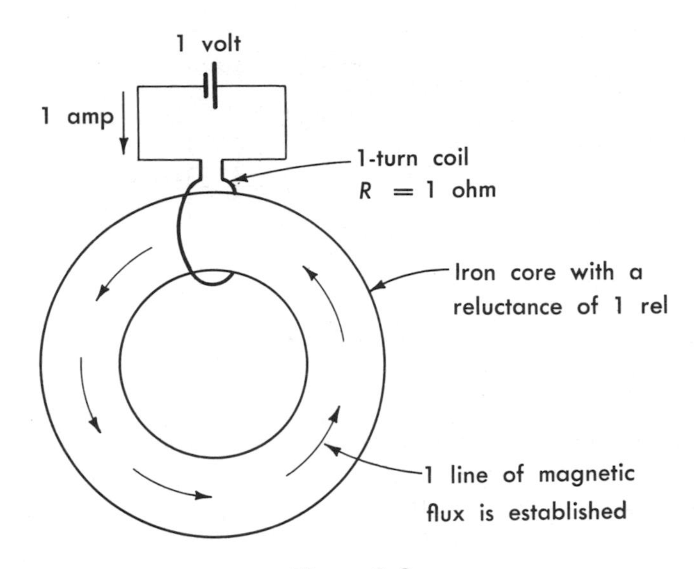

Figure 8-2
One amp-turn establishes one line of flux in a reluctance of 1 rel.

reluctance of 1 rel. This means that air has 1800 times the reluctance of this particular sample of iron, when equal volumes are considered. Otherwise stated, the *reluctivity* of air is 1800 times the reluctivity of the iron.

Although a magnetic circuit is similar to an electric circuit, it must not be supposed that the analogy is complete. For example, a magnetic circuit cannot be entirely opened. Neither air nor a vacuum will provide magnetic insulation. Hence, a magnetic circuit is more nearly analogous to an electric circuit which is submerged in water. When such an electric circuit is broken, it is not entirely open because some current will be conducted through the water across the gap. Although the current flow might be greatly decreased, it cannot be reduced to zero.

When such a submerged electric circuit is closed, current flow is not completely confined to the circuit wires. There will also be some current flow through the water surrounding the conductors, although most of the current might be confined to the conducting wires. Again, magnetic flux is not strictly analogous to electric current, because current is a rate of flow; magnetic flux is more precisely described as a state or condition of the medium (such as iron) in which the flux is established.

Although there is no such thing as a magnetic insulator, a flux field can be greatly attenuated by a magnetic shield, as depicted in Figure 8-3. Highly sensitive galvanometers are sometimes placed inside many con-

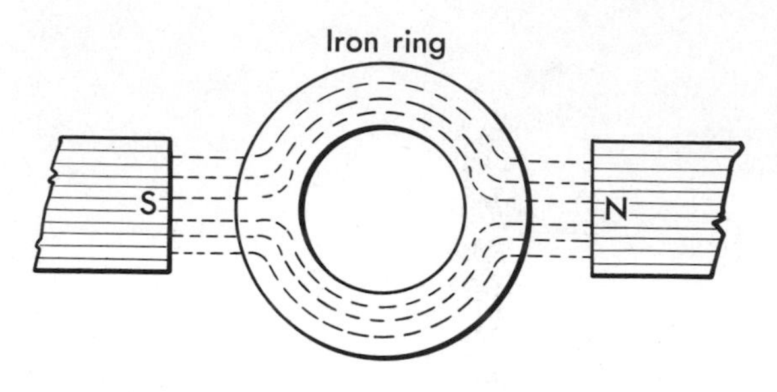

Figure 8-3
Action of a magnetic screen.

centric cases constructed from iron sheets. Each concentric case progressively attenuates the strength of the earth's magnetic field, or stray magnetic fields in the vicinity of the galvanometer.

Let us analyze the magnetic circuit in greater detail. If 1 amp-turn produces one line of magnetic flux in an iron core of a certain length, this core has a reluctance of 1 rel. If the length of the core is reduced to one-half, its reluctance becomes ½ rel; consequently, 1 amp-turn will produce two lines of flux in the shorter magnetic circuit. Hence, the reluctance of a core is directly proportional to its length. Note that the

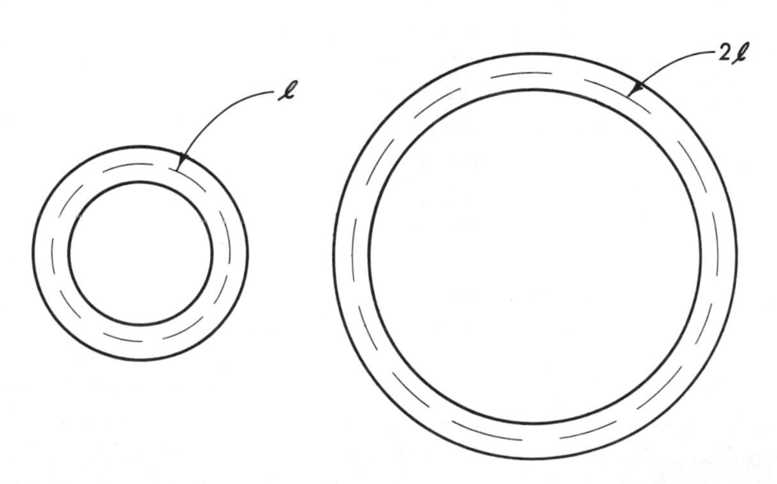

Figure 8-4
A large ring that has twice the reluctance of the small ring.

length of the magnetic circuit in a toroidal (circular) core is given by the median circumference or diameter, as shown in Figure 8-4.

The length of the magnetic circuit in a rectangular core is determined in the same manner, as seen in Figure 8-5. Suppose that the length of a magnetic circuit remains the same, but the cross-sectional area of the core is doubled. Note that this is equivalent to stacking two of the original cores beside each other. Evidently, the reluctance of the magnetic circuit

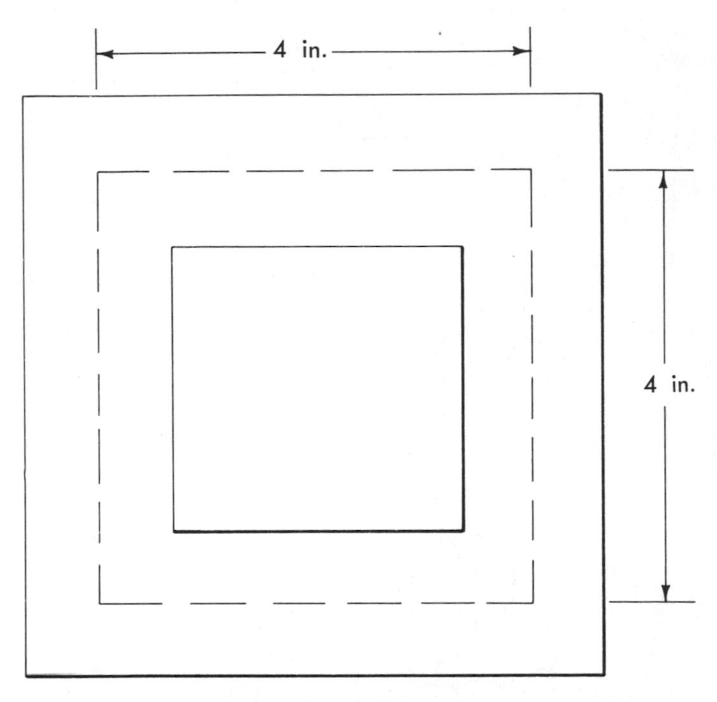

Figure 8-5
Illustration of the length of a magnetic circuit.

is reduced to one-half. On the other hand, if the cross-sectional area of the core is halved, the reluctance of the magnetic circuit is doubled.

If we wish to find how many ampere-turns will be required to produce a certain number of magnetic flux lines in a core, the required mmf, of course, will depend on the reluctance of the core. If the magnetic circuit is doubled in length, the number of ampere-turns must also be doubled to obtain the same number of flux lines. This relation follows from the basic fact that 1 amp-turn establishes one line of flux in a magnetic circuit that has a reluctance of 1 rel. The required mmf will also depend on the cross-sectional area of the core. Hence, it is convenient to consider a core with a cross-sectional area of 1 sq in.; the mmf is stated in terms of ampere-turns per inch of core length.

Figure 8-6 shows a simple example of a core in which the magnetic

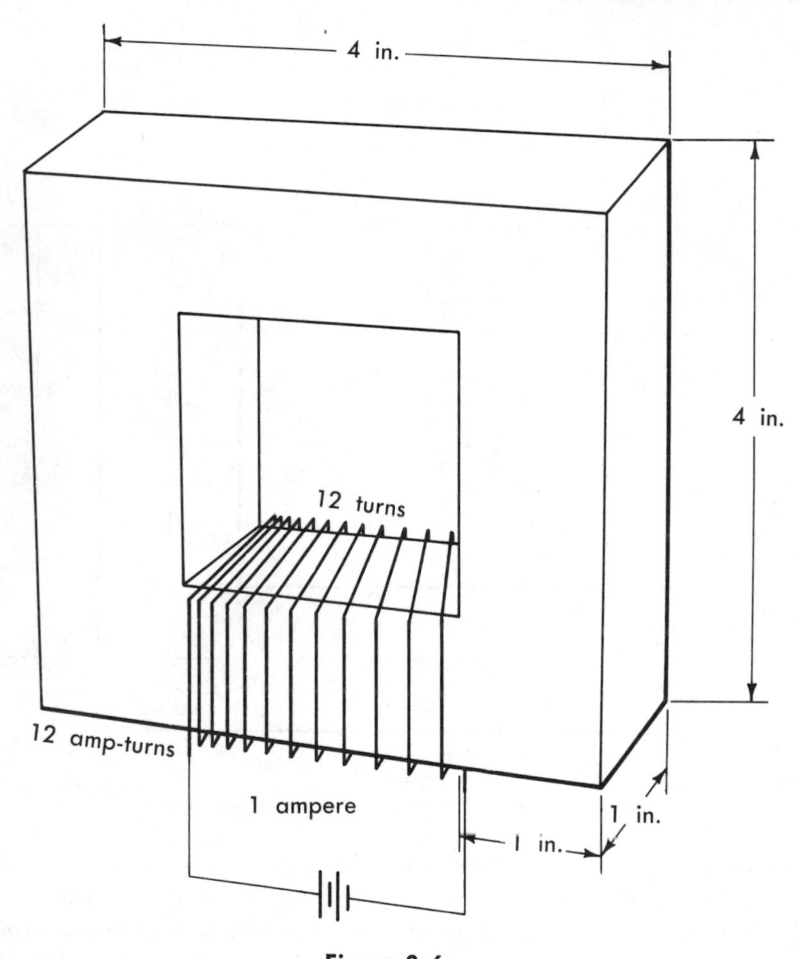

Figure 8-6
Illustration of a magnetizing force of 1 amp-turn per in.

field intensity is 1 amp-turn per in. The core has a cross-sectional area of 1 sq in. Its median length is 12 in. Hence, 12 amp-turns will establish a magnetic field intensity of 1 amp-turn per in. The 12 amp-turns in this example are provided by 12 turns with a current flow of 1 amp. If the median length of this core is increased to 20 in., 20 amp-turns will be required to produce a magnetic field intensity of 1 amp-turn per in.

We know that the number of flux lines produced in the core (Figure 8-6) by 1 amp-turn per in. depends upon the reluctivity of the core material. We divide the reluctivity into the number of ampere-turns per inch to calculate how many flux lines are established. For example, the reluctivity of a certain type of core iron might be 0.001. In this case, 1000 flux lines will be present in the magnetic circuit of Figure 8-6. If you know the type of iron to be used in a core, charts are generally available to determine the reluctivity. Otherwise, you will have to make a measurement of the reluctivity.

IRON HAS A NONLINEAR RELUCTIVITY CHARACTERISTIC

Why must reluctivity be found from a chart? It is because the reluctivity characteristic of iron is nonlinear. A typical chart of mmf versus flux is seen in Figure 8-7. When the magnetizing force is 1 amp-turn per in., there will be 750 flux lines in the magnetic circuit of Figure 8-6. This is the same as saying that when the magnetic field intensity is 1 amp-turn per in., the reluctivity of this core material is 0.0013. Observe that if the magnetic field intensity is increased to 50 amp-turns per in., the reluctivity of the core material is only 0.0006.

The curve in Figure 8-7 is plotted on semilog graph paper. This makes it easier to read values in the region where the curvature changes rapidly. If semilog graph paper were not used in this example, the data between 1 and 10 amp-turns per in. would be compressed, and correspondingly difficult to read accurately. It is inconsequential that the data between 10 and 100 amp-turns per in. are compressed, because the number of flux lines does not change greatly in this interval.

At 100 amp-turns per in., the iron represented in Figure 8-7 is approaching saturation. At a still higher value of mmf, the iron will become completely saturated. We recall that the reluctivity of iron becomes the same as air past the saturation point. The reluctivity of air is 0.313, since a volume of air 1 in. sq and 3.19 in. long has a reluctance of 1 rel. Note that our discussion thus far has been concerned with an unbroken ferromagnetic circuit. Many practical magnetic circuits consist partly of iron, and partly of air. We will now analyze such magnetic circuits.

8.2 MAGNETIC PULL

Figure 8-8 depicts a magnetic circuit of iron that comprises a horseshoe and a bar. The bar contacts the poles of the horseshoe so that there is no air gap in the magnetic circuit. How many pounds of force does the

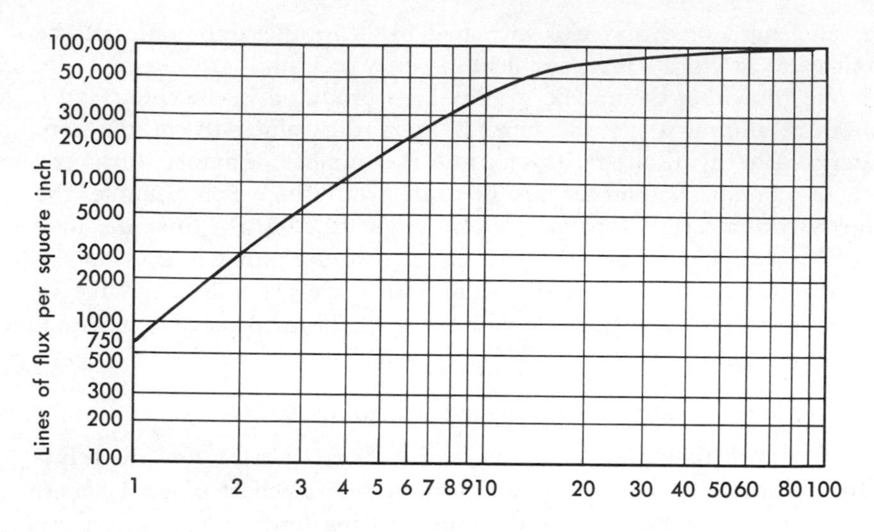

(*a*)

Figure 8-7

(*a*) Flux lines versus magnetizing force for an iron sample. (*b*) The stored energy is proportional to the shaded area in the diagram when the current flow is 20 amps. (*Continued on facing page.*)

horseshoe exert upon the bar? The magnetic pull is stated by

$$F = \frac{B^2 A}{7213 \times 10^4} \tag{8.3}$$

where F is the force in pounds, B is the flux density in each pole, and A is the cross-sectional area of each pole.

The magnetic circuit in Figure 8-8 has a cross-sectional area of 1 sq in. There are 120 amp-turns, and the magnetic circuit is 12 in. long. Hence, we have 10 amp-turns per in. The flux density will depend upon the type of iron that is used. Assume that we are using the iron represented in Figure 8-7. In this case, 10 amp-turns per in. will establish 40,000 lines per sq in. Therefore,

$$F = \frac{40{,}000^2}{7213 \times 10^4} = 22 \text{ lbs (approx) per pair of poles} \tag{8.4}$$

The total pull exerted on the bar in Figure 8-8 is approximately 44 lb.

Hence, it would be necessary to apply 22 lb of force to separate one end of the bar from the horseshoe in Figure 8-8; or, it would require 44 lb applied at the middle of the bar to separate it from the horseshoe.

After the bar is separated from the horseshoe poles, thereby leaving

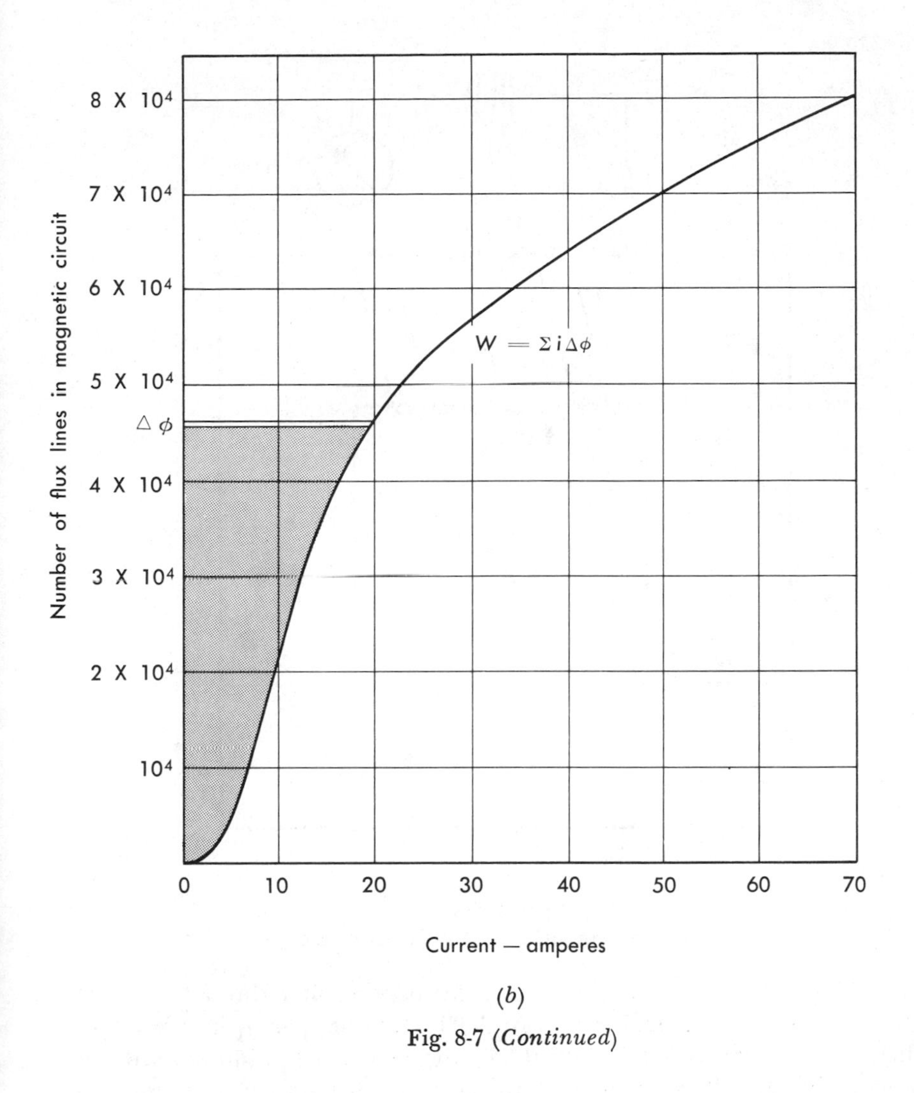

(*b*)

Fig. 8-7 (*Continued*)

an air gap, how many pounds of magnetic pull will be exerted? For example, suppose that there is an air gap of 1/16 in. between each pair of poles. The magnetic circuit is thereby increased in length. This magnetic circuit consists of 12 in. of iron and $\frac{1}{8}$ in. of air. Since the reluctivity of air is 0.313, the reluctance of the $\frac{1}{8}$-in. air gap is approximately 0.04 rel. Note that the reluctance of this air gap is many times greater than the reluctance of the horseshoe and bar. Therefore, it is practical to consider the air gap only, and to disregard the iron-core portion of the magnetic circuit.

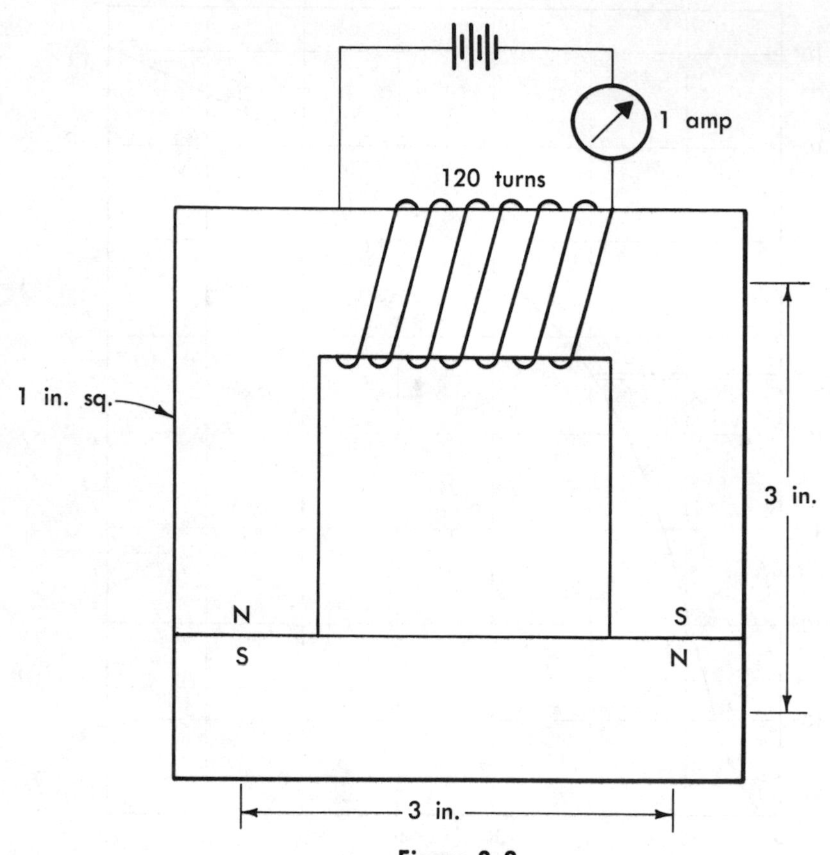

Figure 8-8
The magnetic pull has a value of 44 lb.

In Figure 8-8, there are 120 amp-turns driving flux through a reluctance of 0.04 rel. In turn, 120/0.04 or 3000 flux lines per sq in. are established. Note that this is less than 0.1 of the flux lines produced with an air gap of zero. The magnetic pull with a ⅛-in. air gap present is calculated as follows:

$$F = \frac{3000^2}{7213 \times 10^4} = 0.12 \text{ lb per pair of poles} \tag{8.5}$$

The total force exerted upon the bar in Figure 8-8 is 0.24 lb.

The magnetic pull, which was 44 lb with no air gap, decreases to less than ¼ lb when a 1/16-in. air gap is present at each pair of poles. This large decrease in magnetic pull is due to the fact that air has a much higher reluctance than iron, and because magnetic pull is proportional to the square of the flux density, as stated by Equation (8.3). If you double the flux density, the magnetic pull is increased by a factor of 4.

Permeability, of course, is the reciprocal of reluctivity, just as conductivity is the reciprocal of resistivity. In an electric circuit, conductance is the reciprocal of resistance, or, $G = 1/R$. Similarly, in a magnetic circuit, *permeance* is the reciprocal of reluctance. The reluctivity of common magnetic materials falls in the range from 0.007 to 0.00009, which

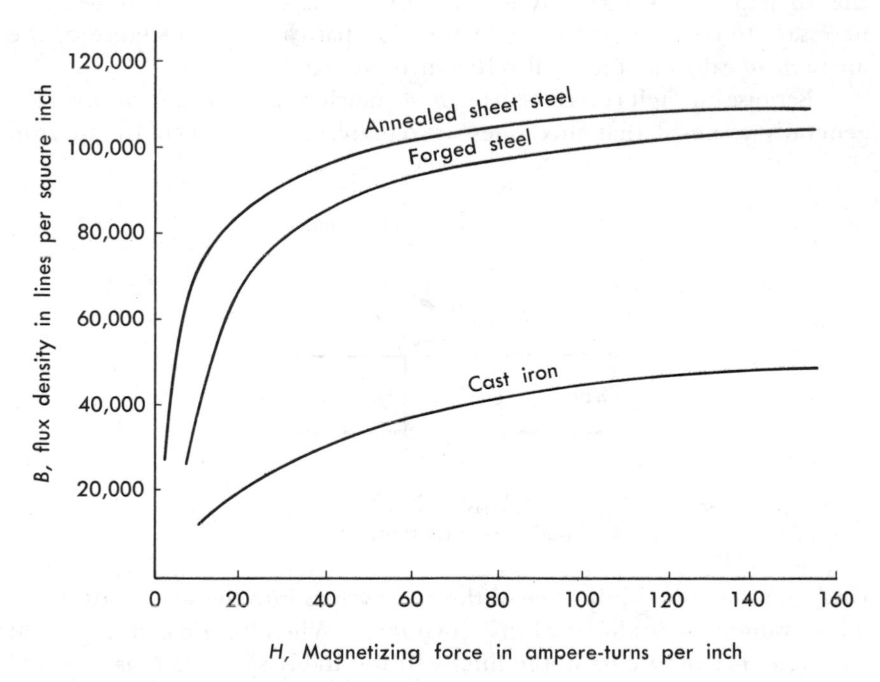

Figure 8-9
Comparative *B-H* curves for three common magnetic materials.

corresponds to permeabilities from approximately 140 to 10,000. Since whole numbers are easier to work with than small fractions, we may prefer to write the laws of magnetic circuits in terms of permeability values instead of reluctivity values.

It is interesting to note comparative *B-H* curves for cast iron, forged steel, and annealed sheet steel, as seen in Figure 8-9. The curves show that annealed sheet steel would be the preferred core material of these three types of iron. Note that the curves have different shapes. In other words, the nonlinearity characteristic of each material is different.

8.3 SERIES MAGNETIC CIRCUITS

Series magnetic circuits obey the series law; the number of flux lines is the same at any point in the series circuit. Figure 8-8 represents a series magnetic circuit, whether the bar contacts the poles of the horseshoe, or is separated from the poles by an air gap. When an air gap is present, we know that the total reluctance of the series circuit is equal to the reluctance of the iron path plus the reluctance of the air path. The total reluctance is practically the same as the reluctance of the air gap, unless the air gap is very small. When the air gap is quite small, it becomes necessary to add the reluctance of the iron path to the reluctance of the air path to calculate the total reluctance accurately.

Because the reluctance of iron is so much less than that of air, it is generally assumed that flux lines are completely contained by an iron

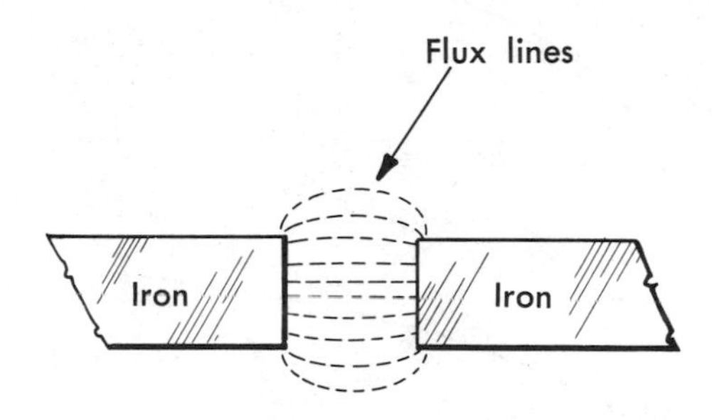

Figure 8-10
Fringing occurs in an air gap.

core, and that practically none of the flux escapes into the surrounding air. This assumption is almost always justifiable. When an air gap is present in a series magnetic circuit, the lines will inevitably spread out as depicted in Figure 8-10. The spreading becomes more pronounced as the gap length is increased. A rule of thumb is useful in this respect. If the air gap is less than 3/16 in. and the core cross-sectional area is 1 sq in. or more, you may assume that the flux lines do not spread out from the air gap appreciably. On the other hand, spreading is appreciable for larger gaps. It is assumed in practical work that the flux fringes out from the gap for a distance equal to the length of the gap.

The number of flux lines is the same at any point in a series magnetic circuit. However, when fringing is present in an air gap, it is evident that the flux *density* is less in the gap than in the core. The same number of flux lines are spread over a larger area. In Figure 8-11, a small piece of soft iron has been brought into the vicinity of a permanent magnet. A magnetic circuit is present in which the air path is longer than the

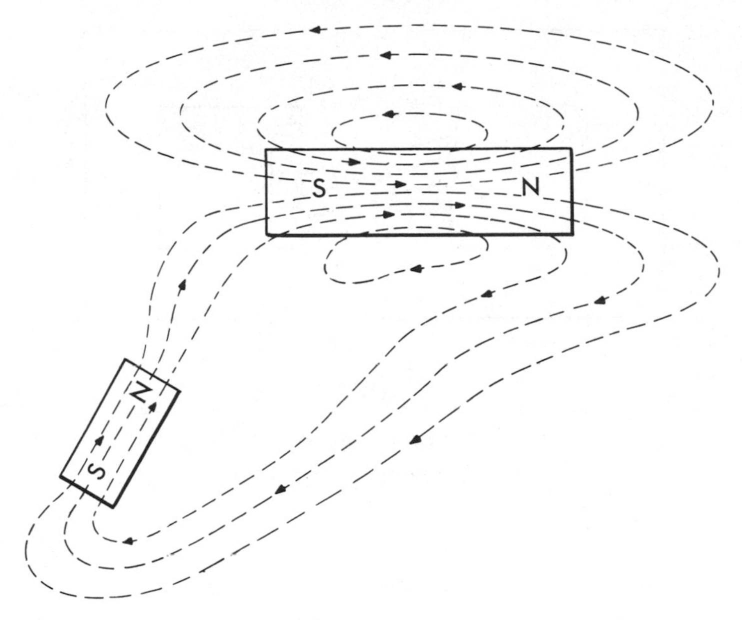

Figure 8-11
The air path is longer than the iron path in this magnetic circuit.

iron path. Hence, fringing is extremely pronounced. Furthermore, note carefully that this is not a series magnetic circuit. The flux from the permanent magnet branches; part of the flux passes through the soft iron, and part passes in an air circuit which does not include the soft iron.

8.4 PARALLEL MAGNETIC CIRCUITS

A parallel magnetic circuit has two or more paths for the flux lines. Figure 8-12 illustrates a common type of parallel magnetic circuit. Here, two series magnetic circuits are arranged end-to-end as depicted by the dotted line. The mmf is applied at the middle leg of the core. Flux in the middle leg divides equally at the top and bottom of the core to pass through the two branch magnetic circuits. Evidently, the reluctance of the parallel magnetic circuit is one-half the reluctance of each branch. This is analogous to the connection of two equal resistances in parallel which have a total resistance equal to one-half the value of an individual resistance.

Parallel magnetic circuits that have air gaps are commonly encountered, as shown in Figure 8-13. The electromagnet winding in this example is split into two sections connected in series-aiding. The flux branches around the top and bottom of the outer magnetic circuit. Across the air gaps, the inner circular portion of the magnetic circuit is magnetized by

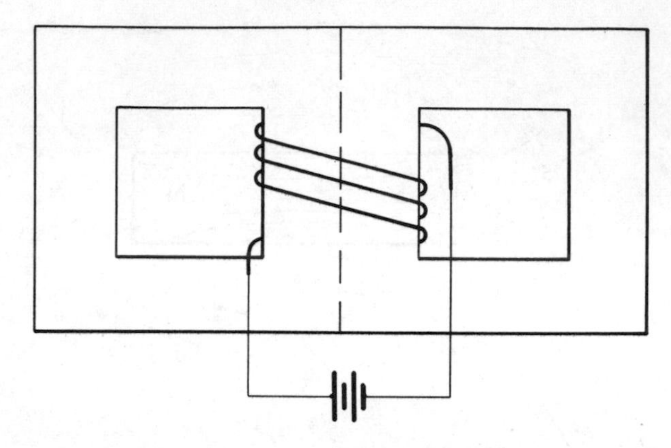

Figure 8-12
A simple parallel magnetic circuit.

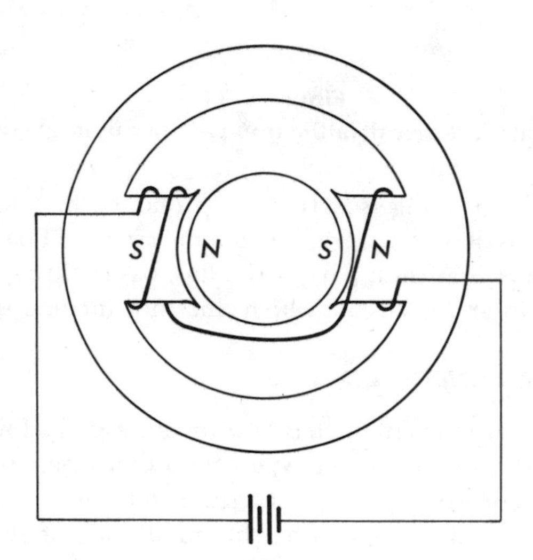

Figure 8-13
A parallel magnetic circuit with air gaps.

induction. Thus, the magnetic pole distribution occurs as depicted in the diagram.

8.5 MEASUREMENT OF FLUX DENSITY

If you do not have a *B-H* chart available for a certain type of iron, it becomes necessary to measure its flux density and to plot a *B-H* curve.

Elaborate techniques are used in advanced work. However, approximate measurements that are satisfactory in many practical applications can be made by simple arrangements such as depicted in Figure 8-8. Various values of current are passed through the coil, and the corresponding force measured which is required to break the bar loose from the horseshoe magnet.

For example, suppose that the magnetic circuit has the same dimensions as shown in Figure 8-8, and the coil is wound with 120 turns of wire. Then, 1 amp will apply 10 amp-turns per in. of magnetic field intensity; 2 amps will apply 20 amp-turns per in. of magnetic field intensity; or, ½ amp will apply 5 amp-turns per in., and so forth. If we rearrange Equation (8.3) and solve for B, we obtain

$$B = 8492\sqrt{F} \tag{8.6}$$

where F is the number of pounds required to separate one end of the bar from the horseshoe and B is the flux density in lines per sq in. To each value of B determined from Equation (8.6) corresponds a value of H, which is the number of ampere-turns per inch of mmf. When corresponding values of B and H are plotted, a B-H chart is obtained, such as illustrated in Figure 8-7 or Figure 8-9.

PRINCIPLE OF MAGNETIC BIAS

An important example of a magnetic circuit is the telephone receiver depicted in Figure 8-14. The telephone was invented in 1876 by Alexander Graham Bell. Two sources of magnetism are provided in a telephone receiver. Voice (audio) currents flow through the winding of the electromagnet A. In turn, the magnetic field that is generated attracts the diaphragm C via the soft-iron pole pieces B and D. A *magnetic bias* is provided by the permanent magnet I. Why is this permanent-magnet field used? It is because the current that reproduces the voice variations is a

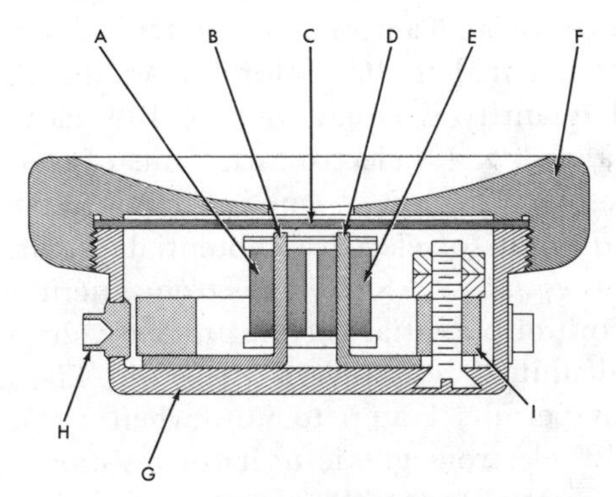

Figure 8-14

Construction of a "watch-case" type of telephone receiver.

pulsating d-c current. As discussed subsequently in greater detail, a pulsating d-c current does not reverse its direction of flow at any time. We will find that the applied voice signal may not be reproduced as a pulsating d-c unless the magnetic bias is provided. Thus, the permanent magnet avoids distortion of the sound waves radiated by the diaphragm.

The magnetic circuit in Figure 8-14 comprises the permanent magnet, soft-iron pieces, a diaphragm, and air gaps between pole pieces and diaphragm. Sensitivity of the receiver is increased by utilizing a very small air gap. On the other hand, there is a limit imposed by the possibility of the diaphragm striking the pole tips at the limit of its downward vibration. Hence, the air gap is adjusted as a compromise between sensitivity and mechanical clearance. If the diaphragm should strike the pole tips, a rattling sound is produced and the voice waves are distorted. The diaphragm is secured by the cap *F,* which is threaded to case *G.* A headband is commonly used with a watchcase receiver. Pivots are provided at the end of the headband, which are inserted into the inserts *H.*

8.6 ELECTRIC AND MAGNETIC UNITS

This book is concerned chiefly with practical units of measurement. However, it is appropriate to note that various systems of electric and magnetic units are in common use. One system of units will be most convenient in a certain area of electronics, while another system of units will be most convenient in another area. The two most basic systems of units are the *electrostatic* and the *electromagnetic* systems.

The *practical* unit of current is the *ampere.* One amp is defined as 0.1 of an electromagnetic unit of current; or, one electromagnetic unit of current is equal to 10 amps. One electromagnetic unit of current is equal to 3×10^{10} electrostatic units of current; 1 amp equals 3×10^{9} electrostatic units of current.

We know that the practical unit of electrical quantity is the *coulomb.* One coulomb is defined as 1 amp per 1 sec. One electromagnetic unit of electrical quantity is equal to 10 coulombs. Again, one electromagnetic unit of electrical quantity is equal to 3×10^{10} electrostatic units; or, 1 coulomb is equal to 3×10^{9} electrostatic units of electrical quantity.

Similarly, the practical unit of emf is the *volt.* One volt is defined as 10^{8} electromagnetic units of electrical potential. Again, one electrostatic unit of potential is equal to 3×10^{10} electromagnetic units of potential; one electrostatic unit of potential is equal to 300 volts.

The practical unit of resistance is the *ohm.* The ohm is defined as the resistance that permits 1 amp to flow when 1 volt is applied. One ohm is equal to 10^{9} electromagnetic units of resistance. One electrostatic unit of resistance is equal to 9×10^{20} electromagnetic units of resistance; one electrostatic unit of resistance is equal to 9×10^{11} ohms.

We know that the practical unit of capacitance is the *farad*. A farad is defined as the capacitance that stores a charge of 1 coulomb when 1 volt is applied. One electromagnetic unit of capacitance is equal to 10^9 farads. Again, one electromagnetic unit of capacitance is equal to 9×10^{20} electrostatic units of capacitance; or, one farad is equal to 9×10^{11} electrostatic units of capacitance.

As previously explained, the *ampere-turn* is the practical unit of magnetomotive force. The electromagnetic unit of mmf is the *gilbert*. One gilbert is equal to 1.257 amp-turns. The electrostatic unit of mmf is equal to 3.3356×10^{-11} gilbert.

The practical unit of reluctance is the *rel*. The electromagnetic unit of reluctance is the *oersted*. The electrostatic unit of reluctance is equal to 1.1122×10^{-21} oersted. One gilbert produces one line of flux in 1 oersted. One amp-turn produces one line of flux in 1 rel. Thus, 1 gilbert produces 1.257 lines in 1 rel; or, 1 oersted is equal to 1.257 rels.

The practical unit of magnetic field intensity is the *ampere-turn per inch*. The electromagnetic unit of magnetic field intensity is the *gauss*. The electrostatic unit of magnetic field intensity is equal to 3.3356×10^{-11} gauss. Note that 1 gauss is equal to 6.452 lines per sq in. It is interesting to note that the intensity of the earth's magnetic field is approximately one-half of 1 gauss. On the other hand, the strongest electromagnet that has been devised has a magnetic field intensity of approximately 250,000 gausses.

One line of magnetic flux is often called a *maxwell*. One kiloline is equal to 1000 lines. One megaline is equal to 10^6 lines, or maxwells.

Engineers often prefer to use a system of units, called the *mks* rationalized system. Mks stands for meter-kilogram-second. In the mks system, the unit of current is the ampere, the unit of electrical quantity is the coulomb, the unit of electromotive force is the volt, the unit of resistance is the ohm, and the unit of resistivity is 1 ohm per meter cube. The unit of conductance is the mho, the unit of capacitance is the farad, the unit of magnetomotive force is the ampere-turn, and the unit of magnetic field intensity is 1 amp-turn per meter.

In the mks system, the unit of magnetic flux is the weber, which equals 10^8 maxwells, or 10^8 electromagnetic units. The unit of magnetic flux density is 1 weber per sq meter.

Thus, this brief presentation shows that the mks system is the nearest to the completely practical system upon which the principles of magnetic circuits were developed in this chapter. Although it is unfortunate that the student must learn the relations between various systems of units, this requirement is inevitable. It is not necessary to memorize these relations—conversion factors are provided in most handbooks. On the other hand, it is essential that the student clearly understand the distinctions among the cgs, mks, and practical systems.

SUMMARY OF FUNDAMENTAL CONCEPTS

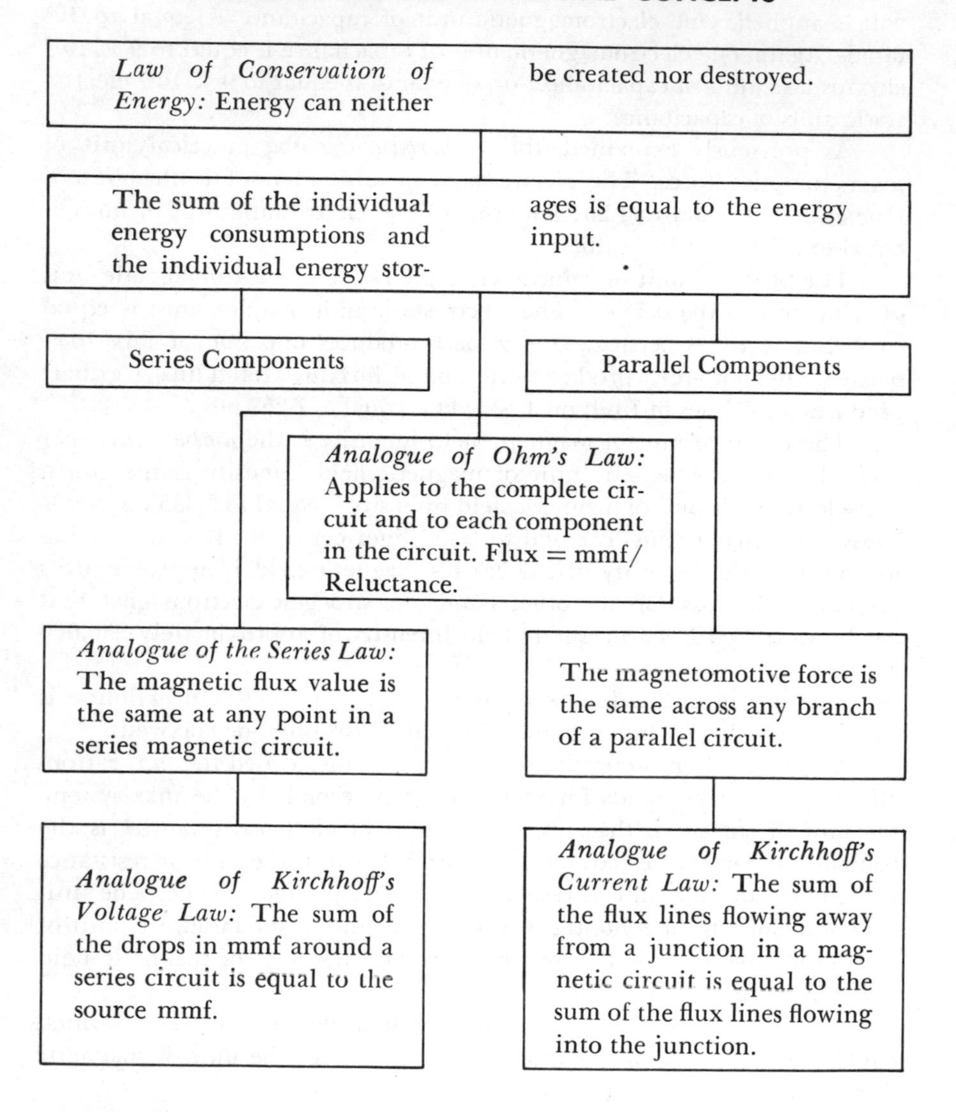

Law of Conservation of Energy: Energy can neither be created nor destroyed.
The sum of the individual energy consumptions and the individual energy storages is equal to the energy input.
Series Components
Parallel Components
Analogue of Ohm's Law: Applies to the complete circuit and to each component in the circuit. Flux = mmf/Reluctance.
Analogue of the Series Law: The magnetic flux value is the same at any point in a series magnetic circuit.
The magnetomotive force is the same across any branch of a parallel circuit.
Analogue of Kirchhoff's Voltage Law: The sum of the drops in mmf around a series circuit is equal to the source mmf.
Analogue of Kirchhoff's Current Law: The sum of the flux lines flowing away from a junction in a magnetic circuit is equal to the sum of the flux lines flowing into the junction.

QUESTIONS

1) Magnetic circuits are analogous to:
(*a*) flow of permeability in an iron core. (*b*) travel around a hysteresis loop. (*c*) electric circuits. (*d*) reluctivity which opposes the flow of magnetic dipoles.
2) Magnetomotive force can be compared with:
(*a*) the force of attraction between two magnetic poles. (*b*) the force of repulsion between two magnetic poles. (*c*) the force of the earth's magnetic field. (*d*) electromotive force.
3) Magnetic flux can be compared with:
(*a*) electrostatic flux. (*b*) electric current. (*c*) magnetic current. (*d*) magnetomotive force.
4) Reluctance can be compared with:
(*a*) conductance. (*b*) capacitance. (*c*) resistance. (*d*) residual magnetism.
5) A volume of air 1 in. sq and 3.19 in. long has a reluctance of:
(*a*) 1 ohm. (*b*) 1 mho. (*c*) 1 amp-turn. (*d*) 1 rel.
6) A magnetic circuit cannot be:
(*a*) connected in series with another magnetic circuit. (*b*) connected in parallel with another magnetic circuit. (*c*) continuous. (*d*) completely opened.
7) The reluctivity characteristic of iron is:
(*a*) the same as its resistivity. (*b*) nonlinear. (*c*) linear. (*d*) the same as its conductivity.
8) Magnetic pull developed by an electromagnet is proportional to:
(*a*) its flux density. (*b*) the square of its cross-sectional area. (*c*) the reciprocal of the cross-sectional area of each pole. (*d*) the square of the flux density in each pole.
9) If two reluctances are connected in series, the total reluctance is equal to:
(*a*) the product of the two reluctances divided by their sum. (*b*) the quotient of the two reluctances. (*c*) the product of the two reluctances. (*d*) the sum of the two reluctances.
10) When an iron core has a large air gap, the total reluctance is practically the same as the reluctance of:
(*a*) the air gap divided by the reluctance of the iron. (*b*) the iron divided by the reluctance of the air gap. (*c*) the iron. (*d*) the air gap.

PROBLEMS

1) If a magnetic circuit has a reluctance of 2 rels, and the magnetomotive force is 10 amp-turns, how many lines of flux are established in the magnetic circuit?
2) There are 10,000 flux lines in a core which has a reluctance of 0.5 rel. How many amp-turns of magnetomotive force are there in the winding around the core?
3) A magnetic circuit is comprised of a horseshoe electromagnet and a soft-iron armature. Both the horseshoe and the armature have smooth surfaces, so that there is no air gap present. There are 1000 flux lines per sq in. in each pole. The cross-sectional area of each pole is 2 sq in. What total force in pounds does the horseshoe exert upon the armature?
4) Another magnetic circuit comprises a horseshoe electromagnet and armature which have a uniform cross-sectional area of 1 in. The electromagnet has 100 amp-turns, and the magnetic circuit is 10 in. long. If the core and armature are fabricated from the iron depicted in Figure 8-7, what total magnetic pull does the magnet exert on the armature? (Assume that there is no air gap.)
5) When the armature is separated 1/16 in. from each pole in Problem 4, what is the total magnetic pull exerted on the armature?
6) One line of flux per sq cm is called a gauss. One line of flux is called a maxwell in the cgs system. Hence, gauss = maxwells/cm^2. If there is a flux of 1000 maxwells through a perpendicular area of 1 sq in., what is the flux density in gauss?
7) In the cgs system, the unit of magnetomotive force per centimeter is the oersted. One oersted exerts a force of 1 dyne on a unit magnetic pole. Oersteds and amp-turns are related as follows: oersteds = 1.26 × amp-turns/cm. If an air-core is 4 cm long and is wound with 10 turns, through which a current of 2 amps flows, calculate the number of oersteds of magnetomotive force per centimeter that are present at the center of the coil.
8) When a soft-iron bar is inserted into the coil in Problem 7, the length of the bar is placed in the denominator, instead of the length of the winding. The resulting answer is the magnetomotive force per centimeter at any point along the iron bar. If the bar is the same in length as the winding, the answer is the same as for an air core. However, if the bar is longer than the winding: oersteds = 1.26 × amp-turns/(bar length in cm). If an iron bar 12 cm in length is placed in the coil of Problem 7, calculate the magnetomotive force in the bar.

9) The gilbert is the unit of magnetomotive force in the cgs system. It follows from Problem 7 that: gilberts = 1.26 × amp-turns. If a coil has 250 turns, and a current flow of 100 ma is passed through the coil, how many gilberts of magnetomotive force are produced?
10) A kiloline is equal to 1000 lines of flux. If there are 10,000 maxwells in a certain core, how many kilolines are present?
11) If the reluctivity of an iron sample is 0.0001, what is its permeability?
12) If the reluctance of a magnetic circuit is 2 rels, what is its permeance in $rels^{-1}$?
13) A magnetic circuit with a reluctance of 0.5 rel is paralleled with another magnetic circuit, having a reluctance of 0.3 rel. What is the total reluctance of the parallel combination?
14) In the mks system, the unit of magnetic flux is the weber, equal to 10^8 maxwells in the cgs system. The unit of magnetic flux density in the mks system is 1 weber per sq meter. If the flux density in a core is equal to 0.5 weber, calculate the flux density in gauss.
15) If the flux density is 1 weber, calculate the flux density in lines per sq in.

REVIEW SUMMARY

Chapters 1 through 8 have been concerned with the laws of direct-current electricity. The following review summary presents the basic laws with which you should now be familiar.

1. The force between two electric charges varies directly as the product of the two quantities of charge, and inversely as the square of the distance between them.
2. The force between two electric charges varies inversely as the dielectric coefficient of the medium in which the charges are placed.
3. The work done by a quantity of electricity q when it flows from a point at potential V_1 to a point at potential V_2 is equal to $q(V_1 - V_2)$.
4. Ohm's law states that current flow is directly proportional to voltage, and inversely proportional to resistance.
5. Capacitance is directly proportional to the area of the electrodes and inversely proportional to their separation.
6. Capacitance is directly proportional to the dielectric coefficient of the insulating substance between the electrodes.
7. The force of attraction between two capacitor plates is directly proportional to their area, directly proportional to the square of the voltage between them, and inversely proportional to the square of the distance between the plates.
8. The increase in resistance of a conductor over its resistance at 0°C is equal to its temperature coefficient multiplied by the temperature in °C.
9. If an electron falls through a potential of V volts, its final velocity in meters per second is equal to $5.93 \times 10^5\sqrt{V}$.
10. Conductance is the reciprocal of resistance.
11. The power rate in watts is equal to volts multiplied by amperes.
12. The power quantity in watt-seconds is equal to the power rate in watts multiplied by the time in seconds.
13. The energy in ergs of a quantum is equal to its frequency in cycles per second multiplied by Planck's constant.
14. The number of electrons multiplied by the number of holes in a semiconductor is equal to the square of the number of electron-hole pairs in the corresponding intrinsic material.
15. The series law states that the current has the same value at any point in a series circuit.

16. Kirchhoff's voltage law states that the sum of all the voltage drops around a circuit is equal to the source voltage.

17. Source resistance is equal to the difference between the open-circuit voltage and the closed-circuit voltage, divided by the current flow on closed circuit.

18. Kirchhoff's current law states that the algebraic sum of the currents at any junction of conductors is equal to zero.

19. The input resistance of an infinite ladder is called its characteristic resistance.

20. If an infinite ladder is broken, and the finite section is terminated by the characteristic resistance of the infinite section, the input resistance of the finite section is equal to the characteristic resistance.

21. Negative resistance causes current flow to decrease when the applied voltage is increased.

22. The force between two magnetic poles is directly proportional to the product of the pole strengths, and inversely proportional to the square of the distance between them.

23. Two magnetic poles exert a mutual force that is inversely proportional to the permeability of the medium in which the poles are placed.

24. The magnetic field intensity inside a coil is directly proportional to the number of amp-turns, and inversely proportional to the length of the coil.

25. The total magnetomotive force developed by a coil is expressed in ampere-turns.

26. Flux density is equal to the magnetic field intensity in air multiplied by core permeability.

27. The flux in a magnetic circuit is directly proportional to the magnetomotive force and inversely proportional to the reluctance.

28. An electromagnet exerts a magnetic pull that is directly proportional to the cross-sectional area of each pole, and directly proportional to the square of the flux density in each pole.

29. A series magnetic circuit has a reluctance that is equal to the sum of the individual reluctances.

30. A parallel magnetic circuit has a reluctance that is equal to the product of the individual reluctances, divided by their sum.

9

ELECTROMAGNETIC INDUCTION

9.1 INDUCED ELECTRIC CURRENTS

Electric current (charges in motion) produce a magnetic field. Conversely, a magnetic field in motion produces an electric current. For example, Figure 9-1 illustrates a practical demonstration of electromagnetic induction. A coil of wire is connected to an electrical meter. When

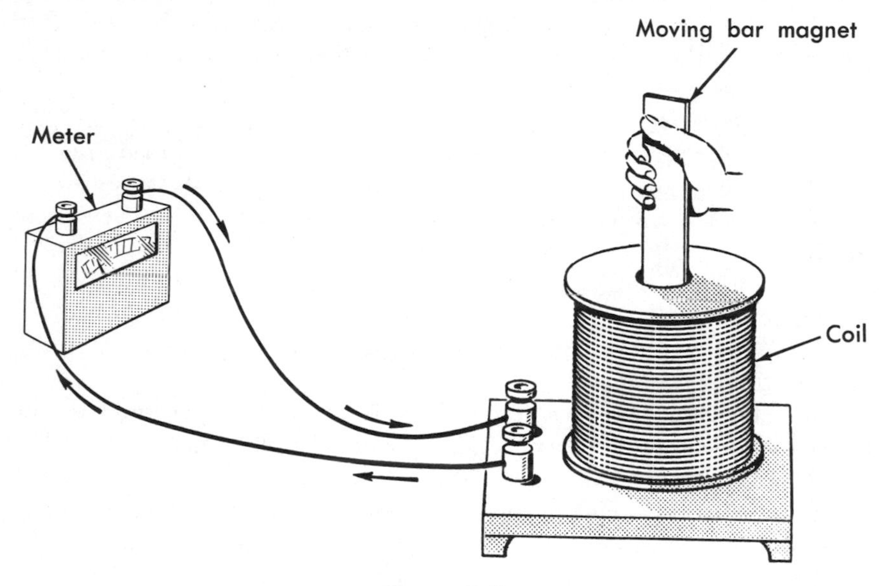

Figure 9-1
Motion of the permanent magnetic induces an electric current in the coil circuit.

a permanent magnet is moved with respect to the coil, the pointer deflects on the meter scale. No current flows when the magnet is motionless. If the magnet is moved downward, the pointer deflects in one direction on the scale. On the other hand, if the magnet is moved upward, the pointer deflects in the other direction.

It is relative motion that generates induced currents. Figure 9-2 depicts a conductor *AB* moving downward through a magnetic field. Current flows in the wire as long as the conductor moves through the field. Note carefully that the direction of current flow indicated in Figure 9-2 is *conventional* flow. Electrons actually flow in the opposite direction. It is customary in this area of electronics to state electrical laws in terms of conventional current flow.

Lenz' law is a right-hand rule that states the relations shown in Figure 9-2. Note that magnetic flux lines cross the air gap from the north pole to the south pole of the magnet. Lenz' law, illustrated in Figure 9-3, states that if your forefinger points in the direction of the flux lines, and your thumb points in the direction that the conductor moves, your middle finger will point in the direction of induced current flow; it points in the direction of conventional current flow. To restate Lenz' law for electron flow, it is necessary to use a left-hand rule instead of the right-hand rule.

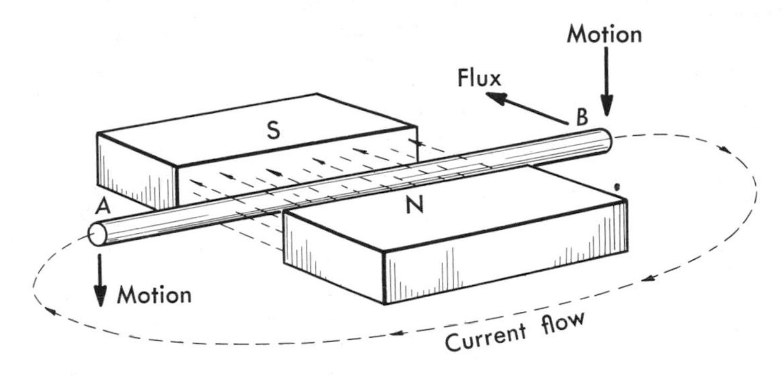

Figure 9-2
Motion of the conductor *AB* through the magnetic field induces an electric current in the conductor circuit.

Suppose the external circuit is open in Figure 9-2. Current cannot flow; however, a voltage exists across the open circuit while the conductor is moving through the magnetic field. How much voltage is generated? If the conductor "cuts" 10^8 flux lines per sec, an emf of 1 volt is generated in the conductor. To *cut* a flux line means that the conductor moves at right angles to the flux line. If the conductor should move parallel to the flux lines, no emf would be induced. It is necessary that the conductor have a component of motion at right angles to the flux lines to generate an emf.

If you use three conductors instead of one (Figure 9-4), how much voltage will be generated? If the conductors cut 10^8 flux lines per sec, an emf of 1 volt will be generated in each conductor. Since the conductors are connected in series-aiding, the total generated emf is equal to 3 volts. It is evident that the current which flows in the external circuit depends upon its resistance, and must obey Ohm's law.

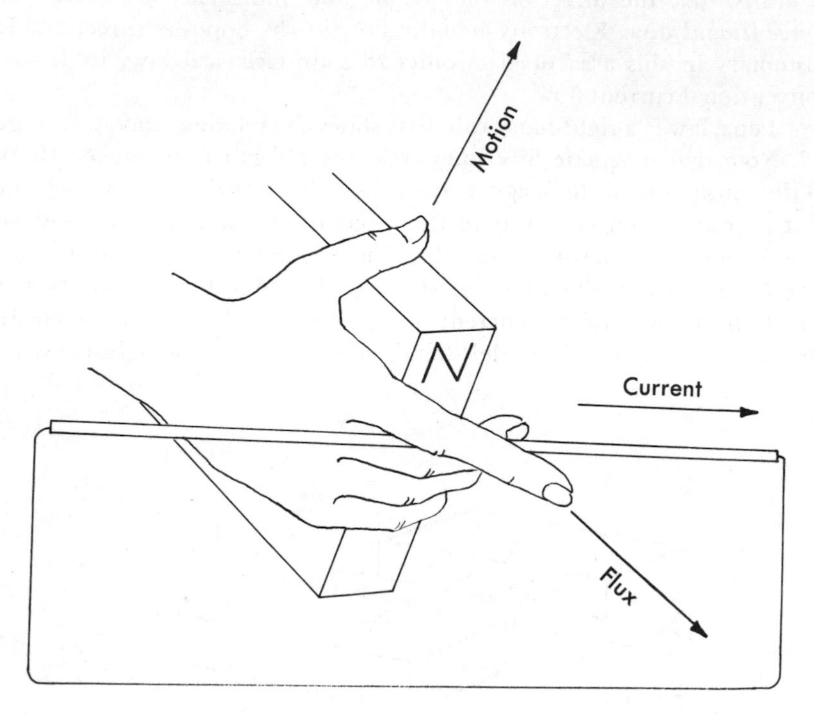

Figure 9-3
Lenz' right-hand law for induced current flow.

CONSERVATION OF ENERGY

When the circuit in Figure 9-2 is open, the motion of the conductor is unopposed. On the other hand, when the circuit is closed, current flows and work must be done to move the conductor through the field. This fact is apparent, because current flow in the circuit consumes power equal to I^2R. The law of conservation of energy requires that this I^2R value be equal to the work being done in moving the conductor through the magnetic field. In other words, the current induced in the conductor necessarily flows in a direction that produces a magnetic field opposing motion of the conductor.

It is inconceivable that the magnetic field produced by the induced current could aid the motion of the conductor. If this were the case, the magnetic field thus produced would speed up the motion of the conductor, which in turn would induce still more current. Thus, we would have the phenomenon of perpetual motion. We can now restate Lenz' law to assert that the induced current flows in a direction establishing a magnetic field that opposes the force applied to the conductor.

An example of these relations is depicted in Figure 9-5. The conductor is being moved up from the plane of the diagram through the magnetic flux lines H at (a). Induced current flows around the circuit as shown by the arrows. This induced current is accompanied by a magnetic field indicated by the circular arrows. Note that the top of the conductor is enclosed by flux lines which aid the external flux lines H as shown at (b). Hence, the total flux density is greater above the conductor than below it. Flux

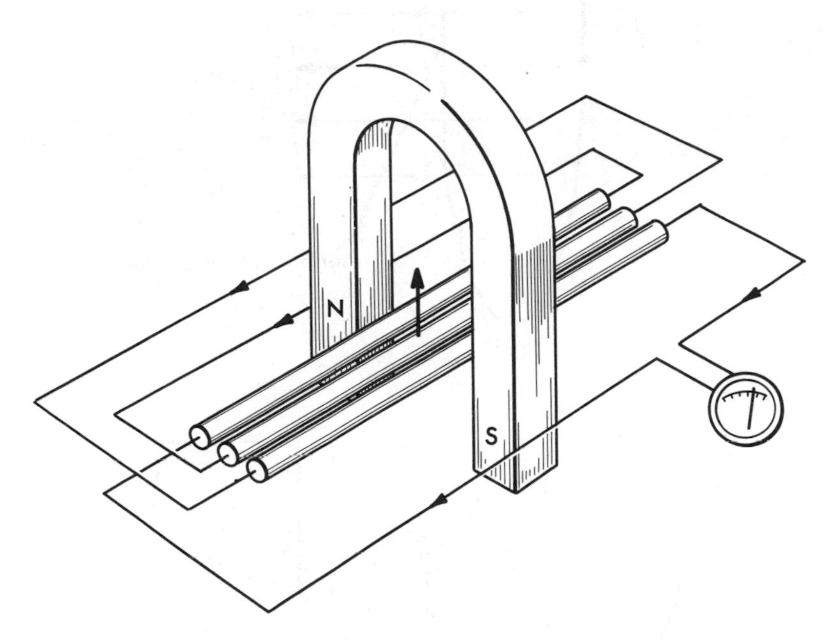

Figure 9-4
The three conductors connected in series-aiding provide three times the emf of a single conductor.

lines repel one another; therefore, the flux distribution in Figure 9-5 exerts a downward force on the conductor. The greater the induced current, the greater is this downward force that opposes upward motion of the conductor.

The equation for induced voltage in a conductor can be written

$$E = \frac{\phi \times 10^{-8}}{t} \tag{9.1}$$

where E is the induced emf, ϕ is the number of flux lines that are cut, and t is the time in seconds over which the lines are cut.

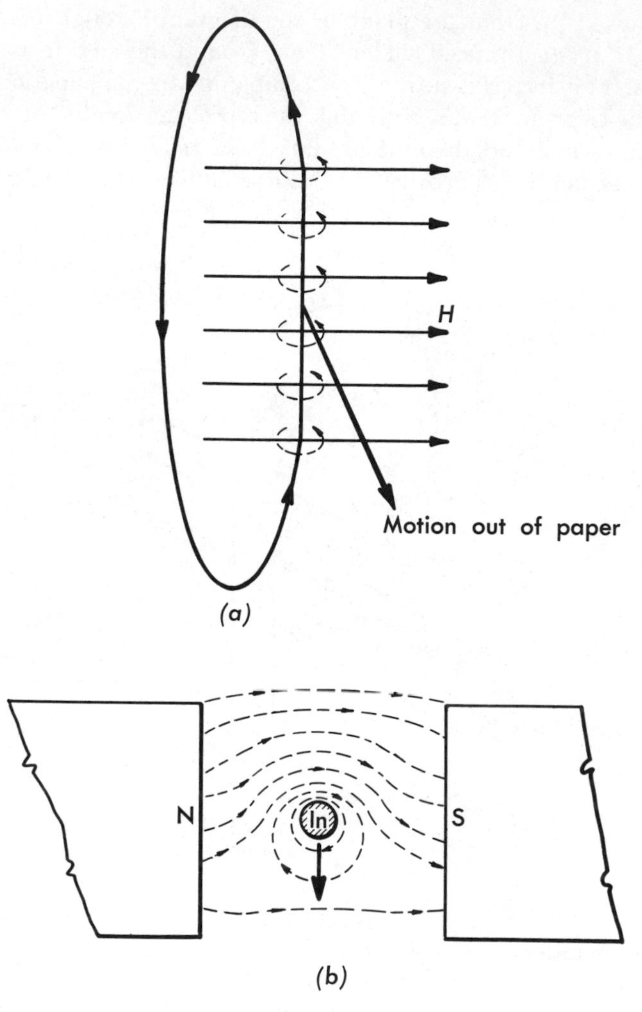

Figure 9-5
(a) Induced current in the conductor establishes magnetic flux encircling the conductor. *(b)* The total flux is concentrated ahead of the conductor, and exerts an opposing force on the conductor.

INSTANTANEOUS VOLTAGE

Equation (9.1) makes two assumptions: First, it is assumed that the flux density is uniform during the time that the flux lines are cut by the conductor; second, it is assumed that the motion of the conductor is uniform during time t. Of course, there are many practical situations in which these assumptions will not be correct. In such case, we must consider the *instantaneous* induced voltage. For instance, suppose that the flux density is not uniform, and that the motion of the conductor is not uniform. Nevertheless, at any instant that we choose, the flux density does have a certain value, and the conductor does have a certain velocity.

For example, let us suppose that the flux density varies from 10,000 lines per sq in. at the top of the gap to 5000 lines per sq in. at the bottom of the gap. Between the top and bottom of the gap, let us take a *very small interval* over which the average flux density is 7500 lines per sq in. We will call this flux density $\Delta\phi = 7500$, in which Δ is the symbol for "very small interval." The conductor traverses this very small interval in a very short time, and the time that is required to traverse the tiny interval will be called Δt. It is clear that an "instantaneous" emf will be induced in the conductor as it traverses $\Delta\phi$ in time Δt. We could call this emf ΔE; however, it is customary to symbolize an instantaneous emf simply as e. Therefore,

$$e = \frac{\Delta\phi \times 10^{-8}}{\Delta t} \tag{9.2}$$

We see that as the conductor passes from top to bottom of the gap which has nonuniform flux density with a nonuniform speed, the induced emf at any chosen instant has a value proportional to $\Delta\phi$ divided by Δt, where the values of $\Delta\phi$ and Δt prevail only at the chosen instant.

Equation (9.2) is used much more widely than Equation (9.1) because many practical devices do not provide uniform flux density, or do not operate at constant speed, or both. Since Equation (9.2) is perfectly general, it applies to any condition of nonuniform flux density and/or nonuniform speed. It follows from previous discussion that when the flux density is constant, and the speed of the conductor is constant, Equation (9.2) becomes identical with Equation (9.1).

Next, let us suppose that the flux density is uniform, and that the motion of the conductor is uniform. The conductor does not cut the flux lines at right angles, but instead cuts the lines at a 60 degree angle as depicted in Figure 9-6. How shall we rewrite Equation (9.1) to take this angle into account? We perceive that the conductor in Figure 9-6 has a downward *component* of motion which does cut the flux lines at right angles. This component is equal to the sine of 60 degrees or 0.866. Evidently, the induced voltage is equal to 0.866 of the value stated by Equation (9.1). In general terms, therefore, we shall write

$$E = \frac{\phi \times 10^{-8} \times \sin\theta}{t} \tag{9.3}$$

where θ is the angle at which the conductor cuts the flux lines.

Figure 9-6 represents a situation in which all the variables have been chosen as linear. Consider the situation, on the other hand, in which the flux density is not uniform, the conductor motion is not uniform, and the cutting angle is not uniform. In this case, Equation (9.3) must be written in a more general form

$$e = \frac{\Delta\phi \times 10^{-8} \times \sin\theta_t}{\Delta t} \tag{9.4}$$

where θ_t is the average angle that prevails during the very small chosen interval.

It has appeared in the foregoing derivations for nonuniform situa-

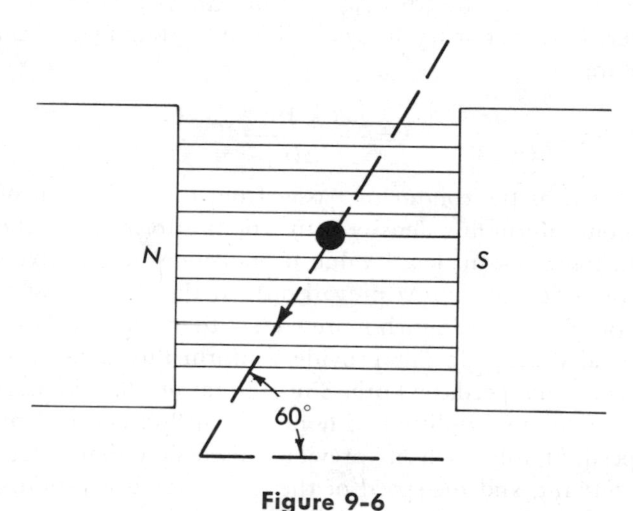

Figure 9-6
The conductor cuts the flux lines at an angle of 60 degrees.

tions that average values must be taken over a very small interval. Because an average value is used, there is an inevitable, though small, error in calculation. This error can be made as small as we please by choosing an appropriately small interval. However, it is evident that absolute accuracy cannot be realized unless the chosen interval is equal to zero. In advanced mathematics, you will learn how to find the limit that is approached as the interval approaches zero.

9.2 INDUCED VOLTAGE IN A ROTATING COIL

Let us now consider an important practical situation in which a single-turn coil rotates at constant velocity in a uniform magnetic field, as depicted in Figure 9-7. The emf induced in the left-hand side of the coil has opposite polarity from the induced emf in the right-hand side of the coil. Hence, the two induced emf's add and give twice the voltage generated by one conductor. Recall that when the coil is in position *ae*, zero emf is generated—the conductors are moving parallel with the flux lines and $\sin 0° = 0$.

As the coil rotates to position *bf*, its conductors are moving at an angle to the flux lines, and an emf is accordingly generated. This emf has a value that is proportional to the height of ordinate *b* in Figure

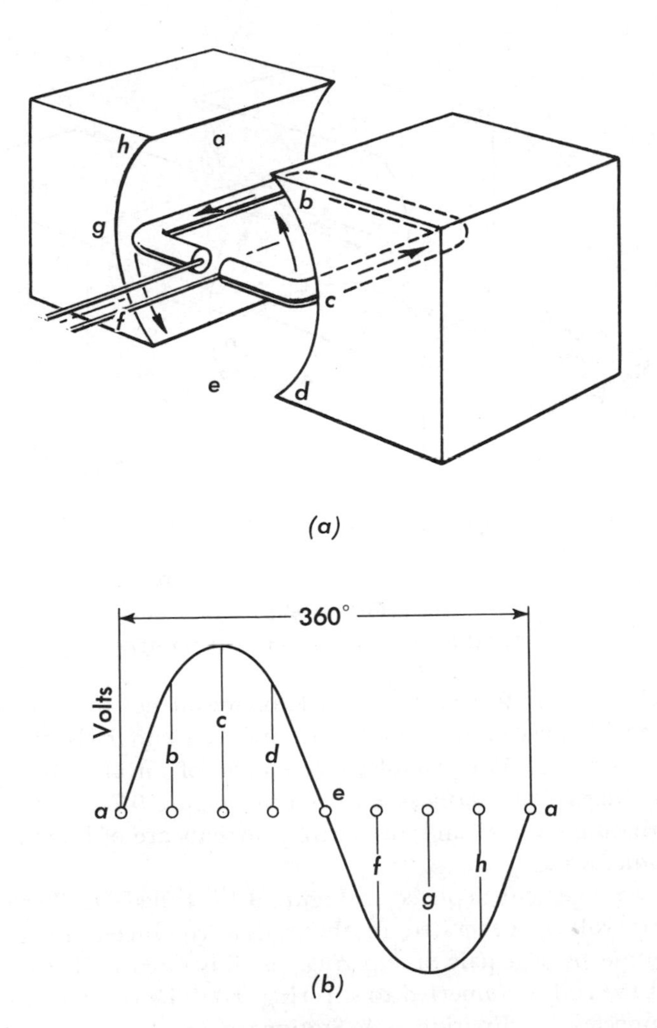

Figure 9-7
(*a*) Single-turn coil rotating in a uniform magnetic field. (*b*) Sinusoidal voltage induced in the rotating coil.

9-7(b); this height, of course, is proportional to sin θ. When the coil rotates farther to position *cg*, the conductors are moving at right angles to the flux. Therefore, the maximum emf is generated at this instant ($\sin 90° = 1$). Note that at position *dh*, the generated emf is the same as at position *bf*, as indicated by ordinate d in Figure 9-7(b). Again, at position *ea*, the generated emf has fallen to zero as at the beginning of the cycle.

When the coil advances to position *fb*, each conductor must have a reversed polarity of generated emf. The value of the emf is indicated by

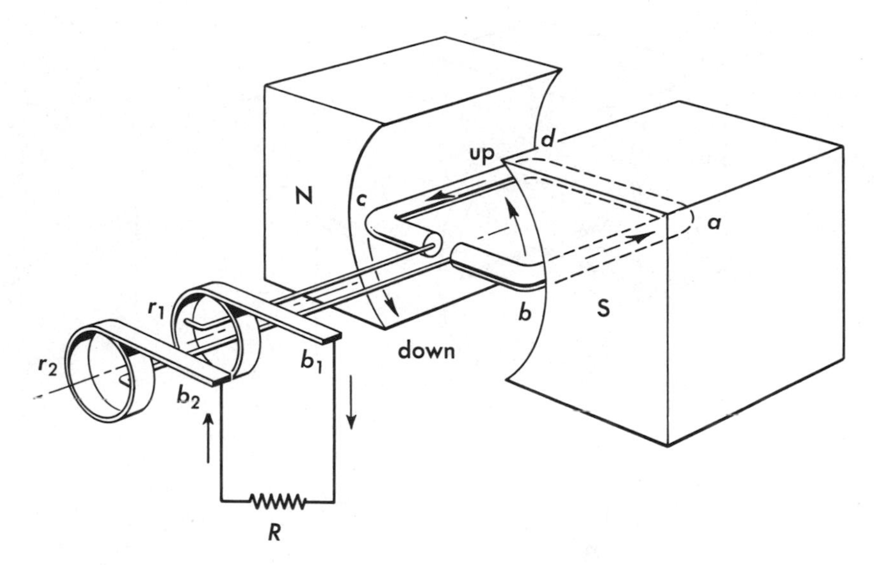

Figure 9-8
An alternator has a pair of slip rings.

ordinate f in Figure 9-7(b). As the coil rotates farther to position *gc*, the induced emf is maximum. Finally, the induced emf falls once more to zero at position *ae*. This completes *one cycle* of an *alternating voltage.* An alternating voltage has a *sine waveform* [Figure 9-7(b)]. We shall find that alternating voltages and alternating currents are of basic importance in electronics work.

The arrangement depicted in Figure 9-7 is called an *alternator*. The alternating voltage generated in the coil is conducted to an external circuit by means of a pair of *slip rings* as illustrated in Figure 9-8. One end (c) of the coil is connected to slip ring (r_1). The other end of the coil (b) is connected to slip ring (r_2). Stationary *brushes* (b_1 and b_2) make sliding contact with the rings and conduct the induced current to load resistance R. Since an alternating voltage is applied to R, an alternating current flows through R.

COMMUTATOR ACTION

Observe that if the pair of slip rings is replaced by a single split ring, as depicted in Figure 9-9, automatic switch action ensues. In other words, the coil connection reverses at the same instant that the induced emf reverses. This split ring is called a *commutator.* The commutator was invented in 1838 by an engineer named Sturgeon. We perceive that its switch action causes the induced emf to always appear with the same polarity in the external circuit. This is not a steady voltage; it necessarily has the half-sine waveform depicted in Figure 9-9(*b*). A voltage that varies but does not change its polarity at any time is called a *pulsating* d-c voltage. The machine depicted in Figure 9-9 is called a d-c generator. We shall encounter pulsating d-c voltages in many types of electronic equipment.

The value of induced voltage is proportional to the rotational speed of the coil. It is also proportional to the number of turns on the coil; if the coil has ten turns, the induced voltage will be ten times as much as for a single turn at the same speed of rotation. The value of induced voltage is also proportional to the magnetic flux density. If the flux density is doubled, the induced voltage will be doubled, with other things remaining equal. Note that the current flowing in the external circuit is equal to the induced voltage divided by the total resistance of the circuit. When heavy currents are to be drawn from the coil, it must be wound with suitably large wire to avoid overheating.

We recall that the power consumed by the external circuit is equal to I^2R, where R is the value of the load resistance. Power is also consumed by the coil resistance $W_c = I^2R_c$, where W_c is the power dissipated by the coil, and R_c is the coil resistance. Evidently, it is desirable to minimize the coil resistance to minimize waste power and thereby maximize the system efficiency. Typical generators operate at 85 percent efficiency. Suppose that an ideal generator develops 746 watts in the external load. In turn, 1 horsepower of mechanical energy is consumed in rotating the coil. But if the generator is 85 percent efficient, approximately 1.18 horsepower must be applied to the coil to develop 746 watts in the load.

SHUNT EXCITATION

Direct-current generators are usually constructed to excite their own fields. Several configurations are utilized, all of which are of practical importance. Figure 9-9(*c*) shows the basic methods of exciting the field magnets. In *separate* excitation, the current for the field coils is taken from an independent source, such as a battery. However, in *shunt* excitation, the current from the armature divides. Some of the current goes to the load circuit, and some to the field coils. When the armature current divides in

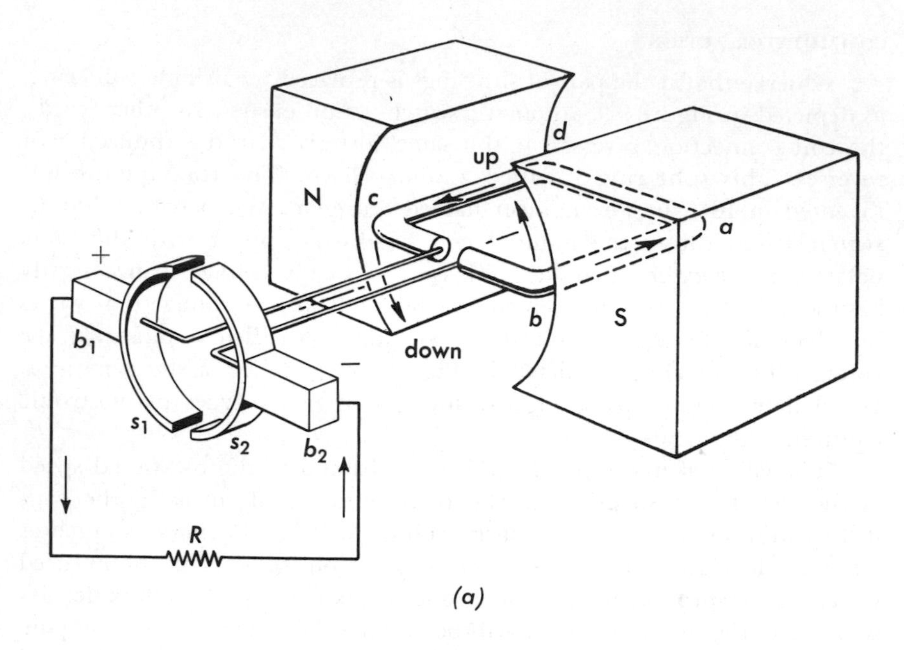

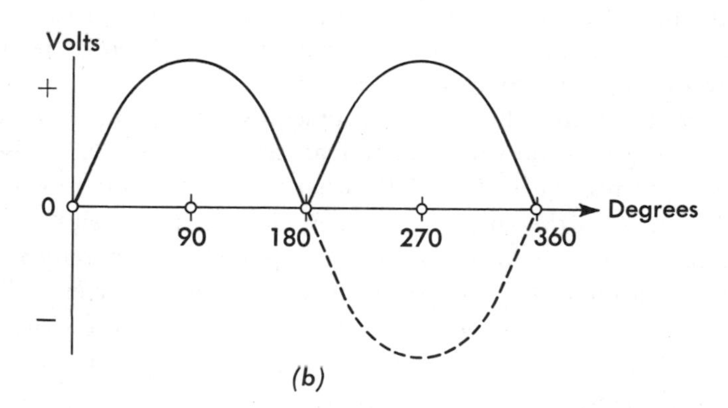

Figure 9-9

(a) A commutator operates as an automatic switch. *(b)* Half-sine waves of induced emf are applied to the external circuit. *(c)* Field-excitation methods for d-c generators. *(d)* Generator terminal voltage versus load. *a*: Separately excited. *b*: Shunt excited. *c*: Series excited. *d*: Compound excited.

(Continued on facing page.)

this manner, the machine is called a *shunt generator*. Only a small fraction of the total current generated is required for field excitation. This might be 5 percent for a 1-kw generator, and as little as 2 percent for a 100-kw generator.

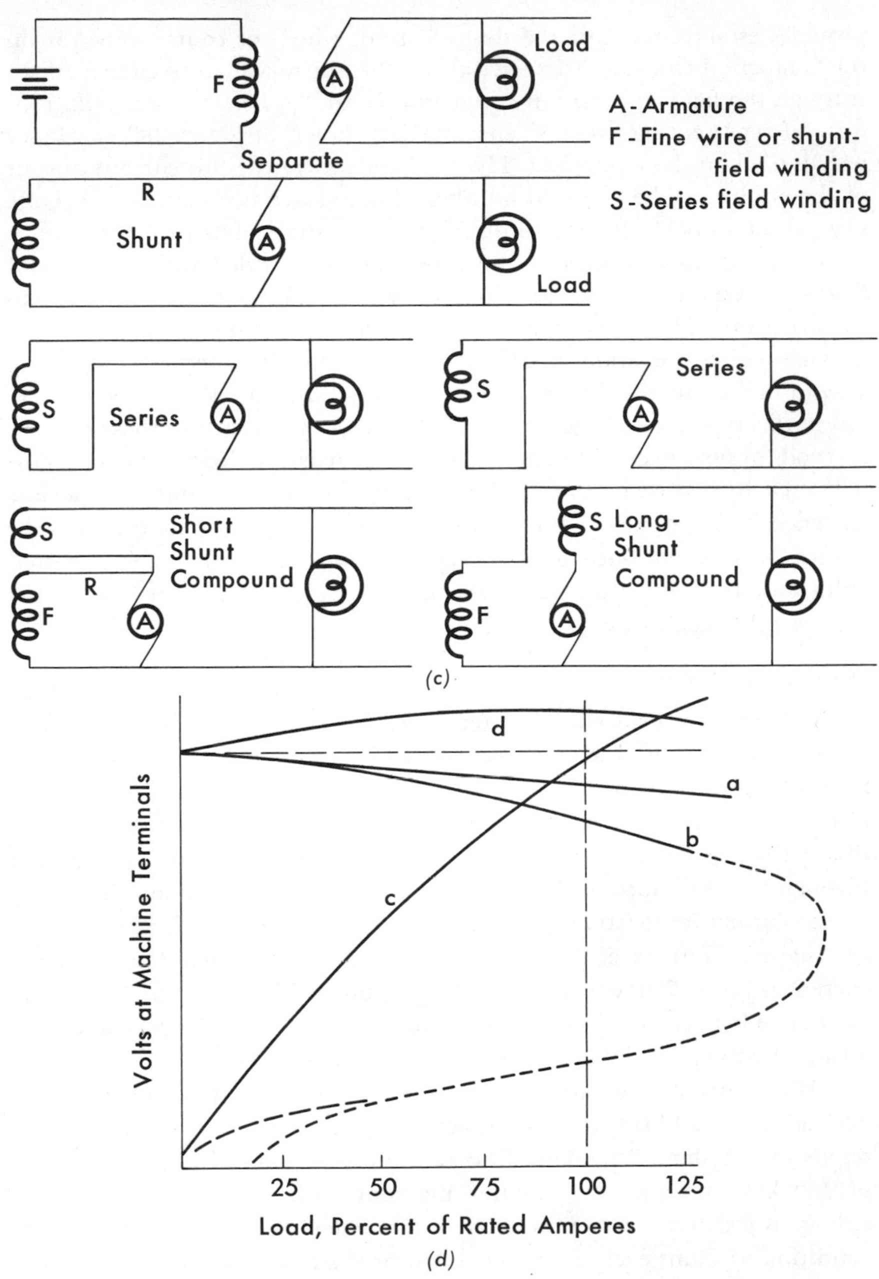

Fig. 9-9 (*Continued*)

Shunt field windings consist of many turns of fine insulated wire. There may be 2000 or 3000 turns employed. A typical field winding has 2800 turns of wire 0.01 in. in diameter. Because of its high resistance, it permits only a small current flow. However, the large number of turns provides establishment of the desired mmf, which of course depends on the "ampere-turns." In *series* excitation, the entire armature current flows through the field coils, and the machine is said to be *series excited.* Two ways of representing a series generator are shown in Figure 9-9(*c*). Heavy wire is used on the series coils. The field coils carry the full current output of the machine. The required number of amp-turns is obtained by a large number of amperes flowing through a comparatively few turns of wire.

In *compound* excitation, the generator is provided with two sets of field coils. One coil is wound with fine wire and is connected in shunt to the armature. The other coil is wound with heavy wire and is connected in series with the armature. This arrangement is called a *compound-wound* or "compound" generator. Two ways are commonly used to represent this type of machine, as seen in Figure 9-9(*c*). Why are these various methods of field excitation employed? Ordinarily, the load on a generator will vary. By this we mean that there are changes in the number of devices switched into the load. Lamps may be turned on or off; motors may be started or stopped. Such load changes automatically affect the terminal voltage of the generator, but they affect it differently, according to the type of field excitation.

GENERATOR CHARACTERISTICS

To see why load effects differ in each case, consider the generator driven at steady speed without load. Then, imagine the load current (current through the armature) to be successively increased. If separate excitation is used, a certain emf is generated at no load. When current flows in the armature, some of this emf is cancelled in the flowing of current through the resistance of the armature itself. There is also another effect due to "armature reaction" that weakens the magnetic field, as explained in Chapter 17. Hence, the terminal voltage is less when the armature current is large. Curve *a* in Figure 9-9(*d*) shows this characteristic graphically. The load current in amperes is plotted along the horizontal axis, and terminal voltage is plotted along the vertical axis.

If the current is greater, the voltage is lower. The difference between no-load and full-load voltage shown in the diagram corresponds to a *regulation* of about 8 percent. This percentage is found in large machines of 100 kw, or more. For smaller machines, the variation in terminal voltage is greater. Let us now analyze the generator characteristic for the condition of shunt excitation. When shunt excitation is used, the reduced terminal voltage sends a reduced current through the field coils, so that the magnetic flux decreases as the armature current increases. Hence, the terminal voltage falls off more than in the case of separate excitation. Curve *b* in Figure 9-9(*d*) shows the characteristic of a shunt generator; the dashed portion depicts how the terminal voltage falls off when the machine is greatly overloaded.

With series excitation, on the other hand, the situation is quite different. When no current flows, only the weak residual magnetism of the iron is present, and the generated emf is accordingly very small. Curve *c* in Figure 9-9(*d*) shows this characteristic; note that the graph starts slightly above the zero value. When current is taken from the machine, the current flow through the field coils strengthens the magnetic field, causing a greater emf to be generated. Thus, curve *c* rises rapidly.

Finally, in the compound generator, series and shunt effects are combined. Depending on the relative proportions of the two windings, the voltage at full load may be made equal to that at no load, or greater, or less. (The latter choice is rarely employed in practice.) Curve *d* in Figure 9-9(*d*) depicts a generator that is somewhat "over-compounded." If the full-load voltage were the same as the no-load voltage, the generator would be "flat-compounded."

9.3 RMS VALUES OF VOLTAGE AND CURRENT

We know that power in a d-c situation is given by $W = EI$. Figure 9-9(*b*) illustrates a d-c situation, but this is not a steady d-c function. As previously noted, it is a pulsating d-c waveform that consists of half-sine waves. It is obvious that we cannot state that the power in load resistance R [Figure 9-9(*a*)] is equal to EI until we derive the *effective* values of E and I, which correspond to a steady direct current. Evidently, the effective value of a half-sine wave will fall somewhere between its zero value and its maximum (peak or crest) value. Let us see how this effective value is derived.

First, we shall ask what the *average* value of a half-sine wave means. The average of the half-sine waveform depicted in Figure 9-10 simply means its equivalent steady d-c value. The quantity of electricity that flows in response to a steady d-c voltage is equal to current multiplied by time. How do we multiply current by time in Figure 9-10? This is basically very simple. The amplitude (height) of the half-sine waveform at any point is proportional to instantaneous current flow. Furthermore, the horizontal intervals are proportional to time. Hence, electrical *quantity* in Figure 9-10 is proportional to *area*. Each square in the coordinate system represents a specific quantity of electricity.

Note that if we "chop off" a suitable area from the top of the first half-sine wave, this area will "fill in" the open space between the first and second half-sine waves. In other words, the upper shaded area is equal to the lower shaded area in Figure 9-10. In turn, the level indicated by the dotted line is the equivalent steady d-c value of the half-sine wave-

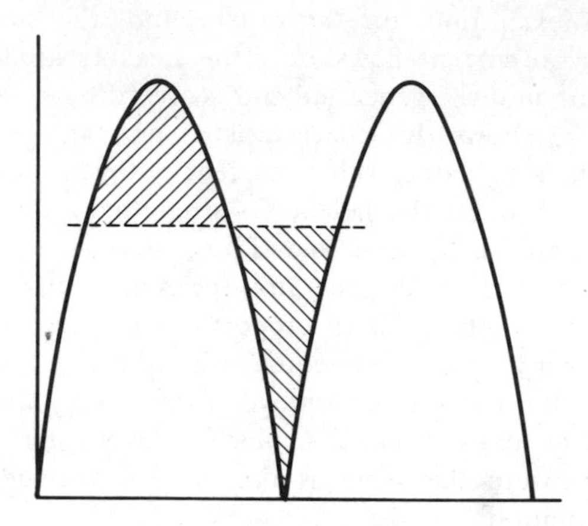

Figure 9-10
Average value of a half-sine waveform.

form; the dotted line falls at the average value of the half-sine waveform. Just how do we find this average value?

We can approximate the average value in Figure 9-10 by counting squares; there are the same number of squares in each of the shaded areas. But this is only an approximate determination, because we have to count up various fractional squares, and this involves an estimation error. However, if we tally up the squares and portions of squares carefully, we will find that the average value which separates equal areas in Figure 9-10 falls somewhere between 60 percent and 65 percent of the peak waveform value. In advanced mathematics courses, you will learn a method whereby this average value can be calculated, to eliminate estimation error. You will then find that the average value of the half-sine waveform is 0.636 of the peak value.

Here is a practical example of peak-value indication in electronics work. If you apply a half-sine waveform that has a peak voltage of 10 volts to a d-c voltmeter, the pointer will indicate 6.36 volts on the scale. Thus, it is much quicker to measure the average value than to calculate it.

To summarize, horizontal intervals in Figure 9-10 are proportional to time, vertical intervals are proportional to voltage (or current), and areas are proportional to electrical quantity (coulombs). A point on the graph represents an instantaneous voltage (or current) value. The same graph can be used to analyze either voltage or current, because, when a given voltage waveform is applied to a resistive load, the current waveform is the same.

EFFECTIVE VALUE OF HALF-SINE WAVE

We shall now turn to the question of what the effective value of a half-sine waveform may be. The term *effective value* is the value of the half-sine waveform that will dissipate the same power in a resistive load as an equal steady d-c value. We perceive that the effective value cannot be the same as the average value, because power is equal to I^2R or E^2/R in a resistance. Since power is proportional to voltage squared (or current squared), our first question is what the average value of $\sin^2 \theta$ may be.

In Figure 9-11, we see the half-sine waveform at $\sin \theta$; we also see that the graph of $\sin^2 \theta$ is a smooth sine wave. Of course, this comes as

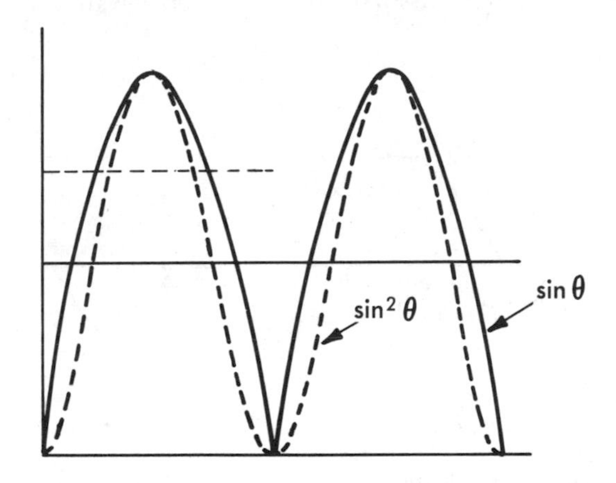

Figure 9-11
Average value of $\sin^2 \theta$

no surprise when we recall the trigonometric formulas. The graph of $\sin^2 \theta$ is obviously located on an axis that is halfway up to the peak value of the waveforms. We note from inspection that the portion of the $\sin^2 \theta$ curve above this axis will exactly fill the "empty space" in the $\sin^2 \theta$ curve below the axis. No counting of squares is required, because we know that a sine wave is symmetrical.

Thus, Figure 9-11 demonstrates that the average value of $\sin^2 \theta$ is equal to one-half the peak value of the waveforms. Power is proportional to E^2. Accordingly, we ask what value of effective voltage squared is equal to one-half of the peak voltage squared. We can find this value at once by writing our question as an equation:

$$E_{\text{eff}}^2 = \frac{E_{\text{peak}}^2}{2} \qquad \textbf{(9.5)}$$

or,

$$E_{\text{eff}} = \frac{E_{\text{peak}}}{\sqrt{2}} \tag{9.6}$$

The effective voltage of the half-sine wave is equal to 0.707 of its peak voltage. In practical terms, this means that the power dissipated in a resistance by a half-sine wave of voltage is equal to $(0.707E_{\text{peak}})^2/R$. Another practical example is the fact that a half-sine waveform with a peak voltage of 10 volts will dissipate just as much power in a resistance as 7.07 volts of steady d-c. We use the effective values of sine waveforms to calculate power just as we use steady values of d-c to calculate power.

Refer back to the sine wave depicted in Figure 9-7(*b*). It is evident that this sine wave will dissipate the same power in a resistance as the

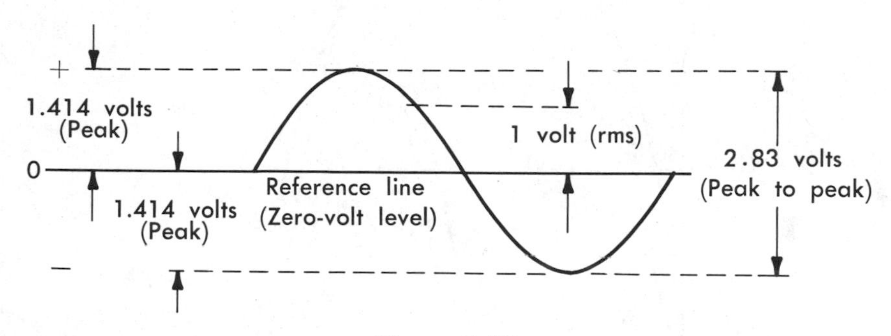

Figure 9-12
Corresponding rms, peak, and peak-to-peak voltages of a sine wave.

half-sine wave depicted in Figure 9-9(*b*). The reason is, of course, that the square of a negative number is a positive number. Hence, the $\sin^2 \theta$ curve in Figure 9-11 represents the square of either a sine wave or the square of a half-sine wave.

In your advanced mathematics courses, you will learn another method of finding the effective value of a sine wave. This attack determines the effective value in terms of the square root of the average sum of the squares. Hence, the effective value is often called the root-mean-square value, or simply the *rms value*. Whether a discussion uses the term effective value or rms value, it always means 0.707 of the peak value of the sine wave.

To fix the foregoing facts firmly in mind, observe the diagram of a sine wave in Figure 9-12. This waveform has an rms value of 1 volt. Hence, its peak voltage is 1.414 volts. Otherwise stated, $0.707 \times 1.414 = 1$. Note also that the *peak-to-peak* voltage of a sine wave is double its peak voltage. Thus, the peak-to-peak voltage of this wave is 2.83 volts. It might seem beside the point to specify the peak-to-peak voltage in this case. However, as we proceed with our study of electronics, we will find it essential to occasionally work with peak-to-peak values.

9.4 FREQUENCY OF A GENERATED VOLTAGE

Each complete revolution of the coil in Figure 9-7 generates one complete cycle. Suppose the alternator is driven at a speed of 3600 revolutions per min (rpm). This is a speed of 60 revolutions per sec. Hence, the generated voltage has a *frequency* of 60 cycles per sec (cps). The standard

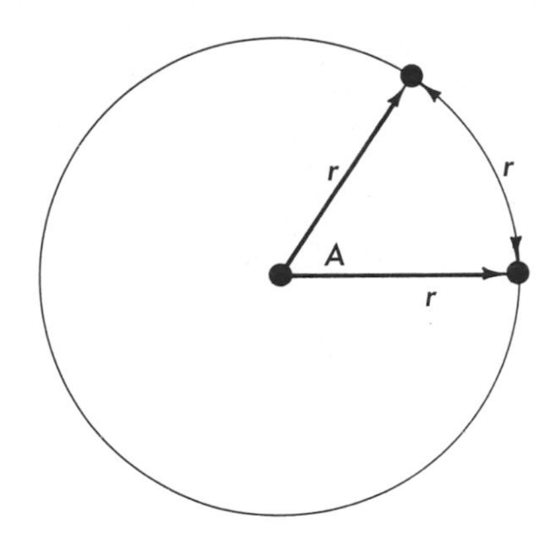

Figure 9-13
Angle A is equal to 1 radian, or approximately 57.3 degrees.

electric-power frequency in the United States is 60 cps. However, various other countries utilize an electric-power frequency of 50 cps. Alternators have been devised that provide frequencies as high as 22,000 cycles per sec (22 kc). Note that the human ear cannot respond to tones higher than 10 kc, approximately. We often speak of frequencies without any time reference, such as "60 cycles" or "1000 cycles." In all such cases, it is implied that the second is the time unit.

We have seen that an alternator generates a sine wave of voltage that has a certain frequency. The instantaneous voltage is a function of the angular position of the coil depicted in Figure 9-7. This function is $E \sin \theta$, where E is the peak value of the generated voltage, and θ is the coil's angular position in degrees. A complete circle, of course, contains 360 degrees. In electronics technology, it is found most convenient to measure angles in *radians*. A radian is the angle that is subtended by an

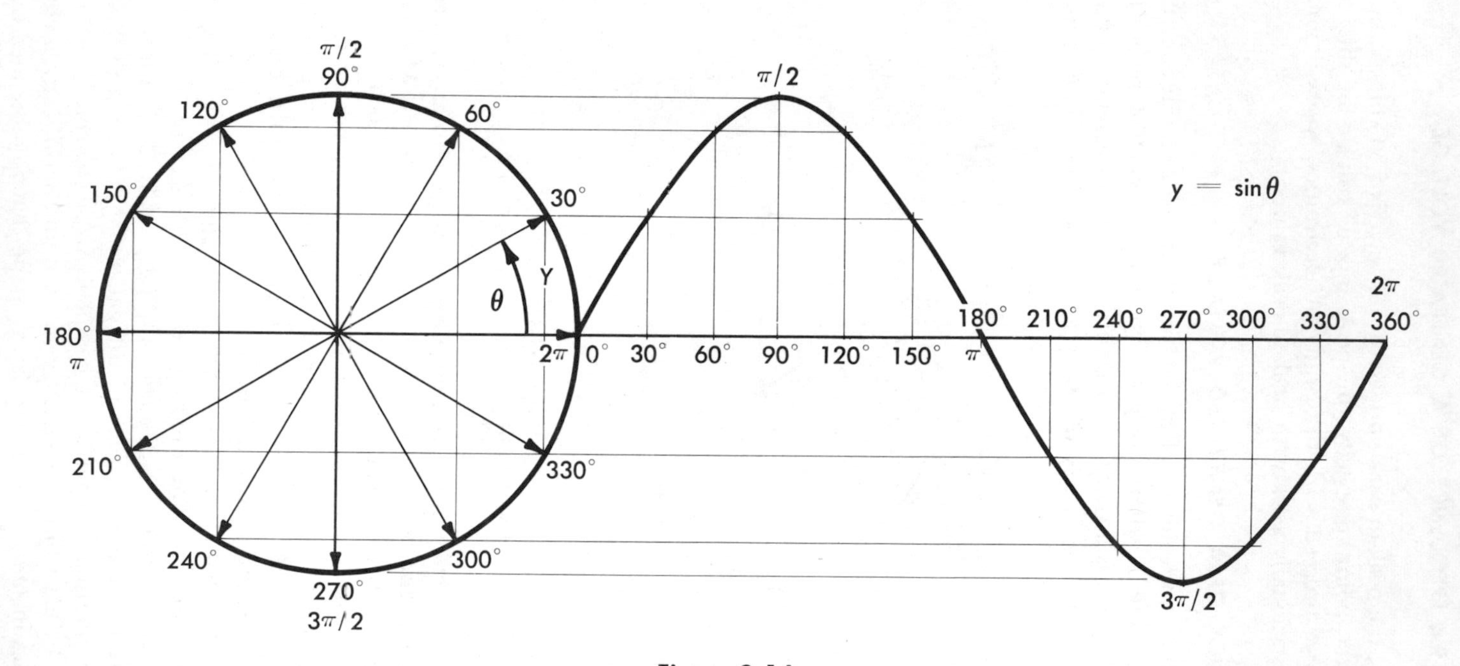

Figure 9-14
A sine wave is generated geometrically by counterclockwise rotation of a radius vector.

arc equal in length to the radius of a circle, as seen in Figure 9-13; it is approximately equal to 57.3 degrees.

It follows that there are 2π radians in a complete circle; or, one complete cycle of a sine wave contains 2π radians. The constant 2π is, of course, equal to approximately 6.28. Note carefully how a sine wave is mathematically generated, as depicted in Figure 9-14. The radius vector

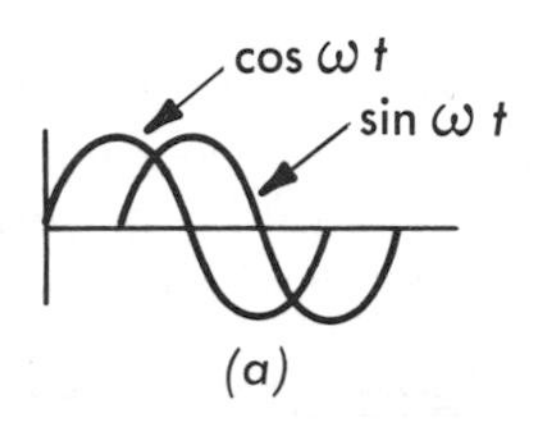

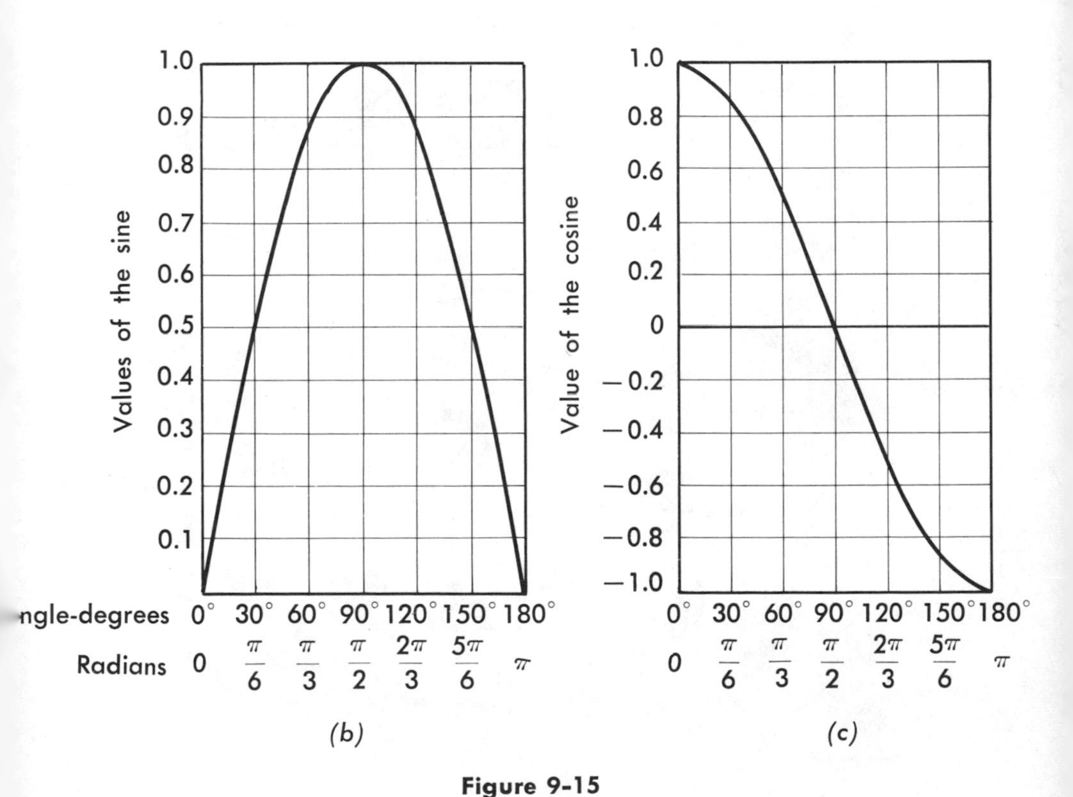

Figure 9-15

(a) Graphs of $\sin \omega t$ and $\cos \omega t$. *(b)* Progressive values of $\sin \omega t$. *(c)* Progressive values of $\cos \omega t$.

rotates *counterclockwise*. Its projection on the horizontal axis defines the instantaneous values of the sine wave. At 90 degrees, the radius vector has traversed $\pi/2$ radians; at 180 degrees, π radians; at 270 degrees, $3\pi/2$ radians; and at 360 degrees, 2π radians. It is essential to remember that the radius vector rotates counterclockwise by convention; otherwise, subsequent topics will be confusing.

Electronics workers commonly express the equation of a sine wave as

$$e = E \sin 2\pi ft \tag{9.7}$$

where e is the instantaneous voltage of the sine wave, E is its peak voltage, f is its frequency in cycles per second, and t is the time in seconds.

An inspection of Equation (9.7) shows why it is so useful; it formu-

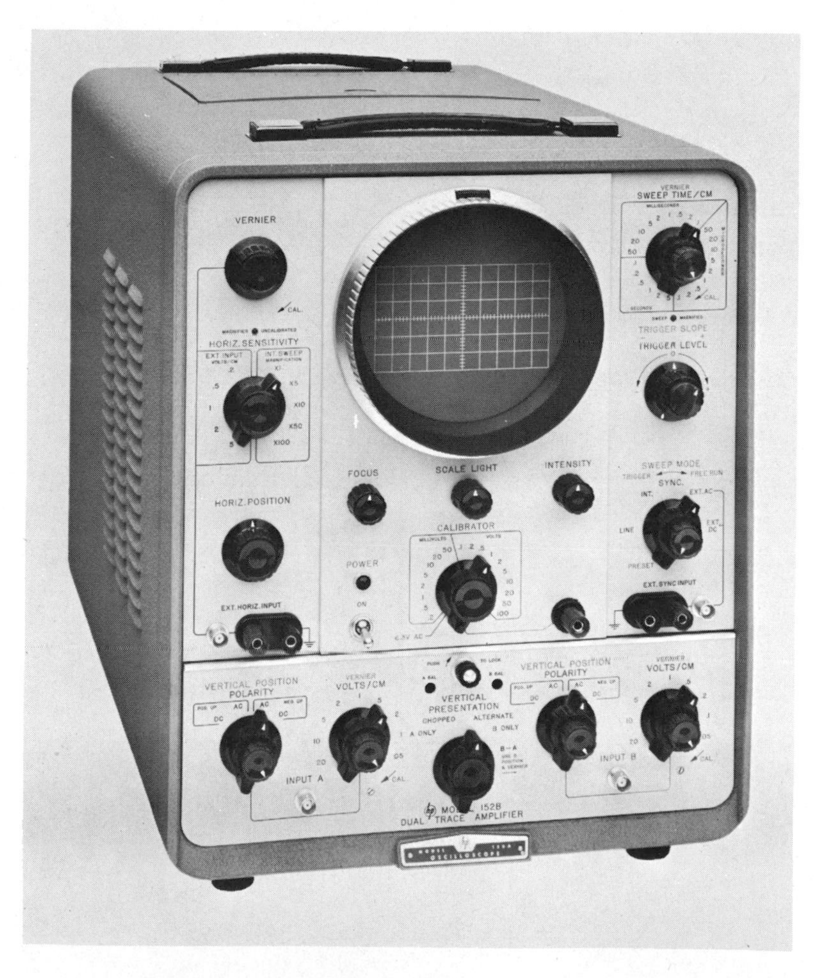

Figure 9-16

A typical laboratory-type oscilloscope. (Courtesy Hewlett-Packard.)

lates the sine wave in terms of its frequency and the time from zero forward. This equation will be met many times again in subsequent discussion. You will also find Equation (9.7) often expressed in the form

$$e = E \sin \omega t \tag{9.8}$$

where ω stands for $2\pi f$.

We call omega (ω) the *angular velocity*. Note that a sine wave is variously termed a *sinusoidal* wave or simply a *sinusoid*. You will recall that a cosine function passes through the same values as a sine function. The only difference is that the radius vector of a cosine wave is displaced 90 degrees or $\pi/2$ radians from the radius vector of a sine wave. Hence, the instantaneous voltage of a cosine wave is expressed

$$e = E \cos \omega t = E \sin (\omega t + \pi/2) \tag{9.9}$$

Both sine waves and cosine waves will be encountered many times again when we analyze alternating-current circuits. Figure 9-15 shows graphs of sine and cosine waves that have the same amplitude and frequency. It is evident that the two waves differ only in their starting times. The cosine wave starts one-quarter cycle before the sine wave. Hence, we say that the two waves differ in *phase angle* (or simply *phase*) by 90 degrees. Since their radii vectors are necessarily at right angles, we sometimes state that sine and cosine waves are in *quadrature* to each other. These waveforms have numerous interesting and basic characteristics which must be reserved for later discussion.

9.5 DISPLAY OF GENERATED VOLTAGE

It must not be supposed that sine and cosine waveforms are only mathematical functions and graphs. There is a basic electronic instrument called the *oscilloscope* that provides a visual display of generated wave-

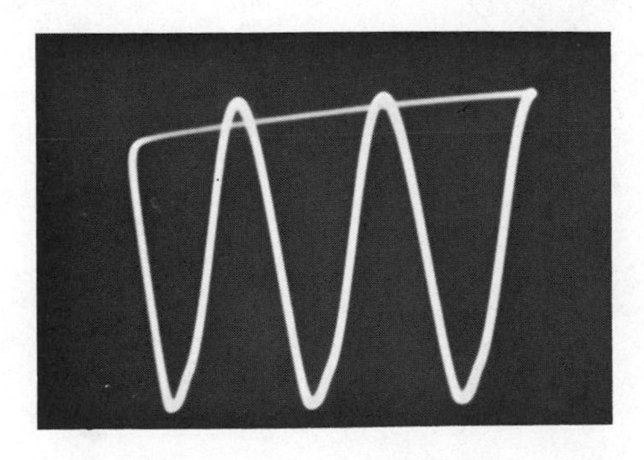

Figure 9-17
Waveform display as seen on the screen of an oscilloscope.

forms for analysis and measurement. A typical oscilloscope is illustrated in Figure 9-16. This instrument shows the physical existence of waveforms that mathematicians previously evolved from the theory of analytical geometry.

Figure 9-17 illustrates a typical waveform display as seen on the screen of an oscilloscope. This waveform has some resemblance to a sine wave. However, we observe that it is not a true sine wave—the pattern has a distorted sine waveshape. It is perhaps surprising to learn that any waveform which is not a true sine wave can be synthesized from a suitable group of true sine waves. This is a fascinating subject to which we shall return in Appendix XIII. Detailed discussion of oscilloscope theory and operation is not included. We merely note at this point that the oscilloscope is a basic tool for checking the waveforms produced by alternators and d-c generators.

9.6 *ANALYSIS OF DEFECTS IN GENERATORS*

Preliminary analysis of generator operation is made by checking its output voltage with a voltmeter. A d-c voltmeter is used in the case of a d-c generator. The output voltage from an alternator must be measured with an a-c voltmeter. If the rotating coil has a broken wire or loose connection, the output voltage will be zero. In Figure 9-9, a single-turn coil was depicted to explain the theory of generator operation. However, in practice, numerous turns are utilized, as seen in Figure 9-18. The rotating element of a generator carries a number of identical multiturn coils.

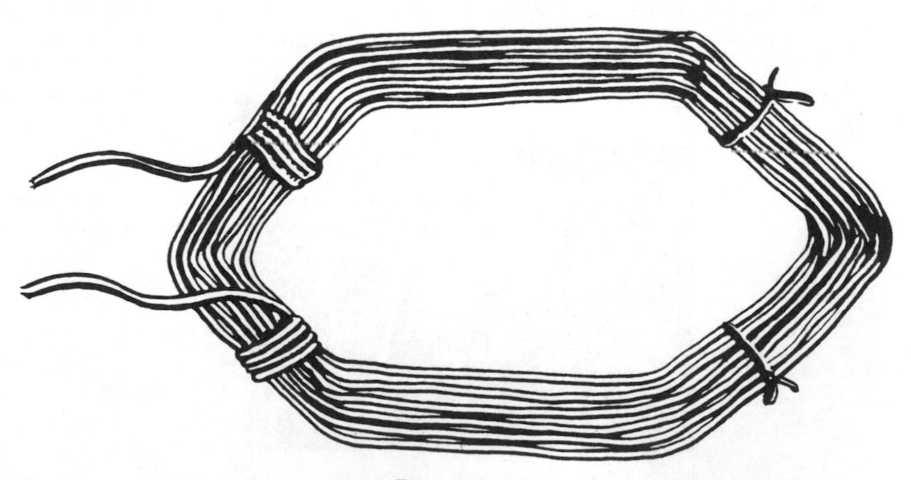

Figure 9-18
A coil of wire utilized in the rotating element of a generator.

If a generator becomes severely overheated due to overload, for example, the insulation of the coil wires may become charred. In such case, one turn in the coil may short-circuit its neighbor. The resulting current that circulates wastes power and causes the generator to overheat at less than normal load. You will measure subnormal output voltage when a coil has shorted turns. Overheating can also melt the solder connections of the wires to the commutator (see Figure 9-19). In this instance, it is often necessary to rewind the coils and solder the ends of the replacement coil wires to their correct commutator bars. This is a highly specialized task that should not be attempted by an inexperienced person.

A generator will supply no output voltage if the *brushes* do not make

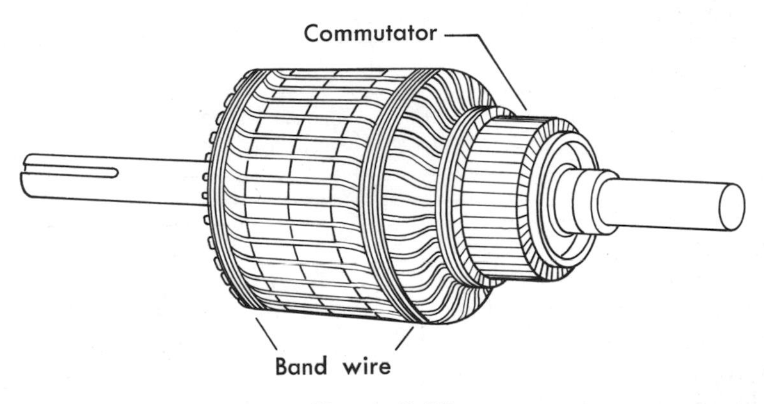

Figure 9-19
View of a commutator.

a good sliding contact to the commutator bars. Brushes eventually wear out and must be replaced. If a brush makes poor or intermittent contact to a commutator, arcing occurs, burning both brush and commutator. When a commutator becomes rough, it must be turned down in a lathe. If excessively worn, a commutator can only be replaced. Commutators sometimes become defective because the copper bars wear down faster than the mica sheeting between the commutator bars. This is called *high mica* and can usually be corrected by careful rubbing with a strip of fine emery paper or cloth.

Many specialized tests are made with meters, glow lamps, and suitably designed electrical devices by generator repair technicians. These tests provide rapid and accurate analysis of almost any fault that can occur in a generator. Discussion of these specialized tests can be referred to in standard handbooks of generator maintenance.

SUMMARY OF FUNDAMENTAL CONCEPTS

Law of Conservation of Energy: Energy can neither be created nor destroyed.

The electrical energy generated by a moving conductor in a magnetic field is obtained from the mechanical energy applied to the conductor.

Lenz' Law: The direction of generated current flow in a moving conductor opposes the mechanical force applied to the conductor.

One volt is induced in a moving conductor which cuts 10^8 magnetic flux lines per sec.

The a-c power supplied to a resistive load has a value in watts which is equal to the rms value of the sine-wave voltage multiplied by the rms value of the sine-wave current.

A sine waveform of voltage (or current) is induced in a coil which rotates at a constant rate in a uniform magnetic field.

A power waveform has twice the frequency of its component voltage or current waveform.

QUESTIONS

1) A magnetic field in motion:
   (*a*) generates current in a circuit if the field flux cuts a conductor.
   (*b*) generates current in a circuit if the field flux moves parallel to

the conductor. (*c*) magnetizes a circuit and causes a magnetic current to flow in its conductors. (*d*) becomes the equivalent of a single magnetic pole.

2) A circuit in motion:
(*a*) reverses the polarity of a magnet in its path of motion. (*b*) exhibits an induced current if a conductor is cut by the flux of a magnetic field. (*c*) exhibits an induced current if a conductor moves parallel to the flux of a magnetic field. (*d*) attempts to orient itself in a North and South direction.

3) Conventional current flow implies:
(*a*) that an electric current consists of electrons in motion. (*b*) that an electric current is a subtle fluid flowing from the positive point of potential in a circuit to the negative point of potential. (*c*) that the sum of the current drops around a complete circuit is equal to zero. (*d*) that the algebraic sum of the voltages at a junction of conductors is equal to zero.

4) Lenz' law is a right-hand rule that:
(*a*) states the direction of induced electron-current flow. (*b*) states the direction of induced conventional-current flow. (*c*) states the polarity of a coil through which electron current is flowing. (*d*) states the polarity of a coil through which conventional current is flowing.

5) If a magnetic field cuts an open-circuited conductor:
(*a*) an induced current flow takes place. (*b*) no voltage is induced in the conductor. (*c*) there is maximum flow of magnetism in the magnetic circuit. (*d*) an induced voltage occurs in the conductor.

6) One volt is induced in a conductor when:
(*a*) the conductor cuts 10^{-8} lines of flux per sec. (*b*) an induced current of 1 amp flows in the open circuit. (*c*) the resistance of the conductor is 1 ohm. (*d*) the conductor cuts 10^8 lines of flux per sec.

7) If current is induced in a circuit when flux lines are cut:
(*a*) the reluctance of the magnetic circuit is reversed. (*b*) mechanical work must be done that is equal to the work done by the induced current. (*c*) voltage is induced in the magnetic circuit. (*d*) an equal and opposite current is induced in the magnetic circuit.

8) An alternator is a device that generates:
(*a*) a pulsating d-c voltage. (*b*) a steady d-c voltage. (*c*) an a-c voltage. (*d*) a sinusoidal d-c voltage.

9) A commutator is:
(*a*) an alternating magnetic field. (*b*) a rotating magnetic field. (*c*) the same as a slip ring. (*d*) an automatic switch.

10) The root-mean-square value of a sine wave is:
(*a*) equal to 0.636 of its peak value. (*b*) equal to 0.707 of its peak

value. (*c*) equal to the square root of its peak value. (*d*) equal to 2.83 times its peak value.

PROBLEMS

1) A conductor cuts 10^4 lines of magnetic flux in 10^{-4} sec. What is the voltage value induced in the conductor?
2) If the conductor in Problem 1 is connected to a load resistance that has a value of 1 ohm, what value of current flows in the load?
3) How many foot-pounds of work per second will be required to force the conductor through the magnetic field in Problem 2?
4) Suppose 100 conductors are used instead of a single conductor in Problem 2. If the conductors are connected in series, what value of current will flow in the load?
5) If the conductors in Problem 4 cut the magnetic flux lines at an angle of 30 degrees, what value of current will flow in the load?
6) A generator is 80 percent efficient. It supplies 1 kw of energy to a load. How much mechanical power does the generator consume?
7) An alternator generates a sinusoidal voltage which has a peak value of 117 volts. A commutator is substituted for the slip rings on the machine. What value of d-c voltage will be indicated by a d-c voltmeter connected to the commutator brushes?
8) If a lamp consumes 60 watts of power when connected to a 117-volt a-c generator, how much power will it consume when connected to a 117-volt d-c generator?
9) A 117-volt a-c line has a 60-cycle frequency. When a lamp is connected across the line, what is the frequency of the power consumed by the lamp?
10) What is the effective voltage of a sine wave which has a peak voltage of 10 volts?
11) What is the peak-to-peak voltage of a sine wave that has a root-mean-square voltage of 10 volts?
12) If a sine-wave voltage of 117 peak volts drives a current of 1 peak amp through a resistive load, what value of power is consumed in the load?
13) Suppose that a sine-wave voltage of 117 peak volts drives a current of 3 root-mean-square amps through a resistive load. What is the value of power consumed in the load?
14) A 117-volt generator drives a 60-cycle current of 117 amps through a load resistance. The generator is then slowed down to 50 cycles per

sec, but its magnetic field is increased so that the voltage remains at 117 volts. What is the difference in power consumed by the load at the 50-cycle frequency?

15) What is the frequency of the power waveform in Problem 14 for 50-cycle operation?

16) An a-c voltage has a frequency of 60 cycles per sec. To what value of angular velocity does this frequency correspond?

10

PRINCIPLES OF CAPACITIVE REACTANCE

10.1 ANALYSIS OF CAPACITIVE REACTANCE

We know that a capacitor consists basically of two conducting plates separated by an insulator. Now we will ask how a capacitor *reacts* to the application of d-c or a-c voltage. Let us briefly note the electrical laws needed:

1. Kirchhoff's voltage law states that the algebraic sum of all the voltage drops around a closed circuit is equal to zero at any instant.

2. Ohm's law states that $I = E/R$.

3. One of Coulomb's laws states that the quantity of electricity stored in a capacitor is equal to the applied voltage multiplied by the capacitance value

$$Q = CE \tag{10.1}$$

where Q is the stored charge in coulombs, C is the capacitance in farads, and E is the voltage across the capacitor.

The voltage across a capacitor becomes greater as the stored charge is increased. The terminal voltage becomes less if the capacitance value is increased: These facts are clearly evident from rearrangement of Equation (10.1):

$$E = \frac{Q}{C} \tag{10.2}$$

4. The series law states that the current value is the same in all parts of a series circuit at any instant.

A *transient voltage* is simply a random voltage change; thus, a lightning flash is a transient voltage. When you close or open a switch, a transient condition of voltage and current prevails in the associated circuit for a short time. We think of a transient as a sudden surge, as contrasted to a steady flow of direct current. Similarly, a surge is contrasted to a steady flow of sine-wave alternating current. It is easy to understand how a capacitor reacts electrically if we analyze the result of applying a d-c voltage to the capacitor.

If you connect a battery to a capacitor by closing the switch in Figure 10-1, you will initiate the following results. A transient surge of current occurs at the instant the switch is closed, producing a deficiency of electrons at the positive terminal of the battery. When the positive battery

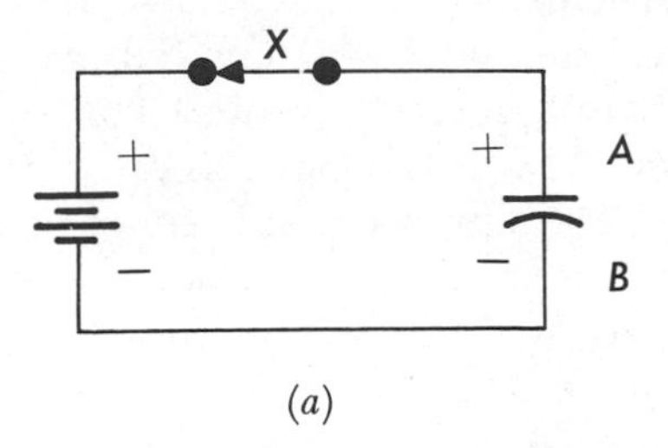

(*a*)

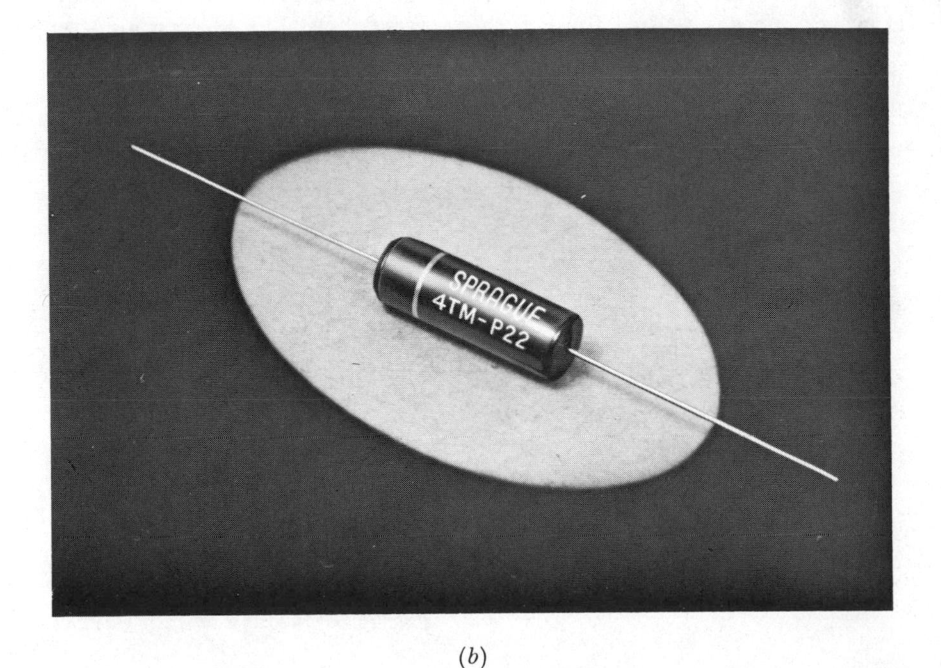

(*b*)

Figure 10-1
(*a*) Switch X connects the battery to the capacitor. (*b*) Typical molded tubular fixed capacitor. (Courtesy of Sprague Products Co.)

terminal is connected to plate A of the capacitor, electrons leave plate A to overcome this deficiency. Similarly, there is an excess of electrons at the negative terminal of the battery. Hence, electrons enter plate B to overcome the excess at the battery terminal.

EQUILIBRIUM CONDITION

It is apparent that there must be a limit to this current flow. This limit is reached when enough electrons have left plate A to establish the same deficiency at the plate as at the battery terminal. At this time, the voltage across the capacitor is exactly equal to the battery voltage. Furthermore, the algebraic sum of the battery and capacitor voltages is zero, since these voltages have opposite polarities. The extremely short current surge that occurs when the switch is closed is called the *charge cycle.*

Now consider a free electron in the vicinity of switch *X*, if you disconnect the battery in Figure 10-1, and connect a battery with less terminal voltage to the capacitor. This electron must be attracted to the higher positive potential of plate *A* in the capacitor. Accordingly, electrons flow from the positive terminal of the battery into plate *A*; simultaneously, electrons flow out of plate *B* into the negative terminal of the battery. However, there is again a limit to this current flow. The surge stops after

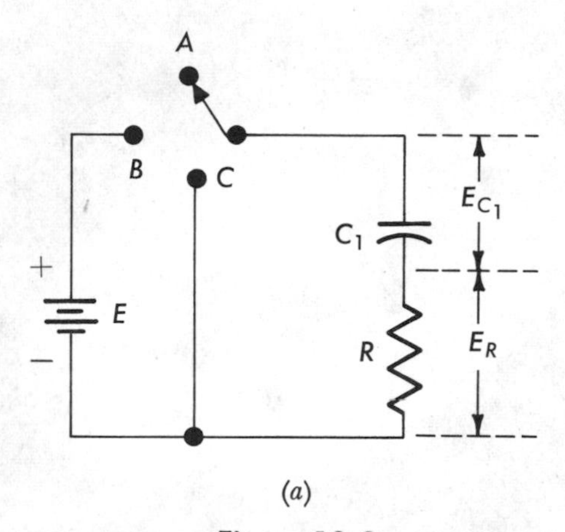

(*a*)

Figure 10-2

(*a*) A series circuit comprising a voltage source, resistance, and capacitance. (*b*) Typical oil-filled rectangular capacitor. (Courtesy of Sprague Products Co.) (*Continued on facing page.*)

an extremely short time during which the capacitor voltage is brought exactly equal to the new value of battery voltage.

If you replace the battery with a short-circuit, it is clear that all of the electrons that previously left plate *A* would return and reduce the capacitor voltage to zero. Then, if you reconnect the battery in Figure 10-1 in reverse polarity, a reversal of electron flow will occur until the capacitor voltage assumes a charge of opposite polarity. Thus, reduced battery voltage, a short-circuit in place of the battery, or a battery with reversed polarity will reduce, eliminate, or reverse the charge that was assumed on the initial charge cycle. Any one of these three conditions is called a *discharge cycle.*

The charge and discharge cycles neither occur in zero time nor with the speed of light. The surge requires a finite and very short time to attain circuit equilibrium. We recall that conductors have resistance and that a

(*b*)
Fig. 10-2 (*Continued*)

battery has internal resistance, although it might be very small. We shall now find that series resistance slows down the charge and discharge cycles. Note that the charged capacitor in Figure 10-1 *reacts* against the battery much as if it were another battery connected in series with the physical battery.

TRANSIENT ANALYSIS

How does series resistance slow down the transient current flow, or surge? In Figure 10-2, the switch is open. Note that the current E_{C_1} and E_R are zero, in accordance with Ohm's law, Coulomb's capacitance law, and again Ohm's law, respectively; the voltage drops around the complete circuit are in agreement with Kirchhoff's voltage law. We substitute the values from Figure 10-2 into the foregoing laws to verify these statements.

Now, let the switch be thrown to position B (Figure 10-3). At zero time, electrons have had no finite interval to flow into the capacitor. Hence, we may write

$$E_{C_1} = \frac{Q}{C_1} = \frac{0}{C_1} = 0 \tag{10.3}$$

Application of Kirchhoff's voltage law will prove that the change of voltage across R at the first instant is equal to the change of applied voltage:

$$\Delta E = \Delta E_R + \Delta E_{C_1} \tag{10.4}$$

where Δ denotes a small though finite value.

We solve Equation (10.4) for E_R:

$$\Delta E_R = \Delta E - \Delta E_{C_1} \tag{10.5}$$

But E_{C_1} is zero at the first instant. Therefore,

$$\Delta E_R = \Delta E \text{ at the first instant} \tag{10.6}$$

Hence, *the voltage across a resistance can always follow the applied change of voltage instantaneously.*

Let us analyze this fact with respect to Ohm's law, $I = E/R$. Since E_R is maximum at the first instant, the "maximum current" must be flowing through R at this instant. By maximum current we mean the current which would flow from the application of E to R, with C replaced by a short-circuit. The series law implies that relative positions of R and C in the circuit have no effect upon circuit response.

What is the condition of the circuit in Figure 10-3 after a brief time

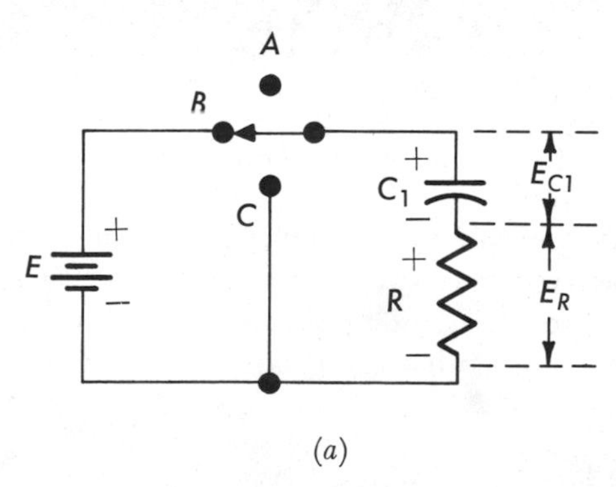

(*a*)

Figure 10-3

(*a*) The capacitor charges through the resistor. (*b*) Typical ceramic capacitors. (Courtesy of Sprague Products Co.)

(*Continued on facing page.*)

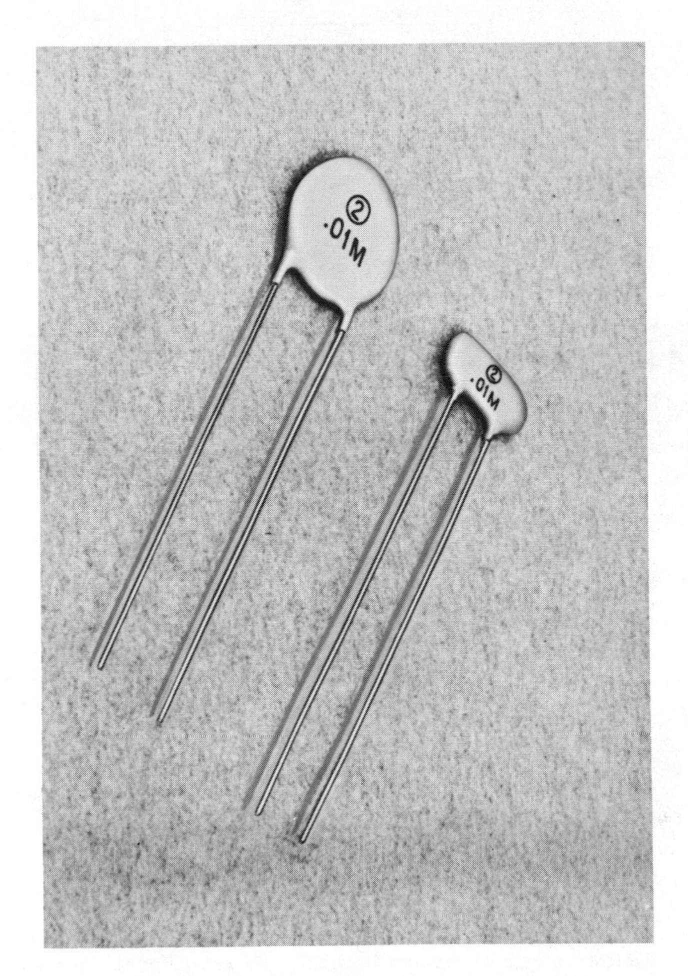

(*b*)

Fig. 10-3 (*Continued*)

has passed? Evidently, the upper plate of C_1 loses electrons, and the lower plate acquires electrons. The capacitor builds up a charge Q, with an accompanying voltage drop E_{C_1}. We know that this charge starts to build up from maximum current flow, which means that the start of build-up obeys Ohm's law as if the capacitor did not react against the battery (see Figure 10-4).

CAPACITIVE REACTANCE

We perceive that this initial rate of current flow and the initial rate of increase of E_{C_1} cannot be sustained because E_{C_1} reacts against E. These two voltages are opposed, which is equivalent to a decrease in available

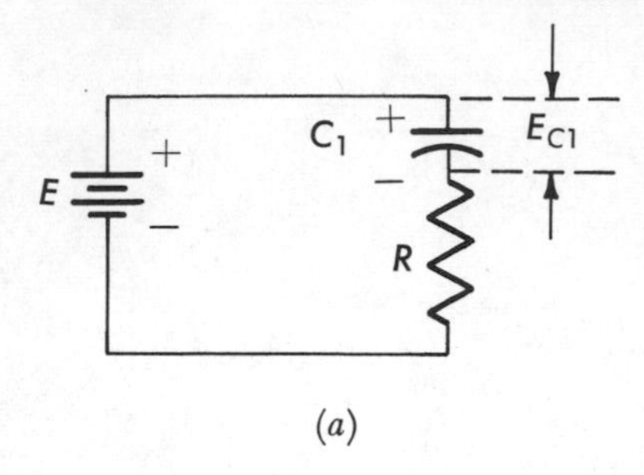

(a)

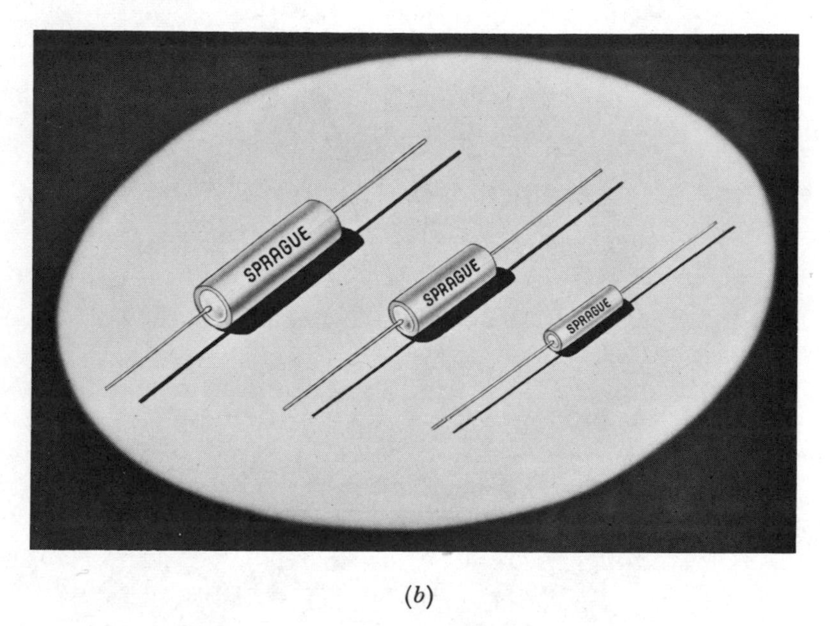

(b)

Figure 10-4

(a) The capacitor voltage E_{C1} reacts against E by reducing the available voltage to drive electrons through the circuit. *(b)* Typical subminiature paper capacitors sealed in metal cases. (Courtesy of Sprague Products Co.)

voltage to move electrons as E_{C_1} rises. Note that if the capacitor did *not* react upon the source voltage, the value of E_{C_1} would rise in a constant or linear manner. Thus, in the absence of *capacitive reactance,* the value of E_{C_1} would rise as depicted in Figure 10-5.

This graph states that the number of electrons per unit time, $\Delta c/\Delta d$, at *any* point along the time axis, is exactly equal to the number of electrons per unit time at the first instant, $\Delta a/\Delta b$. However, we have seen that the rate of change of the capacitor voltage (and the charging current) must, in fact, decrease with the passage of time. Since the capacitor reacts

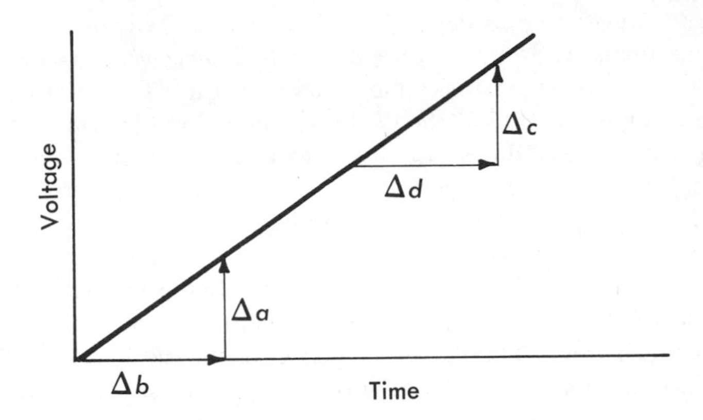

Figure 10-5
This graph indicates a linear relation between voltage and time.

upon the source voltage, the graph must be drawn to show a continual *change* in the *rate of change* of capacitor voltage. In other words, we perceive that E_{C_1} follows a drooping curve instead of a straight line (Figure 10-6).

Note that $\Delta c/\Delta d$ (rate of change) in smaller than $\Delta a/\Delta b$. Still later, $\Delta e/\Delta f$ is smaller than $\Delta c/\Delta d$; the voltage increase at each successive interval of time depends on what has preceded it. Refer to Figure 10-5; this is a voltage-time plot showing the rise of voltage across the capacitor, provided the capacitor does not react against the battery. But, the capacitor

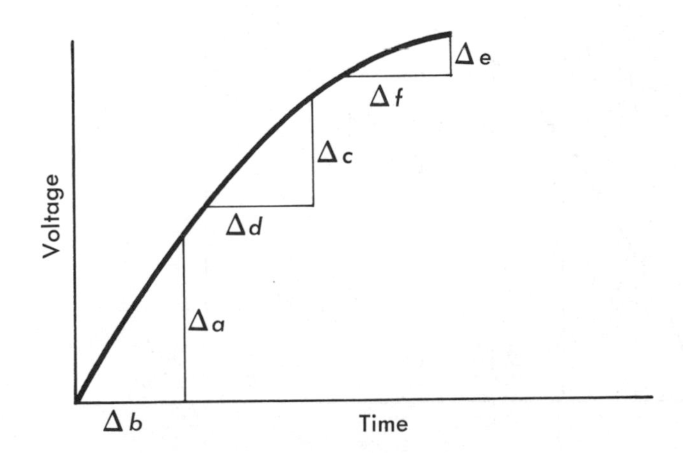

Figure 10-6
This graph indicates a nonlinear relation between voltage and time.

does react against the battery, and it is apparent that this reaction must change the voltage-time plot depicted in Figure 10-6. This insight can be expressed mathematically by a procedure, called *piece-wise construction.*

Piece-wise construction simply means that we apply Ohm's law to find the voltage a (Figure 10-6). We then subtract the value of a from the battery voltage and apply Ohm's law again to find the next increment of voltage rise. The procedure is perhaps a bit tedious, but it permits us to construct the graph of voltage rise across the capacitor without the use of higher mathematics. Now, observe the piece-wise construction illustrated in Figure 10-7. This step-by-step graph is obviously approaching a limit, which, in this example, is 10 volts; a value of 10 volts has been assigned to the battery. The curve is *asymptotic* to the 10-volt level; it will eventually approach 10 volts as closely as we choose, but will never *quite* reach 10 volts, no matter how much time has passed.

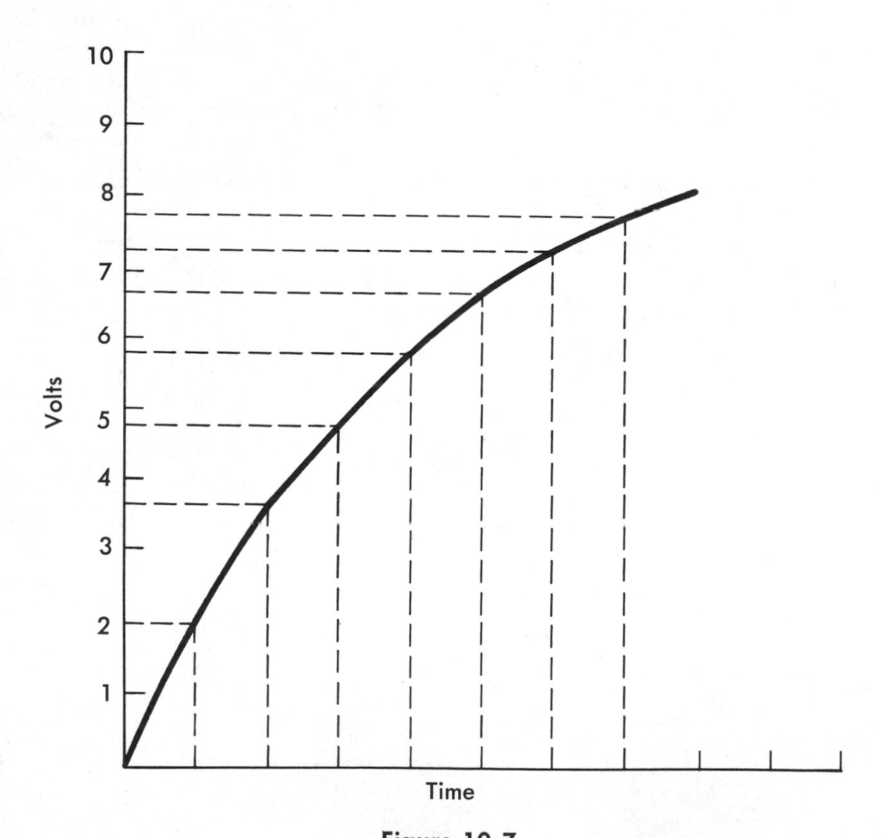

Figure 10-7
A piece-wise construction of voltage rise across the capacitor in Figure 10-3.

EXPONENTIAL CURVE

This type of curve, in which what is ahead depends on what has gone past, is called an *exponential* curve. It is basically an expression of the *natural law of growth.* If we choose very small increments of time in Figure 10-7, we can make the piece-wise graph much smoother. If we can use infinitely small increments of time, the graph will be a continuous curve. You will learn how to use infinitely small increments of time in your courses of higher mathematics. For our present purpose, we need only to understand clearly how capacitor reaction affects current flow in a circuit, and how to approximate the curve of voltage rise across a capacitor.

Refer back to Figure 10-3. Note that $E_{C_1} + E_R$ *must* equal E at any instant to satisfy Kirchhoff's voltage law. It follows that if E_{C_1} *increases* at an *exponential* rate, then E_R must *decrease* at exactly the same rate, so that the sum of the two voltages will always be equal to E. These facts establish an important basic rule: Any instantaneous change in applied

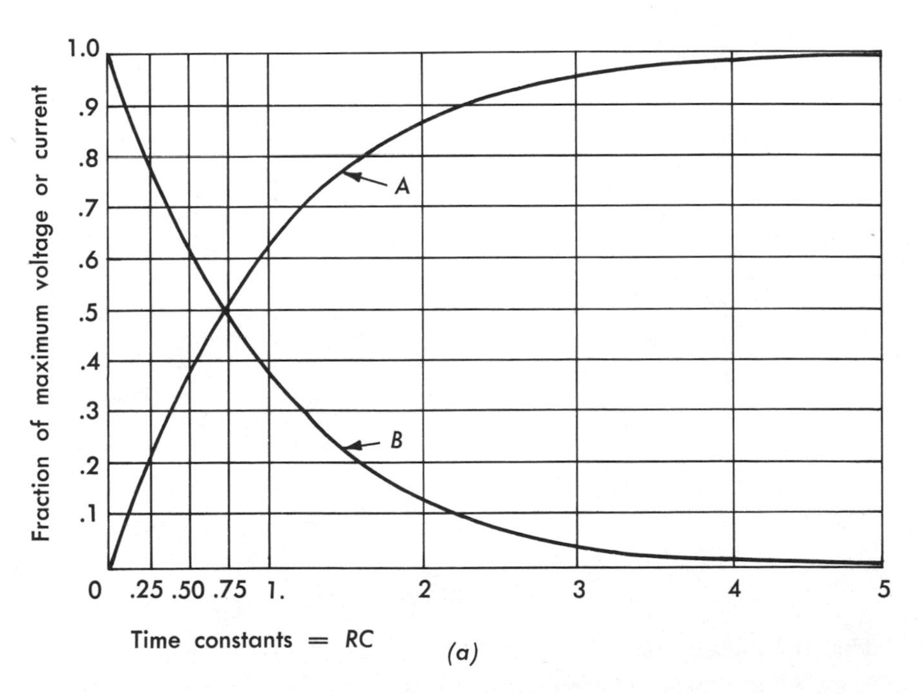

Figure 10-8
(*a*) The universal time-constant chart. (*b*) RC charging circuit. (*c*) Visualization of $Q = \Sigma\, i\, \Delta\, t$. (*d*) $W = CE^2/2$; the energy stored at t_1 is proportional to $e_1{}^2$, and so forth. (*Continued on page 272.*)

voltage (such as ensues when the switch is thrown) is followed by *exponential* voltage changes across R and C. This means that the exponential curve represented by the construction in Figure 10-7 is as basic in its own way as the *sine waveform* that we considered in Chapter 9.

We shall find it very helpful to learn the meaning of a *time constant.*

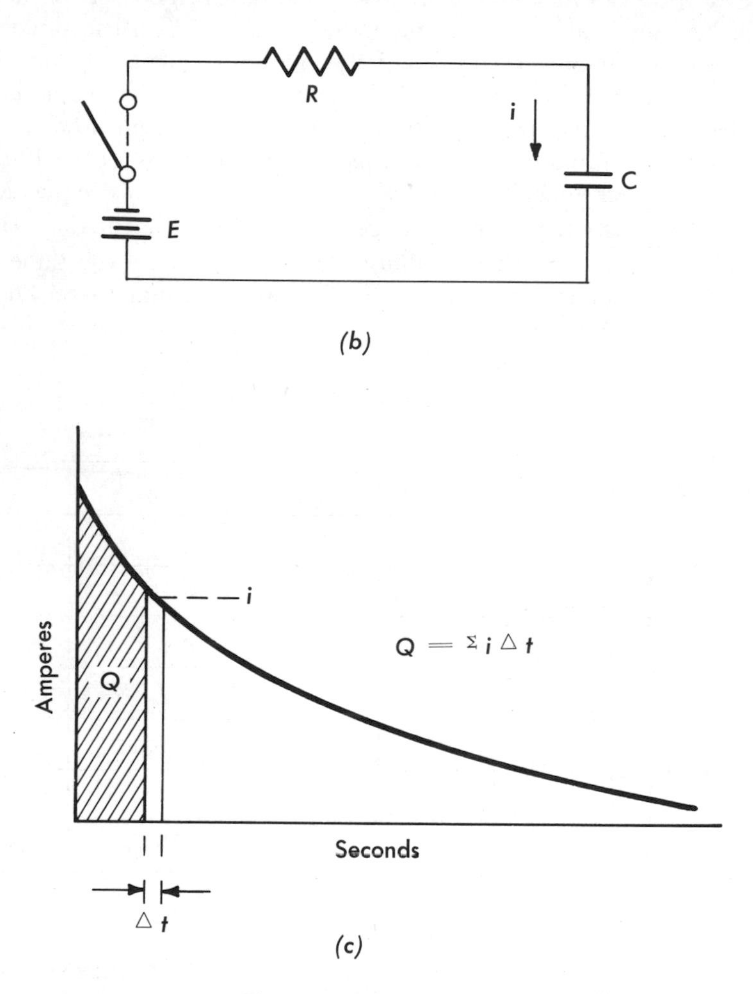

Fig. 10-8 (*Continued*)

The RC time constant in Figure 10-3 (and in Figure 10-7) is the time in seconds required for the voltage across the capacitor to rise to 63 percent of its final value; or, the RC time constant is the time in seconds required for the voltage across the resistor to change 63 percent from its initial value. It is a more general definition to state the voltage change across the resistor, because this takes into account the possibility that the capacitor

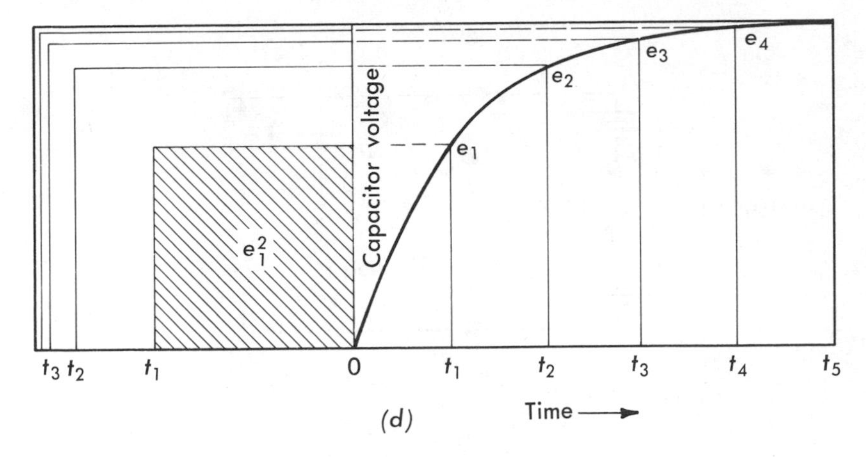

Fig. 10-8 (*Continued*)

voltage might be some value other than zero at the start of a charge or discharge period.

The RC time constant is the product of the resistance in ohms and the capacitance in farads:

$$T = RC \tag{10.7}$$

where T is the time constant in seconds, R is the resistance in ohms, and C is the capacitance in farads.

We perceive that the product of megohms and microfarads will give the same answer, and the use of these units is often more practical and convenient. Let us observe Figure 10-8. This is a graph of percentage change (of voltage or current) versus time (in units of the RC product, or time constant).

10.2 APPLICATION OF EXPONENTIAL FUNCTIONS

In Figure 10-9, let us assume that C_1 is completely discharged, and that the switch has just been thrown to position B. We shall first determine the voltages across R and C_1 at this instant. The curve that is sweeping *downward* in Figure 10-8 shows the percentage of applied voltage *change* across the resistance at any time. This curve indicates that 100 volts, or *all* of the *change* of applied voltage appears across the circuit resistance at the first instant.

The curve that is sweeping upward in Figure 10-8 shows the voltage *change* across C_1. It indicates that the capacitor voltage is zero at the first instant. Now, let us calculate the time constant of the circuit in Figure 10-9. The time constant is the product of all the resistance in the circuit and the capacitance. Resistor R has a value of 990,000 ohms, but this is not the total circuit resistance. The battery in this example has 10,000

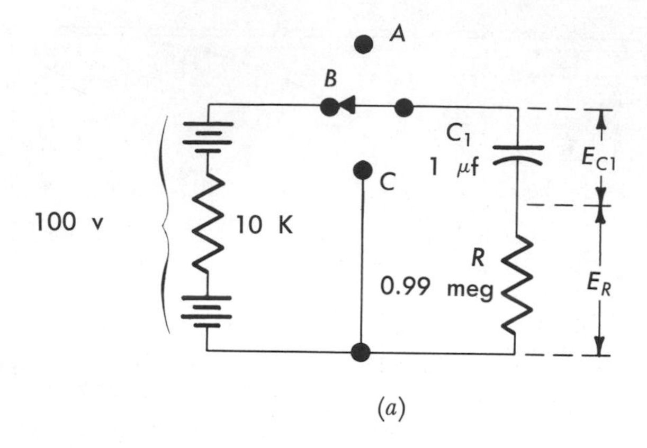

(a)

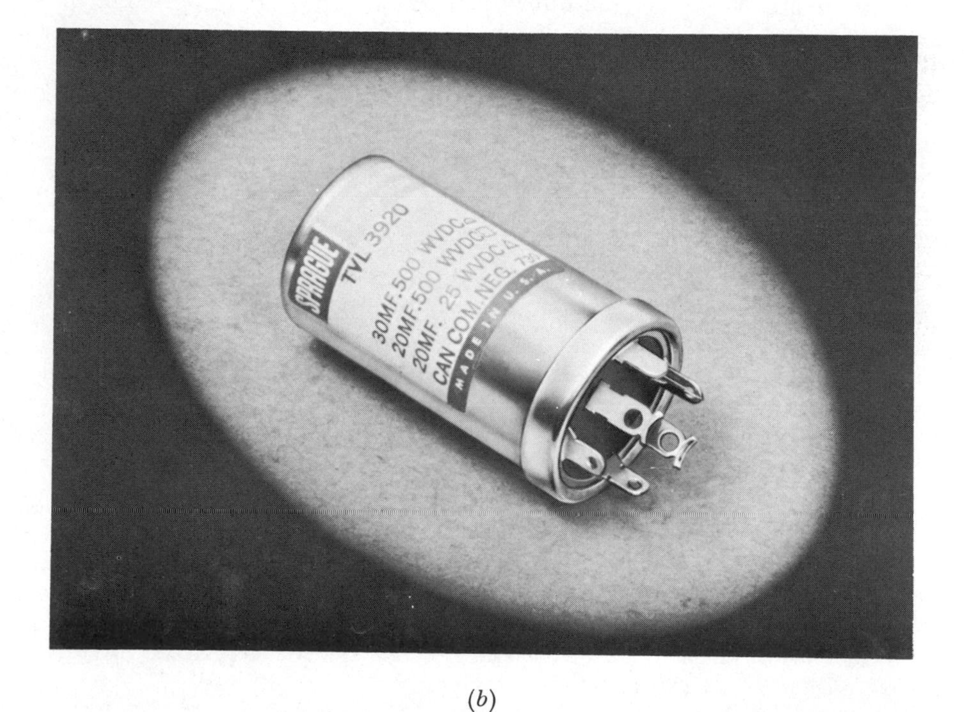

(b)

Figure 10-9

(a) This circuit is easily analyzed by use of the universal time-constant chart. *(b)* Capacitors which have large values of capacitance usually have electrolytic construction. The dielectric is a chemically deposited film. (Courtesy of Sprague Products Co.)

ohms of internal resistance. Hence, the total circuit resistance is 1 megohm. The product of 1 megohm and 1 microfarad is 1; or, the time constant of this circuit is 1 sec. Otherwise stated, it requires 1 sec for the voltage across R to change 63 percent or *to* 37 percent of the voltage that appeared across R at the first instant.

Observe that the intersection of curve B in Figure 10-8 with $RC = 1$ projects to 0.37 on the voltage axis; or, the voltage across R at the end of 1 sec is 37 volts. Since the applied voltage change was 100 volts, the capacitor voltage at the end of 1 sec must be $100 - 37 = 63$ volts, in accordance with Kirchhoff's voltage law. This value is indicated by curve A and its intersection with $RC = 1$. Evidently, the RC chart shows the voltage values across R and C at still later times. We perceive that the capacitor will eventually build up a terminal voltage nearly equal to the applied change of voltage. In theory, E_{C_1} in Figure 10-9 can never *exactly* equal 100 volts, but from a practical viewpoint, E_{C_1} is considered to be approximately equal to 100 volts after $5RC$.

If you throw the switch to position C, another change of voltage is immediately applied to R. This change is provided by the only "battery" that remains in the circuit, viz., the capacitor. We see that the circuit consists of only one battery and one resistor. Since E_R can follow the applied change of voltage instantaneously, but E_{C_1} cannot, it follows that E_R must equal E_{C_1} at the first instant that the switch is thrown to position C. Furthermore, E_R must have opposite polarity with respect to E_{C_1} in accordance with Kirchhoff's voltage law. After a time equal to RC_1, E_R changes 63 percent or *to* 37 percent of the original change that took place when the switch was thrown to position C.

10.3 CAPACITIVE REACTANCE WITH A-C APPLIED

The current that flows "through" a capacitor when a change in voltage is applied can be formulated

$$I = C\frac{\Delta E}{\Delta t} \tag{10.8}$$

where I is the current flow, ΔE is the voltage change over a small interval, and Δt is the time duration of the small interval.

The current flow through the capacitor doubles if the applied voltage changes twice as fast; current flow is directly proportional to the rate in change of voltage. If a change of 1 volt during 1 sec is accompanied by a current of 1 amp, the capacitor has a capacitance of 1 farad, in accordance with Equation (10.8).

We see that capacitance imposes opposition to current flow when the applied voltage changes, analogously to the opposition of resistance to current flow when the applied voltage is constant. The *reaction* of a capacitor to a voltage change is, of course, the basis of this opposition. A sine wave of voltage is continually changing in value. Accordingly, when a sine-wave voltage is applied to a capacitor, a continually changing current flows in response to the continually changing voltage.

The time required to complete one cycle of a sine wave is called its *period.* It follows from the definition of frequency that the period of a sine wave is equal to $1/f$. We recall that the wave rises from zero to peak value in ¼ cycle; or, the first voltage change is completed in $1/(4f)$ sec. Let us consider an a-c voltage with a peak value of E volts and a frequency of f cycles per sec, which is applied to a capacitor with a capacitance value of C farads. Equation (10.8) can be written in terms of *average* current flow over an appreciable interval

$$I_{av} = \frac{C(E_2 - E_1)}{t_2 - t_1} \tag{10.9}$$

where I_{av} is the average current flow from t_1 to t_2, and E_1 and E_2 are the voltage values at the beginning and end of the interval.

For applied sine-wave voltage, the time interval of the voltage rise occupies $1/(4f)$ sec, which, when substituted into Equation (10.9), gives

$$I_{av} = \frac{CE_2}{\frac{1}{4f}} = 4fCE_2 \tag{10.10}$$

Note that E_1 is zero in this case and E_2 is the peak voltage of the sine wave. In Chapter 9, we learned that the average value for a sine waveform is 0.636 of its peak value. Mathematically, you will find that this value of 0.636 is derived as $2/\pi$. This term may be substituted in Equation (10.10):

$$\frac{2I_2}{\pi} = 4fCE_2 \tag{10.11}$$

where I_{av} has been replaced by its equal, which is the peak current I_2 multiplied by $2/\pi$.

Equation (10.11) can be rearranged:

$$I_2 = 2\,\pi\, fCE_2 \tag{10.12}$$

Since the effective value of a sine wave is proportional to its peak value, we can replace I_2 and E_2 in Equation (10.12) with effective values I and E:

$$I = 2\,\pi\, fCE \tag{10.13}$$

The *reaction* of the capacitor to a voltage change is evidently denoted by $2\,\pi\, fC$. Let us rearrange Equation (10.13) in an Ohm's law formulation:

$$I = \frac{E}{\dfrac{1}{2\,\pi fC}} \tag{10.14}$$

We see that $1/(2\,\pi fC)$ in an a-c situation is analogous to resistance in a d-c situation. The opposition that a capacitor imposes to a-c current flow is called *reactance*. Reactance is measured in ohms (a-c ohms). Equation (10.14) states that 1 a-c volt produces 1 amp of a-c current flow through a reactance of 1 ohm. It is often convenient to write reactance as X_C for a capacitor, instead of $1/2\,\pi fC$. Thus, Equation (10.14) will be written

$$I = \frac{E}{X_C} \tag{10.15}$$

This equation can be used with effective (rms) values, peak values, or peak-to-peak values. It is only necessary to be consistent in assignment of values. Let us calculate the reactance of a 26.5 microfarad capacitor at 60 cycles. X_C is equal to $1/(2\,\pi fC)$ or 100 ohms. Note carefully that the reactance of a capacitor is inversely proportional to frequency. This is a basic difference between reactance and resistance, because the resistance of a resistor does not change with frequency.

10.4 PHASES OF VOLTAGE AND CURRENT

We shall find that there is another basic distinction between reactance and resistance. Previous discussion has made it obvious that the greatest current flows through a capacitor when the voltage changes most rapidly. In the case of a sine wave, inspection of Figure 10-10 reveals that the voltage is changing most rapidly as the sine wave passes through zero; but the voltage is not changing at all as it passes through its peak value. Hence, the sine wave is steepest as it passes through zero. As it passes through its peak, the sine wave is neither going downhill nor uphill.

We say that the slope of the sine wave is positive as it rises from zero to its peak value; its slope is negative as it falls from its peak value to zero. The slope of the sine wave is simply the inclination of a tangent line drawn to the curve at a chosen point. Obviously, the slope of a tangent line at the peak of the sine wave is zero; but the slope of a tangent line to the curve as it crosses the axis is maximum, as seen in Figure 10-11.

The slope of the tangent is the ratio of y/x as depicted in Figure 10-12. If you calculate y/x step-by-step along the sine curve, you will find that the value of y/x is proportional to the value of the cosine at each chosen point. Thus, *the slope of a sine curve is a cosine curve.* Recall that if a sine wave of voltage is applied to a capacitor, the current that flows is

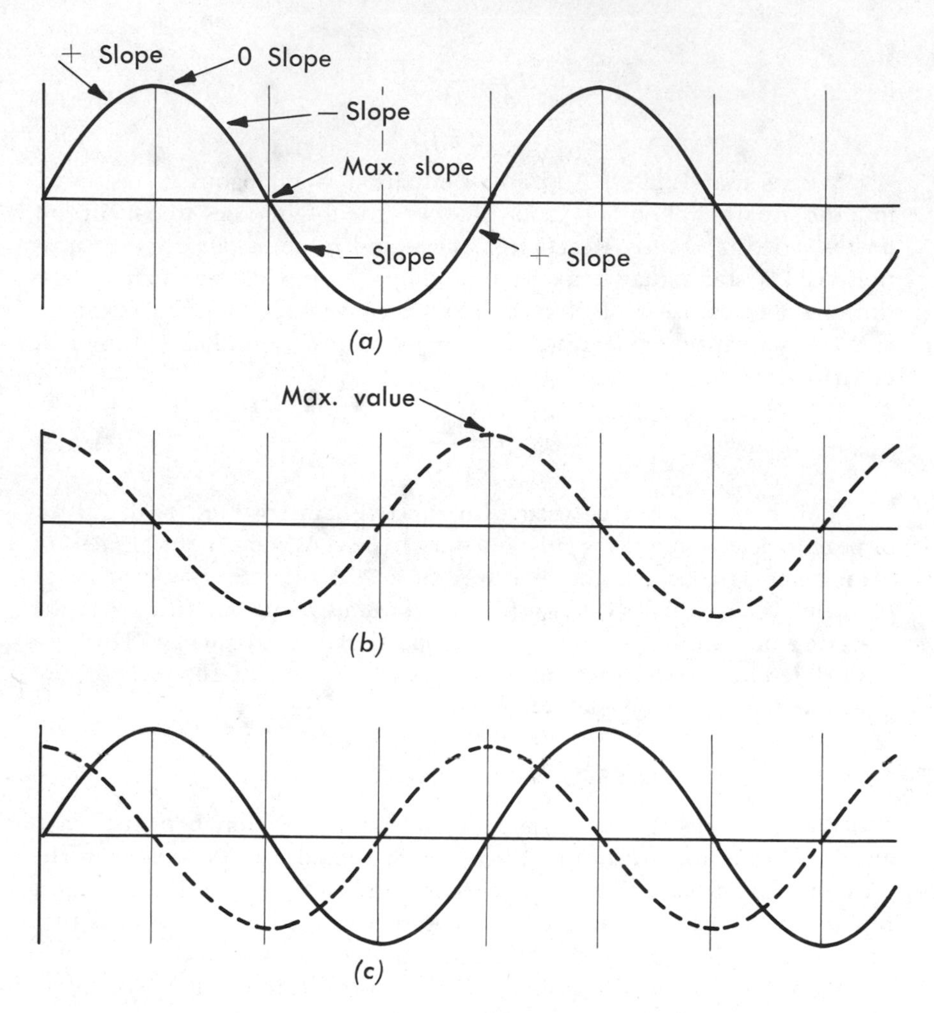

Figure 10-10

(a) Curve of a sine wave, which has a changing slope. *(b)* Change in slope of a sine wave, which plots as a cosine curve. *(c)* Curves *(a)* and *(b)* are compared; sine and cosine waves are separated by 90 degrees in phase. *(d)* Laboratory generator, providing a wide frequency range for generating sine-wave voltages. (Courtesy of Heath Co.)

(Continued on facing page.)

proportional to the rate of voltage change. The rate of voltage change is proportional to the slope of the sine wave; therefore, the current wave that flows in response to a sine wave of voltage is a cosine current wave.

Thus, the solid curve in Figure 10-10(*c*) represents the sine-wave voltage impressed across a capacitor; the dotted curve represents the cosine-wave current flowing through the capacitor. Evidently, the current wave

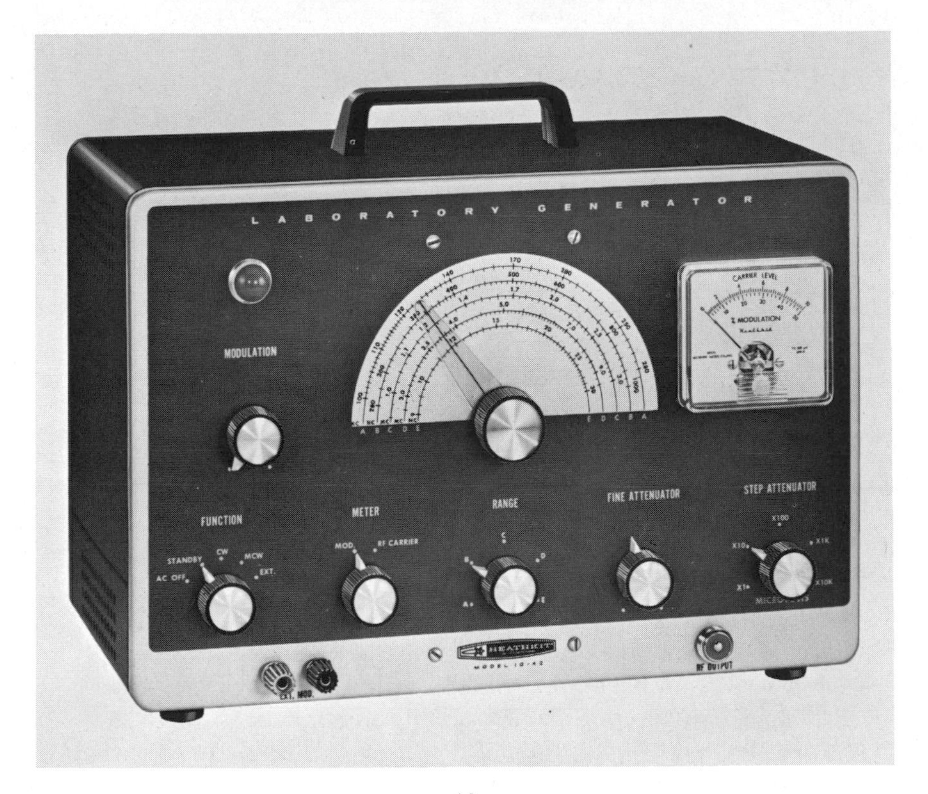

(*d*)
Fig. 10-10 (*Continued*)

is displaced 90 degrees in phase from the voltage wave; or, we say that the current drawn by a capacitor is 90 degrees out of phase with the applied voltage. Inasmuch as the current passes through its peak value in Figure 10-10(*c*) before the voltage passes through its maximum, *the current is said to lead the voltage by 90 degrees.*

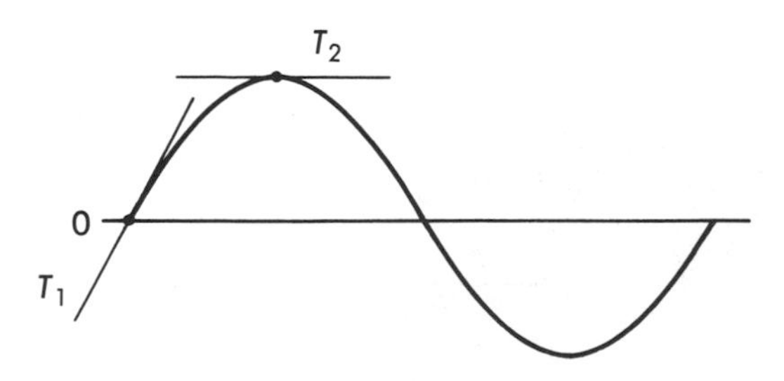

Figure 10-11
Tangent T_1 has maximum slope; tangent T_2 has zero slope.

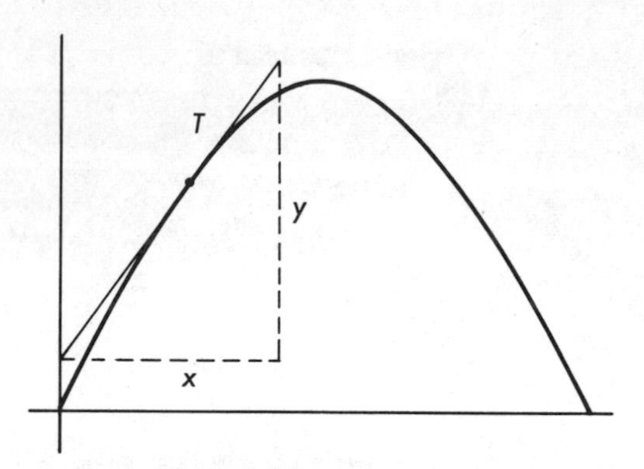

Figure 10-12
The slope of tangent T is the ratio y/x.

10.5 VECTOR REPRESENTATION

A sine wave is generated by a radius vector rotating counterclockwise around a circle; a cosine wave is generated by a radius vector that is displaced 90 degrees in phase from the sine-wave radius vector. In electronics technology, a radius vector is called simply a *vector*. Accordingly, a vector represents the value (amplitude) of a voltage or current by its length; it represents the phase of the voltage or current by its angular position with respect to the time axis. These facts are illustrated in Figure 10-13.

It is much simpler to discuss sine and cosine waves in terms of vectors, instead of drawing the waves in point-by-point detail. Note in Figure 10-13 that the current vector is leading the voltage vector, because it is

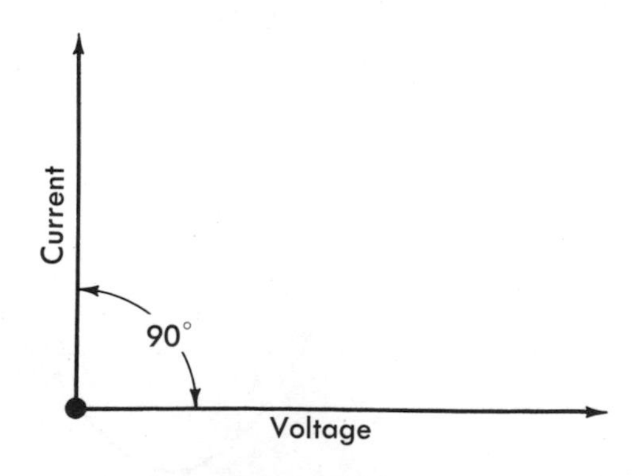

Figure 10-13
Vector representation of voltage and current values and phases for a capacitor.

advanced counterclockwise by 90 degrees from the voltage vector. The length of the voltage vector indicates the value of the applied voltage. The length of the current vector indicates the current value that flows through the capacitor. We have learned previously how to calculate the current value with Ohm's law for a-c.

Although the vectors are represented as stationary in Figure 10-13, it is implied that they are rotating counterclockwise, and that they rotate at all times with a 90 degree phase angle between them. Thus, the two vectors actually imply the generation of a sine wave and a cosine wave simultaneously, as illustrated in Figure 10-10(*c*). To summarize, vector representation is a form of technical shorthand that greatly simplifies the analysis of reactive circuits. You have probably learned in your physics courses to add and subtract vectors; this is also basic in a-c circuit analysis.

10.6 POWER FACTOR

We know that the power in a d-c load resistance is equal to the voltage multiplied by the current. Similarly, the power in an a-c load resistance is formulated:

$$W = E_{\mathrm{rms}} I_{\mathrm{rms}} \tag{10.16}$$

where W is the power in watts, E_{rms} is the effective value of the sine-wave voltage, and I_{rms} is the effective value of the sine-wave current.

Equation (10.16) is true only for a resistive load, as depicted in Figure 10-14, the voltage and current are *in phase* in a *resistive* load. Voltage

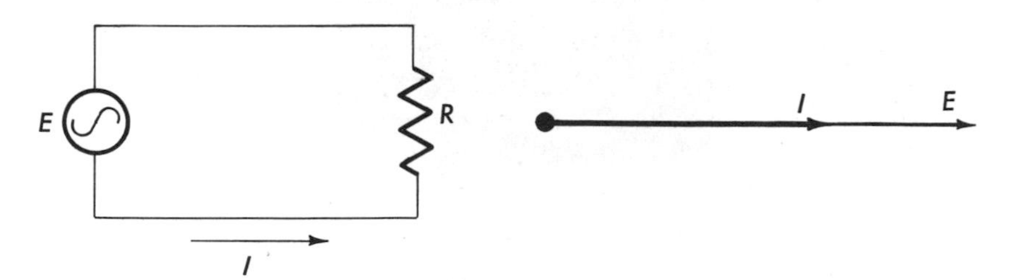

Figure 10-14
Current and voltage are in phase in a resistive load.

and current are in phase because a resistance stores no energy and has no reaction—a resistance merely dissipates energy.

However, the power formula must be written in more general terms to calculate the power in a capacitor. The formula must make quantitative note of the fact that the current is not in phase with the voltage. It must state the component of the current that *is* in phase with the voltage:

$$W = E_{\mathrm{rms}} I_{\mathrm{rms}} \cos \theta \tag{10.17}$$

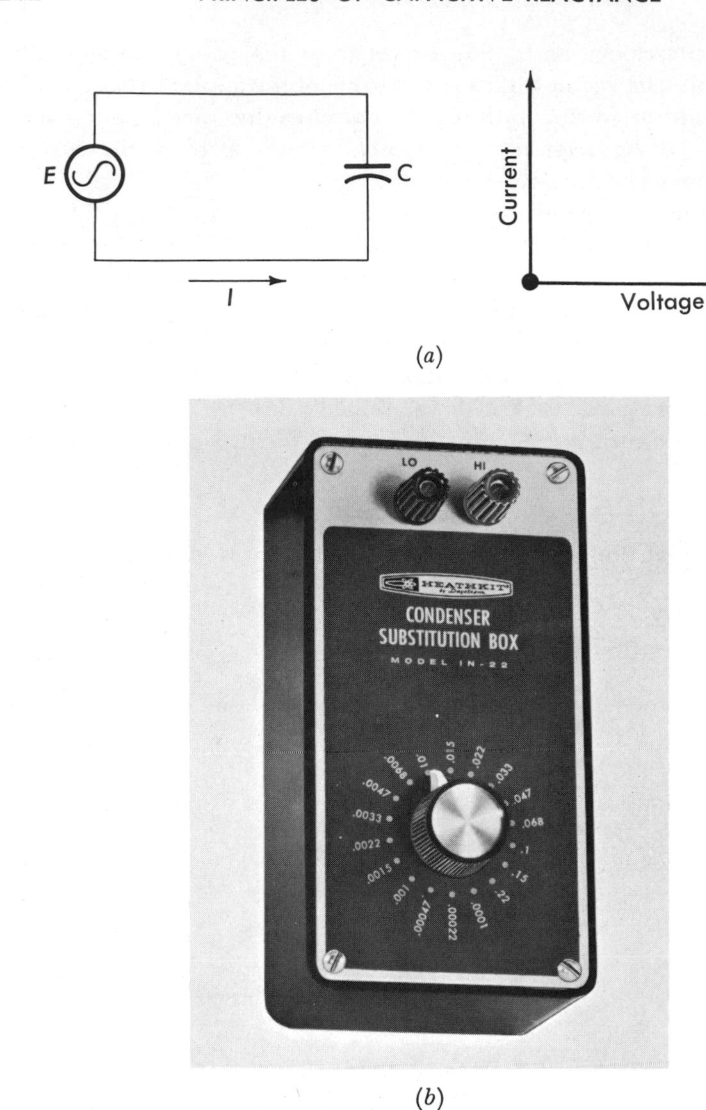

Figure 10-15
(a) Current and voltage are 90 degrees out of phase in a capacitor. *(b)* Laboratory experiments and test work are facilitated by capacitor substitution boxes. This unit provides values from 0.0001 μf to 0.22 μf in 18 steps. (Courtesy of Heath Co.)

where θ is the angle between the voltage and current vectors. W is called *real power.*

Note carefully the relations in Figure 10-15; the current is 90 degrees out of phase with the voltage; the cosine of 90 degrees is zero. Hence,

Equation (10.17) states that there is zero power in the capacitor. This simply means that no power is *consumed* by the capacitor. To put it another way, all the energy stored in the capacitor over the charging interval is returned to the generator over the discharging interval. Hence, the generator does no work on the capacitor.

Since current flows in the circuit of Figure 10-15, and voltage is dropped across the capacitor, it is evident that there is *some* form of power in the capacitor. This power, that does no work, is called *reactive* power. Reactive power is equal to

$$W = E_{rms} I_{rms} \sin \theta \qquad (10.18)$$

where W now denotes the reactive or *wattless* power.

Since the sine of 90 degrees is unity, we see that the reactive power in a capacitor is equal to the product of the effective voltage and the effective current. A visualization of the foregoing facts is presented in Figure 10-16. The power waveform is a double-frequency waveform, as required by the trigonometric formula for $\sin^2 \theta$ and $\cos^2 \theta$. The product of the voltage and current in a capacitor is half positive power and half negative power. Therefore, the average power in a capacitor is zero. But the product of voltage and current in a resistor is all positive; hence, the average power in a resistor is not zero (Figure 10-16).

POWER FACTOR

Let us return briefly to Equation (10.17). Note carefully that $\cos \theta$ is called the *power factor*. The power factor for a capacitor is zero; the power factor for a resistor is 1. Various instruments are used in electronics technology to measure the power factor. Among these are meters and oscilloscopes. The oscilloscope is most informative because it simultaneously indicates voltage, current, and power factor from its screen pattern. Details of instrument design and operation are discussed subsequently.

What about *standards* of capacitance? We recall that the Weston cell is the primary standard of voltage, that the coulometer is the primary standard of current, and that a specified column of mercury serves as a laboratory standard of resistance. Evidently, the unit of capacitance is a derived unit, based on voltage, current, and time. Thus, there is no primary standard of capacitance. On the other hand, laboratory standards of capacitance are universally employed. These laboratory standards feature high stability, high accuracy, low-temperature coefficient of capacitance, and low dielectric losses. Some capacitance standards are continuously variable, and these are designed for high precision of setting, such as 1 part in 25,000.

Standard fixed air-dielectric capacitors have values which range typically from 0.01 $\mu\mu$f to 1000 $\mu\mu$f, each of which has 10 times the capaci-

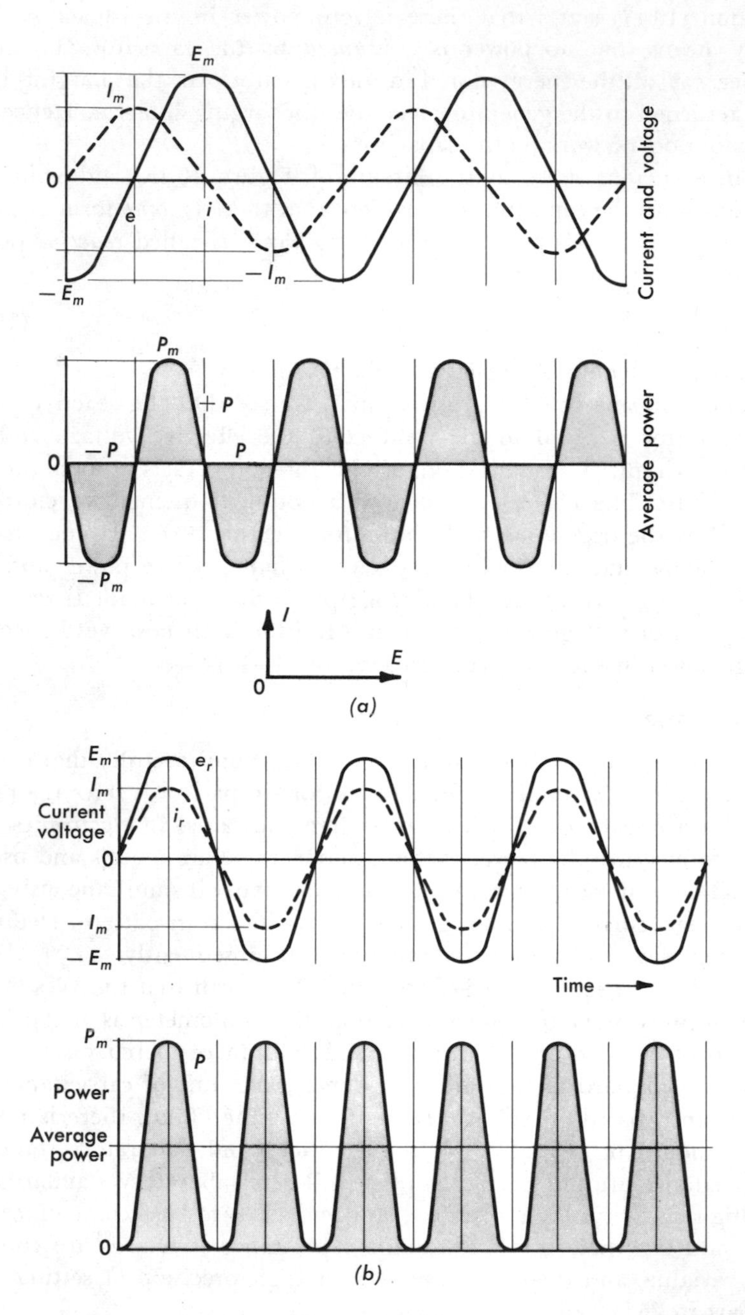

Figure 10-16

(a) Voltage, current, and power in a capacitor. *(b)* Voltage, current, and power in a resistor.

tance of its predecessor. Rated accuracies range from $\pm$ 0.1 to $\pm$ 0.3 percent. Voltage ratings range from 700 to 1500 volts, maximum. Larger values of standard fixed capacitors are fabricated from silvered mica and foil. Capacitance values range typically from 0.001 μf to 1 μf. Rated accuracy is typically $\pm$ 0.05 percent. A 500-volt maximum rating is common. Continuously variable capacitance standards are typically rated for an accuracy of $\pm$ 0.1 percent, and a maximum voltage of 1000 volts. The smallest standards are commonly variable from 0.05 to 1.1 $\mu\mu$f and the largest from 100 $\mu\mu$f to 1150 $\mu\mu$f.

Obviously, standard capacitors must be connected into suitably designed circuits. We know that connecting wires have stray capacitance which can defeat the accuracy of a standard capacitor. You will have an opportunity to learn good practices in application of standard capacitors in your laboratory experiments.

10.7 ANALYSIS OF CAPACITOR DEFECTS

Three principal defects are encountered in commercial capacitors. In most trouble situations, the dielectric between the plates deteriorates and is no longer a satisfactory insulator. This fault permits electric current to "leak" through the capacitor, much as if the capacitor were shunted by a resistance. When leakage is considerable, you can measure the leakage resistance of a capacitor with an ordinary ohmmeter. However, comparatively high values of leakage resistance can cause difficulties in various electronic circuits, and specialized ohmmeters with a high resistance range are commonly utilized to test capacitors.

A typical capacitor tester is illustrated in Figure 10-17. This instrument applies 200 volts to a capacitor under test, and measures leakage resistance up to 1000 megohms. This is d-c voltage test. A pulse voltage (surge test) is also available; it is adjustable from 0 to 900 peak volts. This test indicates the ability of a capacitor to withstand its rated working voltage, such as 400 volts or 600 volts. The instrument also measures capacitance values from 10 micromicrofarads to 1000 microfarads.

It is necessary to measure capacitance values, because capacitors sometimes become defective by "opening up." This implies that the lead of the capacitor does not make contact with the plates inside the capacitor. An open capacitor will measure zero capacitance. Another type of fault concerns partial loss of capacitance; this defect results in measurement of a capacitance value that is less than the rated capacitance value. Large capacitors, in the range from 10 to 1000 microfarads, commonly become defective because of partial loss of capacitance. Such large capacitors often become objectionably leaky as their capacitance value declines. We will examine these situations in more detail in Chapter 22.

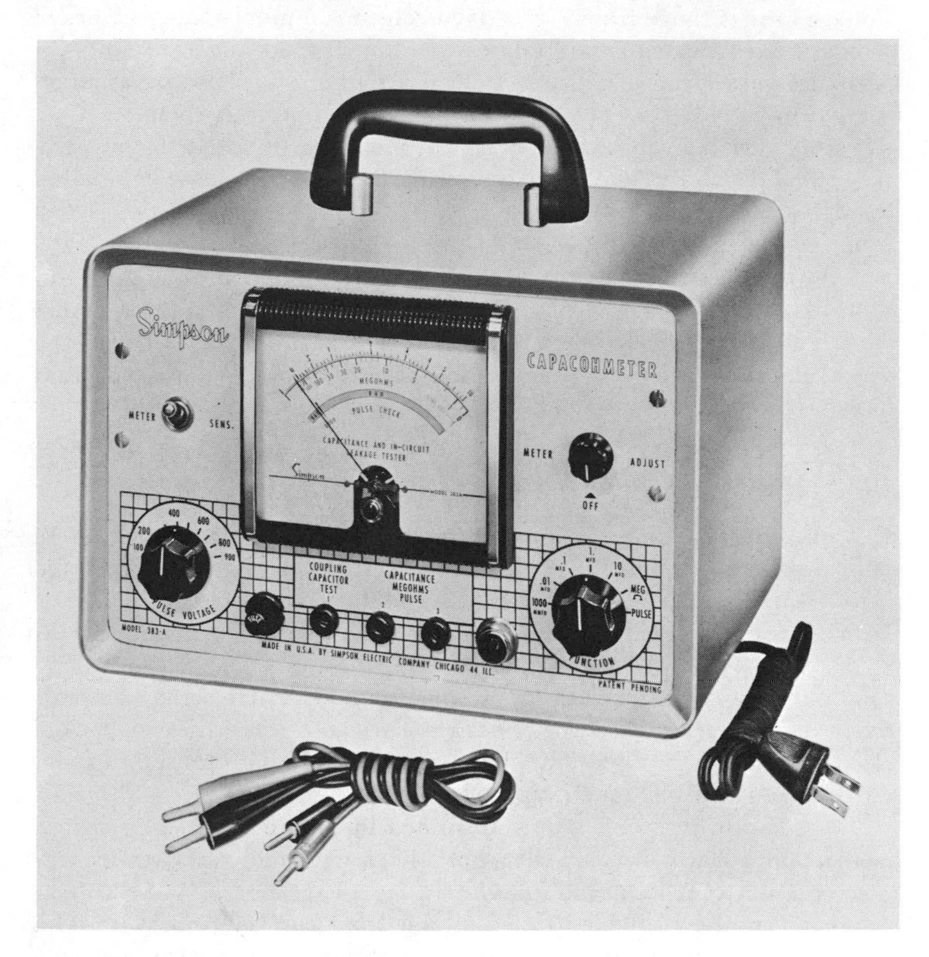

Figure 10-17
A typical capacitor tester. (Courtesy of Simpson Electric Co.)

A capacitor occasionally becomes intermittent. In this case, you might measure a capacitance value of zero until the capacitor is tapped sharply; then, the defective internal connection may be temporarily restored and the capacitor will measure its rated capacitance value until it is tapped again. In other intermittent situations, the capacitor may become temporarily short-circuited. You will also encounter defective capacitors that are thermally intermittent; the capacitor develops a defect when its temperature is raised. Such defects are caused by thermal expansion of the plates and dielectric.

SUMMARY OF FUNDAMENTAL CONCEPTS

Capacitive reactance stores and returns electrical energy, but does not consume energy.

Capacitive reactance and resistance in series cause an exponential current flow in response to a suddenly applied d-c voltage.

The time constant of a series *RC* circuit is equal to the product of *R* and *C*. $T = RC$.

The voltage drop across the capacitor attains 63 percent of its final value in one time constant.

The a-c current flow through a capacitor leads the applied sine-wave voltage by 90 degrees.

Capacitive reactance opposes sine-wave current flow in accordance with Ohm's law. $I = E/X_c$.

The power consumed by an *RC* circuit energized by a sine-wave voltage is equal to the product of voltage, current, and the cosine of the phase angle between voltage and current.

Notes: *R* is equal to the resistance in ohms. *C* is equal to the capacitance in farads. *T* is equal to the time in seconds. *I* is equal to the current in amperes. *E* is equal to the voltage in volts. X_c is equal to the reactance in ohms, or $1/(2\pi fC)$.

QUESTIONS

1) To calculate the quantity of electricity stored in a capacitor: (*a*) multiply the voltage across the capacitor terminals by its resistance. (*b*) multiply the voltage across the capacitor terminals by its capacitance. (*c*) divide the voltage across the capacitor terminals by its resistance. (*d*) divide the voltage across the capacitor terminals by its capacitance.
2) Transient electric currents are the same as: (*a*) random current changes. (*b*) sinusoidal electric currents. (*c*) direct currents. (*d*) a sinusoidal current plus a direct current.
3) An exponential curve is: (*a*) the natural law of growth and decay. (*b*) the difference between a sine wave and a cosine wave. (*c*) equivalent to an asymptotic sine wave. (*d*) equivalent to an asymptotic cosine wave.
4) To calculate the time constant of a series RC circuit: (*a*) find the time required to charge the capacitor to the value of the source voltage. (*b*) find the time required to charge the capacitor to 0.707 of the source voltage. (*c*) multiply the source voltage by the capacitance value. (*d*) multiply the resistance value by the capacitance value.
5) If a resistance is connected across a charged capacitor, the terminal voltage of the capacitor will decrease to: (*a*) 70.7 percent at the end of one time constant. (*b*) 63 percent at the end of one time constant. (*c*) practically zero at the end of one time constant. (*d*) 37 percent at the end of one time constant.
6) To calculate the period of a sine wave: (*a*) multiply its peak voltage by 2.83. (*b*) multiply its frequency by 2.83. (*c*) divide its rms voltage into 1. (*d*) divide its frequency into 1.
7) Capacitive reactance is equal to: (*a*) ωC. (*b*) $2\pi fC$. (*c*) $1/(\omega C)$. (*d*) $1/(\pi fC)$.
8) Current flow through a capacitor is: (*a*) 90 degrees ahead of the voltage. (*b*) 90 degrees behind the voltage. (*c*) in step with the voltage. (*d*) 90 degrees leading on charge and 90 degrees lagging on discharge.
9) Power in a capacitor is called: (*a*) watt power. (*b*) wattless power. (*c*) cosine power. (*d*) in-phase power.
10) The power factor of a capacitor is equal to: (*a*) 0.707 of the applied peak voltage. (*b*) 2.83 times the applied voltage. (*c*) ωC. (*d*) zero.

PROBLEMS

1) If a 0.25-μf capacitor is charged to 600 volts, how many coulombs of charge are stored by the capacitor?
2) If a 6-volt battery is switched into an *RC* series circuit that comprises a 1-megohm resistor and a 1-μf capacitor, what is the voltage value across the resistor at the instant that the switch is closed?
3) In Problem 2, suppose that the 6-volt battery is disconnected after the capacitor is fully charged, and the switch is opened. A 12-volt battery is connected in place of the former 6-volt battery with the same polarity. What is the voltage value across the resistor at the instant the switch is closed?
4) Suppose in Problem 3 that the 12-volt battery is disconnected after the capacitor is fully charged and the switch is opened. The original 6-volt battery is connected in place of the 12-volt battery, but with opposite polarity. What is the voltage value across the resistor at the instant that the switch is closed?
5) What is the time constant of the circuit in Problem 4?
6) What is the reactance, in ohms, of a 1-μf capacitor at 60 cycles per sec?
7) If you connect a 1-μf capacitor across a 117-volt 60-cycle line, how much current will flow through the capacitor?
8) If you connect a 1-μf capacitor across a 1.5-volt dry cell, how much current will flow through the capacitor?
9) An *RC* series circuit comprises a 0.25-μf capacitor and a 4-megohm resistor. The circuit is connected to a 6-volt battery for 1 sec. The battery is then disconnected and replaced by a 4-megohm resistor. Current is permitted to flow for 1 sec. What is the final voltage across the capacitor?
10) Another *RC* series circuit comprises a 10-$\mu\mu$f capacitor and a 1-ohm resistor. If the circuit is connected to a 100-volt d-c source, what is the initial rate of current flow?
11) How long does it take for the capacitor in Problem 10 to charge to 63 volts?
12) A 6-volt storage battery has an internal resistance of 0.005 ohm. A 1-$\mu\mu$f capacitor is connected across the battery terminals. What is the initial rate of current flow?
13) If a 1-μf capacitor is connected across a 117-volt 60-cycle line, what is the value of current flow at the instant the voltage goes through zero?
14) What is the value of current flow in Problem 13 at the instant the voltage rises to 58.5 volts?
15) How much reactive power is present in the capacitor (Problem 14) at the instant the voltage rises to 58.5 volts?

11

PRINCIPLES OF INDUCTIVE REACTANCE

11.1 ANALYSIS OF INDUCTIVE REACTANCE

A coil reacts against an applied voltage. Before voltage is applied to a coil, it has no magnetic field. Current flow in response to applied voltage establishes a magnetic field about the coil similar to the field of a permanent magnet (see Figure 11-1). If the current flow stops, the magnetic field collapses. At the instant that current starts to flow in a coil, magnetic flux lines spread out at the speed of light; if the current flow in a coil is steady, the flux lines remain fixed, as depicted in Figure 11-1(*b*). However, the flux lines cannot remain in fixed position when current flow stops; they then collapse into the coil at the speed of light and disappear simultaneously with the disappearance of the current.

We know that when a conductor cuts magnetic flux lines, a voltage is induced in the conductor. We know also that it is relative motion which induces voltage. If magnetic flux lines are moved to cut a conductor, a voltage is induced in the conductor. It follows that when a flux field collapses into a coil, as depicted for one of the conductors in Figure 11-2, a voltage must be induced in the conductor while the field is collapsing. Similarly, when flux lines spread out from a coil in response to current flow, a voltage must be induced in the conductors while the field is spreading out.

It is this self-induction that causes a coil to react against an applied voltage. Lenz' law requires that the emf of self-induction oppose a suddenly applied voltage, thereby opposing current flow through the coil. Let us see what this means in a very simple circuit, as shown in Figure 11-3. This is a representation of an ideal situation in which the coil and its circuit have no resistance (we can consider that it has been cooled near absolute zero, so that it is superconductive). Although the circuit has zero resistance, current flow is not infinite when the switch is closed. Build-up of magnetic flux induces a *counter emf* in the coil which is exactly equal and opposite to the applied battery voltage.

In accordance with Kirchhoff's voltage law, the algebraic sum of the voltages around the circuit in Figure 11-3(*a*) is zero. The graph in Figure 11-3(*b*) states that the voltage drop across the coil does not change. This constant counter emf requires that the magnetic flux field continue to

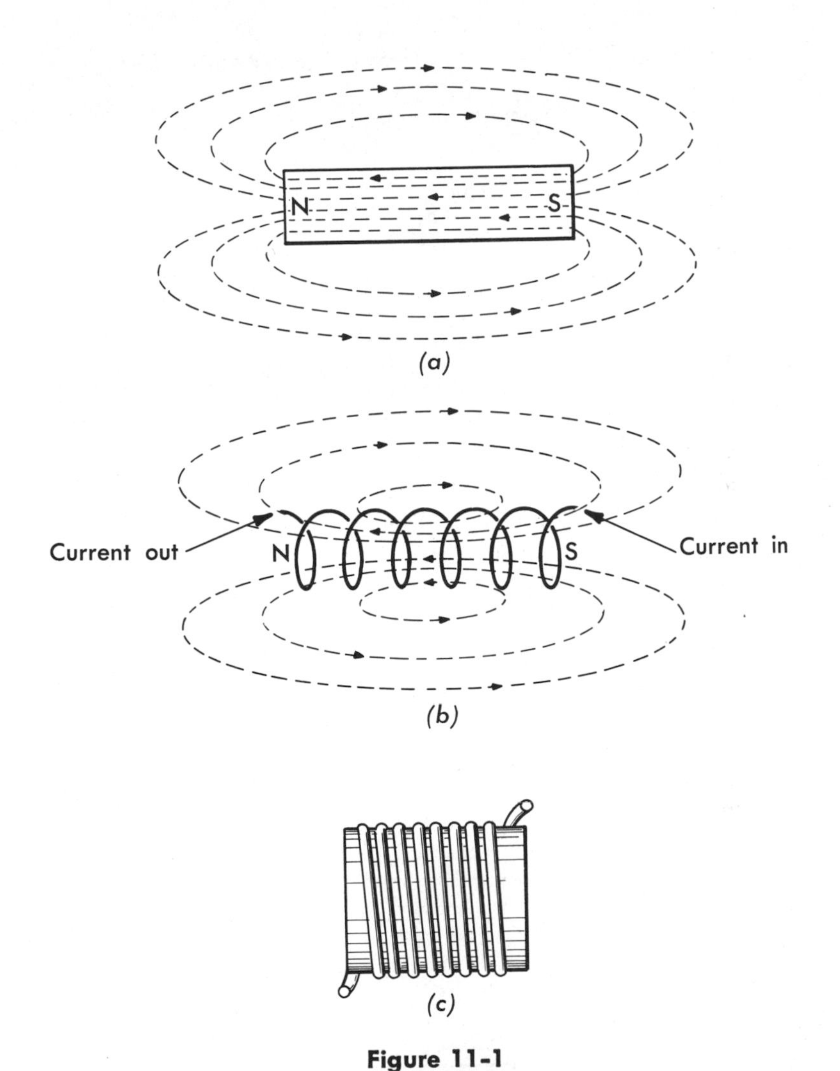

Figure 11-1

(a) Representation of magnetic field surrounding a permanent bar magnet. *(b)* Representation of magnetic field surrounding a current-carrying coil. *(c)* Construction of a small air-core coil.

build up at a constant rate; in turn, the current increases linearly as depicted in Figure 11-4. Thus, there is a steady opposition to current flow, and over an indefinite length of time, the current will increase without limit. Of course, this is an ideal situation; it clearly illustrates the way in which a coil reacts against an applied voltage.

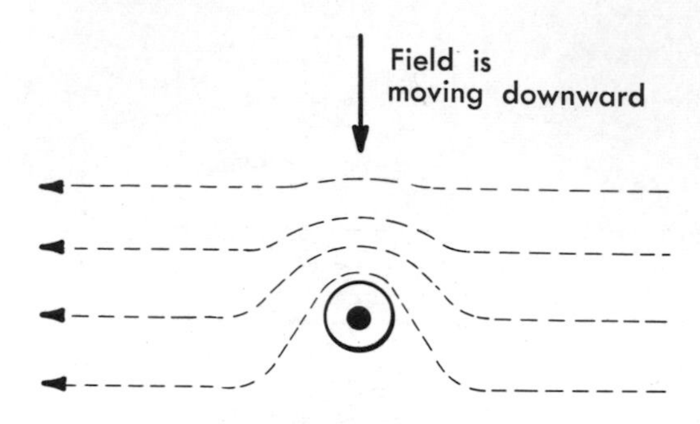

Figure 11-2
The flux lines induce a voltage in the conductor when they collapse and cut the conductor.

CONCEPT OF INDUCTANCE

This reaction is evidently measured by the number of flux lines that are spreading out and cutting the coil turns. We know that 1 volt is induced in a conductor when it is cut at the rate of 10^8 flux lines per sec.

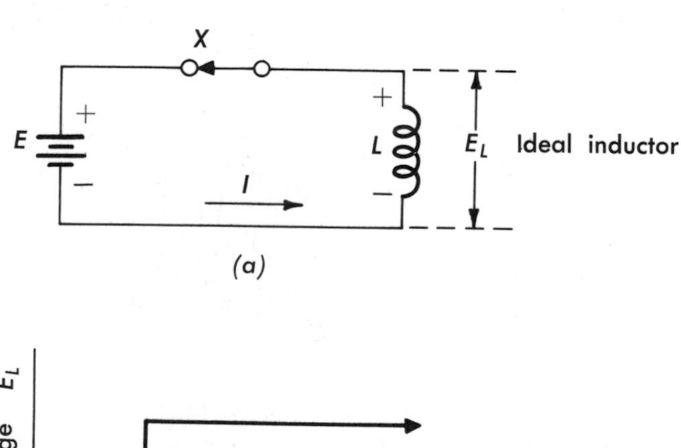

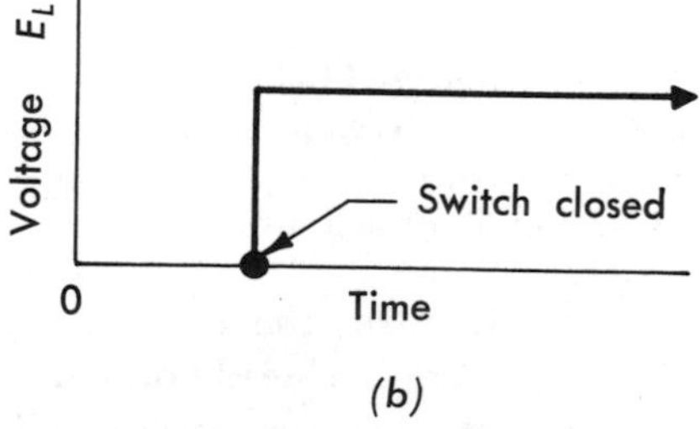

Figure 11-3
(a) A circuit which comprises a battery, coil, and switch. *(b)* Switch closed.

Thus, the *self-inductance*, or simply *inductance*, of the coil can be formulated:

$$L = \frac{N \, \Delta \phi \, 10^{-8}}{\Delta t} \tag{11.1}$$

where L is the inductance, N is the number of turns in the coil, $\Delta \phi$ is the change in the number of *flux loops* over a chosen interval, and Δt is the time over the chosen interval.

Since the current in the coil must increase linearly, as depicted in

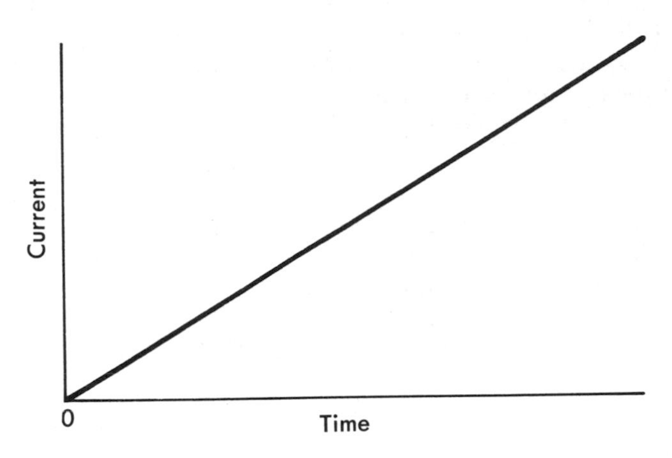

Figure 11-4
The current rises linearly.

Figure 11-4, we can write Equation (11.1) in the form

$$L = \frac{N \, \Delta \phi \, 10^{-8}}{\Delta I} \tag{11.2}$$

If we start our analysis from the instant when the switch is closed in Figure 11-3, the flux and the current start from zero, and we can write Equation (11.2) in the form

$$L = \frac{N \, \phi \, 10^{-8}}{I} \tag{11.3}$$

The product $N \phi$ is referred to as flux linkages, because the flux loops ϕ are linked by N turns. The unit of inductance is called the *henry*. It is evident that 1 henry is the inductance of a coil that produces 10^8 flux linkages per amp of current flow. Since 1 volt of counter emf must be generated by a change of 10^8 flux linkages per sec, it follows that *a coil has an inductance of 1 henry if a change in current at the rate of 1 amp per sec produces a change of 1 volt across the coil.*

We perceive that inductance opposes the build-up of current flow through a coil. This opposition is called *inductive reactance.* Inductive reactance is roughly analogous to resistance. Note carefully that when the switch is opened in Figure 11-3, the collapsing flux lines must now induce a counter emf in opposite polarity, according to Lenz' law. Therefore, the collapsing field maintains current flow in the same direction as before the switch was opened. A spark or arc occurs at the switch contacts to dissipate the energy of the collapsing field.

Hence, inductance is analogous to the inertia of a flywheel. If you apply mechanical energy to a flywheel, the applied force is opposed as the flywheel gradually gains speed. Then, when the force is removed, the flywheel continues to rotate. It can be stopped by braking, dissipating the energy of rotation. Work must be done on the flywheel to give it rotational energy, and this mechanical energy is stored by the moving flywheel. In the same manner, work must be done on an inductor to give it magnetic field energy; this electrical energy is stored in the magnetic field.

The inductance of a single-layer air-core coil is given to an accuracy within practical limits by the empirical formula:

$$\text{Microhenrys} = \frac{0.8\,a^2n^2}{6a + 9b}$$

where a is the radius of the coil in inches, b is the length of the winding in inches, and n is the number of turns (see Figure 11-5).

When a coil is wound with its turns as closely spaced as possible, the number of turns per inch for various wire gages and insulation can be determined from Table 11-1.

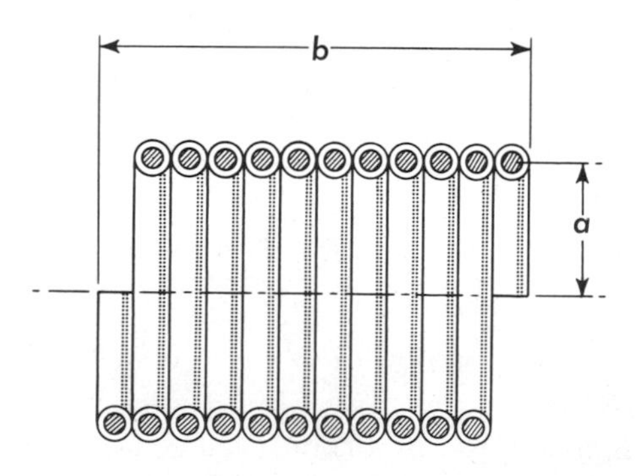

Figure 11-5
Radius of coil is a inches; length of coil is b inches.

Table 11-1

NUMBER OF TURNS PER INCH

B & S Gage	SCE	SCC	DCC	B & S Gage	SCE	SCC	DCC	B & S Gage	SCE	SCC	DCC
8	7.3	7.4	7.0	20	26.1	27.0	24.3	32	73.2	77.2	58.9
9	8.2	8.3	7.9	21	28.9	29.8	26.7	33	78.5	82.8	62.1
10	9.1	9.3	8.9	22	31.7	33.0	29.2	34	84.0	88.4	65.3
11	10.2	10.4	9.9	23	34.9	36.2	31.6	35	89.6	94.3	68.4
12	11.4	11.7	11.0	24	38.1	39.8	34.4	36	95.2	100.0	71.4
13	12.7	12.9	12.1	25	41.8	43.6	37.2	37	100.6	105.8	74.3
14	14.1	15.6	13.6	26	45.7	47.8	40.1	38	106.4	111.6	77.1
15	15.6	16.1	15.1	27	49.7	52.0	43.1	39	111.6	117.2	79.8
16	17.4	17.9	16.7	28	54.0	56.8	46.2	40	116.6	122.8	82.3
17	19.3	19.9	18.2	29	58.8	61.3	49.2				
18	21.4	22.1	20.2	30	63.0	66.5	52.5				
19	23.6	24.4	22.2	31	68.1	71.9	55.8				

SCE: Single cotton-covered enamel
SCC: Single cotton covered
DCC: Double cotton covered

11.2 APPLICATION OF EXPONENTIAL FUNCTIONS

It is apparent that the operation of an *LR* circuit is comparable to the operation of an *RC* circuit, as explained in Chapter 10. We deal with reactance and resistance in an *LR* circuit much as we deal with reactance and resistance in an *RC* circuit. Of course, there are important differences of detail, because inductive reactance is in a sense opposite to capacitive reactance. A capacitor reacts to application of d-c voltage, but it does not sustain the flow of direct current. On the other hand, an inductor reacts to application of d-c voltage and does sustain the flow of direct current. When a capacitor discharges, the discharge current flows in a direction opposite to the charging current. However, when the magnetic field of an inductor collapses, the "discharge" current flows in the same direction as the "charge" current.

Let us analyze an *LR* charging circuit. Figure 11-6 shows typical current and voltage waveforms produced in an *LR* circuit. As before, it is assumed that inductance L is perfect; this pure inductance has no d-c resistance. Of course, this can be realized in practice only by cooling the coil to an extremely low temperature. When the switch is open, there is no voltage across the circuit; consequently, the inductor voltage and current are zero. But when you close the switch, the battery voltage E_b is applied across resistor R and inductor L.

Current attempts to flow, but the inductor opposes this current by generating a counter or back emf, that, at the first instant, exactly equals

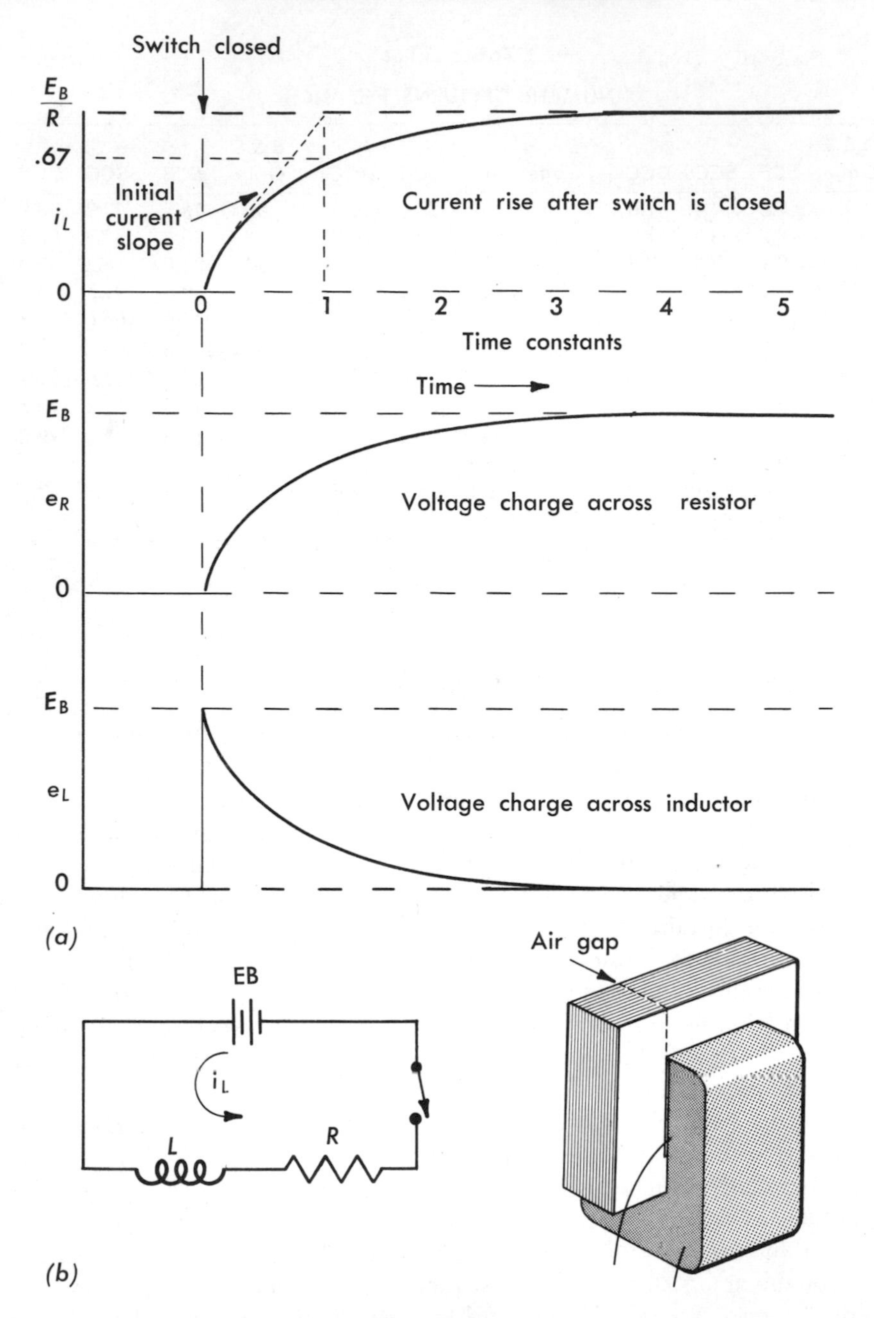

Figure 11-6

(a) Current and voltage curves for an *LR* "charging" circuit. *(b)* Typical iron-cored inductor. The small air gap permits the coil to carry comparatively large currents without saturation of the iron.

the applied voltage E_b. Since no current can flow when the net circuit voltage is zero, there is no voltage drop across resistor R. The two lower curves thus show that at the instant the switch is closed, all the applied voltage is dropped across L, and none is dropped across R. As the current starts to flow, the voltage e_R appears across R, and the voltage e_L across L is reduced by the value of e_R, which prevails at that instant.

EQUILIBRIUM CONDITION

A reduced voltage across the inductor means a less rapid increase in i_L, and thus a less rapid increase in the resistor voltage. The e_L curve in Figure 11-6 shows that e_L finally becomes zero when the current stops increasing; the e_R curve shows that e_R builds up gradually to the value of the battery voltage as the charging current rises. When equilibrium is finally reached, the resistor is the only component that determines current flow in the circuit. Note that in the i_L (instantaneous current) curve, the current starts from zero, and rises rapidly at first. Then, the current flow tapers off to practically a zero rate of increase at the end of 5 time constants.

The initial current slope shown in Figure 11-6 is the same current slope as depicted in Figure 11-4; it is the presence of R in Figure 11-6 that causes the current flow to taper off. What is the initial current slope in Figure 11-6? From previous discussion, it is clear that we can write

$$e_L = \frac{L\,\Delta i}{\Delta t} \tag{11.4}$$

Equation (11.4) states that the voltage drop across an inductor is equal to its inductance multiplied by the rate of change in current flow. The initial current slope in Figure 11-6 is, of course, $\Delta i/\Delta t$. Hence, let us rearrange Equation (11.4) to solve for the rate of change in current flow

$$\frac{\Delta i}{\Delta t} = \frac{e_L}{L} \tag{11.5}$$

Equation (11.5) states that the initial current slope in Figure 11-6 is equal to e_L/L. The initial current flow is determined entirely by the inductance, and not by the resistance. Now, refer back to Figure 11-4, in which the circuit has no resistance, so that the initial rate of current increase is maintained as time passes. We can write a form of Ohm's law for the circuit in Figure 11-3 as follows:

$$\frac{I}{T} = \frac{E}{L} \tag{11.6}$$

where I/T is the current increase in amperes per second, E is the applied voltage in volts, and L is the inductance in henrys.

If you have a 1-volt battery connected to a 1-henry inductor, the current flow in Figure 11-3 increases steadily at the rate of 1 amp per sec. In accordance with Ohm's law, the instantaneous voltage drop across the resistor in Figure 11-6 is directly proportional to current flow. Therefore, the e_R curve is similar in shape to the i_L curve. Since the algebraic sum of the voltages around a series circuit equals zero, and since the applied voltage is constant, the inductor voltage is always equal to the difference between E_b and e_R.

The inductor voltage equals E_b when e_R equals zero; the inductor voltage equals zero when e_R is maximum. If you were to reverse the polarity of the e_L curve, you could also consider it to represent the counter emf in the inductor. The polarity of a counter emf is always opposite to that of the applied voltage. At first, the counter emf is high because the initial current slope is high. This high counter emf opposes the applied voltage and keeps the current from assuming its final value at the outset.

But the initial current slope cannot be maintained as time passes, because higher current values produce higher voltage drops across the resistor. The resistor voltage drop must decrease the voltage applied to the inductor. Consequently, the counter emf decreases as the current increases. It is clear from previous discussion that the three waveforms in Figure 11-6 are exponential curves. In other words, we can use the universal time-constant chart previously illustrated for a series *RC* circuit to analyze a series *RL* circuit.

11.3 TIME CONSTANT OF AN LR CIRCUIT

The meaning of the time constant for an *LR* circuit is rather closely analogous to the meaning of the time constant in an *RC* circuit. An *LR* time constant is defined as the time required for the current through the inductor to increase to 63 percent of its maximum value. If you make a piece-wise graphical construction of current versus time in an *LR* circuit, it will appear that the current attains 63 percent of its maximum value in L/R sec. Thus, we can write

$$T = \frac{L}{R} \tag{11.7}$$

where T is the time constant in seconds, L is the inductance in henrys, and R is the resistance in ohms.

Note that the ratio L/R also represents the time required for the resistor voltage to equal 63 percent of the applied voltage. Also, the ratio L/R is the time required for the inductor voltage to equal 37 percent of the applied voltage. Let us review the following basic problems which illustrate how to find instantaneous values of current and voltage in *LR*

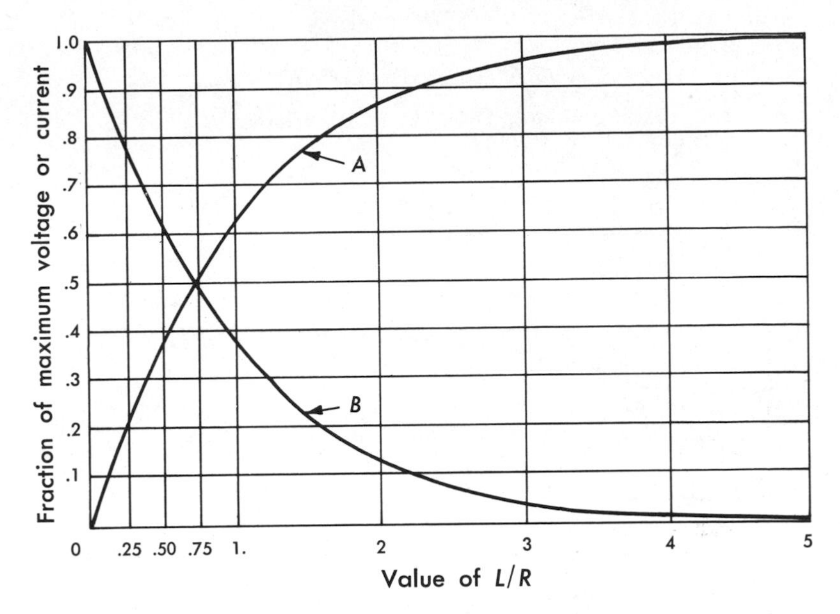

Figure 11-7
Universal time-constant chart.

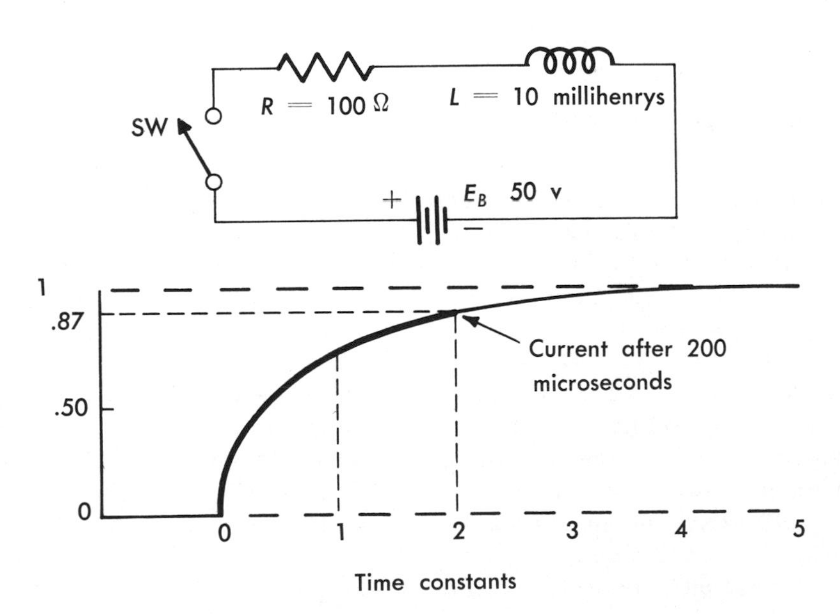

Figure 11-8
A practical *LR* circuit problem.

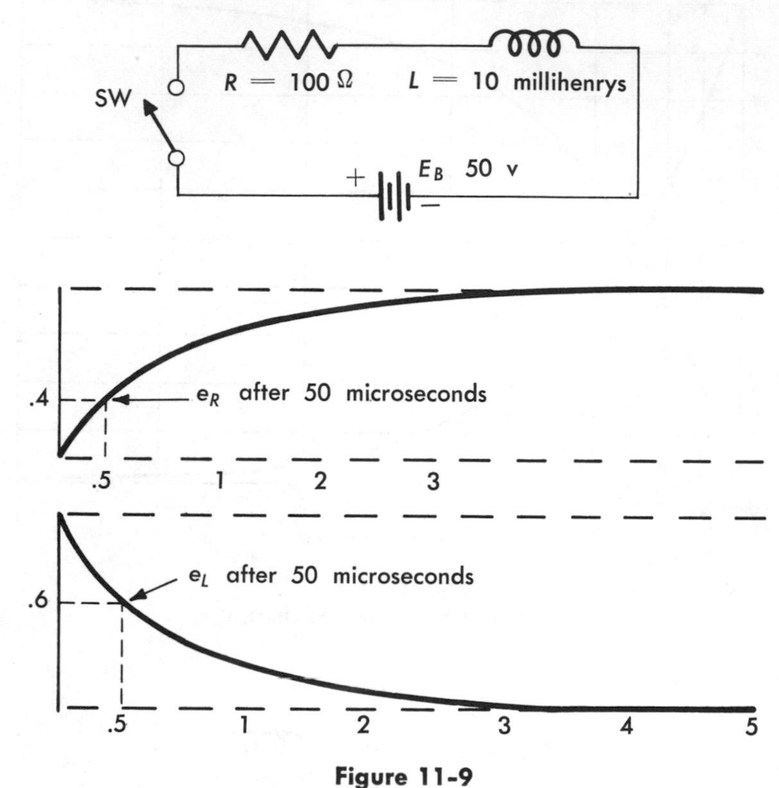

Figure 11-9
Values of e_R and e_L are to be determined after the switch is closed for 50 microsec.

circuits. We will solve the problems with the aid of the universal time-constant chart shown in Figure 11-7.

Our first problem is illustrated in Figure 11-8. With the values indicated in the circuit diagram, find the current value 200 microsec after the switch is thrown. First, we calculate the time constant L/R. Thus, $T = 0.01/100 = 100$ microsec. Since the time constant is 100 microsec, and the time interval of the problem is 200 microsec, the "charge" cycle lasts for 2 time constants; or, the exponential curve shows that the current is 87 percent of maximum at the end of 2 time constants. We know the maximum current from Ohm's law, $I = E/R$, whereby $I = 50/100 = 0.5$ amp. Therefore, at the end of 200 microsec, the current value will be 0.85×0.5, or 0.425 amp.

Our second problem is illustrated in Figure 11-9. With the values indicated in the circuit diagram, find e_R and e_L 50 microsec after the switch is closed. The time constant is the same as before. From Figure 11-7 we observe that e_R will be 0.4 of maximum, and e_L will be 0.6 of maximum at the end of $L/R = 0.5$. Therefore, $e_R = 0.4 \times 50$ volts or 20 volts; $e_L = 0.6 \times 50$ volts or 30 volts, at the end of 50 microsec.

Note in passing that the universal time-constant curves can be expressed as exponential *equations*, which permit us to make an algebraic solution of such problems, instead of a graphical solution. However, the exponential equations are comparable to trigonometric equations, and require the use of exponential tables for numerical evaluation. You will become familiar with exponential functions and tables in your advanced mathematics courses; then, you will no longer need to use the universal time-constant chart to solve *RL* and *RC* circuits.

DISCHARGE ACTION

Let us analyze the discharge action in an *LR* circuit. The curves shown in Figure 11-10 are generated when the battery voltage is removed from an *LR* circuit and instantaneously replaced by a short-circuit. (You use a fuse and switch in an experimental arrangement to replace a battery by a short-circuit.) At the instant the battery voltage is thus dropped to zero, the stored energy in the magnetic field of the inductor is returned to the circuit because of the collapsing flux.

What amount of energy is stored in a magnetic field? This stored energy is equal to the work done against the counter emf over the charge cycle, and is formulated as

$$W = \frac{LI^2}{2} \tag{11.8}$$

where I is the current in amperes, L is the inductance in henrys, and W is the stored energy in watt-seconds (joules).

We recall that a capacitor also stores energy. In the case of a capacitor, the stored energy is equal to the work done against the back voltage of the capacitor over the charging cycle, and is formulated as

$$W = \frac{CE^2}{2} \tag{11.9}$$

where E is the voltage across the capacitor, C is the capacitance in farads, and W is the stored energy in watt-seconds (joules).

At the first instant when the battery in an *LR* circuit is replaced by a short-circuit, the resistor voltage e_R (Figure 11-10) attempts to decrease to zero; however, the inductor tends to maintain current flow because of its collapsing flux field. The counter emf is now the source voltage in the circuit. As the discharge current i_d begins to decrease, the voltage across R also decreases. Since $e_R + e_L = 0$, the value of e_L also decreases. This

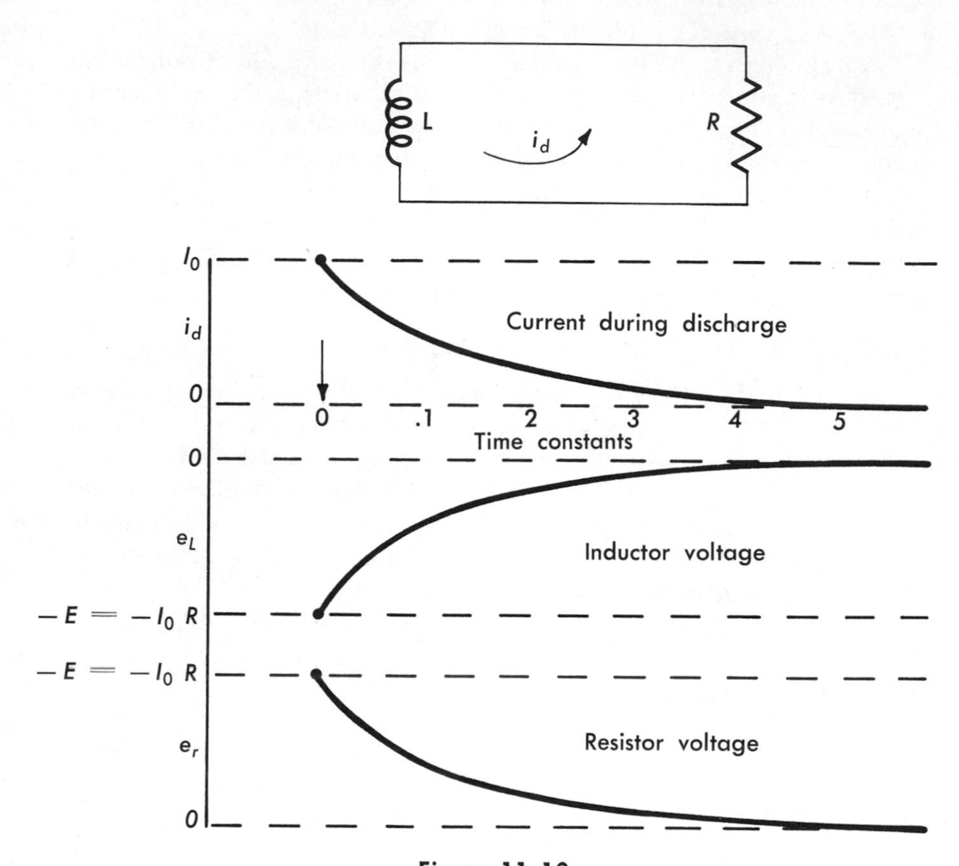

Figure 11-10
Discharge action in an *LR* circuit.

change continues as shown in the e_R and e_L curves until the e_R and e_L voltages are both zero, and no current is flowing. The discharge current at the end of one time constant is 37 percent of maximum.

To solve a practical problem, consider the component values indicated in Figure 11-11. Let us find the current which is flowing 150 microsec after the discharge cycle starts. The time constant is evidently 100 microsec. Since the period specified is 150 microsec, the number of time constants is 1.5. The universal time-constant chart (Figure 11-7) shows that the current drops to 22 percent of its initial value after 1.5 time constants. The initial current is 100 ma; therefore, the current after 150 microsec is 22 ma.

INDUCTIVE REACTANCE VERSUS CAPACITIVE REACTANCE

Observe in Figure 11-9 that the inductor voltage is a falling waveform, and that the resistor voltage is a falling waveform. Suppose we replace the inductor with a capacitor; the capacitor voltage will then be a rising waveform, and the resistor voltage will be a falling waveform. Similarly, we observe that the inductor voltage in Figure 11-10 is a rising waveform, and that the resistor voltage is a falling waveform. Suppose we replace the inductor with a charged capacitor. Then, the capacitor voltage will be a falling waveform, and the resistor voltage will be a rising waveform. It follows that inductive reactance is the opposite of capacitive reactance.

Again, let us see how the circuit in Figure 11-9 (and Figure 11-10) may be classified as a *differentiating* circuit, or as an *integrating* circuit. If you take output from across the inductor, you are operating the *LR* circuit as a differentiating circuit. However, if you take output from across the resistor, you are operating the *LR* circuit as an integrating circuit. The terms *differentiating circuit* and *integrating circuit* are based on analyses that you will learn in your advanced mathematics courses.

If you replace the inductor with a capacitor in Figure 11-9 (and Figure 11-10), these descriptive terms are then reversed. When you take output from across the capacitor, you are operating the *RC* circuit as an integrating circuit. On the other hand, when you take output from across the resistor, you are operating the *RC* circuit as a differentiating circuit. It is evident from previous discussion that if an *LR* circuit has the same time constant as an *RC* circuit, the output waveforms as classified above have identical shapes.

11.4 INDUCTIVE REACTANCE WITH A-C APPLIED

The voltage that drops across an inductor in response to a change in current can be formulated:

$$E = L\frac{\Delta I}{\Delta t} \tag{11.10}$$

where E is the voltage across the inductor, ΔI is the current change over a small interval, and Δt is the time duration of the small interval.

The voltage drop across the inductor doubles if the current changes twice as fast. We know that the period of a sine wave is $1/f$ sec. The sine wave rises from zero to its peak value in $1/(4f)$ sec. Thus, Equation (11.10) can be written in terms of *average* voltage change over an appreciable interval:

$$E_{av} = \frac{L(I_2 - I_1)}{t_2 - t_1} \tag{11.11}$$

where E_{av} is the average voltage change from t_1 to t_2, and I_1 and I_2 are the current values at the beginning and end of the interval.

Since the effective value of a sine wave is proportional its peak value, can substitute these values in Equation (11.11):

$$E_{av} = \frac{LI_2}{\frac{1}{4f}} = 4fLI_2 \tag{11.12}$$

Recall that the average value of a sine wave is equal to $2/\pi$ times its peak value. Accordingly, we can substitute this term in Equation (11.12) to obtain

$$\frac{2E_2}{\pi} = 4fLI_2 \tag{11.13}$$

When Equation (11.13) is rearranged,

$$E_2 = 2\pi fLI_2 \tag{11.14}$$

Since the effective value of a sine wave is proportional its peak value, we can replace E_2 and I_2 in Equation (11.14) with effective values E and I:

$$E = 2\pi fLI \tag{11.15}$$

The *reaction* of an inductor to a current change is evidently denoted by $2\pi fL$. We rearrange Equation (11.15) in an Ohm's law formulation:

$$\frac{E}{I} = 2\pi fL \tag{11.16}$$

INDUCTIVE REACTANCE

We see that $2\pi fL$ in an a-c situation is analogous to resistance in a d-c situation. This opposition is called *inductive reactance.* It is often convenient to write reactance as X_L for an inductor, instead of $2\pi fL$. Thus, Equation (11.16) will be written

$$I = \frac{E}{X_L} \tag{11.17}$$

This equation can be used with effective (rms) values, peak values, or peak-to-peak values. It is only necessary to be consistent in assignment of values. Note carefully that the reactance of an inductor is directly proportional to frequency. This is a basic difference between inductive reactance and resistance, because the resistance of a resistor does not change with frequency. Note also that while the reactance of an inductor is directly proportional to frequency, the reactance of a capacitor is inversely proportional to frequency. We often treat inductive reactance as positive reactance, and we treat capacitive reactance as negative reactance.

Equation (11.17) states that if you apply 1 a-c volt across an inductive reactance of 1 ohm, 1 a-c amp will flow. A typical volt-ampere-wattmeter is illustrated in Figure 11-11. All a-c instruments are calibrated in rms values for sine waves, unless otherwise specified. The instrument illustrated indicates d-c values or rms a-c values. In other words, the pointer will indicate 100 volts whether the meter is connected to a 100-volt d-c source, or to a 100 rms-a-c source.

Figure 11-11
A typical volt-ampere-wattmeter. (Courtesy of Simpson Electric Co.)

11.5 PHASES OF VOLTAGE AND CURRENT

We learned why current and voltage are 90 degrees out of phase in a reactive circuit in our previous analysis of capacitive reactance. In the same manner, the current must be 90 degrees out of phase in an inductive reactance. However, there is one important difference of detail. We recall that an inductor reacts oppositely to the way a capacitor reacts. This simply means that the current through an inductor *lags* the applied voltage by 90 degrees, as depicted in Figure 11-12.

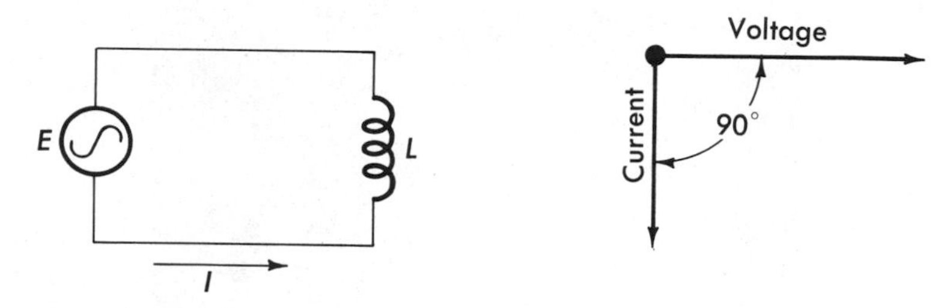

Figure 11-12
The current is 90 degrees out of phase with the voltage in an ideal inductor, and the current lags the voltage.

If you connect an a-c ammeter and an a-c voltmeter into an inductive circuit, as shown in Figure 11-13, the indicated values will be in accordance with Equation (11.17). The ammeter and voltmeter do not provide any information concerning the relative phases of voltage and current. However, if you also connect the wattmeter of Figure 11-11 into the circuit depicted in Figure 11-13, the wattmeter reads zero, no matter what the voltage and current values may be. This is because no real power is present

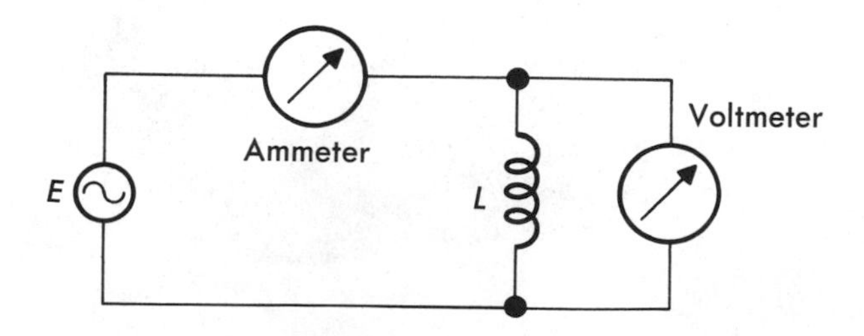

Figure 11-13
The voltmeter and ammeter indicate values in accordance with Ohm's law for a-c circuits.

when the voltage and current are 90 degrees out of phase with each other.

The equation for real power, we recall, is written

$$W_{\text{real}} = I_{\text{rms}} E_{\text{rms}} \cos \theta \tag{11.18}$$

where θ is the phase angle between voltage and current.

Since the cosine of 90 degrees is zero, there is no real power in an inductor. Thus, the power in an inductor can be compared with the power in a capacitor. The energy stored in the field of an inductor is returned to the source on alternate half cycles of the power waveform; hence, the arrangement in Figure 11-13 does no work in the physical sense. This is why the wattmeter reads zero when connected into the circuit of Figure 11-13. The basic a-c wattmeter is designed to indicate the value of real power which is present in a circuit.

Suppose $E = 100$ volts and $I = 1$ amp in Figure 11-13. We then say that there are 100×1 or 100 volt-amps supplied to the inductor. However, only inductive reactance is present in the circuit; the current is 90 degrees out of phase (in quadrature) with the voltage. Hence, the 100 volt-amps are associated with zero real power. Of course, there are 100 watts of *reactive* power present in this example, but reactive power does no work in the physical sense. You will find another type of wattmeter used in some circuits which does *not* measure real power; instead the meter indicates reactive power. This type of wattmeter is called a *VAR meter*; VAR stands for volt-amperes-reactive.

It is perhaps well to recall that the foregoing discussion concerns pure inductive reactance, which has zero resistance. In practice, an inductor does not have zero resistance unless it is cooled to superconductivity. All a-c theory is based on the concept of ideal or pure inductive reactance. At room temperature, it is seldom justified to neglect the resistance of an inductor. Hence, circuit analysis becomes elaborated somewhat over the basic analyses which we have considered thus far.

INDUCTANCE STANDARDS

What about *standards* of inductance? There is no primary standard of inductance, inasmuch as this is a derived unit. We have learned about laboratory standards of capacitance. A standard capacitor can be used to measure inductance values with the aid of a suitable a-c bridge. Again, laboratory standards of inductance are also widely utilized. The characteristics of any inductor to be used as a laboratory standard comprise high accuracy, high stability, small variation of inductance with frequency, small variation of inductance with current, high-Q value, low-temperature coefficient, and minimum external field. Laboratory standards of inductance are often designed as toroids, as depicted in Figure 11-14. This construction provides negligible external magnetic field.

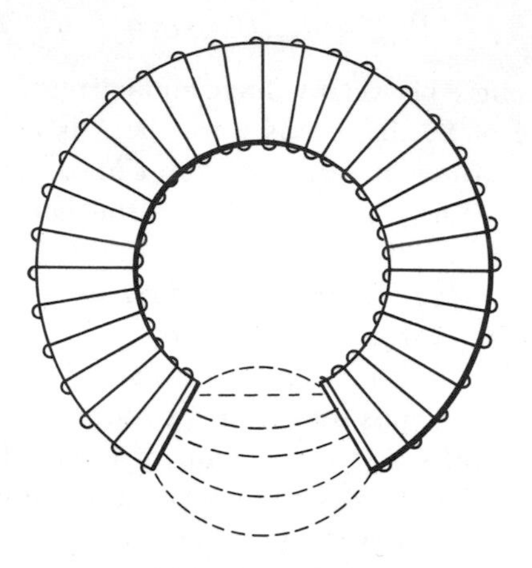

Figure 11-14
Construction of a toroidal coil.

Air-cored inductance standards are preferred, because they have negligible variation of inductance with current change. Inductance values range typically from 100 μh to 10 henrys. Rated accuracies range from $\pm$0.03 percent to $\pm$0.1 percent. Winding resistances range from 0.17 ohm to 8000 ohms for typical standards. Another type of standard inductor is wound on a toroidal molybdenum-permalloy dust core, and has less than 10 percent of the winding resistance of a comparable air-core inductor. On the other hand, accuracy ratings are less, and range typically from $\pm$0.25 percent to $\pm$1 percent. Standard inductors with magnetic cores must be applied with due regard for the *B-H* curve of the core material. You will have an opportunity to learn good practices in application of standard inductors in your laboratory experiments.

11.6 ANALYSIS OF INDUCTOR DEFECTS

Inductors may become defective due to an open-circuit, short-circuit, or partial short-circuit. If the coil wire breaks or becomes severely corroded at some point in the winding, the inductor will be open-circuited and no current can be passed through it. This fault can be determined by an ohmmeter test of the coil—the ohmmeter will read infinite resistance if the coil is open. On the other hand, if the winding is intact, the ohmmeter will read the winding-resistance value. Many inductors used in electronics equipment are rated for winding resistance, to facilitate this test.

When excessive current is passed through an inductor, the winding becomes overheated in consequence of the I^2R loss in its winding resistance. The insulation of the coil wire can become charred, which permits one or more turns to short-circuit with neighboring turns or layers. In this case, the winding resistance will have a subnormal value. Short-circuited turns also reduce the inductance of a coil, because there are effectively fewer turns present to conduct current. An instrument called the *inductance bridge* is used to check the inductance of a coil against its rated value.

Sometimes damaged wire insulation does not produce a complete ("dead") short-circuit between turns or layers. Instead, an effective leakage resistance is established. In such case, the measured winding resistance will be more or less subnormal. The inductance value will be somewhat reduced, and the power factor will measure less than its rated value. An inductance bridge will indicate the power-factor value. An oscilloscope can also be used to measure a power factor. When this type of fault is encountered, the wire insulation may not be damaged mechanically; the coil may have absorbed excessive moisture, which provides leakage paths between turns and layers.

SUMMARY OF FUNDAMENTAL CONCEPTS

Inductive reactance stores and returns electrical energy, but does not consume energy.

Inductive reactance and resistance in series cause an exponential current flow in response to a suddenly applied d-c voltage.

The time constant of a series LR circuit is equal to the ratio of inductance to resistance. $T = L/R$.

The current in the circuit attains 63 percent of its final value in one time constant.

The a-c current flow through an inductor lags the applied sine-wave voltage by 90 degrees.

Inductive reactance opposes sine-wave current flow in accordance with Ohm's law. $I = E/X_L$.

The power consumed by an LR circuit energized by a sine-wave voltage is equal to the product of voltage, current, and the cosine of the phase angle between voltage and current.

Notes: L is equal to the inductance in henrys. R is equal to the resistance in ohms. T is equal to the time in seconds. I is equal to the current in amperes. E is equal to the voltage in volts. X_L is equal to the reactance in ohms, or $2\pi fL$.

QUESTIONS

1) Self-induction operates to:
(*a*) assist the build-up of current in an inductor. (*b*) oppose the build-up of current in an inductor. (*c*) reverse the polarity of the

source voltage. (*d*) reverse the direction of total current flow.

2) Magnetic flux lines spread out from an inductor, or collapse into an inductor:
(*a*) instantly. (*b*) at a velocity proportional to the inductance. (*c*) at a velocity proportional to the source voltage. (*d*) at the speed of light.

3) When magnetic flux lines collapse into an inductor:
(*a*) current flow is reversed. (*b*) current flow continues in the same direction as before the field started to collapse. (*c*) current flow stops at the instant the field starts to collapse. (*d*) current flow starts at the instant the field starts to collapse.

4) If an ideal inductor has an inductance of 1 henry:
(*a*) its terminal voltage will be 10^8 volts when the current through the inductor is changing at the rate of 1 amp per sec. (*b*) its terminal voltage will be 1 volt when the current through the inductor is changing at the rate of 10^8 amp per sec. (*c*) its terminal voltage will be 1 volt when the current through the inductor is changing at the rate of 1 amp per sec. (*d*) its terminal voltage will be 1 volt when its field flux is changing at the rate of 10^{-8} lines per sec.

5) The time constant of an LR series circuit is equal to:
(*a*) $2\pi fL$. (*b*) $\omega L/R$. (*c*) $R/(\omega L)$. (*d*) L/R.

6) An inductor contains stored energy in its magnetic field that is equal to:
(*a*) $CE^2/2$. (*b*) $E/(2\pi fL)$. (*c*) $0.5\,LI^2$. (*d*) L/R.

7) If an a-c voltage is applied to an ideal inductor, the current flow is equal to:
(*a*) E/L. (*b*) $E/(\omega L)$. (*c*) $E \sin \theta$. (*d*) $E \cos \theta$.

8) The reactance of an inductor varies:
(*a*) in direct proportion to the applied voltage. (*b*) in inverse proportion to the applied voltage. (*c*) in direct proportion to the current flow. (*d*) in direct proportion to the applied frequency.

9) If an a-c current flows through an ideal inductor, its terminal voltage:
(*a*) leads the current by 90 degrees. (*b*) lags the current by 90 degrees. (*c*) increases to infinity as a limit. (*d*) decreases to zero as a limit.

10) The reactive power in an ideal inductor is equal to:
(*a*) $EI \cos \theta$. (*b*) $EI \sin \theta$. (*c*) $E/(2\pi fL)$. (*d*) L/R.

PROBLEMS

1) If an ideal coil has 100 turns, and an applied d-c voltage causes an increase of 10^5 flux lines per amp of current increase, what is the inductance value of the coil?

2) An ideal 1-henry coil is connected to a d-c voltage source. How many flux linkages will be established by a current rise from zero to 1 amp?
3) How much energy is stored in the magnetic field of the coil in Problem 2 at the instant that the current attains a value of 1 amp?
4) What is the time constant of a 100-mh coil connected in series with a 1-megohm resistor?
5) If the series combination of Problem 4 is connected to a 6-volt d-c source, how long does it take for the current to rise to 63 percent of maximum?
6) If the series combination of Problem 4 is connected to a 1-microvolt d-c source, how long does it take for the current to rise to 63 percent of maximum?
7) How much energy is stored in the magnetic field of the coil in Problem 5 at the instant that the current attains its 63 percent of maximum value?
8) How much energy is stored in the magnetic field of the coil in Problem 6 at the instant that the current attains its 63 percent of maximum value?
9) An ideal 1-henry coil is connected to a 117-volt 60-cycle line. What is the value of current flow?
10) The coil in Problem 9 is connected to a 117-volt 10,000-cycle source. What is the value of current flow?
11) When a 1-mfd capacitor is connected in series with a certain resistor, the time constant is 1 sec. An ideal 1-henry inductor is substituted for the capacitor. What is the time constant of the *LR* combination?
12) An inductor has a winding resistance of 100 ohms. When it is connected to a 100-volt d-c source, the current rises to 0.63 amp in 0.25 sec. What is the inductance value?
13) After the current has attained its final value of 1 amp in Problem 12, the inductor terminals are short-circuited. A fuse is provided in series with the voltage source, to automatically open the battery lead. Calculate the value of power dissipated in the winding resistance of the inductor.
14) An ideal 1-henry inductor is connected to a 117-volt 60-cycle source through a wattmeter. What is the value of power indicated by the wattmeter?
15) The inductor in Problem 14 is connected to a 6-volt d-c source. At the end of 1 sec, what is the terminal voltage of the inductor?

12

SERIES A-C CIRCUIT ANALYSIS

12.1 RESISTIVE SERIES CIRCUITS

Action and reaction in a-c circuits is more interesting to analyze than elementary d-c circuits. Basic d-c circuit analysis concerns current, voltage, and power values in resistive networks. As would be anticipated, there is no reaction in a resistive circuit when a-c voltage is applied. Hence, the most basic a-c circuit analysis also concerns current, voltage, and power values in resistive networks. This section is essentially a brief summary of certain important facts that were developed in foregoing chapters. With these basic facts clearly in mind, we will be in good position to analyze action and reaction in series a-c circuits that comprise positive and/or negative reactance.

When we speak of a-c current or voltage, it is understood that the current and voltage have sinusoidal waveforms. The equation of an a-c voltage is written

$$e = E \sin 2\,\pi\, ft \qquad \textbf{(12.1)}$$

where e is the instantaneous value of the voltage at any time t, and E is the peak value of the sine-wave voltage.

We will often abbreviate Equation (12.1) to the form

$$e = E \sin \omega\, t \qquad \textbf{(12.2)}$$

where ω stands for $2\,\pi\, f$.

Furthermore, we will often simplify our notation still more, and designate an a-c voltage simply as E. When we write E, we refer to the rms value of the sine-wave voltage, which is, of course, 0.707 of its peak value. Most discussion of a-c circuits entails rms (effective) values, because these values are directly related to a-c power. Regardless of the technical shorthand that we may employ, it is always implied that we visualize a sine wave that is generated by a radius vector rotating counterclockwise in a circle (see Figure 12-1).

The equation of an a-c current may be written

$$i = I \sin 2\,\pi\, ft \qquad \textbf{(12.3)}$$

where i is the instantaneous value of the current at any time t and I is the peak value of the sine-wave current.

Equation (12.3) may also be written in abbreviated form

$$i = I \sin \omega\, t \qquad \textbf{(12.4)}$$

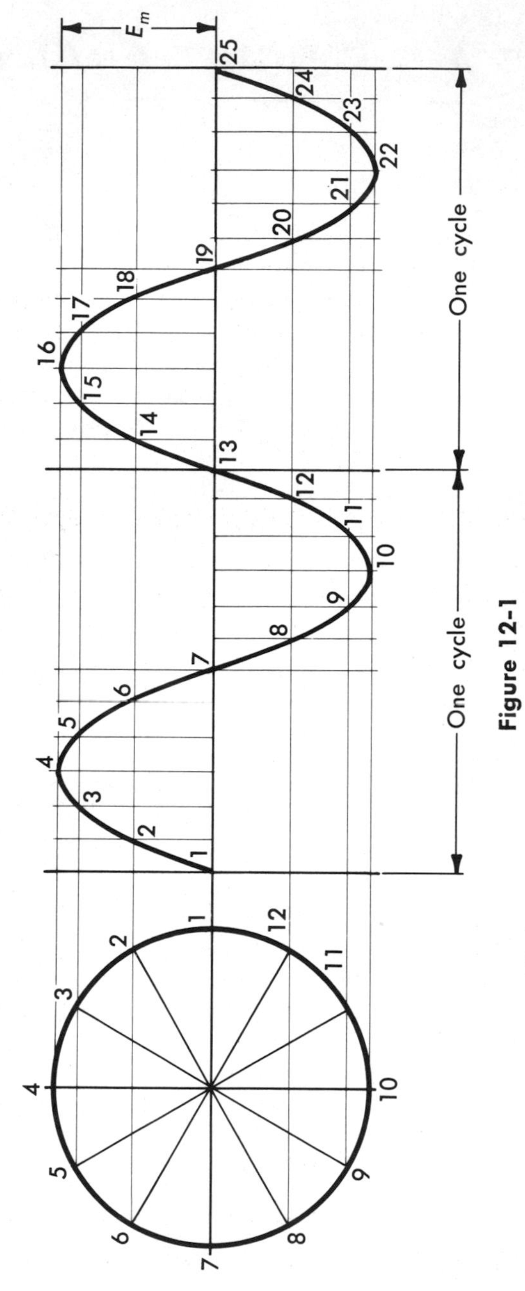

Figure 12-1
All sine-wave notation is based on these geometric relations.

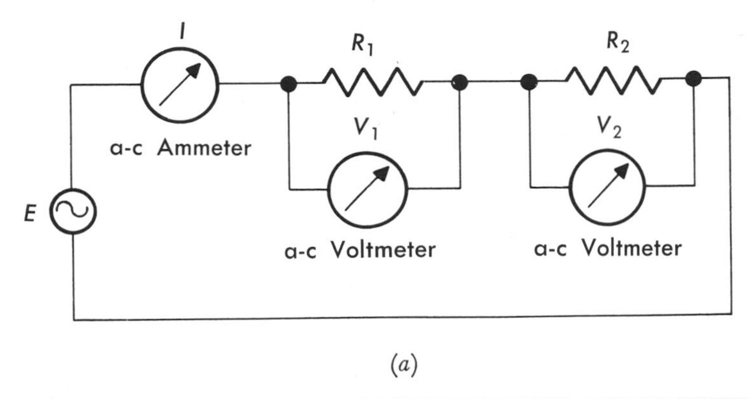

(a)

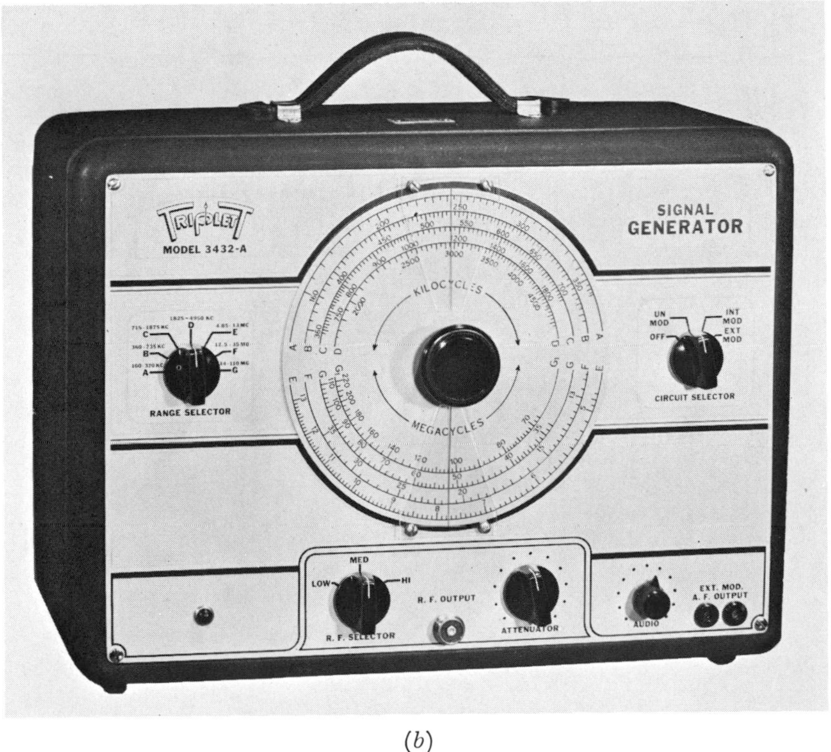

(b)

Fig. 12-2. (*See caption on page 316.*)

When we designate an a-c current as *I*, we refer to its rms value. You will recall that most a-c meters indicate rms values of sine waves. Consider the resistive circuit shown in Figure 12-2. The ammeter indicates the current flow in the series configuration. The voltmeters indicate the voltage drops across the resistors. According to Kirchhoff's voltage law,

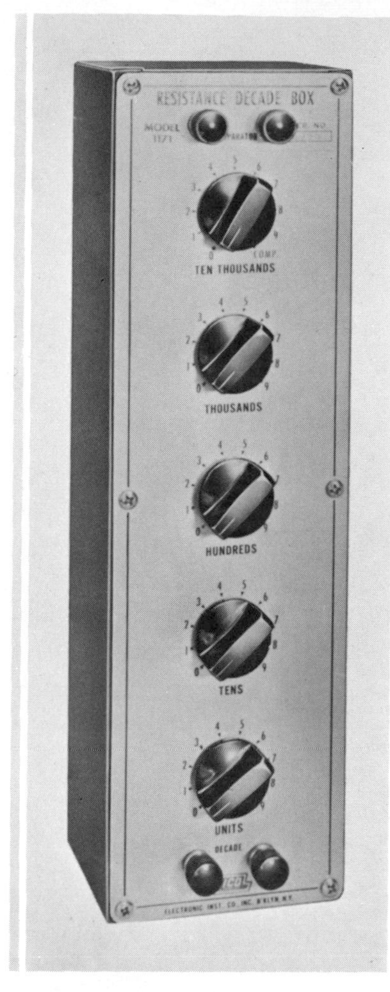

(c)

Figure 12-2
(a) A simple series-capacitor series circuit with resistive components. *(b)* Laboratory experiments often utilize a signal generator as a voltage source. This typical generator provides sine-wave voltages at frequencies from 160 kc to 220 mc. (Courtesy of Triplett Electrical Instrument Co.) *(c)* A typical resistance decade box for laboratory and shop test work. Resistance values are available in steps from 1 to 99,999 ohms. (Courtesy of Electronic Instrument Co.)

$E = V_1 + V_2$. The power supplied by the generator to the series circuit is stated

$$W = EI \tag{12.5}$$

where E and I are in rms values and W is real power that is dissipated as heat by the two resistors.

We know that current and voltage are in phase in a resistive circuit. We also know that $\sin^2 \theta$ is a double-frequency sine waveform, as depicted in Figure 12-3. In other words, if E has a frequency of 60 cycles per sec, the power waveform has a frequency of 120 cycles per sec. These frequency relations are easily demonstrated with a suitable oscilloscope test setup.

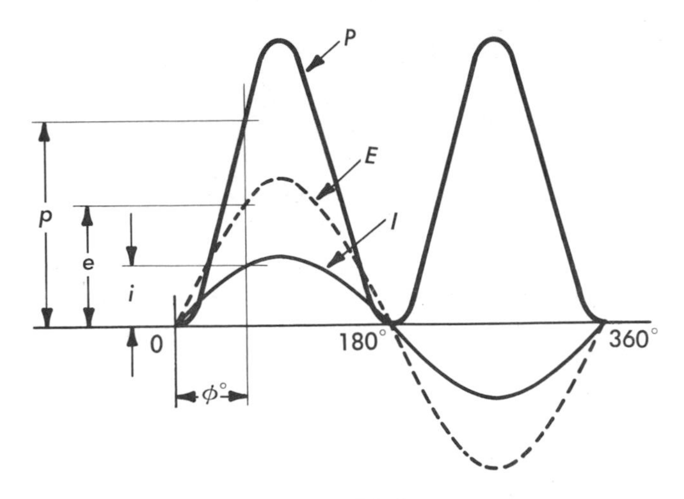

Figure 12-3
The power waveform is a double-frequency sine wave.

Ohm's law applies to parts of an a-c circuit, as well as to the complete circuit. Thus, $R_1 = V_1/I$ and $R_2 = V_2/I$ in Figure 12-2. The power dissipated by R_1 is equal to IV_1, and the power dissipated by R_2 is equal to IV_2. Furthermore, the total power dissipated by the two resistors is equal to the sum of the two power values, which in turn is equal to the power supplied to the circuit by the generator.

When we multiply rms voltage by rms current, we obtain the *average* value of the double-frequency power wave depicted in Figure 12-3. Recall that an rms value is equal to 0.707 of peak value; when we square 0.707, we obtain 0.5. The average power in the double-frequency waveform is equal to half of its peak value, as derived from geometrical considerations explained in Chapter 9. This average value is of most general interest because it is an equivalent d-c power value. It makes no difference whether we apply 117 volts a-c or 117 volts d-c to the circuit of Figure 12-2; the same amount of power will be dissipated by R_1 and R_2 in either case, provided we apply 117 *rms* volts of a-c. The same amount of power is also dissipated regardless of the a-c frequency.

Of course, there are instantaneous and peak power values represented by the double-frequency power wave in Figure 12-3, just as there are instantaneous and peak voltage values represented by the voltage waveform. In some electronics devices we are chiefly concerned with the peak power dissipation. On occasion, we may also be concerned with various instantaneous power values. Thus, p in Figure 12-3 represents an instantaneous power value that corresponds to the product of the instantaneous voltage and current values e and i.

12.2 CAPACITIVE SERIES CIRCUITS

We know that the reactance of a capacitor is measured in a-c ohms, and is expressed by the formula

$$X_C = \frac{1}{2\,\pi\, fC} = \frac{1}{\omega\, C} \tag{12.6}$$

The term X_C is used in Ohm's law for a-c circuits just as R is used in Ohm's law for d-c circuits. In other words, if an a-c voltage E is applied across a capacitor that has a reactance of X_C a-c ohms, the current that flows through the capacitor is given by

$$I = \frac{E}{X_C} \tag{12.7}$$

In this instance, we are concerned with simple series circuits. Hence, we may ask how the series-capacitor circuit shown in Figure 12-4 is to be analyzed. First of all, C_1 has a reactance X_{C_1}, and C_2 has a reactance X_{C_2}. Voltage V_1 is equal to IX_{C_1}; voltage V_2 is equal to IX_{C_2}. Voltage E is equal to the sum of V_1 and V_2, in accordance with Kirchhoff's voltage law. We know that the current leads the voltage by 90 degrees. In turn, the power dissipated by each capacitor is equal to zero, and the generator supplies no real power to the circuit:

$$W = EI \cos\theta \tag{12.8}$$

where θ is the phase angle between voltage and current.

It is apparent that capacitors C_1 and C_2 in Figure 12-4 can be replaced by a single equivalent capacitor. What is the value of this equivalent

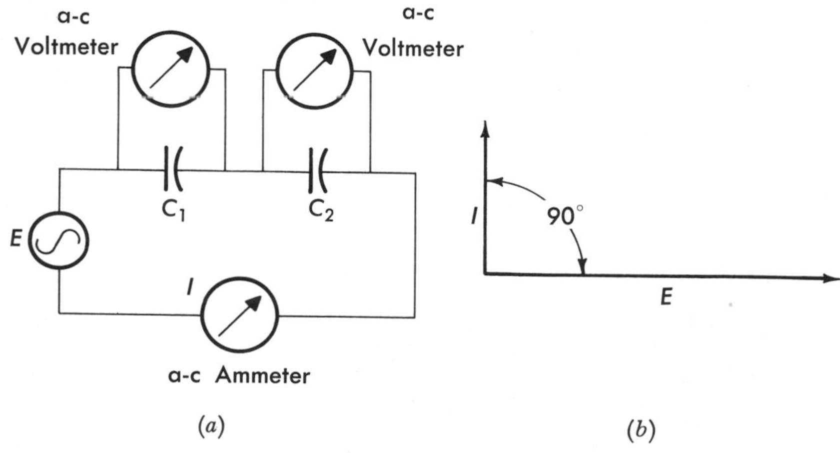

Fig. 12-4. (*See caption on facing page.*)

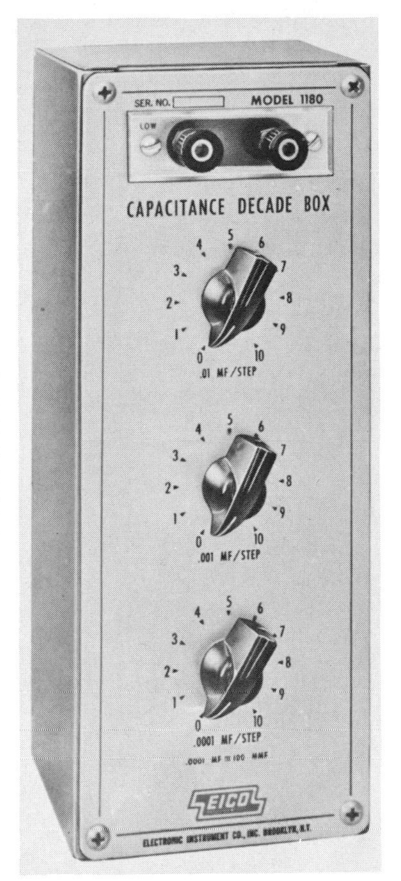

(c)

Figure 12-4
(a) A series-capacitor circuit. *(b)* Current and voltage are 90 degrees out of phase with each other. *(c)* A capacitance decade box facilitates various laboratory experiments and shop tests. This typical decade provides capacitance values in steps from 0.0001 μf to 0.111 μf. (Courtesy of Electronic Instrument Co.)

capacitance? This is a series circuit, and the series law states that the current is same at any point in the circuit. Hence, the same amount of current flows through each capacitor. Current quantity Q, we recall, is formulated

$$Q = CE \tag{12.9}$$

Therefore, $V_1 = Q/C_1$, and $V_2 = Q/C_2$. Kirchhoff's voltage law states that $E = V_1 + V_2$; it follows that $E = Q/C_1 + Q/C_2$. Let us call the equivalent capacitance of the series configuration C_t. Then, $E = Q/C_t$ in accordance with Equation (12.9). In turn, $Q/C_t = Q/C_1 + Q/C_2$. Q cancels out, leaving

$$\frac{1}{C_t} = \frac{1}{C_1} + \frac{1}{C_2} \tag{12.10}$$

This equation states that a reciprocal is equal to the sum of two reciprocals. We may use Equation (12.10) as it stands. However, it is sometimes more convenient to solve for C_t, and write

$$C_t = \frac{C_1 C_2}{C_1 + C_2} \tag{12.11}$$

Equation (12.11) states that the total (or equivalent) capacitance is equal to the product of the two individual capacitances divided by their sum. It is clear that the series circuit in Figure 12-4 can be replaced by an equivalent circuit as shown in Figure 12-5. Exactly the same current flows in the equivalent circuit as in the series circuit. Of course, the generator "sees" the same total reactance in either circuit:

$$X_{C_t} = X_{C_1} + X_{C_2} \tag{12.12}$$

Suppose you have a series circuit comprising three capacitors and a voltage source. Its equivalent circuit can be derived in the same manner as previously explained, and we can write

$$\frac{1}{C_t} = \frac{1}{C_1} + \frac{1}{C_2} + \frac{1}{C_3} \tag{12.13}$$

By algebraic manipulation, we can solve for C_t and restate Equation (12.13) in the form

$$C_t = \frac{C_1 C_2 C_3}{C_1 C_2 + C_2 C_3 + C_1 C_3} \tag{12.14}$$

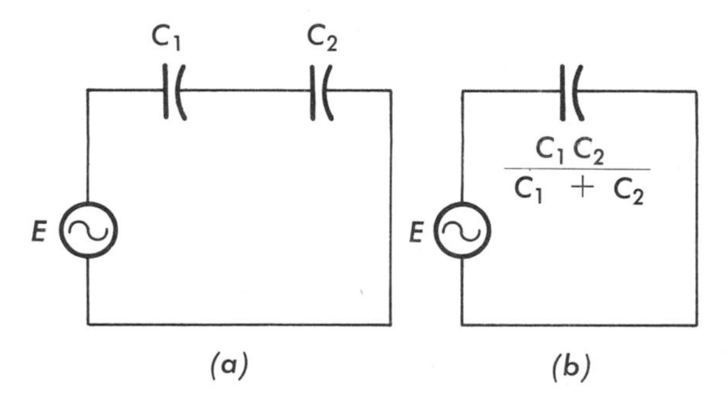

Figure 12-5
(a) A series circuit comprising two capacitors and a voltage source. *(b)* Equivalent circuit comprising an equivalent capacitor and the same voltage source. *(c)* The value of a capacitor is often checked with an instrument which is called a capacitor bridge. This typical bridge also tests a capacitor for leakage. (Courtesy of Heath Co.)

(Continued on facing page.)

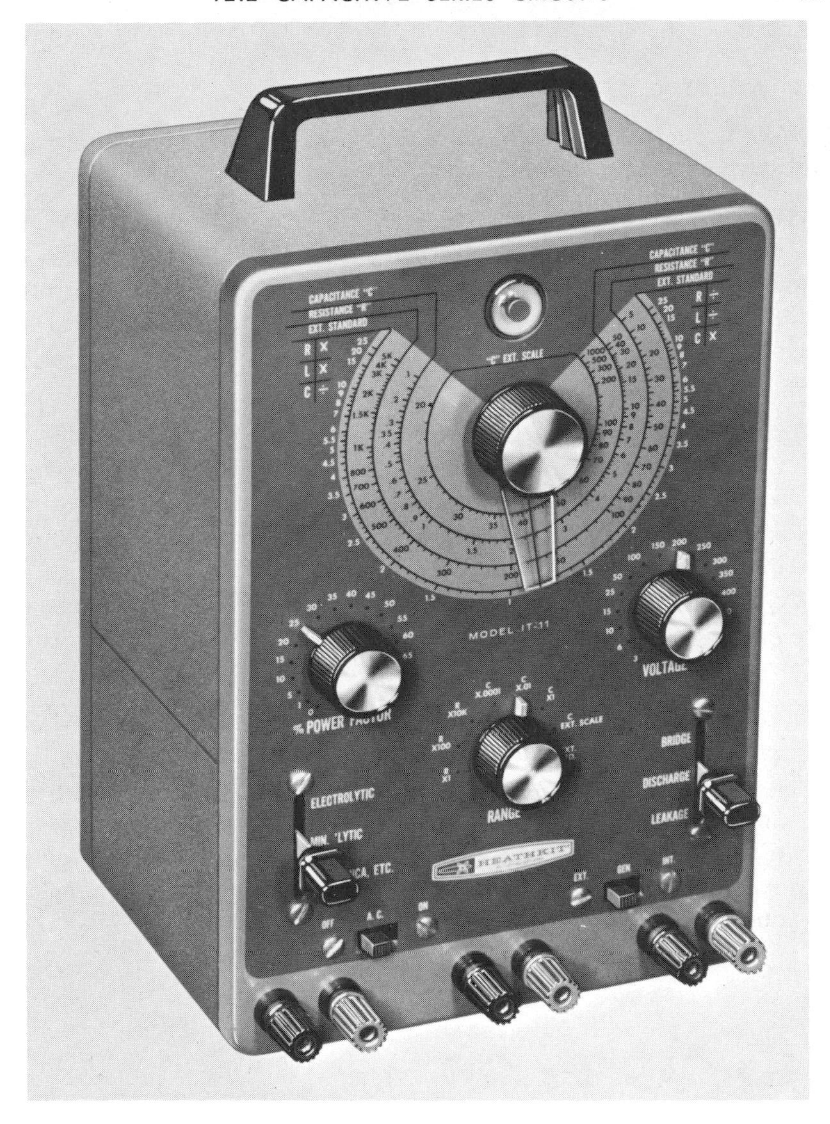

(*c*)
Fig. 12-5 (*Continued*)

We see that if we are concerned with several capacitors connected in series, that it is much easier to compute the equivalent capacitance as a sum of reciprocals instead of using the product-and-sum formulation. However, when only two capacitors are connected in series, it is easier to use the product-and-sum formulation. Later in this chapter we shall return to analysis of circuits that contain capacitors. However, it is instructive at this time to briefly consider simple inductive circuits.

12.3 INDUCTIVE SERIES CIRCUITS

We know that the reactance of an inductor is measured in a-c ohms, and is expressed by the formula

$$X_L = 2\pi fL = \omega L \tag{12.15}$$

Of course, X_L is used in Ohm's law for a-c circuits just as R is used in Ohm's law for d-c circuits. If an a-c voltage E is applied across an inductor that has a reactance of X_L ohms, the current that flows through the inductor is given by

$$I = \frac{E}{X_L} \tag{12.16}$$

Consider the series-inductor circuit depicted in Figure 12-6. Voltage V_1 is equal to IX_{L_1} Voltage V_2 is equal to IX_{L_2} $E = V_1 + V_2$. Neither of the inductors dissipates any power, and the generator supplies no power to the circuit. The same current flows through L_1 and L_2; hence, $IX_{L_1} + IX_{L_2} = IX_{L_t}$, where X_{L_t} represents the total or equivalent circuit inductance. The factor I cancels out, leaving $X_{L_1} + X_{L_2} = X_{L_t}$. Similarly, $2\pi f$ cancels out from the reactance terms, giving

$$L_t = L_1 + L_2 \tag{12.17}$$

The total inductance in the circuit is equal to the sum of the individual inductances. We can replace L_1 and L_2 in Figure 12-6 with their equivalent inductance, and the same current will flow as in the original circuit. The current, of course, lags the voltage by 90 degrees. The reactive power in either circuit is equal to $EI \sin\theta$, or simply EI, as previously explained.

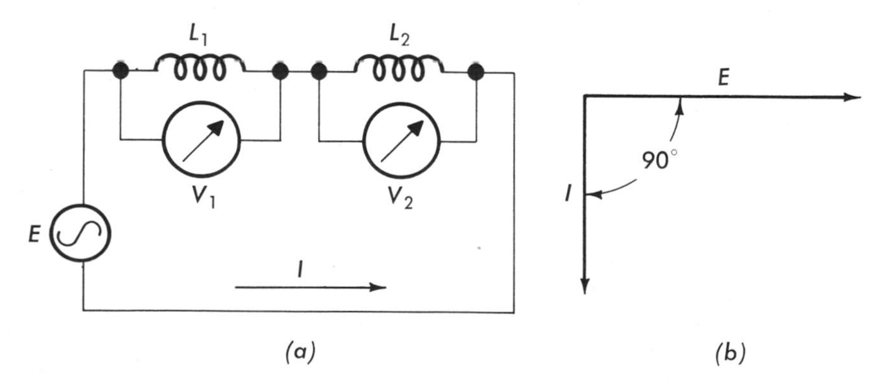

Figure 12-6
(*a*) A series-inductor circuit. (*b*) Voltage and current are 90 degrees out of phase with each other.

12.4 SERIES CAPACITANCE AND RESISTANCE

Let us analyze a series *RC* circuit, such as the configuration shown in Figure 12-7. At first glance, the voltage values might seem to violate Kirchhoff's voltage law; in other words, how can a source voltage of 100 volts drop 44.7 volts across the resistor, and drop 89.4 volts across the capacitor? Remember that the voltage is in phase with the current in a resistor, but that the voltage is 90 degrees out of phase with the current in a capacitor. Hence, to state Kirchhoff's voltage law for the circuit in Figure 12-7 requires that the resistor voltage be added at right angles to the capacitor voltage, as illustrated in Figure 12-8. When we combine

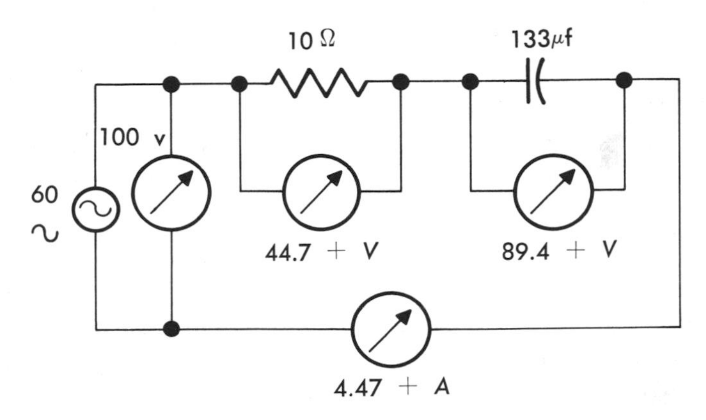

Figure 12-7
A series *RC* circuit with all voltage and current values indicated.

the radius vectors (or simply *vectors*) of the resistor voltage and capacitor voltage correctly, we see that their sum is indeed 100 volts, as indicated in Figure 12-7. The addition depicted in Figure 12-8 is a *vectorial addition*.

What is the reactance of the capacitor in Figure 12-7? We can calculate its reactance from Ohm's law: $X_C = E/I = 89.4/4.47 = 20$ ohms. We can also calculate the reactance of the capacitor according to the formula $X_C = 1/(2\pi fC)$. Note that C is equal to 133 microfarads and f is equal to 60 cycles per sec. If you work the arithmetic, you will confirm that the value of X_C is 20 ohms. Next, we note that the resistor voltage is equal to IR, and that the capacitor voltage is equal to IX_C in Figure 12-8. The 100-volt vector corresponds to IZ, where Z is the *impedance* of the circuit in a-c ohms. In other words,

$$I = \frac{E}{Z} \tag{12.18}$$

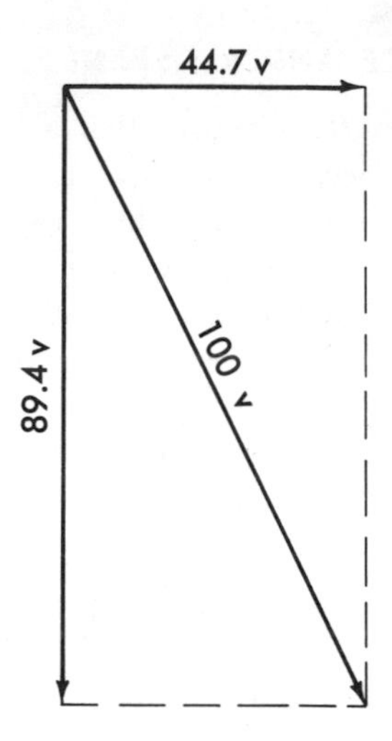

Figure 12-8
Kirchhoff's voltage law as displayed for the circuit in Figure 12-7.

We see that Z in Equation (12.18) is analogous to the total resistance of a d-c resistive circuit which comprises two resistors. Impedance Z is the *vector* sum of a *resistance* and a *reactance.* The sum of the squares on the hypotenuse of a right triangle is equal to the sum of the squares on its two sides. Hence,

$$IZ = \sqrt{(IX_C)^2 + (IR)^2} \tag{12.19}$$

This is the Pythagorean theorem applied to the triangle of voltages depicted in Figure 12-8. Since I cancels out from Equation (12.19), we simply write

$$Z = \sqrt{X_C^2 + R^2} \tag{12.20}$$

Equation (12.20) states that reactance and resistance combine at right angles to form an *impedance triangle,* as shown in Figure 12-9. The impedance triangle in Figure 12-9 is, of course, similar to the voltage triangle in Figure 12-8. If you multiply each length of the impedance triangle by the current value, you will obtain the voltage triangle.

REAL, IMAGINARY, AND COMPLEX NUMBERS

In your algebra courses, you have probably become familiar with complex numbers. A complex number has the formulation $a + ib$, where i represents the $\sqrt{-1}$. Mathematicians call a a real number; they call ib

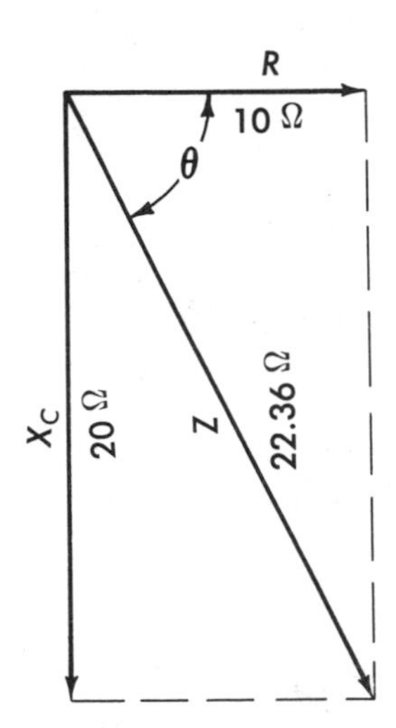

Figure 12-9
The impedance triangle for the circuit in Figure 12-7.

an imaginary number. In electronic circuits, *a* corresponds to resistance, and *b* corresponds to reactance. Thus, from a mathematical viewpoint, we can say that the current which flows through a capacitor is an "imaginary current." However, do not let this terminology mislead you—you can receive a shock just as quickly by an "imaginary current" as by a "real" current.

We learn in analytic geometry that real numbers are represented along the horizontal axis, and imaginary numbers are represented along the vertical axis of a coordinate system. Thus, $a + ib$ form the sides of a right triangle, of which the resultant or hypotenuse is a complex number (compare with the diagram in Figure 12-9). Although mathematicians use the symbol i for *imaginary* notation, electronics technicians use the symbol j. This avoids the possibility of confusion between the symbol for current and the symbol for imaginary. Thus, the electronics worker writes $R - jX_C$ to denote a resistance connected in series with a capacitive reactance. A minus sign is used, of course, because capacitive reactance is negative. Thus, Equation (12.20) can also be written

$$Z = R - jX_C \tag{12.21}$$

It makes no difference how we describe the impedance triangle in Figure 12-9; the answer must always be the same when we assign numerical values to R, X_C, and Z. But, as we shall learn, it is much easier to

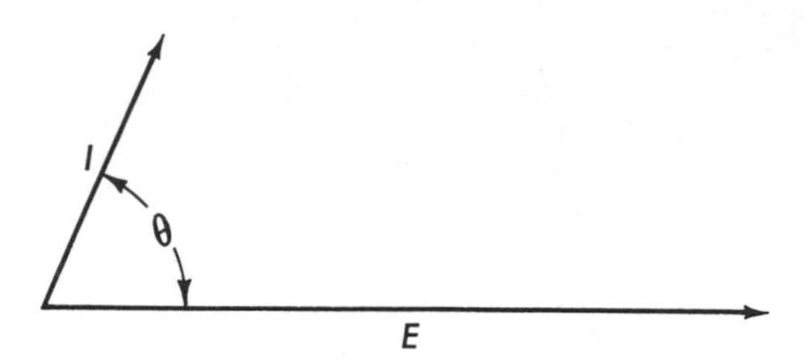

Figure 12-10
Current and voltage vectors for the circuit in Figure 12-7.

make impedance calculations with the operator j than to write out the square root of the sum of the squares of resistance and reactance.

Now, let us refer again to Figure 12-7. We know from principles previously established that the 10-ohm resistor dissipates real power. This power is equal to I^2R or $4.47^2 \times 10 = 200$ watts. On the other hand, the capacitor dissipates zero power. Hence, the generator supplies 200 watts of real power to the circuit. It is clear that the generator does *not* supply 100×4.47 watts, simply because the generator current is out of phase with the generator voltage. The current is in phase, of course, with the R vector in Figure 12-9; the generator voltage is in phase with the Z vector. But the Z vector *does* have a *component* which is in phase with the R vector, and this component is equal to $Z \cos \theta$. θ is simply the power-factor angle of the circuit in Figure 12-7.

Hence, let us draw the voltage and current vectors in a separate diagram, as shown in Figure 12-10. We know from elementary trigonometry that θ is equal to $\cos^{-1} R/Z$, or 63° 26′. The generator voltage is represented by the horizontal vector. The current leads the voltage by 63° 26′. We know that the power supplied by the generator to the circuit is formulated:

$$W = EI \cos \theta \tag{12.22}$$

When we substitute values from our example into Equation (12.22), we again obtain a power value of 200 watts, which confirms the I^2R value determined previously. Thus, $\cos \theta$ is the power factor of the circuit, and its value in this example is 0.4472. What is the reactive power in the capacitor (Figure 12-7)? We learned that reactive power is formulated

$$W = EI \sin \theta \tag{12.23}$$

Therefore, by elementary trigonometry, the reactive power is equal to 400 VARS. Observe that the generator supplies 447 volt-amps to the circuit. It is now clear from previous discussion that the 200 watts of real power is in phase with the resistance vector in Figure 12-9, the 400 watts of reactive power is in phase with the reactance vector, and the 447 volt-amps are in phase with the impedance vector. Thus, we find that the real power, reactive power, and volt-amps form a right triangle as depicted in Figure 12-11.

We have now solved the *RC* circuit completely. Only the basic electrical laws that were established in foregoing chapters were required.

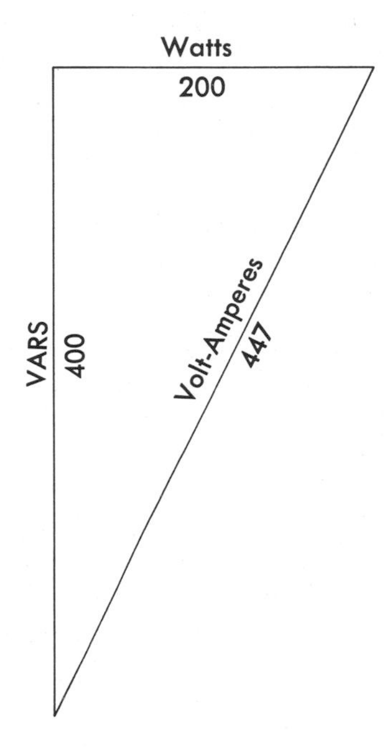

Figure 12-11
The power triangle for the circuit in Figure 12-7.

When these laws are applied with due regard for the fact that the current is 90 degrees out of phase with the voltage in a capacitor, we perceive that it is very easy to solve an *RC* circuit. Laws of a-c circuit action and reaction are merely simple extensions of the laws used to solve d-c circuits.

12.5 SERIES INDUCTANCE AND RESISTANCE

Next, let us analyze a series *RL* circuit, as depicted in Figure 12-12. This configuration is similar to the circuit shown in Figure 12-7, except that the capacitor has been replaced by an inductor. Kirchhoff's voltage

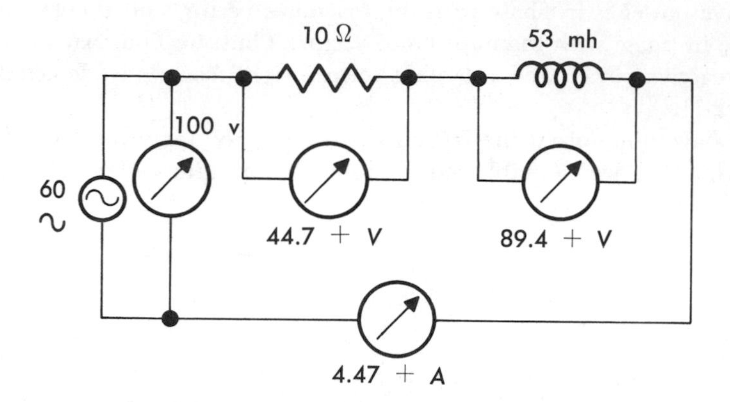

Figure 12-12
A series *RL* circuit, with all voltage and current values indicated.

law for Figure 12-12 is illustrated in Figure 12-13(*a*). Note that the inductor voltage leads the resistor voltage; the resistor voltage is in phase with the current, and the current lags the inductor voltage. Thus, the voltage diagram in Figure 12-13(*a*) is the opposite of the voltage diagram in Figure 12-8.

What is the reactance of the inductor in Figure 12-12? In accordance with Ohm's law, $X_L = E/I = 89.4/4.47 = 20$ ohms. Alternatively, we can calculate the inductive reactance from the formula $X_L = 2\pi fL$. The frequency is 60 cycles per sec, and L is equal to 53 mh, which yields a value of 20 ohms for X_L. The impedance of the *RL* circuit is evidently expressed by the formula

$$Z = \sqrt{X_L^2 + R^2} \qquad \textbf{(12.24)}$$

The corresponding impedance triangle for Figure 12-12 is seen in Figure 12-13(*b*). Compare this impedance triangle with that in Figure 12-9. Inductive reactance is positive; hence, we draw the X_L vector upward in Figure 12-13(*b*). It follows from a previous discussion that we can write Equation (12.24) in the form

$$Z = R + jX \qquad \textbf{(12.25)}$$

Compare Equation (12.25) with Equation (12.21). A plus sign appears in the former because inductive reactance is positive. The 10-ohm resistor in Figure 12-12 dissipates real power; this power is equal to I^2R, or 200 watts. Of course, the inductor consumes no real power. Hence, the generator supplies 200 watts of real power to the circuit. Note the current and voltage vectors for the *RL* circuit, separated by the power-factor

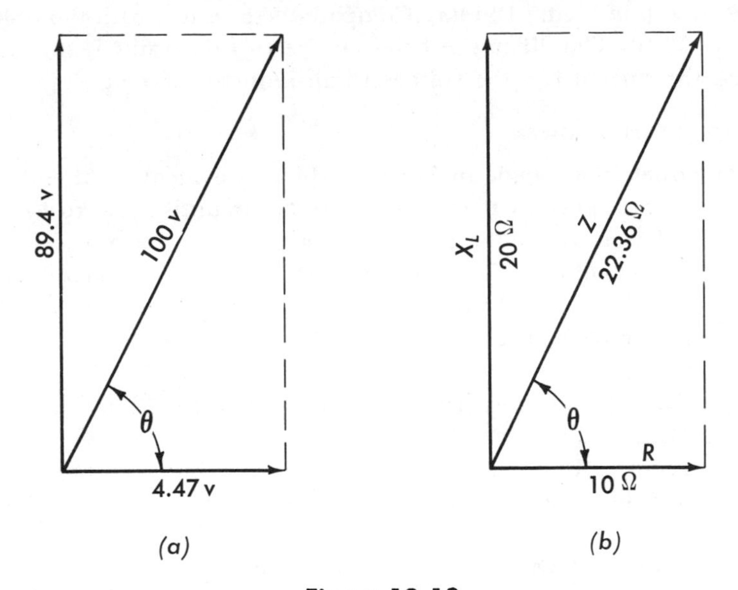

Figure 12-13
(a) Kirchhoff's voltage law displayed for the circuit in Figure 12-12. *(b)* The impedance triangle for the same circuit.

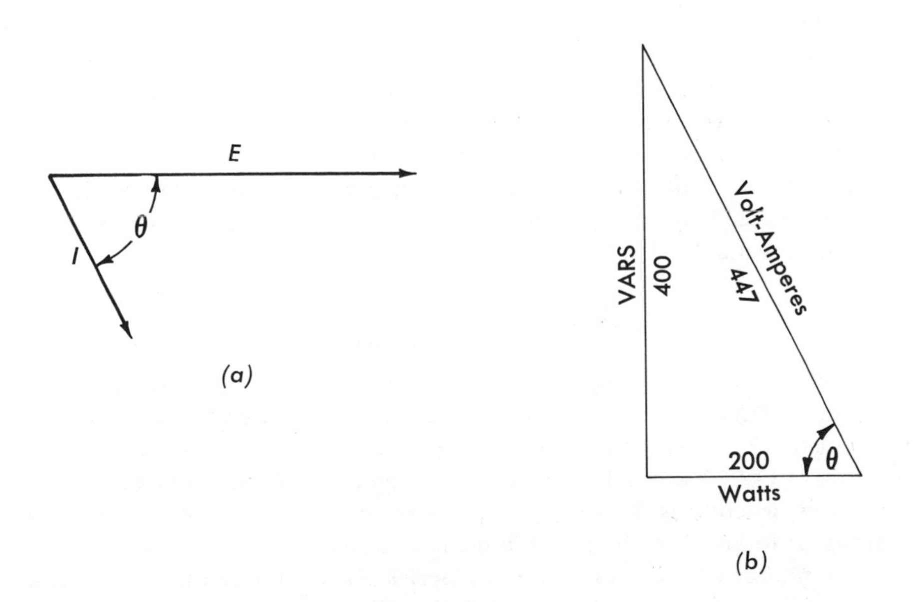

Figure 12-14
(a) Voltage and current vectors for the circuit in Figure 12-12. *(b)* The power triangle for the same circuit.

angle θ, as seen in Figure 12-14(*a*). Compare these vectors with those shown in Figure 12-10. The difference between the two diagrams is due to the fact that the current lags the voltage in an inductive circuit.

REAL AND REACTIVE POWER

The power factor angle in Figure 12-14(*a*) is evidently 63° 26′. Since the real power supplied by the generator to the circuit is equal to $EL \cos \theta$, a short calculation will confirm the value of 200 watts that was calculated above on the basis of I^2R. Since the reactive power in the inductor is equal to $EI \sin \theta$, it follows that the reactive power is equal to 400 VARS. In turn, the power triangle for Figure 12-12 is drawn as shown in Figure 12-14(*b*).

Note that the foregoing discussion assumes that the 53-mh inductance in Figure 12-12 is ideal; in other words, it is assumed that the inductor has no resistance. In practice, however, the winding resistance of an inductor can seldom be neglected. Thus, the 10-ohm resistance in Figure 12-12 might actually be the winding resistance of the inductor. This assumption does not change the analysis of the RL series circuit whatsoever, but when we make this assumption, note that the voltage drop across the resistance and the voltage drop across the inductor cannot be measured separately. In such case, a voltmeter connected across the 53-mh coil with its 10 ohms of winding resistance would read 100 volts.

The power factor of the RL series circuit remains the same, whether the 10-ohm resistance appears as depicted in Figure 12-12, or whether it is associated with the coil winding. How could you measure or calculate the power factor when the 10-ohm resistance is associated with the coil? The most common method is to use a volt-amp-wattmeter. When connected into the circuit of Figure 12-12, the meter will measure 100 volts, 4.47 amps, and 200 watts (of real power). Figure 12-14(*b*) shows that $\cos \theta$ is equal to watts divided by volt-amps. Thus,

$$\text{Power factor} - \frac{\text{Watts}}{\text{Volt-amps}} \tag{12.26}$$

Note in passing that real power is equal to I^2R, reactive power is equal to I^2X_L, and volt-amps are equal to I^2Z. Similarly, real power is equal to V^2/R, where V is the voltage drop across R; reactive power is equal to V^2/X_L, where V is the voltage drop across L; volt-amps are equal to E^2/Z, where E is the voltage applied to the circuit. These various relations all follow directly from Ohm's law for a-c.

Another practical example of a series RL circuit similar to the configuration in Figure 12-12 may be taken by assuming that the physical resistor has a value of 5 ohms, and that 5 ohms of winding resistance are associated with the 53-mh inductor. In this case, the circuit current is 4.47

amps as before, and the power factor remains the same. A voltmeter connected across the 5-ohm resistor will read 22.35 volts. The 20 ohms of inductive reactance combines with the 5 ohms of winding resistance to form an impedance of 20.6 ohms. Hence, a voltmeter connected across the inductor will read 92 volts.

12.6 LOCUS OF OPERATION

Trigonometric formulas are of basic application to a-c circuit analysis. We know that $\sin^2 \theta + \cos^2 \theta = 1$. Refer to Figure 12-13(*a*). Note that the power-factor angle θ is given by the angle between the resistor voltage and the source voltage. If we call the source voltage E, the resistor voltage

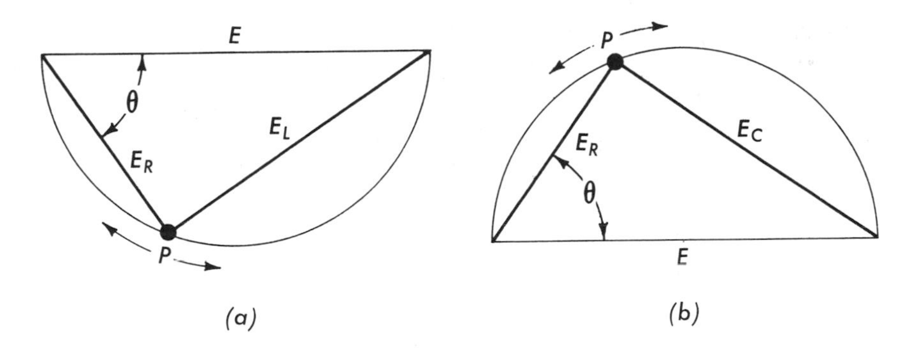

Figure 12-15
(*a*) Locus of P describes a semicircle; E_R lags E. (*b*) Locus of P describes a semicircle; E_R leads E.

is given by $E \cos \theta$. Similarly, the inductor voltage is given by $E \sin \theta$. Moreover, the square of the source voltage is equal to the sum of the squares of the resistor voltage and the inductor voltage, in accordance with the Pythagorean theorem. We can also write

$$E^2 = (E \sin \theta)^2 + (E \cos \theta)^2 \qquad \textbf{(12.27)}$$

The factor E cancels out, yielding $\sin^2 \theta + \cos^2 \theta = 1$. We learn in analytic geometry that this is the equation of a circle. This equation states that the locus of operation of an RL circuit is the arc of a circle, as seen in Figure 12-15(*a*). Point P falls on the circumference of a semicircle that has the source voltage E for a diameter. No matter what values you select for R and L in Figure 12-12, the intersection of the resistor voltage E_R with the inductor voltage E_L must always fall on the circumference of this semicircle.

This is perhaps a surprising conclusion; it is also a very useful and practical conclusion. For example, it shows that if you vary the value of R from zero to a very high (theoretically infinite) value, the phase angle of the circuit varies from 90 degrees to zero. Also, if you vary the value of L from zero to a very high (theoretically infinite) value, the phase angle of the circuit varies from zero to 90 degrees. A voltage with variable phase is sometimes required in electronic equipment. It is evident that we can make the resistance variable and take E_R as an output voltage. Then, the output voltage can be varied in phase with respect to the input voltage E over a range of 90 degrees to zero by varying the resistance value.

Of course, as the phase of E_R is varied with respect to E in this manner, the output voltage changes. This is a disadvantage in some applications. Accordingly, an elaboration of circuitry is often made that maintains the output voltage constant as its phase is varied. This is explained in engineering texts. You will observe that the locus of operation for the RC circuit in Figure 12-7 must also fall along a semicircle [see Figure 12-15(b)]. Hence, if we make the resistance variable in the RC circuit, the voltage across R will vary in phase over a 90 degree range.

Suppose that the inductor in a phase-shifting circuit has appreciable winding resistance. How does this affect the locus of operation in Figure 12-15? This situation simply means that E_R has a certain minimum voltage, and a certain maximum phase. The component of resistance associated with the inductance is not accessible for purposes of variation in a phase-shifting circuit. On the other hand, a commercial capacitor has negligible associated resistance. Hence, phase-shifting circuits are usually designed around RC configurations. Another advantage of an RC configuration is the comparatively low cost of capacitors.

12.7 TROUBLESHOOTING SERIES A-C CIRCUITS

Troubleshooting in series a-c circuitry usually starts with voltage measurements. If no voltage is present in the circuit, a fuse may have blown. An accidental short-circuit sometimes causes a fuse to blow. In such case, it is merely necessary to replace the open fuse. On the other hand, if a short-circuited capacitor, for example, causes excessive current drain and blows a fuse, a replacement fuse will blow promptly. The short-circuit must be cleared before the fuse can be replaced.

In this situation, voltage measurements indicate only that the fuse is blown. The full supply voltage is dropped across the blown fuse, and zero voltage is dropped across the series circuit components. Consequently, troubleshooting usually proceeds with resistance measurements. A short-circuited capacitor can be localized with ohmmeter measurements. Most inductors have appreciable winding resistance. Hence, a short-circuited inductor can often be localized with ohmmeter measurements.

A series circuit may draw excessive current, although the excess is insufficient to blow a fuse. A current measurement can be made by breaking the circuit and connecting an ammeter in series. However, this is often very inconvenient. Hence, expedients are commonly used in this situation. Let us consider a simple example. Suppose the resistor and the inductor overheat in Figure 12-12. If the ammeter is not wired into the circuit, you can make a current measurement by connecting a voltmeter across the 10-ohm resistor. The current value then follows from Ohm's law. This expedient is not completely reliable, because it assumes that the resistor is not defective, and has its rated resistance value.

Hence, the electricians often use a specialized instrument called the *clamp-around ammeter* to measure current flow. This type of meter does not make electrical connection to the circuit. Instead, it has an external iron core that is clamped around a current-carrying wire. We know that a conductor that carries current is surrounded by a magnetic field. The clamp-around core senses this magnetic field, and its strength is indicated by the ammeter. The ammeter, of course, has a scale that is calibrated in amperes, instead of flux.

SUMMARY OF FUNDAMENTAL CONCEPTS

Ohm's law for a-c applies to a complete series circuit, to any component in the circuit, or to a combination of two or more components: $I = E/R$; $I = E/X$; $I = E/Z$.

Kirchhoff's voltage law applies to reactive series circuits; resistive and reactive voltage drops are added in quadrature.

Impedance (series resistance and reactance) is expressed quantitatively as a complex number.

For the *LR* circuit: $Z = R + jX_L$.

For the *RC* circuit: $Z = R - jX_C$.

The locus of operation for an *RC* or *LR* series circuit is a semicircle.

Power is consumed only by the resistance in an *RC* or *LR* circuit.

Real Power $= I^2R$

Power is stored and returned by the reactance in the circuit.

Reactive Power $= I^2X$

Real power and reactive power are added in quadrature to obtain volt-amperes.

Notes: I equals a-c voltage. E equals a-c current. X equals inductive or capacitive reactance. Z equals impedance. L equals inductance. R equals resistance. X_L equals inductive reactance. X_C equals capacitive reactance.

QUESTIONS

1) If a 117-volt 60-cycle line is connected to a 117-ohm resistor, the load reactance is:
(*a*) 1 ohm. (*b*) 1 amp. (*c*) 117 watts. (*d*) zero.

2) The frequency of a power waveform is:
(*a*) equal to the frequency of the source voltage. (*b*) equal to the frequency of the load current. (*c*) equal to twice the frequency of the source voltage. (*d*) equal to the difference between the frequency of the source voltage and the frequency of the load current.
3) In any *RC* series circuit, the source voltage is equal to:
(*a*) the sum of the voltage drops across the resistance and the capacitance. (*b*) the square root of the sum of the squares of the voltage drops across the resistance and the capacitance. (*c*) the product of the current and the resistance. (*d*) the product of current squared and resistance.
4) To find the power factor of a series *RC* circuit:
(*a*) divide the resistance by the impedance. (*b*) divide the impedance by the resistance. (*c*) divide the resistance by the source voltage. (*d*) divide the source voltage by the resistance.
5) The symbol j stands for:
(*a*) a junction of current-carrying conductors. (*b*) the symbol i in the expression for a complex number. (*c*) the joint resistance of a series combination. (*d*) the juncture of voltage and current.
6) Capacitive reactance is:
(*a*) 90 degrees out of phase with inductive reactance. (*b*) negative. (*c*) positive. (*d*) 180 degrees out of phase with resistive reactance.
7) In any *RL* series circuit, the source voltage is equal to:
(*a*) the current flow multiplied by the resistance. (*b*) the current flow multiplied by the reactance. (*c*) the current squared multiplied by the load resistance. (*d*) the current flow multiplied by the impedance.
8) The volt-amp value in any reactive circuit is equal to:
(*a*) the square root of the sum of the squares of the resistive power and the reactive power. (*b*) the sum of the generator voltage and the generator current. (*c*) the product of the generator voltage and the in-phase current. (*d*) the generator voltage divided by the generator current.
9) The locus of operation for a series circuit that comprises resistance and reactance is:
(*a*) a right triangle. (*b*) $Z \cos \theta$. (*c*) a square which has an area equal to the impedance triangle. (*d*) a semicircle.
10) If the frequency of operation varies in an *RL* circuit, the power factor:
(*a*) remains the same as long as the values of R and L remain the same. (*b*) is always equal to the reactance divided by the resistance. (*c*) varies as a function of frequency. (*d*) is always equal to the resistance divided by the reactance.

PROBLEMS

1) A series circuit comprises a 100-ohm resistor and a 0.1-henry inductor that has negligible resistance. If 117 volts at 60 cycles are applied to this series circuit, what is the value of impedance presented to the voltage source? If 234 volts at 60 cycles are applied to this series circuit, what is the value of impedance presented to the voltage source?
2) What are the values of current flowing in Problem 1 for a 117-volt source and for a 234-volt source, both of which have a frequency of 60 cycles?
3) Calculate the voltage drops across the resistor and across the inductor in Problem 1 for a 117-volt source and for a 234-volt source, both of which have a frequency of 60 cycles.
4) When a series circuit that comprises a 1000-ohm resistance and a 300-μh inductor is connected to a 10-volt 1-kc source, what value of current flows through the inductor?
5) If the voltage is maintained at 10 volts in Problem 4, but the frequency is increased until the current flow through the inductor is one-half its former value, calculate the new operating frequency, and the impedance which the circuit presents to the source voltage.
6) A series circuit that comprises a 100-ohm resistor and a 1-μf capacitor is connected to a 117-volt 60-cycle source. Calculate the current flow through the resistor.
7) Another capacitor is connected in series with the 1-μf capacitor in Problem 6. The current flow through the resistor is reduced to one-half. What is the value of the added capacitor?
8) With reference to Problem 6, another resistor is connected in series with the 100-ohm resistor. The current through the resistors is reduced to one-half of its original value. What is the value of the added resistor?
9) Calculate the value of power consumed by each resistor in Problem 8. Calculate the reactive power in the capacitor.
10) A 6-volt 1-kc source supplies 3 volt-amps to an *RC* series circuit. The power factor is 0.5. How much power is consumed in the resistance?
11) If the resistance is doubled in Problem 10, what is the value of the power factor?
12) With reference to Problem 10, what is the value of the power factor if the operating frequency is increased to 2 kc?
13) A 117-volt 60-cycle source supplies 2 volt-amps to an *RC* series circuit

which has a power factor equal to $1/\sqrt{2}$. Calculate the value of the resistor and the value of the capacitor.

14) What is the time constant of the series circuit in Problem 13?
15) If a 117-volt d-c source is substituted for the a-c source in Problem 13, what value of energy has been consumed by the resistance when the capacitor is fully charged?
16) If the 117-volt d-c source is removed in Problem 15 after the capacitor is fully charged, and the voltage source replaced by a short-circuit, how much power has been consumed by the resistance when the capacitor is fully discharged?

13

PARALLEL A-C CIRCUIT ANALYSIS

13.1 RESISTIVE PARALLEL CIRCUITS

The simplest a-c parallel circuits comprise resistive components only. A typical parallel configuration is shown in Figure 13-1(*a*). In accordance with Kirchhoff's current law, the sum of the branch currents is equal to the total current. Thus,

$$I_T = I_1 + I_2 + I_3 + I_4 \tag{13.1}$$

Equation (13.1) can be assigned rms, peak, peak-to-peak, or corresponding instantaneous values. It is only necessary that we be consistent throughout. An equivalent circuit for the parallel configuration is seen in Figure 13-1(*b*). The current value is, of course, given by Ohm's law for a-c

$$I_T = \frac{E}{R_{eq}} \tag{13.2}$$

The value of R_{eq} is calculated most conveniently in terms of conductances. Thus, $G_1 = 1/R_1$, $G_2 = 1/R_2$, and so forth. In turn, $G_{eq} = G_1 + G_2 + G_3 + G_4$. Equation (13.2) can then be rewritten

$$I_T = EG_{eq} \tag{13.3}$$

It is evident that except for the arbitrary choice of rms, peak, peak-to-peak, or instantaneous values, the analysis of a-c resistive parallel circuits is the same as the analysis of d-c resistive parallel circuits.

13.2 CAPACITIVE PARALLEL CIRCUITS

Capacitive parallel circuits are analogous to resistive parallel circuits; however, additional considerations apply to parallel circuits. For example, the current that flows in the circuit of Figure 13-1 is independent of frequency. On the other hand, the current that flows in the circuit of Figure 13-2 increases as the frequency is increased. Previous discussion established that the current leads the voltage in Figure 13-2, while the current is in phase with the voltage in Figure 13-1. The resistive parallel circuit dissipates real power equal to EI_T, whereas the capacitive parallel circuit dissipates zero real power.

Capacitive reactance $X_C = 1/(2\pi fC)$. Hence, it follows directly that

$$C_{eq} = C_1 + C_2 + C_3 + C_4 \tag{13.4}$$

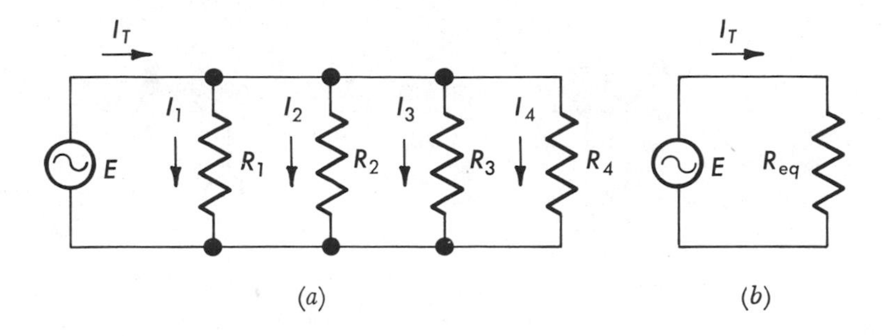

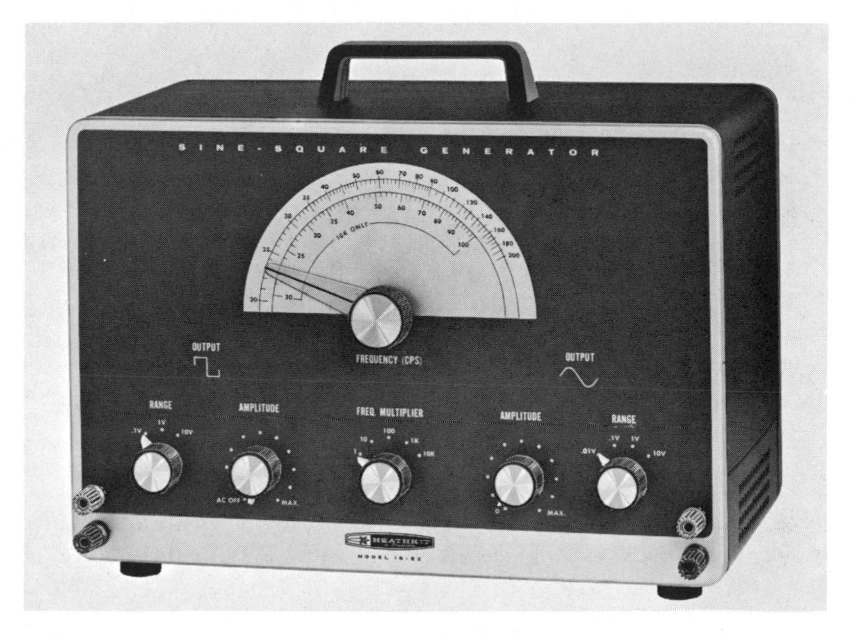

(c)

Figure 13-1

(a) A resistive parallel circuit. *(b)* Equivalent circuit. *(c)* A generator that supplies sine-wave voltages for tests of circuits in laboratories or shops. This type of generator will also supply square-wave voltages for transient tests. (Courtesy of Heath Co.)

What is the total reactance of the circuit in Figure 13-2? The reactances in Figure 13-2(*a*) combine in the same manner as the resistances in Figure 13-1(*a*). In other words,

$$\frac{1}{X_{C_T}} = \frac{1}{X_{C_1}} + \frac{1}{X_{C_2}} + \frac{1}{X_{C_3}} + \frac{1}{X_{C_4}} \tag{13.5}$$

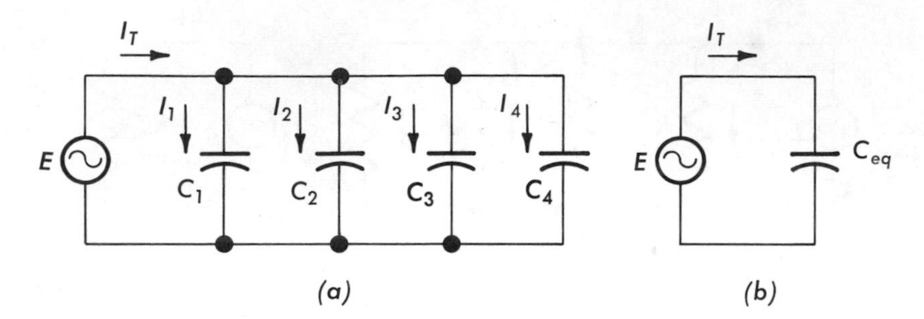

Figure 13-2
(a) A capacitive parallel circuit. *(b)* Equivalent circuit.

The term $1/X_C$ is analogous to the term $1/R$. Just as we write $G = 1/R$, we write

$$B = \frac{1}{X_C} \tag{13.6}$$

The term G, of course, is called conductance; similarly, the term B is called *susceptance*. Susceptance is a measure of the ease with which a-c current flows through a reactance. It is often convenient to rewrite Equation (13.5) in the form

$$B_T = B_1 + B_2 + B_3 + B_4 \tag{13.7}$$

It is evident that Equation (13.7) provides the same facility in combining reactances in parallel that is provided in combining parallel resistances by corresponding conductance values. The susceptance of a capacitor is obviously written

$$B = 2\,\pi\, fC = \omega\, C \tag{13.8}$$

The current that flows in a capacitive parallel circuit is written

$$I_T = EB_T \tag{13.9}$$

Now, let us briefly review the j operator and see how it enters into the expression for susceptance. Capacitive reactance is negative reactance. Thus,

$$X_C = \frac{-j}{\omega\, C} \tag{13.10}$$

In turn,

$$B_C = \frac{1}{X_C} = \frac{1}{\dfrac{-j}{\omega\, C}} = \frac{\omega\, C}{-j} = j\,\omega\, C \tag{13.11}$$

Note that when j is brought from the denominator to the numerator, its sign must be changed. Hence, we see that although capacitive reactance is negative, capacitive susceptance is positive. This fact is consistent vectorially; that is, if we draw the susceptance as a positive vector, and then draw its reciprocal, the resulting reactance vector points in the opposite direction and depicts negative reactance.

13.3 INDUCTIVE PARALLEL CIRCUITS

An inductive parallel circuit is illustrated in Figure 13-3. The total current is evidently given by Kirchhoff's current law

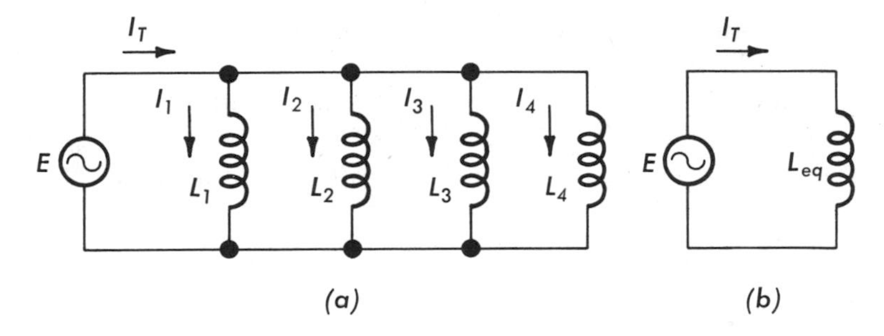

Figure 13-3
(a) An inductive parallel circuit. *(b)* Equivalent circuit.

$$I_T = I_1 + I_2 + I_3 + I_4 \tag{13.12}$$

Inductive reactance $X_L = 2\pi fL$. Hence, it follows directly that

$$\frac{1}{L_{eq}} = \frac{1}{L_1} + \frac{1}{L_2} + \frac{1}{L_3} + \frac{1}{L_4} \tag{13.13}$$

Therefore, inductances in parallel combine like resistances in parallel. What is the total reactance in the circuit of Figure 13-3? It is evident that the individual reactances must combine like resistances

$$\frac{1}{X_{L_T}} = \frac{1}{X_{L_1}} + \frac{1}{X_{L_2}} + \frac{1}{X_{L_3}} + \frac{1}{X_{L_4}} \tag{13.14}$$

The susceptance of an inductor is the reciprocal of its reactance

$$B = \frac{1}{X_L} \tag{13.15}$$

Hence, we can rewrite Equation (13.14) in the form

$$B_T = B_1 + B_2 + B_3 + B_4 \tag{13.16}$$

The susceptance of an inductor is obviously written

$$B = \frac{1}{\omega L} \tag{13.17}$$

In terms of the j operator, we note first that inductive reactance is positive reactance. Thus,

$$X_L = j\,\omega\,L \tag{13.18}$$

In turn,

$$B_L = \frac{1}{X_L} = \frac{1}{j\,\omega\,L} = \frac{-j}{\omega\,L} \tag{13.19}$$

As we would anticipate, the algebra shows that while inductive reactance is positive, inductive susceptance is negative.

The total current I_T which flows in the circuit of Figure 13-3 is obviously equal to $E/(X_{L_{eq}})$. Branch current I_1 is equal to $E/(X_{L_1})$, and so on. The total current and the branch currents are all in phase. However,

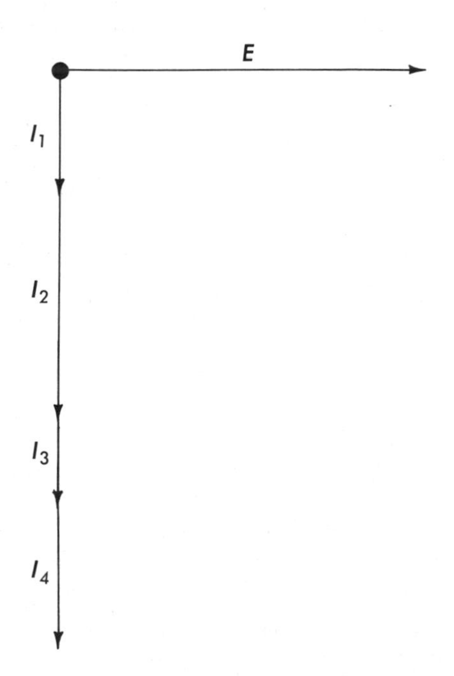

Figure 13-4
Voltage and current vectors for the circuit in Figure 13-3*(a)*.

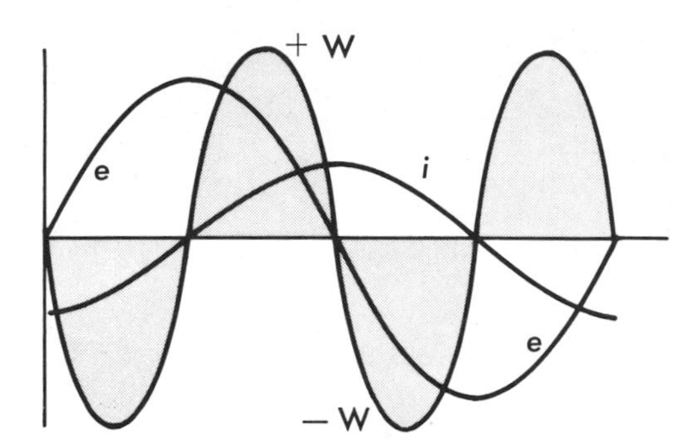

Figure 13-5
The power value in a pure inductance is alternately positive and negative, with an average value of zero.

each current lags the applied voltage by 90 degrees. A voltage and current vector representation for the circuit is seen in Figure 13-4. The power factor is zero. The inductors consume no real power, and the generator supplies no real power to the circuit. (See Figure 13-5.)

13.4 PARALLEL CAPACITANCE AND RESISTANCE

Let us consider action and reaction in a parallel circuit comprising resistance and capacitance, as depicted in Figure 13-6. We know that the current through the resistor is in phase with the voltage, and that the current through the capacitor leads the voltage by 90 degrees. Thus, the current vectors combine as seen in Figure 13-6(*b*) to give the total current. We can write the formula for the total current in *j* notation as follows:

$$I_T = I_R + jI_C \tag{13.20}$$

The power-factor angle is θ, and the power factor is evidently equal to I_R/I_T. The Pythagorean theorem states that

$$I_T = \sqrt{I_R^2 + I_C^2} \tag{13.21}$$

Hence, we can also write Equation (13.20) in the polar form

$$I_T = \sqrt{I_R^2 + I_C^2}\angle\theta \tag{13.22}$$

Equation (13.22) states that the total current is equal to the square root of the sum of the squares of the two branch currents, and that the total current makes an angle of θ with the current through the resistor. As previously pointed out, θ is the power-factor angle. We perceive that in an

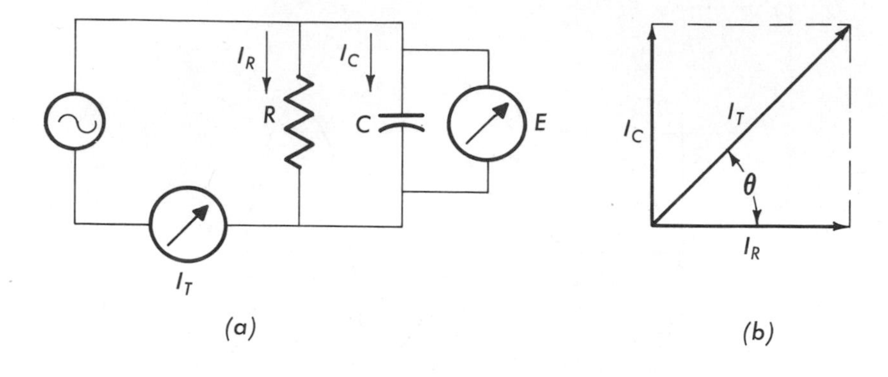

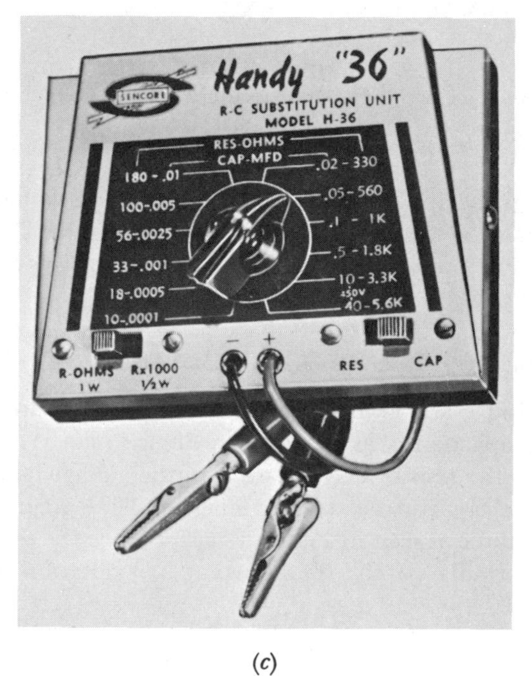

(c)

Figure 13-6

(a) An RC parallel circuit. *(b)* Current vectors for the circuit. *(c)* An RC substitution box is often useful in the laboratory or shop. (Courtesy Sencore, Addison, Illinois.) *(d)* An RC network box for test or experimental applications. Various RC series circuits and RC parallel circuits can be obtained by suitable control settings. (Courtesy of Electronic Instrument Co.)

(Continued on facing page.)

RC circuit, the power-factor angle will fall somewhere between zero and 90 degrees, depending upon the proportions of resistance and capacitance.

The resistor current I_R is equal to E/R, and the capacitor current is equal to E/X_C. Kirchhoff's current law states that I_R, I_C, and I_T must form

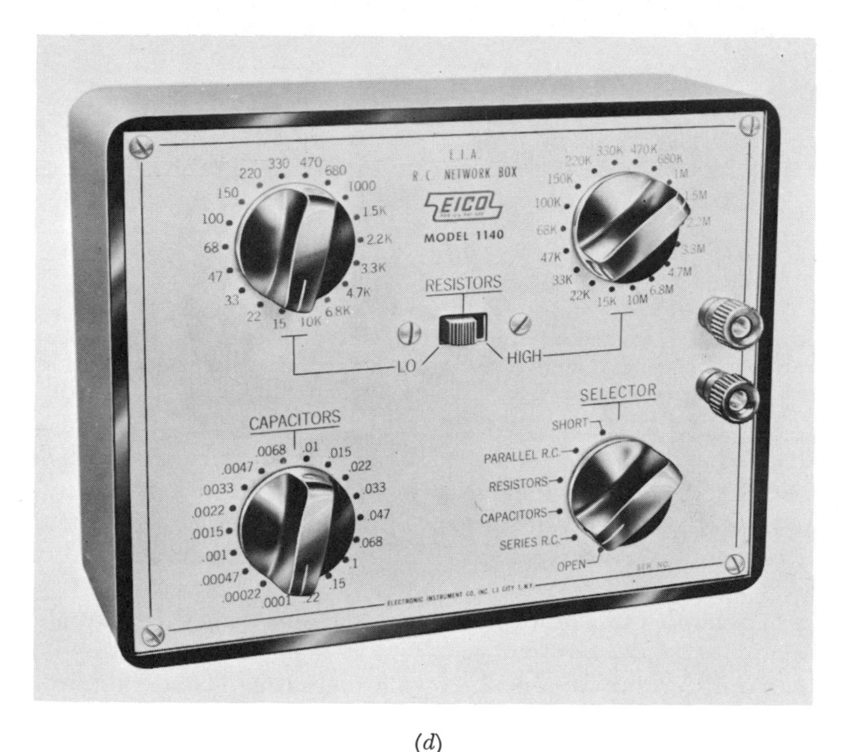

(*d*)

Fig. 13-6 (*Continued*)

a closed triangle, and we observe from Figure 13-6(*b*) that this is so. The real power in the circuit is equal to $I_R{}^2R$; or, $EI_T \cos \theta$. The reactive power is equal to $I_C{}^2X_C$; or, $EI_T \sin \theta$. The generator supplies EI_T volt-amps to the circuit.

It is very interesting and helpful to know that, at any chosen frequency, every parallel circuit has an equivalent series circuit, and vice versa. In other words, there are certain values of R and C, which, when connected in series, draw the same current at the same phase angle as R and C in Figure 13-6(*a*). With our knowledge of vectors, it is very easy to visualize the relations of equivalent series and parallel circuits.

Observe in Figure 13-7(*a*) that R and X combine to give Z for a series circuit as shown. This is merely a restatement of what we learned earlier. Next, suppose that these same values of R and C are connected in parallel. The impedance of the parallel combination is formulated

$$Z = \frac{-jRX}{R - jX} \tag{13.23}$$

Equation (13.23) states that the impedance of the parallel combina-

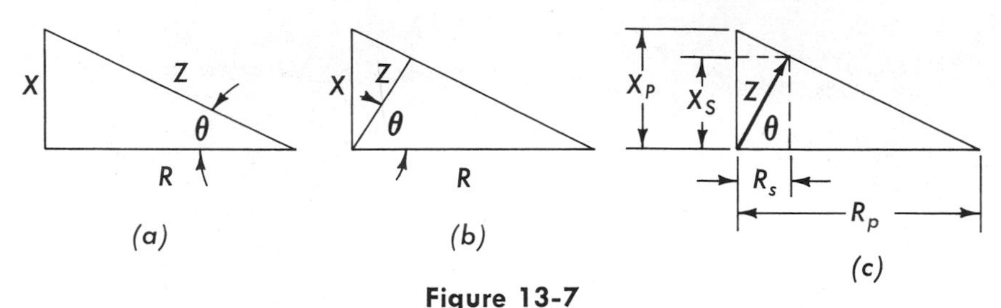

Figure 13-7

(a) Impedance Z is formed by connecting R and X in series. *(b)* Impedance Z is formed by connecting R and X in parallel. *(c)* Impedance Z can be formed either by connecting R_S and X_S in series, or by connecting R_P and X_P in parallel.

tion is equal to the product of the resistance and reactance vectors, divided by the difference between the resistance and reactance vectors. When you studied complex numbers in your algebra courses, you learned that:

1. To multiply two vectors, we multiply their lengths and add their angles.

2. To subtract two vectors, we reverse the direction of the subtrahend and add.

3. To divide two vectors, we divide their lengths and subtract the angle of the divisor from the angle of the dividend.

GRAPHICAL CONSTRUCTION

The end result is that if a resistance R is connected in parallel with a reactance X, the impedance Z is found by dropping a perpendicular to the hypotenuse of the impedance triangle, as shown in Figure 13-7(*b*). When we compare Figure 13-7(*a*) with Figure 13-7(*b*), it is evident that R and X have a much smaller impedance when connected in parallel than when they are connected in series. Furthermore, we see that the power-factor angle θ is different when R and C are connected in parallel than when they are connected in series.

Now we ask the question: If we choose a certain impedance Z, with a certain power-factor angle, what values of R and X connected in parallel will give this value of Z, and what other values of R and X connected in series will also give the value of Z, with the same power-factor angle? The answer is very simple, when we relate the data of Figure 13-7(*a*) and (*b*) into a composite diagram, as depicted in Figure 13-7(*c*). Observe in (*c*) that we have chosen a certain value of impedance Z, which has a power-factor angle θ. We see that $Z \angle\theta$ can be formed by connecting R_S and X_S in series, or by connecting R_P and X_P in parallel.

Hence, Figure 13-7(*c*) depicts the equivalent series and parallel circuits at some selected frequency. Of course, when you select another frequency of operation, you must draw another diagram and start with the changed length and angle of Z. As in any circuit problem, there is more than one point of entry; that is, you do not have to start construction of Figure 13-7(*c*) with $Z \angle\theta$. For example, you might be given specified values of R and C with the operating frequency and asked to find the impedance of their series combination, with the changed values of R and C required in an equivalent parallel circuit. In this case, we start by finding the reactance of C at the given frequency and combine R and X to find Z, as depicted by X_S, R_S, and Z in Figure 13-7(*c*). This gives the impedance of the series combination. We then draw a perpendicular line to the end of Z, and extend X_S and R_S to determine X_P and R_P; then, X_P can be solved for C, which is the changed value required in an equivalent parallel circuit.

You will find in practical work that it is much faster and easier to solve such problems graphically, instead of laboriously working out the algebraic equations. Of course, a graphical solution necessarily involves constructional error. However, the slight experimental error can usually be neglected in practical work. If you use a slide rule in making numerical calculations, there will be a slight computational error from this source. Hence, a graphical solution has the same basic validity as a slide-rule calculation.

Slide-rule calculations of reactance values can be speeded up by use of special slide rules that require only one setting. Reactance slide rules are often used by engineers and technicians; these are specialized and simplified types of slide rules that are used only to calculate inductive and capacitive reactance values. Somewhat more elaborate slide rules will also indicate impedance and phase angles directly from resistance and reactance values. (See Appendix XV for further descriptions of the slide rule.)

13.5 PARALLEL INDUCTANCE AND RESISTANCE

Except for reversal of reactive current flow, a parallel LR circuit is quite similar to a parallel RC circuit. Figure 13-8(*a*) shows a basic parallel LR configuration. The source voltage is in phase with I_R. Reactive current, on the other hand, lags E and I_R by 90 degrees. We know from previous discussion that the total current I_T must be the resultant of I_R and I_L, as shown in (*b*). The power-factor angle θ is evidently the phase difference between I_R and I_T. Furthermore, I_R, I_L, and I_T must form a closed right triangle, in accordance with Kirchhoff's current law.

The parallel circuit in Figure 13-8 has an equivalent series circuit, as illustrated in Figure 13-7(*c*). In other words, there are values of X_{LS} and R_S that operate in a series circuit in the same manner as X_{LP} and R_P in a

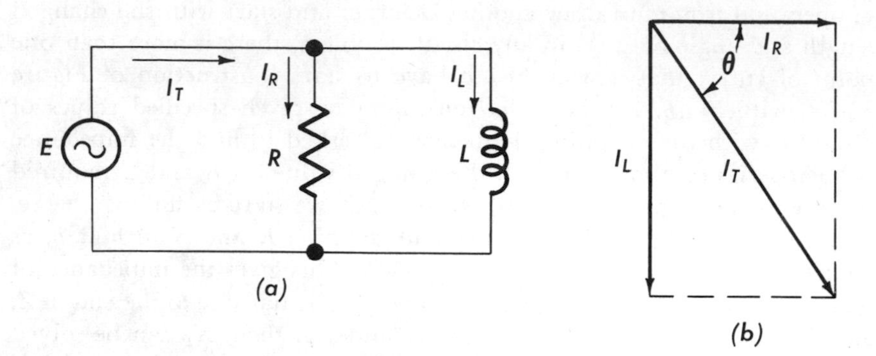

Figure 13-8
(a) A basic *LR* parallel circuit. *(b)* Current vectors for the circuit.

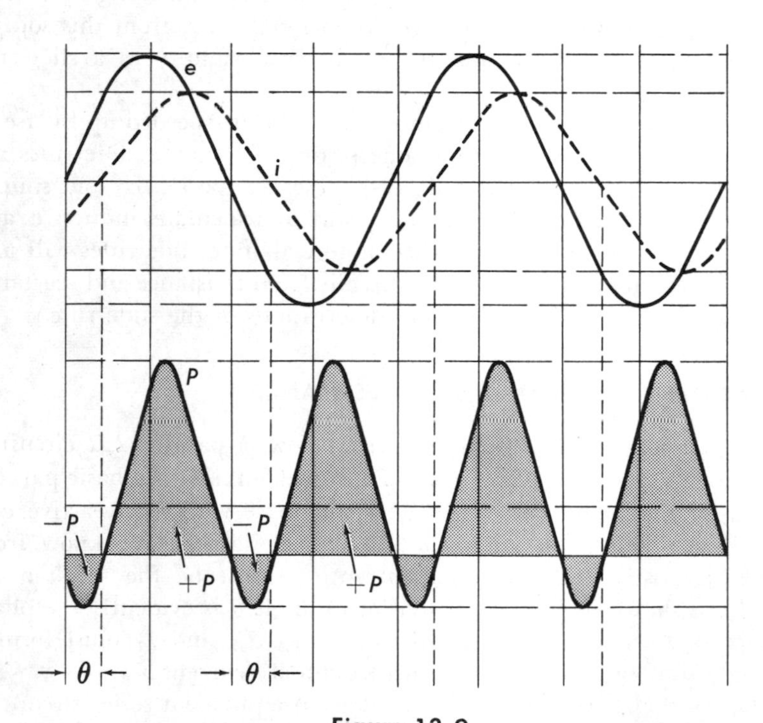

Figure 13-9
Power waveform for a parallel *LR* circuit, derived from voltage and current waveforms in the equivalent series *LR* circuit.

parallel circuit. The power factor in Figure 13-8 is a lagging power factor, and is exactly the same in an equivalent series circuit. The resistor consumes real power, but the inductor merely stores reactive power and then returns it to the source. Let us observe the voltage, current, and power waveforms for the equivalent series circuit; the power waveform, of course, is exactly the same in the parallel circuit.

Figure 13-9 illustrates these voltage, current, and power waveforms. The current waveform is displaced to the right of the voltage waveform. Accordingly, the current goes through its peak value after the voltage goes through its peak value; that is, the current through the inductor lags the applied voltage. When we multiply corresponding instantaneous values of voltage and current, we obtain the double-frequency power waveform. The real power consumed by the resistor is represented by the shaded area above the axis, and the reactive power in the inductor is represented by the shaded area below the axis in the power waveform.

As previously noted, the real power above the axis in the power waveform is called *positive* power; the reactive power below the axis is called *negative* power. Positive power is in phase quadrature to negative power.

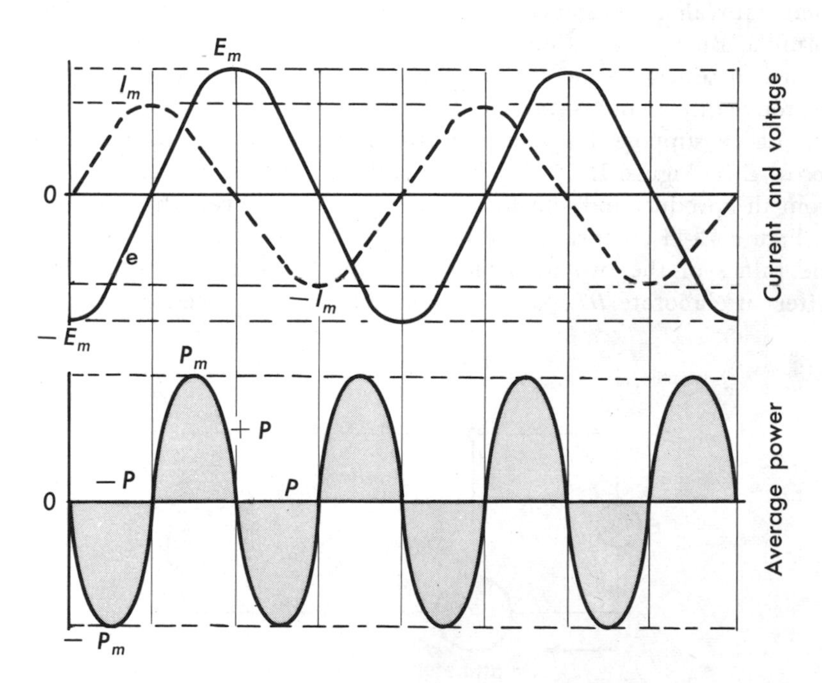

Figure 13-10

The power waveform crosses the axis when the voltage goes through zero, and when the current goes through zero.

Real power, reactive power, and volt-amperes form a closed right triangle, as we have learned. Note in Figure 13-10 that the power waveform crosses the axis at the time that the voltage waveform goes through zero, and at the time that the current waveform goes through zero. Thus, the negative power excursion defines the power-factor angle θ.

We recall that a conventional wattmeter indicates real power. The wattmeter requires an input voltage and an input current. Accordingly, a wattmeter has three terminals. It is connected into a circuit as depicted in Figure 13-11. Voltage E enters the wattmeter across the circuit; current I flows through the wattmeter in series with the circuit. The wattmeter performs the calculation $EI \cos \theta$ electrically and indicates the answer on its scale.

13.6 NETWORK REDUCTION

The basic principles of network reduction have been detailed previously. However, it is instructive to briefly consider these principles with respect to a parallel *LR* circuit. Consider Figure 13-11. Suppose there should be two resistors instead of one connected across E. We know that their equivalent resistance can be calculated from the product-and-sum formula. But if the resistor, in Figure 13-11, comprises two resistors connected in series, we merely add the values of the two resistances to find the total equivalent resistance.

Let us suppose that there are two inductors instead of one connected across E in Figure 13-11. Their equivalent inductance can be calculated from the product-and-sum formula. Suppose, however, that the inductor in Figure 13-11 comprises two inductors connected in series. We then add the values of the two inductances to find their equivalent inductance. After an elaborate *RL* parallel circuit has been reduced to a simple *RL*

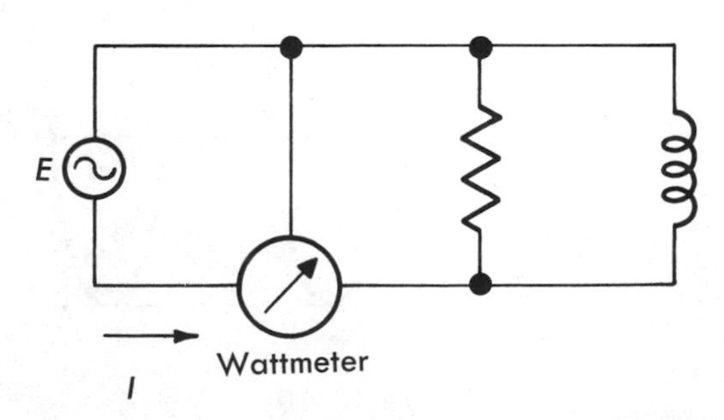

Figure 13-11
Three circuit connections are made to a wattmeter.

parallel circuit, we can change the simple parallel circuit to an equivalent series circuit at a specified operating frequency.

13.7 CONSTANT-CURRENT SOURCE

All the analyses explained thus far have been made on the basis of a *constant-voltage* source. A battery that has negligible internal resistance is a constant-voltage source. This simply means that the source voltage does not change in value if the current demand varies. Similarly, a generator with negligible internal resistance is a constant-voltage source. The 117-volt line that powers lamps and appliances in your home is regarded as this type of source.

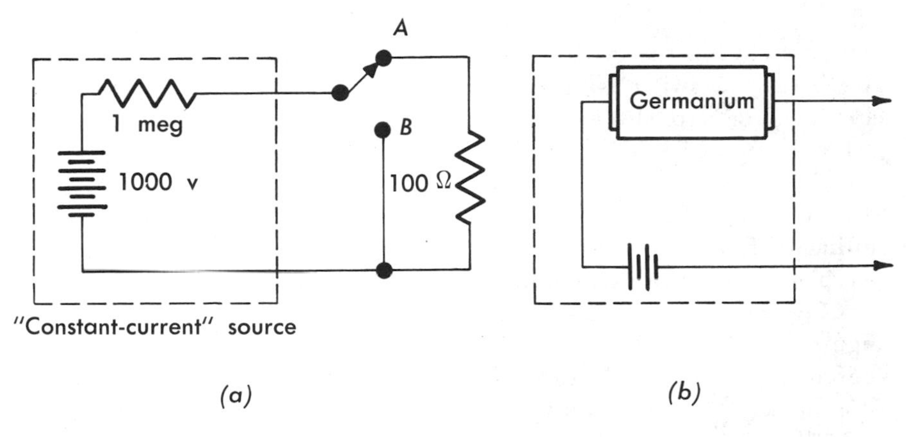

Figure 13-12
(a) A simple and practical approximation of a constant-current source. *(b)* A block of germanium and a battery provide a constant-current source, because the saturation current through the germanium is temperature-limited.

Some types of electronic equipment utilize constant-current sources. This source supplies a *fixed current* to a circuit, just as a constant-voltage source supplies a *fixed voltage* to a circuit. For example, a constant-current source might supply 1 milliamp to a circuit; in this case, the input current to the circuit is always 1 milliamp, regardless of the load imposed by the circuit. This concept might seem a bit confusing at first, but a practical example will make it clear.

The simplest approximation to a constant-current source is shown in Figure 13-12. Here, a battery is depicted that has an extremely high internal resistance. This constant-current source supplies 1 milliamp to the external circuit. Note that whether the switch is thrown to position *A* or to position *B*, the current flow remains 1 milliamp from a practical

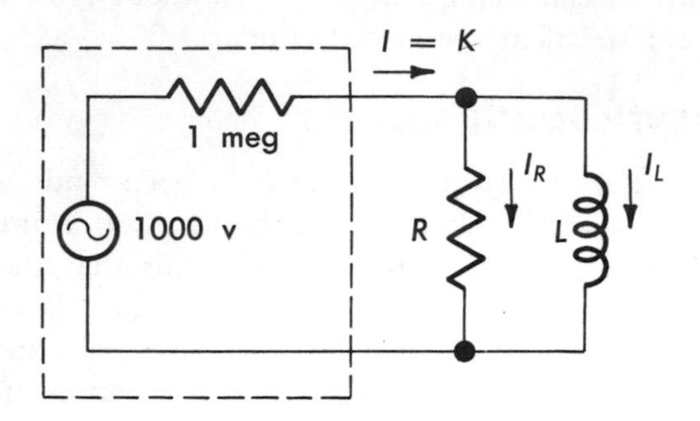

Figure 13-13
The constant-current source supplies 1 milliamp to the parallel *RL* circuit.

viewpoint. When the switch is in position *A*, the voltage drop will be 0.1 volt. When the switch is in position *B*, the voltage drop across the short-circuit will be zero. However, the current flow remains essentially constant at 1 milliamp while the voltage across the load changes.

Next, let us replace the 1000-volt battery in Figure 13-12 with a 1000-volt a-c generator, as depicted in Figure 13-13. It is apparent that 1 milliamp of a-c current is supplied to the parallel *LR* circuit; $I = k = 1$ ma. This 1 ma must divide into I_R and I_L. According to Kirchhoff's current law, I, I_R, and I_L must form a closed right triangle as depicted in Figure 13-14(*a*); furthermore, I is constant. Therefore, regardless of the resistance and inductance values we select, the locus of operation for the constant-current circuit must fall on a semicircle, as depicted in Figure 13-14(*b*). This is a very helpful visualization of constant-current circuit operation.

We recall that the locus of operation for a constant-voltage circuit is

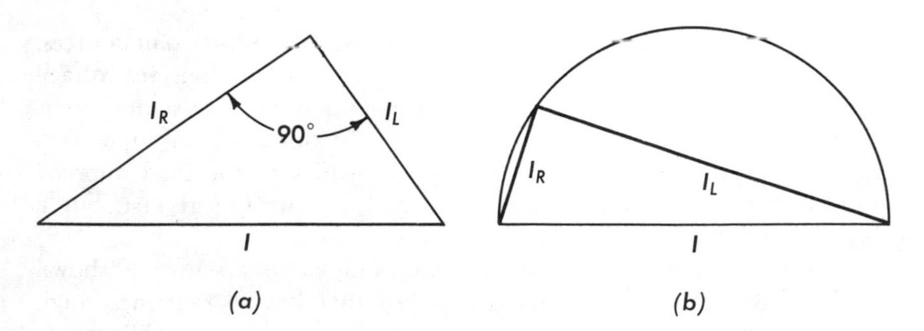

Figure 13-14
(*a*) Current vectors for the circuit in Figure 13-13. (*b*) Locus of operation for a constant-current source.

described in terms of voltage vectors. These voltage vectors illustrate Kirchhoff's voltage law for a series circuit. On the other hand, the locus of operation for a constant-current circuit is described in terms of current vectors. These vectors illustrate Kirchhoff's current law for a parallel circuit. When you analyze various elaborated types of electronic circuits, you will learn to inspect the circuit to see whether it might be considered to have a constant-voltage or a constant-current source. If the circuit can be classified in this manner, analysis is greatly facilitated.

Of course, you will encounter many configurations in which the source is neither a constant-current nor a constant-voltage source. For example, when the internal resistance of a generator is in the same order as the resistance or impedance of the external circuit, the generator cannot be considered either a constant-voltage or a constant-current source. In this situation, we must analyze the circuit as a series-parallel circuit, as explained in Chapter 14.

How do we calculate the values of I_R and I_L in Figure 13-13? First, we must find the voltage drop across the load. Hence, we calculate the impedance of the paralleled resistance and inductance as previously explained. The voltage across the impedance is given by Ohm's law for a-c:

$$E = IZ \tag{13.24}$$

where I is equal to k.

The values of I_R and I_L also follow from Ohm's law. $I_R = E/R$, and $I_L = E/X_L$. Note that after we solve for E in Equation (13.24), we can draw an equivalent circuit for Figure 13-13, in which we replace the constant-current generator with a constant-voltage generator which has a terminal voltage E. This equivalent circuit helps to remove any confusion that might arise in calculation of power factor, real power, reactive power, and volt-amperes.

Suppose the constant-current circuit in Figure 13-12 is opened; what will we encounter? The circuit might be opened momentarily, for example, while switching from A to B. While the circuit is open, no current can flow. Therefore, this circuit condition does not fulfill the definition of a constant-current circuit. It can be properly considered as a constant-current circuit only when a comparatively low-resistance load is connected to the source. When the circuit is opened, the voltage across the open circuit immediately rises to 1000 volts.

What is the upper limit of load resistance which we can use, and still consider that the source operates as a constant-current source? In practical work, it is usually considered that the load resistance shall not be greater than 1 percent of the source resistance to meet the terms of practical constant-current definition. Since the source resistance is 1

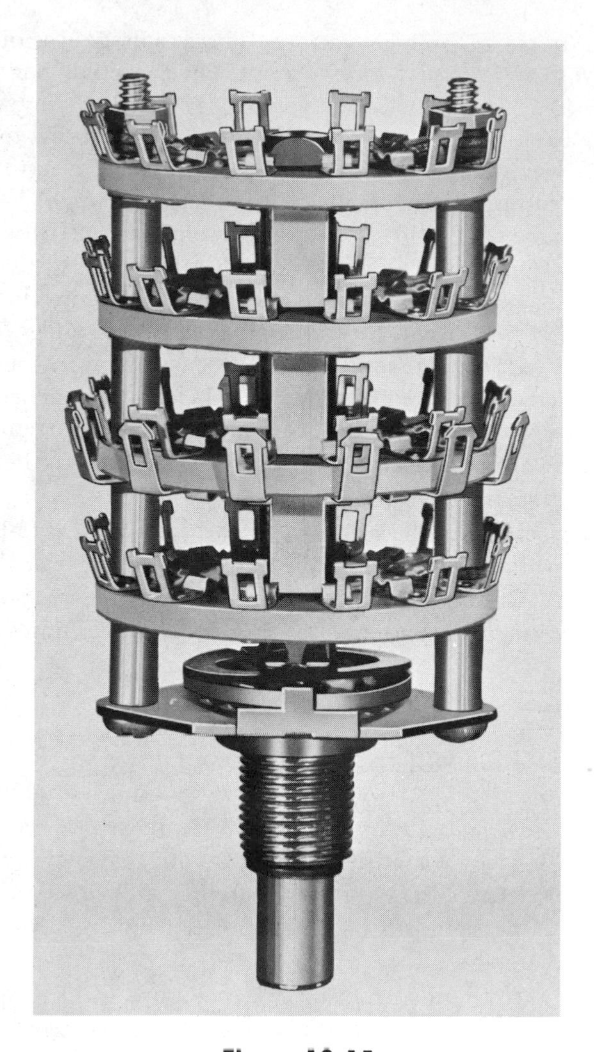

Figure 13-15
Appearance of a typical rotary switch. (Courtesy of Centralab, the Electronics Division of Globe-Union, Inc.)

megohm in Figure 13-12, we would not consider a load value in excess of 10,000 ohms.

Note in passing that rotary switches (Figure 13-15) are fabricated in "shorting" or "nonshorting" types. When it is desired to switch without opening the circuit, a shorting-type switch is used. On the other hand, when it is desired that the circuit shall be open while going from one contact to the next, a nonshorting type of switch is used. Switches are rated for current-carrying capability, and for the maximum voltage which may be permitted to exist between contacts.

13.8 TROUBLESHOOTING PARALLEL A-C CIRCUITS

Since the voltage is the same across each branch of a parallel circuit, branch-current measurement is a basic troubleshooting approach. If you use a clamp-around type of ammeter, it is not necessary to open a branch circuit to measure the current flow. If current flow is zero, the branch component is open-circuited. On the other hand, if the branch current is abnormal, the associated capacitor is leaky, or the associated inductor has shorted turns or layers. Components that draw excessive current become overheated, and can often be localized by noting their temperature.

If a branch component is short-circuited, the protective fuse will blow and power cannot be applied to the circuit until the fault is cleared. In such case, it is common practice to open each branch circuit in turn, and measure the resistance of the component with an ohmmeter or similar instrument. Inductors and capacitors can be checked for inductance and capacitance values on an impedance bridge. The design and operation of resistance bridges is explained subsequently. It is clear from what we have learned about inductors that there is no relation between an inductance value and a winding-resistance value. Hence, a conclusive test of an inductor can only be made with an impedance bridge.

In general, an inductor should not be disconnected from a "live" circuit. It is advisable to turn the power off before making a disconnection, not only because of shock hazard, but because of possible damage to the inductor. If an inductor has a large inductance value and carries substantial current, considerable energy is stored in its magnetic field. When the inductor lead is suddenly opened, the field collapses and generates a counter emf. This counter emf will immediately rise to any potential, no matter how high, which may be required to discharge the stored energy as a spark or arc across the air gap. If the gap is established very quickly, the stored energy may break down the insulation between turns or layers of the inductor and cause damage.

Consider the parallel circuit depicted in Figure 13-11. Here, the inductor is shunted by a resistor. If you suddenly disconnect the generator from the circuit, the counter emf from the inductor drives current through the resistor. Hence, the voltage rise across the inductor terminals is limited. On the other hand, if you disconnect the inductor from the circuit, with current flowing through it, the resistor does not shunt the inductor to limit the surge voltage. This precaution cannot be stressed too strongly. Most of us forget it at some time, and learn from unfortunate experience that the power should be turned off in an inductive cir-

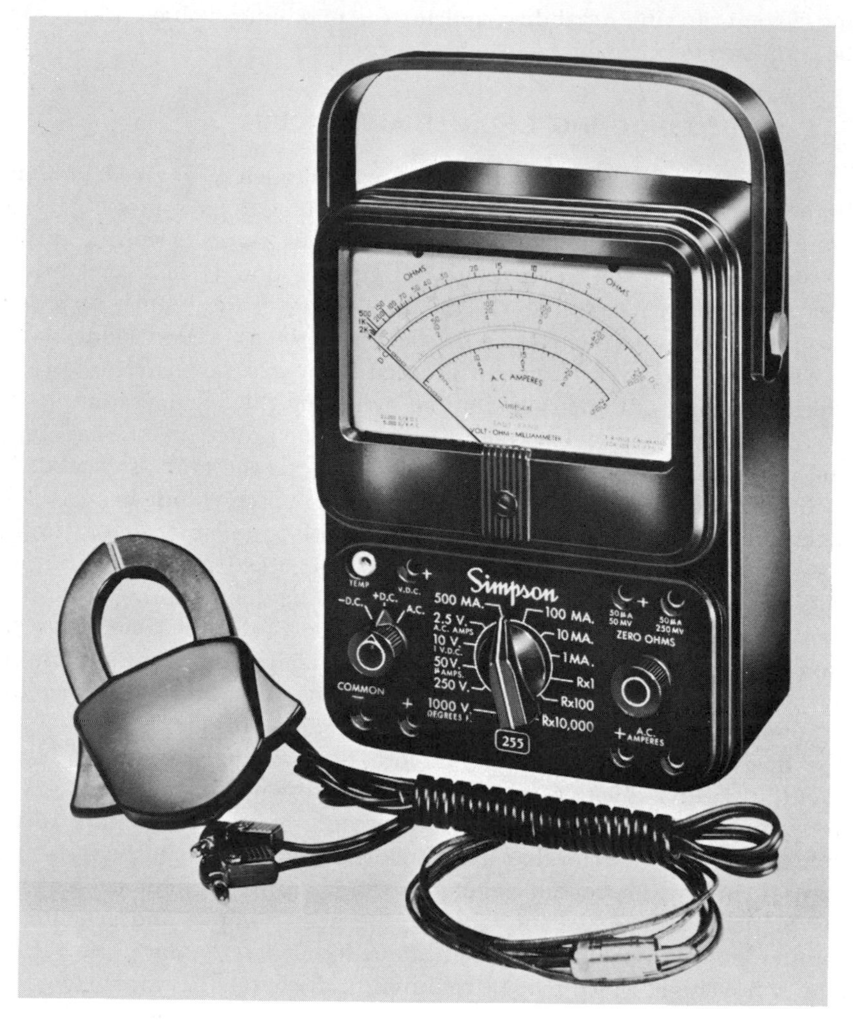

Figure 13-16
A clamp-around type of ammeter. (Courtesy of Simpson Electric Co.)

cuit before an inductor is disconnected. The a-c current flow through any branch circuit can be measured without disconnecting the leads or otherwise opening the circuit if an a-c clamp-on adapter is used with an a-c voltmeter, as illustrated in Fig. 13-16. An adapter operates on the transformer principle which is discussed subsequently.

SUMMARY OF FUNDAMENTAL CONCEPTS

Ohm's law for a-c applies to a complete parallel circuit, to any component in the circuit, or to a combination of two or more components: $I = E/R$; $I = E/X$; $I = E/Z$.

Kirchhoff's current law applies to reactive parallel circuits; resistive and reactive currents are added in quadrature.

A parallel circuit has an equivalent series circuit at a chosen operating frequency.

$$Z = \frac{\pm jRX}{R \pm jX}$$

for resistance connected in parallel with reactance.

Resistive and reactive components of an equivalent series circuit are obtained by rationalizing the expression for Z.

Power is consumed only by the resistance in an RC or LR circuit.

Real Power $= I_R{}^2R$

Power is stored and returned by the reactance in the circuit.

Reactive Power $= I_X{}^2X$

Real power and reactive power are added in quadrature to obtain volt-amperes.

Notes: I equals a-c current. E equals a-c voltage. R equals resistance. X equals inductive or capacitive reactance. Z equals impedance. I_R equals current flow through resistance. I_X equals current flow through reactance.

QUESTIONS

1) The reciprocal of resistance is called:
(*a*) reactance. (*b*) inductance. (*c*) conductance. (*d*) impedance.
2) The reciprocal of reactance is called:
(*a*) reluctance. (*b*) permeance. (*c*) elastance. (*d*) susceptance.
3) Capacitive susceptance is:
(*a*) positive. (*b*) negative. (*c*) positive or negative depending upon the direction of current flow. (*d*) positive when the power is real, but negative when the power is reactive.
4) Inductive susceptance is:
(*a*) equal to $2\pi fL$. (*b*) the opposition imposed by an inductor to a-c current flow. (*c*) always positive. (*d*) a measure of the ease with which a-c current flows through an inductor.
5) The total current flow I_T in a parallel RC circuit is equal to:
(*a*) $I_R + jI_C$. (*b*) $I_R - jI_C$. (*c*) $\sqrt{I_R^2} + (jI_C)^2$. (*d*) E/X_C.
6) Every parallel RC circuit has an equivalent:
(*a*) series RC circuit at all frequencies of operation. (*b*) series RC circuit at zero frequency. (*c*) series RC circuit at the same operating frequency as the parallel RC circuit. (*d*) magnetic circuit.
7) To multiply two voltagc vectors, we:
(*a*) apply Ohm's law. (*b*) apply Kirchhoff's voltage law. (*c*) apply Kirchhoff's current law. (*d*) multiply the vector magnitudes and add the vector angles.
8) To divide two current vectors, we:
(*a*) calculate the algebraic sum of the two vectors. (*b*) divide the vector magnitudes and subtract the angle of the divisor from the angle of the dividend. (*c*) apply Kirchhoff's current law. (*d*) apply Kirchhoff's voltage law.
9) To subtract two voltage vectors, we:
(*a*) complete the parallelogram and draw the resultant. (*b*) calculate the square root of the sum of the squares of the two voltage vectors. (*c*) calculate the root-mean-square value of the two voltage vectors. (*d*) reverse the direction of the subtrahend and find the vectorial sum.
10) To add two voltage vectors, we:
(*a*) calculate their arithmetical sum. (*b*) calculate their algebraic sum. (*c*) complete the parallelogram and draw the resultant. (*d*) add the vector magnitudes and multiply the vector angles.

PROBLEMS

1) An ideal 0.5-henry inductor is connected in parallel with a 500-ohm resistance. If the parallel combination is energized from a 117-volt 60-cycle line, how much power is consumed by the resistance?
2) Calculate the inductance and resistance values to form an equivalent series circuit for the parallel combination in Problem 1. How much power is consumed by the series resistance?
3) A capacitor with a reactance of 20 ohms at 1 kc is connected in parallel with a 30-ohm resistor. If the parallel combination is energized by a 5-volt 1-kc source, what is the value of reactive power present in the capacitor?
4) Calculate the capacitance and resistance values to form an equivalent series circuit for the parallel combination in Problem 3. What is the value of reactive power present in the series capacitor?
5) If a capacitor has a susceptance of 0.1 mho at 600 cycles, and is connected to a 10-volt 600-cycle generator, how much reactive power is present in the capacitor?
6) Five capacitors that have values of 5, 10, 20, 25, and 50 $\mu\mu$f, respectively, are connected in parallel. What is the susceptance of the parallel combination at 1 mc?
7) Five ideal inductors that have values of 50, 100, 200, 250, and 500 mh, respectively, are connected in parallel. What is the susceptance of the parallel combination at 1 mc?
8) A 100-μh ideal inductor is connected in parallel with a 100-ohm resistor. This parallel combination is energized from a 1-mc voltage source. Calculate the capacitance and resistance values to form an equivalent series circuit for the parallel combination that will draw the same value of current (disregarding the phase angle) from the source.
9) What is the power factor of the parallel combination in Problem 8? Is this power factor the same as that of the series *RC* circuit?
10) Two 1-henry inductors are connected in parallel. Hence, they are equivalent to a single 0.5-henry inductor. If half of the turns are removed from one of the 1-henry inductors, will its inductance become 0.5 henry?
11) Two 0.1-μf capacitors are connected in parallel. Hence, they are equivalent to a single 0.2-μf capacitor. If the spacing is reduced to ½ in one of the 0.1-μf capacitors, will its capacitance become 0.2 μf?

12) A rheostat rated for 2 watts maximum power dissipation is connected in parallel with a 1-μf capacitor. The parallel combination is energized from a 117-volt 60-cycle line. The rheostat has a maximum resistance of 10,000 ohms. When set to its maximum value, what is the value of total current drawn by the parallel combination? How much power is dissipated by the rheostat?
13) With reference to Problem 12, what is the minimum value of resistance to which the rheostat may be set, without exceeding its rated power dissipation? When set to this resistance, what is the value of total current drawn by the parallel combination?
14) An ideal inductor with an inductance of 100 mh is connected in parallel with a resistance of 20 ohms. What is the Q of the equivalent circuit at 60 cycles per sec?

14

ANALYSIS OF *LCR* SERIES CIRCUITS

14.1 NETWORK REDUCTION

We know that the total resistance in a series circuit is equal to the sum of the individual resistances. Similarly, the total inductance in a series circuit is equal to the sum of the individual inductances. The total inductive reactance in a series circuit is equal to the sum of the individual reactances. We recall that the total capacitance in a series circuit is found by successive application of the product-and-sum formula. The total capacitive reactance in a series circuit is equal to the sum of the individual reactances. These are the basic facts used in reduction of *LCR* series circuits.

Accordingly, after all series resistances are combined, series inductances combined, and series capacitances combined, a basic *LCR* series circuit is obtained, as depicted in Figure 14-1. This approach to network reduction disregards reactance values. Next, general analysis requires that we express the total reactance in algebraic terms. X_L, of course, or jX_L, is positive; on the other hand, X_C, or jX_C, is negative in an algebraic expression. Therefore, the total reactance in a series circuit is equal to the sum of the individual reactances, with due attention to the sign of the reactance.

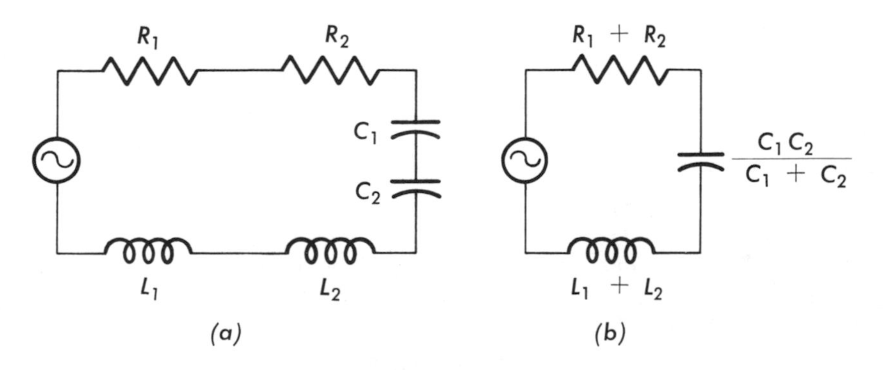

Figure 14-1
(a) An *LCR* series circuit. *(b)* Reduction to a basic *LCR* series circuit.

For example, if we have an inductive reactance of 100 ohms, and a capacitive reactance of 150 ohms, the total reactance of the series combination is a capacitive reactance of 50 ohms, which we will write as $-j50$. Again, if we have an inductive reactance of 75 ohms, and a capacitive reactance of 50 ohms, the total reactance of the series combination is an inductive reactance of 25 ohms, which we will write as $+j25$. It follows that the impedance of either circuit in Figure 14-1 is written

$$Z = R \pm jX \qquad \textbf{(14.1)}$$

where R is the total resistance and X is the total reactance. Note that the sign of the reactance depends upon whether the inductive reactance or the capacitive reactance is the greater.

It is evident that X_C and X_L values might be specified in Figure 14-1(*a*), instead of L and C values. In this case, we calculate the equivalent circuit by algebraic addition of the reactance values. This approach disregards inductance and capacitance values. Thus, our approach is based upon the given data. In some cases, we will have a choice of approach to network reduction, and then our choice is based merely upon convenience of calculation.

We perceive that reduction of an *LCR* series circuit to a basic *LCR* circuit, as exemplified in Figure 14-1, admits to further reduction at a single frequency of operation. For example, suppose that the total reactance in Figure 14-1(*b*) is $-j50$ ohms, and that the total resistance is 13 ohms. The circuit then reduces to two components, as shown in Figure 14-2. Engineers sometimes represent reactance as seen in Figure 14-2(*b*), to denote X by a symbol that is different from the capacitance or inductance symbol. This is chiefly a matter of personal preference in notation.

The basic fact for us to observe here is that the *LCR* circuit in Figure 14-1 has been reduced to an *RC* circuit in Figure 14-2. At the selected

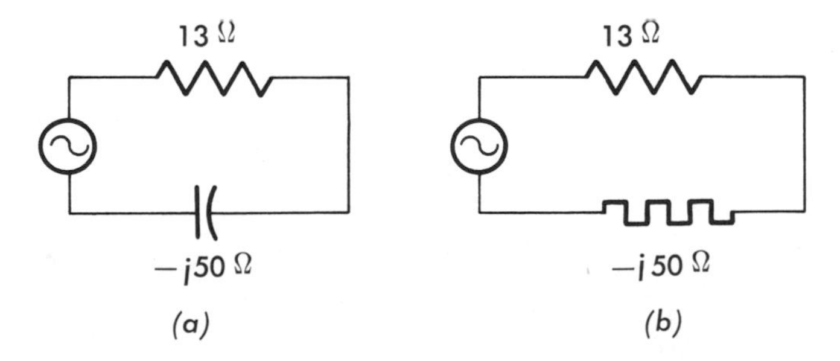

Figure 14-2
(*a*) Further reduction of the *LCR* circuit in Figure 14-1 (*b*), at a selected operating frequency; (*b*) alternative symbolism for (*a*).

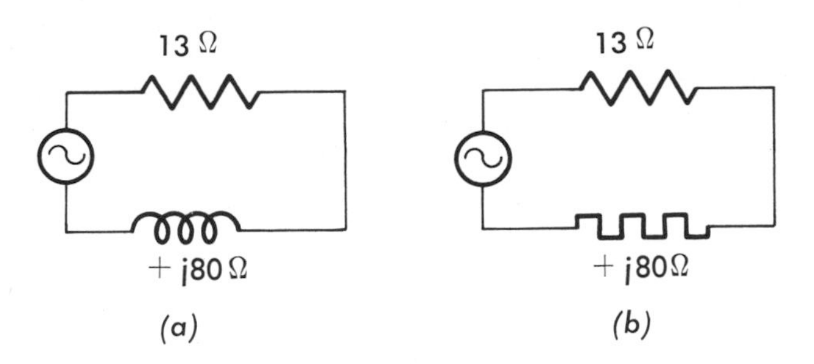

Figure 14-3
(*a*) Further reduction of the *LCR* circuit in Figure 14-1(*b*) at another operating frequency; (*b*) alternative symbolism for (*a*).

operating frequency, the inductive reactance is more than cancelled out by the capacitive reactance. Thus, the current leads the applied voltage in Figure 14-2. We say that the *LCR* circuit is *capacitive* at the selected operating frequency.

Consider circuit operation at some other frequency, which causes the capacitance reactance to be more than cancelled out by the inductive reactance. For example, suppose that the total reactance in Figure 14-1(*b*) is $+j80$ ohms, and the total resistance is 13 ohms. Again, the circuit reduces to two components, as shown in Figure 14-3. At the new frequency of operation, the current lags the applied voltage. We say that the *LCR* circuit is *inductive* at the new operating frequency.

14.2 REACTANCE VARIATION

Thus, an *LCR* series circuit will reduce to an *RC* circuit in some situations, but will reduce to an *RL* circuit in other situations. We will see next that any *LCR* circuit is capacitive up to a certain frequency, and that it is inductive at all higher frequencies. This general statement follows from the variation of capacitive reactance and inductive reactance in response to frequency variation. We know that the reactance of an inductor is directly proportional to frequency. The reactance of a capacitor, however, is inversely proportional to frequency.

The inductive reactance in a series circuit increases as the frequency increases. But the capacitive reactance in the series circuit decreases as the frequency increases. These relations are visualized in Figure 14-4. Evidently, there is a certain frequency for an *LCR* circuit below which the total reactance is capacitive. Above this certain frequency, the total reactance is inductive. Note carefully, that *at this certain frequency the total*

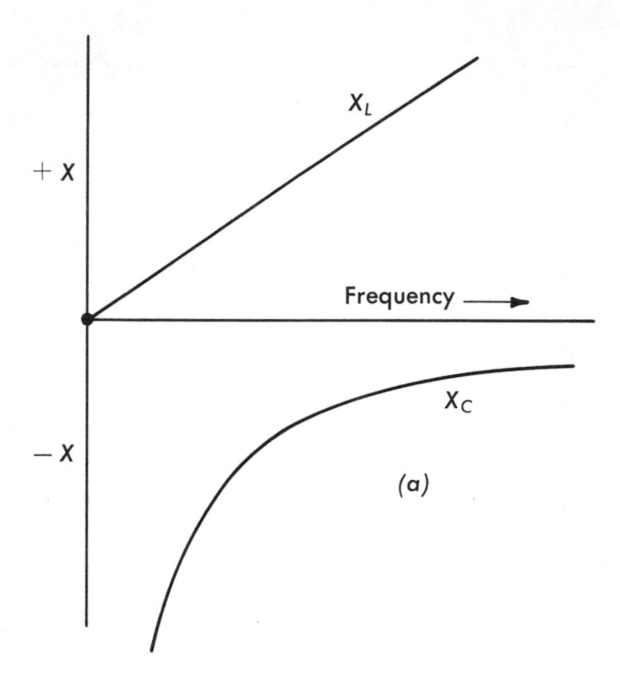

Figure 14-4
(a) Variation of X_L and X_C with frequency of operation. *(b)* At the resonant frequency f_r, the sum of X_L and X_C is equal to zero.

(Continued on facing page.)

reactance is zero. Only resistance is left in the *LCR* circuit to oppose current flow at this certain frequency. We call this the *series-resonant frequency,* or simply the *resonant frequency* of the circuit.

14.3 ANALYSIS OF SERIES RESONANCE

Now, let us see what this resonant frequency may be, and how the circuit parameters vary as the operating frequency is increased from a low value to a high value. Equation (14.1) may be written in the form:

$$Z = R + j\left(\omega L - \frac{1}{\omega C}\right) \tag{14.2}$$

At the resonant frequency, $\omega L = 1/(\omega C)$. Hence, at resonance, $Z = R$. At its resonant frequency, the inductance and capacitance of the *LCR* circuit are effectively absent; or, at its resonant frequency, the *LCR* circuit reduces to R. Evidently, the current is in phase with the applied

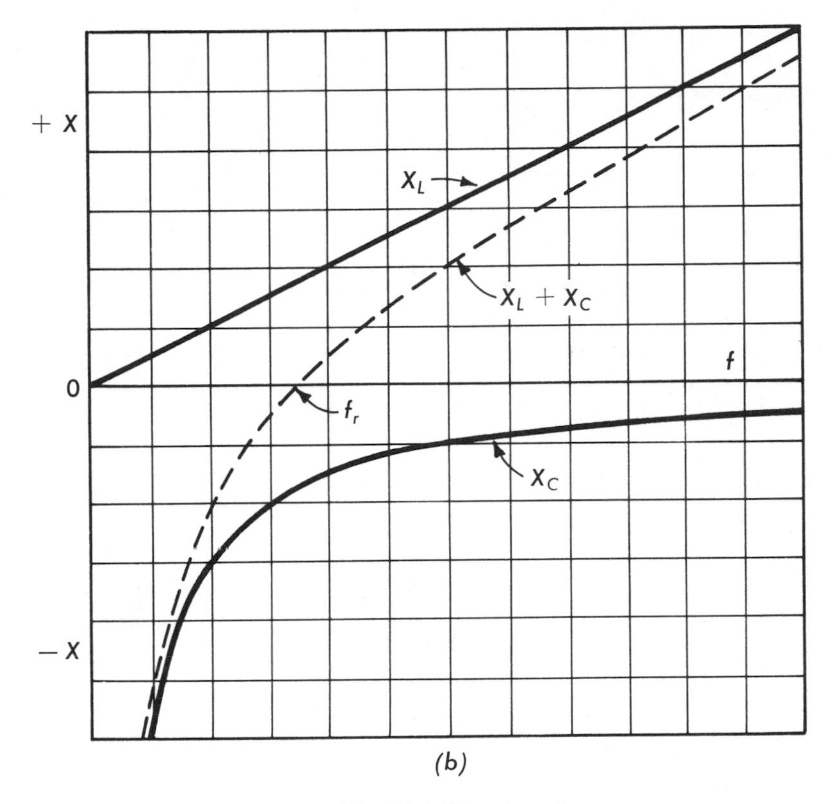

Fig. 14-4 (*Continued*)

voltage at resonance. To calculate the resonant frequency, we simply write $\omega L = 1/(\omega C)$ and solve for f. This simple calculation yields

$$f = \frac{1}{2\pi\sqrt{LC}} \tag{14.3}$$

Electronics engineers and technicians must often calculate the resonant frequency of an *LCR* series circuit. This is somewhat laborious, and slide-rule calculations are commonly employed. Special slide rules are available that require only one setting to calculate a resonant frequency. These are in extensive use by most professional electronics personnel.

Equation (14.3) states that the resonant frequency of a series *LCR* circuit is independent of any resistance value in the circuit. It also states that the resonant frequency depends only upon the *LC* product. Hence, if you double *L* and halve *C*, the resonant frequency remains unchanged.

It is clear that if you maintain the applied voltage constant, and vary

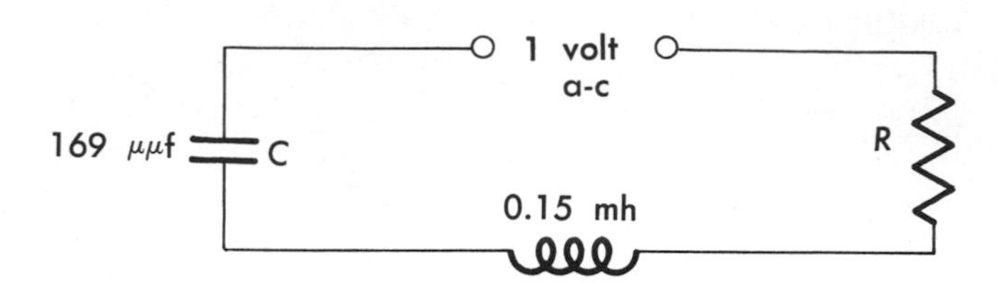

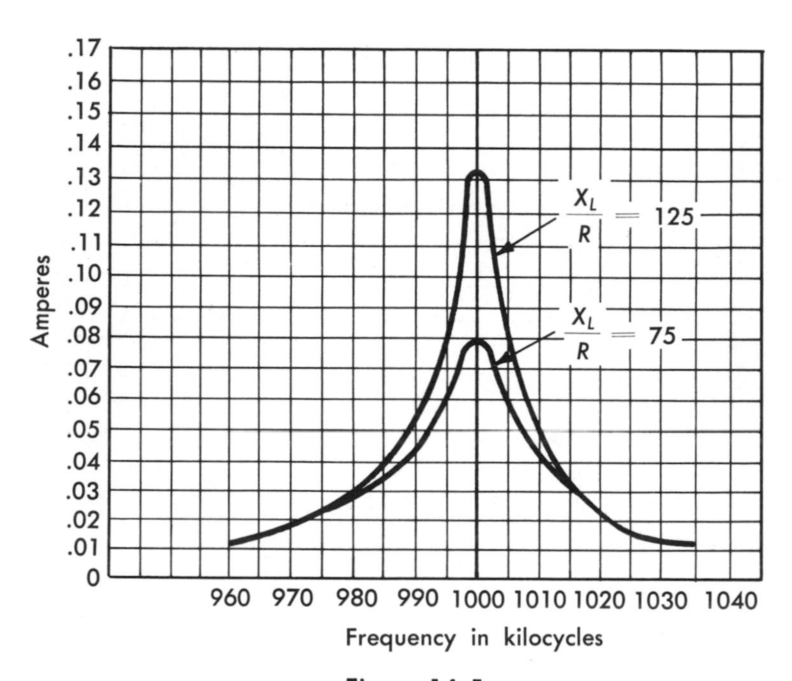

Figure 14-5

Current flow versus frequency in an *LCR* circuit for two different values of *R*.

the operating frequency, maximum current must flow in an *LCR* series circuit at resonance. This fact is obvious because only resistance opposes current flow at resonance. On the other hand, at any frequency other than the resonant frequency, both reactance and resistance will oppose current flow. It is helpful at this point to visualize the current flow versus frequency. Figure 14-5 illustrates how the current rises to a maximum at the resonant frequency, and decreases on either side of resonance.

In this example, the capacitance value is 169 μμf, and the inductance value is 0.15 mh. Curves are plotted for two different values of *R*. We know that the resonant frequency must be 1000 kc, regardless of the resistance value. However, the current flow at resonance depends upon R, and is given by Ohm's law: $I = E/R$. Observe that at frequencies far from resonance, such as 970 kc or 1030 kc in Figure 14-5, the current flow depends primarily upon the total *reactance* of the circuit. Thus, although R is completely dominant at resonance, we can practically neglect R at frequencies far from resonance.

We will observe that the curves in Figure 14-5 are approximately symmetrical, but not entirely so. Dissymmetry results from nonlinearity of the capacitance characteristic (Figure 14-4). The dissymmetry in Figure 14-5 is more evident for the lower value of R. Note that, at resonance, X_L is necessarily the same for both curves. However, the *ratio* X_L/R is large when R is small. This ratio is associated with an interesting and perhaps surprising property of a series-resonant circuit.

14.4 QUALITY FACTOR

The circuit depicted in Figure 14-5 depicts ideal inductance, capacitance, and resistance. We call the ratio X_L/R the quality factor, or Q, of the circuit. At resonance, the reactances X_L and X_C are each equal to 940 ohms, and cancel each other out. Current flow is approximately 0.133 amp. It follows that the voltage drop across L is 125 volts, and the voltage drop across C is 125 volts. This might appear surprising in view of the fact that only 1 volt is applied to the circuit. The drop across R at resonance is, of course, 1 volt. Voltages E_C and E_L are 180 degrees out of phase, and cancel each other when we go around the circuit, in accordance with Kirchhoff's voltage law.

Note that the Q of the circuit is 125 for a value of R, permitting a resonant-current flow of 0.133 amp. The voltage drop across the capacitor is 125 volts, and the voltage drop across the inductor is 125 volts. Application of Ohm's law at resonance shows that there is a *resonant rise of voltage* across the inductor and across the capacitor. This resonant rise is simply written

$$E_0 = QE \quad (14.4)$$

where E_0 is the voltage at resonance across either the capacitor or the inductor, and E is the voltage applied to the circuit.

In most practical situations, capacitors can be considered ideal, and to have no appreciable resistance; however, practical inductors generally have appreciable resistance. Hence, R in Figure 14-5 would be the resistance of the inductor plus the value of the resistor in the circuit. For this reason, we usually consider that the Q of a coil is the limiting factor in resonant rise of voltage. Thus, if there were no resistor placed in the circuit, there would not be an infinite resonant rise of voltage, because of the resistance inherent in a practical inductor.

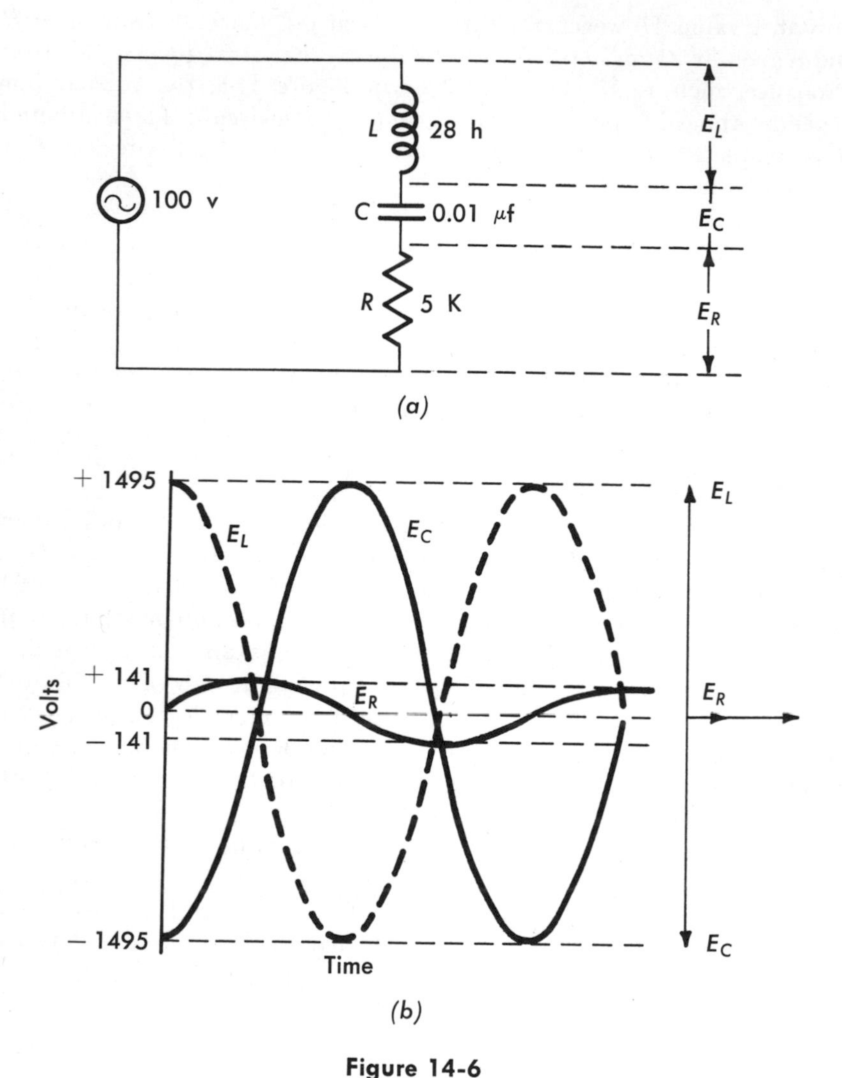

Figure 14-6
(a) An *LCR* circuit with coil which has zero internal resistance. *(b)* Graph and vector diagram for *(a)*.

It is instructive to follow the solution of a typical problem. Figure 14-6 shows an *LCR* series circuit which we will solve for resonant frequency, current flow, and voltage drops. From Equation (14.3) we calculate the resonant frequency:

$$f = \frac{1}{2\,\pi\sqrt{28 \times 0.01 \times 10^{-6}}} = 300 \text{ cps}$$

$X_L = 2\pi fL = 53$ kilohms; similarly, $X_C = 53$ kilohms. Since the inductive and capacitive reactances cancel, $Z = 5 \text{ K} \angle 0^\circ$. $I = E/R = 100/5 \text{ K} = 20 \angle 0^\circ$ ma. Next, $E_C = IX_C = 53 \times 10^3 \angle -90^\circ \times 20 \times 10^{-3} \angle 0^\circ = 1060 \angle -90^\circ$ volts. In other words, the input voltage of 100 volts undergoes a resonant rise and appears as 1060 volts across the capacitor. Since this voltage has a −90 degree phase angle, it lags the resistor voltage drop by 90 degrees.

The inductor voltage drop $E_L = IX_L = 53 \times 10^3 \angle 90^\circ \times 20 \times 10^{-3} \angle 0^\circ = 1060 \angle 90^\circ$ volts. Thus, the input voltage of 100 volts undergoes a resonant rise and appears as 1060 volts across the inductor. Since this voltage has a +90 degree phase angle, it leads the resistor voltage drop by 90 degrees. The resistor voltage drop $E_R = IR = 5 \times 10^3 \times 20 \times 10^{-3} \angle 0^\circ = 100 \angle 0^\circ$ volts. These sinusoidal voltages and their vector diagram are seen in Figure 14-6. Note that the circuit $Q = X_L/R = X_C/R = 53{,}000/5000 = 10.6$.

INTERNAL RESISTANCE

In the foregoing problem, we assumed that the inductor had zero resistance. We know that practical inductors usually have internal resistance which cannot be neglected. In such case, it is impossible to *measure* the inductive voltage drop E_L because the voltage drop across the inductor is the vector sum of its resistive drop and its reactive drop. Hence, it is instructive to solve for the values required in the foregoing problem when the inductor is assigned an internal resistance of 520 ohms, as depicted in Figure 14-7.

As before, the resonant frequency is 300 cycles; $X_L = X_C = 53$ kilohms. The total series resistance is greater because of the inductor resistance:

$$Z = j53 \text{ K} - j53 \text{ K} + 5 \text{ K} + 0.52 \text{ K} = 5.52 \text{ K}$$

Thus, the circuit impedance at resonance is equal to the sum of the inductor's internal resistance and the external circuit resistance. The current flow and voltage drops are

$$I = \frac{1}{5.52 \text{ K}} = 18 \text{ ma}$$

$$E_L = 954 \angle 90^\circ \text{ volts}$$

$$E_C = 954 \angle -90^\circ \text{ volts}$$

$$E_{R\text{-in}} = 9.36 \text{ volts}$$

$$E_R = 90.64 \text{ volts}$$

Accordingly, the terminal voltage across the inductor is the vector sum of $E_{R\text{-in}}$ and E_L, or $9.36 \angle 0^\circ + 954 \angle 90^\circ = 954.04 \angle 89.4^\circ$. The terminal voltage is slightly greater than the inductive drop in this

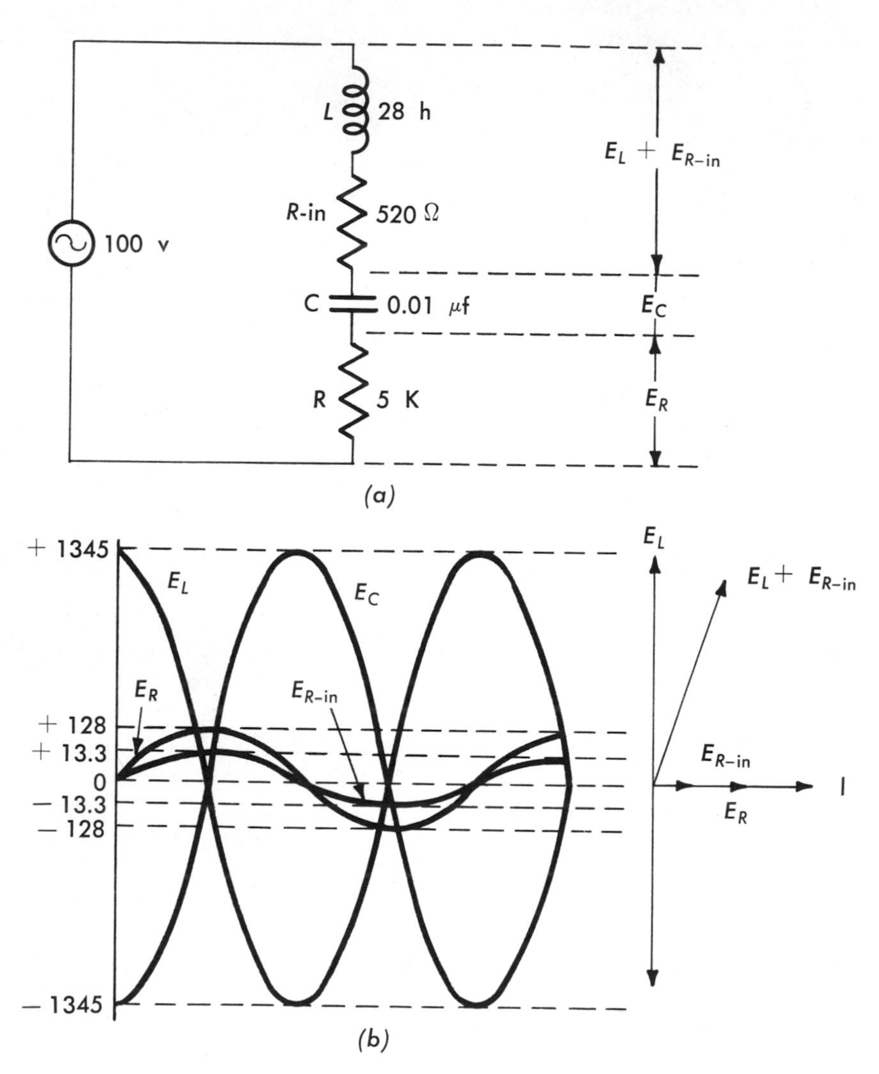

Figure 14-7

(a) LCR circuit with a coil having internal resistance. *(b)* Graph and vector diagram for *(a)*. *(c)* The bandwidth of a frequency-response curve.

(Continued on facing page.)

example. If we compare the values in this problem with those in the previous problem, we note that the inductor's internal resistance lowers the drop across E_L and E_C. This reduction corresponds to a lower Q value. We note also that the current flow was reduced from 20 ma to 18 ma by the inductor's internal resistance. Compare Figure 14-7(*b*) with Figure 14-6(*b*).

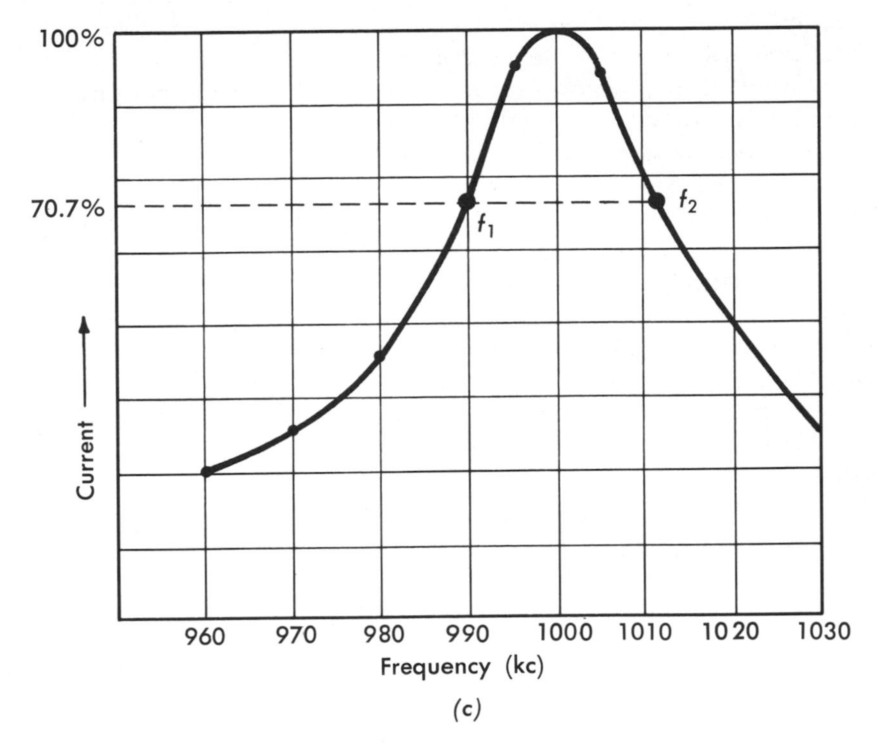

(c)

Fig. 14-7 (*Continued*)

Suppose the 5-K resistor was omitted in the circuit of Figure 14-7. Then, the current flow would be equal to 100/0.52 K, or 192 ma. Furthermore, if an inductor having the same inductance value, but wound with larger wire, were utilized, the current flow would be still greater. However, there is a practical limit to the maximum circuit Q which we can realize, due to the extremely large size required for a 28-henry inductor wound with large-diameter wire. The inductor depicted in Figure 14-7 has a Q value of 53,000/520, or 102 at 300 cps.

Capacitors normally have much less loss than inductors. In many practical situations we regard capacitors as ideal components. However, no capacitor is perfect. The current flow through a capacitor is not quite 90 degrees out of phase with the applied voltage. The loss of energy that occurs in a capacitor is measured in terms of its *dissipation factor*. We denote the dissipation factor by the symbol D:

$$D = R/X_C = \omega CR \tag{14.5}$$

where R is the effective resistance of the capacitor in ohms, C is its capacitance in farads, and ω is equal to $2\pi f$, where f is in cycles per second.

We observe that D is the reciprocal of Q with respect to the capacitor parameters. Since D has a very small value for most capacitors, it can usually be neglected. However, the dissipation factor finds useful application in comparing various designs of capacitors. A well-designed mica capacitor has a typical dissipation factor of 0.0003.

The power consumed in the resistance of an LCR series circuit is equal to I^2R. A frequency-response curve depicts current flow versus frequency, as seen in Figure 14-7(*c*). Since power dissipation is equal to I^2R, the circuit consumes half of maximum power at its 70.7 percent of maximum points. Hence, f_1 and f_2 designate the *half-power points* on the frequency-response curve. In many applications, the number of cycles between the half-power points is defined as the *bandwidth* of the LCR circuit. For example, in Figure 14-7(*c*), maximum power is obtained at a frequency of 1000 kc. Half-power is obtained at 990 kc and at 1012 kc. Hence, the bandwidth in this example is 22 kc.

We know that a frequency-response curve is not quite symmetrical. Hence, it is not surprising to note that f_1 is located 10 kc to one side of the resonant frequency, while f_2 is located 12 kc to the other side of the resonant frequency. When the Q of the circuit is comparatively high, you can determine its value with practical accuracy from the bandwidth: $Q = f_r/(f_2 - f_1)$, where f_r is the resonant frequency. Thus, the approximate Q of the LCR circuit corresponding to Figure 14-7(*c*) is equal to 1000/22 or 45. This topic is considered in greater detail in Chapter 15.

If one LCR circuit has less bandwidth than another LCR circuit, the first is often said to be more *selective*. Selectivity denotes the ability of the circuit to discriminate against currents that have frequencies other than the resonant frequency. This is a consideration of major importance in many electronic devices and systems. A resonant circuit is said to separate or *filter* a desired frequency from a mixture of different frequencies. We will observe a simple example of filter action by a series-resonant circuit in the next section.

14.5 APPLICATION OF *LCR* SERIES CIRCUITS

An interesting application of a series-resonant circuit is to prevent an unwanted a-c current from flowing through a load circuit. For example, Figure 14-8 depicts a 24-volt d-c generator with a 400-cps ripple, connected to a resistive load. Observe that if C and L resonate at 400 cps, a very low resistance is shunted across the load at this frequency. Hence, most of the 400-cps ripple current flows through the resonant circuit. On the other hand, all of the d-c current flows through the load. In an ideal situation, the winding resistance R_L of the inductor would be zero, and all of the 400-cps a-c current would flow through the resonant circuit. In

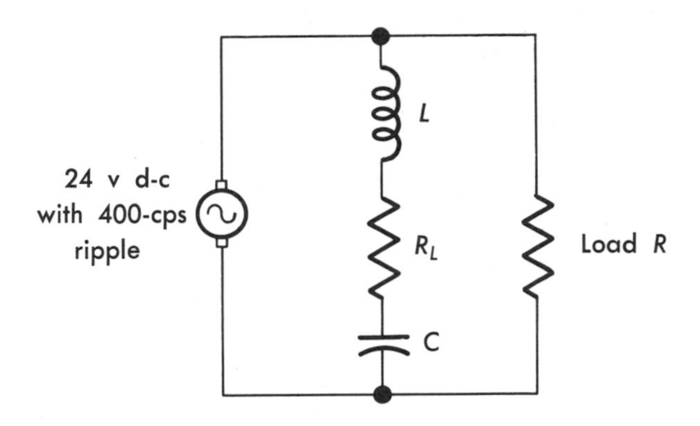

Figure 14-8
Most of the 400-cycle ripple current flow flows through the series-resonant circuit.

practice, however, winding resistance is present, causing a certain fraction of the 400-cycle a-c voltage to proceed through the load resistance.

Another interesting application of a series-resonant circuit is in the measurement of frequency. For example, the a-c voltmeter in Figure 14-9 indicates the drop across R; or, it indicates current flow in the series circuit. Maximum current flows when C is tuned to resonance. Thus, a calibrated dial may be provided for the variable capacitor to indicate the frequency of operation. It follows from Figure 14-5 that if R has a small value, the variable capacitor will tune sharply. However, this sharp tuning entails a large current flow, which may be objectionable. In such case, a higher value can be chosen for R, to limit the current flow at resonance. The variable capacitor tunes less sharply when R has a large value.

14.6 RESPONSE TO D-C VOLTAGE

A series LCR circuit cannot sustain d-c current flow. However, a surge current flows when d-c voltage is suddenly applied to a de-energized LCR circuit. Again, if the d-c voltage source is disconnected and replaced by a short-circuit, a reverse surge current flows to discharge the capacitor. The surge waveform depends on the proportions of R, L, and C. There are three categories of surge waveforms. These waveforms are of great importance in various areas of electronic technology.

Consider the configuration shown in Figure 14-10(a). When R has a comparatively large value, capacitor C must charge slowly when the switch is closed. The current builds up to a peak value, and then decays to zero as the capacitor becomes fully charged. When the switch is first closed,

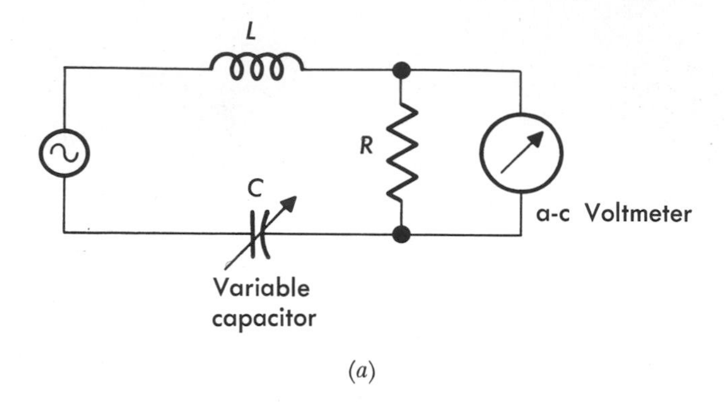

(*a*)

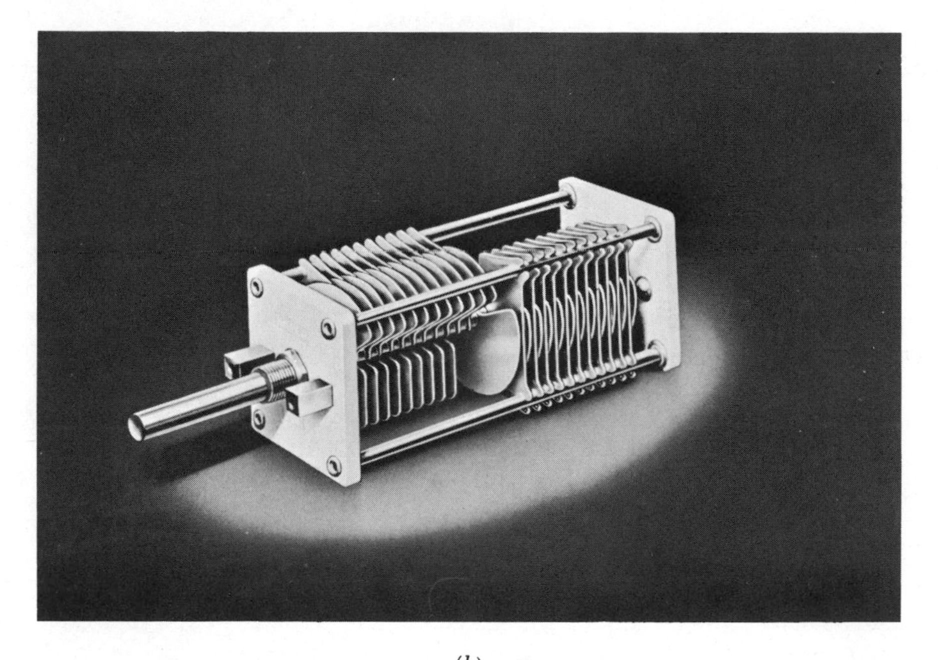

(*b*)

Figure 14-9
(*a*) An operating dial for C can be calibrated in frequency values. (*b*) A variable capacitor; most have air dielectric. (Courtesy of James Millen Mfg. Co.)

the source voltage E appears across L, and there is no voltage drop across C. In other words, the current flow must rise slowly due to the counter emf of the inductor. The circuit current (and voltage across R) has a typical waveform as illustrated in Figure 14-10(*b*). This is called the case of

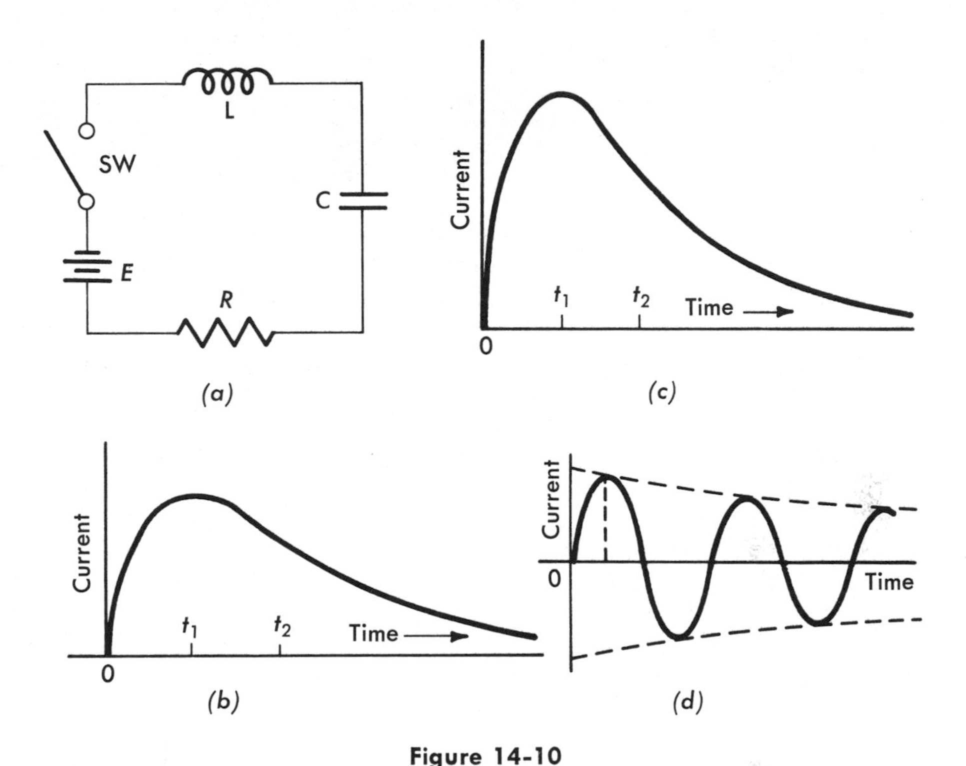

Figure 14-10

(a) LCR circuit with a d-c voltage source. *(b)* Waveform of aperiodic current flow. *(c)* Waveform of current flow for critical damping. *(d)* Waveform of oscillatory current flow.

aperiodic current flow, occurring when R^2 is greater than $4L/C$. *Aperiodic* means that the current is pulsating d-c, and not a-c.

If we reduce the value of R, we will find that there is a limiting value, below which current flow becomes oscillatory instead of aperiodic. This limiting value is $R^2 = 4L/C$. When R has this value, the circuit is said to be *critically damped.* The circuit current (and voltage across R) is illustrated for critical damping in Figure 14-10(*c*).

If we now reduce the value of R below the critical value, the surge current becomes oscillatory. In other words, when R^2 is less than $4L/C$, the surge has a waveform, as illustrated in Figure 14-10(*d*). This is a *damped sine wave.* The waveform decays exponentially. What is the frequency of oscillation? The exact formula is written as

$$f = \frac{1}{2\pi}\sqrt{\frac{1}{LC} - \frac{R^2}{4L^2}} \qquad \textbf{(14.6)}$$

Equation (14.6) states that series resistance causes a lower frequency of oscillation. We observe that if $R = 0$, the frequency of oscillation becomes simply

$$f = \frac{1}{2\pi\sqrt{LC}} \tag{14.7}$$

MAGNITUDE OF ERROR

Note that Equation (14.7) is identical with Equation (14.3). It is apparent that when R is comparatively small, Equation (14.7) will give practically the same answer as Equation (14.6). A bit of algebraic calculation shows that when R is 10 percent of the critical resistance, the error in Equation (14.7) is only ½ of 1 percent. This error is negligible in practical work. When R is 30 percent of the critical resistance value, the error in Equation (14.7) is 4.6 percent, which may be objectionable in some practical situations. If so, we will use Equation (14.6) instead.

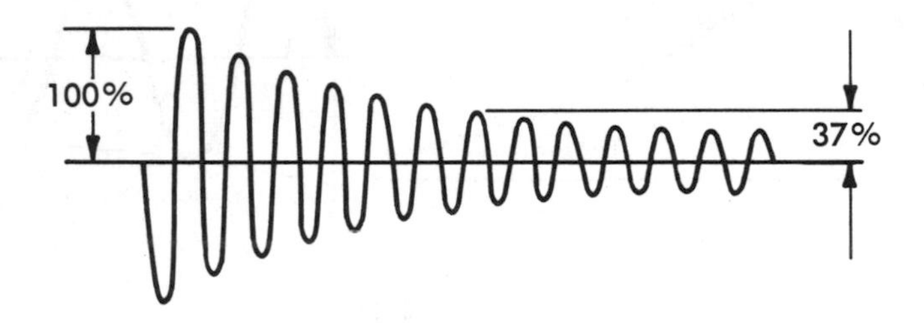

Figure 14-11
The number of cycles from the 100 percent point to the 37 percent point indicates the Q of the circuit.

It is interesting to note that the circuit Q is implicit in the ringing waveform. With reference to Figure 14-11, the ringing waveform decays from 100 percent to 37 percent amplitude in a time interval that may be called T, and which corresponds to the time constant of an RL or RC circuit. The equation of the ringing waveform is written

$$i = \frac{V}{\omega L} \epsilon^{-\alpha t} \sin \omega t \tag{14.8}$$

where i is the instantaneous current value, V is the applied voltage, ω is equal to $2\pi f$, f is given by Equation (14.6), L is the inductance in henrys, ϵ is equal to 2.718, α is equal to $R/2L$, and t is equal to time.

Observe in Figure 14-11 that there are 6 cycles (or peaks) from the 100 percent to the 37 percent. Let us call the time interval of each cycle t. Then, the total time interval T from the 100 percent point to the 37 percent point is equal to nt. Since $t = 1/f$, $T = n/f$. Note in Equation

(14.8) that i will have a value of 37 percent when $\alpha t = 1$; or, $T = 2L/R$. Hence, $n/f = 2L/R$; or $n = 2fL/R$. We know that $Q = 2\pi fL/R$. Therefore,

$$Q = n\pi \tag{14.9}$$

This is a very convenient method of measuring the Q of a resonant circuit. In practice, the battery and switch in Figure 14-10 are replaced by a square-wave generator. The generator operates like a battery with an automatic switch. The voltage drop across R is fed to an oscilloscope, to display the ringing pattern. Note that this measurement gives the Q value at the ringing frequency. At some other frequency, the Q value will be different. Since $Q = 2\pi fL/R$, it might be supposed that a measurement at one frequency would permit calculation of the Q value at another frequency. In general, this is not possible.

You will find that the Q value varies in a generally unpredictable manner over a wide range of frequencies. The reason for this situation is the fact that an inductor has an a-c resistance, which is higher than its d-c resistance. This a-c resistance is a largely unpredictable function of frequency. Accordingly, it is necessary to measure the Q value at a specified frequency. The value measured at this frequency can be extrapolated only for frequencies in the immediate vicinity of the reference frequency. With this brief introduction to the topic of a-c resistance, the subject will be deferred for subsequent discussion.

14.7 FERRORESONANCE

An air-core coil is a linear inductance; that is, its inductance remains constant, regardless of the current value. We recall that an iron-core coil is a nonlinear inductance; its inductance value decreases as the current flow increases. Evidently, if we use an iron-core coil in a series LCR circuit, the resonant frequency will shift when the current value is changed. This frequency shift is the basis of all *ferroresonant* circuits. Consider the LCR series circuit depicted in Figure 14-12. Inductor L is provided with an iron core. If the cross-sectional area of the core is comparatively small with respect to the current value I, its inductance value decreases as I increases. We say that L operates as a *saturable* reactor.

Suppose that the inductance value for small current values resonates with C in Figure 14-12 at a frequency somewhat lower than the frequency of E. Let us consider the change in voltage E_{LC} as the current I is increased. At first, E_{LC} rises with increase in I. However, L decreases in value, causing the circuit to approach resonance. The voltage drops across L and C become more nearly equal, and are of course, 180 degrees apart in phase. Hence, increasing current causes E_{LC} to pass through a maximum value

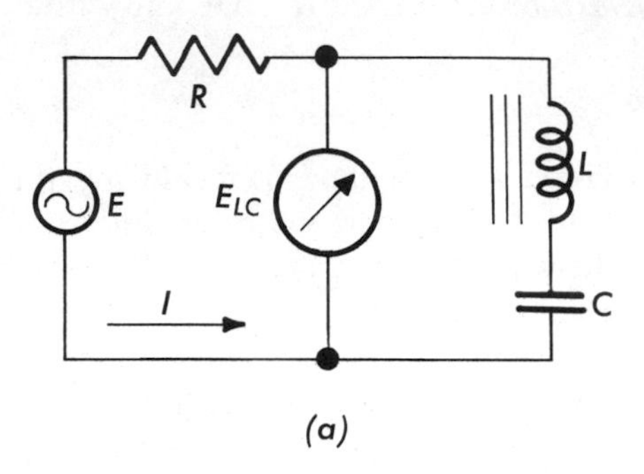

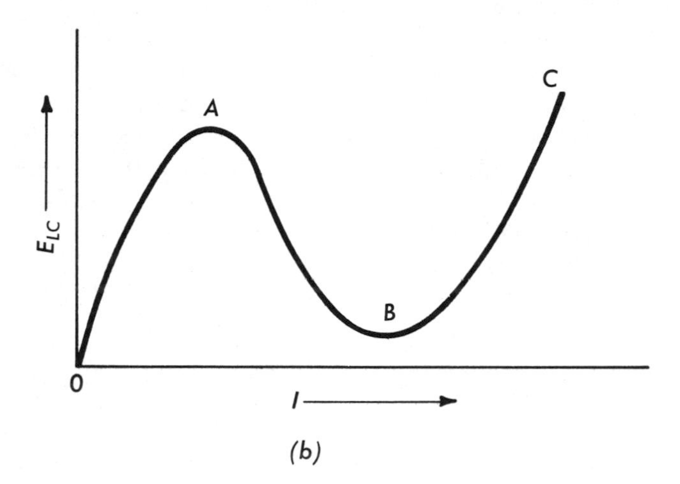

Figure 14-12
(a) LCR series circuit with an iron-core inductor. *(b)* Ferroresonance occurs at point *B*.

at *A* [Figure 14-12(*b*)], and then to pass through a minimum at *B*. Point *B* occurs at the series-resonant point. E_{LC} does not fall completely to zero at point *B*, due to the winding resistance of *L*. As the current is further increased, E_{LC} again rises to point *C*.

An interesting characteristic of the ferroresonant circuit is its reactance variation. It is clear that the circuit is "inductive" for small current values, and becomes "capacitive" for high current values. In other words, the current lags the applied voltage to the left of *B* in Figure 14-12(*b*), but the current leads the applied voltage to the right of point *B*. At point *B*, current and voltage are in phase.

Let us analyze the variation of E_{LC} versus *I* in Figure 14-12(*b*). At first, increasing current is accompanied by increasing voltage. However, over the region from *A* to *B*, increasing current is accompanied by decreasing voltage—the current decreases as the voltage increases. Hence, the voltage-current characteristic defines a *negative impedance* over the interval from *A* to *B*. On the other hand, the characteristic defines a positive impedance from zero to *A*, and from *B* to *C*. Thus, the term negative impedance simply means that increasing voltage values are accompanied by decreasing current values. Extensive use is made of negative impedance in various modern electronic devices.

When we return to analysis of semiconductor devices in Chapter 21, we will find that certain types of capacitors have a nonlinear capacitance characteristic. Otherwise stated, the capacitance value is a function of the voltage drop across the capacitor. Evidently, an *LCR* series circuit comprising linear resistance, linear inductance, and nonlinear capacitance, can be arranged to exhibit negative impedance over a certain range of applied voltage. Hence, extensive use is made of nonlinear capacitance in various modern electronic devices.

14.8 TROUBLESHOOTING *LCR* SERIES CIRCUITS

Voltage, current, and resistance measurements provide basic data for trouble analysis in *LCR* series circuits. The same general approaches apply, which have been explained for series *RC* and *RL* circuits. For example, you will often make measurements of capacitance values; you may also make measurements of inductance values. In addition, since an *LCR* series circuit has a resonant frequency, electronics technicians often measure resonant frequencies. If the circuit resonates at an incorrect frequency, or if it exhibits no resonant response, the observation can be evaluated with respect to the particular circuit.

Measurement of resonant frequencies is often made with an instrument, called a *grid-dip meter*. A typical grid-dip meter is illustrated in Figure 14-13. This instrument is basically a small a-c generator that can be adjusted over a wide frequency range. In practice, the external coil of the grid-dip meter is placed near the inductor of an *LCR* circuit. The operator then adjusts the instrument frequency to a value, producing a "dip" or minimum reading on the microammeter scale. Then, the frequency scale of the instrument indicates the resonant frequency of the *LCR* circuit.

This method of frequency measurement is made with no power applied to the *LCR* circuit. In other words, the grid-dip meter is a test substitute for the normally applied a-c voltage. The instrument *induces* a small current in the *LCR* circuit, and indicates the resonant frequency of this induced current. Accordingly, a resonant-frequency measurement

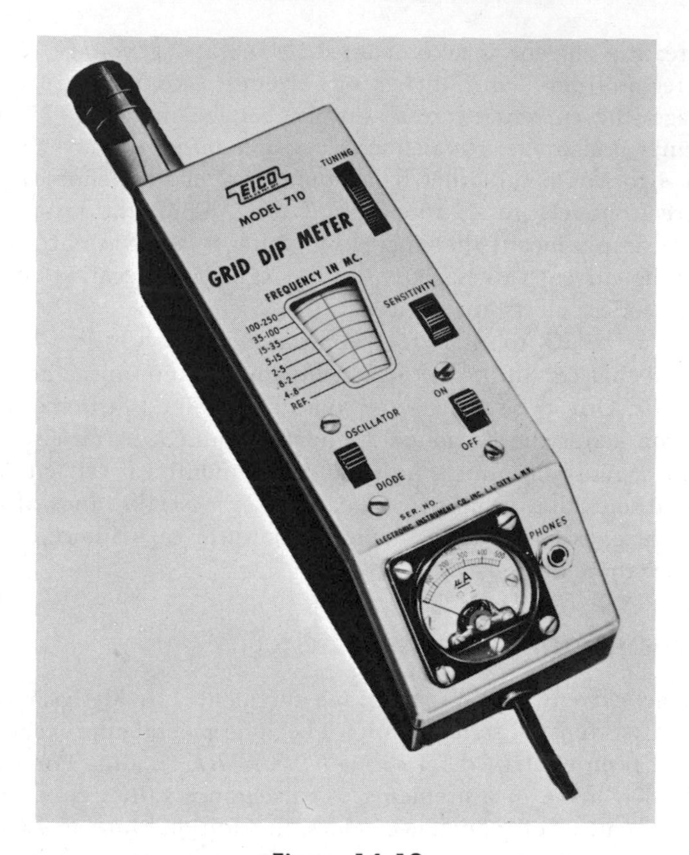

Figure 14-13
A grid-dip meter which has a frequency range from 400 kc to 250 mc. (Courtesy of Electronic Instrument Co.)

can be made quickly, without calculations, and without any electrical connection to the *LCR* circuit.

A grid-dip meter is also used to measure the operating frequency of an *LCR* circuit. In this case, the frequency measurement is made with power applied to the circuit. As before, the external coil of the grid-dip meter is placed near the inductor of the *LCR* circuit. However, the instrument is switched to operate as a *wavemeter*. In this mode of operation, the grid-dip meter does not generate an a-c voltage; instead, the inductor *induces* a voltage in the external coil of the instrument. The operator adjusts the grid-dip meter for a maximum reading on the microammeter scale. Then, the frequency scale of the instrument indicates the operating frequency of the *LCR* circuit.

Figure 14-14 illustrates the simplest example of resonant-frequency measurement. Here, a small inductor is connected to a fixed capacitor.

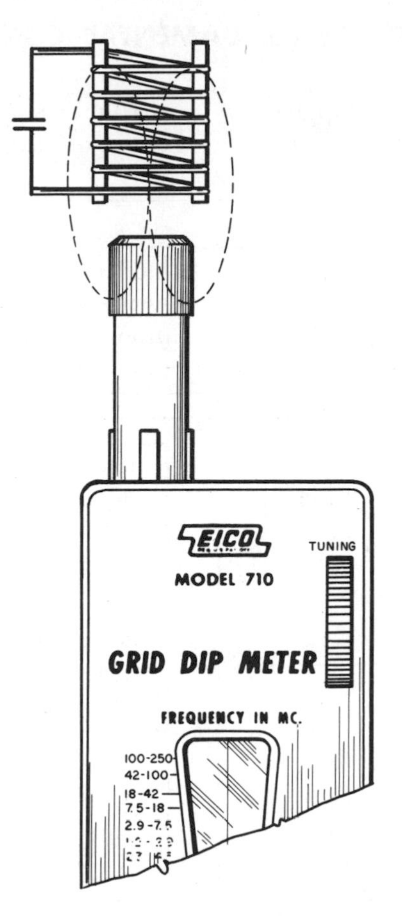

Figure 14-14
A simple example of resonant-frequency measurement with a grid-dip meter.

The grid-dip meter is operated as an a-c generator. When the external coil of the instrument is brought near the inductor, the coil's magnetic field induces an a-c current in the inductor turns. It is evident that this induced current absorbs power due to the I^2R loss in the winding resistance of the inductor. If you adjust the instrument to the resonant frequency of the circuit under test, maximum current is induced. In turn, maximum power is consumed as I^2R loss. This power must be supplied by the grid-dip meter. Hence, the microammeter indicates a minimum reading.

SUMMARY OF FUNDAMENTAL CONCEPTS

Ohm's law for a-c applies to a complete series circuit, to any component in the circuit, or to a combination of two or more components.

Kirchhoff's voltage law applies to a reactive series circuit; a capacitive voltage drop is subtracted from an inductive voltage drop; resistive and reactive voltage drops are added in quadrature.

Capacitive reactance and inductive reactance values are equal at the resonant frequency. $X_L = X_C$.

$$f = \frac{1}{2\pi\sqrt{LC}}$$

The impedance of an *LCR* series circuit is minimum and is purely resistive at the resonant frequency. $Z = R$.

The Q value of an *LCR* circuit is the ratio of inductive reactance to resistance. $Q = X_L/R$.

The voltage drop across the capacitance or across the inductance at resonance is equal to Q times the source voltage.

Power is consumed only by the resistance in an *LCR* circuit.

Power is stored and returned by the reactance in the circuit.

Maximum power is dissipated in the resistance at the resonant frequency of an *LCR* series circuit.

The power factor of an *LCR* series circuit is unity at the resonant frequency.

An *LCR* series circuit is capacitive at frequencies below resonance, and is inductive at frequencies above resonance.

QUESTIONS

1) An *LCR* series circuit operated at a frequency below its resonant frequency is:
(*a*) purely resistive. (*b*) inductive. (*c*) capacitive. (*d*) wattless.
2) An *LCR* series circuit operated at a frequency above its resonant frequency is:
(*a*) reluctive. (*b*) inductive. (*c*) capacitive. (*d*) wattless.
3) At its resonant frequency, an *LCR* series circuit has:
(*a*) a total resistance equal to zero. (*b*) a total conductance equal to zero. (*c*) a total reluctance equal to zero. (*d*) a total reactance equal to zero.
4) The frequency-response curve for an *LCR* series circuit is:
(*a*) symmetrical about its resonant frequency. (*b*) symmetrical about its maximum current point. (*c*) not quite symmetrical about its resonant frequency. (*d*) symmetrical about its maximum power point.
5) An *LCR* frequency-response curve has:
(*a*) two maximum-power points. (*b*) two half-power points. (*c*) two resonant-frequency points. (*d*) two bandwidths.
6) The Q of an *LCR* series circuit is related to:
(*a*) its impedance at resonance. (*b*) its maximum power dissipation. (*c*) its half-power points. (*d*) its current flow at resonance.
7) Aperiodic current flow in an *LCR* series circuit means that:
(*a*) the voltage drop across the resistance is an a-c voltage. (*b*) the voltage drop across the resistance is a pulsating d-c voltage. (*c*) R^2 is less than $4L/C$. (*d*) the circuit conductance is zero.
8) Critical damping in an *LCR* series circuit means that:
(*a*) the circuit conductance is infinite. (*b*) R^2 is equal to $4L/C$. (*c*) the resistance value is zero. (*d*) the reluctance is equal to the resistance.
9) The Q of a series *LCR* circuit is related to:
(*a*) its ringing waveform. (*b*) the source voltage. (*c*) its phase angle at resonance. (*d*) its power factor at resonance.
10) Ferroresonance is a function of:
(*a*) current flow. (*b*) the phase angle at resonance. (*c*) the power factor at resonance. (*d*) the power consumed in the capacitor.

PROBLEMS

1) An ideal 159-μh inductor is connected in series with a 159-$\mu\mu$f capacitor and a 10-ohm resistor. What is the resonant frequency of this circuit?
2) Calculate the Q of the resonant circuit in Problem 1.
3) What is the approximate bandwidth of the circuit in Problem 1?
4) If the 10-ohm resistor is changed to a 20-ohm resistor in Problem 1, what is the resonant frequency of the circuit? What is its Q? What is its approximate bandwidth?
5) The circuit in Problem 1 is energized from a 10-volt variable-frequency source. How much power is dissipated by the 10-ohm resistor at the lower half-power point? How much power is dissipated at the upper half-power point?
6) If the voltage source in Problem 5 is set to the resonant frequency of the circuit, what is the value of the voltage drop across the capacitor?
7) A series *LCR* circuit has a resonant frequency of 1 mc and a Q value of 50. What is its approximate bandwidth?
8) What value of capacitance will be required to resonate a 1-henry inductor at 120 cycles? What is the reactance value of this capacitor at 120 cycles?
9) If the winding resistance of the inductor in Problem 8 is 300 ohms, and the series circuit is energized from a 117-volt 60-cycle line, how much power is dissipated in the winding resistance?
10) With reference to Problem 9, how much power is dissipated in the winding resistance when the 117-volt source has a frequency corresponding to a half-power point?
11) A 159-$\mu\mu$f capacitor is connected in series with a 159-μh inductor and a 100-ohm resistor. If a d-c voltage is suddenly applied to this circuit, what is its exact ringing frequency?
12) How many cycles are included in the ringing waveform (Problem 11) from the 100 percent point to the 37 percent point on the wave envelope?
13) If the resistance is zero in the circuit of Problem 11, what is its exact ringing frequency?
14) How many cycles are included in the ringing waveform (Problem 13) from the 100 percent point to the 37 percent point on the wave envelope? [Hint: The Q value is infinite.]
15) If the resistance is 1 megohm in Problem 11, what is the exact ringing frequency of the circuit?

15

SERIES-PARALLEL A-C CIRCUITS

15.1 NETWORK REDUCTION

Impedances that are connected in parallel, as exemplified in Figure 15-1, can be classified as a series-parallel configuration. Note that the branch components are connected in series, and the branches are connected in parallel. Evidently, this series-parallel circuit must have an

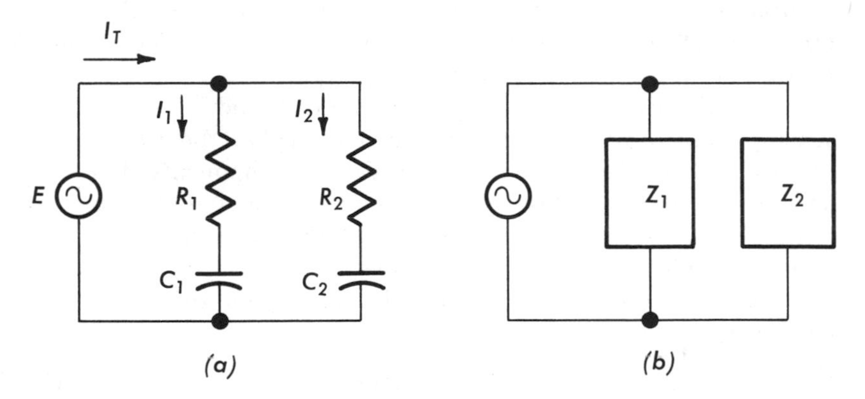

Figure 15-1
(a) An example of a simple series-parallel circuit. *(b)* Block symbolism for impedances.

equivalent *RC* series circuit. The circuit impedance is given by the equation

$$Z_T = \frac{Z_1 Z_2}{Z_1 + Z_2} \tag{15.1}$$

The total impedance Z_T can be expressed in rectangular form, $R - jX$. In turn, R and $-jX$ define the components of the equivalent *RC* series circuit. However, analysis of the configuration in Figure 15-1 can be made without solving for the equivalent circuit at the outset. Instead, we can analyze the circuit action in terms of branch currents, and obtain Z_T at the end of the analysis. Our choice of approach will depend upon the given data in particular cases. Note that the vector sum of I_1 and I_2 is equal to the total current I_T. In turn, Z_T will be equal to E/I_T. First, let us write the equation for Z_1:

$$Z_1 = R_1 - jX_{C_1} = \sqrt{R_1^2 + X_{C_1}^2} \underline{/ -\tan^{-1} X_{C_1}/R_1} \tag{15.2}$$

Next, the current through Z_1 follows from Ohm's law,

$$I_1 = \frac{E}{Z_1 \underline{/-\theta_1}} \tag{15.3}$$

where Z_1 has the magnitude and angle given by Equation (15.2). Since the branch reactance is capacitive, the impedance angle is negative.

We calculate Z_2 and I_2 in the same manner. Now, observe that I_1 and I_2 can be depicted graphically, as seen in Figure 15-2. We take the applied voltage E as a reference in the vector diagram, because E is common to both I_1 and I_2. Note that I_1 and I_2 lead E, because the reactance is capacitive in both branches. If you wish to make a graphical solution for the total current I_T, it is only necessary to complete the parallelogram in Figure 15-2; that is, I_T is the vector sum of I_1 and I_2.

However, a graphical solution is never exact, and will be used only when approximate answers are adequate. To calculate the value of I_T, we must first solve for the resistive and the reactive components of I_1 and I_2. Then, we can add the resistive components, and add the reactive components. Thus, we obtain the resistive and reactive components of the total current. Finally, we compute the magnitude and angle of the total impedance. Accordingly, we will start by solving for the resistive component of I_1:

$$I_1 \underline{/0^\circ} = I_1 \cos \theta_1 \tag{15.4}$$

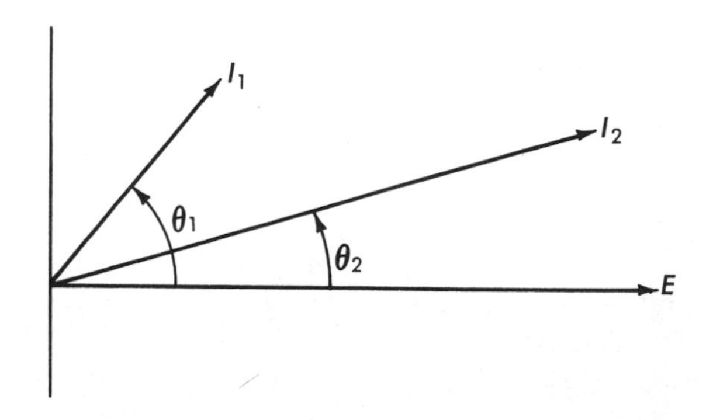

Figure 15-2
Vector diagram for I_1, I_2, and E.

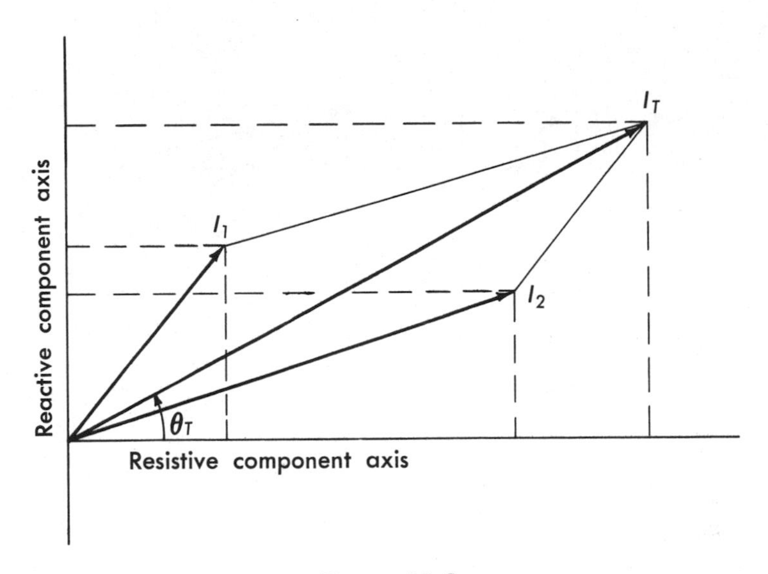

Figure 15-3
Vector diagram for I_1, I_2, and I_T, with resistive and reactive components indicated.

Next, we solve for the reactive component of I_1:

$$I_1 \angle 90^\circ = I_1 \sin \theta_1 \tag{15.5}$$

Similarly,

$$I_2 \angle 0^\circ = I_2 \cos \theta_2 \tag{15.6}$$

$$I_2 \angle 90^\circ = I_2 \sin \theta_2 \tag{15.7}$$

Now that we have the resistive and reactive components of I_1 and I_2, it is clear that the total current is given by

$$I_T = I_1 \cos \theta_1 + I_2 \cos \theta_2 - j(I_1 \sin \theta_1 + I_2 \sin \theta_2) \tag{15.8}$$

We now have I_T in terms of its rectangular components. Since we wish to find the total impedance, we must change Equation (15.8) into its polar form, as we learned previously. Figure 15-3 shows the rectangular components of I_1, I_2, and I_T. Now that we have calculated the magnitude and angle of I_T (either analytically or graphically), the total impedance of the circuit in Figure 15-1 follows from Ohm's law

$$Z_T = \frac{E\angle 0^\circ}{I_T\angle \theta_T} = \frac{E}{I_T} \angle -\theta_T \tag{15.9}$$

Once again, observe that the currents lead the applied voltage in Figure 15-2 and Figure 15-3. Accordingly, we assign positive angles to all currents in this problem. When we divide the total current into the

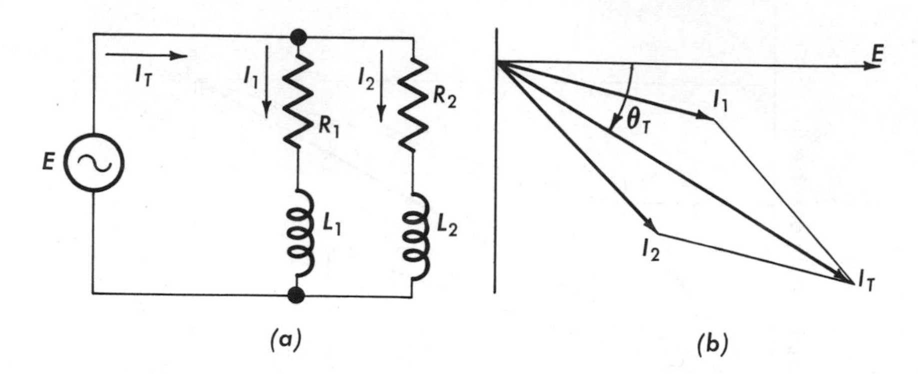

Figure 15-4
(*a*) Two *RL* series branches connected in parallel. (*b*) Vector diagram for *E*, I_1, I_2, and I_T.

voltage [Equation (15.9)], a positive angle is necessarily subtracted from an angle of 0 degrees. The value of the angle is unchanged thereby, but its sign becomes negative. Remember that when we divide two vectors, we divide their magnitudes and subtract their angles. Hence, the total impedance of the circuit in Figure 15-1 is negative. The power factor, of course, is equal to the cosine of the impedance angle.

Next, consider two series *RL* circuits connected in parallel, as depicted in Figure 15-4. The currents all lag the applied voltage. We can find the total current graphically or analytically, as previously explained. Then, the total impedance is given by the quotient of E/I_T. Evidently,

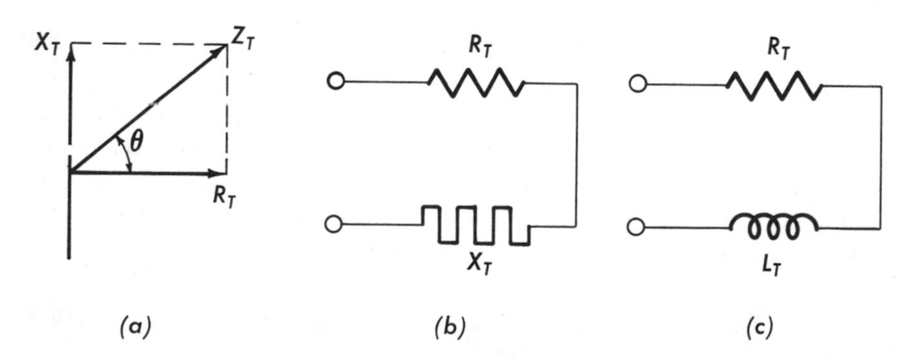

Figure 15-5
(*a*) The total impedance of the circuit in Figure 15-4 has resistive and reactive components. (*b*) Equivalent circuit, comprising resistance and reactance. (*c*) Equivalent circuit comprising resistance and inductance.

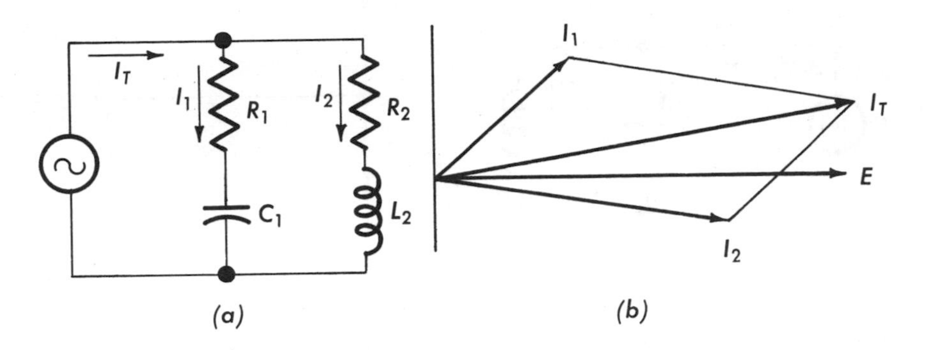

Figure 15-6
(a) A parallel configuration comprising an RC branch and an RL branch. *(b)* Vector diagram for I_1, I_2, I_T, and E.

the phase angle of the circuit is positive, because both branches have inductive reactance. Z_T has resistive and reactive components (see Figure 15-5). These components correspond to the equivalent circuit which comprises series resistance and reactance, as shown in Figure 15-5(*b*). If you divide X_T by $2 \pi f$, the value of L_T is obtained; the equivalent circuit may then be drawn as seen in Figure 15-5(*c*) with resistance and inductance connected in series.

With the foregoing principles in mind, it is easy to understand the circuit action for a configuration such as shown in Figure 15-6. The capacitive branch draws a leading current I_1. On the other hand, the inductive branch draws a lagging current I_2. In this example, the current and phase angles happen to result in a total current I_T, leading the applied voltage. Evidently, the equivalent circuit comprises series resistance and capacitance. Obviously, other values of C_1 and L_2 could be chosen in Figure 15-6 which would cause I_T to lag E. In this case, the equivalent circuit would comprise a series resistance and inductance.

15.2 PARALLEL RESONANCE

We learned in Chapter 14 that inductance and capacitance connected in series exhibit a condition called resonance. Series resonance occurs at a frequency which makes the inductive reactance equal the capacitive reactance. We recall that maximum current flows in a series circuit at its resonant frequency. An analogous resonant condition is encountered in parallel and series-parallel circuits which have inductance in one branch and capacitance in another branch. Let us see how the branch currents and total current are distributed in a simple parallel circuit that has ideal inductance and capacitance. We know, of course, that practical

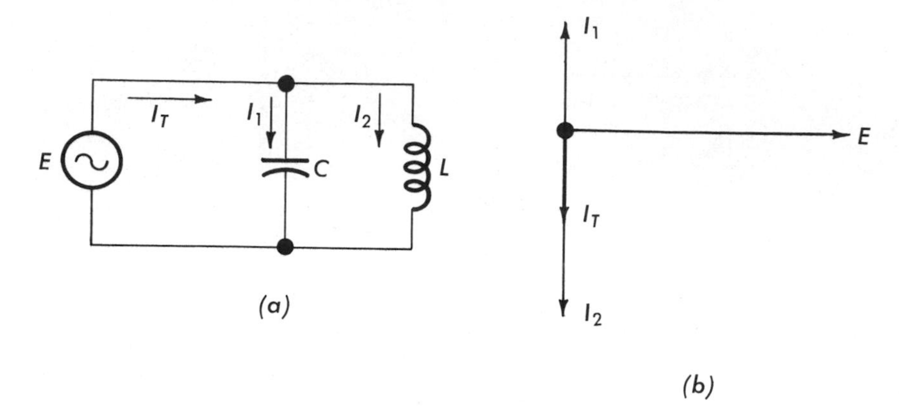

Figure 15-7
(a) A parallel circuit comprising ideal inductance and capacitance. *(b)* Vector diagram for E, I_1, I_2, and I_T.

inductors have winding resistance, unless the winding is cooled to the vicinity of $-273°C$. In the following example, we may assume that this is the case.

Figure 15-7 shows a parallel circuit that comprises an ideal inductance and an ideal capacitance. Branch current I_1 leads E by 90 degrees. However, branch current I_2 lags E by 90 degrees. The value of I_1 is equal to E/X_C. Similarly, the value of I_2 is equal to E/X_L. Since I_2 is greater than I_1 in this example, the equivalent circuit is an ideal inductor. We observe that the total current I_T is the arithmetical difference between I_2 and I_1. It is obvious that other values could be chosen for L and C which would cause I_1 to be greater than I_2. In this case, the equivalent circuit would be an ideal capacitor. As before, the total current would be the arithmetical difference between I_1 and I_2.

Note that we can change the proportions of I_1 and I_2 in Figure 15-7 by varying the frequency of E. At a sufficiently low frequency, I_2 must be greater than I_1. At a sufficiently high frequency, however, I_1 must be greater than I_2. Evidently, there is a certain frequency f at which $I_1 = I_2$. We designate f as the parallel-resonant frequency for the circuit in Figure 15-7. Now, if $I_1 = I_2$, their arithmetical sum is zero, and $I_T = 0$. Hence, *at the parallel-resonant frequency, the generator supplies zero current to this circuit.* (See Figure 15-8.)

RESONANT-FREQUENCY FORMULA

Note that if $I_1 = I_2$, it follows that $X_C = X_L$. When we solve for the resonant frequency f, we obtain

$$f = \frac{1}{2\pi\sqrt{LC}} \qquad \textbf{(15.10)}$$

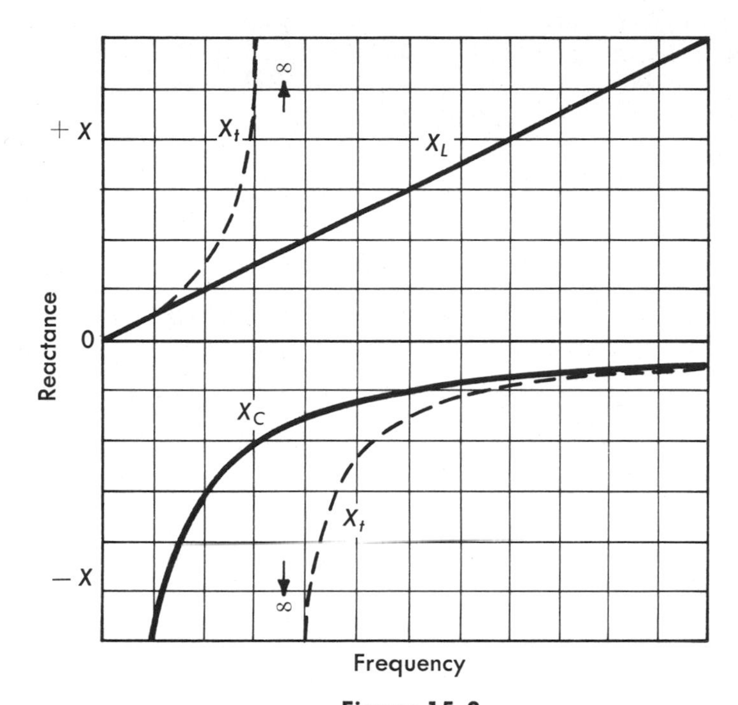

Figure 15-8

Variation of X_L, X_C, and X_T versus frequency for the configuration of Figure 15-7.

This is the same resonant-frequency formula that we derived in Chapter 14 for series resonance. However, the circuit action is "opposite" in the two situations. We know that if an ideal inductor is connected in series with an ideal capacitor, the circuit draws infinite current (in theory) at resonance. On the other hand, we have seen that if an ideal inductor is connected in parallel with an ideal capacitor, the circuit draws zero current (in theory) at resonance.

The circuit action of a parallel *LC* configuration is opposite in another respect from a series *LC* configuration. We recall a series *LC* circuit is capacitive at frequencies below resonance, and is inductive at frequencies above resonance. In other words, the series circuit draws a leading current at low frequencies, and draws a lagging current at high frequencies. But a parallel *LC* circuit is inductive at frequencies below resonance, and is capacitive at frequencies above resonance.

Another interesting respect in which a parallel *LC* circuit is the opposite of a series *LC* circuit is the resonant rise of current in the parallel circuit, compared with the resonant rise of voltage in the series circuit. We recall that the voltage drop across the inductor and the voltage drop across the capacitor in a series-resonant circuit is greater than the supply voltage, and is equal to Q times the supply voltage. On the other hand, we shall find that the current flow through the inductor, and the current flow through the capacitor in a parallel-resonant circuit is greater than the line current I_T, and is equal to Q times the line current.

This resonant rise of current results from the reactance variations depicted in Figure 15-8. As we approach the parallel-resonant frequency, X_C and X_L have finite values which are changing slowly. At resonance, the branch currents are equal:

$$I_1 = E/X_C = I_2 = E/X_L \quad (15.11)$$

As we approach the parallel-resonant frequency, however, X_T is changing rapidly and approaching infinity as a limit. Hence, I_T is approaching zero as a limit. At resonance, each branch current is infinitely larger than the line current. The Q of the inductor is infinite. Or, the branch current is equal to Q times the line current. We shall return to this point in a following discussion.

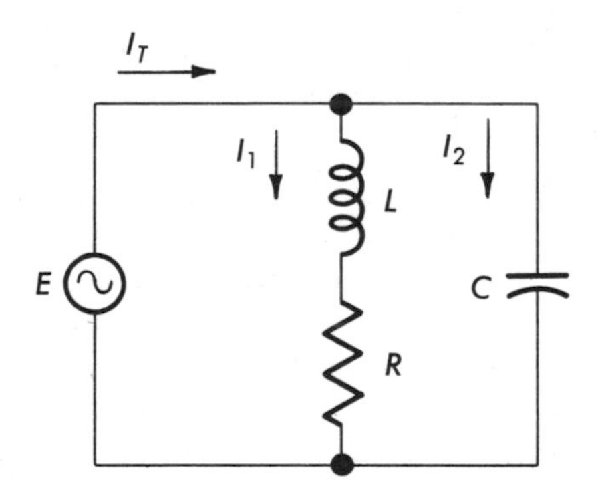

Figure 15-9
A series-parallel circuit comprising series inductance and resistance in parallel with capacitance.

RATIONALIZATION

Next, let us consider the series-parallel circuit shown in Figure 15-9. We know that $I_2 = \omega CE$, and that $I_1 = E/(R + j\omega L)$. We must now *rationalize* I_1, which means to separate its resistive and reactive components:

$$I_1 = \frac{E}{R + j\omega L} = \frac{E}{R + j\omega L} \cdot \frac{R - j\omega L}{R - j\omega L} \quad (15.12)$$

We know that if we multiply the numerator and denominator by the same quantity, the fraction remains unchanged. But Equation (15.12) provides separation of the resistive and reactive components:

$$I_1 = \frac{ER}{R^2 + (\omega L)^2} - j\frac{LE\,\omega}{R^2 + (\omega L)^2} \tag{15.13}$$

Equation (15.13) states that I_1 has a resistive component equal to the first term, and also a reactive lagging component equal to the second term. Let us define parallel resonance for Figure 15-9 in the same manner as we defined parallel resonance for Figure 15-7. In other words, we shall solve for f when jI_1 is equal to $-jI_2$ in Figure 15-9. This is the same as saying that we are defining parallel resonance in Figure 15-9 as the condition in which I_T is in phase with E. Accordingly, if $jI_1 = -jI_2$, we will analyze this condition by equating I_2 to the reactive component of I_1:

$$\frac{\omega LE}{R^2 + (\omega L)^2} = \omega CE \tag{15.14}$$

The term ωE cancels out. We solve for f, and find that

$$f = \frac{1}{2\pi}\sqrt{\frac{1}{LC} - \frac{R^2}{L^2}} \tag{15.15}$$

Equation (15.15) applies to the circuit in Figure 15-9 for any value of resistance. Note, however, that when Q is comparatively large (R comparatively small), R^2/L^2 becomes small also, and may be neglected in many practical situations. In this case, the resonant frequency can be considered to be given by Equation (15.10); that is, Equation (15.15) reduces to Equation (15.10) when R^2/L^2 is assigned a value of zero.

The current I_T at resonance is in phase with E; that is, I_2 in Figure 15-9 is cancelled by the reactive component of I_1. This means that I_T at resonance is equal to the first term in Equation (15.13). Thus, the generator supplies a current at resonance equal to

$$I_T = \frac{ER}{R^2 + (\omega L)^2} \tag{15.16}$$

We should observe that when R is comparatively small, R^2 becomes very small, and it will then be convenient to write Equation (15.16) in the form

$$I_T = \frac{ER}{\omega^2 L^2}, \text{ approximately} \tag{15.17}$$

Since $Q = \omega L/R$, we can write Equation (15.17) in the form

$$I_T = \frac{E}{\omega L} \cdot \frac{1}{Q}, \text{ approximately} \tag{15.18}$$

Equation (15.18) states that the line current I_T is $1/Q$ times the current which flows through the inductor; or, $I_1 = QI_T$. Since I_2 is approximately equal to I_1 at our defined resonance condition, $I_2 = QI_T$. These parallel-resonance approximations (for high Q), resolve the indeterminacy noted earlier, and show that the current rise in the branch circuit at resonance is approximately equal to Q times the line current. As R approaches zero, the approximation evidently approaches complete accuracy as a limit.

IMPEDANCE AT RESONANCE

Another interesting and useful approximation formula for a high-Q parallel-resonant circuit is obtained by solving for the total impedance at resonance. But what is the total impedance of the circuit in Figure 15-9 when R is small? When we solve for Z_T with the approximate value of I_T given in Equation (15.18), we obtain

$$Z_T = Q\,\omega\,L \qquad \textbf{(15.19)}$$

Note particularly that parallel resonance was defined as the condition in which I_T is in phase with E. Accordingly, Z_T in Equation (15.19) is a pure resistance, and can be symbolized as R_T to denote this fact. The general manner in which the impedance of the circuit in Figure 15-9 varies with frequency is depicted in Figure 15-10. As previously explained, the impedance is inductive at frequencies below resonance, but is capacitive at frequencies above resonance.

Another useful equation for Z_T is obtained when we solve for the total impedance at resonance with the approximate value of I_T given in Equation (15.17). Algebraic manipulation yields

$$Z_T = \frac{L}{RC}, \text{ approximately} \qquad \textbf{(15.20)}$$

As before, since we have defined parallel resonance as the frequency at which I_T is in phase with E, we may symbolize Z_T as R_T in Equation (15.20).

The foregoing analysis of parallel resonance was based on the definition of circuit response as a pure resistance. This is the most widely used definition of parallel resonance. On the other hand, we shall find that I_T does not have its minimum value under this condition. The larger the value of R in Figure 15-9, the greater is the deviation from minimum line current when I_T is in phase with E. Therefore, parallel resonance is alternatively defined as the frequency at which the line current attains its lowest possible value. This resonant frequency is given by the formula

$$f = \frac{1}{2\pi}\sqrt{\frac{1}{LC} - \frac{R^4C}{2L^3}} \qquad \textbf{(15.21)}$$

Compare Equation (15.21) with Equation (15.15). We see that when R is comparatively small, either of these equations may be considered as equal to Equation (15.10) for practical applications. The resonant frequency given by Equation (15.15) is higher than given by Equation (15.21). This simply means that when the operating frequency is adjusted for minimum line current, the circuit in Figure 15-9 draws a lagging current.

It follows from foregoing discussion that when you adjust the operating frequency for in-phase line current, X_L is not equal to X_C. Neither is X_L equal to X_C when you adjust the operating frequency for minimum

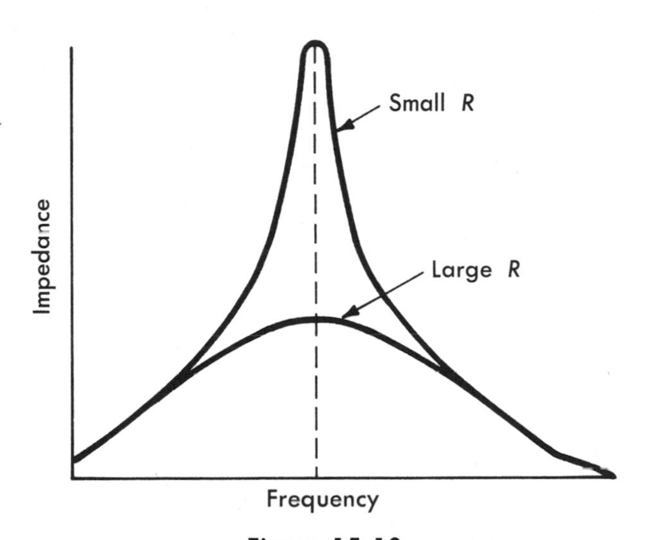

Figure 15-10
Impedance variation versus frequency for an *LCR* series-parallel circuit.

line current. However, there is a certain operating frequency at which X_L *will* be equal to X_C – this is the third definition of parallel resonance. Evidently, if we specify that X_L shall be equal to X_C, this parallel-resonant frequency will be given by Equation (15.10).

15.3 ANALYSIS OF GENERATOR RESISTANCE

The generator in Figure 15-9 is assumed to have zero internal resistance. In turn, the voltage across the two circuit branches is constant and equal to E, regardless of the operating frequency. On the other hand, I_T varies with frequency, because Z_T varies as depicted in Figure 15-10. Thus, I_T decreases to a minimum value at a frequency given by Equation

(15.21). The manner in which I_T varies with frequency is depicted in Figure 15-11.

Now, if the generator has substantial internal resistance, as depicted in Figure 15-12, the voltage across the two circuit branches does not remain constant as the operating frequency is varied. At resonance, the 80-K resistance works into a load resistance of $Q\omega L$, or 20,000 ohms. Hence, 0.2 of the source voltage, or 2 volts, appears at the output. However, at frequencies on either side of resonance, the 80-K resistor works into a lower impedance, and the output voltage is less. This type of circuit is widely used in electronic equipment to develop a maximum output

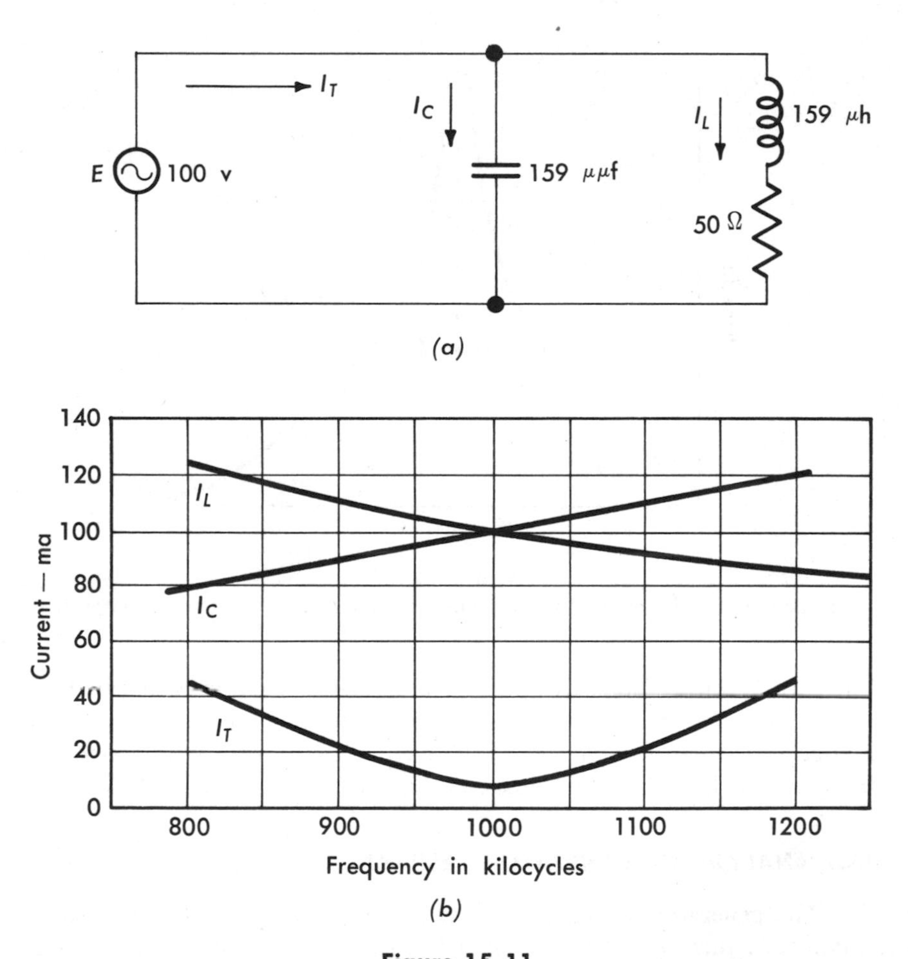

Figure 15-11

(a) The inductor has a Q value of 20 at a frequency of 1 mc. *(b)* Variation of I_T, I_L, and I_C versus frequency.

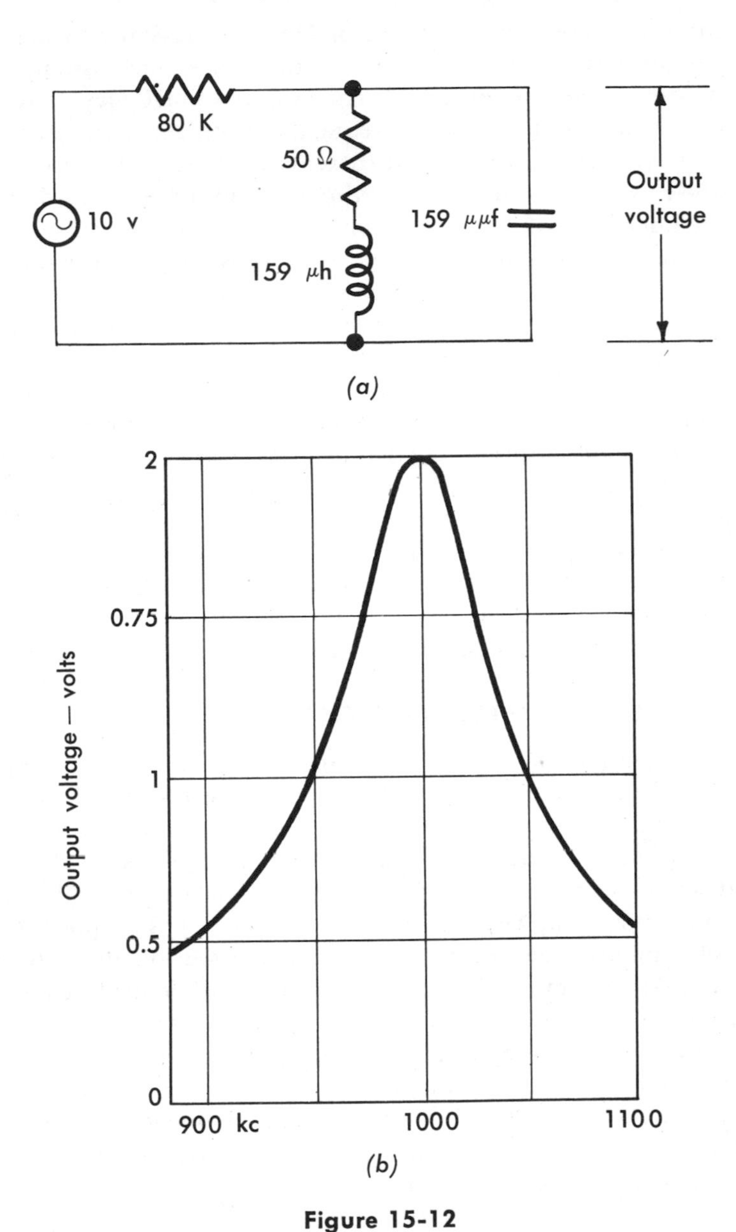

Figure 15-12
(a) Series-parallel *LCR* circuit with substantial generator resistance present. *(b)* Variation of output voltage versus frequency.

voltage at a desired frequency, and to thereby discriminate against unwanted frequencies.

Analytical solution of the circuit in Figure 15-12 starts by *assuming* some value of output voltage at a chosen frequency. Such assumption is necessary, because we do not know what output voltage may correspond to the source voltage at the chosen frequency. With this assumed voltage value, we next compute the branch currents and the total current as in Figure 15-11. Then, we divide the total current into the assumed voltage to find the impedance of the parallel combination at the chosen frequency. This impedance is combined with the 80-K resistance (Figure 15-12) to find the total circuit impedance. Ohm's law then gives the actual value of I_T. Finally, the product of I_T and the impedance of the parallel combination gives the output-voltage value.

Evidently, considerable labor in computation is required to make a point-by-point plot of a frequency-response curve as shown in Figure 15-12(*b*). Fortunately, this is seldom necessary in practical electronics work. We are usually concerned only with the resonant frequency, the impedance of the parallel combination at resonance, and the *bandwidth* of the frequency-response curve. In the great majority of situations, we use Equation (15.10) to find the resonant frequency. Likewise, we use Equation (15.19) to find the impedance of the parallel combination at resonance. The definition and calculation of bandwidth are explained next.

15.4 BANDWIDTH OF A RESONANT CIRCUIT

The basic definition of bandwidth applies to the frequency-response curves of both series and parallel resonant circuits, illustrated in Figure 15-13. Bandwidth is simply the number of cycles from f_1 to f_2, or $f_2 - f_1$. Note that f_1 and f_2 correspond to the 70.7 percent points on the curve. These two points are commonly called the *half-power points*. This terminology follows from the fact that when the response has dropped to 70.7 percent of maximum, the output power has decreased to half of its maximum value. Maximum output power, of course, is obtained at the resonant frequency f_0 in a series circuit.

An approximate formula is commonly used to calculate the bandwidth of a resonant circuit. This formula is satisfactory for any circuit with a reasonably high Q. Given the resonant frequency and the Q of the inductor at the resonant frequency in Figure 15-12, the bandwidth of the frequency-response curve will be

$$\text{Bandwidth} = \frac{f_0}{Q_0}, \text{ approximately} \tag{15.22}$$

where f_0 is the resonant frequency (Figure 15-13), Q_0 is the Q of the inductor at f_0, and the bandwidth is equal to $f_2 - f_1$.

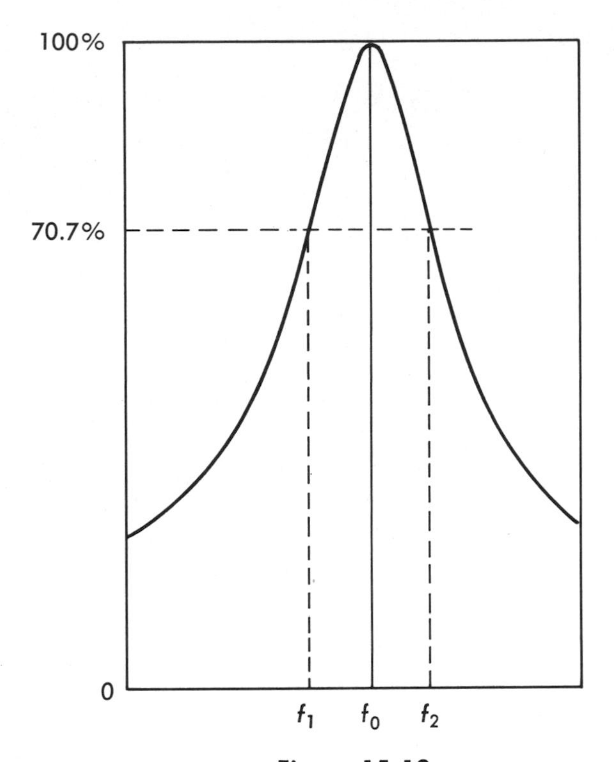

Figure 15-13
Basic definition of bandwidth for a resonant circuit.

Again, you may be given the resonant frequency and the frequency-response curve, but not the Q of the inductor. In such case (Figure 15-13), note the 70.7 percent points on the curve, and project down to find the values of f_1 and f_2. In turn, it follows from Equation (15.22) that the Q of the inductor will be

$$Q = \frac{f_0}{f_2 - f_1}, \text{ approximately} \tag{15.23}$$

where Q is the quality factor of the inductor in Figure 15-12 at the resonant frequency of the circuit.

15.5 ANALYSIS OF SHUNT RESISTANCE

We know that the Q of an inductor with resistance in series is equal to X_L/R. What is the Q of an inductor with resistance in parallel? The parallel combination has an equivalent series combination at the same frequency, as shown in Figure 15-14. Note that $Q = \tan \theta$, where θ is the

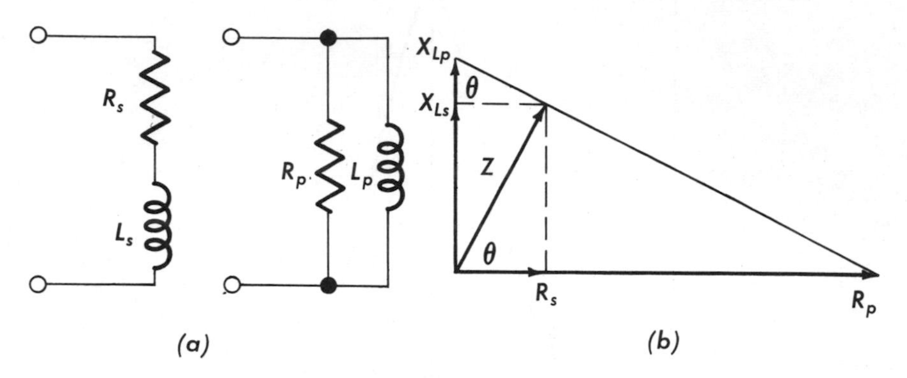

Figure 15-14
(a) Series and parallel *LR* circuits. *(b)* Impedance diagram for equivalent series and parallel *LR* circuits.

power-factor angle. In the equivalent parallel circuit, tan θ is given by R_p/X_{L_p}. Thus, we can write

$$Q = \frac{X_{L_s}}{R_s} = \frac{R_p}{X_{L_p}} \tag{15.24}$$

Equation (15.20) states that the circuit in Figure 15-15(*a*) has an input resistance at resonance that is approximately equal to $L/(R_sC)$. Note that the L and C combination in Figure 15-15(*b*) present an infinite impedance to the generator. Hence, the two circuits in Figure 15-15 are equivalent at their resonant frequency if

$$R_p = \frac{L}{R_sC}, \text{ approximately} \tag{15.25}$$

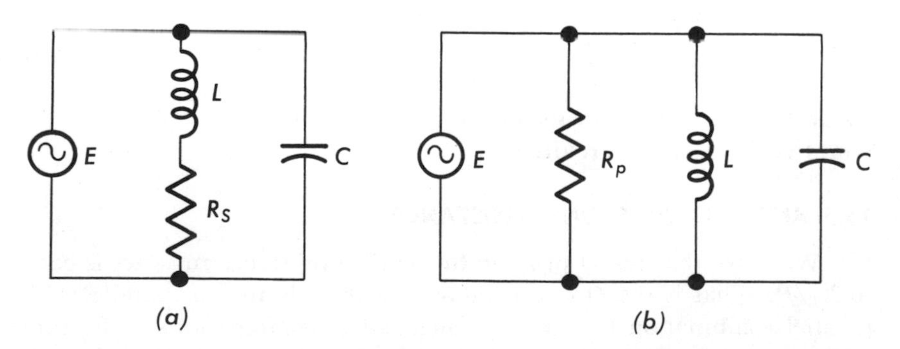

Figure 15-15
(a) Series-parallel configuration. *(b)* Equivalent circuit at resonant frequency.

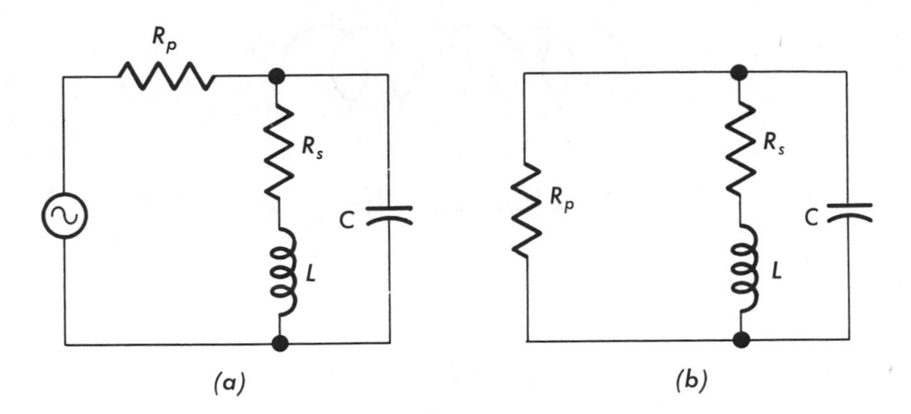

Figure 15-16
(a) Series-parallel configuration. *(b)* Equivalent circuit for calculation of Q value.

Next, consider the series-parallel circuit shown in Figure 15-16(*a*). Insofar as the Q value is concerned, R_p is effectively in shunt to the parallel branches, as depicted in Figure 15-16(*b*). Apply Equation (15.25) to the circuit in Figure 15-16(*b*) to change R_s into an equivalent parallel resistance. This gives us the equivalent circuit shown in Figure 15-17. At its resonant frequency, the impedance of this circuit is evidently equal to the resistance of R_p and $L/(R_sC)$ in parallel. Hence, the resonant impedance can be written

$$Z_T = \frac{1}{\dfrac{1}{R_p} + \dfrac{R_sC}{L}} \tag{15.26}$$

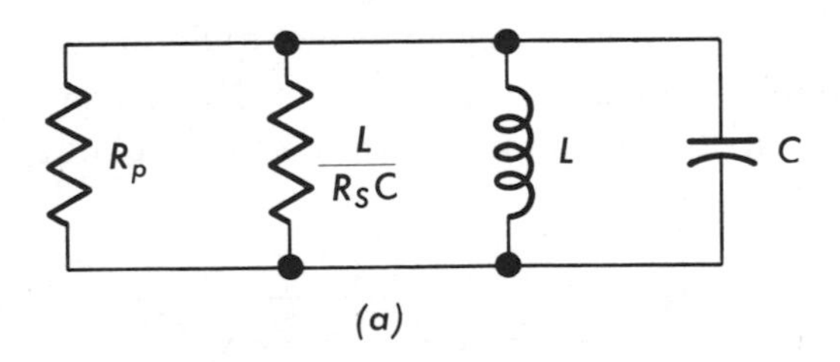

Figure 15-17
(a) An equivalent circuit for Figure 15-16(*b*). *(b)* Inductors have distributed capacitance between turns. *(c)* Equivalent circuit for an inductor. *(d)* The a-c resistance value increases with frequency. *(e)* Skin effect results from a variation of inductive reactance through the cross section of a conductor.

(Continued on page 402.)

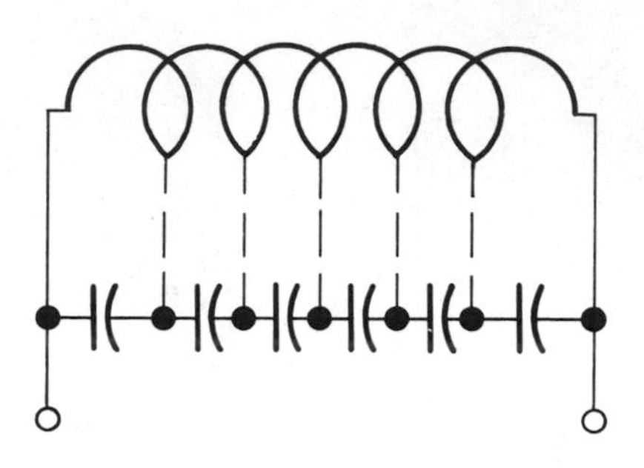

(b)

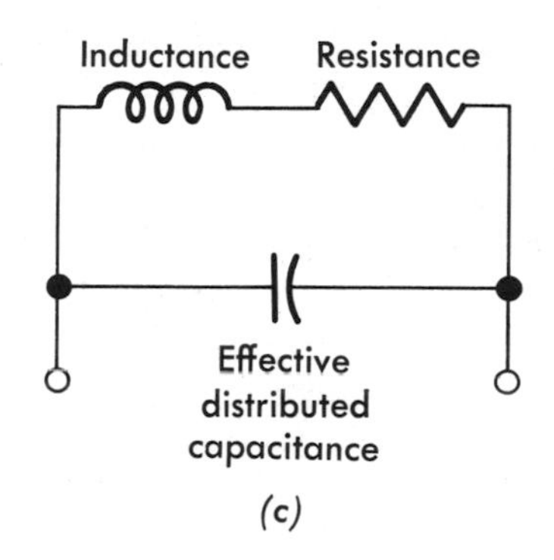

(c)

Fig. 15-17 (*Continued*)

(*Continued on facing page.*)

Since the resonant impedance is a pure resistance, we can symbolize Z_T as R_T. At resonance, $X_L = X_C$. Algebraic manipulation yields $X_L = \sqrt{L/C}$. From Equation (15.19) we know that $Q = R_T/X_L$; or, $Q = R_T\sqrt{C/L}$. Hence, the Q of the circuit in Figure 15-16(a) follows from Equation (15.26)

$$Q = \frac{1}{(1/R_p)\sqrt{L/C} + R_s\sqrt{C/L}} \qquad \textbf{(15.27)}$$

Equation (15.27) is approximate, of course, and has satisfactory accuracy when R_s is comparatively small and R_p is comparatively large. When R_p is very large, as is often the case in electronic circuitry, $1/R_p$ becomes very small and may be neglected in practical work. In this case, Equation (15.27) reduces to the simple form: $Q = 1/(R_s\sqrt{C/L})$.

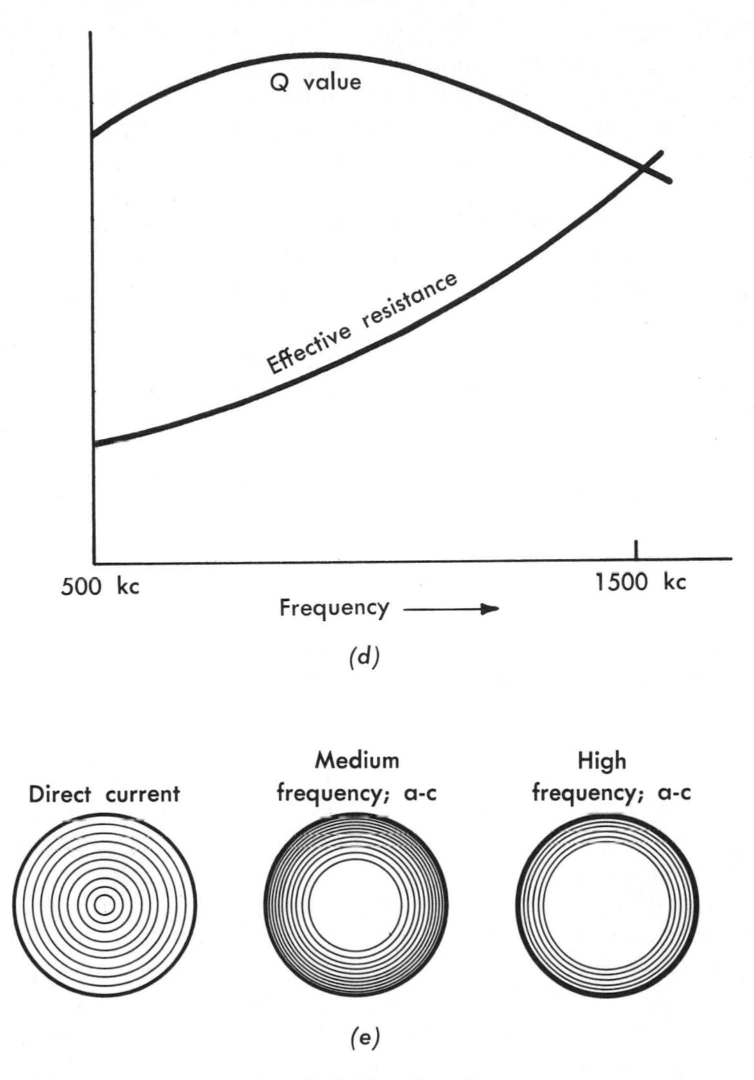

Fig. 15-17 (*Continued*)

DISTRIBUTED CAPACITANCE

Because all inductors have distributed capacitance between turns, as depicted in Figure 15-17(*b*), it follows that any inductor has a self-resonant frequency. This is a case of parallel resonance. It is interesting to note typical self-resonant frequencies of standard air-core inductors used in laboratories. A 1-mh inductor has a self-resonant frequency of 815 kc. This means that the 1-mh inductance is shunted by an effective distributed capacitance of approximately 39 $\mu\mu$f. Again, a 1-henry standard inductor has a self-resonant frequency of 16.6 kc. Its effective distributed capacitance is approximately 92 $\mu\mu$f.

The presence of distributed capacitance causes the inductor to have an impedance at its self-resonant frequency that is much greater than its inductive reactance. The inductor has an impedance at frequencies in the vicinity of resonance which is also substantially greater than its inductive reactance. In turn, when you wish to compare the inductance of a standard inductor with the inductance of an unknown inductor, you must utilize a test frequency far below the self-resonant frequency of either inductor. At low frequencies, practically all the current flows through the inductor, because the distributed capacitance then has an extremely high reactance in comparison with the inductive reactance.

We perceive that a standard inductor (or any inductor) has an equivalent circuit, shown in Figure 15-17(*c*). The winding resistance, or d-c resistance, of a 1-mh standard inductor is typically 0.89 ohm. At low frequencies, the a-c resistance of the inductor is practically the same as its d-c resistance. On the other hand, at high frequencies, the a-c resistance increases, as seen in Figure 15-17(*d*). Since inductive reactance is a linear function of frequency for an air-core coil, the Q value of the coil rises with frequency at first, attains a maximum value, and then falls with further increase of frequency. The effective resistance of a coil comprises its winding resistance and its a-c resistance.

Most of the a-c resistance is attributed to the "skin effect," depicted in Figure 15-17(*e*). When a conductor carries d-c current, magnetic flux is distributed uniformly through the cross-section of the conductor. Inductive reactance is zero at zero frequency. However, when the conductor carries a-c current, inductive reactance is present. The value of the inductive reactance increases as the frequency increases. We perceive that the inductive reactance is greatest at the center of the conductor cross-section, because the center point is surrounded by a maximum number of flux lines. In turn, the center of the conductor has greater opposition to a-c current flow than the surface of the conductor. This means that a-c current is forced away from the center toward the surface. Less of the conductor cross-section is then available for current flow, or, the a-c resistance increases with frequency.

The a-c resistance of a coil increases with frequency also because of dielectric losses in the insulating material. Dielectric losses also increase with frequency. If there are metal structures in the field of the coil, such as mounting brackets, chassis, or a shield, the a-c resistance is further increased because of eddy-current losses. Thus, the a-c resistance of a coil is an involved function of frequency which is usually difficult to calculate. Engineers measure the a-c resistance of coils indirectly; the inductance of an air-coil can be easily measured with an impedance bridge, and its

Q value can be measured at a chosen frequency with a Q meter. From these measured values, the a-c resistance can be calculated at the chosen frequency.

15.6 TROUBLESHOOTING SERIES-PARALLEL CIRCUITS

Defects in series-parallel circuits are analyzed in the same general ways which have been explained for series circuits and parallel circuits. For example, if there were little or no output voltage from the circuit shown in Figure 15-12, we would proceed to make a-c voltage measurements. A generator defect will result in little or no source voltage. If the 80-K resistor is open, there will be no voltage drop across the parallel combination. On the other hand, the same symptom can be caused by a short-circuited capacitor. If the capacitor is suspect, one end is disconnected, and an ohmmeter test is made of its insulation resistance.

Note that the 50-ohm resistor can be checked without disconnection. Its value is very much smaller than that of the 80-K resistor. Hence, an ohmmeter test can be made of the 50-ohm resistor without disconnection. Similarly, the inductor can be checked for a possible "open" without disconnection. The terminal resistance of the inductor is normally very low (this resistance might be as high as 50 ohms, if the 50-ohm resistor in Figure 15-12 is regarded as winding resistance). But if the inductor is open, its terminal resistance will measure 80-K ohms.

Short-circuited turns or layers in the inductor are somewhat more elusive. Technicians commonly measure the resonant frequency of the parallel combination with a grid-dip meter. If a resonant frequency higher than 1000 kc were measured in the configuration of Figure 15-12, suspicion would fall upon both the inductor and the capacitor. Shorted turns or layers in the inductor reduce its inductance value. On the other hand, loss of capacitance or a complete open in the capacitor also increases the resonant frequency. Hence, if a test with a capacitor checker shows that the capacitor has its rated capacitance, it is concluded that the inductor is defective.

Another troubleshooting method is often used by experienced technicians. The generator depicted in Figure 15-12 is disconnected, and a sweep-frequency generator used in its place. As its name indicates, the sweep-frequency generator applies a voltage which varies or "sweeps" over a band of frequencies periodically. This type of waveform is illustrated in Figure 15-18. In the example under discussion, the generator would be set to sweep over a frequency band from approximately 900 kc to 1100 kc. A typical sweep-frequency generator is illustrated in Figure 15-19.

An oscilloscope is connected across the output terminals of the circuit. In turn, the frequency-response curve for the configuration is automatically

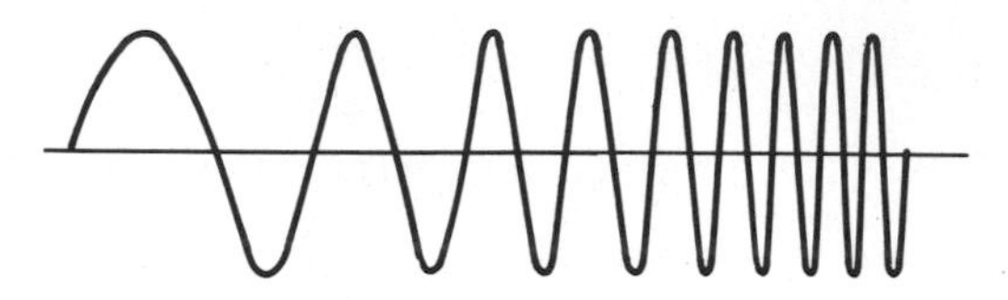

Figure 15-18
A sine wave which is "swept" in frequency.

displayed on the screen of the oscilloscope; hence, the curve depicted in Figure 15-12(*b*) appears as a waveform on the oscilloscope screen. This introductory discussion necessarily omits various details which are essential in practical troubleshooting procedures. Detailed study of sweep-generator operation and application is best made in the laboratory phase of your electronics courses.

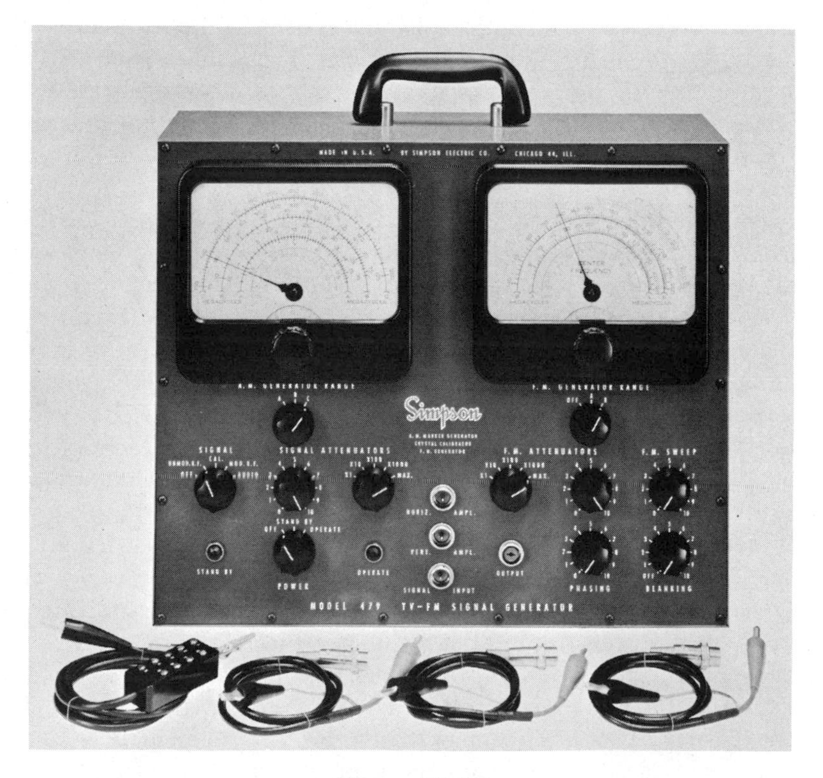

Figure 15-19
Appearance of a typical sweep-frequency generator. (Courtesy of Simpson Electric Co.)

SUMMARY OF FUNDAMENTAL CONCEPTS

Ohm's law applies to a complete series-parallel circuit, to each component in the circuit, and to combinations of two or more components.

Power is consumed only by the resistance in an *LCR* circuit.

Power is stored and returned by reactance in an *LCR* circuit.

Real power and reactive power are added in quadrature to obtain volt-amperes.

Kirchhoff's voltage law applies to series-parallel circuits; resistive and reactive voltage drops are added in quadrature.

Kirchhoff's current law applies to series-parallel *LCR* circuits; resistive and reactive currents are added in quadrature.

A branch current through inductance or capacitance in a parallel-resonant circuit is approximately *Q* times the line current.

A resonant rise of voltage across a parallel-resonant circuit occurs if the generator has appreciable internal resistance.

Three parallel-resonant frequencies are defined for series *L* and *R* shunted by capacitance:

Line voltage and current in phase:

$$f = \frac{1}{2\pi}\sqrt{\frac{1}{LC} - \frac{R^2}{L^2}}$$

Line current minimum:

$$f = \frac{1}{2\pi}\sqrt{\frac{1}{LC} - \frac{R^4C}{2L^3}}$$

$X_L = X_C$:

$$f = \frac{1}{2\pi}\sqrt{\frac{1}{LC}}$$

QUESTIONS

1) A series-parallel configuration can be reduced to an equivalent series circuit:
(*a*) at all frequencies of operation. (*b*) at a single frequency of operation. (*c*) at any frequency less than zero. (*d*) at any chosen pair of frequencies.
2) A series-parallel LCR circuit with R in series with L, has:
(*a*) three basic resonant frequencies. (*b*) a resonant rise of voltage across its inductor. (*c*) the same resonant impedance as a series circuit which comprises the same LCR values. (*d*) zero impedance at its lowest resonant frequency.
3) When a capacitor is connected in parallel with an inductor that has a small winding resistance, each of the branch currents at resonance is approximately equal:
(*a*) to the line current divided by the Q of the inductor. (*b*) to one-half the line current. (*c*) to the product of the line current and the Q of the inductor. (*d*) the source voltage divided by the winding resistance.
4) With reference to Question 3, the impedance of the LCR circuit at resonance is approximately equal to:
(*a*) the product of the inductive reactance and the Q of the inductor. (*b*) RC/L. (*c*) R/CL. (*d*) C/RL.
5) When a resistance R is connected in parallel with a coil L, the Q value of the circuit becomes:
(*a*) X_L/R. (*b*) $1/2\pi fL$. (*c*) R/X_L. (*d*) $R + jX_L$.
6) The bandwidth of a parallel-resonant circuit in which the inductor has a small winding resistance is given approximately by:
(*a*) the Q of the inductor divided by the resonant frequency. (*b*) the resonant frequency divided by the Q of the inductor. (*c*) the Q of the inductor multiplied by the resonant frequency. (*d*) the number of cycles between the half-power points divided by the resonant frequency.
7) The impedance of parallel-resonant circuit at its resonant frequency is directly proportional to:
(*a*) the value of the source voltage. (*b*) the C/L ratio. (*c*) the L/C ratio. (*d*) the reluctance of the inductor core.
8) The impedance of a parallel-resonant circuit at its resonant frequency is inversely proportional to:
(*a*) the resistance in series with the inductor. (*b*) the source voltage. (*c*) the dielectric coefficient of the capacitor. (*d*) the permeability of the inductor core.

9) If an ideal inductor is connected in parallel with an ideal capacitor, the current which flows at the resonant frequency is equal to:
(*a*) the source voltage divided by the source resistance. (*b*) the impedance of the parallel combination divided by the source voltage. (*c*) the inductive reactance divided by the capacitive reactance. (*d*) zero.

10) If it is desired to display the frequency-response curve of an *LCR* circuit on an oscilloscope screen, the source voltage will be obtained from:
(*a*) a 117-volt 60-cycle power line. (*b*) a storage battery. (*c*) a signal generator. (*d*) a sweep-frequency generator.

PROBLEMS

1) A 159-μh inductor with an effective resistance of 707 ohms is connected in parallel with a 159-$\mu\mu$f capacitor. Calculate the parallel-resonant frequency for which the line current is in phase with the applied voltage.
2) Calculate the parallel-resonant frequency in Problem 1 for which the line current is minimum.
3) Calculate the parallel-resonant frequency in Problem 1 for which X_L has the same value as X_C.
4) What is the Q of the inductor in Problem 1? If the source voltage is 10 volts, what is the approximate line current?
5) What is the ratio of the current through the inductor to the line current?
6) What is the approximate impedance of the parallel combination in Problem 1?
7) What is the approximate bandwith of the frequency-response curve in Problem 1?
8) If the voltage source has a value of 10 volts and an internal resistance of 0.5 megohm, what is the approximate voltage across the parallel combination in Problem 1?
9) If an ideal 159-μh inductor and a capacitor are connected in parallel with a 500-ohm resistor, what is the Q value of the parallel combination if the capacitor resonates the circuit at 1 mc?
10) The parallel combination in Problem 1 is connected to a generator that has an internal resistance of 707 ohms. Calculate the approximate Q of this series-parallel circuit.
11) What is the approximate voltage across the parallel combination in Problem 10, at 1 mc if the generator has an emf of 10 volts?

12) How much power is dissipated in the internal resistance of the generator in Problem 11 at 1 mc?
13) How much power is dissipated in the effective winding resistance of the inductor in Problem 11 at 1 mc?
14) If the capacitor is connected in series with the inductor in Problem 1, what is the impedance of the series configuration at its resonant frequency? What is the ratio of this series-resonant impedance to the parallel-resonant impedance which was previously calculated?

REVIEW SUMMARY

Chapters 9 through 15 have been concerned with the laws of alternating-current electricity. The following review summary presents the basic laws with which you should now be familiar.

1. Mechanical energy is changed into electrical energy when a conductor cuts magnetic flux lines.

2. Lenz' law is a right-hand rule which states that if your forefinger points in the direction of magnetic flux lines, and your thumb points in the direction that the conductor moves, your middle finger will point in the direction of induced (conventional) current flow.

3. One volt is induced in a conductor which cuts 10^8 lines of magnetic flux per sec.

4. A conductor that revolves at a constant rate in a uniform magnetic field generates a sinusoidal waveform of voltage.

5. The average value of a half-sine wave of voltage is numerically equal to a d-c voltage which produces equal deflection of the pointer on a d-c voltmeter scale.

6. A half-sine wave has an average value which is equal to 0.636 of its peak value.

7. Half-sine waves have an effective value which is equal to a d-c value that dissipates the same amount of power in a reference load resistance.

8. A half-sine wave has an effective value equal to 0.707 of its peak value.

9. The peak-to-peak value of a sine wave is equal to 2.83 times its rms value.

10. All alternators and generators obey the law of conservation of energy.

11. The stored charge in a capacitor (in coulombs) is equal to the product of the applied voltage in volts and the capacitance value in farads.

12. A capacitor has a capacitance of 1 farad if it stores 1 coulomb when 1 volt is applied to its terminals.

13. If a d-c voltage is switched into an RC series circuit, current flow obeys the exponential law of decay.

14. The time constant of an RC series circuit (in seconds) is equal to the circuit resistance (in ohms) multiplied by the circuit capacitance (in farads).

15. A capacitor in a sine-wave circuit has a reactance in ohms equal to $1/(2\pi fC)$, where f is expressed in cycles per second and C is expressed in farads.

16. Sine-wave current flow "through" a capacitor leads the applied sine-wave voltage by 90 degrees.

17. The power factor of a capacitor is zero; the power factor of a resistor is 1.

18. No real power is dissipated by a capacitor; only reactive power is present in the capacitor. The stored energy in a capacitor is equal to $0.5CE^2$ joules.

19. An inductor generates a counter emf whenever current flow changes through the inductor; a coil has an inductance of 1 henry if a change in current flow at the rate of 1 amp per sec produces a change of 1 volt per sec across the coil.

20. If a d-c voltage is switched into an RL series circuit, current flow obeys the exponential law of growth.

21. The time constant of an LR series circuit (in seconds) is equal to the circuit inductance (in henrys) divided by the circuit resistance (in ohms).

22. An inductor in a sine-wave circuit has a reactance in ohms equal to $2\pi fL$, where f is expressed in cycles per second and L is expressed in henrys.

23. Sine-wave current flow through an inductor lags the applied sine-wave voltage by 90 degrees.

24. The power factor of an inductor (with pure inductance) is zero.

25. No real power is dissipated by an inductor (with pure inductance); only reactive power is present in the inductor. The stored energy in an inductor is equal to $0.5LI^2$ joules.

26. Ohm's law for a-c (with sine-wave voltage applied) states that $I = E/X$.

27. Power in an a-c circuit is equal to $EI \cos \theta$, where the power is expressed in watts, sine-wave current and voltage are expressed in rms values, and $\cos \theta$ is the power factor of the circuit.

28. The impedance of a reactive circuit expressed in ohms is equal to the square root of the sum of the squares of circuit reactance and circuit resistance, expressed in ohms.

29. A reactive circuit has a power factor, equal to the real power consumed by the circuit divided by the volt-amperes applied to the circuit.

30. Real power, reactive power, and volt-amperes combine vectorially to form a right triangle.

31. The locus of operation of an RC or LR circuit is a semicircle.

32. Every reactive parallel circuit can be reduced to an equivalent reactive series circuit at a chosen frequency of operation.

33. An ideal constant-current source supplies the same value of current to any load.

34. The impedance of an *LCR* series circuit in ohms is equal to $R + j(X_L - X_C)$, where X_L and X_C are expressed in ohms.

35. The resonant frequency of an *LCR* series circuit in cycles per sec is equal to $1/(2\pi\sqrt{LC})$, where L is expressed in henrys and C is expressed in farads.

36. Q, the quality factor of an inductor, is equal to X_L/R, where X_L is the inductive reactance at a chosen frequency and R is the effective resistance of the inductor, both measured in ohms.

37. The Q value of an *LCR* series circuit is equal to the inductive reactance of the circuit at a chosen frequency, divided by the total effective resistance of the circuit, both measured in ohms.

38. At resonance, there is a resonant rise of voltage across the inductor and across the capacitor in a series *LCR* circuit which is equal to QE, where E is the source voltage.

39. The Q value of an *LCR* series resonant circuit is equal to $f_0/(f_2 - f_1)$, where f_0 is the resonant frequency, and f_2 and f_1 are the frequencies of the half-power points.

40. A series-resonant circuit has minimum impedance at its resonant frequency.

41. A parallel-resonant circuit has three possible frequencies of resonance; these are the frequencies at which the line current is in phase with the source voltage, at which the circuit has maximum impedance, and at which the inductive reactance is equal to the capacitive reactance.

42. At resonance, the current flow through the capacitor and the current flow through the inductor is approximately equal to Q times the line current in a parallel-resonant circuit.

43. The Q of a parallel-resonant circuit that contains no parallel resistance is equal to the Q of the inductor (assuming that the capacitor is ideal).

44. If inductance and resistance are connected in parallel, the Q value follows from the equivalent series circuit for the combination.

16

TRANSFORMER PRINCIPLES

16.1 TRANSFORMER FUNCTIONS

Transformers are used for a number of purposes in modern electronic equipment. For example, a tapped inductor, or *autotransformer,* is used to step a-c voltage, a-c current, and impedances up or down. Figure 16-1 illustrates these three functions. A tapped inductor such as depicted in

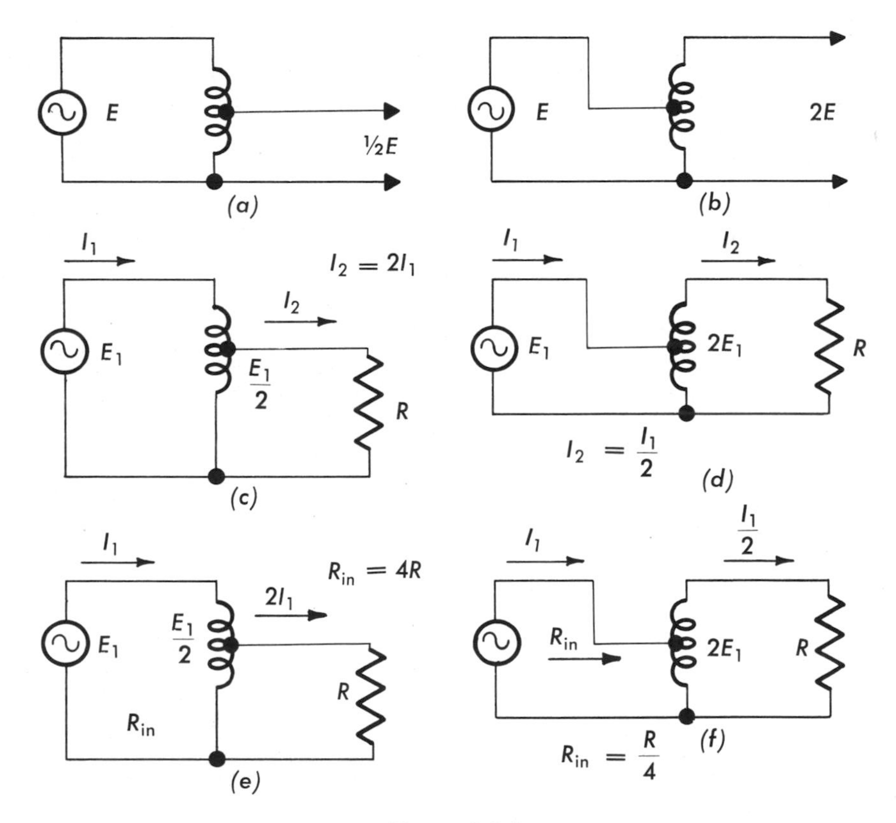

Figure 16-1

(a) Center-tapped inductor. *(b)* Reversal of input and output terminals. *(c)* Current step-up. *(d)* Current step-down. *(e)* Alternating-current resistance step-down. *(f)* Alternating-current resistance step-up.

Figure 16-1(*a*) can be compared with a potentiometer; that is, it operates as a voltage divider. Since the magnetic field in the coil has the same value throughout, the same voltage is induced in each turn of the coil as the field expands and collapses. Hence, if the inductor is tapped at its center point, as in Figure 16-1(*a*), the output voltage is equal to one-half the value of the input voltage.

There is a basic difference, however, between the autotransformer shown in Figure 16-1(*a*) and a potentiometer. A potentiometer is a resistance that consumes power at all times. When zero current is drawn from the arm of a potentiometer, the resistance element still consumes power from the source. On the other hand, an ideal inductor consumes no real power. Accordingly, when an autotransformer is unloaded, as in Figure 16-1(*a*), it consumes no power from the source. Hence, the theoretical efficiency of an autotransformer can be 100 percent, provided the inductor has zero winding resistance, and the voltage source has zero internal resistance.

But a potentiometer cannot have 100 percent efficiency, even if the voltage source has zero internal resistance. Hence, when you make laboratory experiments that require an adjustable a-c voltage source, you will probably use an autotransformer with a slider arm, as depicted in Figure 16-2. This particular arrangement provides a 60-cycle output voltage that is adjustable from zero to 117 volts. Its efficiency is very high, compared with the efficiency provided by a resistive potentiometer. The efficiency of an autotransformer might be 90 percent. The 10 percent loss in efficiency stems from I^2R heat dissipation in the winding resistance, and from minor factors which are discussed subsequently.

Next, observe the autotransformer configuration shown in Figure 16-1(*b*). Here the autotransformer terminals have been reversed. Input voltage is applied to half of the inductor turns. Since the magnetic field established by the input must cut all the turns of the inductor, and induce equal voltage in each turn, it is clear that the output voltage must be twice the value of the input voltage. We call the arrangement in Figure 16-1(*b*) a *step-up* transformer. This terminology implies that the input

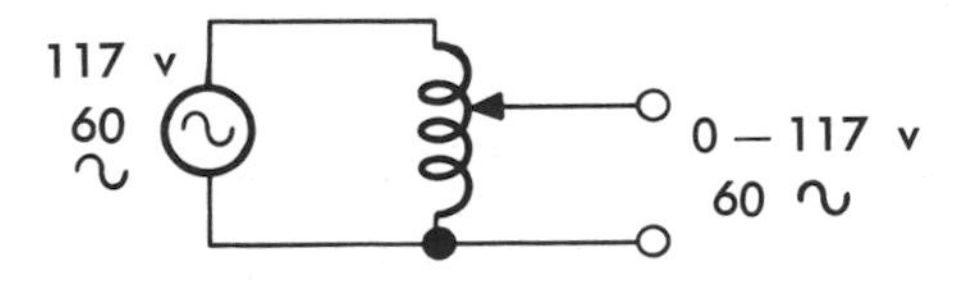

Figure 16-2
Adjustable autotransformer.

voltage is stepped up to a higher value. On the other hand, we call the arrangement in Figure 16-1(*a*) a *step-down* transformer.

The arrangement shown in Figure 16-1(*b*) is highly efficient; moreover, it performs a function that a potentiometer cannot. Evidently, if you substitute a tapped resistance for the tapped inductor in Figure 16-1(*b*), no step-up of voltage occurs. A potentiometer will provide an output voltage equal to the input voltage. Furthermore, a considerable amount of power will be wasted as I^2R heat loss in the potentiometer resistance. Autotransformers that are used as variable-voltage sources in laboratories often have the construction shown in Figure 16-3. It is clear that the slider arm can be set to provide an output voltage that is less than, equal to, or greater than the input voltage.

Observe the configuration depicted in Figure 16-1(*c*). A load resistance R is connected across the output terminals of a step-down autotransformer. Let us analyze the input and output current relation. First, we know that the center-tapped inductor supplies an output voltage which is equal to one-half the value of the input voltage; or, the autotransformer applies a voltage $E_1/2$ to the resistance R. Ohm's law states that $I_2 = E_1/(2R)$. What is the value of power consumed by R? Let us call this power value W_2. Hence, $W_2 = I_2E_1/2$.

CURRENT TRANSFORMATION

Now, if the inductor is ideal, the input power must be equal to the output power. In other words, energy can neither be created nor destroyed. We call the input power value W_1; then, $W_1 = W_2$, and W_1 is obviously equal to E_1I_1. Thus, $E_1I_1 = I_2E_1/2$. When we solve for I_1, we obtain $I_1 = I_2/2$. We see that the system in Figure 16-1(c) *steps down* the voltage as it *steps up* the current; therefore, a *voltage step-down transformer* is also a *current step-up transformer*. It is clear that we can write a general transformer equation as

$$E_1I_1 = E_2I_2 \tag{16.1}$$

where E_1 and I_1 are the input voltage and current values, and E_2 and I_2 are the output voltage and current values.

In the arrangement shown in Figure 16-1(*d*), we have a voltage step-up transformer that is necessarily a current step-down transformer. If you make the same type of analysis as for the configuration in Figure 16-1(*c*), you will perceive that Equation (16.1) applies also to Figure 16-1(*d*). In most laboratory experiments, we are concerned primarily with stepping a voltage up or down. There are various applications, however, in which we are concerned primarily with transforming current values. For example, if resistance R in Figure 16-1(*c*) should be an arc in an arc-welding unit, you will require a very large current flow. In this case, you would

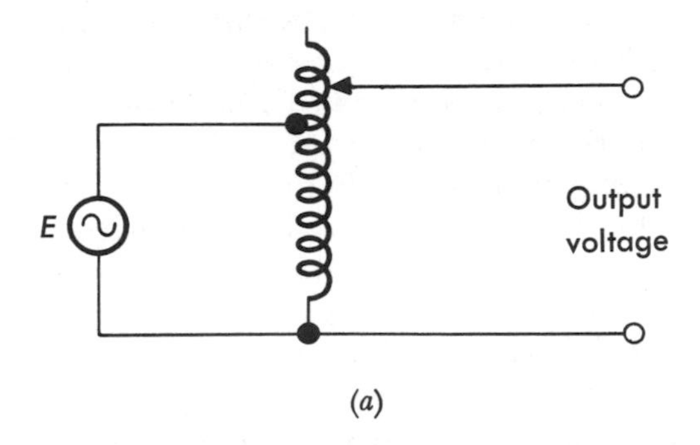

(a)

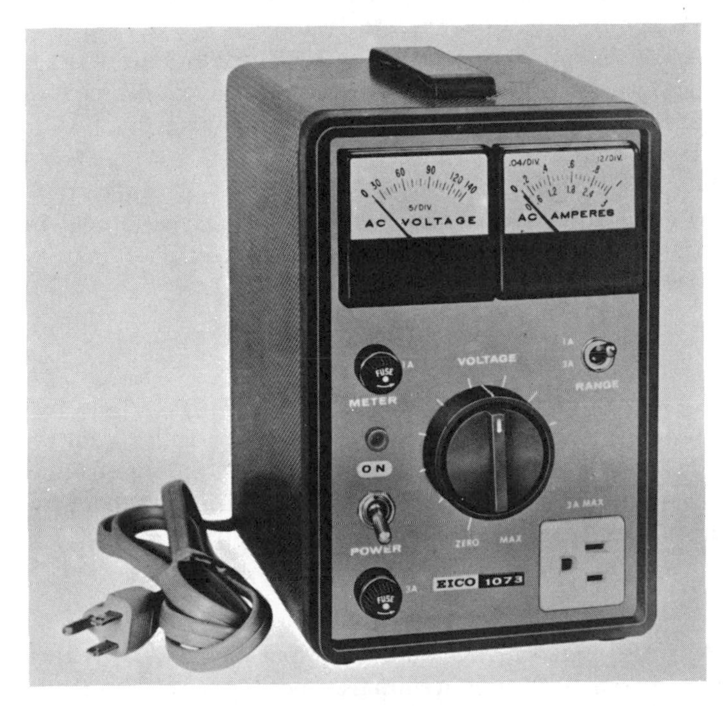

(b)

Figure 16-3

(a) Autotransformer which provides an output voltage less than, equal to, or greater than the input voltage. *(b)* A variable autotransformer with a-c voltage and current meters. (Courtesy of Electronic Instrument Co.)

use an arc-welding transformer which steps up the input current to a very high value.

We understand how a transformer can step voltage or current values up or down. Next, let us see how a transformer can step resistance values up or down. In this procedure, we are concerned only with a-c resistance values; a transformer cannot step d-c resistance values up or down. A transformer cannot be operated from a d-c source because the reactance of an inductor is zero when the frequency of operation is zero. Direct current has zero frequency. Alternating-current resistance is often called impedance, but it is clearly a special case of impedance in which the reactance term is equal to zero. (Reactance can also be transformed.)

Observe the current and voltage relations depicted in Figure 16-1(*e*). Ohm's law defines the value of R as a voltage/current ratio: $R = (E_1/2)/(2I_1)$. Note that the generator "sees" a resistance R_{in} which Ohm's law defines as E_1/I_1. Algebraic substitution yields $R_{in} = 4\,R$. Hence, the center-tapped inductor in Figure 16-1(*e*) has stepped up the load resistance R to an input a-c resistance R_{in} which is four times as great. In this case, we describe the tapped inductor as an *impedance step-down transformer*; the a-c resistance at the input terminals is stepped down to a lower a-c resistance at the output terminals.

The voltage ratio from input to output of an autotransformer is evidently equal to the turns ratio, because the magnetic field in the inductor induces equal voltage in each turn. Thus, we may write the general equation

$$\frac{E_2}{E_1} = \frac{N_2}{N_1} \tag{16.2}$$

where E_2 is the voltage across the output terminals, E_1 is the voltage across the input terminals, N_2 is the number of turns between the output terminals, and N_1 is the number of turns between the input terminals.

On the other hand, the current ratio from input to output of an autotransformer is equal to the inverse ratio of turns:

$$\frac{I_2}{I_1} = \frac{N_1}{N_2} \tag{16.3}$$

where I_2 is the ouput current, I_1 is the input current, N_1 is the number of turns between the input terminals, and N_2 is the number of turns between the output terminals.

IMPEDANCE TRANSFORMATION

Furthermore, the impedance ratio from input to output of an autotransformer is evidently equal to the square of the turns ratio:

$$\frac{Z_2}{Z_1} = \frac{N_2^2}{N_1^2} \tag{16.4}$$

where Z_2 is the output impedance (or resistance), Z_1 is the input impedance (or resistance), N_2 is the number of turns between the output terminals, and N_1 is the number of turns between the input terminals.

The arrangement shown in Figure 16-1(*f*) is called an impedance

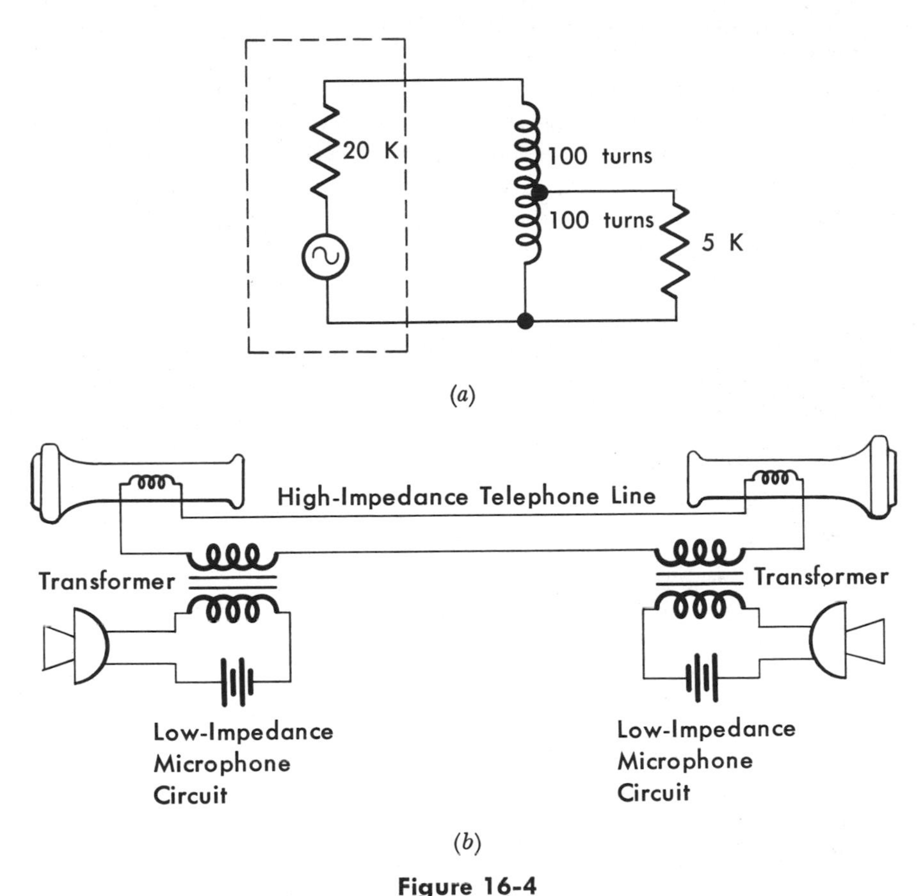

Figure 16-4
(a) A circuit autotransformer, providing maximum power transfer. (b) Transformers are used to match impedances in telephone systems.

step-up transformer. The load resistance R appears at the input terminals as a resistance value equal to $R/4$. Otherwise stated, the a-c resistance present at the input terminals is stepped up four times at the output terminals. Why would you use a transformer to step an impedance (or a-c resistance) up or down? The chief reason is to obtain maximum power transfer. An example is seen in Figure 16-4. Here the generator has an internal resistance of 20,000 ohms. We know that maximum power will be transferred if the load resistance also has a value of 20,000 ohms; however, the load resistance has a value of only 5000 ohms. If we use a suitable impedance step-down transformer, the generator sees an input resistance of 20,000 ohms, and in turn, maximum power is transferred to the 5000-ohm load resistance. The load is then said to be *matched* to the source.

An important and common example of impedance transformation is depicted in Figure 16-4(*b*). Telephone lines that are strung on poles have a comparatively high characteristic impedance. Yet, carbon microphones have a comparatively low internal resistance. In turn, power transfer from a microphone to a line is poor, unless matching transformers are utilized. However, a transformer with suitable turns ratio, as stated by Equation (16.4), provides maximum power transfer. It is clear that the primary must have fewer turns than the secondary in this application. Thus, the microphone sees a low impedance into the primary, and the line sees a high impedance into the secondary.

If the microphone has an internal resistance of 20 ohms, and the line has a characteristic impedance of 1000 ohms, the required turns ratio is approximately 7.1 to 1. With maximum power transfer, one-half of the power generated by the microphone is transferred to the line. The efficiency, therefore, is 50 percent. Half of the generated power is dissipated as heat in the internal resistance of the microphone. You will recall that the same general principles were developed in Chapter 4 for d-c circuits. Thus, maximum power transfer in either a-c or d-c systems is accomplished at an efficiency of 50 percent. Since the power level on a telephone line is comparatively low, this mediocre efficiency is not of great concern. The chief concern is to obtain maximum power transfer, and thereby utilize the low power output of the microphone to best advantage.

DIRECT-CURRENT ISOLATION

Another important function of a transformer is to isolate an output circuit from d-c voltage or current. In this application, an autotransformer is unsuitable. A transformer with separate primary and secondary windings must be used, as exemplified in Figure 16-5. Note that the source voltage consists of a 10-volt 1-kc generator connected in series with a 6-volt battery. The 12-ohm resistance might be the internal resistance of the generator. Although both a-c voltage and d-c voltage are applied to the primary winding, only the a-c voltage appears across the secondary terminals. It is obvious that there can be no d-c transfer from primary to secondary.

Let us analyze the configuration in Figure 16-5 a bit more closely. An iron-cored transformer is depicted, as is customary for use at comparatively low frequencies. If we assume the transformer to be ideal, which is often justified in practical circumstances, all of the magnetic flux produced by the primary winding threads through the secondary and cuts the turns in the secondary winding. It follows from our knowledge of magnetic circuits that the voltage induced in the secondary will be equal to the voltage applied across the primary.

What is the voltage applied across the primary? First, the 6-volt battery drives a current of 0.5 amp through the primary winding. But since the primary was assumed to have no winding resistance, there is no

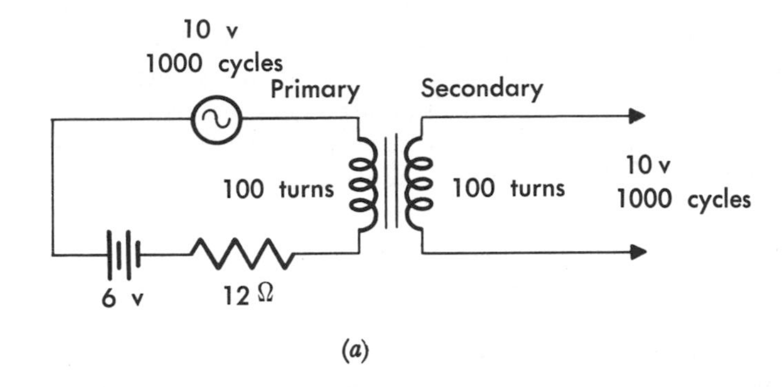

(a)

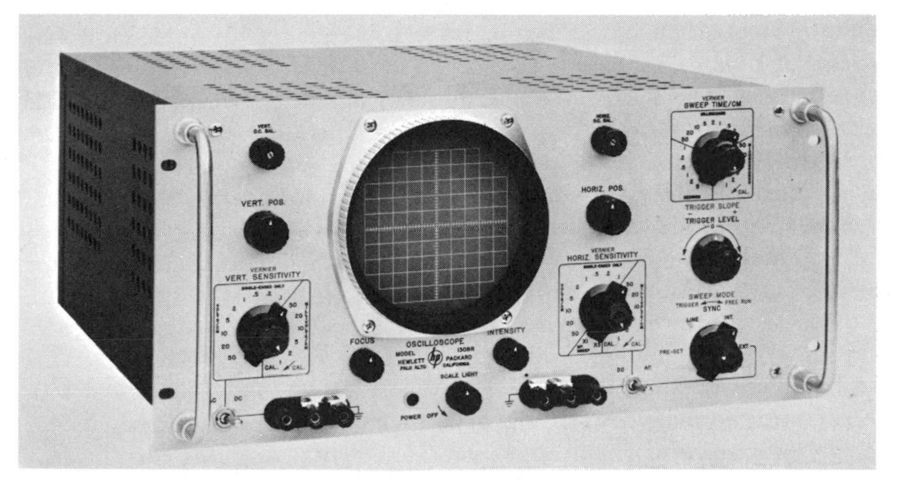

(b)

Figure 16-5

(a) The transformer provides d-c isolation. (b) An oscilloscope which can be used with suitable auxiliary equipment to display the *B-H* curve of a transformer core. (Courtesy of Hewlett-Packard Co.)

d-c voltage drop across the primary terminals. Even if the primary had a substantial winding resistance, the resulting d-c voltage drop could not be transformed, because a steady magnetic flux cannot induce a voltage in the secondary winding. Next, the a-c generator applies its voltage to the primary winding through the 12-ohm resistance. Observe that the reactance of the primary winding will be extremely large, compared with 12 ohms. Hence, for all practical purposes, we can assume that the voltage drop across the primary terminals is 10 volts. In turn, the voltage drop across the secondary winding will be approximately 10 volts.

If you connect a 12-ohm resistance across the secondary terminals in Figure 16-5, the 12-ohm resistance in the primary circuit becomes significant. From previous discussion, it is evident that this is the same situation as if you connected the generator in series with two 12-ohm resistances. Hence, the voltage across each of these resistances becomes 5 volts at 1 kc. This is a practical example of the fact that a loaded transformer provides reduced output voltage. It is quite easy to calculate the secondary voltage for any value of secondary load resistance in the configuration of Figure 16-5.

16.2 TRANSFORMER REACTANCE

It is interesting and important to consider the reactance of transformer windings. Since the windings are coils, they have inductive reactance. Hence, it might seem puzzling at first glance to understand why a resistance connected across the secondary terminals is transformed to a pure resistance at the primary terminals. Actually, the answer is quite simple. In Figure 16-4, we assume that the operating frequency is sufficiently high that the inductive reactance of the transformer is very high; E/X_L can be neglected in practical work. Therefore, when the 5-kilohm resistance is disconnected, the generator can drive practically no current through the very high inductive reactance. We can also say that the no-load current of the transformer is practically zero.

Next, when we connect the 5-kilohm resistance to the autotransformer, as in Figure 16-4, a voltage is applied across the resistor. Since the 5-kilohm resistor demands in-phase current, it draws in-phase current from the autotransformer. In turn, the generator must supply in-phase current to the autotransformer. Since the generator is supplying this current, it is readily apparent that the 5-kilohm resistance connected across the output terminals is transformed to an effective 20-kilohm resistance at the input terminals of the autotransformer.

If a transformer draws appreciable current from the generator under no-load conditions, its efficiency becomes less. Hence, a sufficient number of primary turns are customarily used to reduce the no-load current to a negligible value. Accordingly, the number of secondary turns will depend upon the number of primary turns with respect to the turns ratio which is required for the particular application. Evidently, if a transformer is to be used at an operating frequency of 60 cycles, high efficiency requires that the primary have a greater number of turns than if the transformer is to be used at an operating frequency of 1000 cycles. It is not good practice, nor is it economical to use more primary turns than are required to bring the no-load current to a desired minimum. An excessive number of primary turns impose an excessive winding resistance, and we have seen that the winding resistance produces an I^2R power loss which reduces transformer efficiency.

We recall that iron cores increase the inductance of a coil, compared with the inductance of an air-core coil. Hence, transformers used in 60-cycle power applications and audio-frequency applications always have iron cores. High-permeability types of iron are used to minimize the number of primary turns required to obtain the desired inductance. The conventional transformer symbol, seen in Figure 16-5, appears to indicate a magnetic circuit that has a long air path. However, the symbol is generalized, and is used to represent *any* form of core. In 60-cycle and audio-frequency work, transformer cores are fabricated as iron magnetic circuits, with little if any air gap. A continuous iron magnetic circuit provides maximum inductance for a given number of primary turns.

There are four basic core constructions, as illustrated in Figure 16-6.

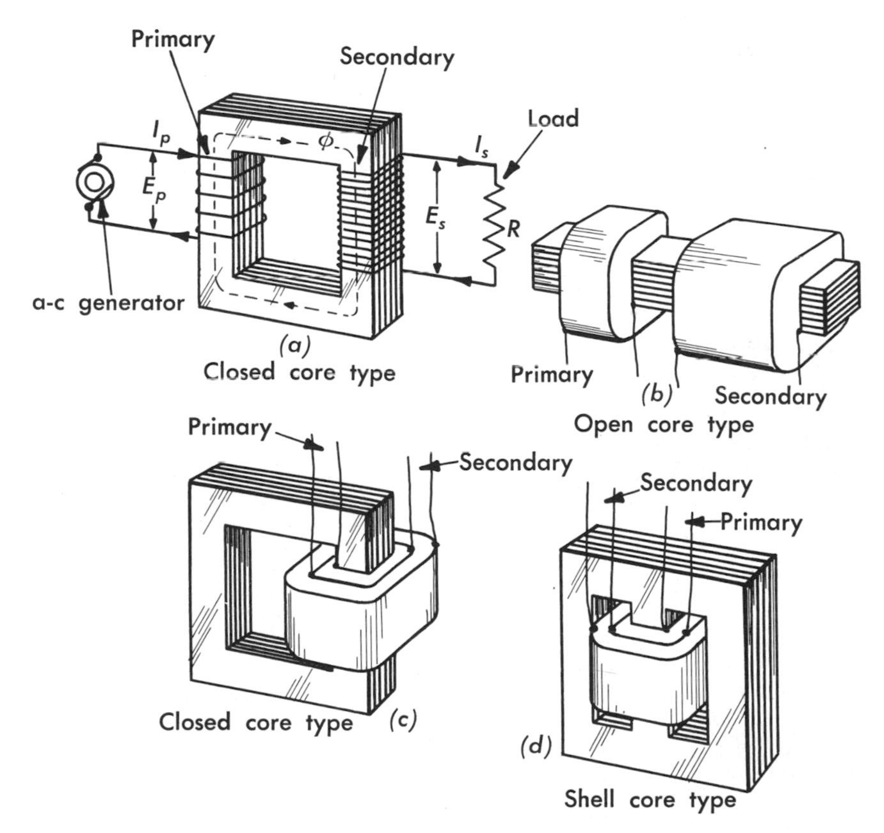

Figure 16-6

(a)-(d) Four basic core constructions. *(e)* Appearance of an isolation transformer with a shell-type core. (Courtesy of United Transformer Corp.)

(Continued on page 424.)

(*e*)
Fig. 16-6 (*Continued*)

The closed-core type depicted in Figure 16-6(*a*) is easy to manufacture and to assemble. However, some of the magnetic flux escapes into the surrounding air in passage from the primary side to the secondary side. This *leakage flux* reduces operating efficiency. Leakage flux does not reduce the secondary voltage if the secondary is unloaded. In other words, the emf induced in the secondary is proportional simply to the rate of change of flux. But when the secondary is loaded, leakage flux causes the secondary voltage to decrease. Figure 16-7 shows the equivalent circuit when leakage flux is present. It is as if an inductor were connected in series with the generator, and another inductor were connected in series with the

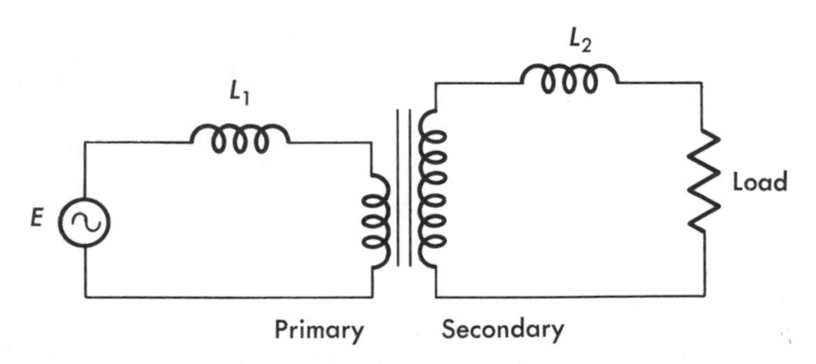

Figure 16-7
Equivalent circuit for a transformer depicting leakage reactances.

load. As soon as current is demanded from the transformer, more or less voltage is dropped across the equivalent leakage reactances L_1 and L_2.

Leakage reactance is very high for the open-core type of transformer, depicted in Figure 16-6(*b*). This construction is economical to manufacture, but is unsuitable for applications in which appreciable current must be supplied by the secondary. An improved type of closed-core construction is illustrated in Figure 16-6(*c*). Leakage flux is reduced in comparison with (*a*) because the secondary is wound over the primary. Nevertheless, some flux does escape from the iron core into the surrounding air. To further minimize flux leakage, a shell-type core is used, as illustrated in Figure 16-6(*d*). Since primary and secondary windings are more nearly enclosed by iron, less flux strays into the surrounding air. Evidently, the shell-type core is comparatively costly and difficult to assemble.

16.3 CORE LAMINATION

Very few transformers utilize solid iron cores. Iron is a conductor of electricity; hence, as the magnetic field rises and falls in strength, it induces a current in an iron core. Currents induced in cores are called *eddy currents,* imposing a power loss in transformer operation. Power is consumed as heat in the I^2R core loss. Hence, eddy currents are minimized by *laminating* transformer cores, as depicted in Figure 16-8. A lamination is a thin sheet of iron. Sheets are stacked to build up the complete core.

Laminations must be inserted into the transformer windings; hence,

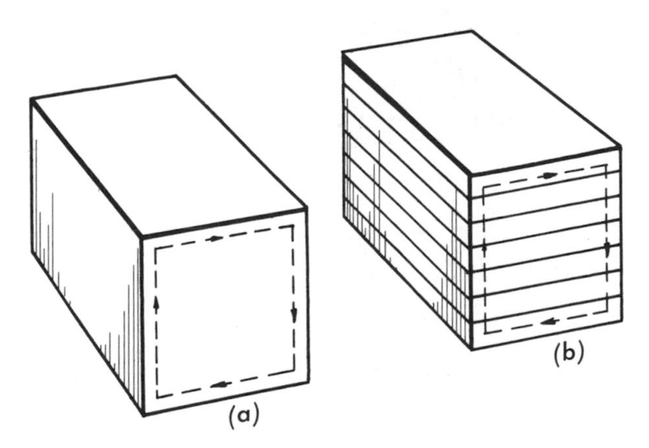

Figure 16-8

(*a*) Eddy-current flow in a solid iron core. (*b*) Laminations break up the path of eddy-current flow.

they are stamped into separate sections, as depicted in Figure 16-9. There is necessarily a small air gap where the sections butt together. These small air gaps cause a certain amount of flux leakage. When this leakage must be strictly minimized, the sections are alternated during assembly, so that the air gaps in each lamination are covered above and below by

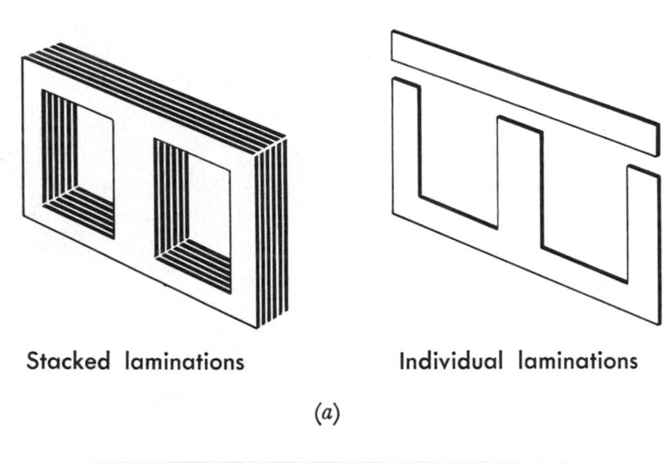

(*a*)

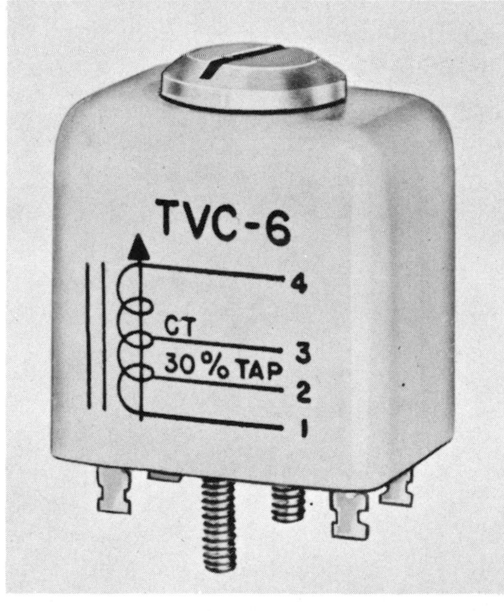

(*b*)

Figure 16-9

(*a*) Core laminations fabricated in separate sections. (*b*) An autotransformer with an adjustable open core. (Courtesy of United Transformer Corp.)

unbroken surfaces. Of course, it is more costly to alternate the laminations, and you will find many transformers in which core laminations are stacked without alternation. Laminations are always coated with some insulating substance. Unless insulated from their neighbors, a conducting path would be present, as shown in Figure 16-8(*a*), and no advantage would be gained.

When transformers are operated at comparatively high frequencies, eddy-current loss becomes increasingly troublesome. Hence, laminations must be thinner for high-frequency operation. There is a practical limit encountered in this regard, and when a transformer is designed for 1-mc or 20-mc operation, for example, it is impractical to use laminated cores. However, eddy-current losses can be satisfactorily minimized and the advantages of high permeability are retained by forming cores from a mix of powdered iron and insulating binder. Another widely used technique employs ferrites for high-frequency transformer cores. When iron oxide reacts with nickel oxide, a nickel ferrite $NiFe_2O_4$ is formed. Ferrite cores are formed by powdering the oxides and compacting them under pressure in suitably shaped molds. The cores are then fired at high temperature. Since the resistivity of the nickel ferrite is very high, eddy-current flow is minimized.

In addition to eddy-current losses, there is a hysteresis loss in a magnetic core. You will recall that the *B-H* curve for iron or other magnetic substances has the form of a loop. The area of this loop is proportional to the hysteresis loss. Hysteresis is a form of magnetic friction, and causes flux energy to be dissipated as heat in the core. Hysteresis loops for some types of iron have much less area than for other types. Hence, an iron that has high permeability and a small hysteresis loop is most desirable for use as core material.

16.4 TUNED TRANSFORMERS

Tuned transformers are widely used in electronic equipment. The primary and secondary windings are designed to have resonant response at a chosen frequency, or over a comparatively small band of frequencies. A small variable capacitor, often called a *trimmer* capacitor, is connected across one of the windings to resonate the transformer at the desired frequency; or, a trimmer capacitor may be connected across each winding. Transformers are tuned in order to pass a certain frequency or band of frequencies, and to reject other frequencies.

Figure 16-10 depicts a transformer that has an untuned primary and a tuned secondary. An air core is used, and the flux leakage is very high by ordinary standards of power-transformer design. The frequency-response curve shown in Figure 16-10 is a graph of secondary current versus fre-

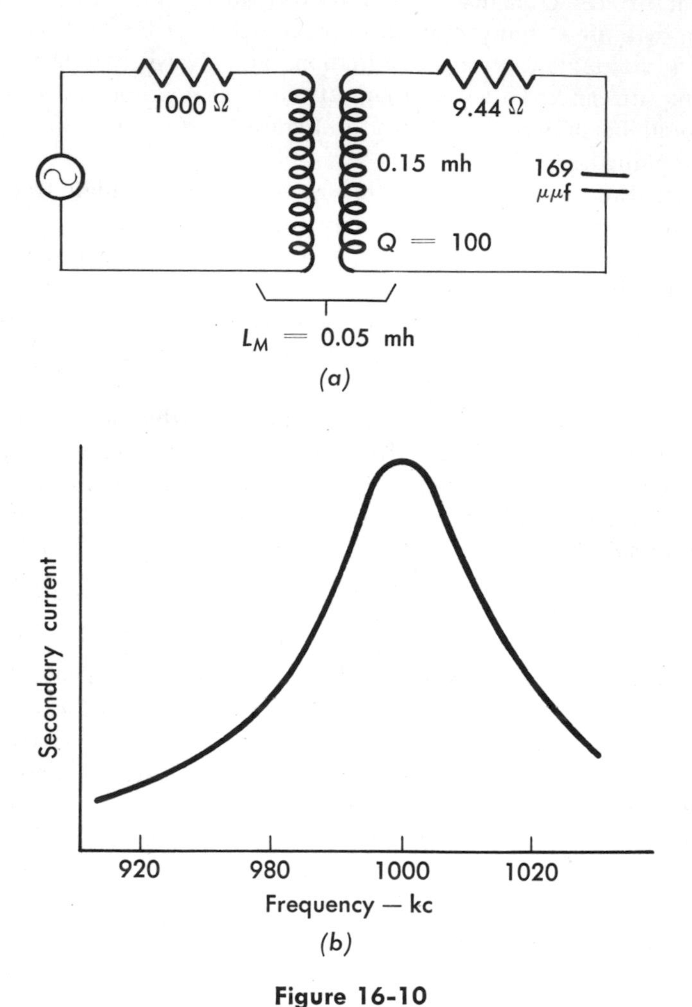

Figure 16-10

(a) Air-core transformer with untuned primary and tuned secondary. *(b)* Variation of secondary current with frequency.

quency of the primary voltage. The primary voltage is held constant, as its frequency is varied. This curve has the same shape as an ordinary series-resonant frequency-response curve, although it may be noted that the secondary has a lower Q than if the primary were withdrawn from its vicinity.

Why does the Q of the secondary winding become less in the presence of the primary? Evidently, magnetic flux that links both primary and secondary windings has the effect of coupling some resistance into the secondary from the primary. Let us see how this takes place. Note in Figure 16-10(*a*) that a term $L_M = 0.05$ mh is bracketed from primary to secondary. We call L_M the *mutual inductance* of the two windings. Figure 16-11 shows the meaning of mutual inductance. An air-core transformer has an equivalent circuit, as seen in Figure 16-11(*b*), and although the equivalent circuit does not provide d-c isolation, it nevertheless has exactly the same a-c characteristics as the air-core transformer. The mutual in-

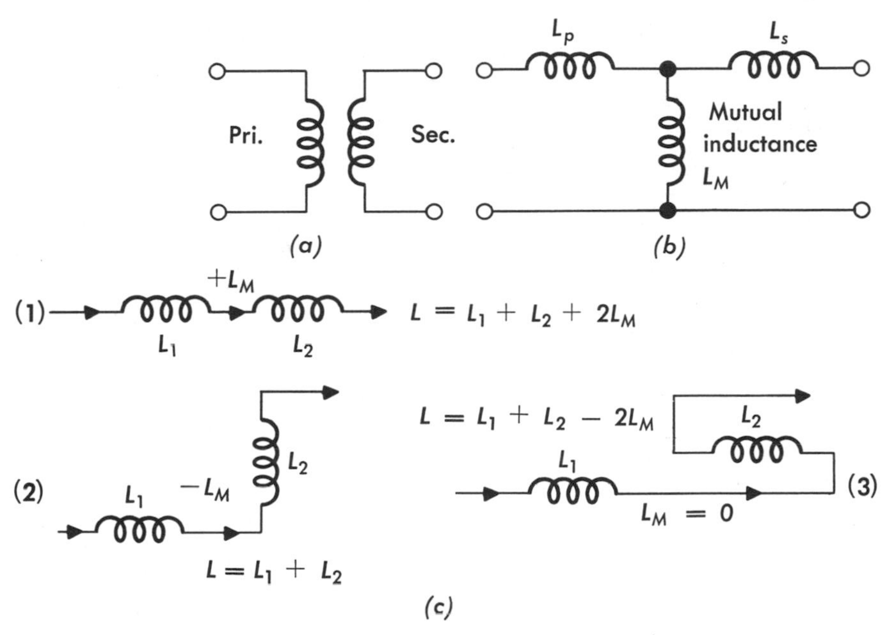

Figure 16-11
(a) An idealized air-core transformer. *(b)* Equivalent circuit. *(c)* Total inductance of two coils connected in series. (1) Magnetic fields aid and total inductance equals $L_1 + L_2 + 2L_M$. (2) Magnetic fields induce zero voltage in adjacent coil and total inductance equals $L_1 + L_2$. (3) Magnetic fields oppose and total inductance equals $L_1 + L_2 - 2L_M$.

ductance is simply the inductance that is common to the primary and the secondary.

Mutual inductance in Figure 16-11(*a*) corresponds to the amount of magnetic flux that is common to the primary and to the secondary. Thus, when primary and secondary windings are placed closely together (closely coupled), the mutual inductance is large. However, when primary and secondary windings are separated widely (loosely coupled), the mutual inductance is small. If the primary and secondary are placed so close together (coupled so tightly) that all of the primary flux cuts the secondary turns, the mutual inductance then has its maximum possible value. The equation for maximum mutual inductance is

$$L_M\,(\text{max}) = \sqrt{L_1 L_2} \tag{16.5}$$

where L_1 is the inductance of the primary alone and L_2 is the inductance of the secondary alone.

The equivalent circuit shown in Figure 16-11 is for an ideal air-core transformer. However, a practical transformer has winding resistance, and the primary may include some internal resistance from the generator (Figure 16-10). Hence, there is mutual resistance present in addition to mutual inductance. This is the reason that the Q of the secondary becomes less when the primary is coupled more closely.

COEFFICIENT OF COUPLING

Instead of working directly with the mutual inductance value, electronics engineers and technicians more commonly use a term which is called the *coefficient of coupling*. The coefficient of coupling is the ratio of the mutual inductance which is present to the maximum possible value of mutual inductance. Thus,

$$k = \frac{L_M}{\sqrt{L_1 L_2}} \tag{16.6}$$

where k is the coefficient of coupling.

Now, let us see how the frequency-response curves of tuned transformers change when the coefficient of coupling is varied. Most communications equipment makes use of transformers in which the primary and secondary are tuned to the same frequency. Therefore, let us consider frequency-response curves for this common application. Figure 16-12 illustrates responses for a transformer with both primary and secondary tuned to 1 mc. Only the coefficient of coupling is changed to obtain the various frequency-response curves.

The first characteristic we see is the fact that some of the curves have a single peak, while others have double peaks. This is actually more appearance than fact; careful analysis of the transformer action will reveal that the single-peaked curves actually have double-peaked response. However, the two peaks are sufficiently close together that they appear to be a single peak. Observe the curves for secondary current in Figure 16-12. When $k = 0.002$, coupling is very loose, and the induced secondary current is small; the bandwidth is comparatively narrow. However, when k is increased to 0.01, the secondary current is at its maximum amplitude and the bandwidth is considerably greater.

When $k = 0.01$, we say that the transformer is *critically coupled*. This term means that this is the highest coefficient of coupling for which the

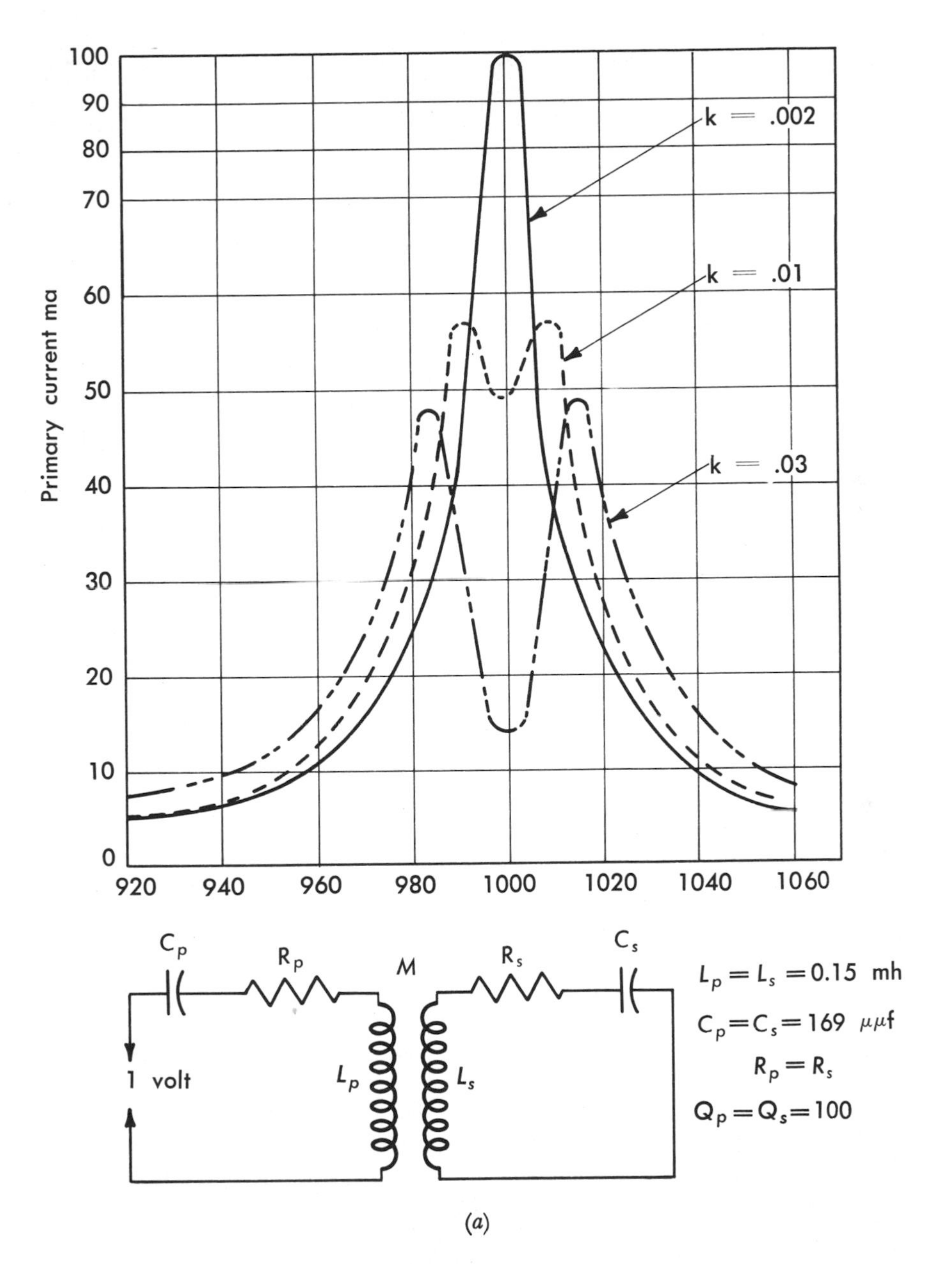

Figure 16-12

(a) and *(b)* Frequency-response curves for tuned transformers with various coefficients of coupling. *(c)* Typical transformer with tuned primary and secondary. (Courtesy of James Millen Mfg. Co.)

(Continued on page 432.)

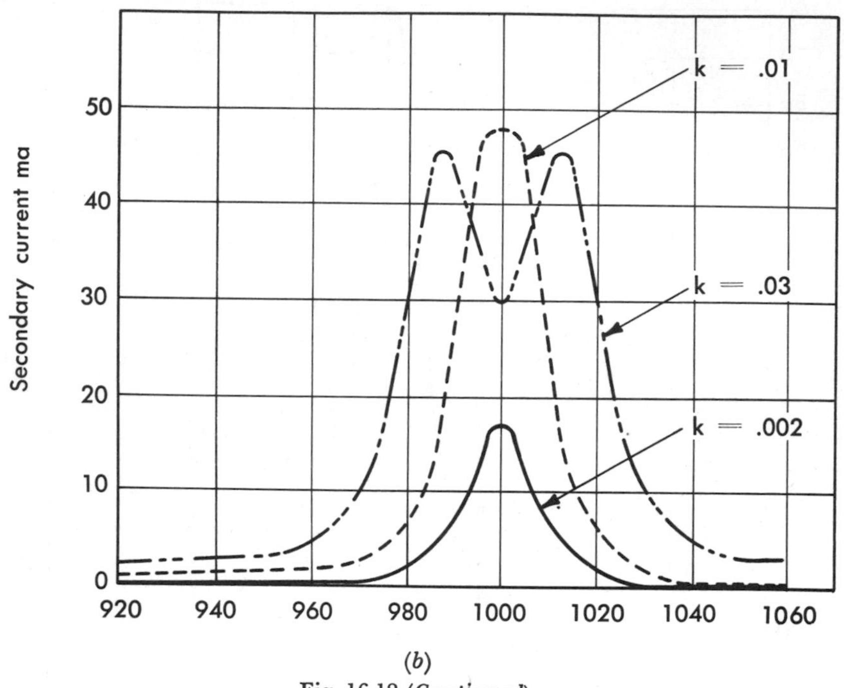

(*b*)
Fig. 16-12 (*Continued*)

(*Continued on facing page.*)

curve appears to have a single peak. At higher coefficients of coupling, the curve exhibits a visible dip between two peaks. Critical coupling also means that the secondary current has its maximum amplitude. The coefficient of critical coupling is given by the formula

$$k_{\text{(critical)}} = \frac{1}{\sqrt{Q_1 Q_2}} \tag{16.7}$$

where Q_1 is the Q value of the primary alone, and Q_2 is the Q value of the secondary alone. .

When the coefficient of coupling exceeds the critical value, the bandwidth increases rapidly. Double peaks appear symmetrically on either side of the center frequency. What is the source of double peaks? Observe the equivalent circuit depicted in Figure 16-13. Trimmer capacitor C_p is not connected directly across L_p because mutual inductance L_M is reflected into the primary winding. Similarly, trimmer capacitor C_s is not connected directly across L_s because mutual inductance L_M is reflected into the secondary winding. In turn, the network has two resonant frequencies, one of which corresponds to C_p connected across L_p and L_M in series. This is the same resonant frequency that corresponds to C_s connected across L_s

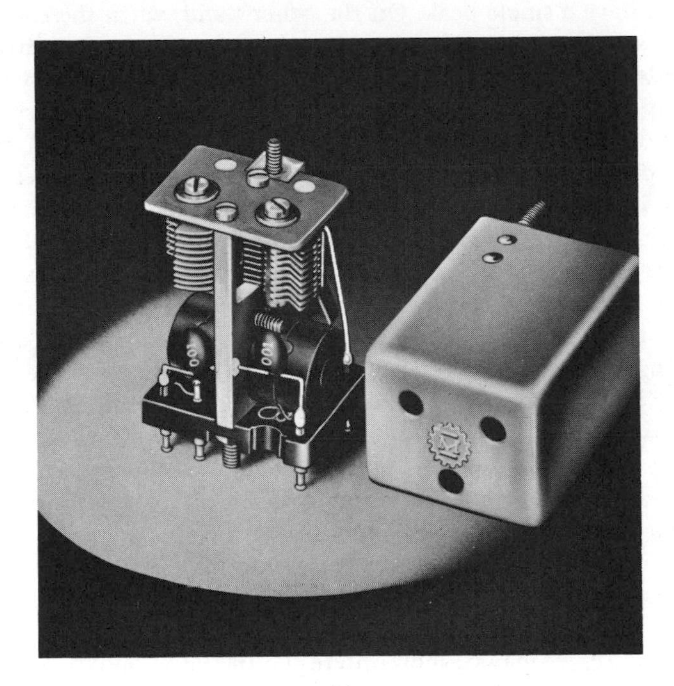

(c)
Fig. 16-12 (*Continued*)

and L_M in series. The other resonant frequency corresponds to C_p and C_s in series connected across L_p and L_s in series.

PRIMARY AND SECONDARY CHARACTERISTICS

If the coefficient of coupling is small, L_M is also small. Hence, the two resonant frequencies are almost the same. The frequency-response curve

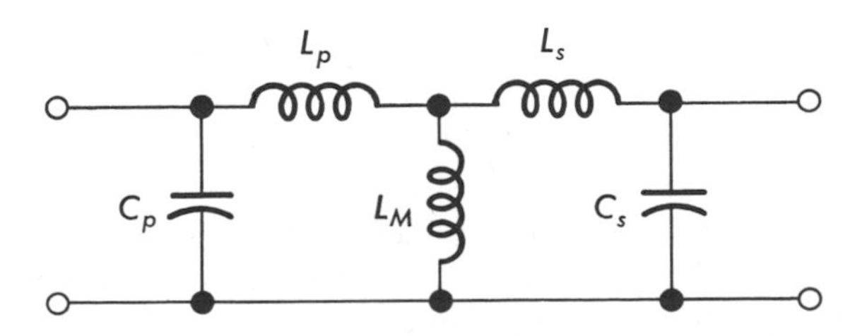

Figure 16-13
Equivalent circuit for a transformer with tuned primary and tuned secondary has two resonant frequencies.

appears to have a single peak. On the other hand, when the coefficient of coupling is large, L_M is also large. Hence, the two resonant frequencies are considerably different. In turn, the frequency-response curve has two widely separated peaks, and the response at center frequency forms a visible and often prominent dip. The larger the coefficient of coupling, the more prominent is the dip between the widely separated peaks.

Note in Figure 16-12 that the frequency-response curves for the primary have the same general forms as those for the secondary. However, the primary current is always greater than the secondary current at a given coefficient of coupling. This difference results from the I^2R loss in the secondary resistance R_s. The difference is most striking at low coefficients of coupling, such as 0.002. The leakage flux is then so excessive that comparatively little current is induced in the secondary winding.

Observe also in Figure 16-12 that the primary frequency-response curve exhibits a noticeable double peak before the secondary curve exhibits double peaks. For example, when the coefficient of coupling is critical (0.01), the secondary curve still appears to have a single peak, yet the primary curve has a prominent dip between double peaks. This difference also results from the fact that primary current is larger than the secondary current.

In practice, we may be more interested in the secondary voltage than in the secondary current. If so, we will observe that the secondary voltage curves have practically the same shape as the secondary current curves in Figure 16-12. It is customary to take the secondary voltage from the terminals of C_s. Hence, the secondary voltage is equal to $I_sX_{C_s}$. Although the reactance of C_s varies slightly over the pass band, this variation can be neglected from a practical viewpoint. What is the value of the secondary voltage in Figure 16-12 for a coupling coefficient of 0.01? The secondary current is 47.5 ma at 1000 kc. Since the 169-$\mu\mu$f capacitor C_s has a reactance of approximately 942 ohms at 1000 kc, the secondary voltage is approximately 45 volts.

Although 1 volt is applied to the primary, 45 volts are obtained across the secondary capacitor at critical coupling. This increase is due to the resonant rise of voltage across the capacitor. Note that the secondary is *not* a parallel-resonant circuit, as it might appear superficially. The secondary is a *series-resonant circuit* because the magnetic flux induces a voltage in each turn of the secondary. In turn, the secondary voltage source is effectively a series source. Although the Q of the secondary alone is 100 at 1000 kc, the resistance reflected into the secondary from the primary at critical coupling reduces its effective Q to approximately 45.

When the Q's of the primary and secondary are equal, as in Figure 16-12, the frequency-response curves are symmetrical with respect to the center frequency. Furthermore, the primary and secondary are tuned to the same frequency in this example. Suppose, on the other hand, that you tune the primary and secondary to slightly different frequencies. The effect of such *stagger tuning* is the same as if the coefficient of coupling were increased and the two circuits were tuned to the same frequency. However, although the bandwidth is increased, the secondary voltage is somewhat less than if the same bandwidth were obtained by increasing the coupling coefficient and maintaining identical tuning.

Next, if primary and secondary do *not* have the same Q values, you will find that the frequency-response curves are not symmetrical, regardless of the tuning adjustments. In the vast majority of applications, it is desired to obtain a symmetrical response curve. Hence, the Q values of the primary and secondary are usually made equal. In most applications, it is also desired to obtain maximum secondary output voltage. Consequently, the primary and secondary are tuned to the same frequency, and the coefficient of coupling is set to provide the required bandwidth.

AUDIO-FREQUENCY TRANSFORMERS

We find that *audio-frequency transformers* have characteristics that are based on the principles of both tuned and untuned operation. For example, Figure 16-14 depicts the frequency response of an audio transformer that has a rising response at high frequencies with a peak output at about 8 kc. This perhaps unexpected characteristic is due to the presence of distributed capacitance in the primary and secondary windings. To understand the response of an audio transformer, it is helpful to consider the three equivalent circuits shown in Figure 16-15.

To simplify the equivalent circuits as far as possible, it is assumed that the transformer has a 1-to-1 winding ratio. In turn, the effective

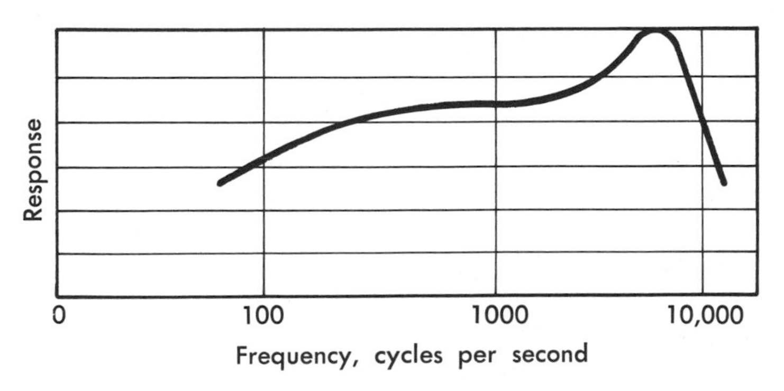

Figure 16-14
Frequency-response curve.

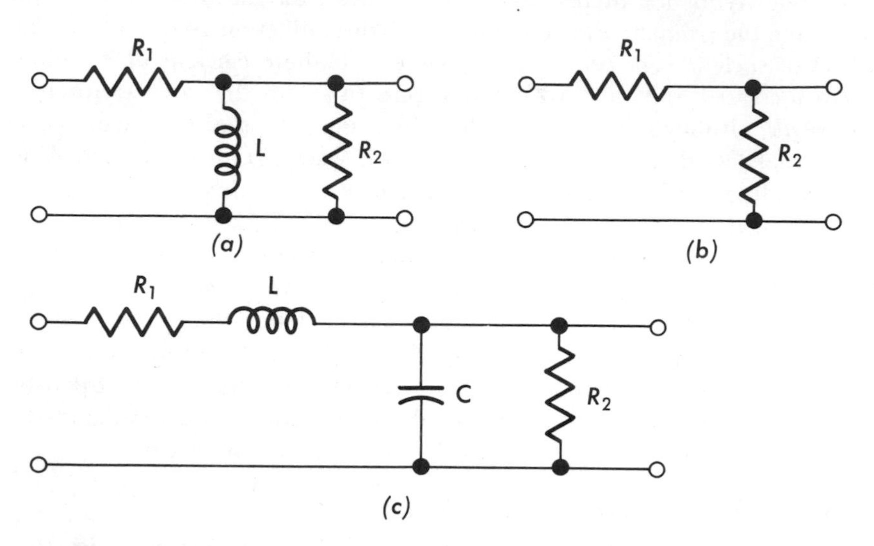

Figure 16-15

(a) Distributed capacitance is disregarded at low frequencies. *(b)* Inductive reactance and distributed capacitance are disregarded over the mid-range. *(c)* Distributed capacitance and inductance become series-resonant at high frequencies.

inductance is represented by a single coil L. R_1 is the effective series resistance of this coil, and R_2 is the load resistance into which the secondary works. In practice, R_2 may be a low value, or it might be practically infinite. It is apparent that if R_2 has a low value, the peak response of the transformer at high frequencies will be reduced, or perhaps eliminated entirely. In other words, the Q of the system is reduced by secondary loading.

At low frequencies [Fig. 16-15(*a*)], the reactance of the distributed capacitance is so high that it can be disregarded. Inductive reactance is small and cannot be neglected. Thus, the transformer draws a lagging current, and this current demand is very significant at very low frequencies. Most of the source voltage drops across R_1 at very low frequencies. In turn, the response depicted in Figure 16-14 falls off rapidly below 200 cps.

In mid-range [Figure 16-15(*b*)], the inductive reactance has a sufficiently high value that it can be neglected. Distributed capacitance also has a sufficiently high reactance that it can be disregarded. In this mid-range, we observe conventional untuned-transformer action. The output amplitude depends solely on the winding ratio of the transformer, minus the loss due to resistance drop. Frequency response is practically flat over the mid-range (Figure 16-14), because reactances are not significant.

However, at high frequencies, distributed capacitance cannot be disregarded. Effectively, the distributed capacitance forms a series-resonant circuit with the inductance as depicted in Figure 16-15(*c*). A resonant rise of voltage occurs across both the inductance and the distributed capacitance. Since the total distributed capacitance can be regarded as a capacitor shunted across the output terminals, the peak response in Figure 16-14 represents the resonant rise of voltage across this equivalent capacitor.

Audio-transformer design, particularly for hi-fidelity equipment, is a fine art. Note that if L were absent in Figure 16-15(*c*), that C would cause a falling response past mid-range. Again, if L were very large, the peak response would be shifted to a low frequency. Hence, inductance is proportioned with respect to distributed capacitance in such manner that the resonant peak serves to maintain response at high audio frequencies. To avoid excessive response at high frequencies (and consequent frequency distortion), the value of R_2 is controlled to lower the Q of the LC resonant system as required. If the winding resistance of the transformer is insufficient to obtain optimum Q, a physical resistor can be connected across the external circuit to reduce the value of R_2.

16.5 TRANSFORMER TROUBLESHOOTING

Power transformers can be damaged by heavy overload. If a secondary winding is short-circuited, excessive current flow can heat the coil sufficiently to char its insulation, or to melt the wire. Damaged insulation often results in short-circuited turns or layers in the winding, although current flow is insufficient to open the winding. In this case, the output voltage is reduced and the transformer operates at an abnormally high temperature. A current measurement will indicate the flow of excessive no-load current.

Occasionally, a transformer winding makes electrical contact with the core. Such contact may be direct, in case defective insulation permits the bare wire to make connection with the laminations or their supports. Or, contact may be indirect, via leakage resistance between winding and core. Leakage resistance is commonly caused by charred insulation, or by entry of moisture. Although a transformer is basically unaffected by this fault, the core is a source of possible shock. Technicians often make ohmmeter checks of the insulation resistance from windings to core to insure against this hazard.

When moisture has permeated the windings, or after a transformer has been damaged by heavy overload, leakage resistance may also occur between windings. In such case, a transformer no longer provides d-c isolation between the primary and secondary. An ohmmeter test will usually disclose the presence of leakage resistance. However, transformers that operate at comparatively high voltages, such as the so-called "flyback" transformer in a television receiver, may develop leakage resistance that cannot be localized by an ohmmeter test. However, special types of ohmmeters, called *meggers,* can localize leakage resistance which becomes apparent only when high test voltages are applied.

Nearly all transformers are impregnated with special waxes to prevent entry of moisture. Windings that operate at comparatively high voltage are commonly coated with suitable plastics to prevent spark-over or arcs. If the coating is cracked or chipped, sparks or a blue-glow discharge will occur in normal operation. Technicians can sometimes repair damaged coatings with commercial plastic pastes or sprays. On the other hand, when impregnating waxes break down between layers in a winding, it is seldom practical to attempt repair of a high-voltage transformer.

Tuned transformers can also become defective in case of overload. If a circuit defect causes accidental flow of excessive current, a winding may be burned open, or leakage between turns or layers may be established through charred insulation. If a tuned transformer has internal leakage or short-circuited turns, it will exhibit an abnormal frequency-response curve. The frequency-response curve can be checked easily with a sweep-frequency generator and oscilloscope. Trimmer capacitors occasionally become open, shorted, or leaky. These defects also result in abnormal frequency-response curves.

Most tuned transformers in familiar communications equipment provide d-c isolation in addition to band-pass response. Leakage between the primary and secondary permits entry of d-c voltage into the secondary circuit. This defect can ordinarily be determined by measurement of d-c voltage in the secondary circuit with the equipment turned on. Technicians compare measured d-c voltage values with specified normal values published in service data or schematic diagrams. You will often find tuned transformers provided with adjustable powdered-iron or ferrite cores, instead of trimmer capacitors. If a core becomes damaged, or its adjustment assembly becomes defective, an abnormal frequency-response curve will be observed.

Abnormal frequency-response curves will have incorrect center frequencies, incorrect bandwidths, incorrect contours, or incorrect amplitude. Electronic test equipment is designed to display a frequency-response curve, and to identify its center frequency. Provisions are made for measuring bandwidth. The more elaborate types of sweep-frequency generators also have calibrated output facilities, to permit convenient checks of amplitude values. You will probably have an opportunity to become familiar with sweep-frequency equipment in your laboratory experiments.

SUMMARY OF FUNDAMENTAL CONCEPTS

A transformer changes electrical energy into magnetic energy; the magnetic energy is then changed back again into electrical energy.

Untuned transformers with tight coupling are used to step a-c voltage, current, or impedance up or down.

Voltage transformation is directly proportional to the primary/secondary turns ratio.

Current transformation is inversely proportional to the primary/secondary turns ratio.

Impedance transformation is directly proportional to the square of the primary/secondary turns ratio.

The efficiency of a transformer depends on the I^2R loss in the windings, eddy-current loss in the core, and hysteresis loss in the core.

The primary reactance is made sufficiently large to demand negligible primary current at no load.

The core cross-section is made sufficiently large to avoid saturation under the ampere-turns value at full load.

Cores fabricated from conductive substances are laminated to minimize eddy-current core loss.

Tuned transformers with loose coupling are used to pass a certain range of frequencies, and to reject other frequencies.

The turns ratio of a tuned transformer is not directly related to its voltage transformation.

The frequency characteristic of a tuned transformer is determined by its coefficient of coupling, Q values of primary and secondary, resonant frequencies of its windings, and amount of loading imposed.

QUESTIONS

1) An autotransformer has:
(*a*) separate primary and secondary windings. (*b*) a single tapped or adjustable winding. (*c*) a tuned secondary, with a copper core. (*d*) tuned primary and secondary windings, with copper cores.
2) If a transformer steps up an a-c voltage, the:
(*a*) primary has fewer turns than the secondary. (*b*) primary has more turns than the secondary. (*c*) primary has the same number of turns as the secondary. (*d*) core is constructed from laminated copper sheets.
3) If a transformer steps up a-c current, the:
(*a*) primary has a laminated winding. (*b*) secondary has a laminated winding. (*c*) primary has fewer turns than the secondary. (*d*) secondary has fewer turns than the primary.
4) The impedance ratio provided by a transformer depends upon:
(*a*) its turns ratio. (*b*) diameters of wires in the primary and secondary windings. (*c*) the value of primary current. (*d*) the square of the turns ratio.
5) To match a load to a source means:
(*a*) to obtain maximum power transfer. (*b*) to obtain maximum load voltage. (*c*) to minimize core losses. (*d*) to minimize power dissipation in the load.
6) If a transformer has separate primary and secondary windings, d-c current flow in the primary causes:
(*a*) no d-c current flow in the secondary. (*b*) maximum d-c voltage output from the secondary. (*c*) increase of core permeability. (*d*) decrease of core reluctance.
7) Leakage reactance is caused by:
(*a*) an open circuit in a winding. (*b*) leakage resistance from coil to core. (*c*) leakage resistance between primary and secondary. (*d*) escape of magnetic flux from the core to surrounding air.
8) Cores are laminated to:
(*a*) minimize leakage flux. (*b*) minimize eddy-current losses. (*c*) minimize hysteresis losses. (*d*) match the load to the source.
9) The coefficient of coupling denotes:
(*a*) the rate of change of magnetic flux. (*b*) the turns ratio of primary to secondary. (*c*) the relative separation of primary and secondary coils. (*d*) the I^2R loss in a powdered-iron core.
10) Double-peaked frequency-response curves occur when:
(*a*) the mutual inductance is comparatively high. (*b*) a primary winding is short-circuited. (*c*) a primary winding is open-circuited. (*d*) primary and secondary windings are connected in parallel.

PROBLEMS

1) An inductor is connected to a 117-volt 60-cycle source. What voltage value will be measured from a center tap on the inductor to either end of the winding?
2) If the source voltage in Problem 1 is connected between the center tap and one end of the winding, what voltage value will be measured across the complete winding?
3) An ideal inductor is connected to a 1000-ohm resistor. What a-c resistance value will be found between a center tap on the inductor and one end of the winding?
4) A 100-ohm resistor is connected across the output of an ideal variable autotransformer. A 117-volt 60-cycle source is applied to the input terminals. As the output voltage is varied, how does the ratio of output power to input power change?
5) If a load resistance of 1000 ohms is to be matched to a source resistance of 10 ohms by an autotransformer, at what point must the winding be tapped?
6) Calculate the power in the load resistance of Problem 5, when a source voltage of 5 volts at 500 cycles is applied to the autotransformer. (The source resistance is 10 ohms.)
7) If a 117-volt 60-cycle source supplies 5 amps to an ideal welding transformer, and the secondary applies 0.5 volt across its load, what is the value of current flow through the load?
8) Calculate the efficiency of a power transformer that supplies a real power value of 1 kw to a load when the real power input to the transformer is 1.2 kw.
9) If a certain transformer has a step-down ratio of 100-to-1, and is followed by a transformer with a step-up ratio of 1 to 1.5, what is the step-down ratio of the system?
10) Consider that the two transformers are to be replaced in Problem 9 by a single transformer. If the step-down ratio applies to current transformation, what is the required ratio of primary turns to secondary turns?
11) Calculate the maximum mutual inductance which can be realized in an air-core transformer which has a primary inductance of 150 mh and a secondary inductance of 200 mh.
12) What is the value of mutual inductance in Problem 11 when the secondary is placed at an infinite distance from the primary?
13) If the coefficient of coupling in an air-core transformer is 0.01, and the maximum realizable mutual inductance is 100 mh, what is the value of mutual inductance between the primary and secondary?

14) Calculate the coefficient of critical coupling for an air-core transformer that has a primary Q value of 75, and a secondary Q value of 125.
15) Consider an air-core transformer that operates at 465 kc. The secondary trimmer capacitor has a value of 35 $\mu\mu$f. If the secondary current is 0.2 ma, what is the value of the voltage drop across the capacitor?

17

MOTOR PRINCIPLES

17.1 CONVERSION OF ELECTRICAL ENERGY TO MECHANICAL ENERGY

The basic construction of an electric motor is quite similar to that of a generator. However, a motor converts electrical energy into mechanical energy, in contrast to a generator which converts mechanical energy into electrical energy. We will find that almost any motor can be operated as a generator, and vice versa. Recall that when electric current flows in a wire near a compass needle, the needle is deflected, as depicted in Figure 17-1; that is, it exerts mechanical force. Evidently, an equal and

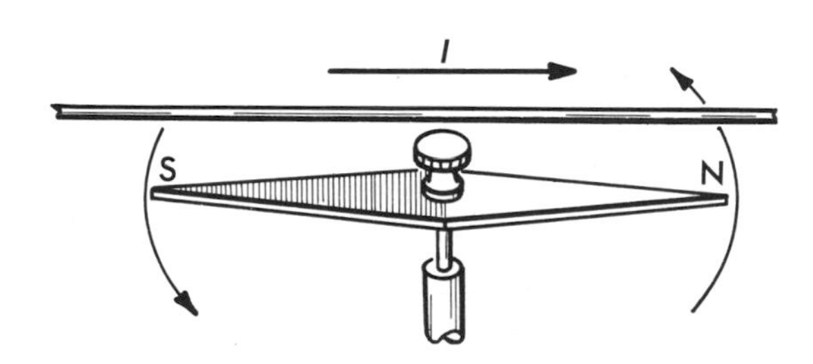

Figure 17-1
Current flow through a wire produces forces of action and reaction with respect to a nearby compass needle.

opposite mechanical force is exerted upon the wire. As the needle tends to orient itself with respect to the current-carrying wire, so does the wire tend to orient itself with respect to the compass needle.

When a current-carrying conductor is placed in a magnetic field (Figure 17-2), the conductor tends to move at right angles to the magnetic flux lines. The larger the current flow, and the stronger the magnetic field, the greater is the mechanical force exerted by the conductor. The relation between current, flux, and conductor motion is stated by Fleming's left-hand rule for motor action, illustrated in Figure 17-3. Note carefully that Fleming's rule applies to conventional current flow, *not* to electron flow. If you wish to observe electron flow, you must substitute a right-hand rule for motor action.

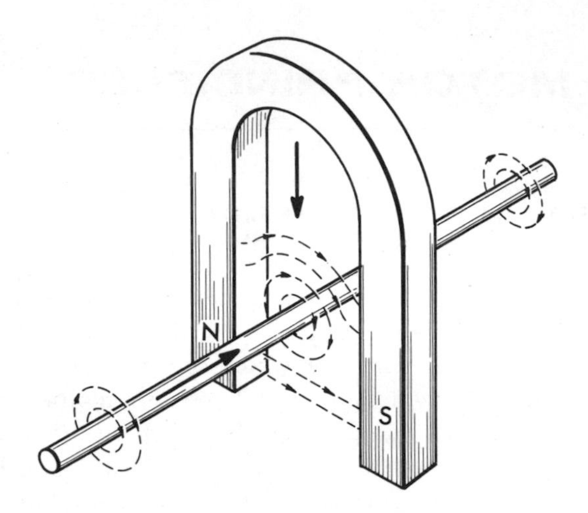

Figure 17-2
A magnetic field exerts force upon a current-carrying conductor.

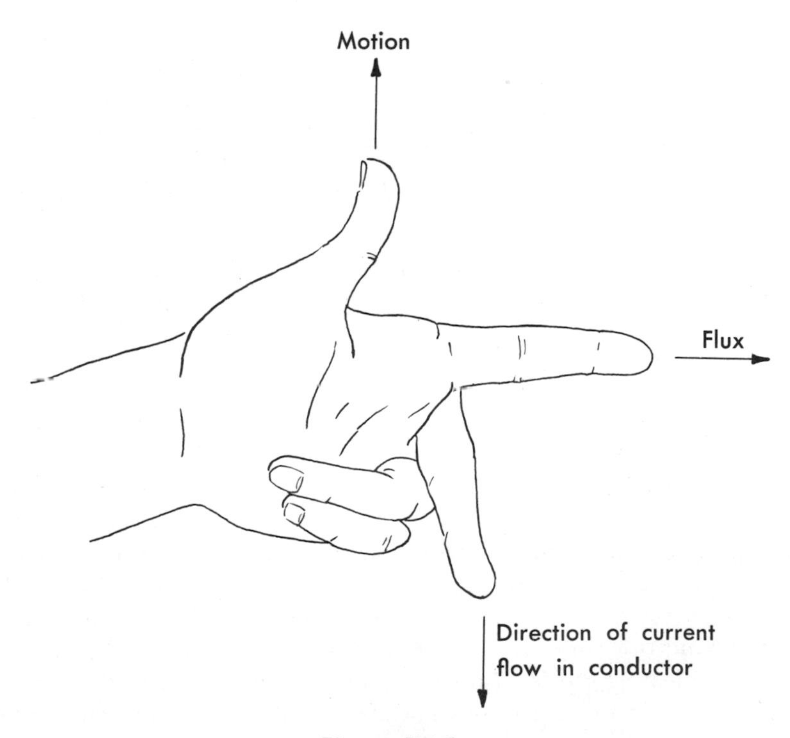

Figure 17-3
Fleming's left-hand rule for motor action.

If a loop of wire is pivoted as shown in Figure 17-4, it is clear that this basic armature arrangement will rotate when current flows through the loop. Note that in Figure 17-4, conventional current flow is indicated. How much mechanical force will the conductor in Figure 17-2 develop? This force is proportional to the flux density, current value, and length of the conductor in the magnetic field. Quantitatively, the force is expressed by the equation

$$F = \frac{BIL}{10} \quad (17.1)$$

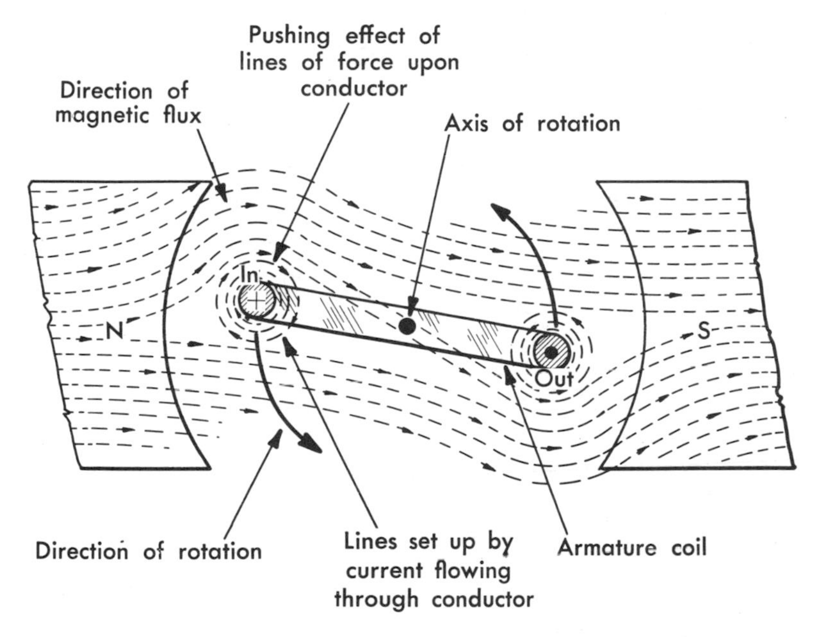

Figure 17-4
A rotational force is exerted.

where F is the force in dynes, B is the flux density in lines per square centimeter, I is the current in amperes, and L is the length in centimeters of the conductor in the magnetic field.

Let us see how Equation (17.1) is derived. Assume that one pole of a long bar magnet is placed at the center of a coil, as shown in Figure 17-5. Let the magnet have a strength M. The coil has a radius r, consists of N turns, and the current flow is I amps. In turn, the force that acts on the magnetic pole is given by the equation

$$F = MH \quad (17.2)$$

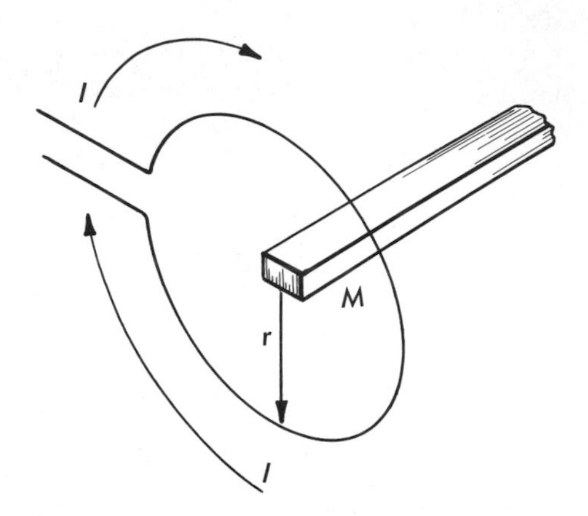

Figure 17-5
Basic diagram for derivation of Equation (17.1).

where H is the field strength established by the current flow in the coil.

The value of H is expressed by the equation

$$H = \frac{2\pi NI}{10r} \tag{17.3}$$

where the notation is the same as above, and H is the magnetic field intensity in oersteds.

If we substitute this value for H in Equation (17.2), we obtain

$$F = \frac{M2\pi NI}{10r} \tag{17.4}$$

We can multiply both numerator and denominator of Equation (17.4) by r to obtain the formula

$$F = \frac{M}{r^2} \cdot \frac{I}{10} \cdot 2\pi rN \tag{17.5}$$

where M/r^2 is the flux density of the magnetic field at r cm from the pole of strength M, and $2\pi rN$ is the length of the conductor.

We know that flux density is given by

$$B = \mu H \tag{17.6}$$

Hence, we can replace M/r^2 in Equation (17.5) by B. Then, by substituting the single quantity L for the length of the conductor $2\pi rN$, we obtain Equation (17.1). When the conductor does not move at right angles to flux field, but at some angle θ with respect to the field, the vectorial length of the conductor becomes effectively $L \sin \theta$, and Equation (17.1) will be written

$$F = \frac{BIL \sin \theta}{10} \tag{17.7}$$

For example, the conductors depicted in Figure 17-4 move at a progressively smaller angle with respect to the flux as their rotation continues.

Technicians often prefer to use practical units in computation. Thus, Equation (17.1) can be rewritten

$$F = \frac{8.85\ BIL}{10^8} \tag{17.8}$$

where F is the force in pounds, B is the flux density in lines per square inch, L is the length in inches of the conductor in the field, and I is the current in amperes.

For example, if a conductor extends 6 in. through a magnetic field that has a flux density of 50,000 lines per sq in., and if a current of 10 amps flows through it, the conductor develops a mechanical force of $8.85 \times 50{,}000 \times 10 \times 6 \times 10^{-8} = 0.26$ lb, approximately.

17.2 ARMATURE TORQUE

Simplified motors have only two poles, as depicted in Figure 17-6. The field flux may be obtained from a field coil through which current flows; it also may be obtained from a permanent magnet. Toy motors often utilize permanent field magnets to reduce manufacturing cost. In any case, a cylindrical iron armature revolves between the field poles. There is necessarily a small air gap between the armature and the field poles. We can assume for practical purposes that the flux in the air gap is uniform, and that the direction of flux lines in the gap is toward the axis of the armature. Therefore, the armature conductors cut the flux lines at right angles as the armature rotates.

In Figure 17-4, the mechanical force exerted by each conductor is given by Equation (17.1) or by Equation (17.8). But the *torque* that is exerted by each conductor is equal to this mechanical force multiplied by the radius of the armature. Thus, if we use Equation (17.8) to obtain F in pounds, we will multiply F by r, where r is the radius of the armature in feet. The product Fr is called pound-feet. Accordingly,

$$T = Fr \tag{17.9}$$

Consider the armature shown in Figure 17-7, which has 12 conductors. Of these, six conductors are in the magnetic field. The radius of the armature is 2 in. or ⅙ ft. Hence, the torque exerted by each conductor

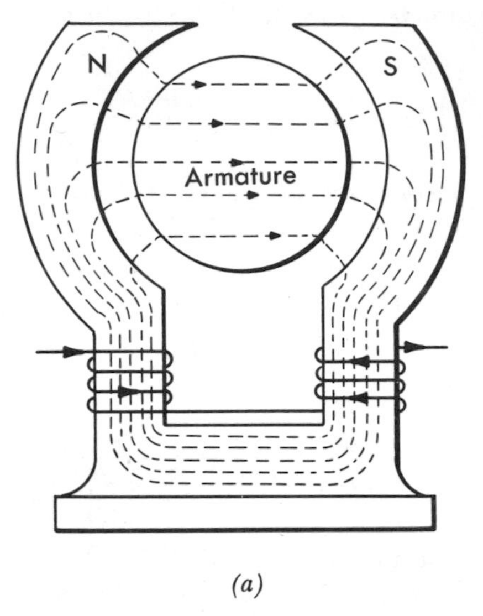

(*a*)

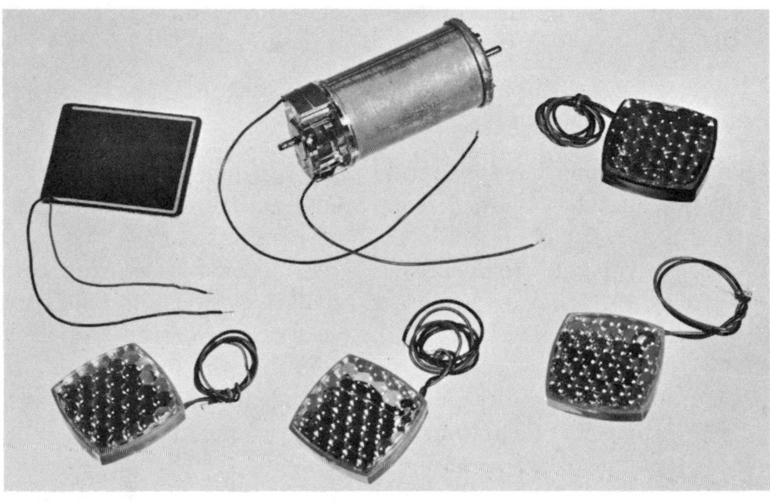

(*b*)

Figure 17-6

(*a*) Basic plan of a two-pole motor, showing the armature, field, and field coils. (*b*) A small motor, powered by solar cells. (Courtesy of Edmund Scientific Co.)

is equal to $F/6$. Since six conductors are in the field, the torque exerted by the armature is equal to F lb-ft. Suppose that the current flow in each conductor is 10 amps, the flux density is 50,000 lines per sq in., and each conductor is 3 in. long. Then, the torque developed is equal to $8.85 \times 50{,}000 \times 10 \times 3 \times 10^{-8}$, or 0.13 lb-ft, approximately.

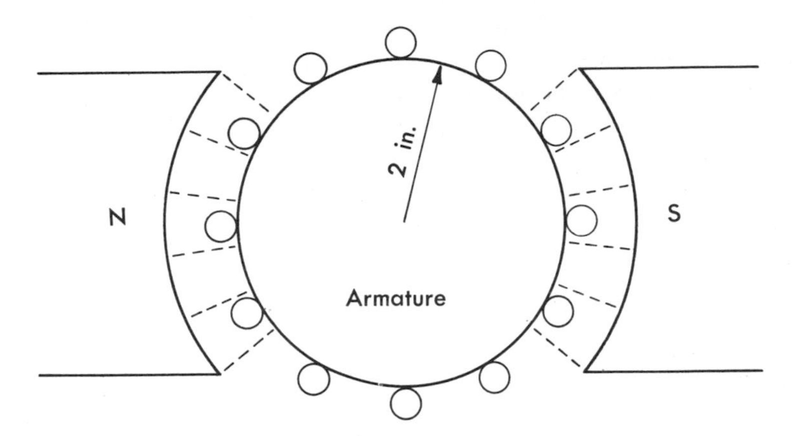

Figure 17-7
Conductors placed in a magnetic field.

17.3 COUNTER EMF

We know that when a conductor cuts lines of magnetic flux, a voltage is induced in the conductor. Hence, when a motor armature rotates, a voltage must be induced in the armature wires. If you apply the right-hand rule for induced voltage, it is clear that armature rotation results in a voltage that opposes the applied voltage. Hence, we say that a motor armature develops *counter emf,* which is sometimes called *back voltage.* The value of counter emf is directly proportional to the speed of armature rotation and to the strength of the field. If a motor is unloaded, its armature revolves very rapidly; in turn, the counter emf is large. The actual voltage available to produce motor action is the difference between the applied emf and the counter emf. However, if a motor "stalls" due to an excessive load, the counter emf is zero, and the motor draws an extremely large current.

For example, a 1/4-horsepower 117-volt motor has a terminal resistance of 4 ohms. When the motor runs under no load, it does not draw 29 amps from the line; instead, it draws a very small current. As the motor is progressively loaded, it draws an increasing value of current; hence, the counter emf approaches the line voltage when the motor supplies no mechanical energy. However, the counter emf approaches zero when the motor is very heavily loaded. In theory, an ideal motor that had no mechanical friction, no winding resistance, and no iron loss would generate a counter emf equal to the line voltage under no-load conditions.

Motors that are rated at several horsepower have much lower armature resistance than small motors. Thus, a typical 6-horsepower motor has an armature resistance of 0.09 ohm. Like a small motor, the 6-horsepower motor draws only a small current when it is unloaded; yet, if the large motor is stalled, its armature resistance is so low that the resulting abnormal current flow will burn out the armature winding. It is clear that the current drawn by a motor under any condition of loading is stated by the equation

$$I = \frac{E_s - E_c}{R} \tag{17.10}$$

where E_s is the source (line) voltage, E_c is the counter emf, and R is the terminal resistance of the motor.

If 220 volts, for example, are applied to a motor that has an armature resistance of 0.09 ohm, under load conditions, the motor might develop a counter emf of 218 volts. In this case, the line current will be approximately 22 amps. This line current is required to supply load power, I^2R losses in the armature resistance, iron losses, air-friction (windage) losses, and bearing-friction losses.

If we multiply both sides of Equation (17.10) by I, and rearrange, we obtain the following power relations:

$$W_{\text{in}} = W_{\text{out}} + I^2R \tag{17.11}$$

where W_{in} is the electrical power drawn by the motor from the line, W_{out} is the mechanical power developed by the armature, and I^2R is the heat dissipated in the winding resistance.

All of the mechanical power W_{out} is not available as useful output power. Some of it is lost, as previously noted, in bearing friction, air friction, and heat due to iron losses. Since the magnetic flux rises and falls in the armature in step with its rotation, there is necessarily an eddy-current loss and a hysteresis loss (see Figure 17-8), plus a small loss due to leakage flux. In the case of large well-designed motors, it can be assumed for practical purposes that W_{out}, or IE_c, is equal to the available output power from the motor. Hence, the available horsepower output is approximately

$$\text{HP} = \frac{IE_c}{746} \tag{17.12}$$

To measure the available mechanical power from a motor, a Prony brake is often utilized, as illustrated in Figure 17-9. You may have used a Prony brake in your physics experiments; now let us see how it measures horsepower. Let F equal the reading of scale B; this is the force in pounds applied to the brake surface. The diameter of the brake cylinder is L ft. When the brake cylinder makes one revolution, force F acts through a distance of $2\pi L$ ft, or it does $2\pi LF$ ft-lb of work. If the brake cylinder

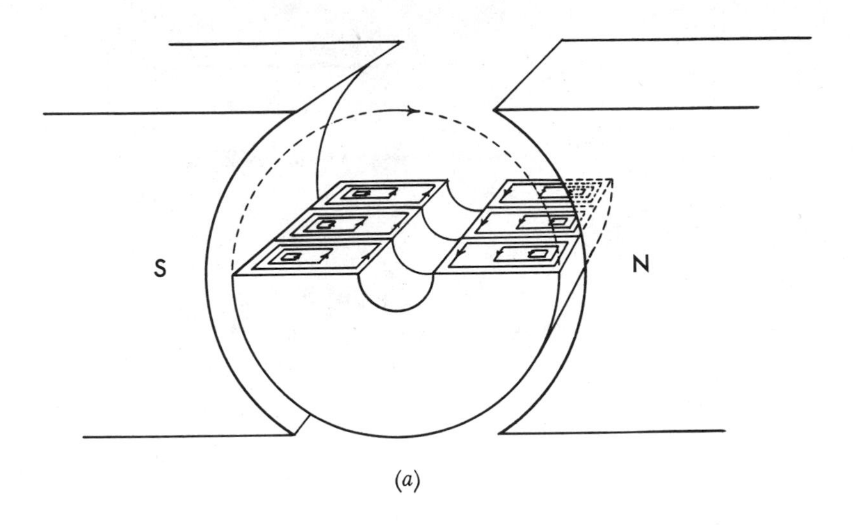

(*a*)

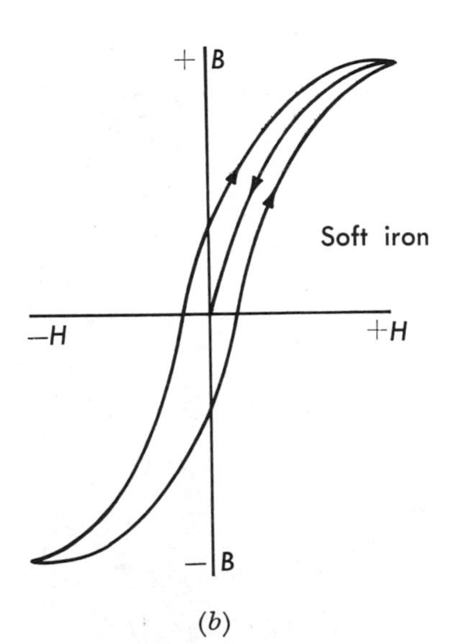

(*b*)

Figure 17-8
(*a*) Eddy currents. (*b*) Hysteresis loop.

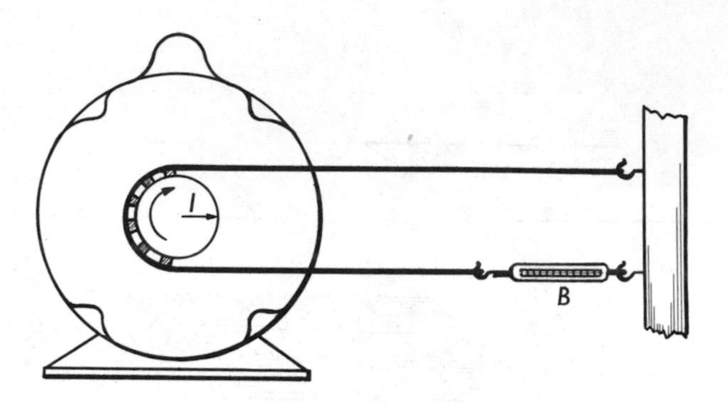

Figure 17-9
Basic plan of a Prony brake.

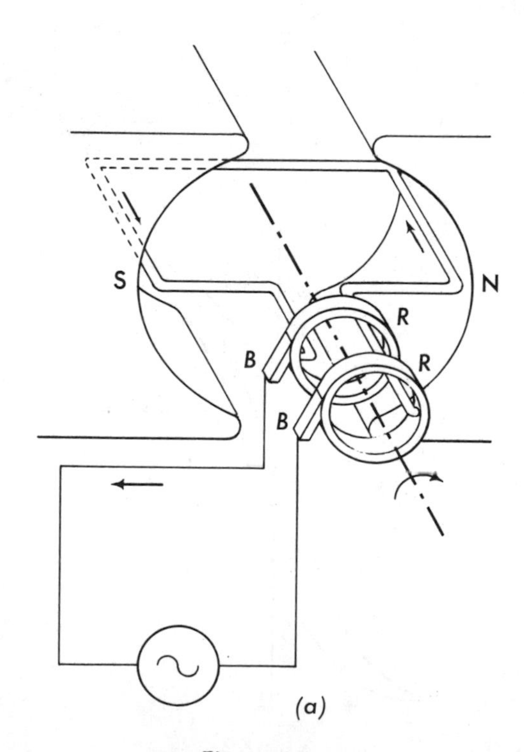

Figure 17-10
(a) The basic a-c motor is provided with slip rings. *(b)* A d-c motor is provided with a commutator.

(Continued on facing page.)

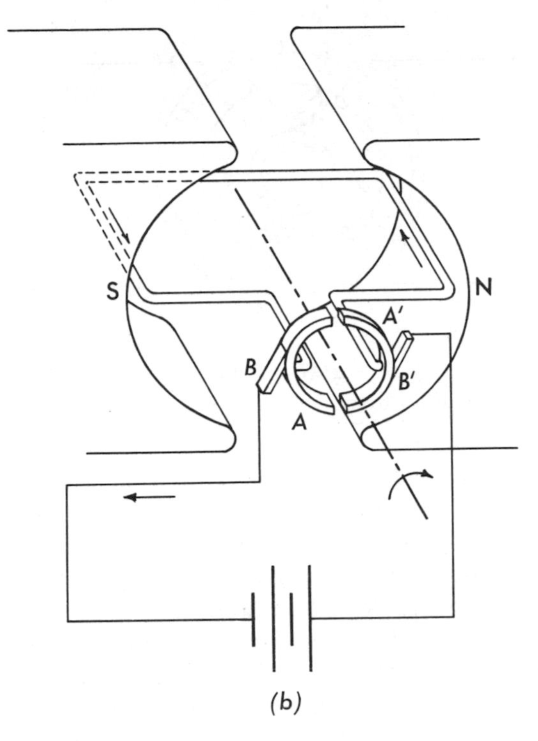

Fig. 17-10 (*Continued*)

rotates N revolutions per min, the work done is equal to $2\pi LFN$ ft-lb. Since 1 horsepower is equal to 33,000 ft-lb of work per min, the number of horsepower delivered by the motor is evidently equal to

$$\mathrm{HP} = \frac{2\pi LFN}{33{,}000} \tag{17.13}$$

The available mechanical power from a motor is customarily measured at a load corresponding to the rated volt-amperes of the motor. Accordingly, we will move back the support in Figure 17-9 until a voltmeter and ammeter show that the motor is drawing its rated volt-ampere value. At this time, the scale B will read a certain number of pounds F_2. Next, when the line is switched open, the scale B will read a lesser value F_1. The value of F in Equation (17.13) is equal to $F_2 - F_1$.

17.4 BASIC MOTOR ARRANGEMENTS

As we would anticipate, d-c motors utilize commutators, while a-c motors utilize slip rings, as depicted in Figure 17-10. The slip rings R-R make electrical connections to the source voltage via brushes B-B. Similarly,

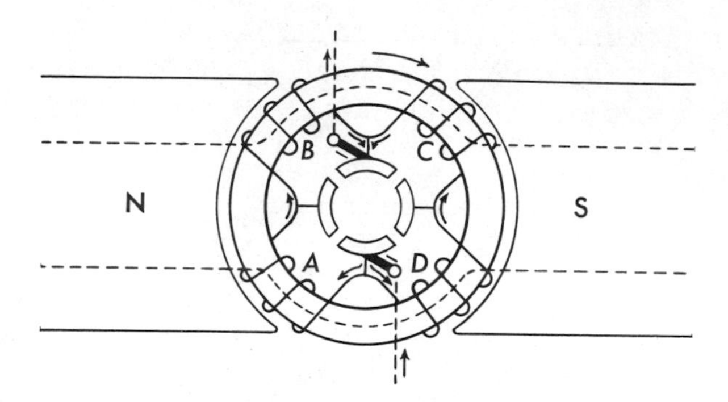

Figure 17-11
Connection arrangement for four armature coils, with basic position of brushes.

the commutator segments *A-A′* make electrical connections to the source voltage via brushes *B-B′*. A d-c motor will operate from an a-c voltage source; and, when operated in this manner, it is called a *universal* motor.

Consider a d-c motor with four armature coils, as seen in Figure 17-11. This is called a *ring-wound* armature, and is rarely used in modern motors. However, the arrangement is instructive, and applies basically to slotted armatures as well. The armature coils are connected in series. Evidently, the branch currents produce aiding torques with resulting clockwise rotation of the armature. Figure 17-12 shows how six armature coils are connected. It is clear that any desired number of armature coils may be

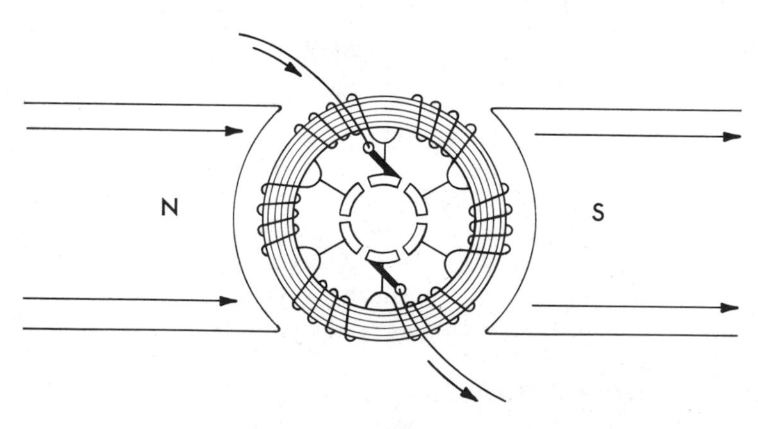

Figure 17-12
Connection arrangement for six armature coils.

utilized. It is helpful to use a large number of coils, because there is less tendency for the brushes to spark at the commutator.

A motor may have four field poles instead of two (Figure 17-13). There are also two positive brushes and two negative brushes, with the two positive brushes connected together, and the two negative brushes connected together. In this example, there are 24 armature coils. The current divides at each of the negative brushes and then passes in parallel through four circuits (two circuits for each brush) to the positive brush.

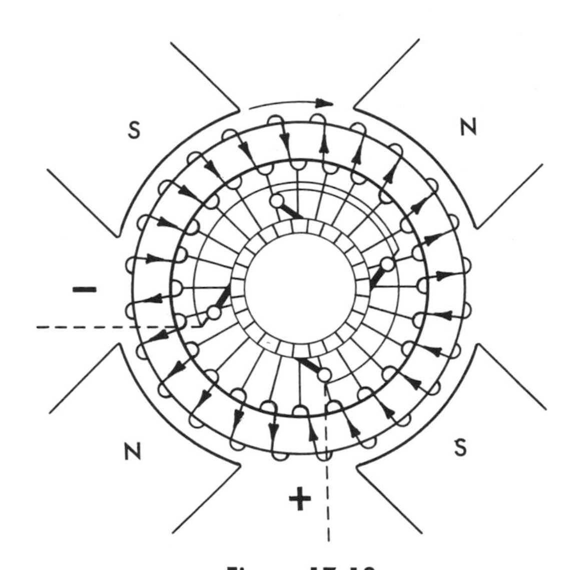

Figure 17-13
Arrangement of a motor with four field poles.

Small motors usually have only two poles; however, large motors may have four or more poles.

Many motors use some variety of the basic *drum* winding, depicted in Figure 17-14. Although it is customary to place the conductors in armature slots, analysis is facilitated by having the wires lie on the surface of the armature. We have seen that in the basic ring winding, conductors are connected in series and are wound over and under the ring core (Figure 17-13). On the other hand, a drum winding (Figure 17-14) has a return portion that also lies *over* the armature. No portion of the winding passes under the armature in a drum winding. Inasmuch as the torques of both portions of the conductor loop must aid in armature rotation, it is evident that the return portion of a loop must fall under a pole of opposite polarity.

Thus, if the forward portion of a loop lies under the south pole in Figure 17-14, the return portion of the loop necessarily lies under the north pole. When the current enters the winding from one brush, it flows in series from turn-to-turn until it arrives at the other brush. For simplicity, only two complete turns are shown in Figure 17-14. Current passes to bar *A* from a conductor, thence to a conductor on the opposite side of the armature, back to bar *B*, and to another conductor on the opposite side of the armature, and so forth. Note that the unconnected conductors (every other conductor) in Figure 17-14 are actually connected to com-

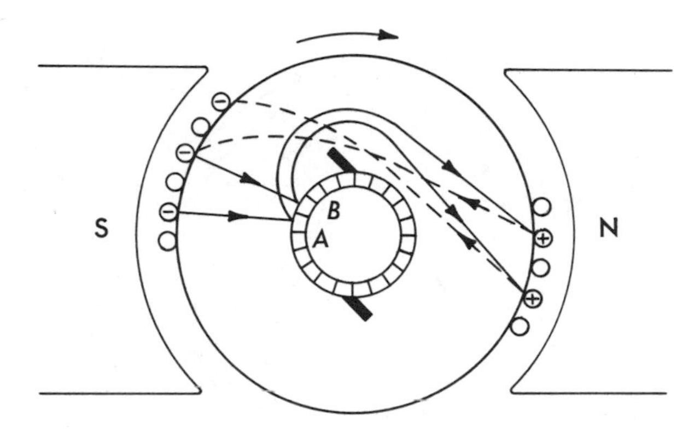

Figure 17-14
The basic drum winding, with two complete turns shown.

mutator bars opposite *A* and *B*—these connections are omitted to avoid confusion.

Figure 17-15(*a*) depicts a complete drum winding with ten commutator bars. With respect to the brushes, we observe that the winding comprises two circuits connected in parallel; in practice, however, each of the coils may have one turn, or a number of turns. Thus, a starter motor for an automobile ordinarily has one-turn coils formed from heavy copper strips. Such motors are designed to operate with very large currents at comparatively low voltages. But a universal motor, such as used in a vacuum cleaner, has a substantial number of turns in each coil [see Figure 17-15(*b*)]. This type of motor operates with comparatively small currents and comparatively high voltages. In addition, a universal motor has a laminated field construction as well as a laminated armature construction. A laminated field [Figure 17-15(*c*)] is required to minimize eddy-current losses, because the field is energized with alternating current in a universal motor.

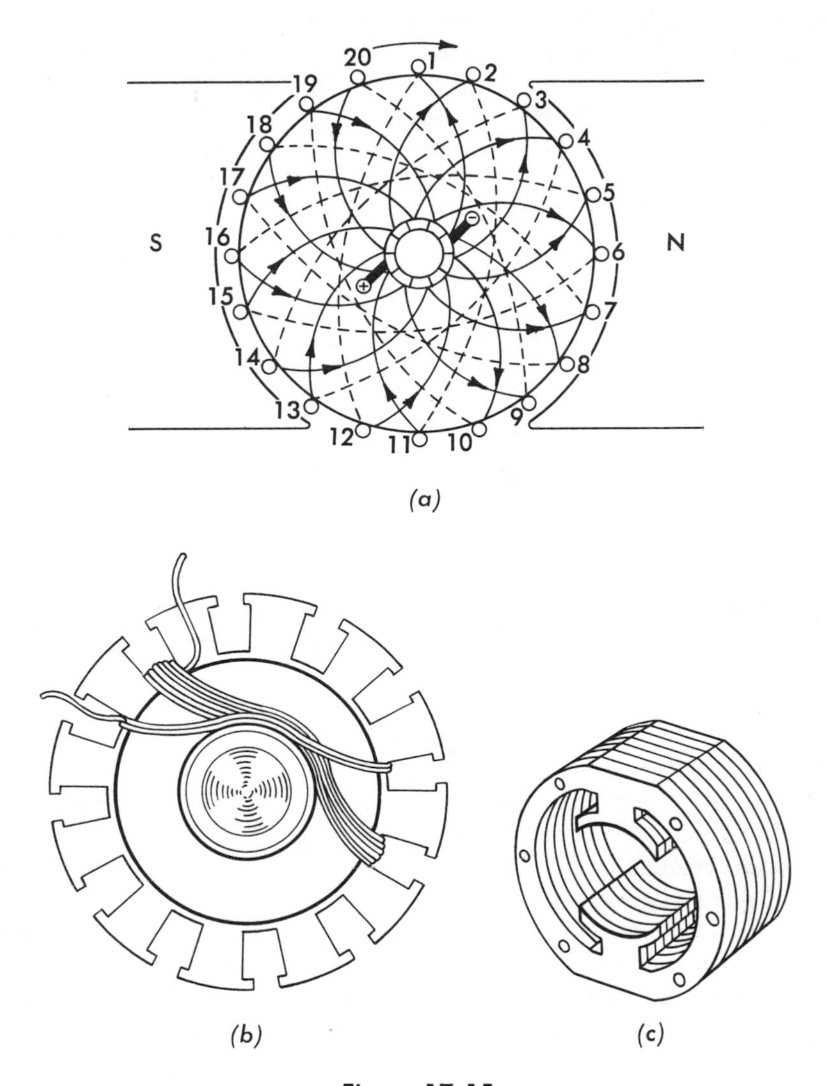

Figure 17-15

(*a*) Plan of a drum winding with ten commutator bars. (*b*) Multiturn coils wound in a slotted armature. (*c*) Laminated field structure.

SERIES MOTOR

Only the smallest type of motors, such as in electric clocks, employ permanent-magnet fields; all others have electromagnetic fields. One basic arrangement is the *series motor,* which has its field coil connected in series with the armature, as seen in Figure 17-16. When operated under no-load conditions, the speed increases to a very high value, because the current demand is small under no-load conditions. In turn, little current flows through the field, and the field flux falls to a very small value. The armature must then rotate with extreme rapidity to generate sufficient counter emf for equilibrium. Small series motors, such as used in vacuum cleaners, may be permitted to run under no-load conditions because friction and windage play a comparatively large part in braking the armature. Yet, a large series motor will be destroyed if operated with no load. The

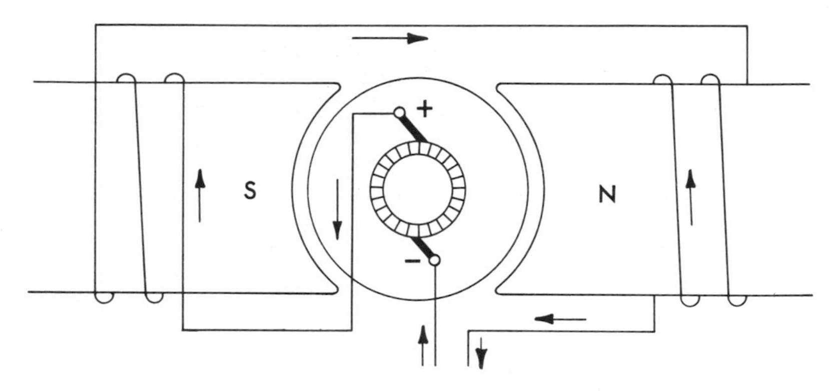

Figure 17-16
Winding connections in a series motor.

armature speed builds up to such an extreme value that centrifugal forces cause the armature construction to fly apart.

Direct-current motors that employ permanent-field magnets reverse their direction of rotation when the polarity of the supply voltage is reversed. It is evident that this must occur, because the direction of current flow through the conductors on the armature is reversed, while the field polarity remains unchanged. However, motors that utilize field electro magnets do not reverse their direction of rotation when the polarity of the supply voltage is reversed. This is true of both series and shunt configurations. When the polarity of the supply voltage is reversed, armature current flow is reversed, but in addition, the field polarity is also reversed. To reverse the direction of rotation, it is necessary to reverse the connections to the field terminals.

SHUNT MOTOR

Another basic arrangement is the *shunt motor* (Figure 17-17), which employs a field winding connected in parallel with the armature. Since the field coils in this type of motor have comparatively high resistance, they do not consume a substantial portion of the total power. You will perceive that a shunt motor cannot speed up excessively under no-load conditions. The field flux remains constant, regardless of load, and the counter emf acts as an effective brake. However, if you open the field circuit under no load, a shunt motor will speed up and destroy itself. The field magnets have some residual magnetism, and consequently the motor speeds up in the same manner as a series motor.

Basically, the efficiency of a shunt motor is approximately the same as the efficiency of a series motor. However, a series motor often operates

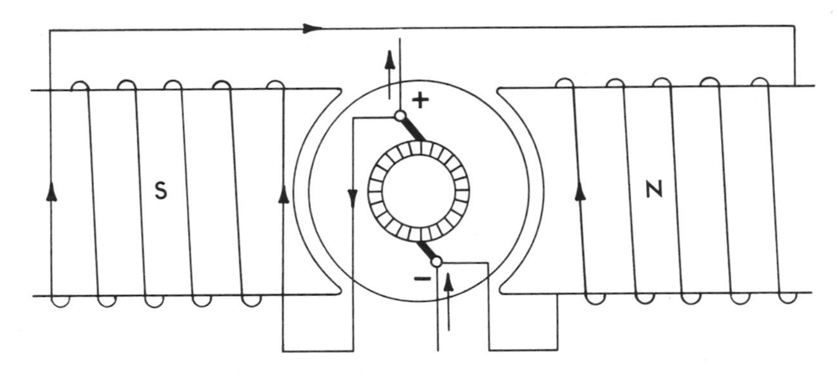

Figure 17-17
Winding connections in a shunt motor.

at widely varying speeds due to load variations; the series motor will then be less efficient than a shunt motor. Observe the characteristics shown in Figure 17-18 for a shunt motor. Its speed does not change greatly from full load to no load; efficiency is nearly maximum at full load. Its torque increases linearly with the load; however, we shall see that the increase of torque versus load is less than for a series motor.

Figure 17-19 depicts typical characteristics for a series motor. Its speed is subject to wide variations with load; efficiency is nearly maximum at full load. Its torque increases more rapidly for appreciable loads than in the case of a shunt motor. Automobile starter motors are series motors. A series motor can respond faster to application of a heavy load. The high speed of this motor under light loads is also an advantage in some applications. When a large series motor is to be operated under varying load conditions, it is essential to maintain the minimum loading at a value which prevents destructive armature speeds.

COMPOUND MOTOR

Another important basic type of motor is called the *compound motor.* As seen in Figure 17-20, part of the field flux is obtained with a series connection, and the remainder of the flux is obtained with a shunt connection. The series circuit may be connected either to aid or oppose the

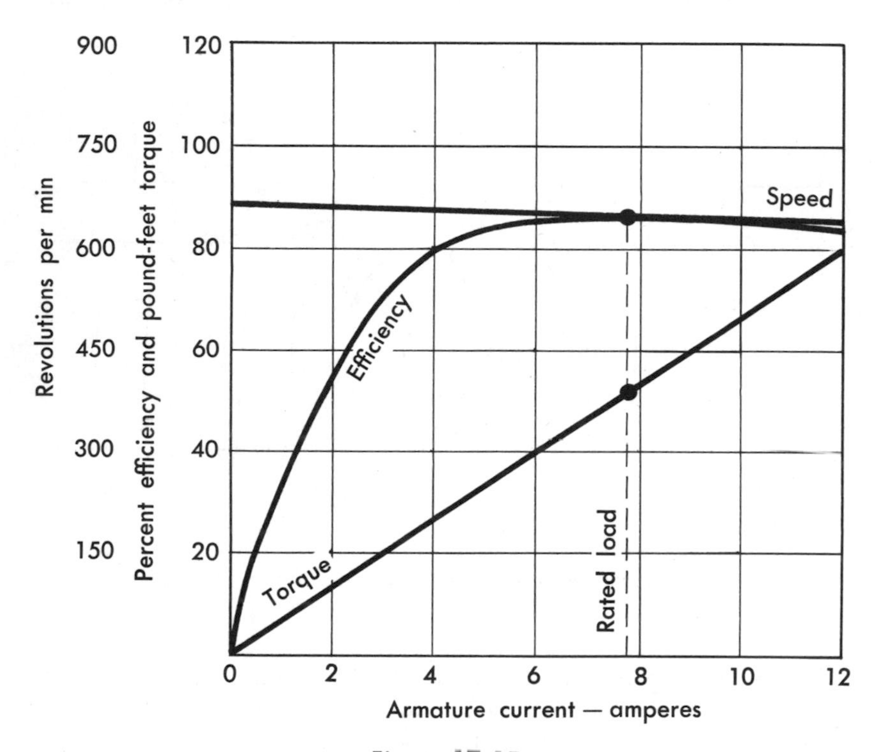

Figure 17-18
Typical operating characteristics for a shunt motor.

parallel circuit. Most compound motors are connected with aiding series and shunt field windings. This arrangement is called a *cumulative compound* motor. Its operating characteristics are intermediate to those of a series motor and a shunt motor. The chief advantage of the compound motor is that its no-load armature speed may be made practically the same as that of a shunt motor at higher torque. Hence, the shunt winding is commonly proportioned to maintain a safe armature speed under no load. Suitable winding proportions permit much better torque character-

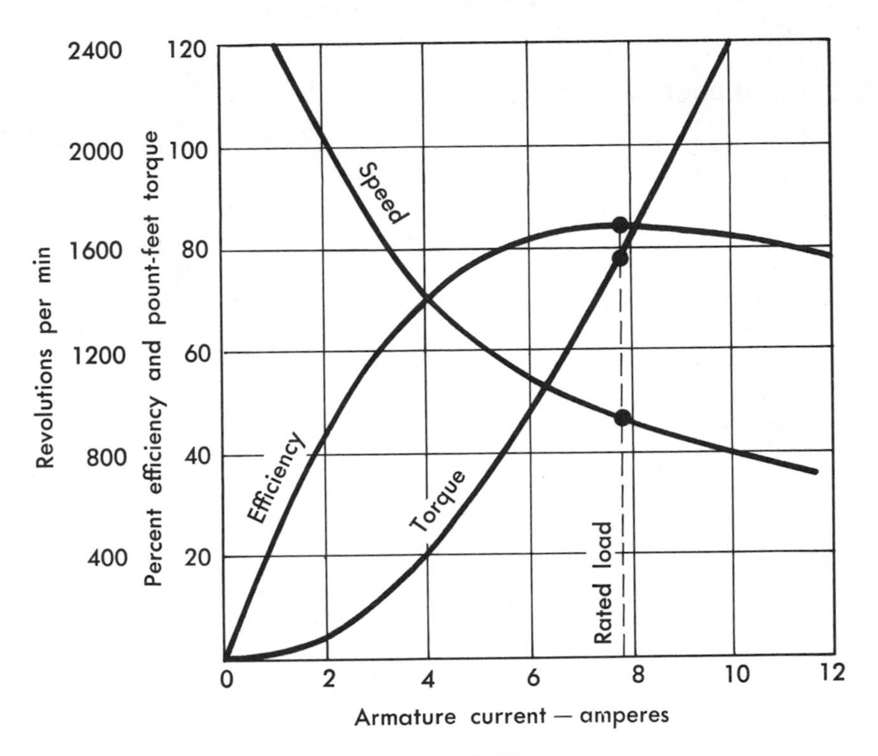

Figure 17-19
Typical operating characteristics for a series motor.

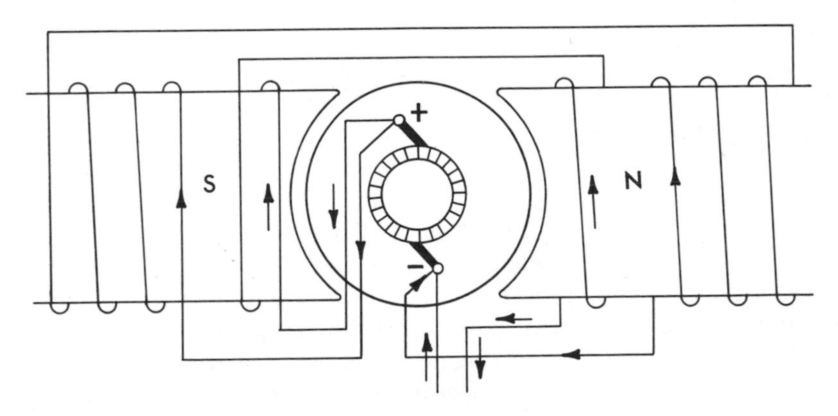

Figure 17-20
Winding connections for a cumulative compound motor.

istics than a shunt motor, without the danger of excessive armature speed at no load.

17.5 THE INDUCTION MOTOR

More a-c motors are in use than d-c motors. All utilities transmit a-c power at a 60-cycle frequency in the United States. Comparatively few a-c motors have commutators, and very few have slip rings. Instead, a-c current flowing in the field winding induces current in an armature arrangement called a *squirrel cage,* depicted in Figure 17-21. Rotation of the armature results from magnetic forces between the induced current

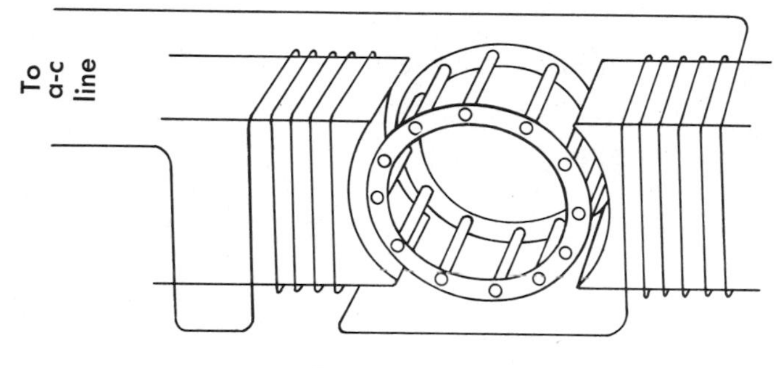

Figure 17-21
A squirrel-cage rotor.

and the field current. Motors that operate on this principle are called *induction motors.*

You will observe in Figure 17-21 that transformer action takes place from the stator to the rotor. Each pair of rods can be considered as a one-turn, low-resistance secondary winding. Like the simple *synchronous* motor [Figure 17-10(*a*)], the simple induction motor is not self-starting. However, if means are provided to give the rotor an initial start, torque will then develop. You may recall the earlier types of electric clocks that were not self-starting, but when the small motor shaft was given a twist of the fingers, the motor developed normal torque and operated until such time as the applied a-c voltage was interrupted. Then, the clock would stop until the motor was again started manually.

Nearly all electric clocks operate from synchronous motors. The reason for this design is that a clock must keep accurate time and the 60-cycle power-line frequency is accurately maintained by utilities. It is apparent from Figure 17-10(*a*) that a synchronous motor necessarily rotates in exact step with the applied frequency. But this is not true of an induction motor for here the rotor current is not applied from the a-c voltage source. Instead, it is induced from the stator. The rotor rods, therefore, do not *cut* the stator flux unless the rotor runs at slightly less than synchronous frequency. This difference in speed is called the *slip* of an induction motor; the heavier the load, the greater is the slip. If slip becomes excessive, the induction motor suddenly loses torque and "stalls."

Under full load, a typical induction motor operates at 1760 rpm,

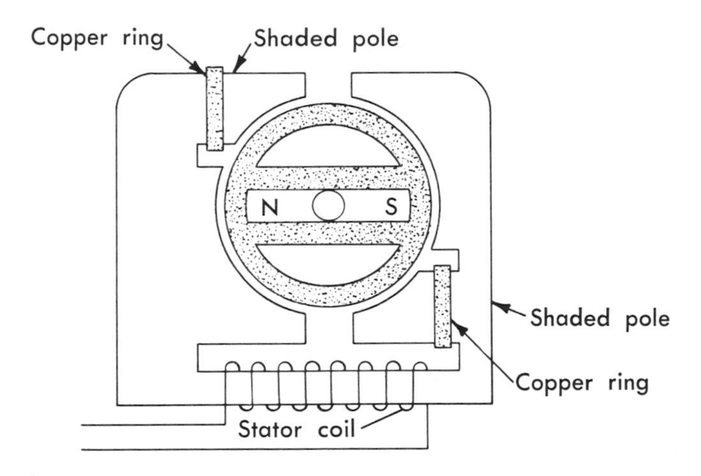

Figure 17-22
Typical shaded-pole construction.

whereas synchronous speed for the same number of field poles would be 1800 rpm. In this example, the slip is 40 rpm. Hence, simple induction motors, like simple synchronous motors, must be provided with auxiliary means to make them self-starting. Various means are employed, but all have the same effect. Either a lagging or leading field is provided in addition to the main field, so that as the north pole, for instance, in the main field is decreasing, a north pole in an adjacent position is increasing. This gives the effect of a *rotating* stator field, which provides starting torque.

One of the simplest starting arrangements is called a *shaded-pole* construction, as depicted in Figure 17-22 for a basic synchronous motor. The same shaded-pole arrangement is suitable for starting an induction motor. Let us see how it works. Note that the shaded pole is a portion of

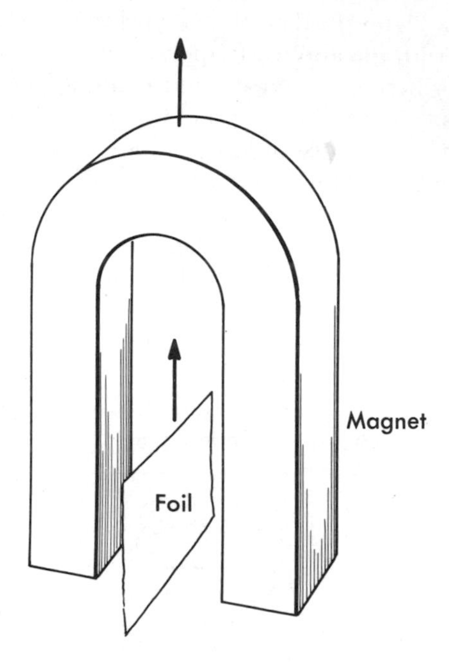

Figure 17-23
A moving magnetic field exerts force upon a metal object.

the stator, surrounded by a copper ring which is a one-turn secondary coil. A current is induced in the ring by the main field flux; however, the induced current is out of phase with the current in the stator coil. The induced current then produces a magnetic field which is out of phase with the main field and, in turn, the resultant field from the shaded pole is out of phase with the main field.

It is clear that as a north pole is decreasing in a main pole, a north pole will be building up in the shaded pole. Thus, the resultant north pole rotates or "sweeps" across the surface of the rotor. You can make an experiment which demonstrates that a sweeping magnetic field drags a conductor along with it. If you place a sheet of metal foil between the poles of a strong horseshoe magnet, and suddenly move the magnet upward, as shown in Figure 17-23, the metal foil is also pulled upward. The reason for this action stems from induced current in the foil; the foil becomes an effective magnet and is attracted to the horseshoe magnet.

17.6 MOTOR TROUBLESHOOTING

Motor troubleshooting is a specialized occupation. However, there are various simple defects which can be corrected by a nonspecialized technician. For example, an appliance motor may be inoperative merely because of a defective line cord. An ohmmeter test can be made to determine whether the cord is open-circuited. A switch may also become defective, but it can usually be replaced without undue difficulty. Short-circuits between turns or layers of the windings in a motor cause the motor to overheat even at no load. A motor can be checked for rated power consumption with a wattmeter. Rewinding of a motor must be done by an experienced technician.

When brushes wear excessively, intermittent contact is made with the commutator. Sparking results, which burns and pits the commutator; then the worn brushes must be replaced. Rough commutator surfaces can be smoothed by placing the armature in a lathe and turning down the commutator surface slightly. In some cases, judicious sanding with a strip of emery cloth suffices to smooth the commutator. The copper commutator bars are insulated from one another by mica sheets. As copper tends to wear faster than mica, the mica protrudes slightly in a worn commutator. This condition is called *high mica,* which can be corrected by slicing off the excess with a small chisel. The mica should be cut slightly below the copper surface.

Badly damaged commutators can be replaced, but this must be done by an experienced technician. Motor bearings must be kept lubricated; however, the commutator must not be lubricated. Another type of difficulty is caused occasionally by excessive absorption of moisture. In this case, a leakage path is set up between the windings and the motor frame. The frame becomes "hot" and may give a person a shock when touched. If the motor is dried out thoroughly in an oven at moderate heat, the leakage will usually disappear; however, if it persists, the motor must be repaired by a specialist. An ohmmeter test will show whether there is leakage resistance between the winding terminals and the motor frame.

Large motors arc quite costly, and are always repaired when any defect occurs. On the other hand, small motors such as used in appliances are modestly priced. Hence, when a time-consuming repair is required, such as rewinding of the armature or field, a small motor may be simply discarded and replaced. Motors used in automobiles are fairly costly, and hence they are usually sent to a motor repair shop when rewinding is required.

SUMMARY OF FUNDAMENTAL CONCEPTS

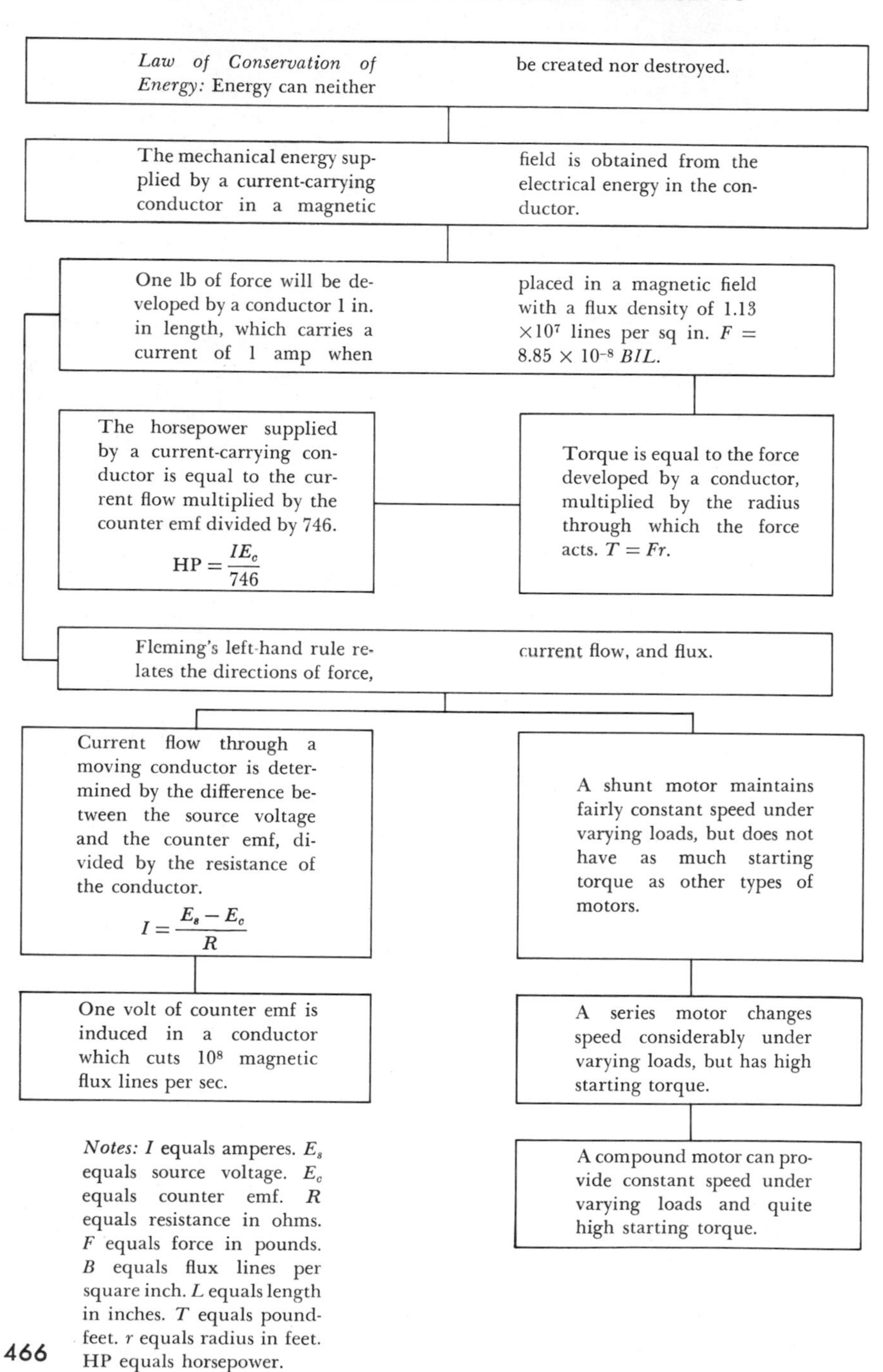

Law of Conservation of Energy: Energy can neither be created nor destroyed.
The mechanical energy supplied by a current-carrying conductor in a magnetic field is obtained from the electrical energy in the conductor.
One lb of force will be developed by a conductor 1 in. in length, which carries a current of 1 amp when placed in a magnetic field with a flux density of 1.13 $\times 10^7$ lines per sq in. $F = 8.85 \times 10^{-8} BIL$.
The horsepower supplied by a current-carrying conductor is equal to the current flow multiplied by the counter emf divided by 746. $HP = \frac{IE_c}{746}$
Torque is equal to the force developed by a conductor, multiplied by the radius through which the force acts. $T = Fr$.
Fleming's left-hand rule relates the directions of force, current flow, and flux.
Current flow through a moving conductor is determined by the difference between the source voltage and the counter emf, divided by the resistance of the conductor. $I = \frac{E_s - E_c}{R}$
A shunt motor maintains fairly constant speed under varying loads, but does not have as much starting torque as other types of motors.
One volt of counter emf is induced in a conductor which cuts 10^8 magnetic flux lines per sec.
A series motor changes speed considerably under varying loads, but has high starting torque.
A compound motor can provide constant speed under varying loads and quite high starting torque.
Notes: I equals amperes. E_s equals source voltage. E_c equals counter emf. R equals resistance in ohms. F equals force in pounds. B equals flux lines per square inch. L equals length in inches. T equals pound-feet. r equals radius in feet. HP equals horsepower.

QUESTIONS

1) If current flows through a wire near a compass needle, the:
(*a*) wire exerts force on the magnet only. (*b*) magnet exerts force on the wire only. (*c*) wire exerts a force on the magnet, and the magnet exerts a force on the wire. (*d*) wire exerts zero force on the magnet, and vice versa.
2) Torque is a function of:
(*a*) force and the radius through which it acts. (*b*) inductance and capacitance. (*c*) leakage flux and conventional current flow. (*d*) the force of attraction and the length of the armature shaft.
3) Counter emf denotes:
(*a*) the speed of electron flow through the armature. (*b*) the speed of conventional current flow through the armature. (*c*) the difference between the speed of current flow through the armature and the field coils. (*d*) a voltage generated by a motor armature winding that opposes the voltage applied to the winding.
4) A Prony brake is used to measure:
(*a*) input power to a motor. (*b*) input power to a generator. (*c*) output power from a motor. (*d*) mechanical power loss in motor bearings.
5) Permanent-magnet fields are used in:
(*a*) chiefly small toy motors and electric-clock motors. (*b*) large saw-mill motors. (*c*) motors for Diesel locomotives. (*d*) starter motors for automobiles.
6) Shunt motors have:
(*a*) capacitors shunted across their field windings. (*b*) shading poles shunted across their armatures. (*c*) squirrel cages shunted across their fields. (*d*) field windings shunted across their armature windings.
7) Series motors have:
(*a*) inductors shunted across their field windings. (*b*) single-turn field windings connected in series-parallel with their armature windings. (*c*) field windings connected in series with their armature windings. (*d*) single-turn armature loops connected in series-parallel with their armature windings.
8) Induction motors always:
(*a*) operate from a d-c voltage source. (*b*) step up the line voltage for application to the field winding. (*c*) have a stator winding which induces current flow in the armature conductors. (*d*) step down the line current for application to the field winding.
9) A simple induction motor is:
(*a*) not self-starting. (*b*) likely to destroy itself under no load. (*c*) al-

ways in synchronism with the power frequency. (*d*) the same as a d-c motor with slip rings.

10) Shading coils are used to:
(*a*) minimize heating of a motor under full load. (*b*) prevent excessive armature speed at no load. (*c*) generate an out-of-phase flux field. (*d*) minimize commutator sparking.

PROBLEMS

1) A wire is placed in a uniform magnetic field that has a flux density of 10,000 lines per sq cm. Two cm of wire are acted upon the field. If a current of 1 amp flows in the wire, what force in dynes will be exerted on the wire?
2) A wire is placed in a uniform magnetic field that has a flux density of 10,000 lines per sq in. Two in. of wire are acted upon by the field. If a current of 1 amp flows in the wire, what force in pounds will be exerted on the wire?
3) How many pounds of force are exerted on the wire in Problem 1?
4) How many dynes of force are exerted on the wire in Problem 2?
5) If a force of 10 lb is applied to a lever 6 in. in length, what is the value of the torque which is exerted?
6) A ¼-horsepower motor rated for 117 volts a-c has a terminal resistance of 4 ohms. The motor is erroneously connected to a 117-volt d-c source, and refuses to run. How much power does the motor consume from the d-c source?
7) When a 220-volt d-c motor is operated at full load, it draws 22 amps. If its armature resistance is 0.1 ohm, calculate the counter emf generated by the armature.
8) If 234 watts of power are supplied to a 117-volt d-c motor, and a Prony brake indicates that 0.26 horsepower are delivered by the motor, what is I^2R loss of the armature in watts?
9) What is the efficiency of the motor in Problem 8?
10) A motor draws 3 amps and develops a counter emf of 115 volts. Approximately how many horsepower does the motor provide?
11) A Prony brake is applied to a 6-in. cylinder on the end of a motor shaft. When the motor is stopped, the scale in Figure 17-9 reads 10 lb. If the scale reads 50 lb when the motor rotates 800 rpm, how many horsepower are being delivered by the motor?
12) If a synchronous motor has two poles, what is the synchronous speed of the armature when the motor is energized from a 60-cycle line?
13) The shunt motor corresponding to the characteristics depicted in Figure

17-18 is operated at half its rated load. What is its speed, efficiency, and torque?

14) If the series motor corresponding to the characteristics depicted in Figure 17-19 is operated at 20 percent over its rated load, what is its speed, efficiency, and torque?
15) An induction motor has an ideal speed of 1800 rpm. When loaded, it runs at 1700 rpm. What is its slip?

18

D-C METERS

18.1 METER MOVEMENTS

Many types of mechanisms, or movements, are used in electrical measuring instruments. However, the d'Arsonval movement depicted in Figure 18-1 is in widest use; it operates on the motor principle. A moving coil is suspended on jeweled bearings in a magnetic field. Spiral phosphor-

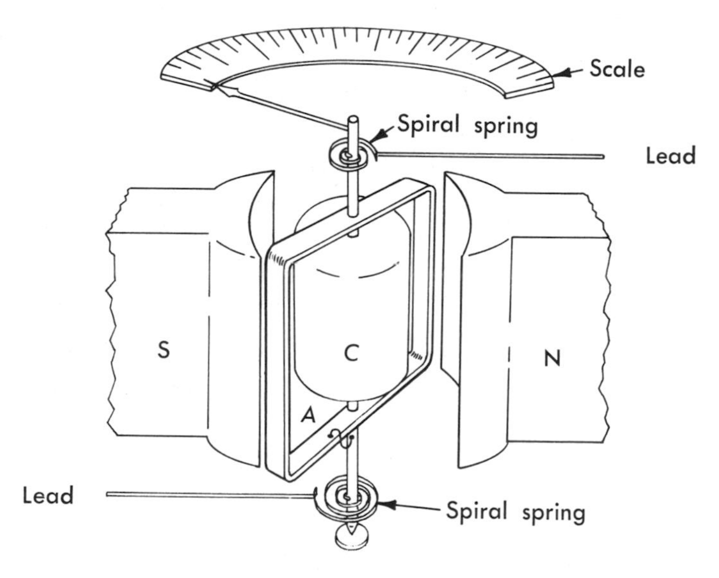

Figure 18-1
The basic d'Arsonval movement.

bronze springs resist the torque that develops when current passes through the coil. Hence, the pointer comes to rest at a point of equilibrium between the two forces. Meters used in the great majority of electronics applications are designed to be highly sensitive; therefore, the magnetic field is designed to have as high a flux density as is practical.

To obtain high flux density, the air gap between the magnet poles and the core *C* in Figure 18-1 must be small. In turn, the moving coil *A* is very thin. Substantial torque at small current values (high sensitivity) requires a large number of turns on the moving coil; hence, the coil is

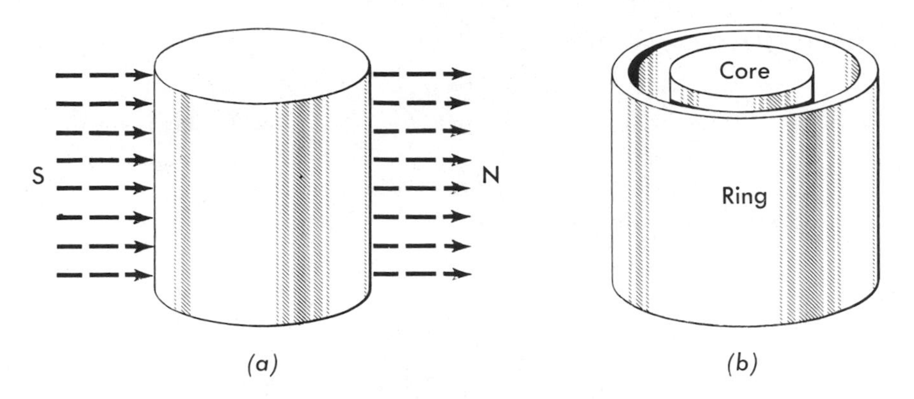

Figure 18-2
(*a*) Permanent magnet for a core-type movement. (*b*) Soft-iron ring surrounds the core.

wound with very small wire. The resistance of a typical moving-coil winding is 2000 ohms. A current of 50 μa develops sufficient torque in this type of movement to provide full-scale deflection. Note that a d'Arsonval movement is basically a current indicator. When current is passed directly through the moving coil, the instrument operates as a microammeter.

Many movements utilize horseshoe permanent magnets; however, the present trend is to core-type magnets. Note in Figure 18-1 that core *C* is fabricated from soft iron. Pole pieces *N* and *S* are part of a horseshoe permanent magnet. But a core-type movement uses a hard-steel or magnetic alloy core, which is strongly magnetized (Figure 18-2). This core-type permanent magnet is also surrounded by a soft-iron ring which provides more compact construction, and also shields the movement to better advantage against stray magnetic fields.

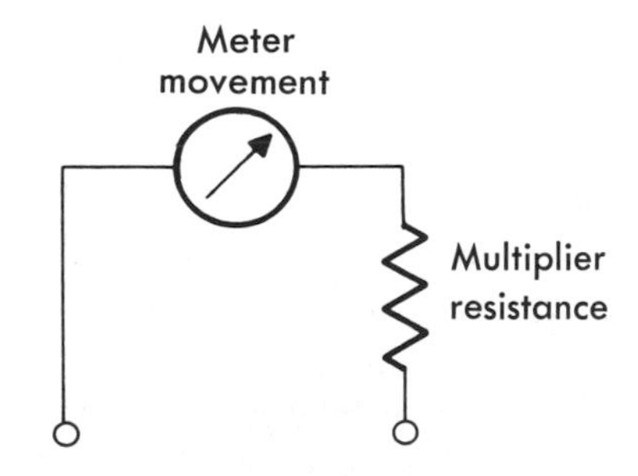

Figure 18-3
Basic d-c voltmeter configuration.

18.2 VOLTMETER MULTIPLIERS

A voltmeter consists basically of a meter movement connected in series with a multiplier resistor, as seen in Figure 18-3. Recall that a voltmeter is always applied across a voltage source, thus drawing a small current from it. Ohm's law states that the current which flows through the multiplier resistance and the meter movement is directly proportional to the

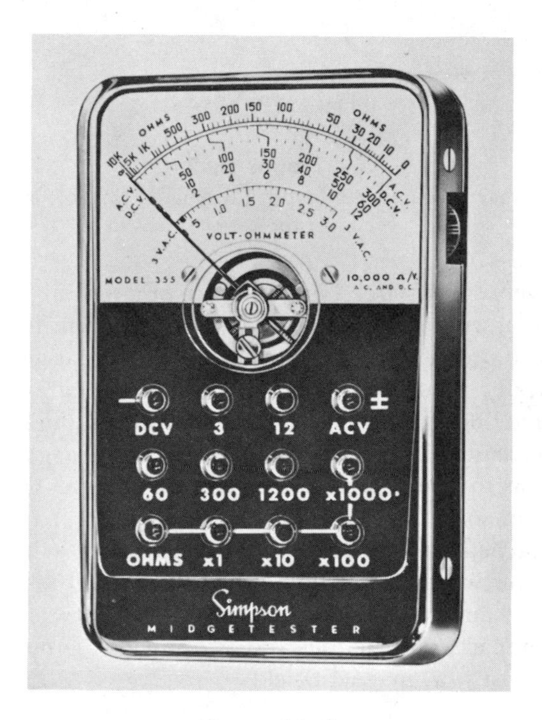

Figure 18-4

Volt-ohmmeter which contains a core-type movement. (Courtesy of Simpson Electric Co.)

applied voltage. Hence, the scale of the voltmeter can be calibrated in volt units.

Most d-c voltmeters have several ranges. Additional ranges (Figure 18-4) are obtained by employing suitable values of multiplier resistance. These values are used, for example, in the volt-ohm-milliammeter illustrated in Figure 18-5. The 80-meg multiplier for the 5-kv range is brought out to a separate terminal. A rotary switch is utilized on the lower voltage ranges, but its insulation resistance will not withstand 5000 volts. Hence, the positive test lead must be changed over to the 5-kv input terminal

Figure 18-5
Typical volt-ohm-milliammeter which utilizes a rotary switch. (Courtesy of Simpson Electric Co.)

when operating on the 5-kv range. In television service applications, d-c voltages up to 25,000 volts are applied to the picture tube. Measurement of such high-voltage values requires the use of an external multiplier resistance, as seen in Figure 18-6.

You will observe that multiplier resistance values are selected in Figure 18-7 to provide 50 microamps current flow for full-scale indication on each range. The value of the multiplier resistance in Figure 18-6 is simi-

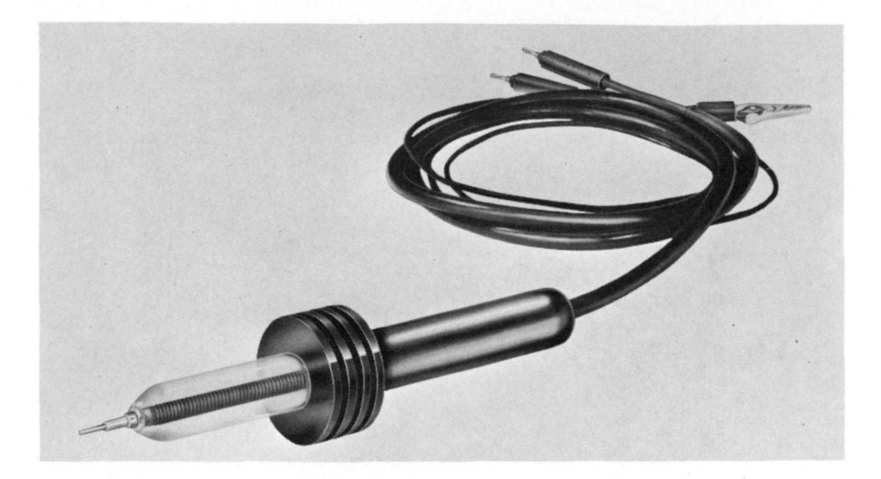

Figure 18-6
External multiplier resistance in probe form. (Courtesy of Precision Apparatus Co.)

larly selected to provide full-scale deflection when 25,000 volts are applied to the probe. When the voltmeter is to be operated on a 25,000-volt range, the high-voltage probe is substituted for the test leads that are used on the lower ranges.

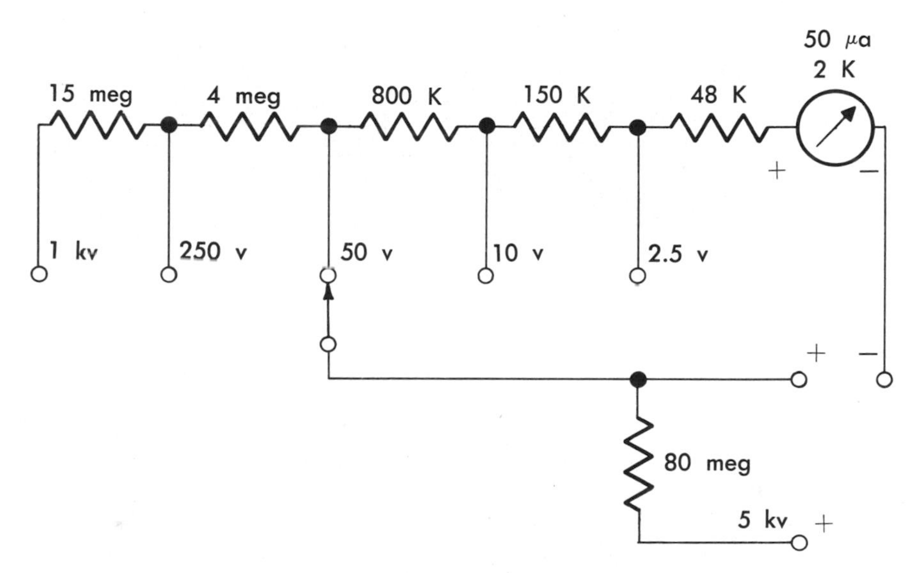

Figure 18-7
Multiplier resistances provide a choice of ranges.

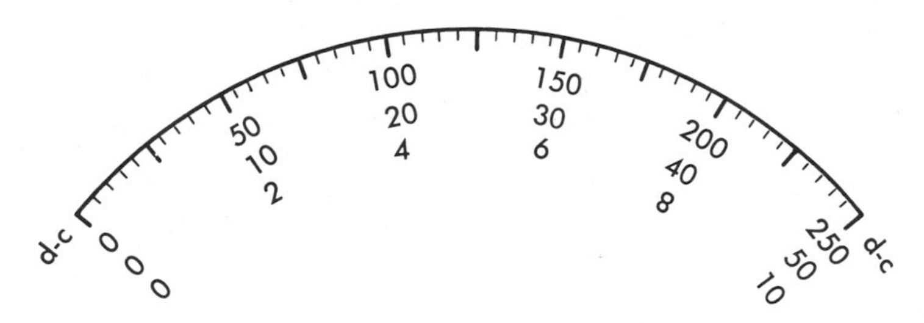

Figure 18-8
A single scale accommodates various ranges.

A few d-c voltmeters provide a separate scale for each range; however, most instruments have a scale arrangement such as seen in Figure 18-8. The "250" scale serves as a 2.5-, 250-, or 25,000-volt indicator. You merely shift the decimal point suitably to read the scale on any one of these three ranges. Similarly, the "50" scale serves as a 50- or 5000-volt indicator; the "10" scale serves as a 10- or 1000-volt indicator.

18.3 VOLTMETER SENSITIVITY

All d-c voltmeters are rated for sensitivity in terms of ohms-per-volt. It is evident from Ohm's law that if an instrument draws 50 microamps for full-scale indication on each of its d-c voltage ranges, the internal resistance on each range is equal to the reciprocal of 50 microamps, or 20,000 ohms-per-volt. Therefore, if you are operating the instrument on its 2.5-volt full-scale range, its internal, or input, resistance is evidently equal to $2.5 \times 20{,}000$ or 50,000 ohms.

However, if you are operating a 20,000 ohms-per-volt instrument on its 10-volt full-scale range, its input resistance on this range will be 200,000 ohms. It is helpful to check the foregoing values of input resistance against the circuit diagram in Figure 18-7. Suppose you are operating the instrument on its 5000-volt full-scale range; its input resistance is now equal to 100 megohms. It is necessary to be aware of the input resistance value, because a voltmeter draws more current on its lower ranges than on its higher ranges. If a voltmeter draws excessive current from a circuit under test, the circuit is abnormally loaded. The voltage distribution in the circuit is then changed appreciably, and the voltmeter will indicate subnormal voltage values. In general, a voltmeter should have an input resistance that is at least 50 times greater than the internal resistance of the circuit under test.

A simple example makes this requirement clear. If you apply a voltmeter directly across the terminals of a new 1.5-volt dry cell, the instrument will read the actual terminal voltage of the cell, for all practical purposes. The internal resistance of a "good" cell is extremely small compared with the 50,000-ohm input resistance of the voltmeter. But you might attempt to measure the emf of a cell that is connected in series with a 50,000-ohm resistor. Because the 50,000-ohm resistor is in series with the test leads to the voltmeter, half of the voltage is dropped across the resistor, and the voltmeter will read 0.75 volt. However, the open-circuit voltage of the cell-and-resistor series combination is 1.5 volts. If you use a voltmeter having an input resistance of 10 megohms, for example, the instrument will indicate practically 1.5 volts.

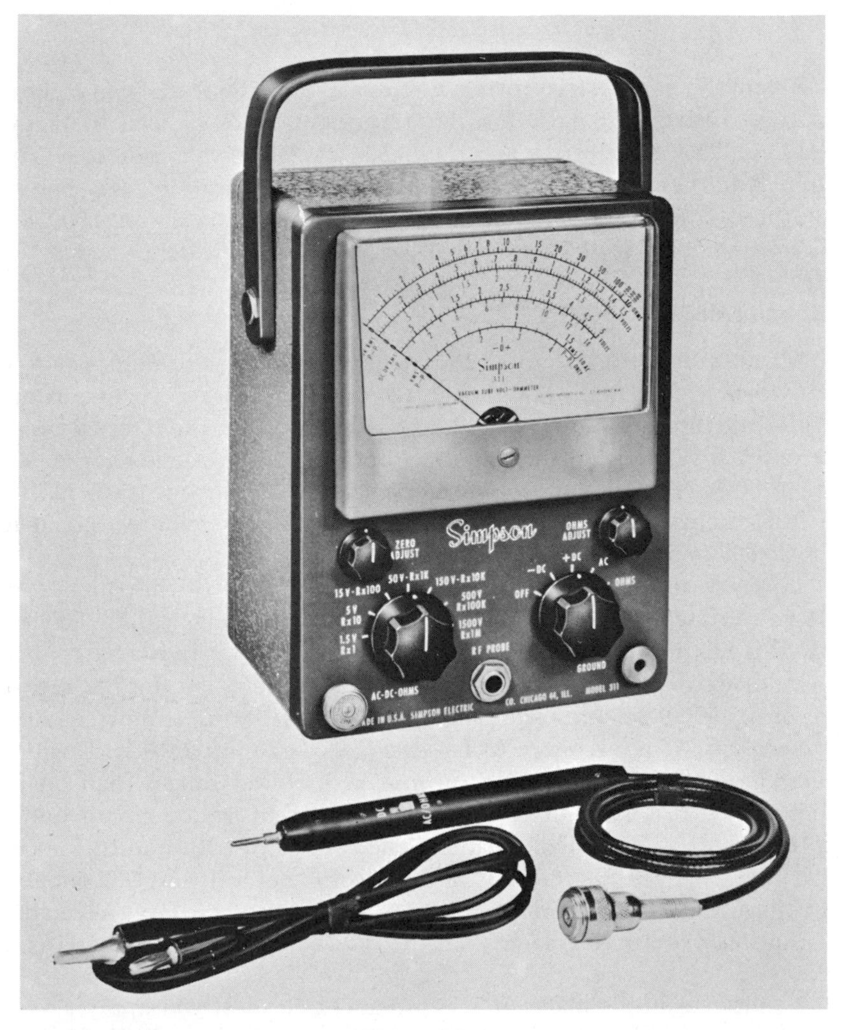

Figure 18-9
A typical vacuum-tube voltmeter. (Courtesy of Simpson Electric Co.)

Although a simple voltmeter has very high input resistance on its high-voltage ranges, it is not practical to measure small voltage values on a high range. The pointer moves so slightly that it is not possible to read the voltage value with satisfactory accuracy. Accordingly, when voltage values are to be measured in circuits that have high internal resistance, another type of voltmeter is used that has high input resistance on its low-voltage ranges. For example, the vacuum-tube voltmeter illustrated in Figure 18-9 has 20 megohms input resistance on all d-c voltage ranges.

18.4 CURRENT MEASUREMENT

If you connect a 50-μa movement in series with a circuit under test, you can read current values from 0 to 50 microamps. When higher values of current are to be measured with the movement, a *shunt* is connected

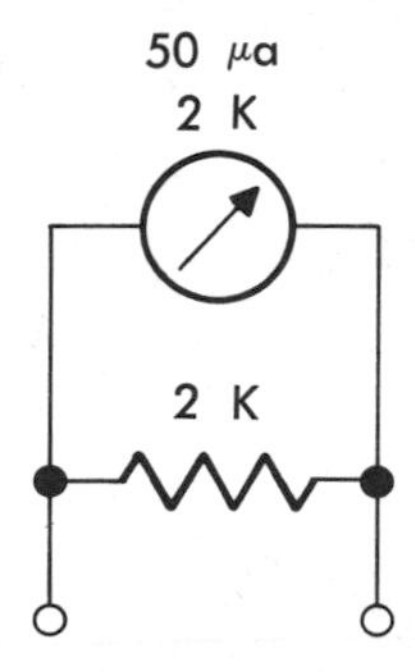

Figure 18-10
The shunt provides 100 microamps full-scale indication.

across the meter terminals, as depicted in Figure 18-10. In this example, the shunt has a resistance value equal to that of the movement. Hence, half of the incoming current flows through the movement, and half flows through the movement in accordance with Kirchhoff's current law. Consequently, the movement indicates 100 microamps at full scale.

A panel-type current meter, such as illustrated in Figure 18-11, has a single shunt resistor. On the other hand, the VOM in Figure 18-5 has several current ranges, and utilizes five shunt resistors, as depicted in Figure 18-12. This configuration is called a *ring shunt.* A ring shunt is generally preferred over other arrangements because the shunt circuit is never open during switching. This feature avoids the possibility of damage to the movement while the switch passes from one contact to the next. Thus, a ring shunt presents a series-parallel circuit to the movement. It is left as an exercise for the student to verify the resistance values noted in Fig-

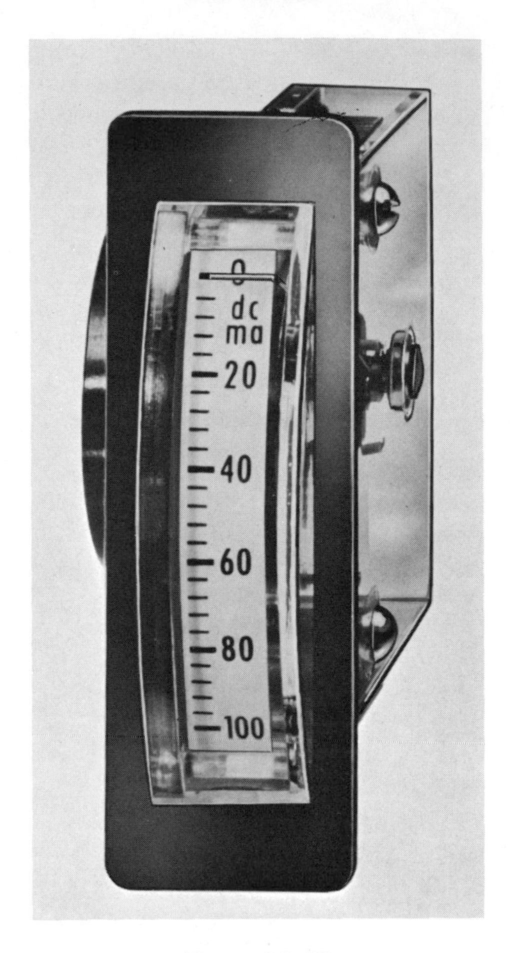

Figure 18-11
A panel-type current meter. (Courtesy of Simpson Electric Co.)

ure 18-12. Note that the resistance values in a ring shunt may *seem* to be slightly off-value in some cases, because the resistance of the leads must be taken into account.

You will also find that high-current ranges often are arranged to bypass the range switch, because rotary switches may have limited current-carrying capacity. For example, the 10-amp range for the VOM illustrated in Figure 18-5 is not wired through the range switch. Instead, the test leads are plugged into the "10-amp" terminals, and connection is made to the 0.025-ohm shunt, as seen in Figure 18-13. Although it might appear that excessive current passes through the movement, remember that the resistance of the test leads for the VOM must be taken into account in

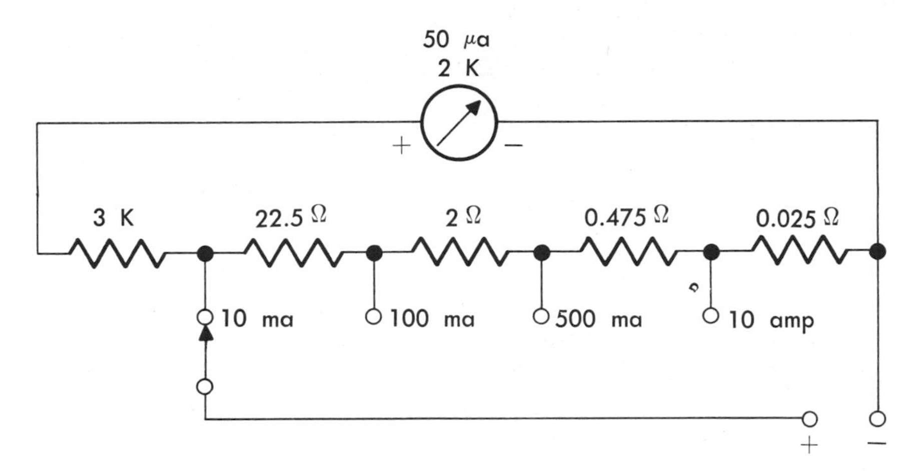

Figure 18-12
A ring-shunt arrangement for a multirange milliammeter.

computing the value of the shunt. This calculation is interesting, and is left as an exercise for the reader.

Observe that the input resistance of a current meter is low on its high-current ranges, but the input resistance is substantial on low-current ranges. When a current meter is connected in series with a circuit under test, the input resistance of the instrument is added to the circuit resistance, and less current is flowing in the circuit. This circumstance may or may not be of practical concern. When the circuit resistance is much higher than the instrument's input resistance, we can neglect the current change in practice. But when the circuit resistance is less than 50 times

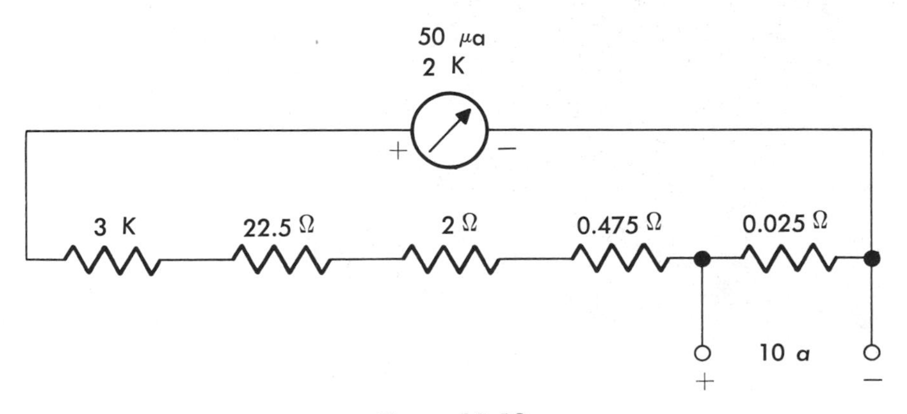

Figure 18-13
A separate terminal provided for high-current measurements.

the instrument's input resistance, it is often necessary to calculate the reduction in current flow caused by insertion of the instrument, and to correct the scale reading accordingly.

18.5 INSTRUMENT ACCURACY

Direct-current voltmeters are commonly rated in terms of full-scale indication accuracy. For example, the VOM illustrated in Figure 18-5 is rated for ±2 percent of full-scale accuracy. This means that if you are operating on the 10-volt range, the indication accuracy is rated at ±0.2 volt at any point on the scale. At full scale, the rated accuracy states that a 10-volt reading corresponds to a voltage from 9.8 to 10.2 volts. When the scale indication is 3 volts, the true voltage value falls between 2.8 and 3.2 volts, on the 10-volt range; or, if the scale indication is 0.5 volt on the 10-volt range, the true voltage value falls between 0.3 and 0.7 volt. The indication accuracy might be better than rated accuracy, but you cannot know this unless you calibrate the voltmeter against a suitably accurate standard.

Laboratory-type instruments are often used as secondary standards. For example, the voltmeter illustrated in Figure 18-14 has a rated accuracy on d-c ranges of ±0.1 percent of the reading at any value. If the volt-

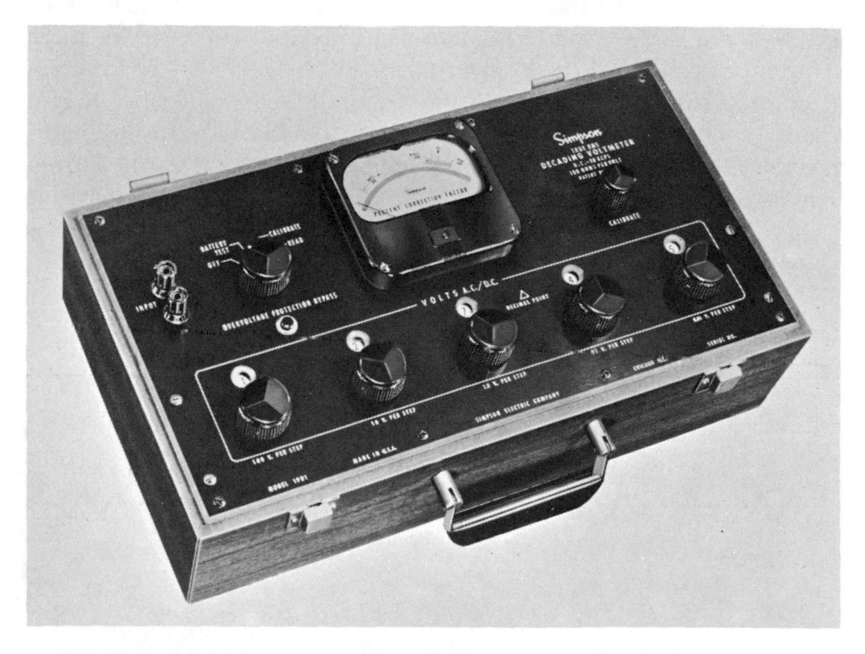

Figure 18-14
A typical decading voltmeter. (Courtesy of Simpson Electric Co.)

meter indicates 100 volts, the true voltage value falls between 99.9 and 100.1 volts; or, if the voltmeter indicates 0.5 volt, the true voltage value falls between 0.4995 and 0.5005 volt. This type of voltmeter is comparatively expensive, and is not used in electronics service applications; however, it finds wide use in design and development work.

18.6 OHMMETER PRINCIPLES

Figure 18-15 depicts a very simple ohmmeter configuration. The movement is connected in series with a small dry cell and a multiplier resistance, which has a value to provide full-scale deflection when the instrument terminals are short-circuited. When a resistor under test is connected between the terminals, current flows in accordance with Ohm's law. Hence, the meter scale can be calibrated to indicate resistance values

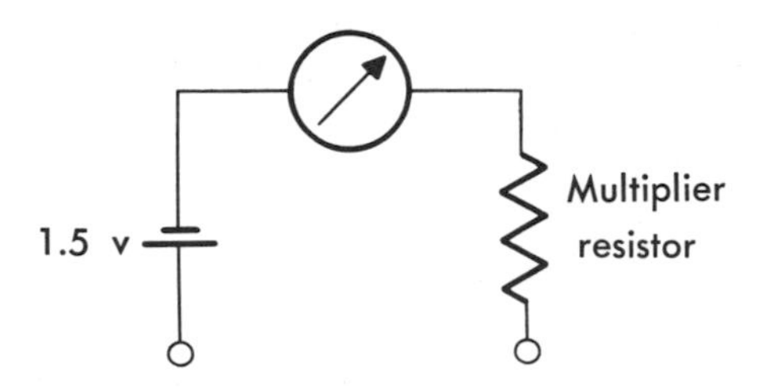

Figure 18-15
An elementary ohmmeter configuration.

in ohms. In practice, a rheostat must be provided to adjust the ohmmeter for full-scale indication when the instrument terminals are short-circuited. This "zero-set" control is required because the terminal voltage of a dry cell declines somewhat with age.

Observe the ohms scale and the zero-set control in the illustration of the VOM in Figure 18-5. The ohms scale is necessarily nonlinear, as you can verify by applying Ohm's law for several different values of test resistance in the circuit of Figure 18-15. An ohms scale for a VOM is also "reversed" with respect to the d-c volts scale. This sequence stems from the fact that an ohmmeter must indicate zero resistance at full-scale deflection. Practical ohmmeters also require several ranges, because the ohms scale is very cramped and difficult to read in the left-hand region.

An ohmmeter configuration with three ranges is shown in Figure 18-16. This is the circuit utilized in the instrument illustrated in Figure 18-5. It is apparent that when you connect a test resistance across the instrument terminals, having a value equal to the internal resistance of the ohmmeter, the pointer will deflect to half-scale. Note that a 110-ohm

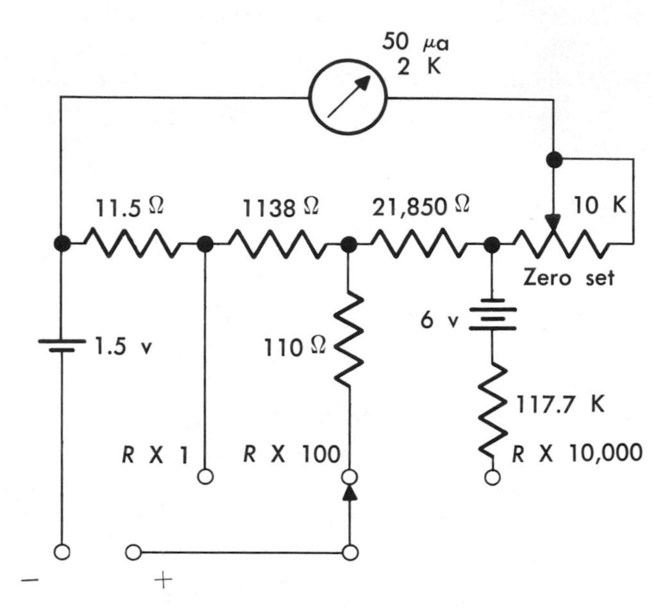

Figure 18-16
Three-range ohmmeter configuration.

resistor is connected in series with the test leads on the $R \times 100$ range; a 117.7-K resistor is connected in series with the test leads on the $R \times 10{,}000$ range. Let us see why these series resistors are required.

When the ohmmeter (Figure 18-16) is set to its $R \times 1$ range, an 11.5-ohm multiplier resistance is utilized. However, there is slightly more resistance in the circuit than one can perceive. The battery, the test leads, the instrument wiring, and range switch all have small resistances. Consequently, the scale calibration is affected by these residual resistances, and the ohmmeter scale is marked with divisions which take the total circuit resistance into account. The effective residual resistance is approximately 1.1 ohms. When you switch the ohmmeter to its $R \times 100$ range, the ohms scale cannot remain in calibration unless a proportional, compensating resistance is connected in series with the test leads. This series resistance necessarily has a value 100 times greater than the residual resistance on the $R \times 1$ range, or a value of 110 ohms.

Next, when the ohmmeter is switched to its $R \times 10{,}000$ range, both a battery and a resistance are connected in series with the test leads. A 6-volt battery is required to obtain necessary current flow through the large multiplier resistance. This 6-volt battery is in series with the 1.5-volt cell, so that the total source voltage becomes 7.5 volts. Now, to make the ohms scale remain in calibration, a 117.7-K series resistance is required.

The location of the zero-set control is somewhat of a design compromise. As a battery ages, its internal resistance increases; hence, the zero-set control will be adjusted for somewhat less resistance in series with the meter. The increase in the battery's internal resistance is then roughly compensated, but, as noted earlier, side reactions in an aging battery also cause its emf to decrease to some extent. Maximum accuracy would require that compensation be provided individually for increasing internal resistance and for declining emf. However, such compensation would increase the production cost of a service ohmmeter, and hence, a single zero set is used. Best accuracy is obtained when the ohmmeter batteries are fresh.

Ohmmeters are widely used in electronics service applications, but are seldom used in the laboratory. Resistance values are customarily measured with Wheatstone bridges in laboratory procedures, since these measurements provide maximum accuracy. Industrial-electronics technicians occasionally employ Wheatstone bridges, although routine service measurements are made with ohmmeters. Both laboratory and industrial-electronics tests occasionally require the use of ohmmeters which have a high source voltage, such as 1000 or 10,000 volts. Such ohmmeters are called *meggers,* and are used primarily to measure insulation resistance. A megger can indicate many thousands of megohms.

18.7 OPERATING PRECAUTIONS

Almost everyone has damaged an electrical instrument at some time. If a current meter is connected across a voltage source, it is almost certain to burn out. A current meter must always be connected in series with a circuit. The circuit resistance limits the current flow through the meter. It is also necessary to set a current meter to a suitable range. If excessive current flows through the movement on any range, the pointer will be slammed, even if the movement does not burn out. Slammed pointers are often bent, requiring that the movement be repaired by a meter specialist.

Good operating practice dictates that a current meter always be set initially to a much higher range than is deemed necessary. Then, the range switch can be set as required to obtain a reading on the upper half of the scale. This simple precaution will avoid much unnecessary expense in meter repair or replacement. A minority of meters, such as illustrated in Figure 18-5, have automatic protective circuitry that eliminates nearly all possibility of damage from misuse. However, most of the meters which you will use are unprotected, and you must observe good practices.

Voltmeters are always connected across the circuit or component under test. If a voltmeter is accidentally connected in series with a circuit, no damage will result to the movement except in unusual situations. However, voltmeter movements and multiplier resistors are often damaged because the user forgets to set the range switch to a suitably high range. For example, if the voltmeter is set to its 2.5-volt range, and is applied across a 5000-volt circuit, serious damage will result. Accordingly, good practice requires that a voltmeter be set initially to a much higher range than is deemed necessary. If a defect in the circuit under test should apply unexpectedly high voltage to the voltmeter, this fact will be immediately apparent.

Ohmmeters are often damaged because they are accidentally applied to a "live" circuit. If an ohmmeter is set to its $R \times 1$ range, and is connected to a live 117-volt circuit, the meter movement will be burned out and at least one multiplier resistor will be burned open. Hence, it is advisable to always operate a VOM first on its d-c voltage function, and if the reading is zero, to then switch the instrument to its ohms function. Even if power is removed from a circuit, the circuit is not necessarily "dead." For example, if a circuit contains an electrolytic capacitor, a very substantial charge may be stored in the capacitor after power is removed. If the capacitor voltage is applied to an ohmmeter, damage is very likely to result.

A pointer does not always rest at zero on a meter scale when the instrument is not energized. The phosphor-bronze hairsprings tend to change their equilibrium position slightly as an instrument ages. Hence, all movements are provided with a set-screw to bring the pointer exactly to zero on the scale when adjustment is required. You will observe the set-screw in Figure 18-5 just below the scales. Sometimes the set-screw must be readjusted when an instrument is changed from a vertical to a horizontal position. The movement is provided with tiny balance weights, but these are sometimes in imperfect adjustment. Hence, the zero set-screw may need a small readjustment to compensate for off-balance. When a movement is seriously out of balance, the balance weights must be readjusted by a meter specialist.

Meter movements should be opened only in a dust-free room. Tiny particles of dust will settle in the air gap and in the jeweled bearings or between the turns of the hairsprings. In turn, indication accuracy will be affected. Movements must not be unduly jarred. Excessive shock or vibration will demagnetize the permanent magnet and make the scale reading subnormal. Jewels are also likely to be chipped or cracked from violent mechanical strain. The shaft points are very sharp, and exert enormous forces on the jewels.

Movements must also be kept out of a-c fields. A substantial field will demagnetize the permanent magnets and affect indication accuracy. Core-type movements are less susceptible to demagnetization from external a-c fields than horseshoe-type movements. However, an a-c field that threads flux axially through a core-type movement will demagnetize the permanent magnet. If a movement is partially demagnetized for any reason, it must usually be sent to a meter repair shop.

A few movements are provided with series and shunt rheostats. These rheostats are maintenance adjustments that are used to compensate for loss of movement magnetization. The shunt rheostat is set to bypass less current around the movement. In turn, the series rheostat is set to maintain rated resistance of the movement. At a certain critical setting of the series and shunt rheostats, the loss of magnetization will be exactly compensated. Of course, when the demagnetization exceeds a certain limit, compensation is no longer possible. The movement must then be sent to a meter repair shop.

Since an ohmmeter applies voltage across the component under test, it is possible to damage certain components when attempt is made to measure their resistance value. For example, it is not advisable to measure the resistance of a meter movement with an ohmmeter. In most cases, the ohmmeter applies sufficient voltage to the movement under test that it will be damaged. Indirect methods are used accordingly, to measure the resistance of a movement.

The half-scale method is often used to measure the resistance of a movement. First, a current is passed through the movement which provides full-scale deflection. A decade resistance box is next connected across the terminals of the movement. The shunt resistance value is adjusted to make the movement indicate at half-scale. Then, the value of the shunt resistance is equal to the resistance of the movement.

SUMMARY OF FUNDAMENTAL CONCEPTS

Most electrical indicating instruments utilize movements which operate on the motor principle.

Utility instruments are generally rated for accuracy (possible error) in terms of percentage of full-scale indication.

Laboratory instruments are usually rated for accuracy (possible error) in terms of percentage of indication at any point on the scale.

Resistive shunts are connected across a movement to measure high values of current.

A current meter is always connected in series with the circuit under test.

An ohmmeter utilizes a series-parallel resistive network and a source of reference voltage in combination with a movement.

A d'Arsonval movement responds to d-c current flow; the movement can be used without a shunt to indicate small current values.

D-c voltage values are indicated by a movement which is connected in series with a multiplier resistance.

A voltmeter is always applied across the component or circuit under test.

An external multiplier resistor, called a high-voltage probe, is used with a voltmeter to measure high-voltage values.

Voltmeters are rated for sensitivity in terms of ohms-per-volt.

QUESTIONS

1) A voltmeter multiplier is:
(*a*) the relation between the full-scale indication and the half-scale indication. (*b*) a resistor connected in parallel with a movement. (*c*) a resistor connected in series with a movement. (*d*) the relation between magnetomotive force and flux density.
2) Voltmeter sensitivity is rated in terms of:
(*a*) ohms-per-volt. (*b*) volts-per-ohm. (*c*) ohms-per-ampere. (*d*) amperes-per-ohm.
3) A current meter shunt is a:
(*a*) relation between the full-scale indication and zero indication (*b*) resistor connected in series with a movement. (*c*) resistor connected in shunt with a movement. (*d*) relation between flux density and magnetomotive force.
4) An accuracy rating in terms of full-scale indication denotes:
(*a*) that the rated accuracy applies at any point from zero to full scale as a percentage tolerance on the particular reading. (*b*) that the rated accuracy applies at any point from zero to full scale as a constant which is added and subtracted from a particular reading to determine the indication tolerance. (*c*) that the indicated value is sufficiently accurate that any residual error can be disregarded. (*d*) that the meter scale is highly cramped in the left-hand region.
5) An ohmmeter is used to:
(*a*) vary the internal resistance of a circuit under test. (*b*) adjust the source resistance of a circuit under test. (*c*) measure the resistance of a meter movement. (*d*) measure the resistance of a component or "dead" circuit.
6) An ohmmeter is connected into a "live" circuit:
(*a*) to measure conventional current flow. (*b*) to measure electron flow. (*c*) to measure source resistance. (*d*) because of an unfortunate accident.
7) Ohmmeters are:
(*a*) more accurate than Wheatstone bridges. (*b*) useful for measuring insulation resistance. (*c*) less accurate than Wheatstone bridges. (*d*) used as primary standards.
8) A current meter is connected across a voltage source:
(*a*) to measure the internal current of the source. (*b*) to measure the conductance of the source. (*c*) to calculate the internal resistance of the source. (*d*) only in consequence of an unfortunate accident.
9) An instrument should always:

(*a*) be set initially to a higher range than is deemed necessary. (*b*) be set initially to the anticipated voltage value which is to be measured. (*c*) have high-resistance test leads. (*d*) have zero-resistance test leads.

10) A zero set-screw is:

(*a*) the same as a zero-ohms control. (*b*) used to compensate for equilibrium drift in the resting position of the phosphor-bronze springs. (*c*) provided to adjust the internal resistance of the movement. (*d*) only used to compensate for ohmmeter battery aging.

PROBLEMS

1) If a moving coil has a resistance of 2000 ohms, and a current of 50 μa flows through the winding at full-scale indication, how much power is dissipated as heat?
2) Calculate the resistance value of a multiplier that will provide a full-scale indication of 3 volts for the movement of Problem 1.
3) Calculate the resistance value of a multiplier that will provide a full-scale indication of 100 millivolts for the movement of Problem 1.
4) Calculate the resistance value of a multiplier that will provide full-scale indication of 30,000 volts for the movement of Problem 1.
5) Calculate the resistance value of a shunt that will provide a full-scale indication of 100 amps for the movement of Problem 1.
6) Calculate the amount of power dissipated in the shunt of Problem 5 for a current flow of 100 amps.
7) A dry cell has an emf of 1.5 volts, and an internal resistance of 5000 ohms (the cell is "dead"). If you measure the cell's terminal voltage on the 2.5-volt range of a 20,000 ohms-per-volt VOM, what is the scale reading?
8) If a sensitive VOM has a rating of 100,000 ohms-per-volt, what is the input resistance of the instrument on its 1000-volt range?
9) What is the possible error in indication when a ±2 percent of full-scale tolerance is applied to a 117-volt reading on a 250-volt scale?
10) What is the possible error in indication when a ±2 percent of full-scale tolerance is applied to a 1.5-volt reading on a 50-volt scale?
11) An ohmmeter has an input resistance of 120 ohms. If a 120-ohm resistor is connected across the instrument's input terminals, how much does the pointer deflect?
12) If a 60-ohm resistor is connected across the test leads in Problem 11, how much does the pointer deflect?
13) Unless the pointer deflects at least 1/25 of full scale, an ohmmeter

measurement is likely to be quite inaccurate. Accordingly, what is the highest value of resistance which you would attempt to measure with the ohmmeter of Problem 11?

14) If an ohmmeter applies 1.4 volts across a resistance of 2000 ohms, how much current would be driven through a 50-μa meter movement with a winding resistance of 2000 ohms—if a person makes the mistake of attempting to measure the winding resistance in this manner?

15) A meter movement draws 100 μa at full scale. When a 750-ohm resistor is shunted across the terminals of the movement, the pointer falls back to half-scale. What is the winding resistance of the movement?

19

A-C METERS

19.1 FUNDAMENTALS OF A-C RESPONSE

Since the d'Arsonval movement responds only to d-c current flow, an instrument that utilizes this movement must have provision for changing a-c current into d-c current. In turn a *rectifier* is required in a basic a-c voltmeter configuration, as seen in Figure 19-1. We will examine the physics of rectifiers in detail subsequently; at this time, we are chiefly interested in the fact that a rectifier permits current flow in one direction, but blocks current flow in the other direction, as depicted in Figure 19-2.

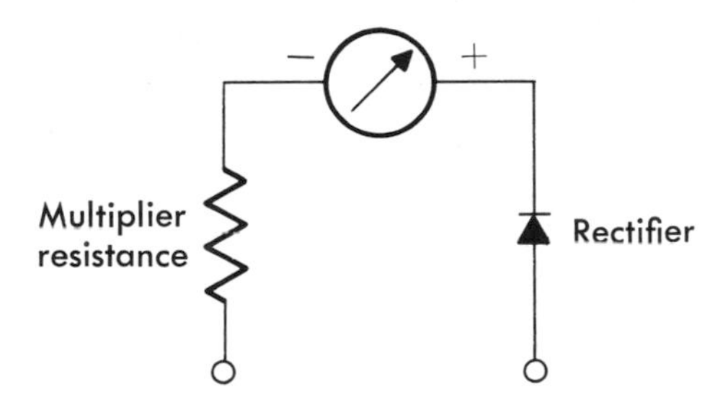

Figure 19-1
Basic a-c voltmeter configuration.

Observe that a rectifier changes a-c current into pulsating d-c current. This pulsating d-c current is suitable for energizing a d'Arsonval movement. Since the current always flows in one direction, the pointer is deflected on the scale. Although the pulsating d-c current rises and falls, the pointer does not vibrate. The reason for this steady pointer indication is found in the weight or inertia of the moving coil and its associated parts. If you apply a 60-cycle a-c voltage to the circuit of Figure 19-1, the pointer actually responds to 60 impulses of energy per sec. However, its movement is so sluggish that it can only indicate the resultant of the rapid impulses.

Of course, if you apply a very low-frequency voltage to the circuit in Figure 19-1, the pointer will then vibrate back-and-forth about its mean indication point. For example, if you connect a VOM to an audio oscillator, pointer vibration becomes visible when you reduce the operating fre-

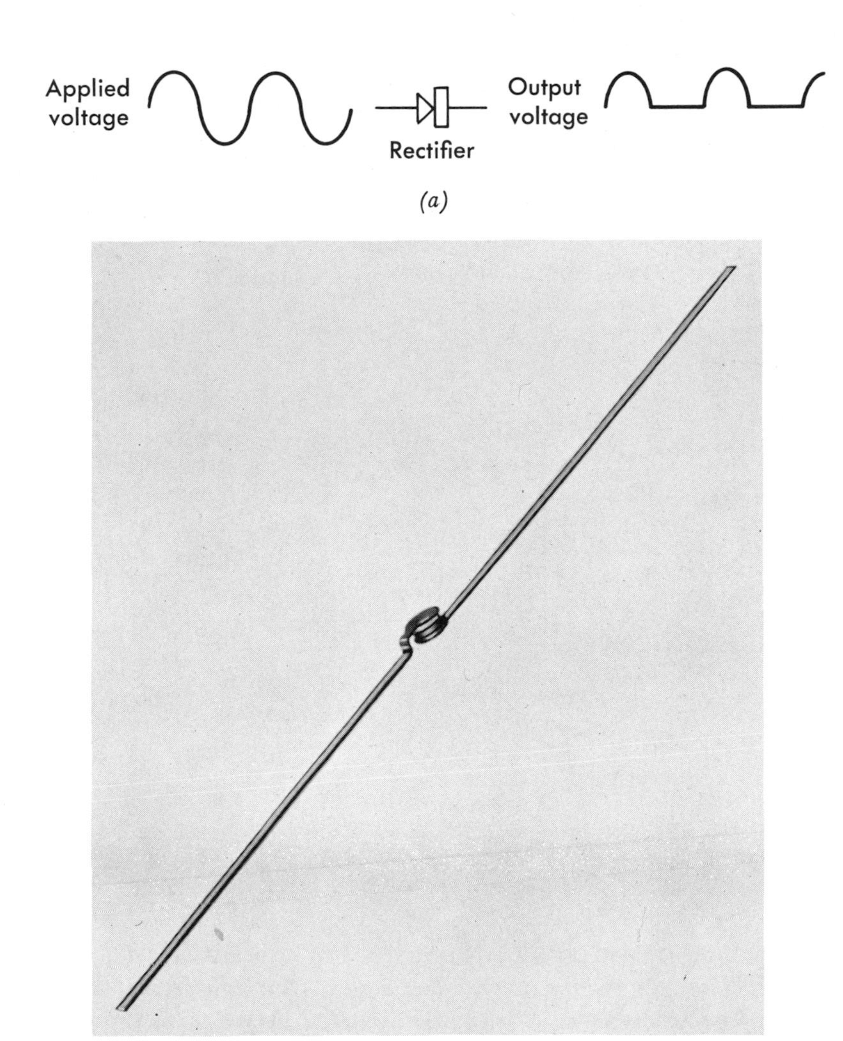

Figure 19-2
(*a*) Current flow through a rectifier. (*b*) Subminiature semiconductor diode. (Courtesy of Semiconductor Products Department, General Electric Co.)

quency to approximately 20 cycles per sec. The lower frequency limit varies for different instruments; however, most commercial VOM's can be operated satisfactorily at frequencies considerably less than 60 cycles.

An ideal rectifier would have infinite resistance in one direction, and zero resistance in the other direction, as depicted in Figure 19-3(*a*). However, commercial instrument rectifiers are represented to a better degree of approximation by the characteristic in Figure 19-3(*b*). This characteristic is idealized to the extent that the rectifier is considered to have infinite "back" resistance, and a finite "forward" resistance. In other words, a rectifier operates as a type of automatic switch, and this switch has more or less internal resistance. This internal resistance is effectively in series with the multiplier resistance of Figure 19-1.

Many instrument rectifiers have copper-oxide construction. A copper-oxide rectifier has a nonlinear "forward" resistance, as seen in Figure 19-4. It also permits a small "back" or "reverse" current flow. Accordingly, a

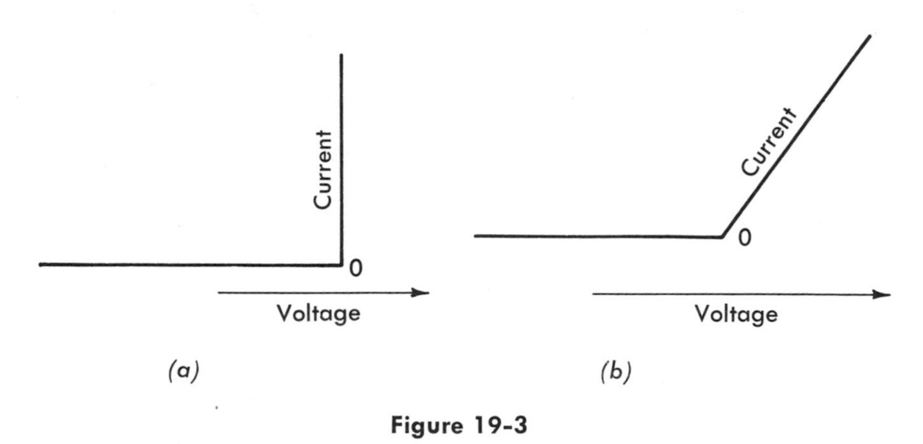

Figure 19-3

(*a*) Ideal rectifier characteristic. (*b*) Ideal characteristic with finite forward resistance present.

copper-oxide rectified has a comparatively low forward resistance, and a comparatively high reverse resistance. You will also note from Figure 19-4 that the forward resistance becomes higher and the reverse resistance becomes lower after extended service. To put it another way, a copper-oxide rectifier gradually ages, and its characteristics drift. These considerations are of central concern to the design engineer.

Commercial tolerances on copper-oxide rectifiers are also wider than on multiplier resistors. Otherwise stated, a multiplier resistor might have a tolerance of ±1 percent, but the copper-oxide rectifier might have a tolerance (when new) of ±2 percent. The movement might have a tolerance of ±1 percent of full-scale indication. Resistive tolerances are not additive. For example, if you connect a 1 percent resistor in series with another 1 percent resistor, the tolerance of the combination is still 1 percent. However, resistive tolerances and mechanical tolerances must be *summed*; that is, if you connect a 1 percent resistor in series with a 1 percent of full-scale movement, the tolerance on the combination becomes 2 percent. Let us see why this is so.

Suppose you connect a 1000-ohm 1 percent resistor in series with another 1000-ohm 1 percent resistor. The series combination has a nominal value of 2000 ohms. Its actual resistance will fall between 1980 ohms and 2020 ohms. We see that this is a tolerance of 1 percent on 2000 ohms; or, the series combination has the same tolerance as the individual resistors. You will find that if the 1000-ohm 1 percent resistors are connected in

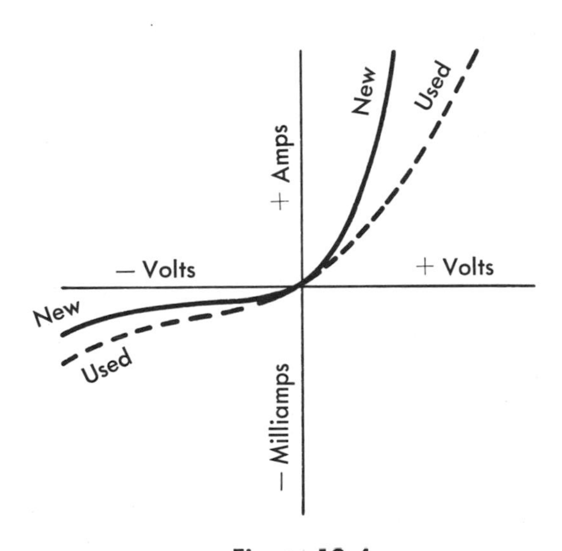

Figure 19-4
Change in characteristic of a copper-oxide rectifier with age. (Courtesy of General Electric Co.)

parallel, the tolerance becomes 1 percent on 500 ohms. Verification of this fact is left as an exercise for the student.

If you connect a 1000-ohm 1 percent resistor in series with a 1 percent movement, however, the movement has a mechanical tolerance, which simply means that its full-scale reading may be 1 percent higher than the maximum resistance value, or 1 percent lower than the minimum resistance value. Obviously, we must add the resistive and mechanical tolerances. Or, the total tolerance of a 1 percent resistor connected in series with a 1 percent movement becomes 2 percent. You will find that if the resistor is connected in shunt with the movement, the same tolerance value applies; the resistor tolerance must be added to the movement tolerance.

Again, suppose you connect a 1000-ohm 1 percent resistor in series with a 1000-ohm 2 percent resistor. The nominal resistance of the series combination is 2000 ohms. Its actual resistance will fall between 2030 and 1970 ohms; or, the tolerance on the series combination is 1.5 percent. Clearly, this is the *average* tolerance on the individual resistors. To put it another way, the 1 percent resistor tightens the tolerance on the average, but the 2 percent resistor relaxes the tolerance on the average.

Consider the flow of half-sine waves (Figure 19-2) through a meter movement. The movement responds to the average value of the pulsating d-c. What is this average value? We recall that the average value of a waveform is found by determination of equal areas, as depicted in Figure

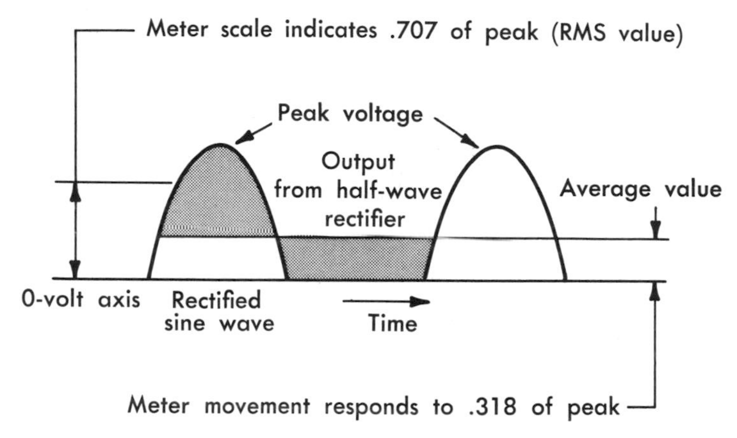

Figure 19-5

The shaded areas depict equal quantities of electricity.

19-5. Note that the shaded area above the average value is equal to the shaded area below the average value. You can approximate this equality by plotting the half-sine wave on graph paper and counting squares. Advanced mathematics will show that the average value of the half-sine waveform is 0.318 of peak value.

The rectifier depicted in Figure 19-1 operates as a *half-wave* rectifier. This terminology means that the rectifier passes half-sine waves. Many a-c voltmeters use half-wave rectifiers. It is apparent that if the output from a half-wave rectifier is passed through a movement, the pointer response is proportional to 0.318 of the peak a-c voltage which is applied. However, most a-c voltmeters are designed to indicate rms values of sine waves; hence, the scale is calibrated in rms units. It follows that if you apply d-c to an a-c voltmeter, the pointer will indicate 2.22 times the d-c voltage; or, $0.707/0.318 = 2.22$. For example, if you apply 1.5 volts d-c to the a-c voltmeter arrangement depicted in Figure 19-1, you will read 3.33 volts on the a-c volts scale.

Of course, if you connect the 1.5-volt d-c source in incorrect polarity, the rectifier will block current flow, and the pointer will indicate zero volts. This might seem to be a trivial point, but it is really very useful in practical work. Because an a-c voltmeter reads 2.22 times the applied d-c voltage, we can quickly check the condition of the instrument rectifier by applying a known d-c voltage to an a-c voltmeter. If the rectifier is old and has excessive internal resistance, the scale reading will be less than 2.22 times the applied d-c voltage. Again, if the rectifier permits appreciable reverse-current flow, the pointer will indicate a reverse voltage when the polarity of the d-c source is reversed.

19.2 A-C VOLTMETER CIRCUITRY

Alternating-current voltmeters that employ half-wave copper-oxide rectifiers are in wide use. The structure of a copper-oxide instrument rectifier is depicted in Figure 19-6. Although details of rectification action are reserved for subsequent discussion, it will be seen from Figure 19-6 that the barrier surface is comparatively thin. This means that you must never overload this type of a-c voltmeter, or the rectifier will be damaged. Always set the range switch initially to a much higher value than is

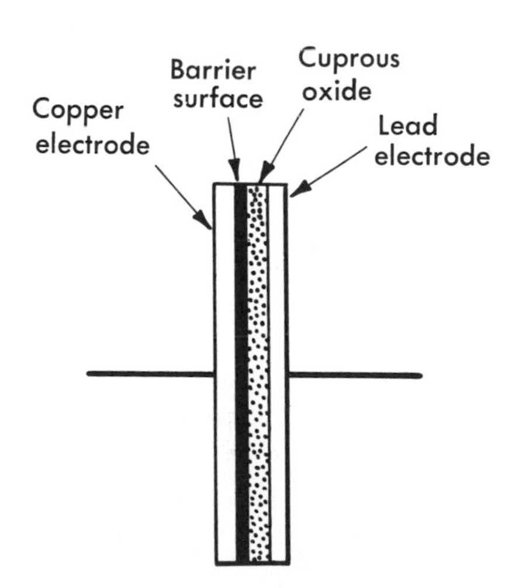

Figure 19-6
Structure of a copper-oxide rectifier.

deemed necessary. Then, after the voltmeter is connected to the circuit under test, you can reduce the range setting as required.

Refer to Figure 19-7 for the circuit configuration of a typical a-c voltmeter. Multiplier resistors are utilized in the same manner as in a d-c voltmeter to provide a multiplicity of ranges. The first novelty that meets the eye is the presence of two copper-oxide rectifiers in the movement circuit. Note that the series rectifier permits current flow through the movement, as in Figure 19-1. On the other hand, the shunt rectifier provides a low-resistance path around the movement when the current flow reverses.

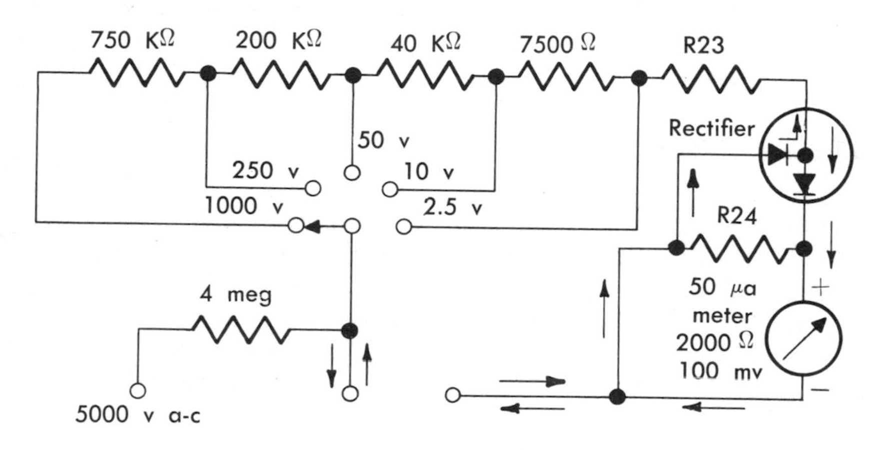

Figure 19-7
Alternating-current voltmeter configuration utilized in a standard volt-ohm-milliammeter.

Why should a shunt rectifier be used to bypass reverse current flow around the movement?

Observe in Figure 19-4 that even a new copper-oxide rectifier has a reverse resistance which is not infinite. To minimize reverse-current flow through the movement, a shunt rectifier is used to present a low-resistance bypass with respect to reverse current. The series-shunt configuration has the effect of greatly increasing the reverse resistance of the series rectifier. The arrows in Figure 19-7 show the current paths for both forward and reverse current flow in the circuit. Note that the arrows represent conventional current flow.

The second novelty we see is the presence of resistors *R*23 and *R*24 in Figure 19-7. These two resistors serve as "swamping" and "calibrating" resistances. They are actually rheostats, and are used as maintenance adjustments. It is apparent from Figure 19-4 that a copper-oxide rectifier has a nonlinear characteristic. It is desirable to linearize scale calibration within practical limits. If we combine a fixed linear resistance with a copper-oxide rectifier, its characteristic becomes more nearly linear. Of course, less current then flows through the movement, because part of the forward current flows through the swamping resistor. However, scale linearity is improved, although the meter sensitivity is reduced.

Evidently, it is not practical to completely linearize the scale indication. The residual nonlinearity shows up most prominently at the low end of the a-c voltage scale, as seen in Figure 19-8. If swamping resistance were not used, the scale nonlinearity would be much greater. In practice, *R*23 and *R*24 also serve another useful purpose. It follows from Figure

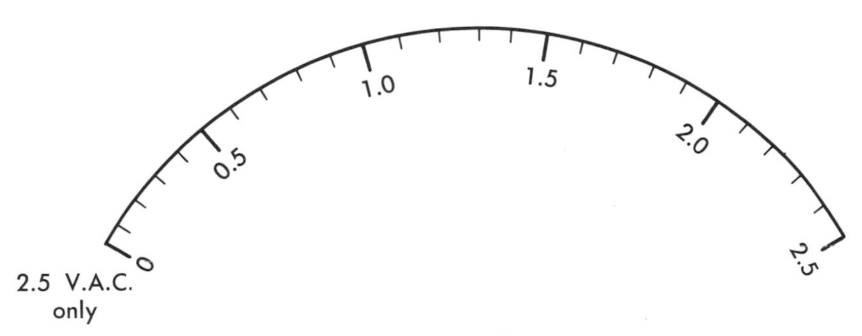

Figure 19-8
The low-range a-c voltmeter scale is nonlinear.

19-4 that the internal resistance of a copper-oxide rectifier is not only nonlinear, but also tends to drift with age. Hence, *R*23 can be adjusted as required to compensate for gradual drift of rectifier characteristics. When the a-c voltmeter can no longer be recalibrated satisfactorily by adjustment of *R*23 and *R*24, the copper-oxide rectifier must be replaced.

Because *R*24 bypasses some of the incoming current around the meter movement in Figure 19-7, the multiplier resistors necessarily have a lower value than in a corresponding d-c voltmeter configuration. In turn, the ohms-per-volt sensitivity of the a-c voltmeter is lessened. For example, a VOM that has a sensitivity rating of 20,000 ohms per volt on its d-c functions might have a rating of only 1000 ohms per volt on its a-c volts function. Moreover, a VOM that utilizes some other type of instrument rectifier and/or elaborated rectifier circuitry might have a sensitivity rating of 5000 ohms per volt on its a-c volts function.

In consequence of the comparatively wide tolerances on copper-oxide rectifiers, the accuracy rating of a VOM is different from its a-c voltage–d-c

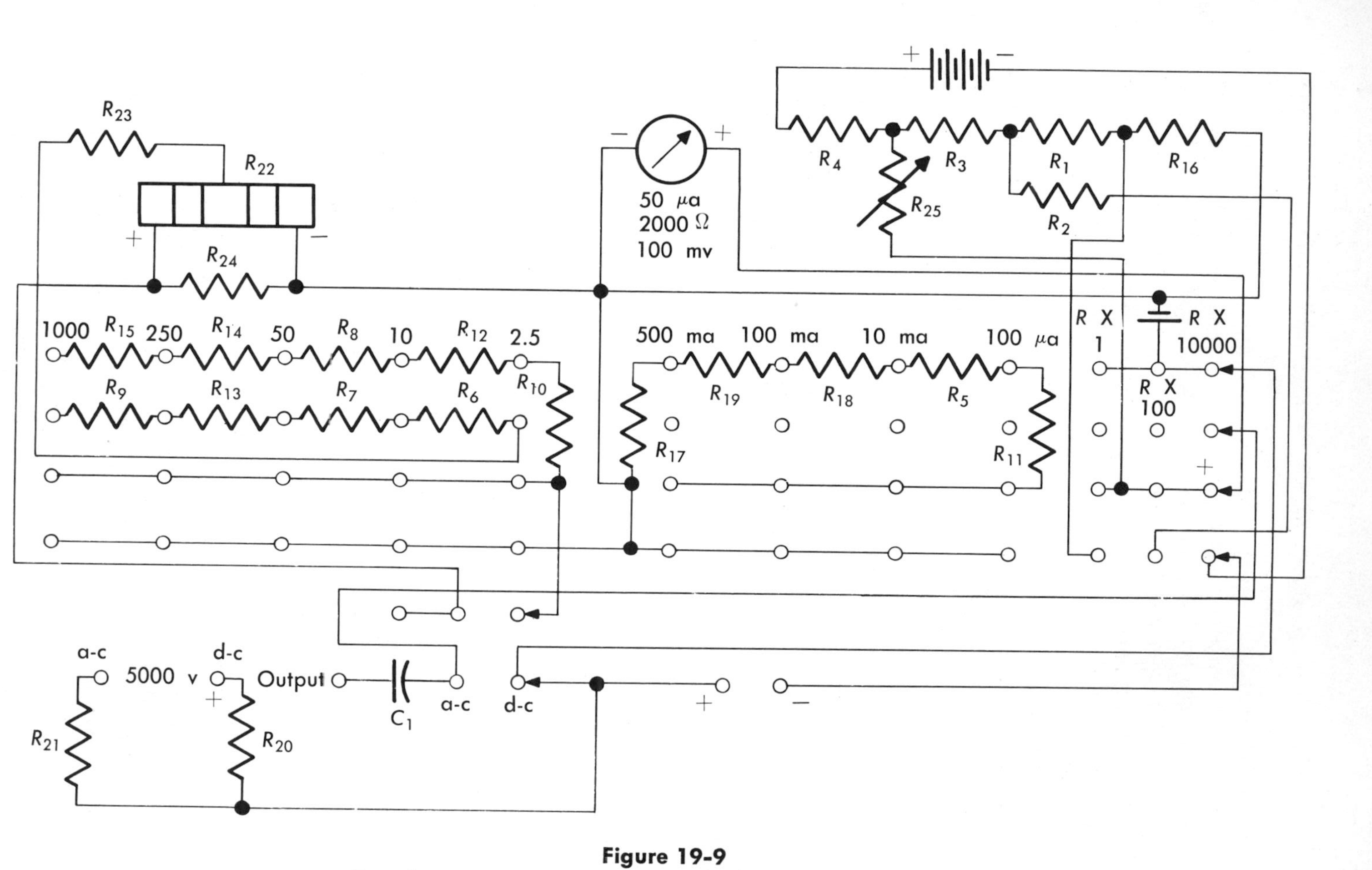

Figure 19-9
Complete VOM configuration. (Courtesy of Simpson Electric Co.)

voltage functions. For example, an instrument that is rated for ±2 percent of full-scale accuracy on d-c voltage indication might be rated for ±5 percent of full-scale accuracy on a-c voltage indication. Some VOM's employ germanium rectifiers instead of copper-oxide rectifiers. A typical instrument with germanium rectifiers is rated for ±2 percent of full-scale accuracy on d-c voltage indication, and ±3 percent of full-scale accuracy on a-c voltage indication.

When the d-c indicating sections discussed in Chapter 18 are combined with the a-c indicating section shown in Figure 19-7, the complete VOM configuration appears as seen in Figure 19-9. This arrangement provides measurement of d-c voltage, resistance, d-c current, and a-c voltage values. Note that an "output" function is also provided. This circuit includes a series capacitor C_1 which prevents d-c current flow into the a-c voltmeter circuitry. This function is used when the source provides a mixture of a-c and d-c voltages. The d-c component can be measured on the d-c volts function of the VOM; the a-c component can be measured on the output function. If a mixture of a-c and d-c voltage were applied on the a-c volts function (without blocking capacitor C_1), the reading would be confused and essentially meaningless.

19.3 FREQUENCY RESPONSE

Recall that an a-c voltmeter has a practical lower-frequency limit at which the pointer begins to vibrate noticeably. Moreover, a high-frequency limit is also imposed by several factors. Figure 19-10 shows how the indication accuracy is uniform up to 10 kc in a typical VOM. On the other hand, substantial error is seen at 100 kc. The error will be high or low, depending on which range of the a-c voltmeter is in use. High-frequency error stems from the inductance of the moving coil, and stray capacitance in the system; in other words, the equivalent circuit of the system is complex, compared with the conventional schematic diagram.

When a VOM is operated on its output function, additional reactance is introduced in series with the a-c voltmeter circuit. This reactance introduces additional frequency error, as seen in Figure 19-11. Its most pronounced effect occurs at the low-frequency end of the curves, and causes the scale to read low on all ranges. Because of the complex equivalent circuit which results, mid-range response is also affected to some extent. In practical work, it is necessary to be aware of the frequency limitations of an a-c voltmeter.

19.4 DECIBEL INDICATION

Many VOM's have decibel scales in addition to a-c voltage scales. The decibel unit is equal to 0.1 bel, and is based upon a power ratio. Decibels are calculated by the formulas:

$$db = 10 \log_{10} \frac{P_1}{P_2} \tag{19.1}$$

or,

$$db = 20 \log_{10} \frac{V_1}{V_2} \tag{19.2}$$

or,

$$db = 20 \log_{10} \frac{I_1}{I_2} \tag{19.3}$$

where P_1/P_2 is a power ratio, V_1/V_2 is a voltage ratio, and I_1/I_2 is a current ratio.

Of course, a VOM does not indicate power values explicitly; however, it indicates the a-c voltage drop across a resistive load. Since power is equal to voltage squared divided by resistance, a VOM can be calibrated for db values across a standard load resistance. The specified load resistance is usually either 500 ohms or 600 ohms. Evidently, if db readings are taken across other than the specified resistance value, the readings will be incorrect. In most cases, an incorrect reading must be corrected by calculation or from a suitable chart.

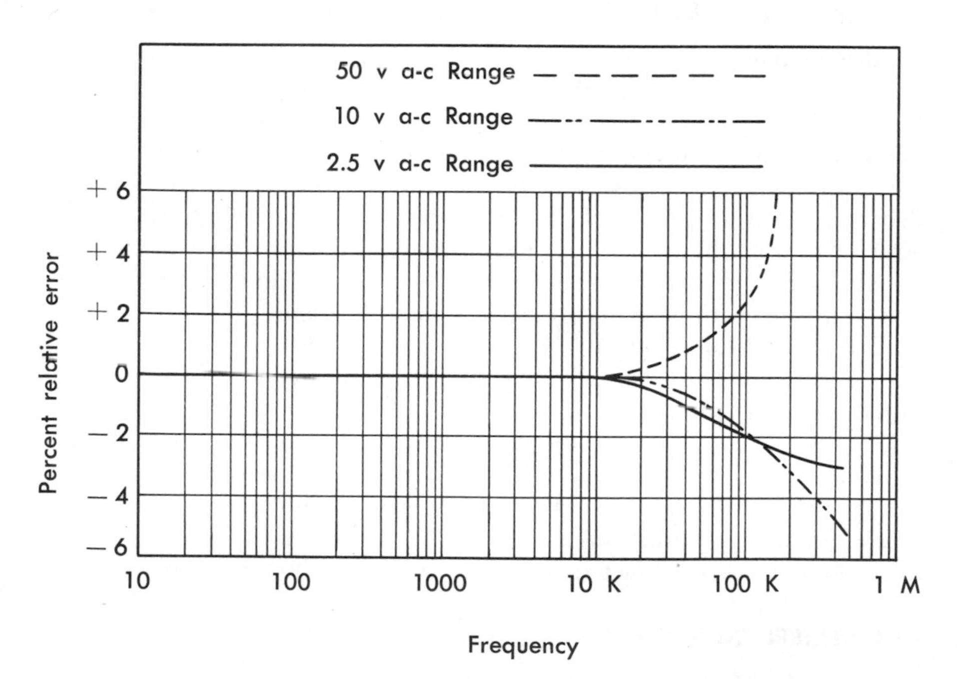

Figure 19-10
High-frequency errors occurring on different ranges of an a-c voltmeter.

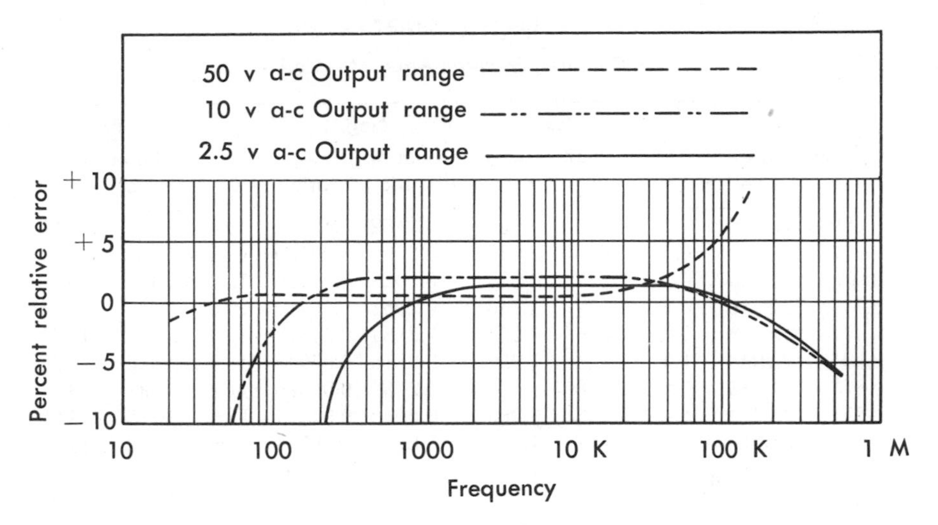

Figure 19-11
An a-c voltmeter may include a series capacitor which affects the instrument's frequency response. (Courtesy of Simpson Electric Co.)

However, there is one situation in which such readings need not be corrected. If you make two decibel measurements across the *same* value of resistance, the *difference* between the two db readings will be correct, although both of the individual readings are incorrect. For example, suppose a VOM is calibrated for decibel measurements across a 600-ohm load. If you take a db reading across a 1000-ohm resistor at one point in a circuit, and across another 1000-ohm resistor at another point in the circuit, the difference between the two db readings will be equal to the actual change in db level.

Let us consider a VOM that is calibrated to read db values across a 500-ohm load. Then, the relations between db indication, voltage ratios, and power ratios are as tabulated in Table 19-1. Zero db is defined as a level of 6 milliwatts in a 500-ohm load, corresponding to 0.707 rms volt. Negative db readings simply mean that the measured voltage happens to be below the reference level of 0 db. However, positive db readings mean that the voltage is above the reference level.

Decibel values are used to measure ratios of electrical values corresponding to sound levels because human perception of sound power has a logarithmic characteristic. Regardless of the prevailing power level, a change of 1 db is the smallest perceptible change in that level. In other words, decibel values are proportional to our subjective judgment of sound intensities.

Table 19-1

DECIBEL CHART

(Courtesy, Precision Apparatus Co.)

Neg.			Pos.		Neg.			Pos.	
Voltage ratio	*Power ratio*	*—Db+*	*Voltage ratio*	*Power ratio*	*Voltage ratio*	*Power ratio*	*—Db+*	*Voltage ratio*	*Power ratio*
1.0000	1.0000	0	1.000	1.000	0.3162	0.1000	10.0	3.162	10.000
0.9772	0.9550	0.2	1.023	1.047	0.3090	0.09550	10.2	3.236	10.47
0.9550	0.9120	0.4	1.047	1.096	0.3020	0.09120	10.4	3.311	10.96
0.9333	0.8710	0.6	1.072	1.148	0.2951	0.08710	10.6	3.388	11.48
0.9120	0.8318	0.8	1.096	1.202	0.2884	0.08318	10.8	3.467	12.02
0.8913	0.7943	1.0	1.122	1.259	0.2818	0.07943	11.0	3.548	12.59
0.8710	0.7586	1.2	1.148	1.318	0.2754	0.07586	11.2	3.631	13.18
0.8511	0.7244	1.4	1.175	1.380	0.2692	0.07244	11.4	3.715	13.80
0.8318	0.6918	1.6	1.202	1.445	0.2630	0.06918	11.6	3.802	14.45
0.8128	0.6607	1.8	1.230	1.514	0.2570	0.06607	11.8	3.890	15.14
0.7943	0.6310	2.0	1.259	1.585	0.2512	0.06310	12.0	3.981	15.85
0.7762	0.6026	2.2	1.288	1.660	0.2455	0.06026	12.2	4.074	16.60
0.7586	0.5754	2.4	1.318	1.738	0.2399	0.05754	12.4	4.169	17.38
0.7413	0.5495	2.6	1.349	1.820	0.2344	0.05495	12.6	4.266	18.20
0.7244	0.5248	2.8	1.380	1.905	0.2291	0.05248	12.8	4.365	19.05
0.7079	0.5012	3.0	1.413	1.995	0.2239	0.05012	13.0	4.467	19.95
0.6918	0.4786	3.2	1.445	2.089	0.2188	0.04786	13.2	4.571	20.89
0.6761	0.4571	3.4	1.479	2.188	0.2138	0.04571	13.4	4.677	21.88
0.6607	0.4365	3.6	1.514	2.291	0.2089	0.04365	13.6	4.786	22.91
0.6457	0.4169	3.8	1.549	2.399	0.2042	0.04169	13.8	4.898	23.99
0.6310	0.3981	4.0	1.585	2.512	0.1995	0.03981	14.0	5.012	25.12
0.6166	0.3802	4.2	1.622	2.630	0.1950	0.03802	14.2	5.129	26.30
0.6026	0.3631	4.4	1.660	2.754	0.1905	0.03631	14.4	5.248	27.54
0.5888	0.3467	4.6	1.698	2.884	0.1862	0.03467	14.6	5.370	28.84
0.5754	0.3311	4.8	1.738	3.020	0.1820	0.03311	14.8	5.495	30.20
0.5623	0.3162	5.0	1.778	3.162	0.1778	0.03162	15.0	5.623	31.62
0.5495	0.3020	5.2	1.820	3.311	0.1738	0.03020	15.2	5.754	33.11
0.5370	0.2884	5.4	1.862	3.467	0.1698	0.02884	15.4	5.888	34.67
0.5248	0.2754	5.6	1.905	3.631	0.1660	0.02754	15.6	6.026	36.31
0.5129	0.2630	5.8	1.950	3.802	0.1622	0.02630	15.8	6.166	38.02
0.5012	0.2512	6.0	1.995	3.981	0.1585	0.02512	16.0	6.310	39.81
0.4898	0.2399	6.2	2.042	4.169	0.1549	0.02399	16.2	6.457	41.69
0.4786	0.2291	6.4	2.089	4.365	0.1514	0.02291	16.4	6.607	43.65
0.4677	0.2188	6.6	2.138	4.571	0.1479	0.02188	16.6	6.761	45.71
0.4571	0.2089	6.8	2.188	4.786	0.1445	0.02089	16.8	6.918	47.86
0.4467	0.1995	7.0	2.239	5.012	0.1413	0.01995	17.0	7.079	50.12
0.4365	0.1905	7.2	2.291	5.248	0.1380	0.01905	17.2	7.244	52.48
0.4266	0.1820	7.4	2.344	5.495	0.1349	0.01820	17.4	7.413	54.95
0.4169	0.1738	7.6	2.399	5.754	0.1318	0.01738	17.6	7.586	57.54
0.4074	0.1660	7.8	2.455	6.026	0.1288	0.01660	17.8	7.762	60.26
0.3981	0.1585	8.0	2.512	6.310	0.1259	0.01585	18.0	7.943	63.10
0.3890	0.1514	8.2	2.570	6.607	0.1230	0.01514	18.2	8.128	66.07

Table 19-1 (*Continued*)

	Neg.		Pos.		Neg.			Pos.	
Voltage ratio	Power ratio	—Db+	Voltage ratio	Power ratio	Voltage ratio	Power ratio	—Db+	Voltage ratio	Power ratio
0.3802	0.1445	8.4	2.630	6.918	0.1202	0.01445	18.4	8.318	69.18
0.3715	0.1380	8.6	2.692	7.244	0.1175	0.01380	18.6	8.511	72.44
0.3631	0.1318	8.8	2.754	7.586	0.1148	0.01318	18.8	8.710	75.86
0.3548	0.1259	9.0	2.818	7.943	0.1122	0.01259	19.0	8.913	79.43
0.3467	0.1202	9.2	2.884	8.318	0.1096	0.01202	19.2	9.120	83.18
0.3388	0.1148	9.4	2.951	8.710	0.1072	0.01148	19.4	9.333	87.10
0.3311	0.1096	9.6	3.020	9.120	0.1047	0.01096	19.6	9.550	91.20
0.3236	0.1047	9.8	3.090	9.550	0.1023	0.01047	19.8	9.772	95.50
					0.1000	0.01000	20.0	10.000	100.00

VOLTAGE RATIOS BEYOND THE RANGE OF THE TABLES

A) *Ratios less than those in tables:* Multiply ratio by 10 successively until the result can be found in the tables. From the decibel value found from the table subtract +20 db for each time the multiple of 10 was used.

Example: Voltage Ratio of 0.02042–find db value:

$0.02042 \times 10 \times 10 = 2.042$ from the table: Voltage ratio of $2.042 = 6.2$ db

6.2 db — 20 db — 20 db = 33.8 db.

B) *Ratios greater than those in tables:* Divide ratio by 10 successively until the result can be found in the tables. To the db value found from the table add +20 db for each time the divisor of 10 was used.

Example: Voltage Ratio of 407.4–find db value:

$407.4 \div 10 \div 10 = 4.074$ from the table: Voltage ratio of 4.074 — 12.2 db

12.2 db + 20 db + 20 db = 52.2 db.

19.5 THE ELECTRODYNAMOMETER MOVEMENT

Wattmeters that indicate real-power values commonly utilize an electrodynamometer movement. This type of meter can be applied to either a-c or d-c sources. No permanent magnets are used in this type of instrument; instead, a moving coil is mounted between fixed coils, as depicted in Figure 19-12. Effectively, it is a combined voltmeter and ammeter, and the scale is calibrated in units of real power. Both the moving coil and the fixed coils generate magnetic fields. These fields interact to produce torque on the moving coil, and this torque is resisted by phosphor-bronze spiral springs.

The current coil (fixed coils) has low resistance and is wound with several turns of large-diameter wire. However, the voltage coil (moving coil) is wound with a comparatively large number of turns of small-diameter wire. The moving coil is connected in series with a multiplier resistance, as seen in Figure 19-12. Note that the current coil is connected in series with the circuit under test; on the other hand, the voltage coil

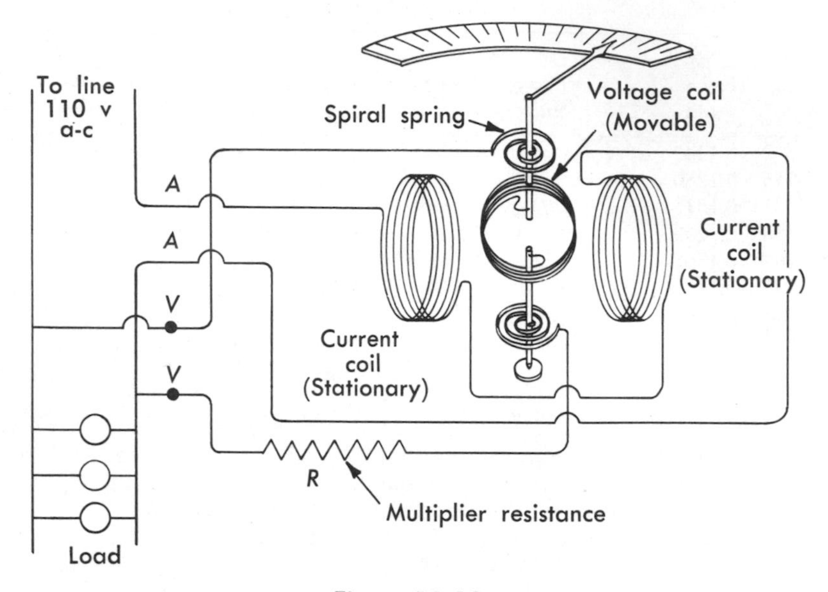

Figure 19-12
Construction of an electrodynamometer-type wattmeter.

Figure 19-13
An electrodynamometer panel-type wattmeter. (Courtesy of Simpson Electric Co.)

is connected across the circuit under test. Evidently, the magnetic field produced by the current coil is proportional to current flow, and the magnetic field produced by the voltage coil is proportional to the voltage value.

Coulomb's law as applied to magnetic fields will show that the torque on the moving coil is proportional to the *product* of the current and voltage values; or, pointer deflection is proportional to power. Furthermore,

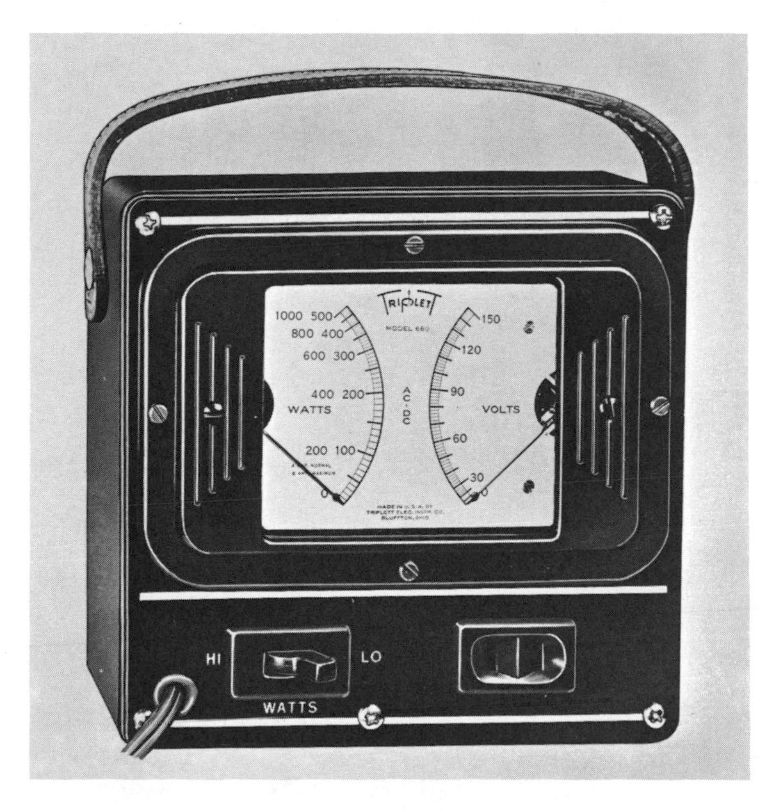

Figure 19-14

A voltmeter-wattmeter which indicates power values in terms of the voltage drop across an internal load resistance. (Courtesy of Triplett Electrical Instrument Co.)

the torque is produced only by the in-phase component of current flow. Hence, the scale indicates real power values. If you apply an electrodynamometer instrument to a 60-cycle circuit, the power waveform is a 120-cycle wave; the average value of the $\sin^2\theta$ power wave defines the torque exerted on the moving coil.

Electrodynamometer movements are not used in all wattmeters. The instrument illustrated in Figure 19-13 is a dynamometer type, and always measures real power. The voltmeter-wattmeter illustrated in Figure 19-14, however, indicates power values in terms of the voltage drop across an internal load resistance. Both type of instruments indicate real-power values, provided the current and voltage are in phase. However, when the power factor is not unity in the circuit under test, only a dynamometer-type instrument indicates real-power values.

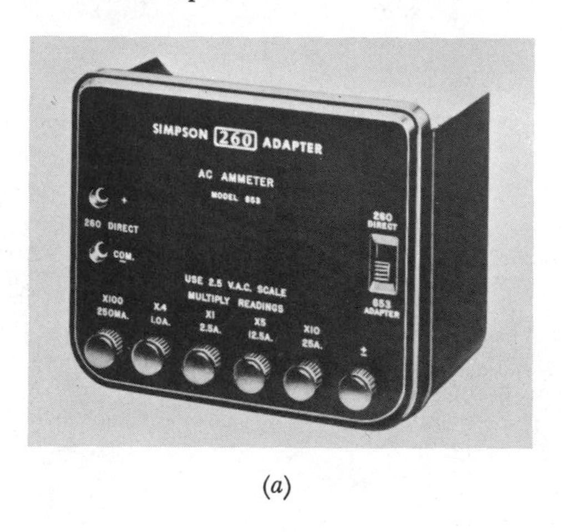

(*a*)

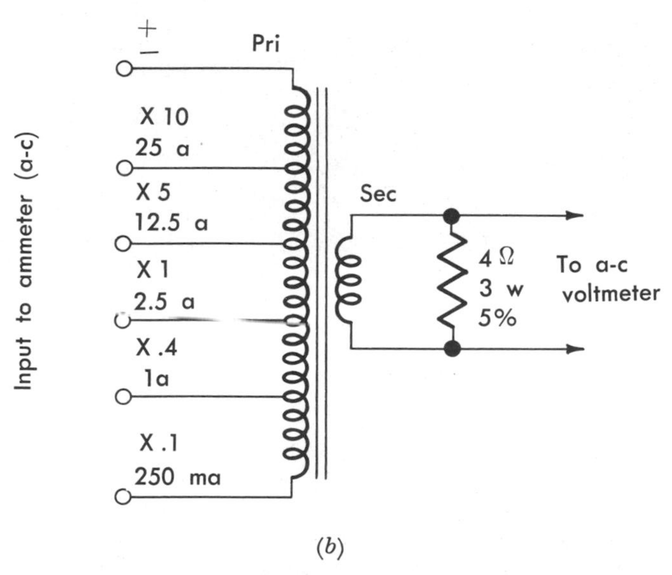

(*b*)

Figure 19-15

(*a*) External appearance of a current transformer. (*b*) Configuration of a current transformer which adapts a VOM for measurement of a-c current values. (Courtesy of Simpson Electric Co.)

19.6 A-C CURRENT MEASUREMENT

Various methods can be used to measure a-c current values. The simplest approach is to connect a resistor in series with the circuit under test, and to measure the voltage drop across the resistor. In turn, Ohm's law can be applied to determine the current flow. Sometimes a known series resistance is present in the circuit under test, eliminating the need to open the circuit. Again, instead of inserting a series resistor in a circuit, a current transformer may be connected in its stead. Figure 19-15 depicts a small current transformer which is used with a VOM to indicate a-c current values. This type of current transformer is designed as an auxiliary plug-in unit for the associated VOM.

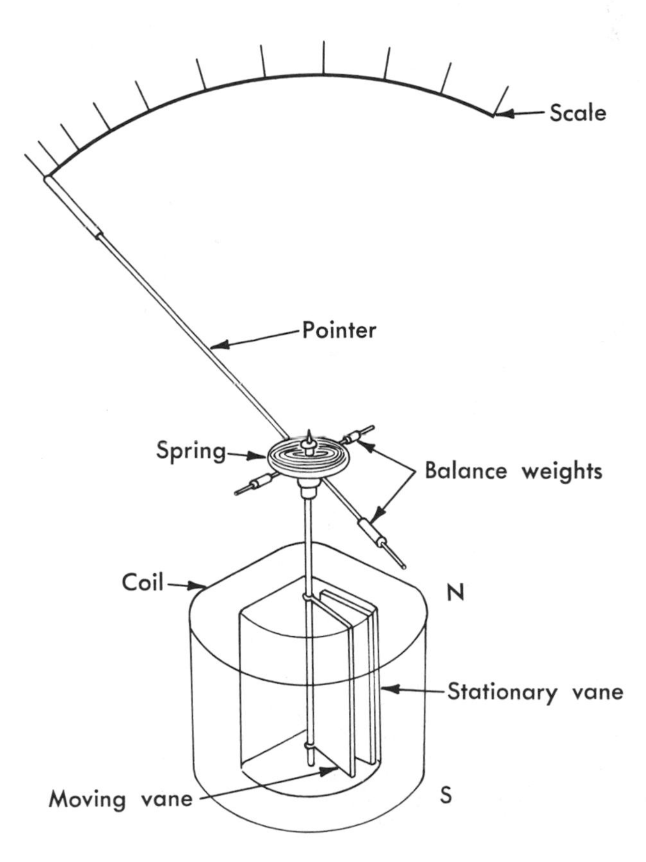

Figure 19-16
A common construction for an iron-vane movement.

Another commonly used type of current transformer is designed as a clamp-around probe device. It consists basically of a small transformer with a core which can be temporarily opened to clamp around a current-carrying conductor. The conductor operates as a one-turn primary, inducing an a-c voltage in a secondary winding on the core. This induced voltage is applied to a VOM which is operated on its a-c voltage function. Current values are indicated on the voltage scale of the instrument. Electricians often use clamp-around current probes to measure the current demand of large motors.

19.7 THE IRON-VANE MOVEMENT

Various other types of movements are utilized to measure a-c voltage and current, which can only be discussed briefly in this chapter. Aside from the d'Arsonval and dynamometer arrangements, the iron-vane type of movement is in fairly wide use. One form of iron-vane construction, depicted in Figure 19-16, utilizes a pivoted moving vane which is repelled by the fixed vane when a-c or d-c current flows through the coil. Mutual repulsion of the magnetic fields from the two soft-iron vanes causes the assembly to open up like a book. Thus, the movement is analogous to the gold-leaf electroscope.

Iron-vane movements, like dynamometer and d'Arsonval movements, have definite frequency limitations. Inductance and distributed capacitance impose the primary deterrents to accurate response at higher fre-

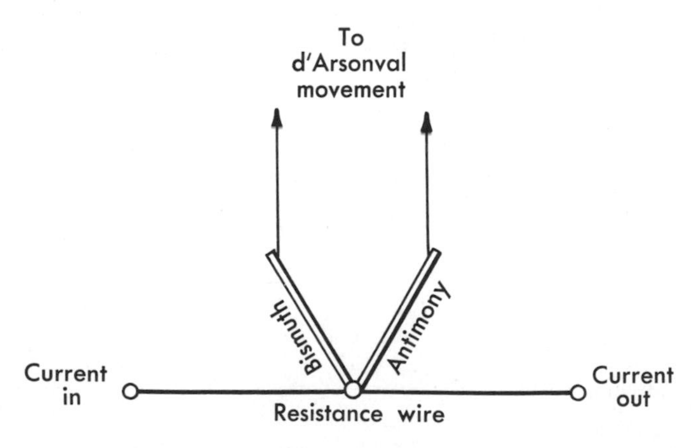

Figure 19-17
Plan of a thermocouple junction.

quencies. Manufacturers rate each type of movement for frequency capability, and these ratings must be strictly observed in practice. When high-frequency voltages or currents are to be measured, specialized types of instruments are employed.

19.8 THERMOCOUPLE AMMETERS

One type of a-c instrument that is useful at comparatively high frequencies is the thermocouple ammeter, depicted in Figure 19-17. The current to be measured flows through a short length of resistance wire, generating heat in accordance with the I^2R law. This heat is applied to a *thermocouple junction* which consists of two dissimilar metals such as bismuth and antimony. When two dissimilar metals are in contact and are heated, some of the heat is converted into electric current. This thermoelectricity is applied to a sensitive d'Arsonval movement, with a scale calibrated in milliamperes or amperes.

A thermocouple current meter can be operated at high frequencies, because the resistance wire has very small inductance and distributed capacitance. But this type of instrument must be used with great care, because the resistance element will burn out on small overloads. It is least rugged of the instruments that have been described. Thermocouple current meters can be operated from a d-c source, but are not used in this application because of their liability to burn-out.

SUMMARY OF FUNDAMENTAL CONCEPTS

A utility a-c voltmeter is basically a d-c voltmeter with a rectifier connected in series with the movement.

Rectifier-type voltmeters have upper and lower frequency limits.

An a-c voltmeter may be used with a current transformer to measure a-c current values.

Rectifier-type instruments indicate correct values only for sine-wave input.

An electrodynamometer movement can be used to indicate real-power values.

Electrodynamometer instruments have a comparatively restricted upper frequency limit.

The movement responds to half-sine waves of current; the scale is calibrated in rms values for sine waves.

Alternating-current voltmeters are rated for sensitivity in terms of ohms-per-volt.

Decibel values are indicated by a-c voltmeters under specified conditions of test.

An output meter is a decibel meter connected in series with a blocking capacitor.

Thermocouple ammeters have very low internal impedance and are suitable for use at high frequencies.

Electrodynamometer instruments indicate correct values for sinusoidal or nonsinusoidal inputs.

QUESTIONS

1) Instrument rectifiers are used to:
(*a*) change d-c into a-c current. (*b*) linearize a fixed resistor. (*c*) compensate for multiplier reactance. (*d*) change a-c into pulsating d-c current.
2) A copper-oxide rectifier:
(*a*) has infinite back resistance. (*b*) has zero forward resistance. (*c*) has characteristics that drift with age. (*d*) has equal forward and back resistance values.
3) An electrodynamometer movement:
(*a*) utilizes two permanent magnets. (*b*) has one permanent magnet and a moving coil. (*c*) comprises a fixed coil and two iron vanes. (*d*) utilizes one fixed coil and one moving coil.
4) An electrodynamometer wattmeter measures:
(*a*) volt-amperes. (*b*) real power. (*c*) reactive power. (*d*) decibels.
5) A current transformer is used with an a-c voltmeter to measure:
(*a*) a-c current values. (*b*) apparent power. (*c*) a-c voltage. (*d*) d-c current.
6) An iron-vane movement is analogous to:
(*a*) a constant-current source. (*b*) an electroscope. (*c*) a Leyden jar. (*d*) a ferrite core.
7) A current probe is constructed as:
(*a*) one-half of a current transformer. (*b*) an enclosed rectifier. (*c*) a swamping resistance. (*d*) an external multiplier resistance.
8) Thermocouple current meters are constructed with:
(*a*) electrodynamometer movements. (*b*) instrument rectifiers. (*c*) iron vanes. (*d*) thermocouple junctions.
9) Thermocouple instruments are chiefly useful for:
(*a*) power-frequency current measurements. (*b*) high-frequency current measurements. (*c*) d-c current measurements. (*d*) decibel measurements.
10) Electrodynamometer instruments are chiefly useful for:
(*a*) power-frequency applications. (*b*) high-frequency applications. (*c*) rectification of a-c currents. (*d*) measuring internal resistance values.

PROBLEMS

1) If a sine wave has an rms value of 117 volts, what will its average value be after half-wave rectification?
2) When a sine-wave voltage is applied to a d-c voltmeter through a half-

wave rectifier, the pointer indicates 10 volts. What is the rms value of the sine-wave voltage?

3) A battery is connected to a VOM which is operated on its a-c voltage function. The VOM utilizes a half-wave rectifier. If the pointer indicates 6.66 volts, what is the value of the battery voltage?
4) If a 10,000-ohm 1 percent resistor is connected in parallel with a 10,000-ohm 3 percent resistor, what is the tolerance on the parallel combination?
5) Suppose the parallel combination in Problem 4 is connected in series with a movement which has a tolerance of 2 percent of full-scale. What is the tolerance on the system?
6) A VOM is calibrated to read decibel values across 600 ohms. An electronic device has 300 ohms input resistance, and 300 ohms output resistance. If you measure −10 db at the input, and 0 db at the output of the device, what is the change in db level through the device?
7) Suppose that you measure −10 db at the input, and +10 db at the output of the device in Problem 6. What is the change in db level through the device?
8) What is the output/input power ratio in Problem 6? In Problem 7? [Hint: Refer to Table 19-1.]
9) An electrodynamometer wattmeter is connected in a 117-volt 60-cycle circuit which draws 1.5 amps at a phase angle of 30 degrees. What power value does the wattmeter indicate?
10) Another power reading is taken in the circuit of Problem 9 with a wattmeter which responds to the voltage drop across an internal resistor. What power value does this wattmeter indicate?
11) If an electrodynamometer wattmeter is connected in a 117-volt 60-cycle circuit which consists merely of a 100-μf capacitor, what power value does the wattmeter indicate?
12) Calculate the difference in power readings of an electrodynamometer wattmeter when the phase angle of the current is changed from 30 degrees leading to 30 degrees lagging.
13) If an electrodynamometer wattmeter reads W watts when the current leads by 30 degrees, what power value does it indicate when the phase angle of the current is changed to 60 degrees leading?
14) A 6-volt storage battery supplies 10 amps to the headlights in an automobile. What power value will be indicated by an electrodynamometer wattmeter?

20

VACUUM TUBES

20.1 ELECTRON EMISSION

In 1863, Thomas Alva Edison was experimenting with an evacuated tube that contained a heated filament and a metal plate. The plate was mounted near, but did not touch the filament. Edison discovered that electric current flowed between filament and plate when the plate was more positive than the filament. He noted that current flow stopped when the plate was negative with respect to the filament. This was the discovery of *thermal emission,* which is the process utilized in vacuum tubes to obtain electrons in the space surrounding a filament.

Thermal emission is also called the *Edison effect.* It is explained by the electron theory of matter, which assumes that the outer electrons in metal atoms are very loosely bound to the nucleus. When a filament is energized in an evacuated tube, free electrons flow through the filament and collide with atoms and other free electrons. These collisions generate heat. They also give some of the moving electrons enough energy to overcome the attractive force within the wire and break out from the surface of the wire. Electrons that have escaped from the metallic wire are called *emitted electrons.*

An emitted electron is a free electron, and it is no longer bound to its parent atom. Thus, it is free to drift in an electrostatic field. There is a fundamental difference between a free electron and an electron which is orbiting about the nucleus of an atom. A free electron is not quantized; thus, it can absorb or radiate an arbitrary amount of energy, and does not obey Planck's law. A free electron moves smoothly and continuously—it does not proceed in "jumps." In other words, an electron becomes quantized only when it approaches the nucleus of an atom closely, in the order of 10^{-8} cm. Thus, a free electron obeys the laws of classical physics.

A filament that emits electrons is called a *cathode.* If a metal plate placed near the filament has an applied voltage, making the plate positive with respect to the filament, the plate attracts emitted electrons. This electron flow in the space between filament and plate is an electric current, as you can demonstrate by connecting a milliammeter in series with the external circuit from plate to filament. However, if the applied voltage makes the plate negative with respect to the filament, no current flows through the milliammeter; the emitted electrons are repelled by the negative plate.

Escape of electrons from the surface of a metal is analogous to the escape of molecules from a liquid by evaporation. In a liquid, the molecules that evaporate are those that possess enough energy to overcome the surface force which tends to keep them within the liquid. In a heated metal, electron emission is a similar process, and in this sense can be considered as the evaporation of electrons from a heated surface. The number of electrons emitted per unit area of a heated surface is expressed by the equation

$$I = AT^2\epsilon^{-b/T} \tag{20.1}$$

where I is the current in amperes per square centimeter, A is the figure of merit which differs for various types of metals (A equals 60.2 for tungsten), T is the absolute temperature of the emitting surface, ϵ is the constant 2.718, and b is the work the electron must do to escape through the surface of the metal.

Although you may have little occasion to use Equation (20.1), it illustrates some significant facts. The electron emission (current I) depends chiefly on the temperature and on the quantity b. Since these values appear in the exponent, any change in either of them will greatly change

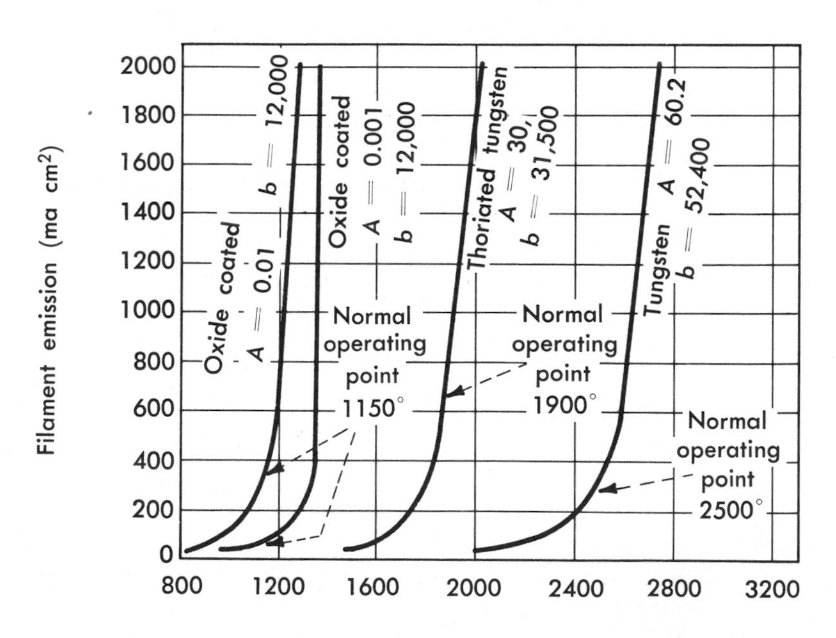

Figure 20-1

Emission versus temperature characteristics for four typical emitters.

the exponent, and in turn, the value of I. The value of A is of secondary importance, because even a large change in its value can be offset by a small change in either T or b.

Figure 20-1 shows electron emission versus temperature for three different types of emitters. In each case, the value of A depends upon the type of emitter. Symbol b represents the work or energy required for the electrons to break through the surface. Filament temperature in Figure 20-1 is indicated in °K. The temperature at which emission becomes appreciable is noted as the normal operating point.

Common substances suitable for use as thermionic emitters in vacuum tubes are tungsten, thoriated tungsten, and oxide-coated metals. Oxide-coated emitters have a much lower normal operating temperature than either tungsten or thoriated tungsten. Tungsten must be operated at a very high temperature to obtain substantial electron emission. Despite the large amount of power required to energize tungsten filaments, its durability is notable, leading to its wide use in high-power vacuum tubes. It is interesting to find that tungsten was also used in most of the earliest vacuum tubes. A filament-heating battery is called an *A* battery.

20.2 DIRECTLY AND INDIRECTLY HEATED EMITTERS

Emitters are heated either by passing current through a filament, or by placing a heating element near the emitter. A vacuum tube in which the emitter is heated directly is called a *directly heated tube.* The emitter is called a *filament.* On the other hand, a tube in which the emitter is heated by a heating element is called an *indirectly heated tube,* and the emitter unit is called a *cathode.* The heating element is termed the *heater.* Either a-c or d-c current can be used to heat either type of tube; however, filaments must be heated with d-c in certain applications that require a very smooth flow of emitted electrons. Cathodes can be heated with a-c in almost any application.

20.3 FILAMENT AND HEATER VOLTAGES

Voltages and currents required for heating emitters to suitable temperatures vary considerably in different tubes. Tube manuals are published by manufacturers which specify the voltage and current ratings for particular types of tubes. Note that even if two different tubes have the same voltage rating, the current rating is often quite different. Common filament or heater voltage ratings for familiar tube types are 1.4, 2.0, 2.5, 5.0, 6.3, 12.6, 25, 50, 70, and 117 volts.

Tubes most commonly used in small electronic equipment are 6.3- and 12.6-volt tubes. The 1.4-volt types are used when voltage is supplied by a dry cell. A 117-volt tube can be energized from a 117-volt a-c line. Tubes are generally referred to with respect to rated filament or heater voltages. Thus, we speak descriptively of a 6.3-volt tube, or a 117-volt tube. Additional descriptive terms are explained subsequently.

20.4 FILAMENT AND HEATER CIRCUITS

Filaments or heaters may be connected in parallel when they have the same voltage rating. Parallel connection is common practice in radio and television receivers which utilize a power transformer to step down the line voltage. For example, a power transformer that has its primary energized from a 117-volt a-c line may have three secondary windings, two of which are used to supply heater voltages to various tubes. A 5-volt tube is supplied by one winding, and all the 6.3-volt tubes are supplied in parallel from the other winding.

An a-c–d-c receiver will operate from either an a-c or a d-c source, and does not utilize a power transformer. Heaters in this type of receiver are connected in series, and energized directly from the power line. This arrangement requires that the combined voltage ratings of all the tubes in the series string be equal to the power-line voltage. A resistor may be connected in the series string to drop the power-line voltage to a lower value. All tubes in a series string must have the same current rating. If a tube with a lower current rating is present, a resistor will be connected in shunt with its heater terminals to equalize its current demand.

Let us consider examples of typical requirements met in connecting filament or heater circuits. Figure 20-2 depicts a circuit that comprises

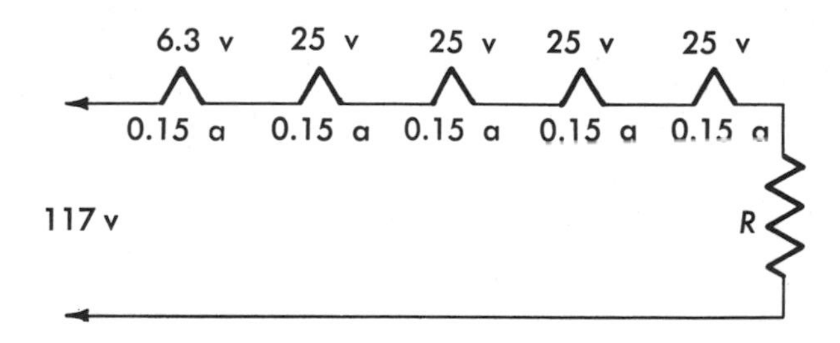

Figure 20-2
A series string in which all tubes are rated for the same current flow.

five filaments connected in series. We are to calculate the resistance value and power rating of resistor R. The sum of the voltage ratings for the five tubes is 106.3 volts. This is 10.7 volts less than the source voltage. Hence, R must drop 10.7 volts at 0.15 amp. Since $R = E/I$, the required

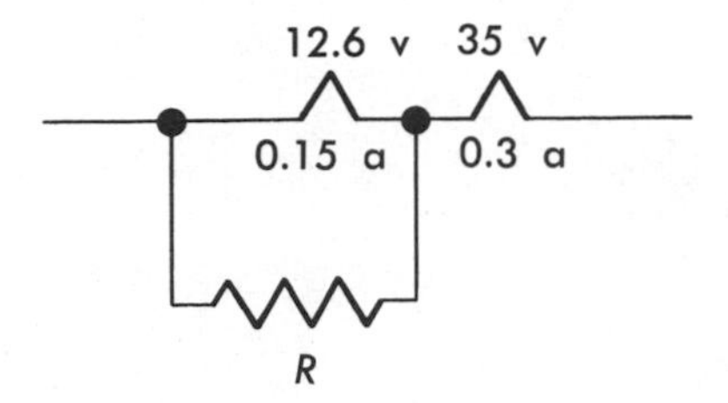

Figure 20-3
The two heaters are rated for different values of current flow, and different voltage drops.

value of R is 71 ohms. $W = EI$, or the power dissipated by R is equal to 1.605 watts.

Another typical heater problem is depicted in Figure 20-3. One heater is rated at 0.3 amp, but the other heater is rated at 0.15 amp. Hence, resistor R is utilized to carry the additional 0.15 amp. $R = E/I = 12.6/0.15 = 84$ ohms. The power dissipated by R is equal to 12.6×0.15, or 1.89 watts. Evidently, calculation of heater-circuit voltages, currents, and resistances is a simple application of the procedures we learned in our studies of general series, parallel, and series-parallel circuits.

20.5 DIODES

The simplest form of electron tube has two electrodes—a filament (or cathode) and a plate (or anode). This type of tube is called a *diode*. The vacuum diode was invented in 1905 by J. A. Fleming. When the plate is made positive with respect to the cathode, electrons, which are emitted from the cathode, flow to the plate and thence through the external circuit back to the cathode. But if a negative voltage is applied to the plate, free electrons in the space surrounding the cathode will be forced back to the cathode, and no plate current will flow. The plate is cold and cannot emit electrons. Thus, a diode permits electron flow from cathode to plate, but not from plate to cathode. Evidently, the vacuum diode is a *rectifier*.

When an a-c voltage is applied to the plate, the plate becomes alternately positive and negative with respect to the cathode. Plate current flows only during the time that the plate is positive, and plate current flows in the form of half-sine waves. Vacuum diode rectifiers are used, for example, in a-c operated radio receivers and transmitters to change a-c energy into d-c energy for operation of associated circuitry (see Figure 20-4).

The relation between plate current and plate voltage in a diode is shown in Figure 20-5. Characteristics are depicted for two different types

Figure 20-4
A small radio transmitter. (Courtesy of Electronic Instrument Co.)

of cathodes at three different operating temperatures. Note that at high plate voltages, the value of plate current (the number of electrons attracted to the plate) is determined chiefly by cathode temperatures. When plate voltage is high, plate current is more temperature-dependent than voltage-dependent. However, at comparatively low plate voltages, plate current becomes a function of plate voltage only.

Tube action at high plate voltages is explained by the fact that the plate attracts electrons from the cathode as rapidly as they are emitted. At very high plate voltage, further voltage increase makes no difference in plate current, because the plate current is simply equal to the total emission of the cathode. The tube is said to be operating at *emission saturation* in this case. Next, if we raise the cathode temperature, the cathode emits electrons at a faster rate and complete saturation occurs at a higher value of plate voltage; the saturation current value is also higher.

At low plate voltages, electrons are emitted by the cathode faster than they are attracted to the plate. Electrons, accordingly, tend to remain in the space between cathode and plate. This "cloud" of electrons are a negative charge, called the *space charge*. The space charge exerts a repelling force upon other electrons which are being emitted by the cathode. At any instant, the number of electrons traveling between cathode and

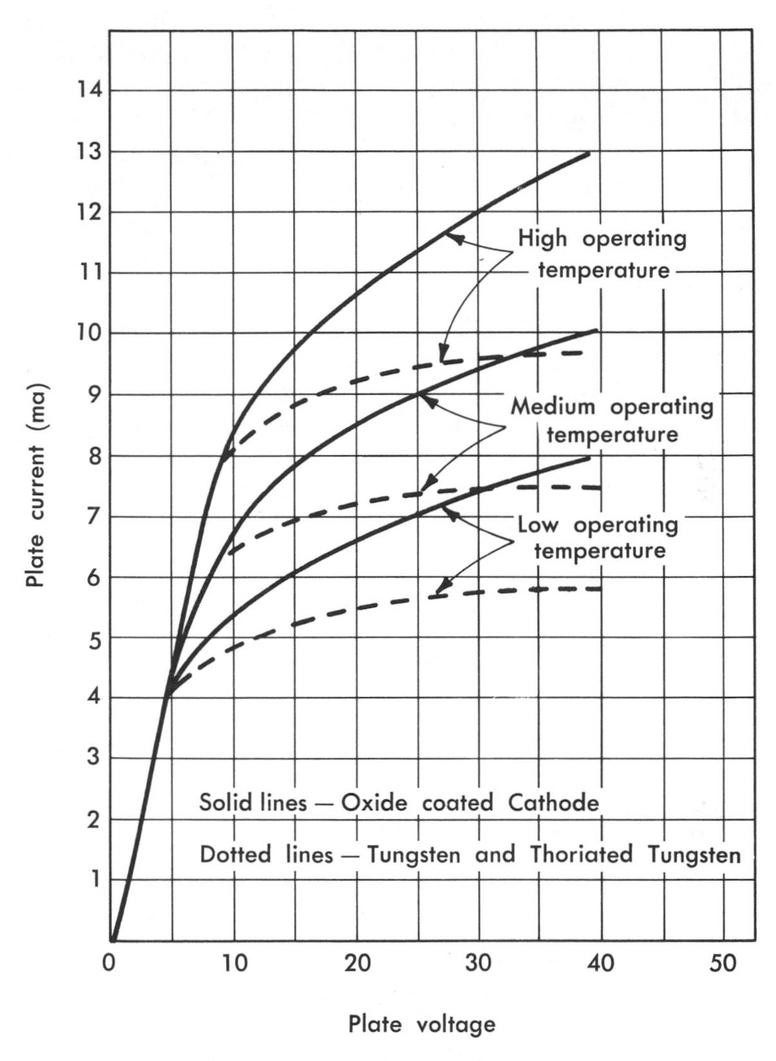

Figure 20-5
Plate-voltage versus plate-current characteristics for vacuum diodes.

plate cannot be greater than the number required to neutralize the attraction of the plate voltage. All electrons in excess of this number are repelled back to the cathode. Consequently, plate current is independent of cathode emission as long as the negative space charge dominates the tube characteristics. A plate-supply battery is called a *B* battery.

We perceive that at higher plate voltages, the plate attracts more of the electrons emitted from the cathode, reducing the tendency for electrons to remain in the space-charge region and to repel emitted electrons. Thus, the higher the plate voltage, the less is the space-charge value. When the plate voltage is increased to the point in which all of the emitted electrons are immediately taken up, and no more plate current can be caused to flow, the tube is said to be operating at its *saturation point*. Thereafter, plate current can be increased only by raising the cathode temperature.

20.6 TRIODES

A triode is a three-element vacuum tube containing a filament (or cathode), a grid, and a plate. The vacuum triode was invented in 1908 by Lee DeForest. The grid structure is usually formed as a coil with spaced turns or mesh of fine wire. It is placed between the cathode and plate (see Figure 20-6). Spacing of the grid wires is sufficient so that electrons may pass through freely. Thus, the plate-current flow in a triode may be almost the same as in a comparable diode. On the other hand, if the grid is made more negative than the cathode, some of the electrons emitted by

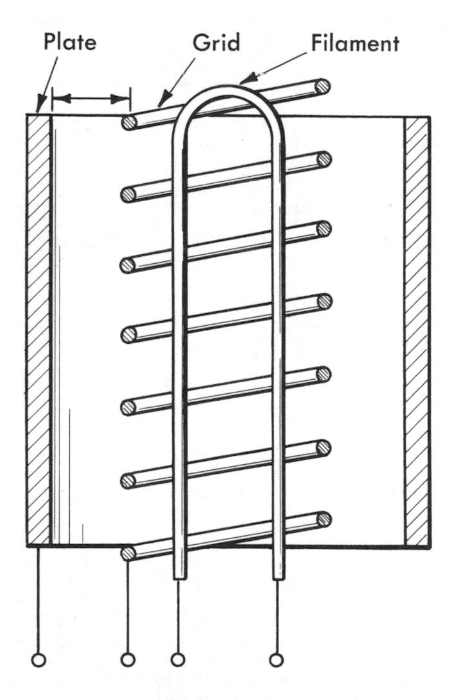

Figure 20-6
Basic construction of a triode tube.

the cathode will be repelled by the grid. These repelled electrons cannot reach the plate, and the plate current is correspondingly decreased.

It follows that as the grid voltage is made increasingly negative, fewer and fewer electrons can reach the plate. Eventually, when the grid is made sufficiently negative with respect to the cathode, no electrons can pass from cathode to plate, and the plate current is cut off entirely. The point at which plates current ceases to flow is called *cutoff*, and the value of negative grid voltage required to stop plate-current flow is called the *cutoff voltage*.

As you make the grid less negative, plate current will increase. When the grid voltage is zero, it has no effect on electrons emitted from the cathode—it is as if the grid were absent. If the grid is made positive with respect to the cathode, it will aid in drawing electrons from the space charge between plate and grid, causing a plate-current increase. However, not all of these electrons will arrive at the plate. The positive grid acts as a form of anode, or plate, and the grid wires draw *grid current*.

If you make the grid sufficiently positive, it will attract the majority of the electrons emitted by the cathode, because the grid is closer to the cathode and the space charge than it is to the plate. Because of the grid's proximity to the cathode, a comparatively small change in grid voltage has the same effect on plate-current flow as a much larger change in plate voltage. It is this feature that gives the triode one of its most useful features: *amplification*. Figure 20-7 illustrates an amplifier that is used in a typical laboratory oscilloscope.

How is amplification achieved? A small a-c voltage applied to the grid causes comparatively large variations in a-c plate current. This plate current has the same frequency as the applied grid voltage. Since the grid is maintained (in most situations) at a negative potential with respect to the cathode over the complete cycle of operation, the grid draws virtually no current. If you place a resistor, called the *load resistor*, in series with the plate circuit, the varying plate current flows through this resistor and drops a voltage which has the same frequency as the applied a-c grid voltage.

The amplitude of the voltage drop across the plate-load resistor will be much greater than that of the applied a-c grid voltage. Since the plate-output voltage is greater than the applied grid voltage, the tube operates as an *amplifier*. Of course, the plate is maintained at a suitable positive d-c potential to attract electrons emitted by the cathode. You will perceive that the grid consumes virtually no power in this example, while substantial a-c power is supplied by the plate to the plate-load resistor. Thus, a triode is a *power amplifier* as well as a *voltage amplifier*. Clearly, the plate converts d-c power into a-c power, and the instantaneous power output depends upon the instantaneous grid voltage.

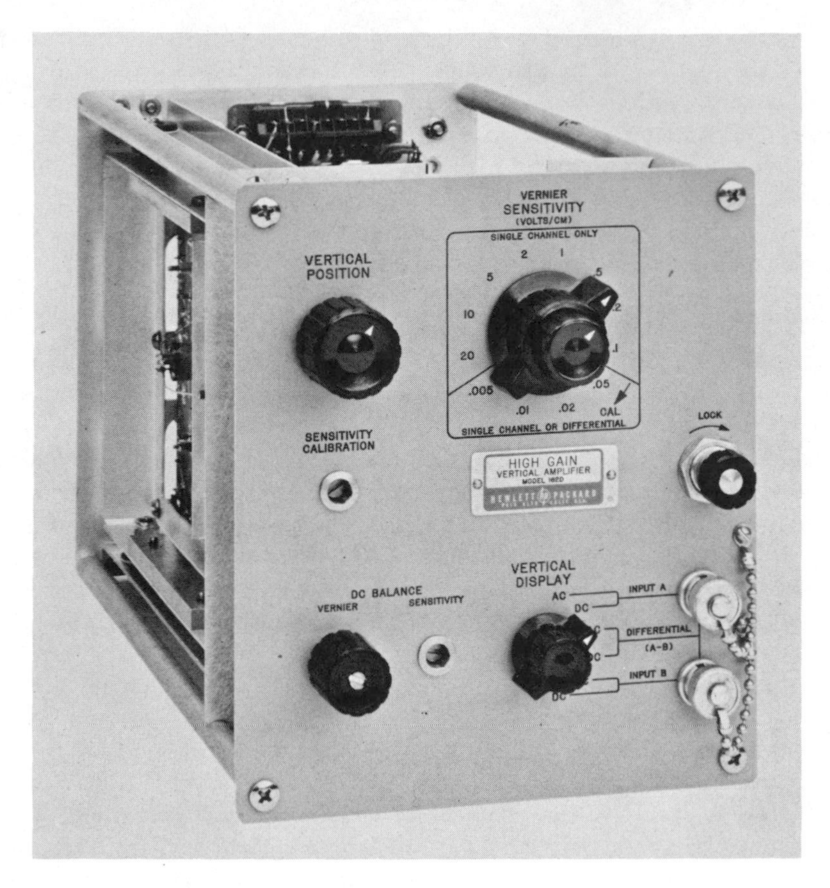

Figure 20-7
An amplifier for a laboratory oscilloscope. (Courtesy of Hewlett-Packard Co.)

20.7 TRIODE CHARACTERISTIC CURVES

You can analyze the action of a triode to best advantage by following its action on an array of curves, called *characteristic curves*. In Figure 20-8, these curves are plotted by keeping one of the three quantities (grid voltage, plate voltage, or plate current) constant, and measuring the related values between the other two quantities. Since you can select any one of the three basic quantities as an experimental constant, you can plot three different families of characteristic curves.

In the three families of curves shown in Figure 20-8, each curve is obtained by applying various voltages to the grid and plate and noting the corresponding plate current. The E_g–I_p curves are obtained by keeping the plate voltage E_p constant, and plotting the plate current I_p against the grid voltage E_g. The E_p–I_p curves are obtained by holding the grid

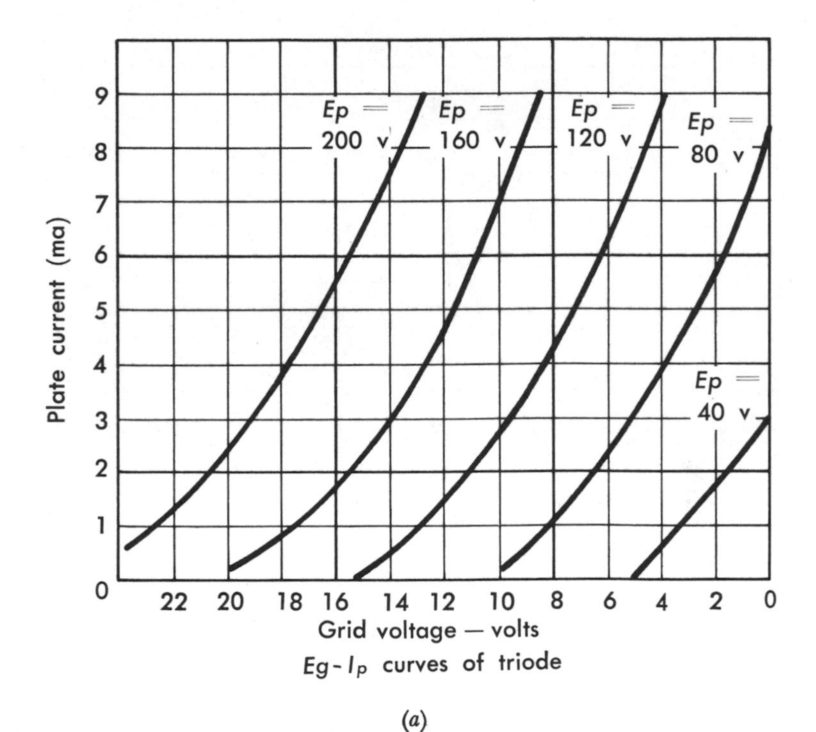

(*a*)

Figure 20-8

(*a*) E_g-I_p characteristic curves. (*b*) E_p-I_p curves. (*c*) E_p-E_g curves.

(*Continued on page 524.*)

voltage E_g constant and plotting the plate voltage E_p against the plate current I_p. The third family, the E_p–E_g curves, are obtained by holding the plate current constant, and plotting the grid voltage E_g against the plate voltage E_p. You will find that the most commonly used curves are the E_p–I_p family, and these are published for the majority of tube types in manufacturer's tube manuals.

Characteristic curves such as depicted in Figure 20-8 are called *static curves,* because they are obtained by application of d-c voltages. Characteristic curves obtained under typical operating conditions with a-c voltage applied to the grid are called *dynamic curves.* We will find that dynamic curves are useful only when circuit elements are operating under the same conditions for which the curve data were measured. Static curves, although obtained under nonoperating conditions, can be analyzed to obtain dynamic characteristics for chosen circuit parameters; in other words, they are basic and generalized.

Let us derive the *amplification factor* for a triode. The ratio of the

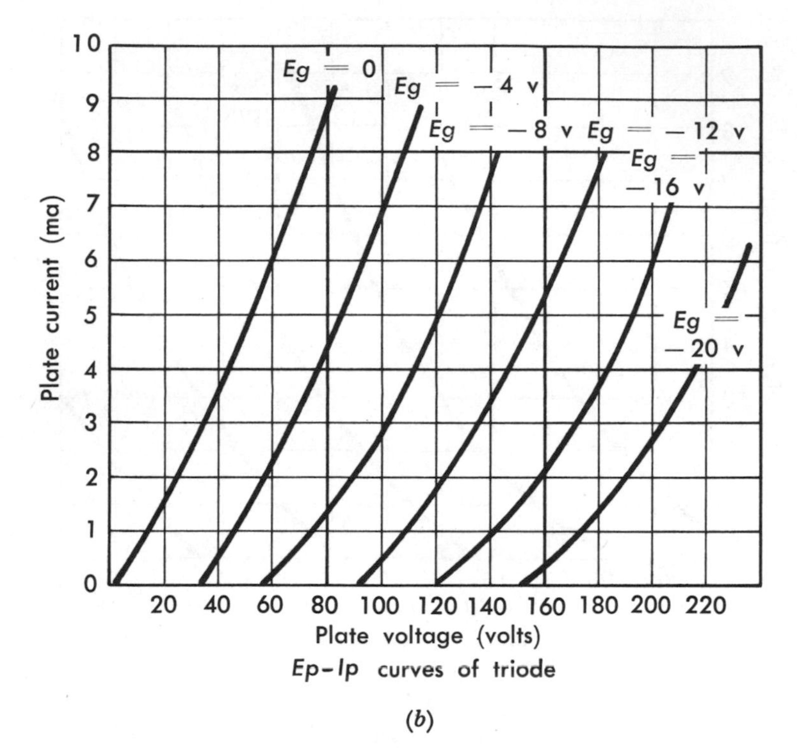

(*b*)

Fig. 20-8 (*Continued*)

(*Continued on facing page.*)

plate-voltage change required for a given change in plate current to the change in grid voltage which will produce the same change in plate current is called the amplification factor of the tube. It is commonly symbolized by the Greek letter mu (μ), and is given by the equation

$$\mu = \frac{\Delta e_p}{\Delta e_g} \tag{20.2}$$

where I_p is held constant, Δe_p represents a small change in plate voltage, and Δe_g represents a small change in grid voltage.

If the curve is approximately linear, you can select a comparatively large interval for Δ without incurring objectionable error. But if the curve is highly nonlinear, you must select a very small interval for Δ to avoid substantial error. It is left as an exercise for the student to calculate a μ value for the triode characteristics in Figure 20-8. Note that the μ value will be different at the top of a curve than at the bottom. The μ value also changes progressively from one curve to the next. Tube

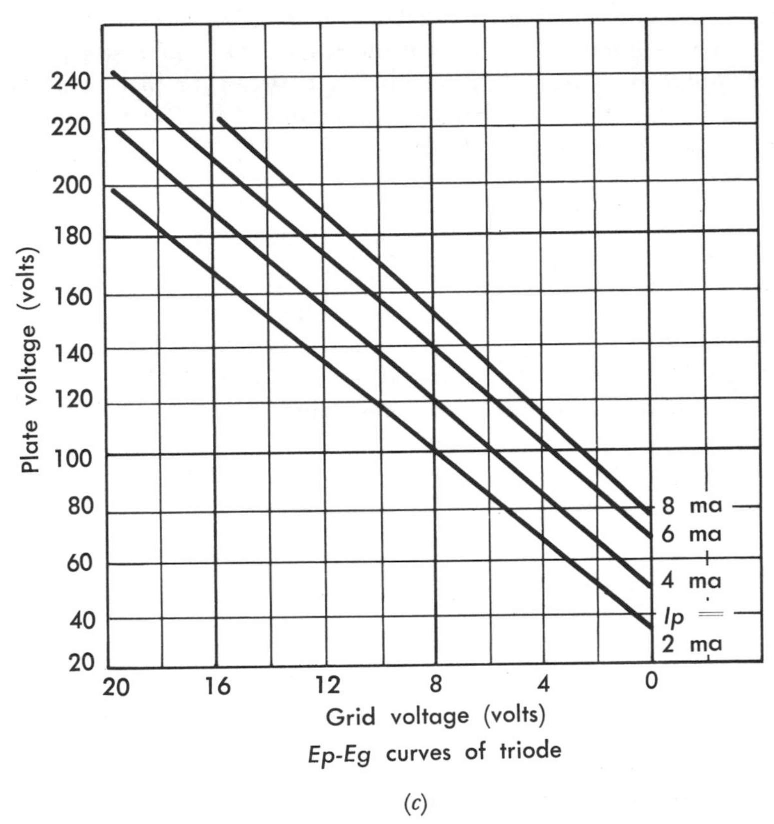

Ep-Eg curves of triode

(c)

Fig. 20-8 (*Continued*)

manuals specify μ values in the center region of a curve family. Typical triodes have specified μ values in the range from about 3 to 100.

Let us next investigate the *plate resistance* of a triode. The tube has a d-c plate resistance and an a-c plate resistance. For example, the d-c plate resistance is simply the E_p/I_p ratio at a chosen point on a curve. As you move up a curve, the d-c plate resistance changes. The amount of change depends on the nonlinearity of the curve. Observe carefully that when an a-c signal voltage is applied to the grid, you will ordinarily apply a comparatively small voltage, which represents only a small variation compared with the value of the d-c plate voltage.

Hence, we find it necessary to ask: "What is the ratio of a small change in plate voltage to the change in plate current which results, when the grid voltage is held constant?" We call this ratio of a small change in E_p to I_p the *dynamic*, or a-c plate resistance of the triode. Dynamic plate resistance is symbolized by R_p. It is apparent that the dynamic plate resistance is different in value from the d-c plate resistance. That is, *the dynamic plate resistance is the slope of the tangent to a curve at a selected operating point.* This important distinction between d-c plate resistance and dynamic plate resistance is shown in Figure 20-9. The value of the dynamic plate resistance is given by the formula

$$R_p = \frac{\Delta e_p}{\Delta i_p} \tag{20.3}$$

where Δe_p and Δi_p are corresponding small increments of plate voltage and current at a chosen operating point (E_g held constant).

The d-c plate-resistance value determines how much power is consumed by the tube as heat (plate dissipation) at a selected operating point. On the other hand, the dynamic plate-resistance value is used in various formulas to calculate the gain (amplification) of an amplifier circuit.

Another important tube parameter is called *transconductance*, symbolized by G_m. Transconductance states how much plate-current change

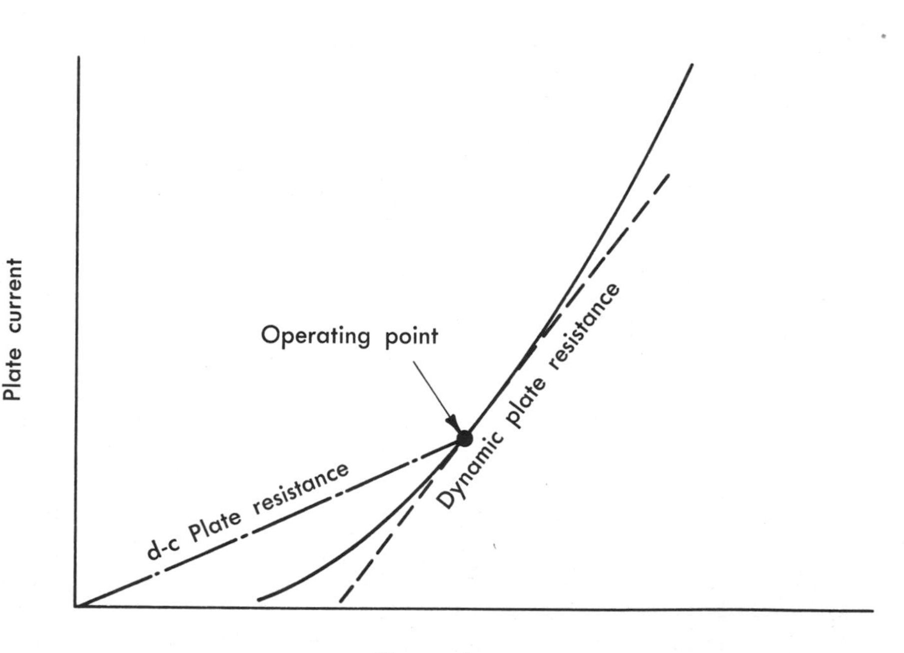

Figure 20-9
Direct-current plate resistance and dynamic plate resistance.

is caused by a small change in grid voltage. The unit of transconductance is the mho, and is expressed by the formula

$$G_m = \frac{\Delta i_p}{\Delta e_g} \tag{20.4}$$

where E_p is held constant.

Note that transconductance is related to the amplification factor and to the dynamic plate resistance of a triode according to the equation

$$\mu = G_m R_p \tag{20.5}$$

In Figure 20-8, the tube parameters μ, R_p, and G_m can be determined with reasonable accuracy from the E_p–I_p curves. Note that when E_g changes from -4 to -8 volts, with I_p remaining at 5 ma, E_p changes from 88 volts to 125 volts. Hence, $\mu = -37/-4 = 9.25$. According to a tube manual, the amplification factor for the tube corresponding to these curves is 9. Thus, for practical purposes, the curves provide values which give reasonably correct operating parameters.

By assuming a value for E_g, and then comparing the change in E_p corresponding to a small change in I_p, you can approximate the dynamic plate resistance R_p. For example, let $E_g = -8$. When I_p changes from 4 ma to 5 ma, E_p changes from 112 volts to 125 volts. Hence, $R_p = 13/0.001 = 13{,}000$ ohms. When calculating the G_m value with the same E_p–I_p curves, assume that E_p is equal to 100 volts. When E_g changes from -4 to -8 volts, I_p changes from 6.4 ma to 2.8 ma. In turn, substitution into Equation (20.4) yields $G_m = 900$ micromhos.

20.8 GRID BIAS

If you add a sufficient value of negative d-c voltage to an a-c voltage, the combined voltage will be a negative pulsating d-c voltage. This means that if an a-c voltage applied to the grid of a tube is made negative by addition of a negative d-c voltage, the grid will not conduct current. This negative d-c voltage applied to the grid, which makes the total applied voltage negative, is called *bias voltage*. In most cases, bias voltage is applied directly and continuously to the grid, not to the applied a-c signal voltage before it reaches the grid.

Bias voltage must not be excessive, or the grid voltage will exceed the cutoff value over more or less of the a-c signal cycle, which causes *distortion*. When distortion occurs, the plate-current waveform is not the same as the grid-voltage waveform. There are three general types of bias methods utilized to provide grid-bias voltage for vacuum tubes. These are classified as *fixed bias, cathode bias,* and *grid-leak resistance bias* (see Figure 20-10). Fixed bias is usually supplied by a battery, called a *C* battery. However, a battery source of bias is often inconvenient.

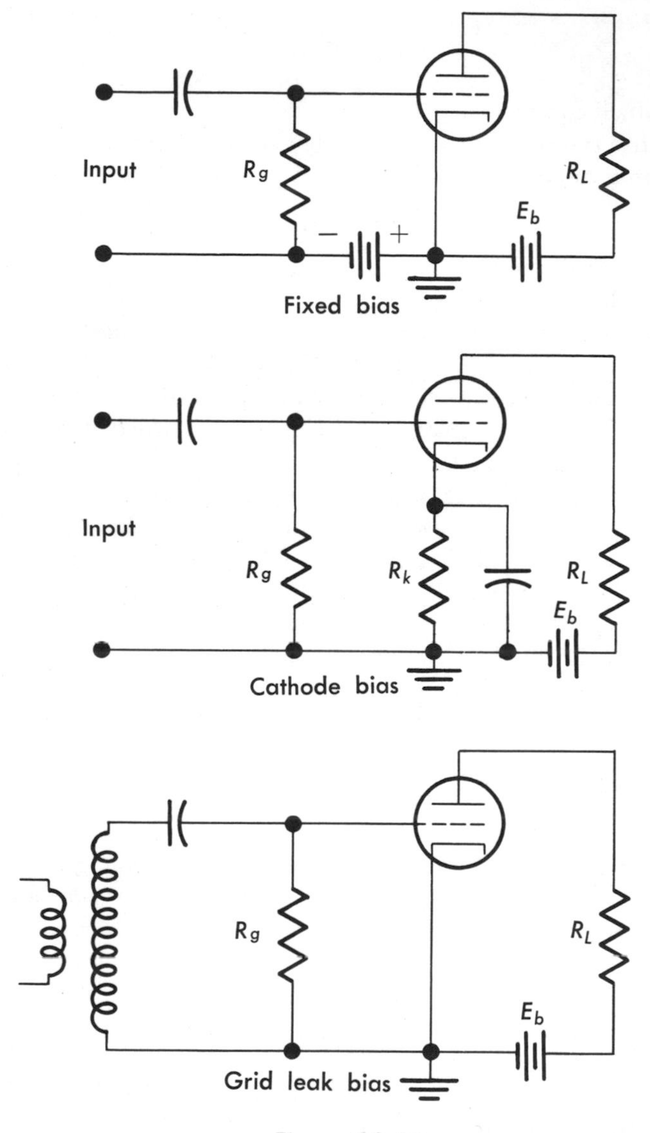

Figure 20-10
Three basic arrangements for provision of grid bias.

One of the simplest methods of supplying a steady negative voltage to the grid of a tube is to utilize cathode bias. Here a resistor is connected in series with the cathode lead of the tube, and the voltage drop across the resistor which results from plate-current flow is used as grid-bias voltage. To eliminate a-c variation from this bias voltage, a capacitor is connected in parallel with the cathode-bias resistor. This capacitor charges to the average value of the drop across the resistor, and cannot change unless the capacitor charge increases or decreases. The capacitor is chosen to have a comparatively long time constant in combination with the resistor, so that the bias voltage is maintained essentially constant.

The capacitor that is shunted across a cathode-bias resistor is called a *bypass capacitor*. In the cathode-bias circuit (Figure 20-10), the grid is connected to ground through the grid resistor R_g. As no d-c current flows through the grid resistor, the grid is at ground potential. The cathode is positive with respect to ground because plate current flows through the resistor between cathode and ground. Thus, the cathode is more positive than the grid. This is the same as stating that the grid is more negative than the cathode.

Grid-leak bias makes use of the flow of grid current during a portion of the input cycle to develop negative voltage which biases the grid. Refer to Figure 20-10. When the voltage across transformer secondary swings positive, grid current flows, charging the grid capacitor. Next, when the secondary swings negative, the grid capacitor discharges through the closed path of the secondary and resistor R_g. Since R_g has a high resistance value, the capacitor discharges slowly over the entire negative portion of the input cycle. The discharge current through R_g is in such direction that the grid is negative with respect to ground. Hence, the average grid potential is negative, provided the grid becomes positive for at least a small portion of each cycle.

20.9 LOAD LINES

You can apply characteristic curves in the analysis of an amplifier circuit, as shown in Figure 20-11. The straight line drawn across the E_p–I_p curves is called the *load line*. It is a plot of corresponding plate-current and plate-voltage values in the triode circuit. One extremity of the load line is located at zero plate current and zero voltage drop across the load resistor. The other extremity is located at the point where the plate current is not limited by the tube; that is, where the tube is replaced by a short-circuit. Current flow at this point is limited only by the load resistance, and its value follows from Ohm's law.

Evidently, when the tube is regarded as a short-circuit, its plate voltage is zero. The slope of the load line is determined by the value of the load resistor. The greater the load resistance, the less is the slope. The load line across the E_p–I_p curves is based on the triode amplifier circuit, depicted in Figure 20-11. If, in the amplifier circuit shown, the plate current drops to zero, the plate voltage will have its maximum value of 240 volts. Hence,

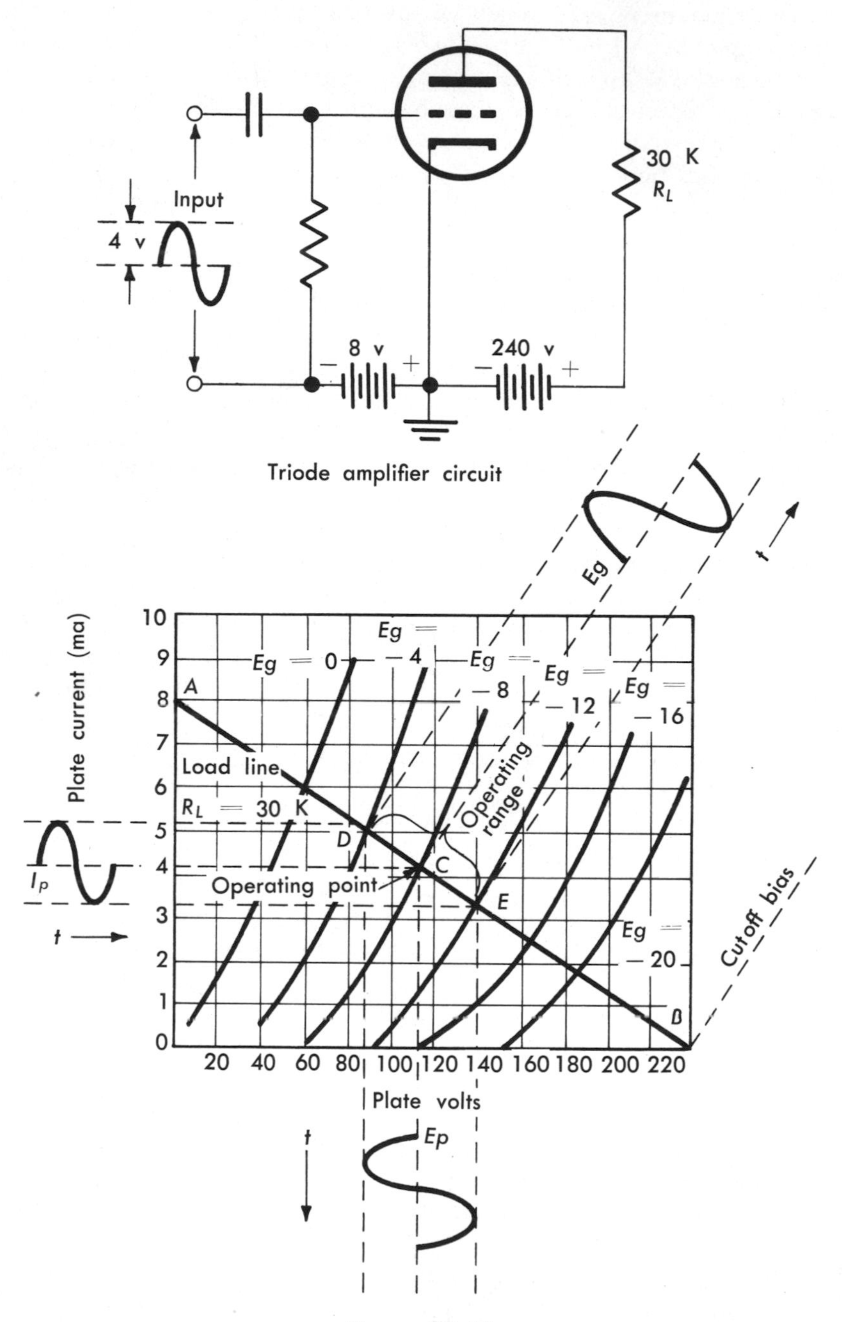

Figure 20-11
Analysis of triode amplifier operation.

one end of the load line is located at a point where $I_p = 0$ and $E_p = 240$. But, when the tube is short-circuited, the plate voltage becomes zero and the current flow is equal to the supply voltage divided by the load resistance: $240/30\ K = 8$ ma. This calculation locates the other end of the load line. Note carefully that the path of operation for the amplifier circuit must always fall along the load line.

The grid bias value in Figure 20-11 is −8 volts. With no signal applied to the grid, you can determine the static E_p and I_p values from the intersection (*C*) of the −8-volt curve and the load line. This point (*C*), called the *operating* point, or *quiescent* point, corresponds to $I_p = 4.2$ ma and $E_p = 114$ volts. Next, suppose you apply an a-c signal voltage of 4-volt peak amplitude to the grid. Since the grid is biased at −8 volts, this 4-volt signal will cause the grid voltage to vary or "swing" between −4 volts and −12 volts. The two curves, $E_g = -4$ and $E_g = -12$, intersect the load line at points (*D*) and (*E*), which correspond to $E_p = 87$ volts and 142 volts, and to $I_p = 5.1$ ma and 3.3 ma, respectively.

The portion of the load line between (*D*) and (*E*) in Figure 20-11 is called the *operating range*, because the applied signal voltage results in a swing between these limits. Wave shapes of the plate-voltage, plate-current,

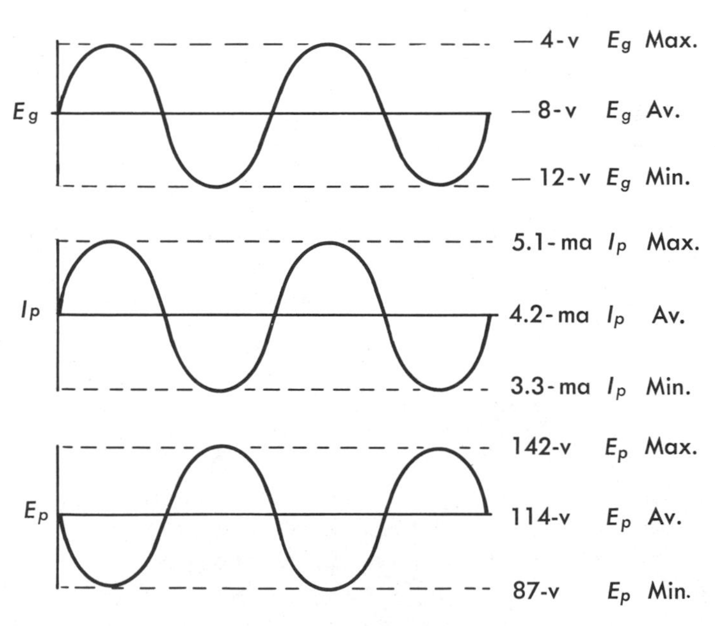

Figure 20-12
Phase relations of E_g, I_p, and E_p.

and grid-voltage variations are shown in Figure 20-12 to depict relative phases. These waveshapes point out that the plate-voltage variation is 180 degrees out of phase with the grid-voltage variation. The grid-voltage variation E_g is the applied signal voltage. It has a peak amplitude of 4 volts. Again, the plate-voltage variation E_p is the a-c component of the plate voltage, and has a peak value of 27 volts.

Amplification of the stage is 27/4, or 6.75. Stage amplification is less than the amplification factor of the tube (μ is 9 in this example), because a voltage divider is formed by the dynamic plate resistance and the load resistance. Only the drop across the load resistance is available as an output

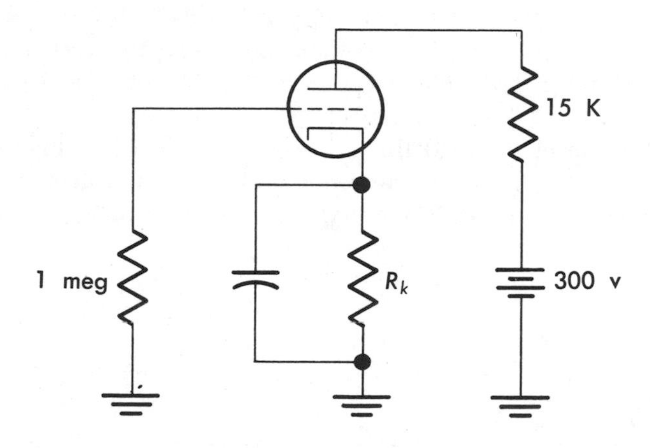

Figure 20-13
Reference circuit for construction of R_k bias values.

voltage. The following problems illustrate other practical applications of load lines.

Let us find the value of R_k in Figure 20-13 that will provide an 8-volt cathode bias. With reference to the family of E_p–I_p curves in Figure 20-14, locate the intersection of the −8-volt curve and the load line. This is point P, which is projected on the vertical axis (point S) to determine I_p, has a value of 5.5 ma. Ohm's law states the required value of R_k. Thus, $R_k = 8/(5.5 \times 10^{-3})$, **or 1450 ohms.**

Next, let us calculate the cathode bias in this same circuit if R_k is reduced to 500 ohms. Assume that $I_p = 4$ ma. Then, the drop across R_k is 2 volts in accordance with Ohm's law. Locate the point of the $E_g = -2$ curve, which is opposite 4 ma on the vertical axis. This gives us point B in Figure 20-14. Next, assume that $I_p = 12$ ma, and then locate a corresponding point in a similar manner (point A). Connect these two points as

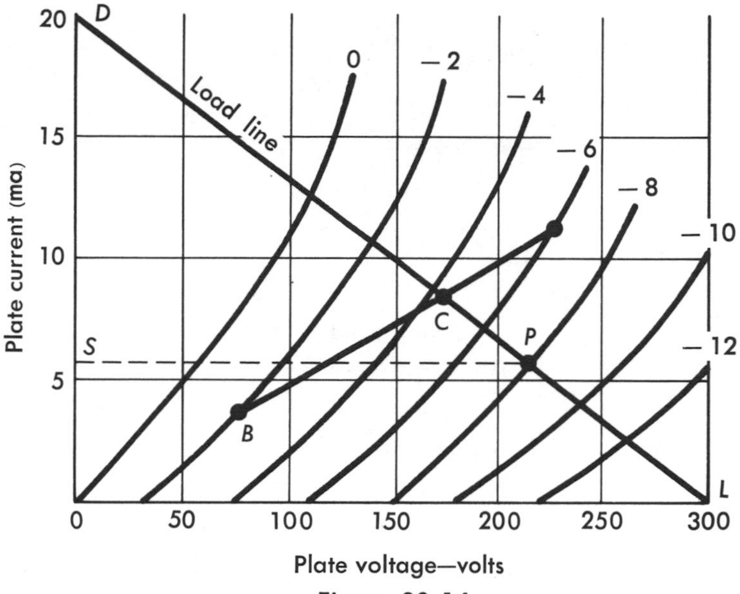

Figure 20-14

Determination of cathode-bias voltages.

shown. This line intersects the load line at point *C*. Point *C* lies between the curves marked −4 and −6. The approximate bias is determined by the proportional distance of point *C* from these two curves. Thus, the bias value is approximately −4.3 volts.

20.10 INTERELECTRODE CAPACITANCE

You are familiar with the fact that two conductors separated by a dielectric form a capacitor. Its capacitance value depends upon the area of the conductors, the distance between them, and the dielectric coefficient. In a vacuum tube, the capacitance between electrodes, called *interelectrode capacitance*, establishes capacitive reactance between the electrodes, as indicated in Figure 20-15. The largest capacitance value usually occurs between plate and cathode because of the comparatively large area involved. C_{gk} is the grid-to-cathode capacitance; C_{gp} is the grid-to-plate capacitance.

Although these capacitance values are small, they provide capacitive coupling between tube elements. At low frequencies, the coupling can be disregarded; however, at high frequencies, this capacitive coupling must be taken into consideration. Grid-to-plate capacitance is most disturbing at high frequencies because it couples a-c energy from the grid circuit to the plate circuit, and vice versa. Thus, there is more than meets the eye in the

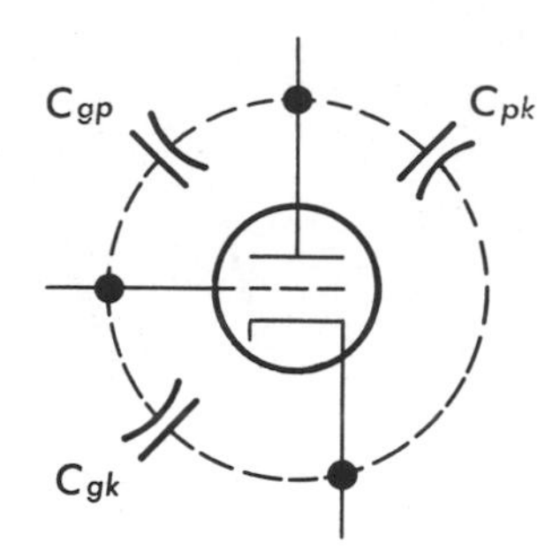

Figure 20-15
Interelectrode capacitances of a triode.

circuit diagram of a high-frequency amplifier. Various means are invoked to cope with this disturbance in high-frequency amplifier operation.

20.11 TETRODES

A tetrode is a four-element vacuum tube. Essentially, it is a triode with the addition of a *screen grid* located between the control grid and the plate. Addition of the screen grid greatly reduces the effective grid-to-plate capacitance. This makes the tetrode more useful than a triode in high-frequency applications. The screen grid is maintained at a positive d-c voltage. In most applications, the plate is operated at a higher potential than the screen grid. No a-c signal is applied to the screen grid in the majority of applications. Since the screen grid is at a-c ground potential, it provides an electrostatic shield or screen between the control grid and plate. This shielding action minimizes transfer of signal voltage from plate to control grid, or vice versa, via interelectrode capacitance.

Shielding action of the screen grid is not affected by its d-c potential. A positive d-c voltage is applied to the screen grid to establish an electrostatic field which will accelerate electrons from the cathode. In general, an increase in screen voltage causes an increase in plate current. Although the screen grid intercepts some of the electrons, its construction is such that most of the electrons pass through and continue to the plate. The number of intercepted electrons (value of screen current) depends upon relative screen and plate voltages. Higher screen voltages cause higher screen currents. Up to a certain limit, the plate current also increases, because the positive screen draws more electrons out of the space charge, thereby increasing the total available number of electrons.

On the other hand, when the maximum number of electrons obtainable from the space charge are utilized, further increase in screen voltage cannot increase the total current. Thereafter, the screen and plate must divide the available electrons between them. Hence, further increase in screen voltage results in higher screen current and lower plate current; that is, the plate current decreases as the screen voltage increases. We recall that this is a condition of *negative resistance*. In this region of operation, a decrease in plate voltage causes an increase in plate current. The negative-resistance interval of a tetrode finds practical application in certain specialized electronic devices.

20.12 SECONDARY EMISSION

We also find an effect called *secondary emission* that occurs when electrons strike the plate or screen grid with sufficient force to knock other electrons out of the metal. Secondary electrons freed in this manner travel to the electrode that exerts greatest electrostatic force upon them. Flow of secondary electrons from screen grid to plate is negligible, because the secondaries are liberated on the side away from the plate. However, flow of secondary electrons from plate to screen grid may be appreciable when the screen grid is more positive than the plate.

At very low plate voltages, the number of secondary electrons produced at the plate is small, and there is a tendency for space-charge electrons to accumulate in a cloud in front of the plate. This electron cloud turns back some of the arriving electrons. Electrons thus turned back are collected by the screen grid. In this region of operation, plate current depends upon plate voltage, and the plate current is much less than the total space current.

20.13 TETRODE CHARACTERISTICS

When the plate voltage is less than the screen voltage, but sufficiently high to eliminate the space charge between screen and plate, the plate current decreases as the plate voltage increases. This negative-resistance interval is seen in Figure 20-16. Although the number of primary electrons received by the plate is independent of plate voltage (being dependent solely upon screen-grid and control-grid voltages), the number of electrons *lost* to the screen via secondary emission increases as the plate voltage increases because the electrons strike the plate with greater force.

A tetrode used as a negative-resistance device is called a *dynatron*. The transition from this negative-resistance region to the region in which plate current is practically independent of plate voltage occurs when the plate and screen grid have approximately the same voltage. Next, when the plate voltage is more positive than the screen voltage, the plate retains all the primary electrons and also collects some secondary electrons from the screen grid. Hence, the plate current is almost equal to the total space current. Furthermore, plate current then becomes almost independent of plate volt-

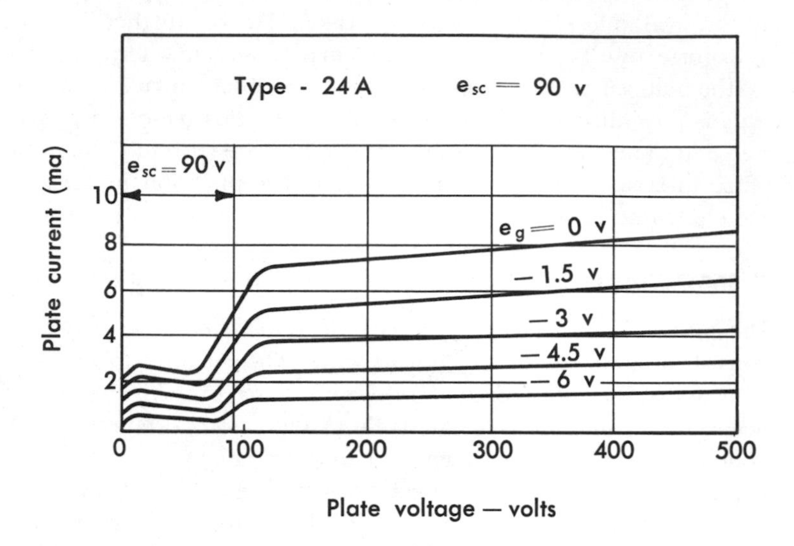

Figure 20-16
The downward-sloping portions of the curves exhibit negative resistance.

age. This is the same as saying that the dynamic plate resistance is very high.

In the majority of applications, negative resistance is undesirable. Hence, a tetrode is usually operated with comparatively high plate voltage. Amplification factors are high compared with triodes. Typical tetrodes have μ values from 500 to 800. However, transconductance values are about the same as for triodes operated with similar plate currents. In addition to high μ, a tetrode also provides a very low effective plate-to-control grid capacitance, as noted previously. Hence, tetrodes are preferred in high-frequency amplifier applications.

20.14 PENTODES

In amplifier application, the negative-resistance interval of a tetrode limits the available "swing" or output which is obtainable. Hence, another type of tube is commonly used to overcome the effects of secondary emission, called a *pentode*. It contains a third grid between the screen and plate, called a *suppressor grid,* which is usually connected directly to the cathode. When the plate emits secondary electrons, these secondaries are repelled back into the plate by the suppressor. Since the suppressor is negative with respect to the plate and screen, it does not materially affect the flow of primary electrons to the plate.

Although the screen grid in either a tetrode or pentode greatly reduces the effect of plate voltage upon plate-current flow, the control grid maintains its effect on plate current as in a triode. This control-grid action in all tubes results from the proximity of the control grid to the cathode. In turn, the transconductance of a pentode or a tetrode is approximately the same as that of a triode having similar structure. As would be anticipated, the μ and the dynamic plate resistance of a pentode is very high compared with these parameters in a triode. The μ of typical pentodes ranges from 100 to 1500. Dynamic plate resistances range from 0.5 to 1 megohm.

A typical set of pentode characteristics is seen in Figure 20-17. The

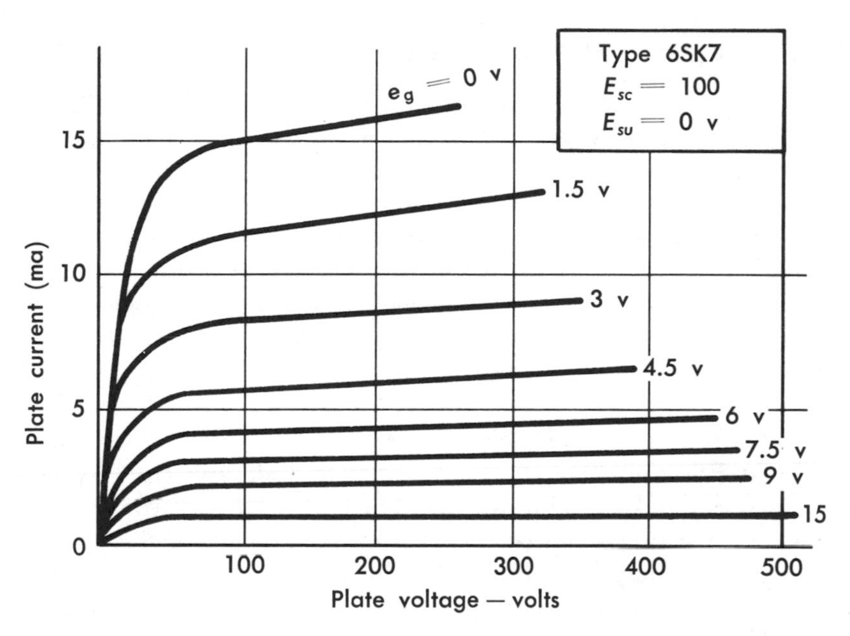

Figure 20-17
Characteristic E_p-I_p curves for a typical pentode.

comparatively small effect of plate voltage upon plate current appears as the small slope of the curves past the point where the plate voltage is high enough to keep the electrons between screen and plate from being attracted back to the screen. The plate voltage at which this occurs is less than the screen voltage, because electrons enter the space with sufficient velocity to travel past the screen to the lower voltage plate. A pentode can accommodate a considerably greater swing than a tetrode. Hence, pentodes find favor as high-power amplifiers. We should note in passing that certain tetrodes are constructed in such manner that they have characteristics comparable to pentodes. Such tetrodes are called *beam-power* tubes. The effect of a suppressor grid is obtained by suitable tube geometry which develops a space-charge distribution analogous to the electrostatic field of a suppressor grid.

There are, of course, a large number of electron tubes other than diodes, triodes, tetrodes, and pentodes. The cathode-ray tube is one example. However, discussion of such tube types cannot be covered in a basic electronics book. You will have an opportunity to learn about specialized electron tubes in your advanced electronics courses. Despite the wide variety in construction and function, you will find that the operation of all electron tubes is based on the principles explained in this chapter.

20.15 TUBE DEFECTS AND TUBE TESTERS

Vacuum tubes have numerous characteristics. New tubes have characteristics and parameters which fall within certain tolerances that are maintained by quality-control procedures in tube factories. As a tube ages, its characteristics and parameters change. Various defects may occur which impair tube function; hence, tube testers are used to check the more important electrical characteristics and common defects of vacuum tubes. It is impractical to check a tube completely, because a very complex tester would be required, and the test procedures would be prohibitively time consuming. Accordingly, commercial tube testers represent a judicious compromise.

One of the most common defects found in tubes which have seen long service is interelectrode short-circuits, or interelectrode leakage. Two electrodes, such as a heater and a cathode, may make electrical contact or a resistance path may develop between the electrodes. This defect impairs tube operation in many applications. Again, a heater (or a filament) may burn open. The tube then becomes inoperative. Simple tube testers, as illustrated in Figure 20-18, are limited to tests for open heaters. A neon bulb is used as an indicator. Operating voltage is obtained from a 117-volt 60-cycle outlet. The tube under test is plugged into the appropriate socket, and the neon bulb is observed.

More elaborate tube testers also provide indication of interelectrode short-circuits and leakage resistance. For example, the neon bulb is connected in series with the heater and cathode and a voltage source. If the heater-cathode insulation is defective, the neon bulb will glow. Again, the neon bulb can be connected in series with the cathode and grid and the voltage source. If the grid-cathode insulation is defective, the neon bulb will glow. Plate-cathode or plate-grid insulation can be checked in the same manner. These tests are usually made with the heater operating at

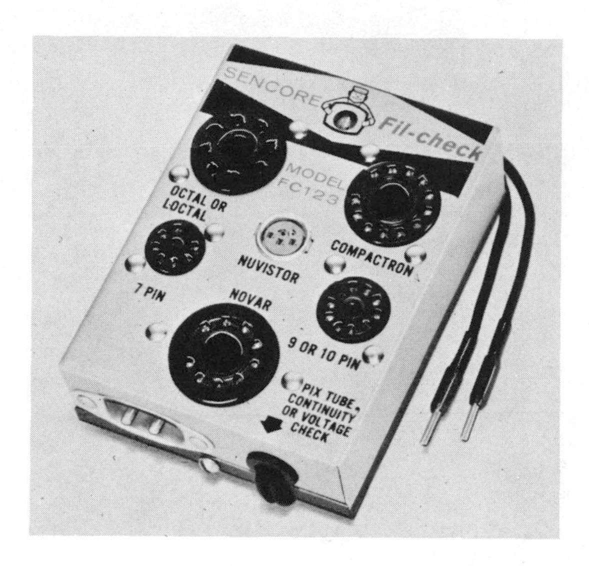

Figure 20-18
A simple tube tester. (Courtesy, Sencore, Addison, Illinois.)

its normal temperature, because insulation defects may become evident only when the electrodes are heated.

Thus, the tube tester illustrated in Figure 20-19 provides a check of insulation resistance between any two electrodes of a tube. The lever switches are thrown, as specified by the chart, and the neon bulb is observed. Correct voltage is applied to the heater by suitable setting of the filament-voltage switch. This type of tester also checks cathode (or filament) emission of a tube. A milliammeter is connected in series with the plate and cathode and a voltage source. The hot cathode emits electrons (unless the tube is dead), and the resulting electron current flow is indicated by the meter. Most tube testers of the emission type do not indicate the current flow in milliamperes, but are provided with an "English" scale with Bad-?-Good sectors. This form of indication is termed a *go–no-go test.*

Tubes become defective most frequently because of open heaters or interelectrode short-circuits (or leakage). The second most common defect is low emission. Hence, an emission-type tester is quite effective in detecting bad tubes. However, it is possible for a tube to pass the foregoing tests satisfactorily and still fail to operate satisfactorily as an amplifier. In other words, the control grid may not "valve" the electron flow normally. Accordingly, more elaborate tube testers provide a transconductance test instead of an emission test. A transconductance test checks the ability of a triode,

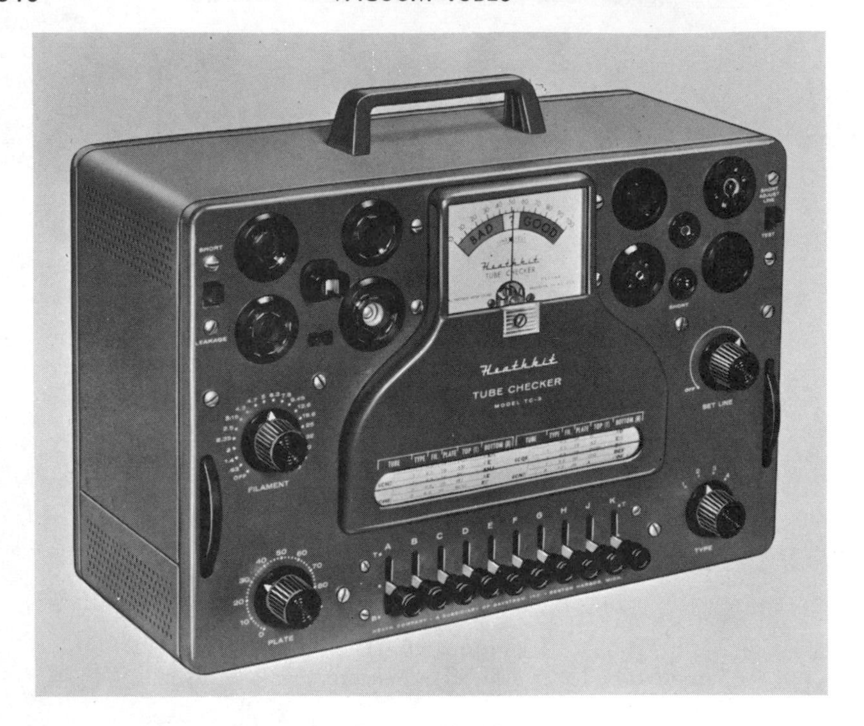

Figure 20-19
A tube tester which provides a check of insulation resistance. (Courtesy of Heath Co.)

tetrode, or pentode to operate as an amplifier. Diodes, of course, can only be checked for emission.

Figure 20-20 illustrates a transconductance (dynamic mutual conductance) type of tube tester. An a-c signal voltage is applied to the control grid, and the resulting a-c plate-signal current is indicated by the meter. Predetermined d-c voltages are applied to each electrode in the tube. In turn, the meter scale can indicate the transconductance value of the tube. An English scale is also provided for rapid go–no-go tests. It has been found that the life expectancy of a tube can be predicted with reasonable accuracy by checking its transconductance at suitable intervals and noting the rate at which the transconductance value decreases with time in service. Life expectancy can also be determined roughly by comparing the transconductance value at normal heater voltage with the transconductance value at 10 percent reduction in heater voltage.

The more elaborate types of tube testers also check a tube for gas. Unless a very high vacuum is maintained, a tube will not operate satisfactorily in some circuits. A trace of gas permits ions to form, and the grid draws appreciable current. In turn, circuit action is disturbed and the tube does not operate properly. The tube tester may also provide a power-output

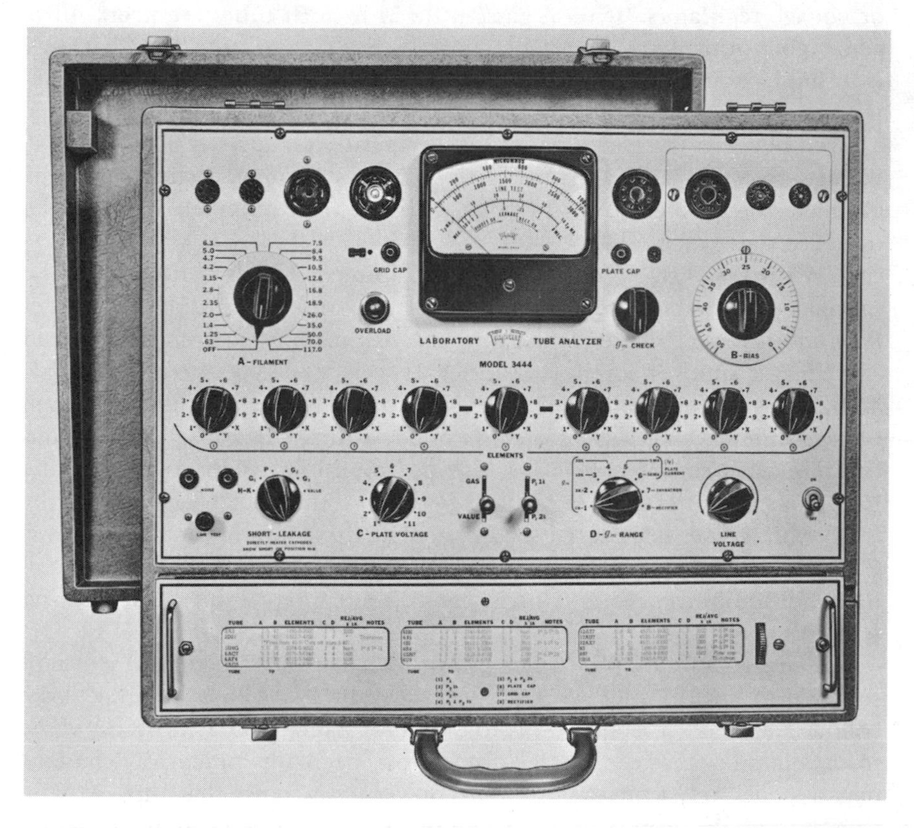

Figure 20-20
A transconductance type of tube tester. (Courtesy of Triplett Electrical Instrument Co.)

test for tubes which are required to supply substantial signal output power. A screen-grid *knee* test is provided by a few tube testers. This function indicates whether the screen-grid characteristic is correct, or whether it is abnormal in a manner which limits the available power output from the tube in typical applications.

Specialized laboratory-type tube testers provide many other tests of tube characteristics and parameters which are significant in particular applications. Details of specialized tube testers are discussed in engineering instrumentation textbooks.

20.16 GAS-FILLED TUBES

We have learned that the presence of gas in a high-vacuum tube is undesirable and may cause the tube to be inoperative. However, there are special-purpose tubes which are gas-filled and are used as electronic switches or voltage regulators. Typical gases utilized in such tubes are neon, nitrogen, argon, or mercury vapor. The neon bulb that was noted in Chapter 4 is a simple example of a gas-filled tube. A neon bulb is a gas diode. You will recall that this bulb is characterized by the fact that the voltage applied between the electrodes causes practically no current flow until the voltage exceeds a critical value. Then, the gas becomes ionized, and the gas molecules lose electrons through collision with other electrons in the interelectrode space.

In turn, positively charged ions are formed, which drift toward the cathode and attract more electrons out of the cathode, causing the current flow to increase. There is no physical distinction between anode and cathode in a simple neon bulb—the negative electrode operates as a cathode and the positive electrode operates as an anode. There is a certain minimum voltage difference between plate and anode which will cause the electrons to move with sufficient velocity to cause ionization. This is termed the ionization potential or firing voltage. Once the tube has been ionized, the anode voltage can be reduced somewhat without stopping the current flow. However, there is a certain minimum value of anode voltage necessary to maintain ionization. This value is termed the extinguishing or de-ionizing voltage.

Thus, a gas-filled tube operates as a switch which opens and closes in response to critical anode-cathode voltage values. When a gas-filled tube conducts current, it is analogous to a low resistance, which varies in value in such manner that the voltage drop across it remains practically constant over a moderately wide range of current. Analysis shows that this virtually constant voltage drop is simply based on the ratio of the circuit resistance to the internal resistance of the gas-filled tube in its conducting state. This characteristic makes gas-filled tubes useful as voltage-regulator and circuit-protective devices.

A *voltage-regulator* tube is specially designed to keep the voltage drop across the tube at a practically constant value regardless of fairly wide changes in source voltage or load current (see Figure 20-21). Another type of gas-filled tube in wide use is termed the *mercury-vapor* tube. This tube contains a small amount of mercury that vaporizes when the cathode is heated. The mercury vapor ionizes when the anode voltage exceeds a critical value. The anode-to-cathode voltage drop in a mercury-vapor tube is practically constant at 15 volts, regardless of the amount of anode current flow. Mercury-vapor diodes are widely used as rectifiers in power supplies which must provide heavy current flow.

A *thyratron* is a gas-filled triode or tetrode in which the grid controls the ionization voltage value. Figure 20-22 shows the ionization-potential characteristic of a typical thyratron triode. Note the plate (anode) voltages necessary to produce ionization at various values of grid voltage. Once the

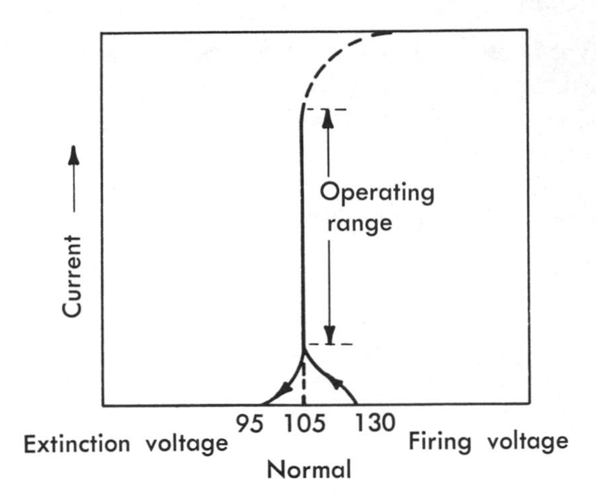

Figure 20-21
A voltage-regulator tube maintains a practically constant voltage drop.

thyratron starts to conduct, the grid loses control. The grid is unable to extinguish the tube. De-ionization occurs when the plate (anode) voltage is reduced below a critical minimum value. After the thyratron is de-ionized, the grid regains control. Thus, both the grid and the plate voltages are involved in thyratron switching circuits.

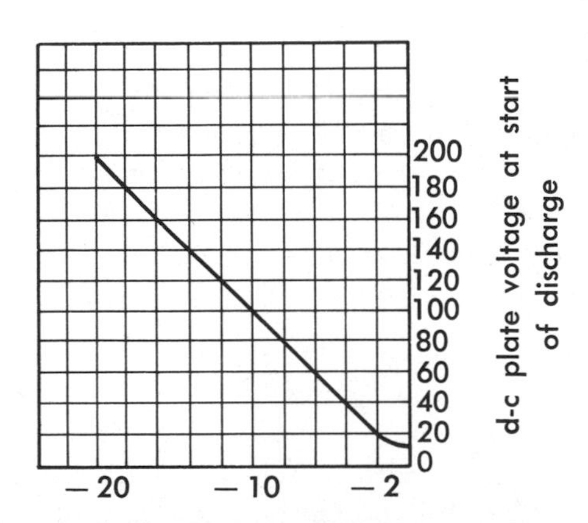

Figure 20-22
Ionization-potential characteristic for a typical thyratron.

20.17 PHOTOTUBES

Another type of electron tube that changes light energy into electrical energy is termed the *photoelectric* tube, or *phototube*. In contrast to the conventional electron tube, a phototube does not use a heated cathode. Instead, electrons are liberated from a specially prepared surface inside the tube when radiant energy strikes the surface. The stream of charges that result is an electric current. A voltage drop appears across the phototube; that is, a voltage output is obtained when visible (or invisible) radiant energy enters the tube. Heinrich Hertz discovered the photoemissive effect of ultraviolet light on metal electrodes in 1887.

Although it is not as versatile as a conventional electron tube, a phototube has many important uses. It provides a method of using light energy to control the operation of devices or of systems. Reproduction of sound from a photographic image on film is a typical example. The automatic doorbell that operates from a beam of light is another familiar example. Photocathodes of chief interest in electronics technology are formed by deposition of a thin film of alkali metal on a metal plate. The alkali metals have comparatively low work functions, and some of them emit electrons when visible light strikes the photocathode. Photocathodes suitable for measurement of ultraviolet light employ metals that have high work functions, such as thorium. You will have an opportunity to learn more about work functions of metals in your advanced physics courses.

It is interesting to note the equation for photoelectric emission:

$$I = A_1 T^2 \epsilon^{-b_0/T} \tag{20.6}$$

where I is the photoelectric current in amps per sq cm, A_1 is an empirical constant, b_0 is proportional to the frequency of the incident light, T is the absolute temperature, and ϵ is the constant 2.718.

The similarity of this equation for photoelectric emission to the previous equation for thermionic emission [Equation (20.1)] is obvious. This similarity does not really come as a surprise, because we know that light and heat are similar forms of energy that differ only in their frequency of vibration.

SUMMARY OF FUNDAMENTAL CONCEPTS

Edison Effect: Negative electricity is given off by a heated filament and can be collected by an electrode placed near the filament inside the evacuated bulb.

Fleming Valve: An application of the Edison effect in rectification of alternating currents, particularly high-frequency alternating currents.

DeForest Triode: A vacuum tube comprising a cathode, grid, and plate; it can convert a source of d-c power into a-c power, and provides an a-c output which is greater than the a-c power input.

Triodes are basically nonlinear devices and can be analyzed to best advantage by graphical methods.

A tetrode contains a screen grid between the control grid and plate, minimizing capacitive coupling between control grid and plate.

The basic parameters of a triode include its amplification factor, plate resistance, and transconductance.

A tetrode can be regarded as a constant-current device because the plate current is little affected by changes in plate voltage.

A pentode contains a suppressor grid between the screen grid and plate, which provides electrostatic shielding and suppresses current flow due to secondary emission.

Tetrodes are basically nonlinear devices, and have a region of negative-resistance operation.

The basic parameters of a pentode include its transconductance, plate resistance, and screen resistance.

The basic parameters of a tetrode include its transconductance, plate resistance, and screen resistance.

QUESTIONS

1) Thermally emitted electrons are:
(*a*) free electrons in the metallic body of an emitter. (*b*) free electrons in the space surrounding an emitter. (*c*) free electrons in a superconducting substance. (*d*) free electrons in a semiconducting substance.
2) A thermal emitter is termed a:
(*a*) cathode. (*b*) space charge. (*c*) source of secondary electrons. (*d*) plate.
3) An electron tube with a cathode and plate is called a:
(*a*) beam-power tube. (*b*) heater. (*c*) diode. (*d*) filament.
4) At emission saturation, the plate resistance of an electron tube becomes:
(*a*) zero. (*b*) reverse. (*c*) indeterminate. (*d*) negative.
5) The cutoff voltage of a triode corresponds to:
(*a*) zero grid current. (*b*) zero plate current. (*c*) zero heater current. (*d*) infinite negative resistance.
6) The amplification factor of a triode is:
(*a*) the step-up in signal voltage which it can provide. (*b*) the step-down in signal voltage which it can provide. (*c*) proportional to its screen-grid voltage. (*d*) inversely proportional to its suppressor-grid voltage.
7) Dynamic plate resistance corresponds to:
(*a*) d-c plate resistance. (*b*) absence of a space charge. (*c*) reverse current flow. (*d*) the slope of the tangent at the operating point on an E_p–I_p curve.
8) Transconductance is a measure of:
(*a*) dynamic plate resistance. (*b*) the ratio of a plate-current increment to a grid-voltage increment. (*c*) heater conductance. (*d*) electron distribution.
9) A load line depicts:
(*a*) the locus of operation for an electron tube. (*b*) the conductivity of the control grid. (*c*) the resistivity of the control grid. (*d*) the magnitude of the heater current.
10) Secondary emission denotes the:
(*a*) emission of electrons from a heated cathode. (*b*) emission of electrons from a transformer secondary. (*c*) emission of electrons by primary electrons striking a plate or a screen grid. (*d*) emission of electrons by a load resistor.

PROBLEMS

1) If a change of 10 microvolts in grid potential corresponds to a change of 100 microvolts in plate potential of a triode when the plate current is held constant, what is the μ of the tube?
2) At another operating point in Problem 1, a change of 10 microvolts in grid potential corresponds to a change of 50 microvolts when the plate current is held constant. What is the amplification factor of the tube at the changed operating point?
3) If a triode is biased to cutoff, and the grid voltage is increased by -10 microvolts, what is the corresponding change in plate voltage when the plate current is held at its cutoff value?
4) If the grid voltage of a triode is held constant, and the plate voltage is changed by 1 volt, the plate current changes by 100 microamps. What is the dynamic plate resistance of the tube?
5) Suppose that the grid voltage in Problem 4 biases the tube to cutoff. If the plate voltage is reduced by 1 volt, what is the value of the tube's dynamic plate resistance?
6) Calculate the transconductance of a tube in micromhos if a grid-voltage change of 0.1 volt causes a plate-current change of 100 microamps when the plate voltage is held constant.
7) The transconductance of a tube is 5000 micromhos. What is the change in plate current if the grid voltage is changed by 0.1 volt, with the plate voltage held constant?
8) A tube has an amplification factor of 15. Its transconductance is equal to 1500 micromhos. What is the value of its dynamic plate resistance?
9) If a tube draws 10 ma of plate current at a plate voltage of 100 volts, what is the value of its d-c plate resistance?
10) The power dissipated by the plate as heat is equal to I_pE_p. Calculate the power dissipated by the plate in Problem 9.
11) If a grid draws current, it dissipates power as heat. This power is equal to E_gI_g. If the grid is biased to $+1$ volt and draws 20 milliamps of current, how much power is dissipated by the grid?
12) A certain tube is rated for a maximum plate dissipation of 1 watt. If the plate is operated at 150 volts, what is the maximum permissible plate current?
13) If a triode is operated with grid-leak bias, and an a-c signal with an amplitude of 2 peak volts is applied to the grid, what is the approximate value of the grid-bias voltage?
14) What is the maximum negative swing of the instantaneous grid potential, approximately, in Problem 13?

21

SEMICONDUCTOR DIODES AND TRANSISTORS

21.1 SEMICONDUCTOR JUNCTIONS

We know that an *N*-type semiconductor has an excess of free electrons, and that a *P*-type semiconductor has an excess of holes. Hence, conduction in *N*-type material takes place chiefly by electron flow. On the other hand, conduction in *P*-type material takes place chiefly by hole flow. Most semiconductor applications require that *N*-type material and *P*-type material be fabricated with a *junction* or transition as depicted in Figure 21-1. A junction is not merely a mechanical juxtaposition of the two materials; instead, the crystalline structure must be uninterrupted across the junc-

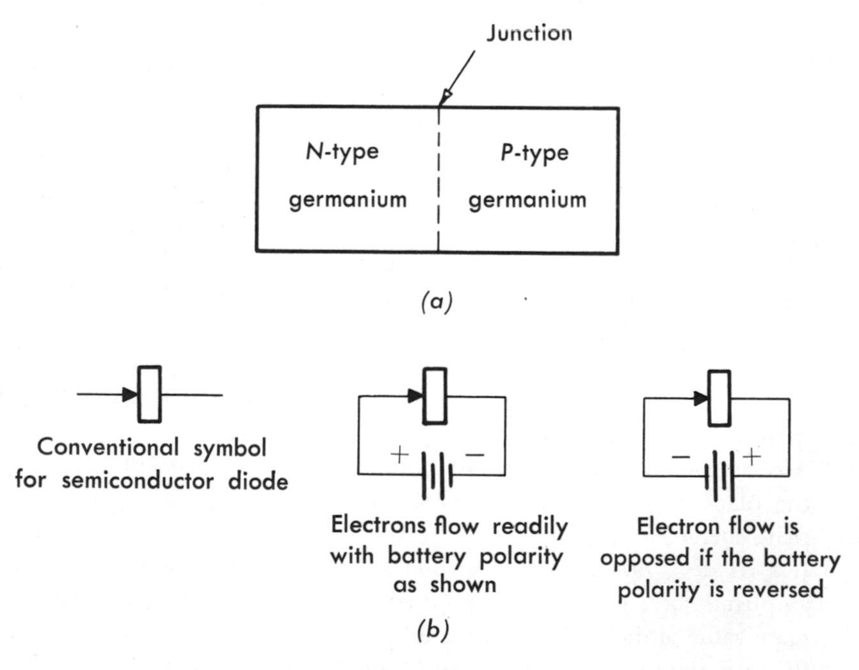

Figure 21-1
(*a*) A junction is the interface between *N*-type and *P*-type materials. (*b*) Polarity considerations in diode symbolism.

tion. Otherwise, the desired electrical characteristics of a junction are not obtained.

Figure 21-2 illustrates the lattice structure through a junction. Note that *N*-type germanium appears to the left of the junction, and *P*-type

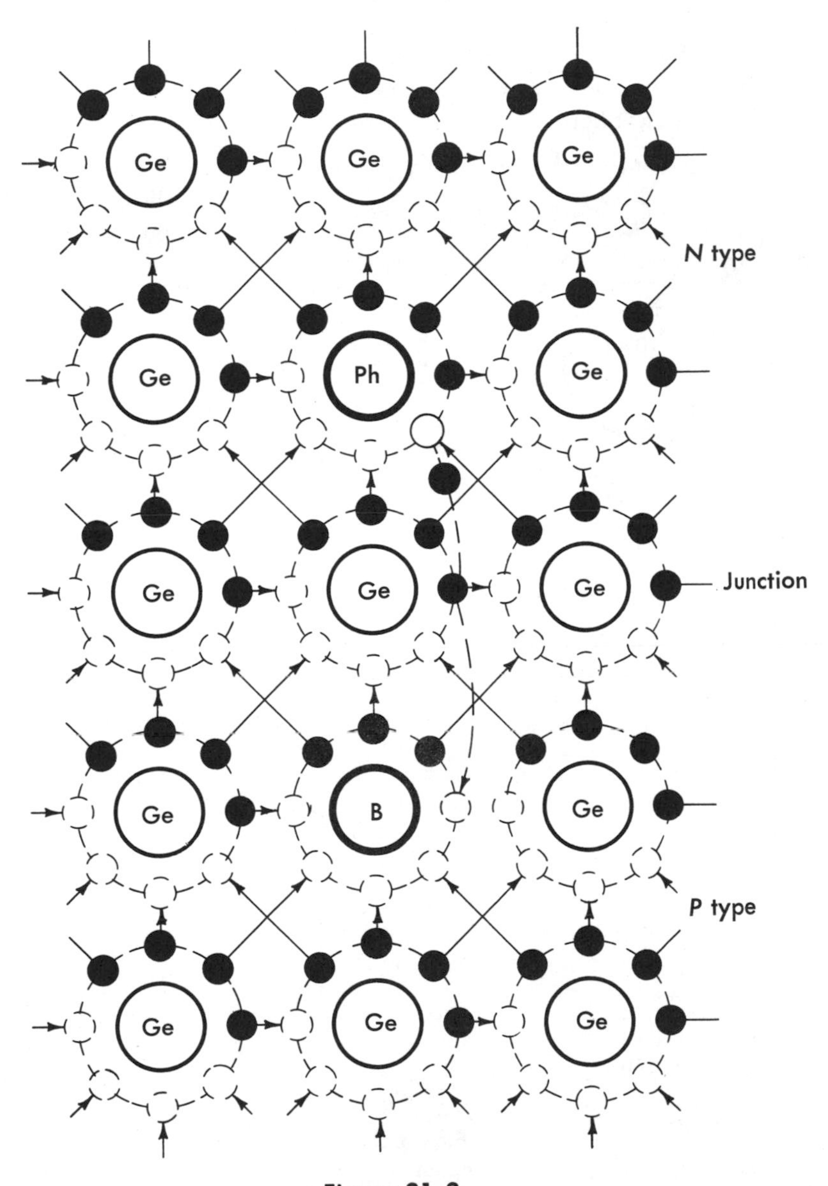

Figure 21-2
Lattice structure across a junction.

germanium appears to the right of the junction. Except for the occurrence of donor and acceptor atoms, the lattice structure is the same as found in intrinsic germanium. Typical junctions are grown from a melt; growth is continuous, but the doping elements are changed to fabricate a junction. Note that the phosphorous atom has an extra electron that cannot be assimilated into the lattice structure. Note also that the boron atom has an electron deficiency, which corresponds to an absent covalent bond.

Since the *N*-type germanium provides a free electron, and the *P*-type germanium needs an electron to complete the lattice structure, the free electron soon wanders across the junction and comes to rest in the shell

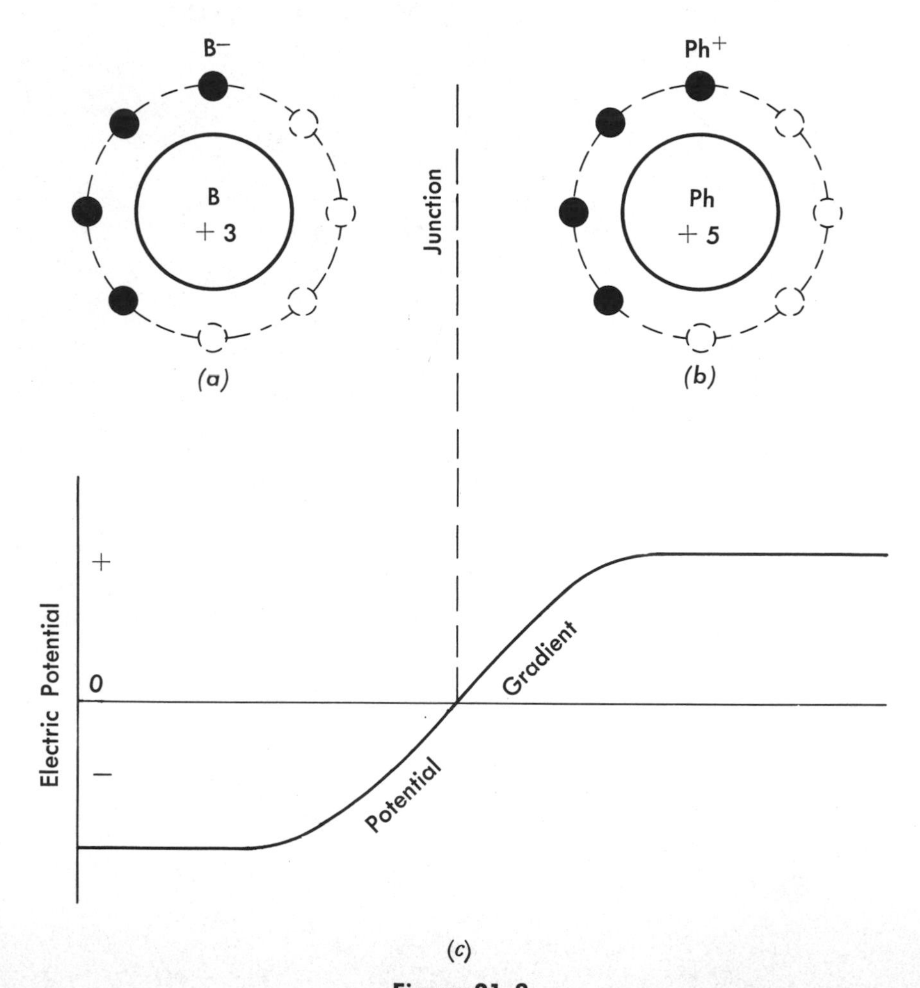

Figure 21-3
Potential gradient across a junction. (*a*) Boron ion. (*b*) Phosphorous ion. (*c*) A "built-in" field.

of the boron atom. This completes the lattice structure, and represents its stable condition. In turn, the phosphorous and boron atoms are left as ions in the lattice. To put it another way, the phosphorous ion represents a positive charge on the left-hand side of the junction; the boron ion represents a negative charge on the right-hand side of the junction.

This situation is depicted in Figure 21-3. The junction is a "built-in" electric field. We see that if a free electron happens to be located at the junction, the field will cause the electron to move away from the boron ion, and toward the phosphorous ion. Similarly, if a hole happens to be located at the junction, the hole will move away from the phosphorous

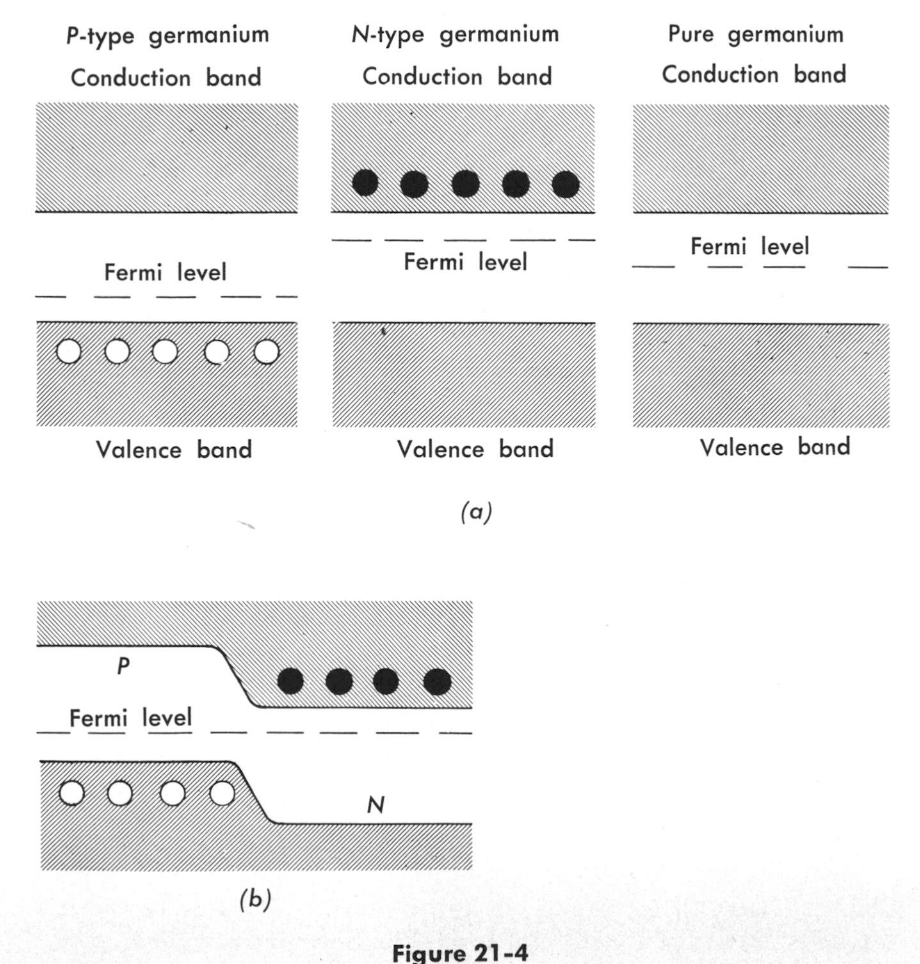

Figure 21-4
Alignment of Fermi levels in a *PN* junction. (*a*) Fermi levels for individual substances. (*b*) Fermi levels aligned through a junction.

ion and toward the boron ion. That is, the potential gradient through the junction will sweep any charge carriers out of the junction region.

The potential gradient across a junction is often described as an alignment of the *Fermi levels.* A Fermi level is simply the average energy level of the charge carriers. In a sample of intrinsic germanium, the number of free electrons is equal to the number of holes. Hence, the Fermi level of intrinsic germanium is in the forbidden region, halfway between the conduction band and the valence band. This fact is depicted in Figure 21-4. Now, in the case of *N*-type germanium, there are more free electrons than holes. Hence, the Fermi level is located nearer the conduction band in *N*-type germanium. But *P*-type germanium has more holes than free electrons; hence, the Fermi level is located nearer the valence band in *P*-type germanium.

Whenever two dissimilar substances are brought into electrical contact, the Fermi levels must have the same value. This can be achieved only by establishing a potential gradient, as seen in Figure 21-4. The greater the doping concentration of the germanium, the greater the potential gradient will be in consequence of Fermi-level alignment. Hence, lattice equilibrium across a junction entails establishment of a built-in electric field. This field is not externally accessible. If you connect a voltmeter across the germanium blocks which form a junction, the meter reads zero volts. The germanium blocks as a whole are electrically neutral.

21.2 DIODE ACTION

The fact that various minerals exhibit widely different resistances when current flow is reversed was first noted by F. Braun in 1874; thus, diode action was discovered long before the physics of semiconductors was understood. We know that *N*-type germanium has an excess of free electrons, and that *P*-type germanium has an excess of holes. When these two types of semiconductors are fabricated into a junction device, it is called a semiconductor *diode.* Figure 21-5 depicts a semiconductor diode, and indicates the excess electrons and holes which are available to conduct electric current. Suppose you connect a battery to the diode with positive voltage applied to the *N*-type material, and negative voltage applied to the *P*-type material. Both electrons and holes are attracted away from the junction.

With the available charge carriers thus attracted away from the junction, it is clear that no current can flow through the diode. The effective resistance of the diode is the same as that of intrinsic germanium, which is an extremely high resistance. However, if you reverse the battery polarity, as shown in Figure 21-5, electrons are urged toward the junction, and holes are also urged toward the junction. At the junction, holes

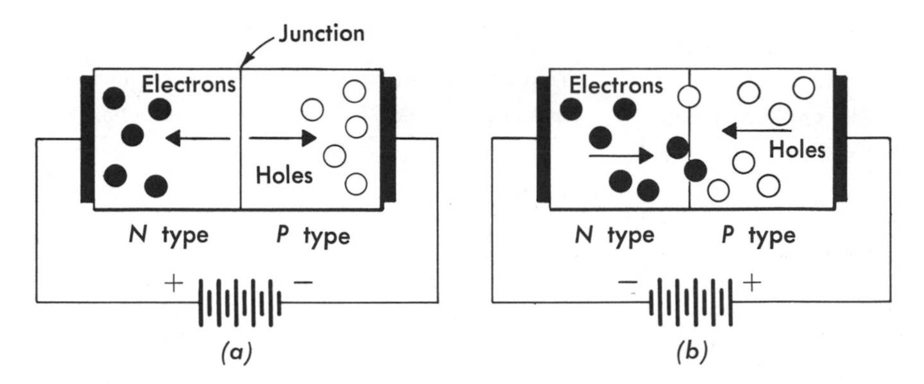

Figure 21-5
(*a*) Junction diode does not conduct. (*b*) Junction diode conducts.

and electrons recombine. Meanwhile, the battery is injecting more free electrons into the *N*-type block, and more holes into the *P*-type block. Hence, current continues to flow as long as the battery voltage is applied.

Doping concentrations are sufficiently high in commercial semiconductor diodes so that the forward resistance is low. Hence, a heavy current flows in the forward direction. If the battery voltage is substantial, the diode will burn out due to the large amount of I^2R power that it must dissipate as heat. Let us see how the potential gradient operates to prevent reverse-current flow, and to permit forward-current flow. When no voltage is applied to the diode (Figure 21-6), the potential gradient is at its normal value. Because the potential gradient will prevent reverse-current flow, it is also called a potential *barrier*. If you apply a voltage in the forward direction to the diode, the barrier is partially neutralized, or, the barrier is lowered. A lowered barrier permits current flow, but if you apply a voltage in the reverse direction, the barrier is enhanced, or raised. In turn, only a very small current can flow.

The tiny current that flows in the reverse direction is called a *saturation current*, and has approximately the same value that would flow in a block of intrinsic germanium. There is a fundamental difference between forward-current flow and reverse-current flow. If you apply more voltage in the forward direction, a higher current flows. A higher voltage injects more charge carriers into the diode, in addition to lowering the potential barrier. Hence, forward current obeys Ohm's law in a general sense. On the other hand, if you apply voltage in the reverse direction, charge carriers are simply swept out of the diode. In addition, the potential barrier is raised. Hence, the only charge carriers that become available are those due to thermal generation, and they are quite few. Saturation current is then *temperature limited* and does not obey Ohm's law. Satura-

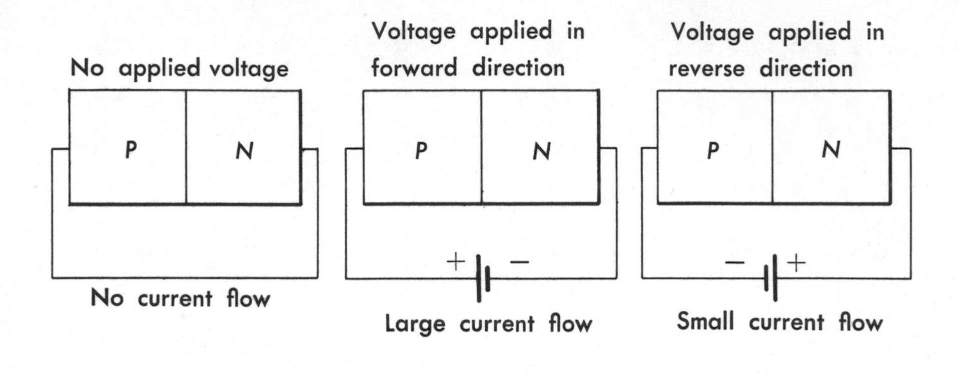

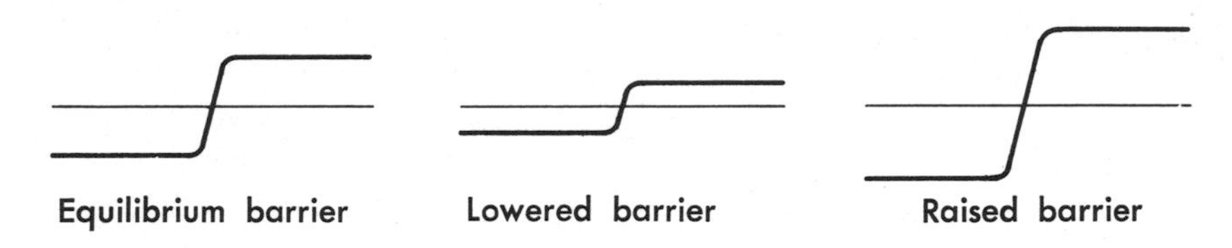

Figure 21-6
A potential barrier may be raised or lowered.

tion current remains virtually constant, regardless of the value of reverse voltage which is applied.

Forward-current flow is given approximately by the formula

$$I = I_s \epsilon^{eV/kT} \tag{21.1}$$

where I_s is the reverse or saturation current in amperes, ϵ is the constant 2.718, e is the charge on an electron (1.602×10^{-19} coulomb), k is Boltzmann's constant (1.38×10^{-23} joule per °K), V is the applied voltage in volts, and T is the junction temperature in °K.

We perceive that since the applied voltage V appears as an exponent, the forward current will increase very rapidly with increase in voltage. A characteristic for a typical semiconductor diode is shown graphically in Figure 21-7. The curve is nonlinear; however, like vacuum-tube curves, the characteristic approaches linearity at higher values of current flow. The d-c resistance at any point on the diode curve is given by the E/I ratio at that point. For small variations about a chosen point on the curve, the dynamic resistance of the diode is a basic parameter. The dynamic resistance at a point is given by the ratio of a small voltage increment to the corresponding current increment.

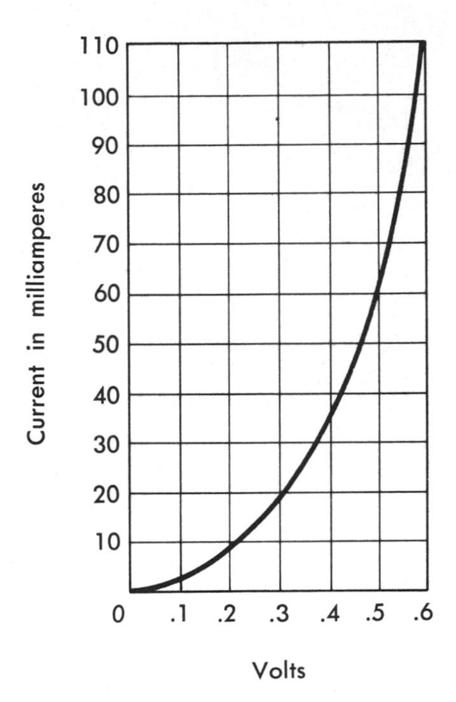

Figure 21-7
Forward-voltage-current characteristic for a typical semiconductor diode.

Load lines are used to analyze the operation of a diode which is connected in series with a resistor, as depicted in Figure 21-8. The diode is connected for forward-current flow. To find the current flow and the voltage drop across the diode, we draw the load line as in Figure 21-8(*b*). The slope of the load line is the E/I locus of R. This load line intersects the diode characteristic at point P. Next, if we project point P to the voltage and current axes, we determine the current flow in the circuit and the voltage drop V_D across the diode. The power which the diode must dissipate as heat is equal to IV_D.

21.3 JUNCTION CAPACITANCE

Since a semiconductor diode has a potential barrier (Figure 21-6), it follows that capacitance is associated with a junction. We perceive that junction capacitance is simply the relation of applied voltage to charge concentration

$$C = \frac{Q}{V} \tag{21.2}$$

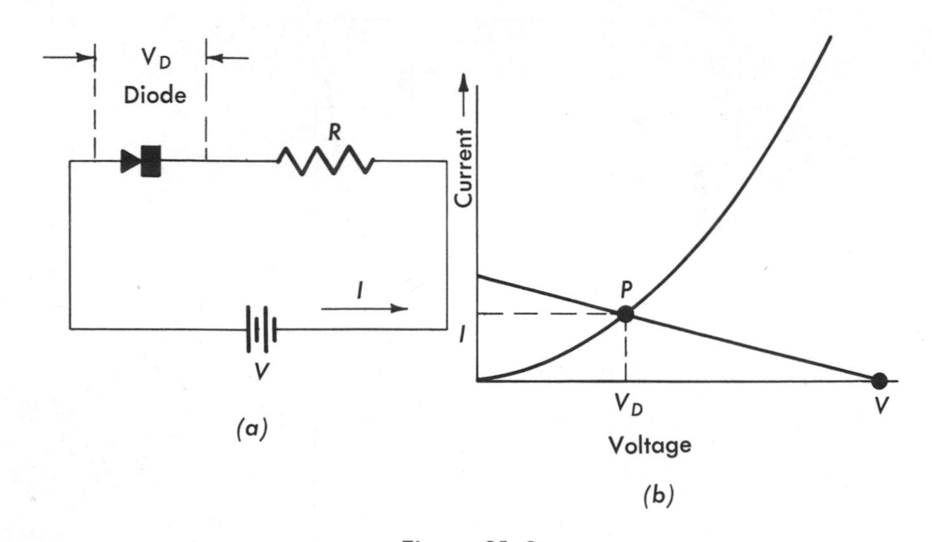

Figure 21-8
(*a*) Diode connected in series with a resistor and a voltage source.
(*b*) Determination of current I and voltage drop V_D.

where C is the capacitance in farads, Q is the charge in coulombs, and V is the potential in volts.

We find that in a reverse-biased diode, the junction capacitance is not constant. Instead, the capacitance value depends upon the value of the applied voltage, as depicted in Figure 21-9. Hence, the junction capacitance must be expressed incrementally

$$\Delta C_j = \frac{q}{\Delta V} \tag{21.3}$$

where Δ denotes a very small change in value.

It was noted that the potential gradient sweeps charge carriers out of the junction. When an external voltage is applied, the barrier is changed in height, with corresponding change in the charge-sweeping force. The effective width of the region from which charge carriers have been swept (Figure 21-9) is called the *depletion region*. As shown in Figure 21-5, increased reverse voltage will attract more holes toward the negative terminal of the diode, and will attract more electrons toward the positive terminal of the diode.

There is a depletion region on each side of the junction. The sum of the region widths is equal to the width of the depletion layer. If the N-type germanium and the P-type germanium have equal resistivities, the depletion-region widths are equal. If one of the substances should have higher

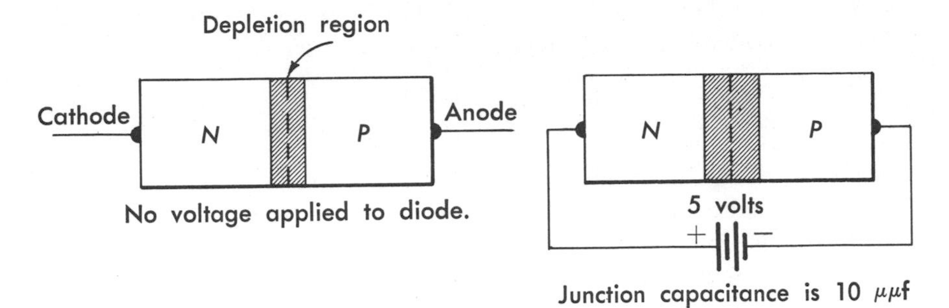

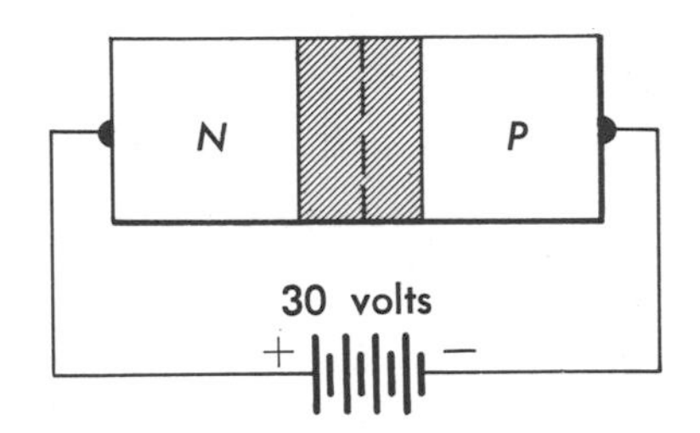

Junction capacitance is 5 μμf

(*a*)

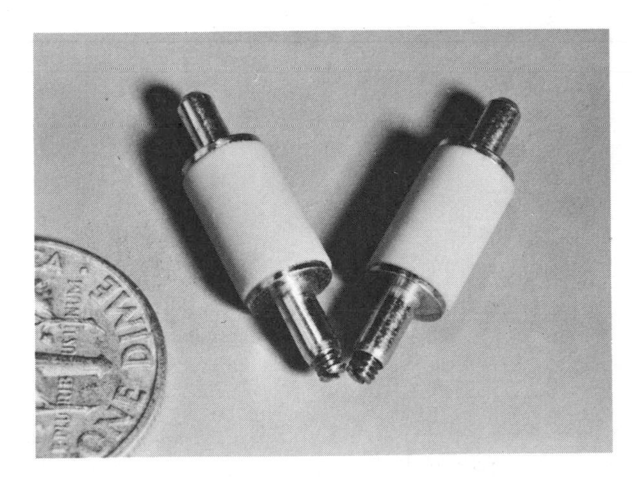

(*b*)

Figure 21-9

(*a*) Variation of junction-capacitance value. (*b*) Semiconductor diodes designed for use as variable capacitors. (Courtesy of Raytheon Mfg. Co.)

resistivity, however, its depletion region will be wider. A simple formula permits us to calculate the width of the depletion layer

$$W_d = \frac{\epsilon A}{C_j} \tag{21.4}$$

where W_d is the width of the depletion layer in meters, ϵ is the permittivity of the semiconductor substance (dielectric constant of the semiconductor substance times the permittivity of a vacuum, 8.855×10^{-12} farad/meter), A is the junction area, and C_j is the junction capacitance.

Junction capacitance is put to use in certain practical applications. For example, a form of variable capacitor is provided by variation of

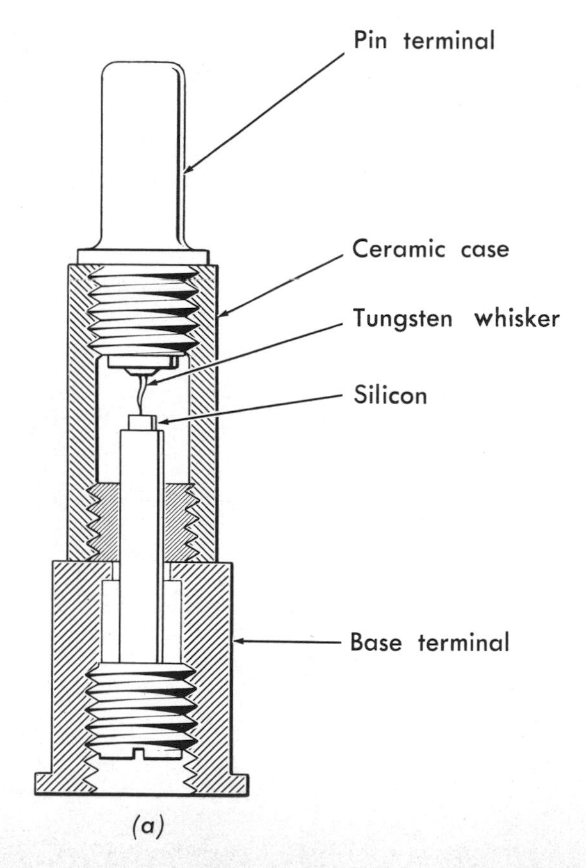

Figure 21-10
(*a*) Construction of a typical point-contact semiconductor diode. (*b*) The *P*-type region of a point-contact diode.

(*Continued on facing page.*)

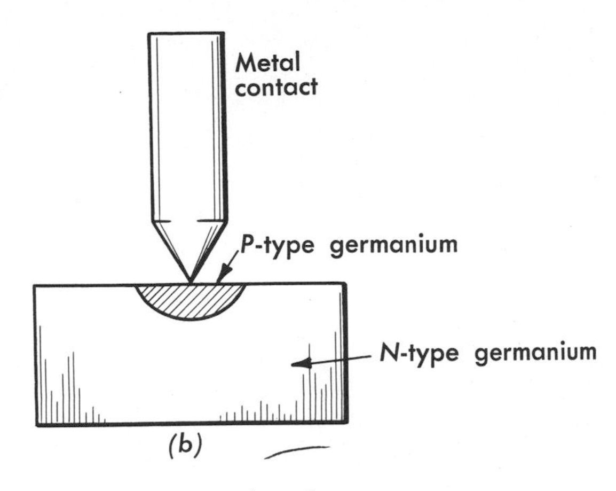

Fig. 21-10 (*Continued*)

reverse-bias voltage applied to a junction diode. Junction capacitance imposes an upper-frequency limit in the operation of high-frequency equipment. Hence, junction diodes cannot be used beyond this frequency limit; instead, point-contact diodes are utilized. A typical point-contact diode is shown in Figure 21-10. A sharp metallic point makes contact with the semiconductor surface. During manufacture, a controlled surge of current is passed through the diode to form a junction, which evidently has a very small area. Hence, a point-contact diode has minimum junction capacitance, and is suitable for operation at extremely high frequencies.

21.4 TUNNEL DIODES

Tunnel diodes are junction diodes formed from very heavily doped semiconductor substances. Typical tunnel diodes are illustrated in Figure 21-11. For example, the doping concentration in high-frequency diodes is about 10^{16} atoms per cu cm. The doping concentration in a tunnel diode, on the other hand, is about 10^{20} atoms per cu cm. Hence, the depletion layer is extremely thin, and is approximately 10^{-6} cm in width. The diode characteristic also has a perhaps unexpected form, depicted in Figure 21-12. The "tunneling" effect that accounts for this characteristic cannot be treated in these pages. However, you will have an opportunity to learn about tunneling action in your advanced electronics courses.

As the forward voltage is increased, current flow rises first to a maximum, called the *peak-current* value. Further increase of forward voltage causes reduced current flow. This is the negative-resistance interval which is the chief operating feature of a tunnel diode. Current flow reaches a minimum value at the valley point. Thereafter, the current flow increases much as in a conventional diode. The voltage range over the negative-resistance region is called the *voltage swing*. The ratio of peak current to valley current is called the *peak-to-valley current ratio*. Note that the negative-resistance value is given by the slope of the downward portion of the characteristic.

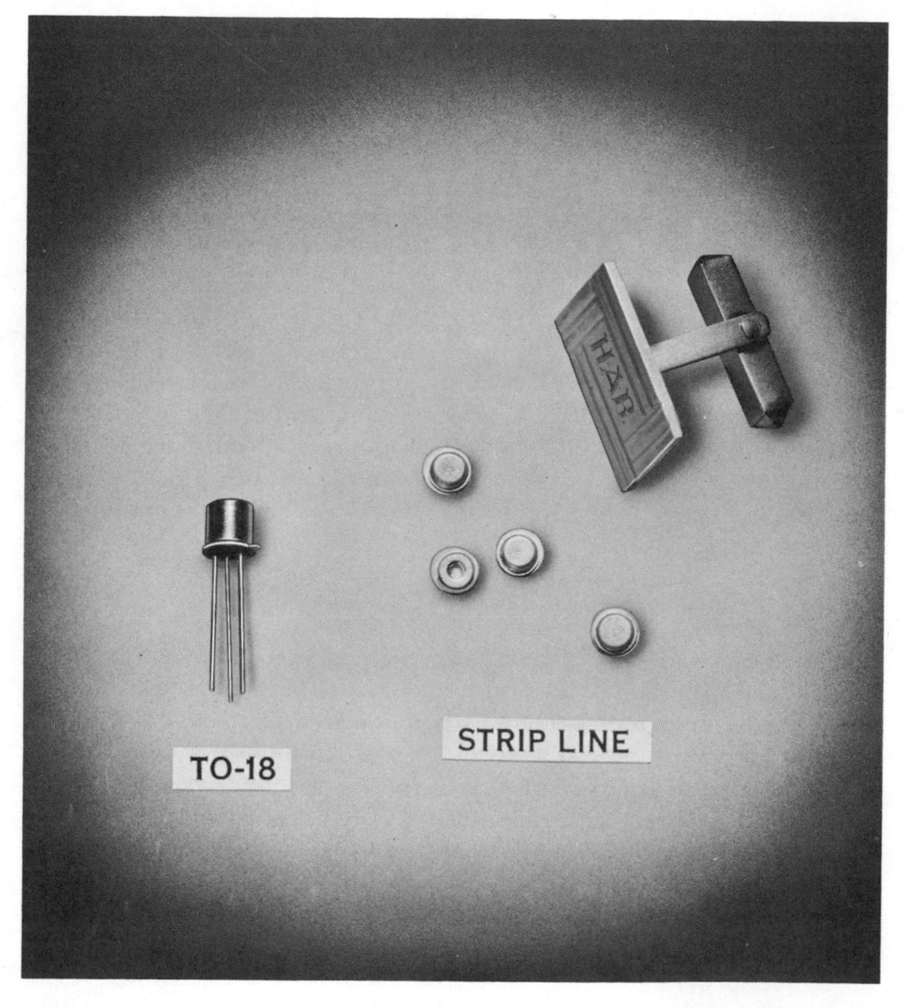

Figure 21-11
Two types of tunnel diodes, shown with cuff link for comparative size. (Courtesy of Semiconductor Products Department, General Electric Co.)

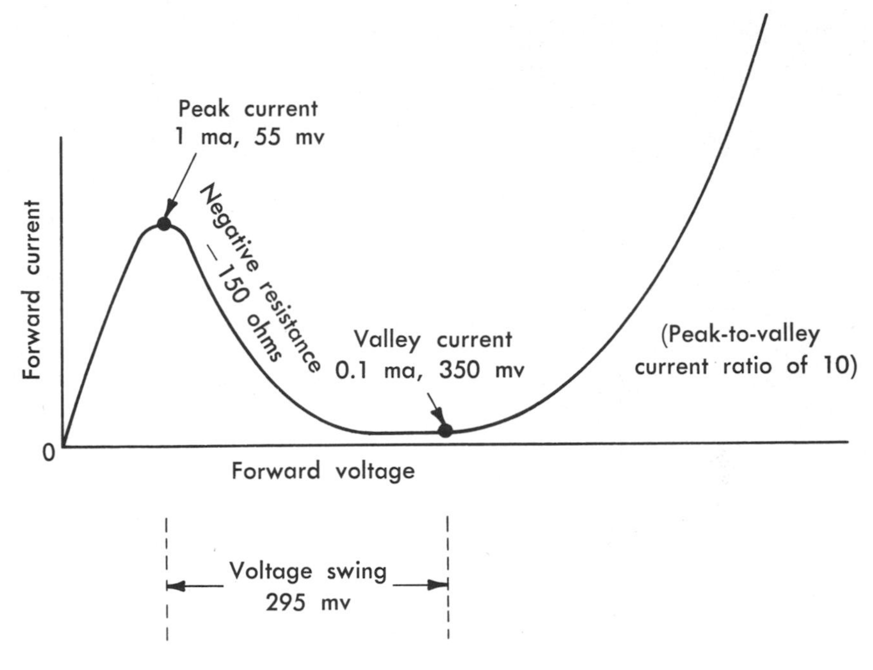

Figure 21-12
Forward characteristic for a tunnel diode.

21.5 ZENER DIODES

When the reverse bias on a semiconductor diode is increased beyond a limiting value, breakdown occurs. Current flow increases with extreme rapidity, or, the diode's internal resistance suddenly becomes extremely small. Breakdown is nondestructive in suitably designed diodes, called *Zener diodes.* Hence, the breakdown, or Zener region, can be put to practical use. Figure 21-13 shows the characteristic of a typical Zener diode. If the operating point is located on the Zener portion of the characteristic, variations in current demand cause very little change in voltage drop across the diode. Hence, a Zener diode can be used as a *voltage regulator.*

The value of reverse voltage required to produce Zener breakdown depends on the doping concentration of the diode substances. When the doping concentration is increased, Zener breakdown occurs at a lower value of reverse voltage. Observe that if the doping is extremely heavy, the Zener-breakdown region will be moved past the origin and into the forward region. This is a basic approach to the derivation of a tunnel-diode characteristic; the negative-resistance interval of a tunnel diode represents

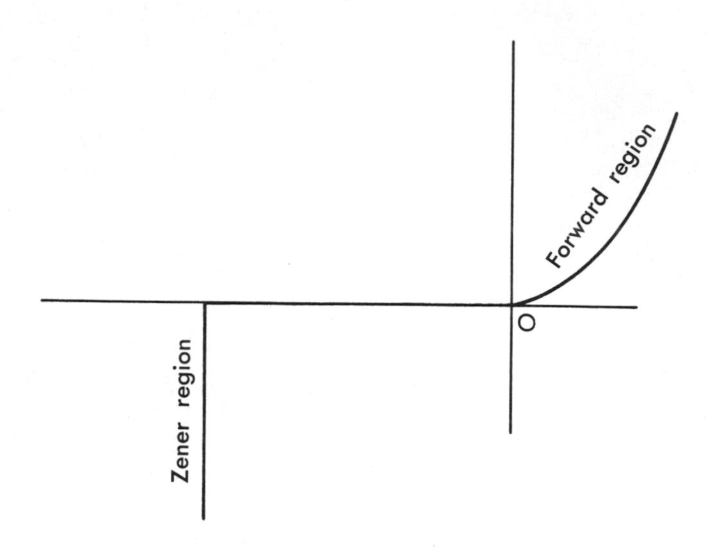

Figure 21-13
Characteristic of a typical Zener diode.

the combined features of a forward characteristic and a Zener characteristic.

21.6 TRANSISTORS

Basic transistors can be compared with triode tubes. A transistor can accomplish most of the functions of a vacuum tube, and, in addition, it provides functions which cannot be realized by tubes. Since a transistor is a solid-state device, its electrical characteristics can be compared only in a general way with vacuum-tube characteristics. Since a transistor has no heater, it can operate at considerably higher efficiency than a vacuum tube. Nearly all transistors are junction types, and have the basic construction depicted in Figure 21-14. It is basically two diodes with continuous lattice structures across the junctions. The center region is comparatively thin, and is called the *base*; end regions are called the *emitter* and the *collector*.

The emitter and collector are made of the same type material, although their doping concentrations are not necessarily the same. The base consists of *N*-type material if the emitter and collector are *P*-type material. The transistor depicted in Figure 21-14 is called a *PNP* transistor. On the other hand, the construction shown in Figure 21-15 is called an *NPN* transistor. Either an *NPN* transistor or a *PNP* transistor

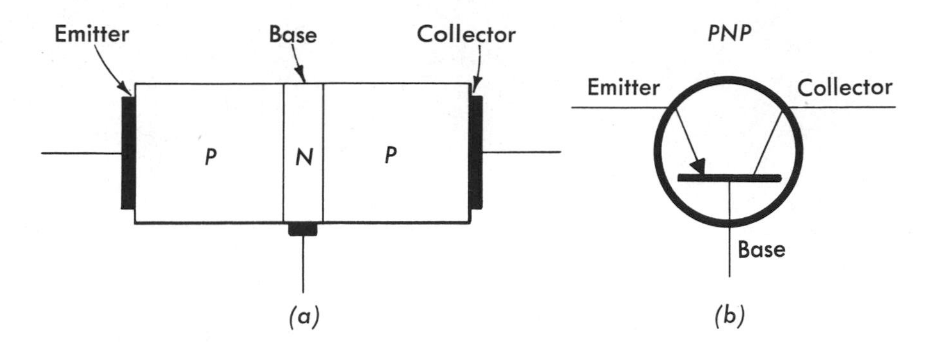

Figure 21-14
(a) Plan of a *PNP* junction transistor. (b) *PNP* transistor symbol.

can be used in general applications; however, the bias polarity is opposite for the two types. Both types are analogous to the triode vacuum tube.

In the great majority of applications, the emitter is forward-biased and the collector is reverse-biased with respect to the base, as seen in Figure 21-16. Forward bias entails appreciable current flow, as in a semiconductor diode; however, reverse bias results in negligible current flow. From previous discussion of the potential gradient and Fermi level in semiconductor diodes, it is evident that the potential gradient in a transistor has the form depicted in Figure 21-17. When forward bias is applied to the emitter, the emitter barrier is lowered. But application of reverse bias to the collector raises the collector barrier, as seen in Figure 21-18.

The emitter provides charge carriers. In Figure 21-19, electrons are supplied by the emitter battery to the *N*-type germanium of the emitter. The majority carriers in the emitter are electrons. Flow of electrons in the emitter circuit results in the injection of these electrons into the base

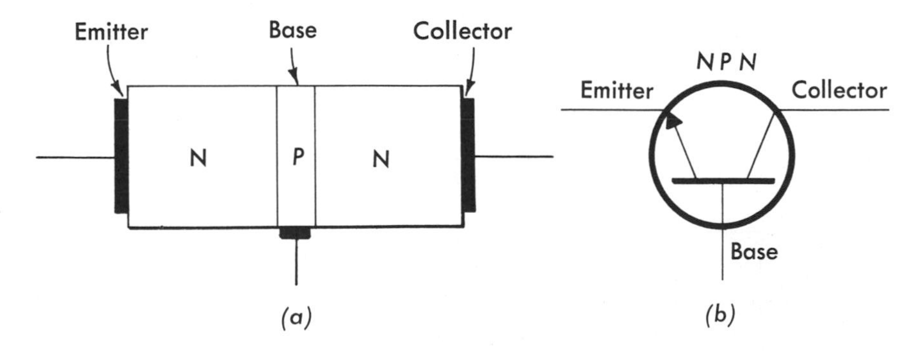

Figure 21-15
(a) Plan of an *NPN* transistor. (b) *NPN* transistor symbol.

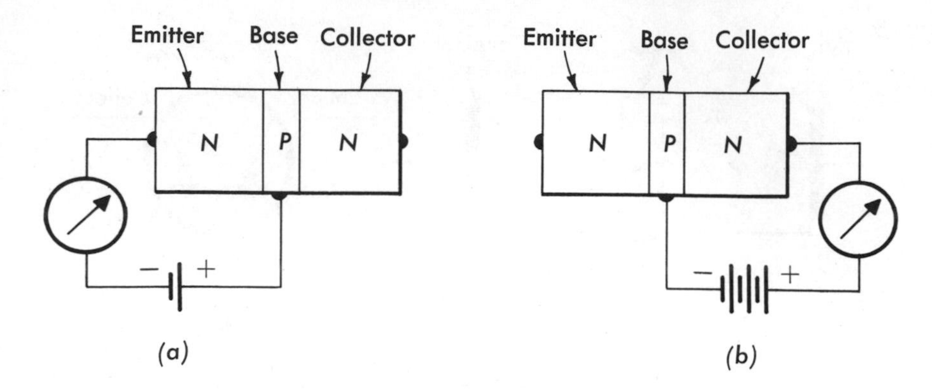

Figure 21-16
(*a*) Forward-biased emitter. (*b*) Reverse-biased collector.

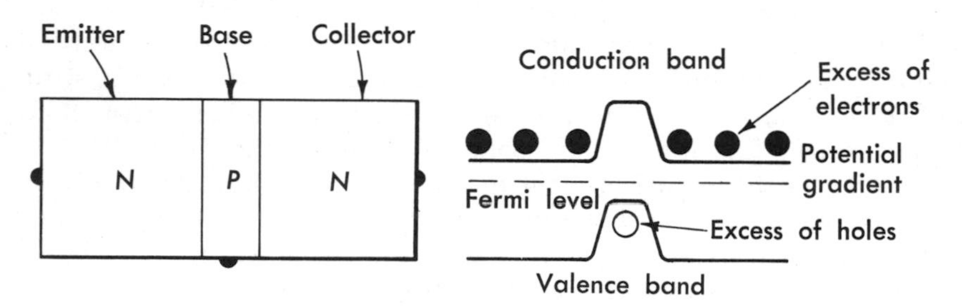

Figure 21-17
Potential gradient in a transistor.

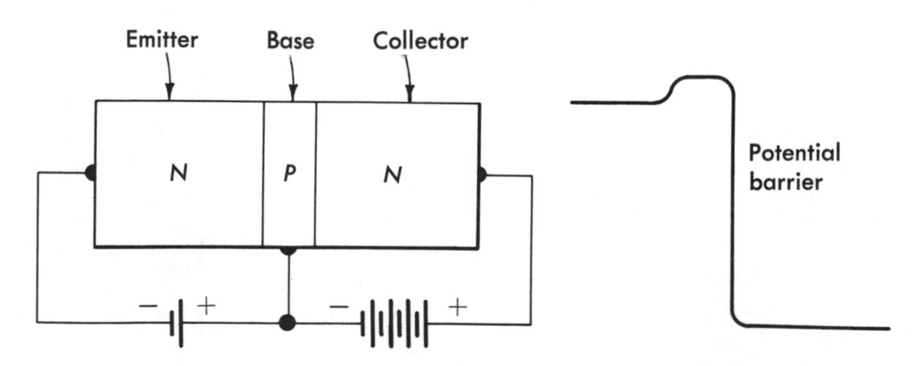

Figure 21-18
Emitter battery voltage lowers the potential barrier between emitter and base. Collector battery voltage raises the potential barrier between collector and base.

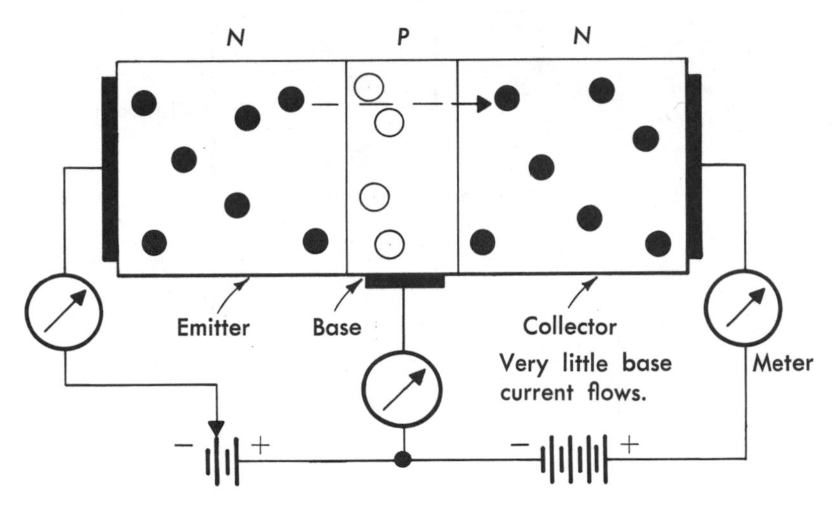

Figure 21-19

Electrons flow from the emitter into the base, and diffuse through the base to the collector.

region. Majority carriers in the base region are holes. Thus, the injected electrons are minority carriers in the base region. There is a small amount of recombination in the base, but most of the injected electrons diffuse to the collector junction. Recombination (and resulting loss of electrons) is slight because the base is very thin, and because the base material is not heavily doped.

Diffusion occurs as depicted in Figure 21-20. Most of the electrons (Figure 21-19) cross the base region without recombination and enter the collector region; they then flow in the collector circuit and establish a collector current. Thus, the collector current is almost as great as the emitter current. Evidently, the base current is slight. There is a very small base current due to occasional recombination of an electron with a hole in the base region. In effect, we can consider the current flow in Figure 21-19 to follow around the outer loop, and disregard the base connection in preliminary analysis.

If a *PNP* transistor is substituted for the *NPN* transistor in Figure 21-19, the configuration employs opposite battery polarities, as depicted in Figure 21-21. Now, holes are majority carriers in the base and collector regions, but electrons are majority carriers in the base region. Holes are injected into the base region by the emitter and diffuse through the base as minority carriers into the collector region. We see that an emitter is

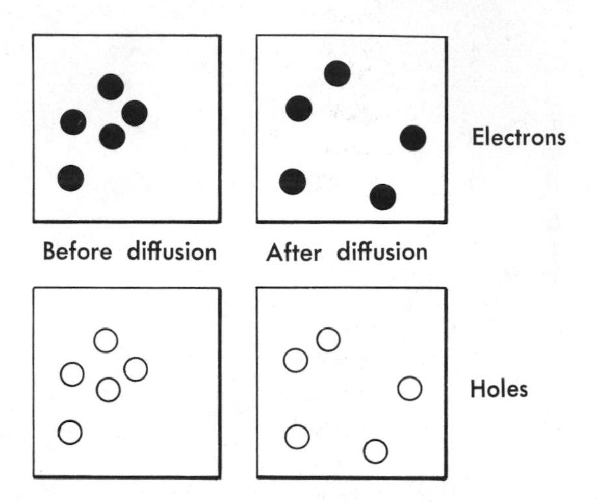

Figure 21-20
Charge carriers diffuse because of their random motion.

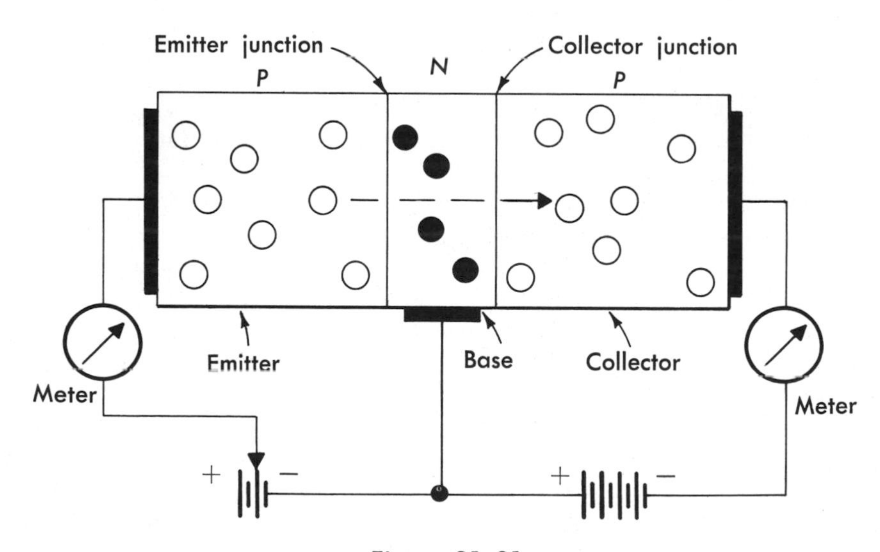

Figure 21-21
Holes diffuse through the base to the collector.

analogous to a vacuum-tube cathode and to a vacuum-tube grid; a collector is analogous to a vacuum-tube plate. If no forward voltage is applied between base and emitter, no current flows in the collector circuit. Figure 21-22 shows the appearance of a typical transistor.

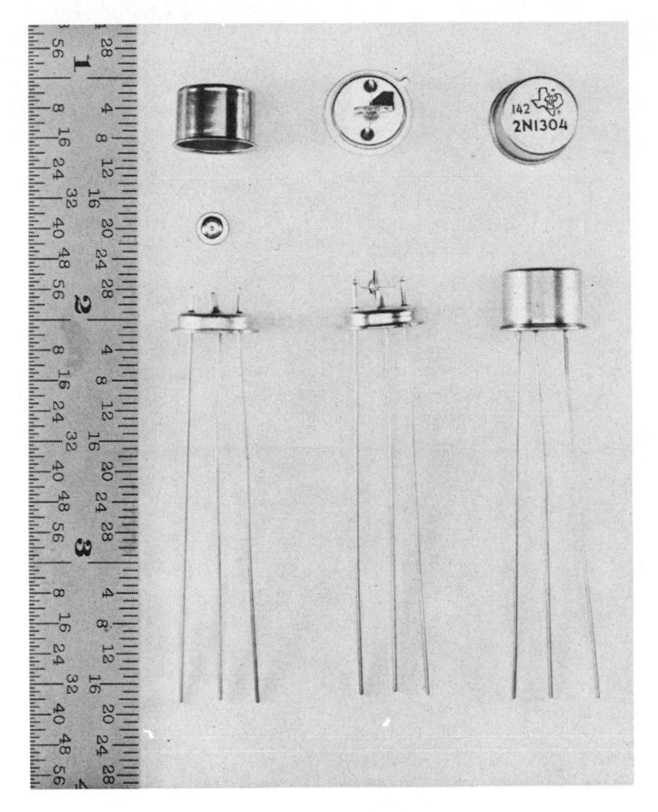

Figure 21-22
Appearance of a typical transistor. (Courtesy of Texas Instruments Co.)

21.7 COMMON-BASE, COMMON-EMITTER, AND COMMON-COLLECTOR CONFIGURATIONS

The common-base, common-emitter, and common-collector configurations shown in Figure 21-23 are basically amplifier circuits. Terminology refers to location of the input signal source and location of the load resistor. Amplication can be calculated with respect to voltage gain, current gain, or power gain. The common-emitter circuit provides highest power gain, the common-base circuit provides high voltage gain, and the common-collector circuit provides high current gain. In some applications, you might be most concerned with obtaining a low output impedance; in this case, you would use the common-collector circuit. But, if you are most concerned with obtaining a high output impedance, you would then use the common-base circuit.

Let us see how a common-base amplifier provides voltage gain. The transistor has a collector family of characteristics, as exemplified in Figure

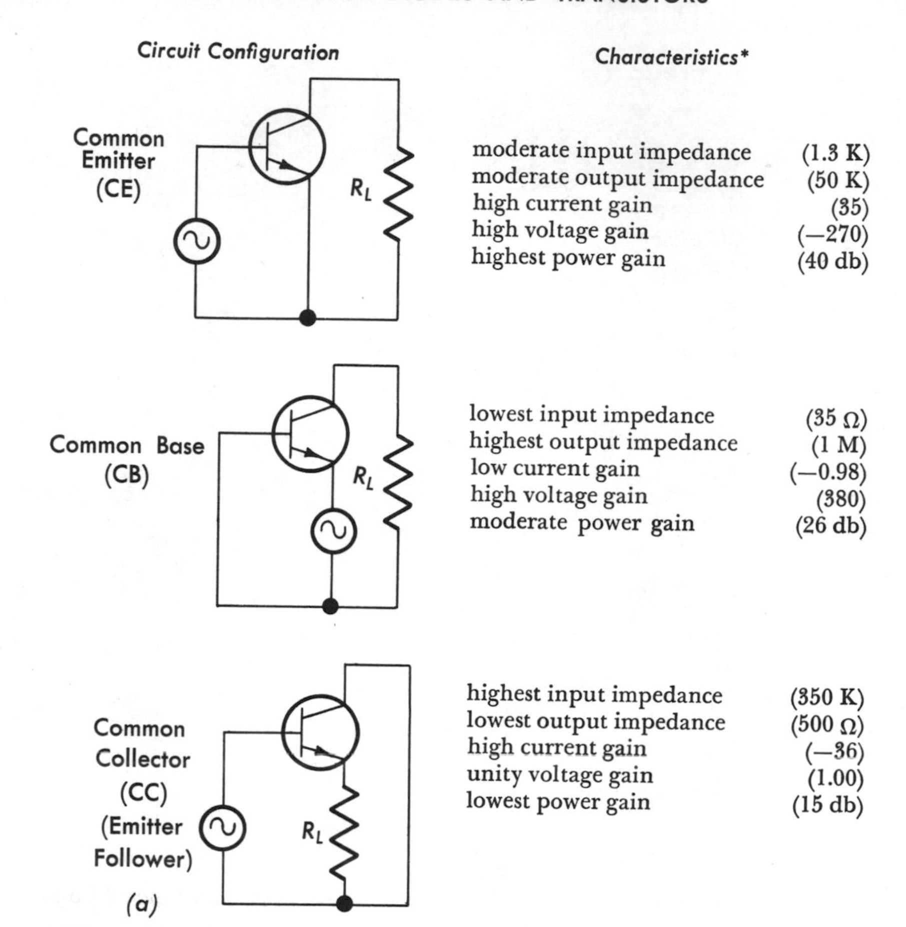

Circuit Configuration
Characteristics*
Common Emitter (CE)
R_L
moderate input impedance (1.3 K)
moderate output impedance (50 K)
high current gain (35)
high voltage gain (—270)
highest power gain (40 db)
Common Base (CB)
R_L
lowest input impedance (35 Ω)
highest output impedance (1 M)
low current gain (—0.98)
high voltage gain (380)
moderate power gain (26 db)
Common Collector (CC) (Emitter Follower)
R_L
highest input impedance (350 K)
lowest output impedance (500 Ω)
high current gain (—36)
unity voltage gain (1.00)
lowest power gain (15 db)
(a)

* Numerical values are typical for the 2N525 at audio frequencies with a bias of 5 volts and 1 ma, a load resistance of 10 K, and a source (generator) resistance of 1 K.

Figure 21-23

(*a*) Elementary common-base, common-emitter, and common-collector configurations. (*b*) A transistorized audio amplifier. (Courtesy of Knight Electronics.)
(*Continued on facing page.*)

21-24. A load line is drawn on the diagram, in the same manner as previously discussed for vacuum tubes. The operating point is determined by the emitter bias. In this example, the operating point occurs at a collector current of 4 ma and 13 volts. Note that the emitter current is practically equal to the collector current, and that the emitter resistance is small (35 ohms in this example). If the emitter voltage is changed by 0.07 volt, the emitter and collector currents are changed by 2 ma. In turn, the voltage

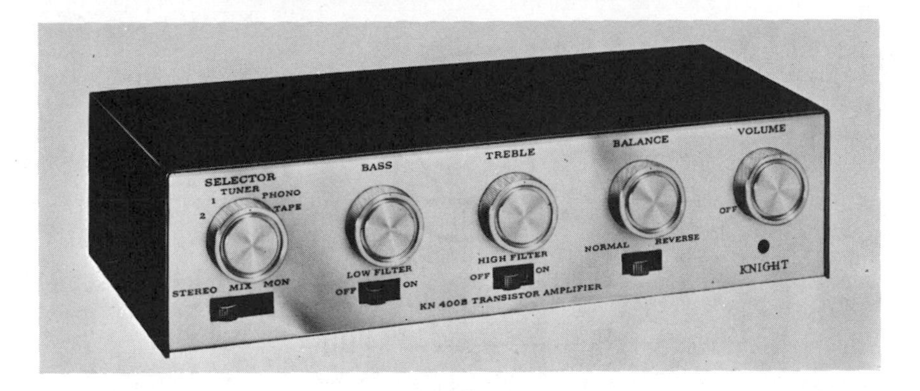

(*b*)

Fig. 21-23 (*Continued*)

drop across the load resistance changes by about 8 volts. This is a voltage amplification of approximately 114 times.

However, the current gain is practically unity. The power gain is approximately proportional to the ratio of load and emitter-input resistances, because practically the same current flows in emitter and collector circuits. Hence, the power gain of the configuration in Figure 21-24 is approximately 123 times.

A typical family of collector characteristics for a transistor in a common-emitter configuration is shown in Figure 21-25. A load line can be drawn on these coordinates in the same manner as for the common-base configuration. In turn, the voltage, current, and power gains may be calculated graphically. When amplifier stages are to be utilized in cascade (one stage following another), the common-emitter circuit is most suitable. Its input and output impedances are in the same order of magnitude, permitting reasonable power transfer.

Just as a vacuum tube has an amplification factor (μ), a transistor also has an amplification factor. If a common-base configuration is utilized, the ratio of output current (collector current) change to input current (emitter current) change is defined as its amplification factor, and is symbolized by alpha (α). In a junction transistor, the value of α varies from 0.9 to 0.997; its value is not equal to unity because of slight recombination in the base region, and some secondary side effects. Expressed as a formula,

$$\alpha = \frac{\Delta I_c}{\Delta I_e} \qquad \textbf{(21.5)}$$

where I_c denotes collector current and I_e denotes emitter current.

Evidently, a transistor will have some other amplification factor when

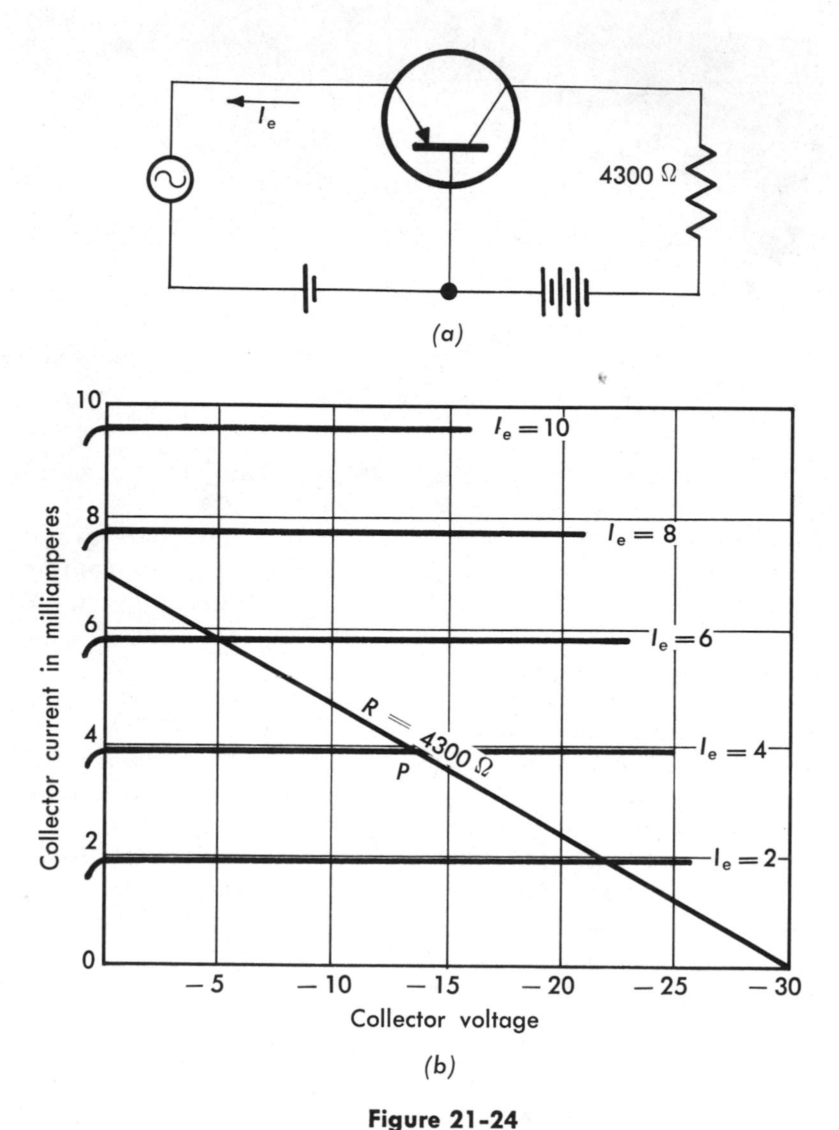

Figure 21-24

This common-base amplifier provides a voltage gain of approximately 114 times.

connected in a common-emitter configuration. This amplification factor is called beta (β), and is defined as the ratio of collector-current change to base-current change. Thus, we can write

$$\beta = \frac{\Delta I_c}{\Delta I_b} \tag{21.6}$$

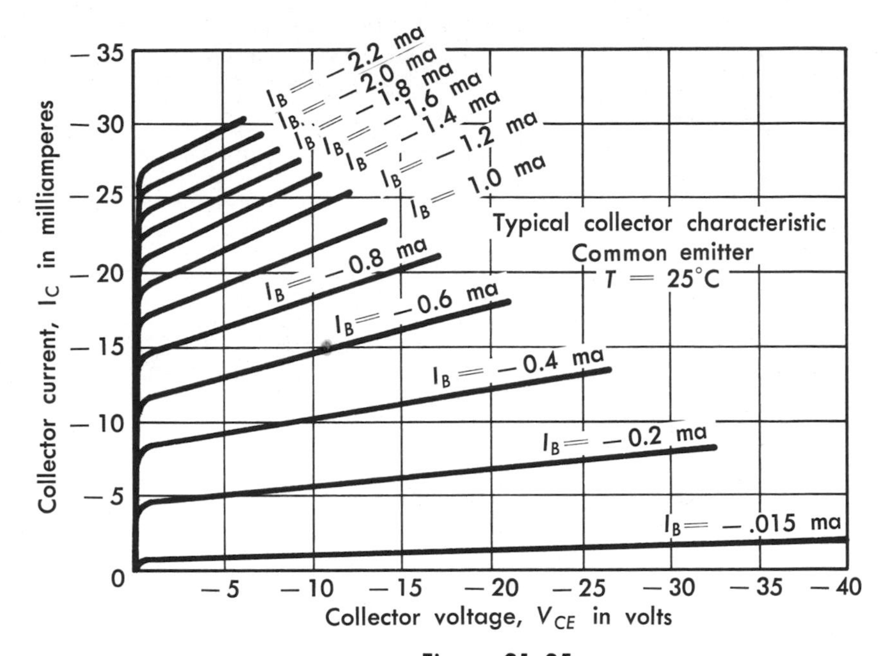

Figure 21-25
Collector family for a Philco 2N858 transistor in the common-emitter configuration. (Courtesy of Philco Corp.)

Inasmuch as both α and β are characteristics of the transistor, and not of the external circuit, it would be anticipated that they are related by some formula. This formula is easily derived, and states

$$\beta = \frac{\alpha}{1 - \alpha} \tag{21.7}$$

or,

$$\alpha = \frac{\beta}{1 + \beta} \tag{21.8}$$

Since a vacuum tube has a transconductance value, it would be anticipated that a transistor will also have a transconductance value. This supposition is correct; however, we find that transconductance is not a widely used transistor parameter. The reason for this is seen in Figure 21-26. Since the characteristic departs substantially from linearity, only an average value can be given for a specified transistor. This limitation might be acceptable for practical approximations, but there is still another drawback.

Unlike a vacuum tube, a transistor is fundamentally a current-operated device; that is, a transistor is a comparatively low-impedance device. We recall that the grid of a vacuum tube draws practically no current in the great majority of its applications. Thus, the grid is voltage-operated. On the other hand, the emitter of a transistor (in the *CB* configuration) or the base (in the *CE* configuration) draw appreciable current. Hence, it is a better approach to characterize a transistor in terms of α or β values, which are current ratios.

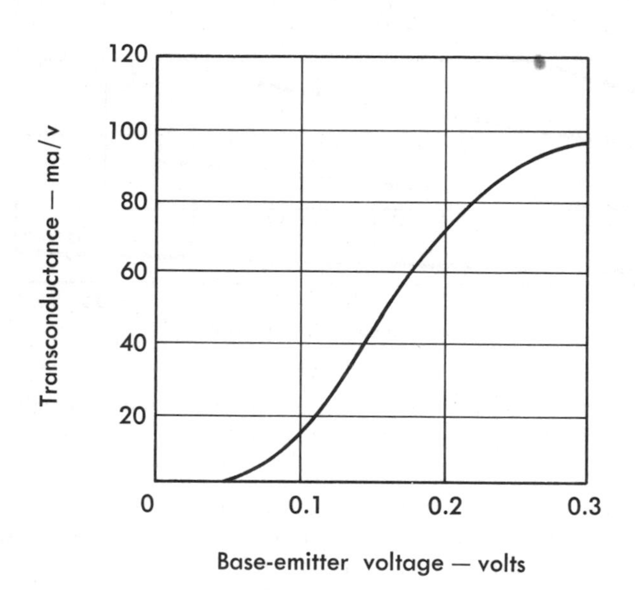

Figure 21-26
Typical transconductance characteristic for a transistor in the common-emitter configuration.

In some applications, the phase of the output voltage with respect to the phase of the input voltage is of interest. A brief study of current flow in the *CB*, *CE*, and *CC* configurations will reveal that:

1. The output voltage from a *CB* circuit has the same phase as the input voltage.

2. The output voltage from a *CE* circuit is 180 degrees out of phase with the input voltage.

3. The output voltage from a *CC* circuit has the same phase as the input voltage.

21.8 TRANSISTOR TESTING

Various types of transistor tests are made from the standpoint of intended application. Since a transistor consists basically of semiconductor junctions, an ohmmeter test can be made of the junctions for front-to-back resistance ratios. This is a simple test approach which is often used

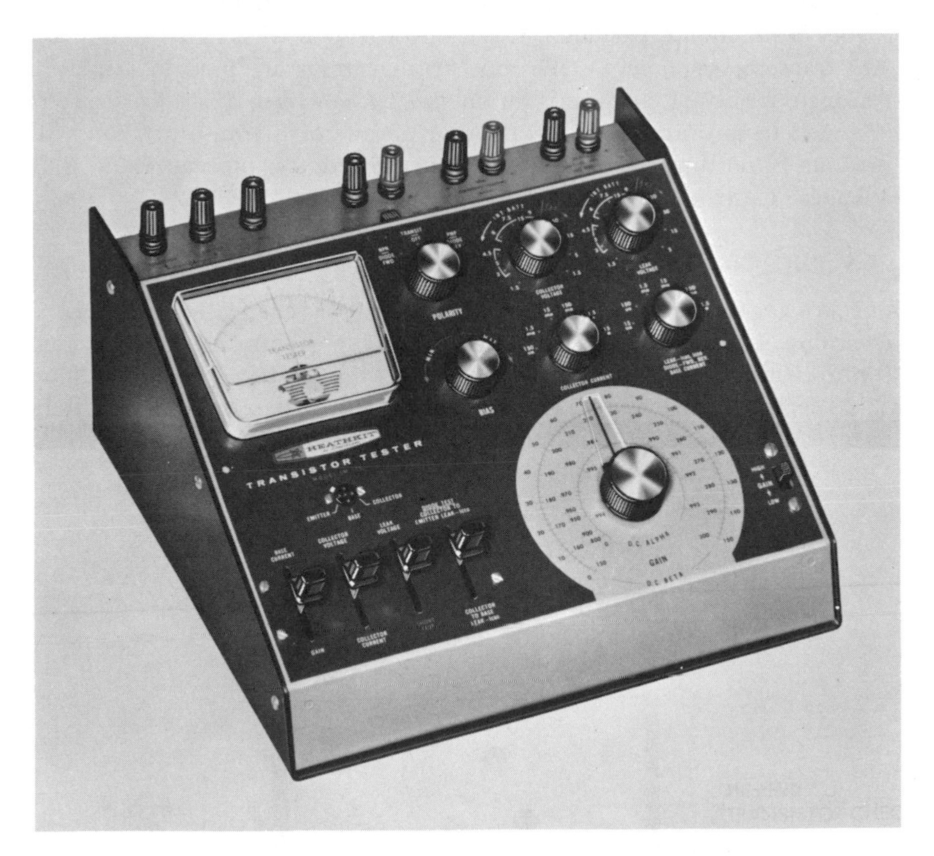

Figure 21-27
A typical transistor tester. (Courtesy of Heath Co.)

by electronic technicians. However, its value is somewhat limited, because it gives no data concerning α or β, which are the basic figures of merit for a transistor. An ohmmeter test shows whether a transistor is open or shorted, or whether a junction might have a poor front-to-back resistance ratio.

A transistor tester such as illustrated in Figure 21-27 provides rather complete test data. The transistor can be connected into a *CB*, *CE*, or *CC* circuit by rotation of a selector switch. In addition, the applied bias voltages can be set as desired for a given type of transistor, and for its intended application. A suitable value of load resistance and source resistance can also be included in the test circuit. Current meters indicate values of input and output current. These current ratios provide α, β, and stage-amplification values.

Laboratory-type transistor testers provide additional data, such as values of junction capacitance, variation of α or β with signal frequency, and transient response. Oscilloscope arrangements are used to display a complete family of characteristics on the *CRT* screen. Specialized testers are used to measure the random noise output of a transistor. You will have an opportunity to learn about specialized test procedures in your advanced electronics courses.

21.9 PHOTODIODES AND PHOTOTRANSISTORS

We recall that phototubes respond to light energy by emission of electrons. Thus, a phototube changes light energy into electrical energy. Semiconductors also change light energy into electrical energy. Figure 21-28 depicts a block of pure germanium connected in series with a battery

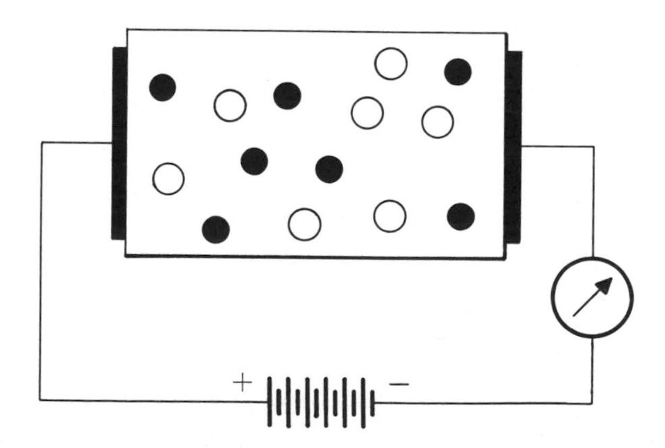

Figure 21-28
Series configuration for measurement of light intensity.

and a current meter. As noted, large numbers of free electrons and holes are present in the germanium crystal. These electrons and holes are generated by thermal energy at room temperature. Next, if light rays are allowed to strike the germanium crystal, the total number of electrons and holes is increased; in turn, the meter indicates a higher value of current flow.

This current flow, of course, does not obey Ohm's law. If we double the battery voltage, the current flow remains practically the same. If we double the intensity of light striking the crystal, however, the current flow is virtually doubled. Hence, pure germanium can be used as a photoelectric

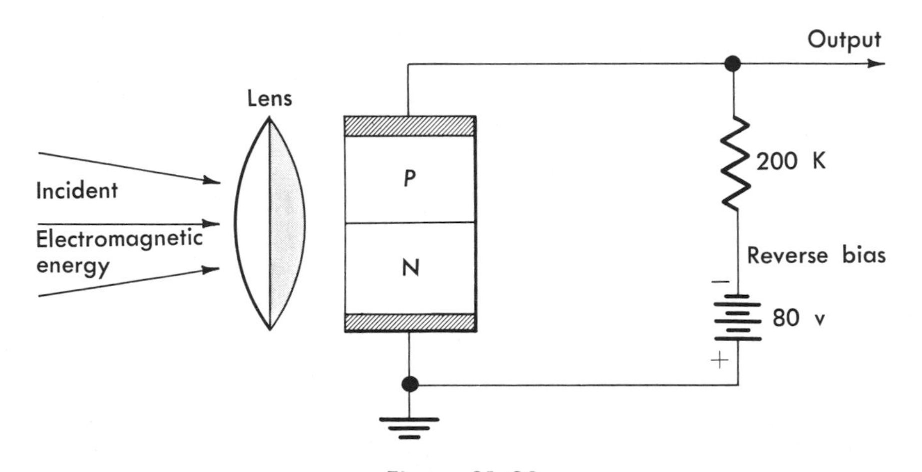

Figure 21-29
Another arrangement for measurement of light intensity.

device. But we recall that saturation currents are quite small. Therefore, it is advantageous to use a semiconductor diode instead of a pure germanium crystal, as depicted in Figure 21-29. Light is focused on the junction of a photodiode. Because a potential gradient is established across the junction by the *P* and *N* substances, the generated electrons and holes are swept in opposite directions toward the electrodes. Electrons are swept into the *N*-type substance, and holes are swept into the *P*-type substance.

The diode is reverse-biased. In turn, the potential gradient across the junction aids the external battery in producing current flow. Furthermore, the resistivities of *P*-type and *N*-type substances are much less than the resistivity of pure germanium. Consequently, the current flow in a photodiode for a given amount of light is comparatively large. Note that saturation-current flow occurs in Figure 21-29 just as in Figure 21-28. More efficient conversion of light energy into electrical energy is obtained in Figure 21-29 simply because of the presence of a potential gradient and the lower resistance of the crystal lattice. We perceive that efficiency can be maximized by focusing the incoming light upon the junction so

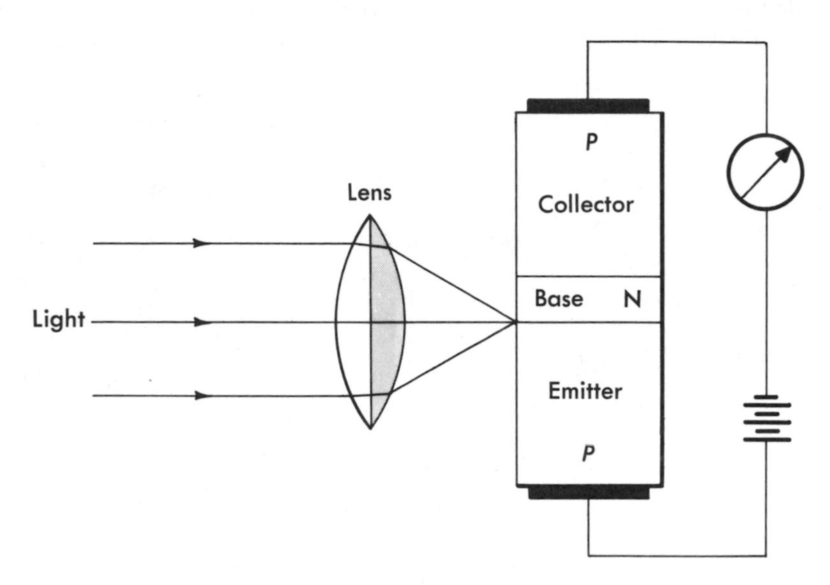

Figure 21-30
Plan of a phototransistor arrangement.

that generated charge carriers can be swept toward the electrodes.

The maximum sensitivity of a photodiode is evidently one electron-hole pair per quantum of light energy absorbed by the junction. You are probably wondering whether the output from the device could be greatly increased by transistor action. This supposition is correct. Figure 21-30 depicts a *phototransistor,* which provides approximately 100 times as much output current as a photodiode. The base may be biased, or left "floating." Light is focused on the base-emitter junction, and its energy generates holes and electrons, which are swept into the emitter and base, respectively. Of course, a base-emitter current flow is thereby established, which is amplified in the collector circuit. If the transistor has a β value of 100 times, for example, the collector current is 100 times as great as the base-emitter current.

We know that charge carriers are swept in opposite directions from a semiconductor junction when electron-hole pairs are generated by light energy which is absorbed by the junction substance. In turn, we would expect that a voltage difference would appear across the diode. Our expectation is correct, and this is the basic principle of operation of a *solar cell.* No external voltage is applied to a semiconductor when it is operated as a solar cell. The voltage that appears across the diode when exposed to the direct rays of the sun measures 0.5 volt in a typical unit. The diode supplies approximately 100-ma short-circuit current.

A solar cell used to power a miniature motor is illustrated in Figure 21-31. It is constructed from arsenic-doped silicon wafers 0.03 in. thick. The surface of this *N*-type material is exposed to boron vapor at high

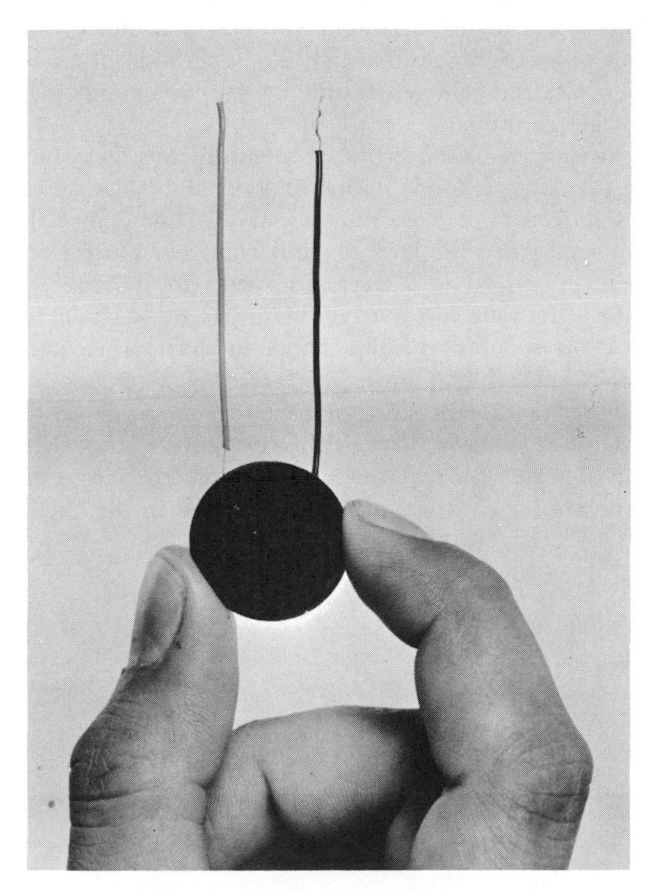

Figure 21-31
A solar cell. (Courtesy of Edmund Scientific Co.)

temperature which produces a very thin *P*-type layer. Contacts are deposited on the *N*-type material and the *P*-type surface, which connect to the external leads. Solar cells can be connected in series to provide increased voltage, and can be connected in parallel to provide increased current capacity. Experimental electric automobiles have been built which have a top fabricated from a very large number of solar cells. The solar cells are not used to power the automobile directly, but serve to charge the car's storage batteries while the sun shines on the solar cells.

You have probably used an exposure meter to measure light intensity for photographic purposes. This is another form of light-sensitive cell that requires no battery, and is similar to a solar cell. Photographers term this type of light-sensitive device a photronic cell. One design employs a junction formed by a selenium film deposited on an iron plate. Another design utilizes a junction formed by a copper-oxide layer deposited on a copper plate. Contact wires to the dissimilar substances conduct the generated electricity out of the light-sensitive cell. The operation of all such devices depends upon electron-hole generation by radiant energy, as previously explained for germanium.

The light-sensitive characteristic of selenium was first observed by an attendant in the Atlantic Cable station at Valencia, Ireland. Selenium was used in the fabrication of fixed resistors. It was noted that the value of resistance changed when the level of light changed. Early workers in the television field attempted to use selenium cells for picture transmission. However, difficulties were encountered, because a rapid change in light did not produce a correspondingly rapid change in electrical response. In other words, the selenium cells had limited high-frequency response. Early workers did not understand semiconductor junction action. Since the junction capacitance must be charged through the resistance of the selenium, a certain amount of time was required to charge or discharge the junction capacitance before the electrical response appeared in the external circuit.

SUMMARY OF FUNDAMENTAL CONCEPTS

Semiconductor devices are characterized by junction action between *N*-type and *P*-type substances.

Junction action is based on the physics of electron flow and hole flow in crystal lattices.

A semiconductor junction can be compared with a diode vacuum tube in that a junction can operate as a rectifier.

Semiconductor diodes and transistors are basically nonlinear devices which are analyzed to best advantage by graphical methods.

The basic parameters of a transistor include its α or β value, collector resistance, and emitter resistance.

Two junctions provided by *NPN* or *PNP* substances provide transistor action, which can be compared with a triode vacuum tube.

Ions in the crystal lattice establish a potential gradient across a junction.

The potential gradient (or barrier) is raised or lowered by an external voltage applied to the semiconductor substances.

Junctions formed by heavily doped substances exhibit a region of negative-resistance operation.

Zener action is a junction characteristic which exhibits a nearly constant voltage drop at different values of current flow.

The saturation current of a junction device does not obey Ohm's law, but is a function of temperature.

QUESTIONS

1) A junction in a semiconductor device is formed by:
(*a*) connecting an *N*-type substance to a *P*-type substance. (*b*) producing a continuous lattice structure from *P*-type material to *N*-type material. (*c*) attaching a central electrode to a block of doped germanium. (*d*) cementing two blocks of intrinsic germanium together.
2) A potential gradient is:
(*a*) the difference between two bias voltages. (*b*) the sum of two bias voltages. (*c*) a "built-in" electric field produced by ions. (*d*) opposite to saturation current.
3) The Fermi level in a semiconductor is:
(*a*) the average energy level of the charge carriers. (*b*) equal to the α value divided by the β value. (*c*) equal to the emitter voltage plus the collector voltage. (*d*) caused by recombination in the base region.
4) Semiconductor diodes conduct in the forward direction because:
(*a*) the applied voltage causes nondestructive breakdown. (*b*) saturation current is neutralized. (*c*) reverse current flow is amplified. (*d*) charge carriers neutralize each other at the junction.
5) Semiconductor diodes do not conduct in the reverse direction because:
(*a*) charge carriers are swept away from the junction. (*b*) saturation current is neutralized. (*c*) reverse current flow encounters a negative resistance. (*d*) the base circuit is reverse biased.
6) Saturation current:
(*a*) obeys Ohm's law. (*b*) is temperature limited. (*c*) equals the α value. (*d*) equals the transconductance value.
7) Diffusion in the base region occurs because:
(*a*) electrons repel one another. (*b*) holes attract electrons. (*c*) of the random motion of charge carriers. (*d*) the collector voltage is higher than the emitter voltage.
8) An α value denotes:
(*a*) the ratio of input current to output current. (*b*) the ratio of output current to input current. (*c*) the ratio of input voltage to output voltage. (*d*) the ratio of output voltage to input voltage.
9) A β value denotes:
(*a*) maximum transconductance of a transistor. (*b*) minimum transconductance of a transistor. (*c*) the ratio of output current to input current. (*d*) the ratio of input current to output current.

10) A common-emitter amplifier circuit:
(*a*) has a current gain of less than unity. (*b*) reverses the phase of the output voltage with respect to the input voltage. (*c*) has a negative-resistance interval. (*d*) uses a semiconductor diode instead of a transistor.

PROBLEMS

1) If 2 volts are applied across a capacitance of 10 $\mu\mu$f, what is the value of the stored charge in coulombs?
2) A tunnel diode has a peak current value of 1.5 ma, and a valley current value of 0.15 ma. What is its peak-to-valley current ratio?
3) If the peak-current value in Problem 2 occurs at 50 mv, and the valley-current value occurs at 300 mv, what is the voltage swing of the tunnel diode?
4) If the slope of the tangent at a point on the characteristic of a tunnel diode is 0.025, and the curve slopes downward through the point, what is the corresponding resistance value and its algebraic sign? [Hint: $I/E = 0.025$ at the point.]
5) The operating point for a Zener diode is placed on the Zener interval of its characteristic. The voltage at this point is 50 volts, and the current flow is 1 ma. How much power is dissipated by the diode as heat?
6) If the input resistance of a transistor is 40 ohms, and 0.04 volt is applied to the emitter, what is the value of the emitter current?
7) Calculate the α value of the transistor in Problem 6, if 97 percent of the emitter current appears in the collector circuit.
8) When connected in a common-emitter configuration, a change of 0.01 ma in base current produces a change of 1 ma in collector current. What is the β value of the transistor?
9) If the α value of a transistor is 0.95, what is its β value?
10) If the β value of a transistor is 99, what is its α value?
11) Calculate the power that must be dissipated as heat at the collector junction if the collector voltage is 10 volts and a current of 2 ma flows.
12) An emitter has an input resistance of 35 ohms. Calculate the power that must be dissipated as heat at the emitter junction when the current flow is 2 ma.
13) A transistor is connected in a common-base circuit. If the base current is 1 percent of the emitter current value, what is the α value of the transistor?
14) What is the efficiency of the circuit in Problem 13?

22

FILTERS

22.1 DEFINITION OF A FILTER

We find many definitions of filters in the literature. The most general definition of a filter is a circuit that contains resistance and reactance. In other words, *any* circuit that comprises resistance and reactance can be regarded as a filter. A filter has an output which is frequency-dependent; or, the amplitude and phase of the output from a filter is a function of frequency. It is the reactance of a filter that makes its output a function of frequency. Thus, a purely resistive network does not function as a filter, but is a special case of a filter configuration.

Let us consider the *RC* coupling circuit depicted in Figure 22-1, which is a simple example of a *high-pass* filter. We see that there can be no current flow through the resistor at zero frequency, but the capacitive reactance becomes less as the frequency is increased. At very high frequencies, capacitor *C* can be replaced with a short-circuit for all practical purposes. It is clear that the output voltage must lead the input voltage by almost 90 degrees at very low frequencies. This phase angle becomes less as the frequency is increased. At very high frequencies, the output voltage is practically in phase with the input voltage.

Again, consider the *RL* circuit depicted in Figure 22-2. At zero frequency, there is no voltage drop across the inductor; the output voltage is equal to the input voltage. However, as the frequency is increased, inductive reactance causes the output voltage to decrease. This decrease is small at first, and becomes more evident at moderate frequencies. At still higher frequencies, the curve tends to flatten, but the output voltage continues to decrease. At very high frequencies, the output voltage approaches zero as a limit. We perceive that the output voltage is practically in phase with the input voltage at very low frequencies. The phase angle increases with frequency, and approaches a lag of 90 degrees as a limit at very high frequencies. The circuit arrangement in Figure 22-2 is a simple example of a *low-pass* filter.

22.2 LCR FILTER NETWORKS

Previous chapters have explained the characteristics of *RC* and *LR* circuits. The curves shown in Figure 22-1 and Figure 22-2 recall the basic principles of these characteristics from the standpoint of filter action. We

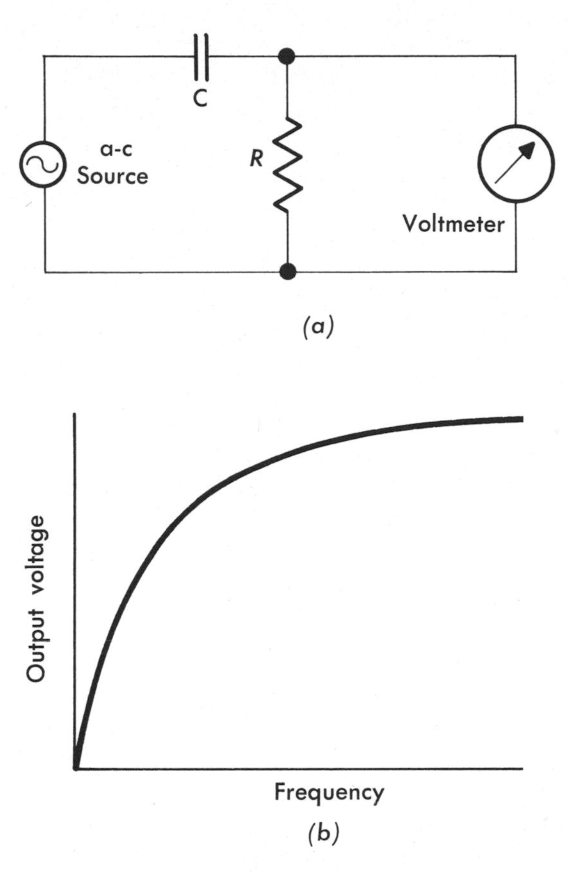

Figure 22-1
(*a*) An *RC* coupling circuit. (*b*) Output voltage versus frequency.

will also recall that a resonant circuit such as shown in Figure 22-3 has an impedance that varies with frequency. If a voltmeter is connected across the capacitor, maximum output will be measured at 1000 kc. This is a simple example of an *LCR bandpass filter*. The circuit develops an output voltage across the capacitor over a band of frequencies centered on 1000 kc.

Note that the voltage and phase-angle curves in Figure 22-3 apply to the parallel-resonant section, and disregard the damping effect of generator resistance R_g. These curves require no practical modification, provided R_g is very large. For example, if the a-c source and R_g were a pentode vacuum tube, R_g would be very large, and its effect on the shapes of the curves can be disregarded from a practical standpoint. On the other hand, if the a-c source and R_g were a transistor, R_g might be of the same order of

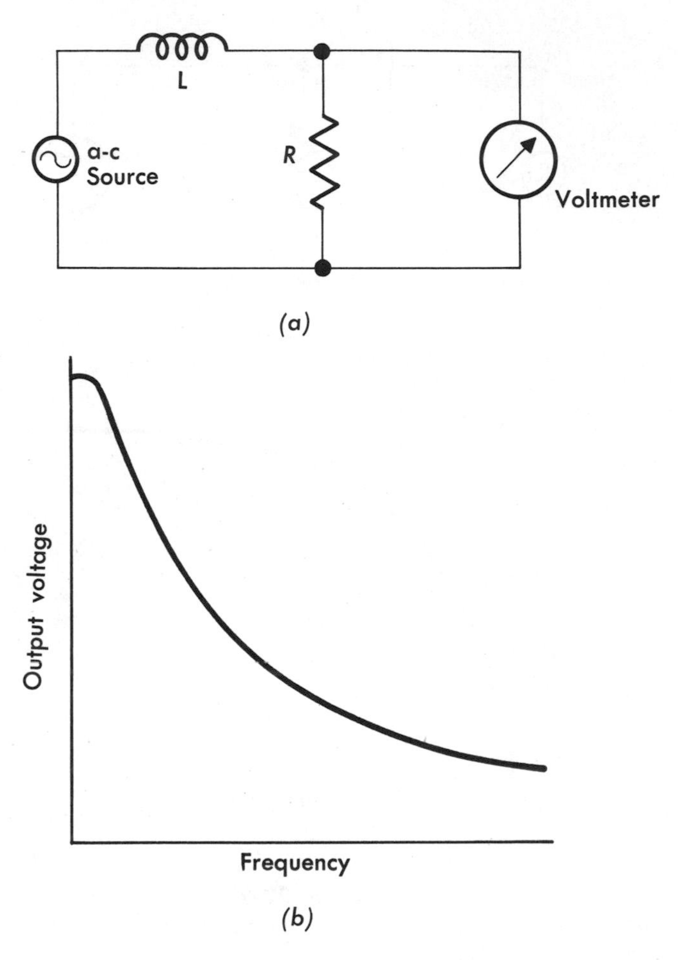

Figure 22-2
(*a*) An *RL* circuit. (*b*) Output voltage versus frequency.

magnitude as R_L. In this case, we recall that the value of R_g will have an appreciable effect on the impedance characteristic.

The circuit shown in Figure 22-3 is usually called a *resonant* circuit, instead of a filter. Nevertheless, it is clear that a resonant circuit has filter action. From the foregoing examples, we can easily understand why the most general definition of a filter is "a circuit that contains resistance and reactance." In Figures 22-1 and 22-2, observe that the output voltage varies continuously with frequency. This continuous variation is also seen in Figure 22-3. There is no range of frequency over which the output voltage

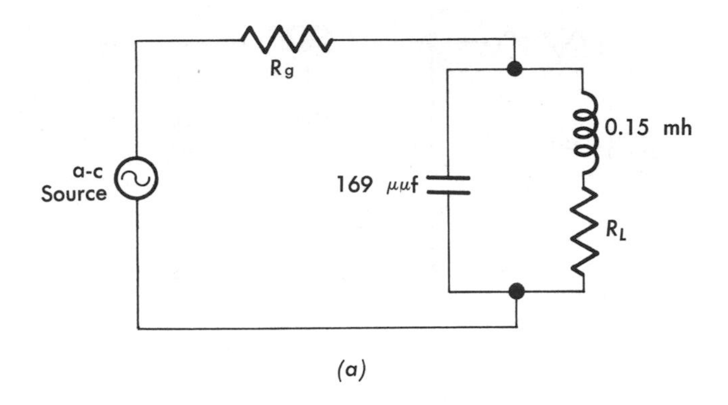

(a)

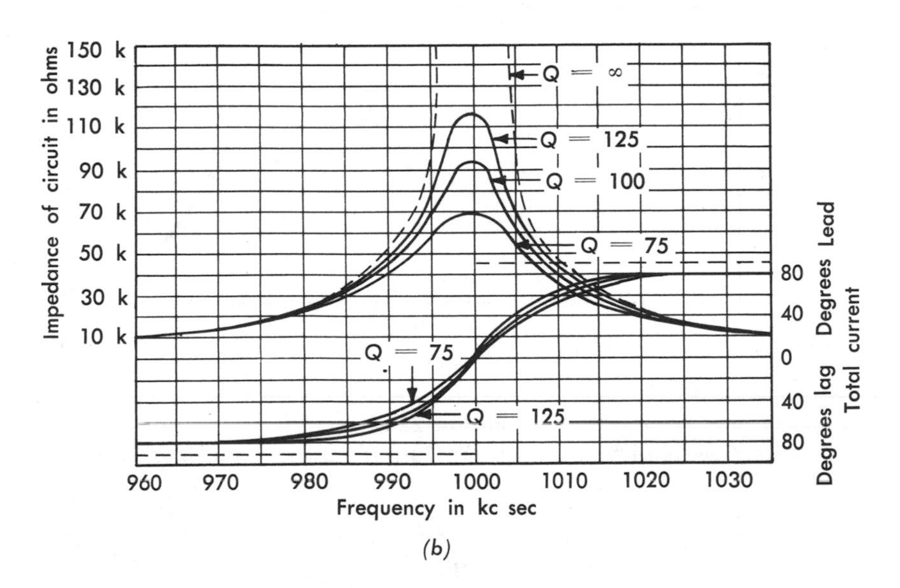

(b)

Figure 22-3
(*a*) Parallel-resonant circuit. (*b*) Magnitude and phase angle of impedance versus frequency.

remains constant. Now, we will find that there are simple *LCR* configurations in which the output voltage *does* remain constant over a chosen frequency range. In the more restricted definition of a filter, such configurations are analyzed by conventional filter theory which will now be considered.

Beginners are usually surprised to find that there is a large class of *LCR* networks that have "flat" response over a chosen frequency range. It is not obvious that these *LCR* circuits exhibit no resonant peak; how-

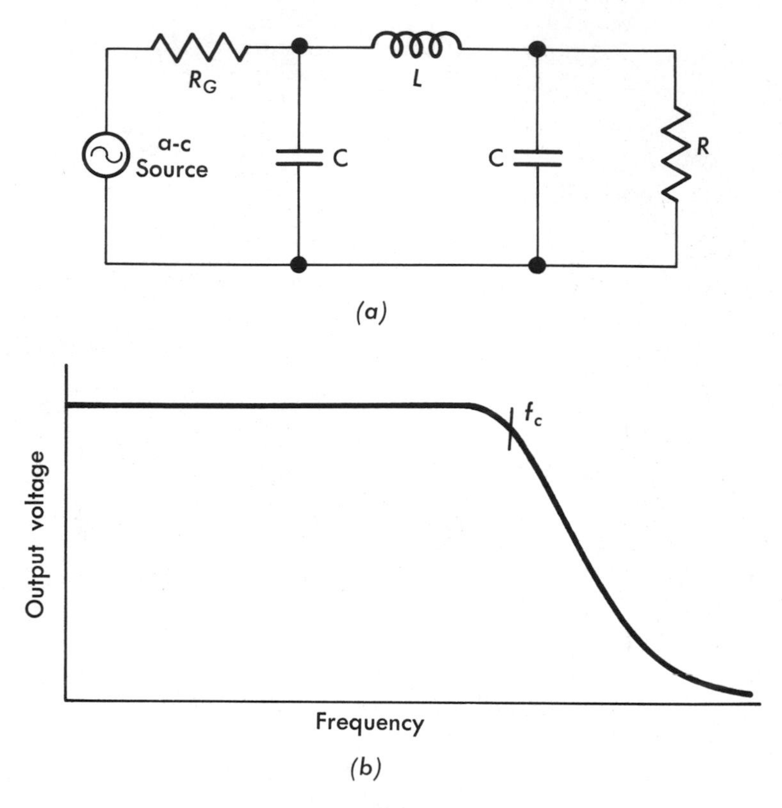

Figure 22-4
(*a*) Pi-section low-pass filter. (*b*) Output voltage versus frequency.

ever, the facts of filter-circuit action become evident from basic a-c theory. Let us look at the series-parallel configuration in Figure 22-4. This is called a *pi-section low-pass filter*. The pi section comprises L, C, and C. It derives its name from its resemblance to the Greek letter π. Of course, this pi section by itself is simply a resonant circuit, and has a characteristic which varies continuously with frequency. However, the pi section does *not* stand alone; its response is modified by R and R_g. The complete filter then has a response depicted in Figure 22-4(*b*).

Since it is laborious to carry out the calculations, we will merely note here that when the components in Figure 22-4(*a*) have suitable values, the output voltage remains constant over the pass band, as depicted in Figure 22-4(*b*). At frequency f_c, the output voltage finally starts to decrease. We call f_c the *cutoff frequency* of the filter. It is interesting to connect inductance, capacitance, and resistance into a filter configuration, and to observe the circuit action experimentally in the laboratory. If we use suitable test equipment, the characteristic depicted in Figure 22-4(*b*) can be observed directly on the screen of an oscilloscope.

Let us briefly consider the slope of the curve following f_c in Figure 22-4(*b*). This slope is not drawn to scale in the illustration. We will find that the steepness of this slope depends upon the filter configuration. Although the pass band remains constant or flat, the steepness of the slope will depend on how many sections we employ in the filter. If one pi section is used, the slope will be rather gradual, but if two pi sections are used, it will be steeper. If we use many pi sections in succession, the slope will become very steep.

Another basic type of low-pass filter is shown in Figure 22-5. This configuration employs *L, L,* and *C* in a *T section.* The section derives its

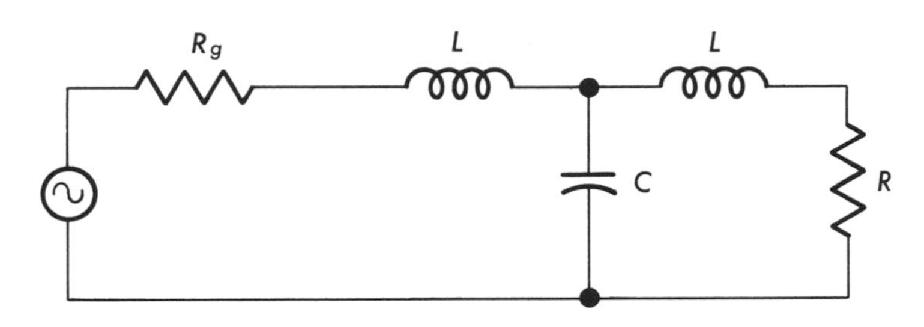

Figure 22-5
A *T*-section low-pass filter.

name from its resemblance to the letter *T*. If the components have suitable values, the output voltage remains constant over a chosen frequency range, as depicted in Figure 22-4(*b*). Every pi section has an equivalent *T* section; hence, whether we use a pi-section filter or a *T*-section filter, we can obtain the same circuit action. Our choice will depend upon incidental considerations, such as component costs. In general, inductors are more costly than capacitors.

As we would expect, inductors and capacitors can be connected into high-pass pi- or *T*-filter sections, as seen in Figure 22-6. As before, a constant output voltage is obtained over a chosen frequency range when suitable component values are used. Below the cutoff frequency f_c, the output voltage drops. Steepness of drop-off depends upon the number of pi or *T* sections used in the filter. We will find in all pi-section and *T*-section filters that flat response requires definite values for *R* and R_g. We call *R* the terminating resistance of the filter. R_g, of course, is the generator or source resistance.

Let us look once again at the low-pass filter configuration in Figure 22-4. At zero frequency, there is no voltage drop across *L*, and the capaci-

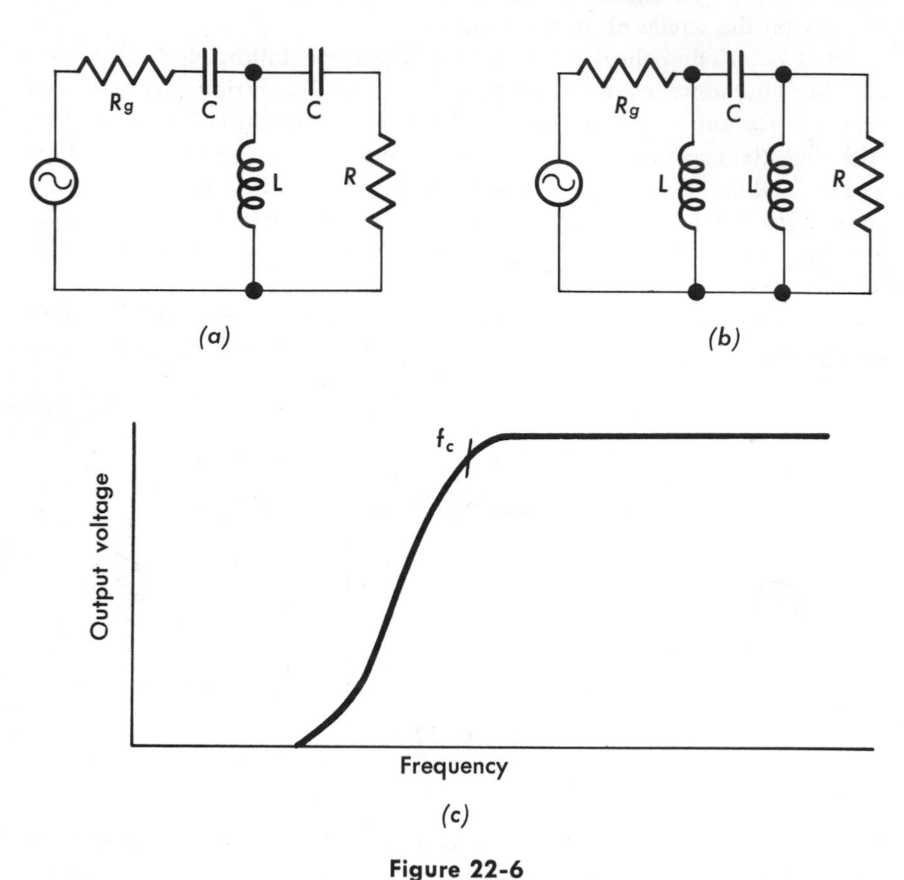

Figure 22-6
(*a*) *T*-section high-pass filter. (*b*) Pi-section high-pass filter. (*c*) Output voltage versus frequency.

tors represent open circuits. Hence, half the source voltage is dropped across R, provided that $R = R_g$. This is the maximum output voltage, represented by the flat top of the graph. Next, as the operating frequency is increased, the capacitors start to draw leading currents, and the inductor starts to draw a lagging current. Inductive reactance is now present, which tends to reduce current flow through the inductor. However, the inductor and the second capacitor form a series circuit, and there is a Q step-up of voltage across the second capacitor. The Q of the LC series combination maintains the voltage across R constant up to the resonant frequency.

However, as the operating frequency becomes higher than the resonant frequency, the circuit action is different. Now, inductive reactance continues to increase, further reducing current flow to the output. Furthermore, the Q step-up of the LC series combination is not increasing—it is decreasing because the resonant frequency has been passed. In turn, both X_L and Q now operate to reduce the voltage across R. This is a preliminary analysis of the network. A complete analysis entails algebraic solution of the series-parallel configuration. This is not necessary for our present purpose.

A similar preliminary analysis applies to the low-pass filter in Figure 22-5. At zero frequency, the inductors impose no reactance, and the capacitor represents an open circuit. Next, as the operating frequency is increased, inductive reactance is present which tends to reduce transfer of voltage to R. However, the first inductor forms a series circuit with the capacitor. There is a Q step-up of voltage across the capacitor which holds the voltage across R constant up to the cutoff frequency. But after the resonant frequency is passed, inductive reactance continues to increase while the Q step-up decreases. Hence, the voltage across R does not remain constant, but must decrease.

22.3 COMPONENT VALUES FOR BASIC FILTERS

A filter has flat response over a chosen frequency range only if its component values are correctly related. Consider the pi section depicted in Figure 22-7(*a*). This is a symmetrical network in which both capacitors have the same value. The pi section is an LC resonant circuit; it is not a flat low-pass filter. However, with terminating resistor R added [Figure 22-7(*b*)], flat response can be obtained over a chosen range of frequencies. Values of R, L, and C are related as follows:

$$L = \frac{R}{\pi f_c} \tag{22.1}$$

$$C = \frac{1}{2\pi f_c R} \tag{22.2}$$

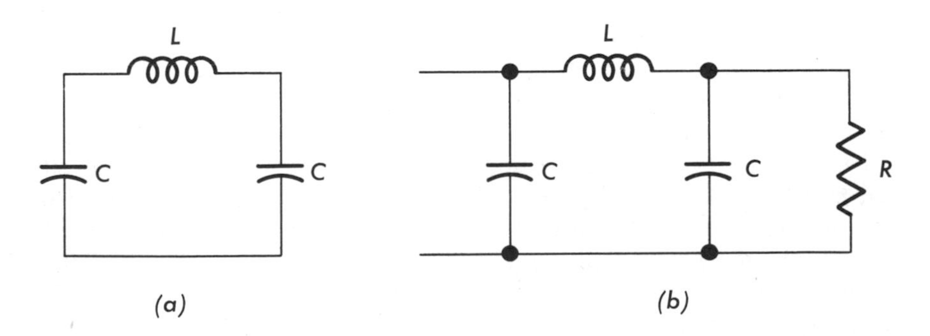

Figure 22-7
(*a*) L and C values determine f_c. (*b*) R is related to L and C values.

where L is in henrys, R is in ohms, f_c is in cycles per second, and C is in farads.

These are the basic design equations for a symmetrical low-pass pi-section filter. We start with a chosen value for terminating resistance R, and a selected cutoff frequency f_c. In turn, the associated values for L and C are calculated from Equations (22.1) and (22.2). Optimum filter action necessitates use of high-Q inductors; note that ideal inductors are assumed in the equations. If we wish to obtain a more abrupt drop-off past f_c than is provided by a single pi section, several sections can be connected in cascade, as depicted in Figure 22-8. Since the output capacitor of the first

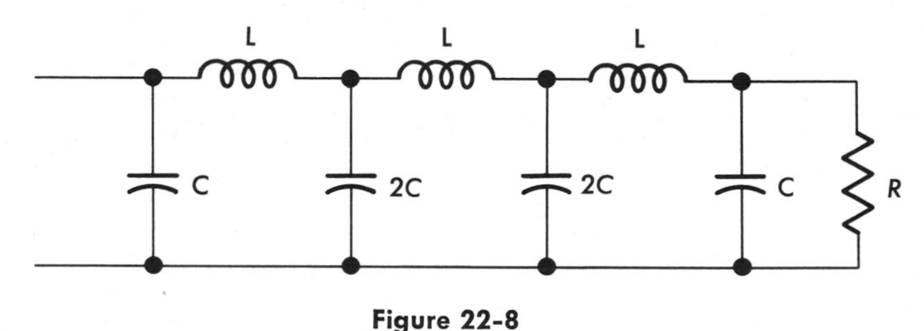

Figure 22-8
Three identical pi sections connected in cascade.

section is in parallel with the input capacitor of the second section, the two capacitors are combined into one capacitor with a value of $2C$. Magnetic coupling is avoided between the inductors in Figure 22-8, since such coupling would distort the filter response. Commercial filters often provide an individual shield box for each inductor.

It is interesting to consider a practical example of the low-pass filter depicted in Figure 22-7(*b*). An electronic test instrument is provided with a filter to pass all frequencies up to 37 mc, and to minimize output at all higher frequencies. This filter operates in a circuit which has a resistance of 100 ohms. Hence, f_c is equal to 37 mc and R is equal to 100 ohms. Substitution of these values in Equations (22.1) and (22.2) yields $L = 0.42$ μh, and $C = 22$ pf. Since one pi section does not provide an abrupt drop-off past f_c, three pi sections are connected in cascade, as shown in Figure 22-8. Each inductor has a value of 0.42 μh. The input capacitor has a value of 22 pf, and the output capacitor also has a value of 22 pf. Each of the intermediate capacitors has a value of 44 pf. The terminating resistor has a value of 100 ohms.

From a practical standpoint, it is essential that R provide a purely resistive termination; otherwise, the frequency characteristic of the filter will be distorted. Hence, a wire-wound resistor cannot be used; it has appreciable inductance, which would prevent R from operating as a purely resistive termination. However, a composition resistor is satisfactory in this application. Suppose we wish to measure the voltage across R. The voltmeter we choose must have a very low input capacitance, because its input capacitance will be placed in shunt to C at the output end of the filter in Figure 22-8. If this shunt capacitance is a substantial fraction of 22 pf, the filter will be disturbed and its frequency characteristic will be distorted.

High-frequency voltmeters are available which have an input capacitance of only 2 or 3 pf. Hence, this type of voltmeter would be used in the laboratory to measure the voltage across R in Figure 22-8. It is essential to remember that a meter always becomes a part of the circuit under test. If an unsuitable meter is utilized, circuit action will be disturbed and incorrect readings obtained. In turn, a defect will be falsely attributed to the circuit under test.

Let us consider the T-section low-pass filter shown in Figure 22-9. Both inductors have the same value. Capacitor C forms resonant circuits with the inductors, which are not magnetically coupled. To obtain a flat characteristic, R, L, and C are related as follows:

$$L = \frac{R}{2\pi f_c} \tag{22.3}$$

$$C = \frac{1}{\pi f_c R} \tag{22.4}$$

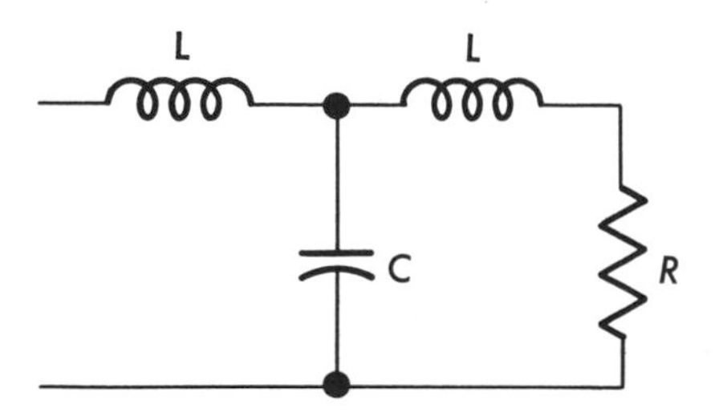

Figure 22-9
L and C values determine f_c, and are related to R.

Figure 22-10 depicts the T-section filter with a driving source. The generator has a resistance equal to the terminating resistance. The value of R in Equations (22.3) and (22.4) is also called the characteristic resistance of the filter; hence, the filter is matched at both input and output

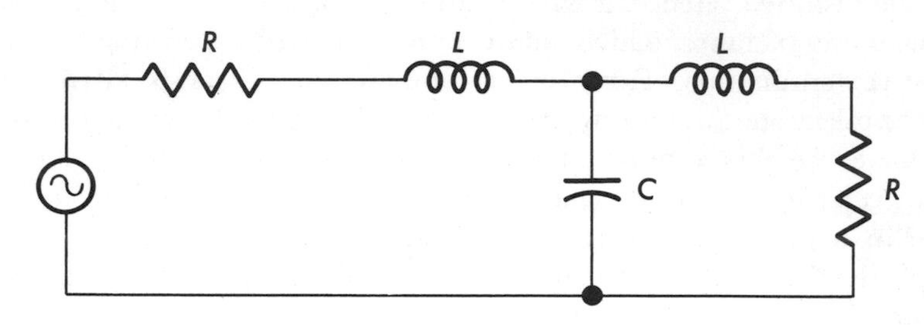

Figure 22-10
The source and terminating resistance values should be the same.

terminals. Half of the source voltage is transferred to the output over the flat-topped region of the filter characteristic, provided the inductors have sufficiently high Q that they impose negligible loss. If desired, several T sections can be connected in cascade to obtain a more abrupt drop-off past f_c.

A high-pass pi filter is depicted in Figure 22-11. Both inductors have the same value. L, C, and R are related as follows:

$$L = \frac{R}{2\pi f_c} \tag{22.5}$$

$$C = \frac{1}{4\pi f_c R} \tag{22.6}$$

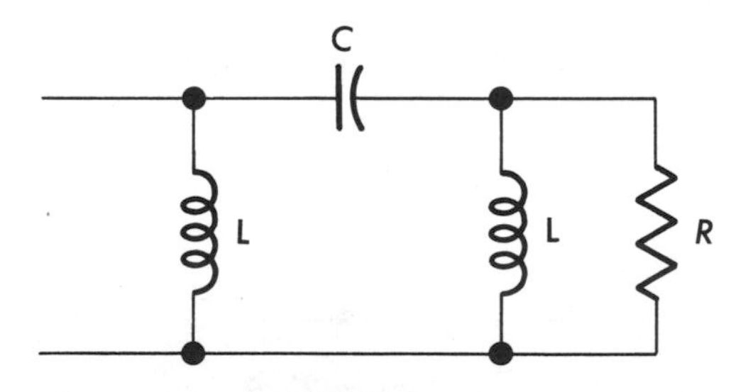

Figure 22-11
L, *C*, and *R* values are related in the high-pass pi filter.

The inductors are not magnetically coupled. As before, the value of terminating resistor R in Equations (22.5) and (22.6) is equal to the characteristic resistance of the filter section. The driving source should have a resistance equal to R. To obtain a more abrupt drop-off, several pi sections can be connected in cascade.

These basic filter configurations that have been described are often called *constant-k* filters. This means that the components are reactances that have a product equal to a constant. For example, the configuration in Figure 22-11 comprises inductive reactances and a capacitive reactance. The product of the reactances is

$$\frac{j\omega L}{j\omega C} = \frac{L}{C} = k \tag{22.7}$$

Because this is a symmetrical filter in which both inductors have the same value, it is a constant-k filter. Figure 22-8 is also a constant-k filter; it is symmetrical throughout, and X_L times X_C is equal to a certain constant k at each section. Remember that since the sections have been cascaded, only half of $2C$ goes with each L. Constant-k filters are one form of prototype filter. The word *prototype* has the meaning of a most basic form. In practice, constant-k filters can be approximated, but not completely realized. Inductors have residual resistance and distributed capacitance. Consequently, X_L becomes an impedance Z and Equation (22.7) is not a strictly true description of the reactive relations.

Next, consider the high-pass T-type filter in Figure 22-12. Values of L, C, and R are related as follows:

$$L = \frac{R}{4\pi f_c} \tag{22.8}$$

$$C = \frac{1}{2\pi f_c R} \tag{22.9}$$

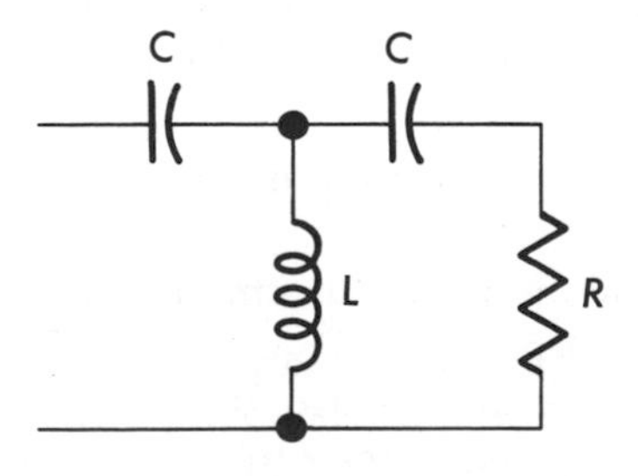

Figure 22-12
High-pass T-type filter.

22.4 POWER-SUPPLY FILTERS

A power-supply filter is a special-purpose low-pass filter which has a very low cutoff frequency. The design equations in previous discussion do not apply to power-supply filters. We recall that the output from a diode rectifier consists of half-sine waves, and is a pulsating d-c voltage. An analysis was made which showed how the half-sine waveform comprises a d-c component. In other words, the output from a rectifier consists of a d-c component plus an a-c component, called the *ripple content*. In a radio or television receiver, for example, only the d-c component is desired. Hence, the half-sine output from the power-supply rectifier is processed by a low-pass filter to minimize the ripple content.

To measure the smoothness of the d-c output from the filter, the terms *ripple factor* or *percent ripple* are defined as follows:

$$\text{Ripple factor} = \frac{\text{rms value of a-c components}}{\text{average value}} \tag{22.10}$$

$$\text{Percent ripple} = \text{ripple factor} \times 100 \tag{22.11}$$

The a-c component or ripple waveform contains many frequencies, or a-c components. This aspect of waveform analysis is not covered in these pages; however, we simply notc that if the ripple component of the waveform is passed through an rms meter, its rms value can be measured. The average value of the waveform is its d-c component, and is the value indicated by a d-c meter. Thus, it is a simple procedure to measure the ripple factor of a power-supply waveform in the laboratory. In Figure 22-13, the output from the half-wave rectifier has a d-c component which is 0.318 of the peak or maximum voltage. The lowest frequency in the ripple component is equal to the source frequency (usually 60 cycles per sec). Finally, the percent ripple is equal to 121 percent.

To suppress the ripple component and to pass the d-c component, a simple capacitor filter may be employed, as seen in Figure 22-14. Resistor R_L represents the load demand on the simple filter. Evidently, the ability of this circuit to reduce the ripple component depends upon the time constant R_LC. Suppose that R_L is infinite. Then, the capacitor charges to peak voltage and maintains a completely constant potential as shown by E_{out} in Figure 22-14(*b*).

But if R_L imposes a small current demand, the filter-output waveform then appears as depicted in Figure 22-14(*c*). Although the capacitor charges up to the peak supply voltage, this charge must now decay to some extent between peaks. In turn, the filter output has a certain ripple content, given quantitatively by Equations (22.10) and (22.11). Note that if capacitor C were not present, the ripple would be 121 percent under any

	Half wave	Center tap	Bridge
Circuit	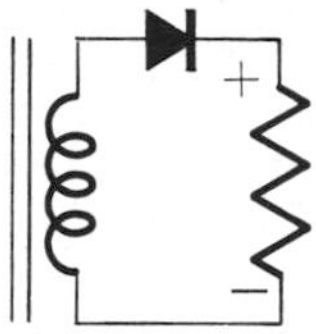	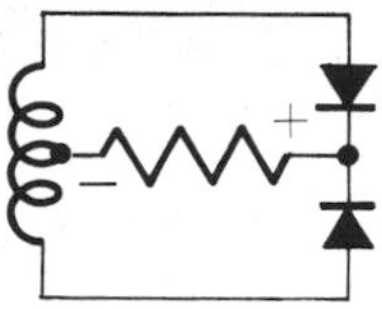	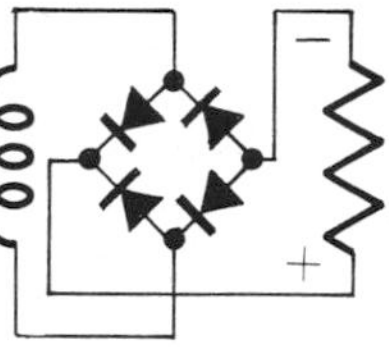
Load voltage	 0 π 2π	 0 π 2π	 0 π 2π
$\frac{E_{d\text{-}c}}{E_m}$	0.318	0.636*	0.636
Lowest ripple frequency	F	$2F$	$2F$
Percent Ripple	121%	48%	48%

*E_m is measured to center tap of winding

Figure 22-13
Output waveforms from half-wave and full-wave rectifiers.

condition of load. But with C in the circuit, the ripple is reduced to a comparatively small percentage. The decay path from 1 to 4 in Figure 22-14 is an exponential curve. We recall that over a period of time equal to one time constant, a capacitor discharges to 37 percent of its initial voltage.

When the load is increased (value of R_L reduced), this discharge time constant is reduced proportionately. Now, the capacitor discharges more between peaks, as seen in Figure 22-14(*d*); percent ripple increases, and the d-c component decreases. It would be possible to improve the filter action by increasing the capacitance of C. However, there are disadvantages to the use of a value substantially greater than 40 μf. An unduly large capacitance can cause damage to the rectifier from excessive surge

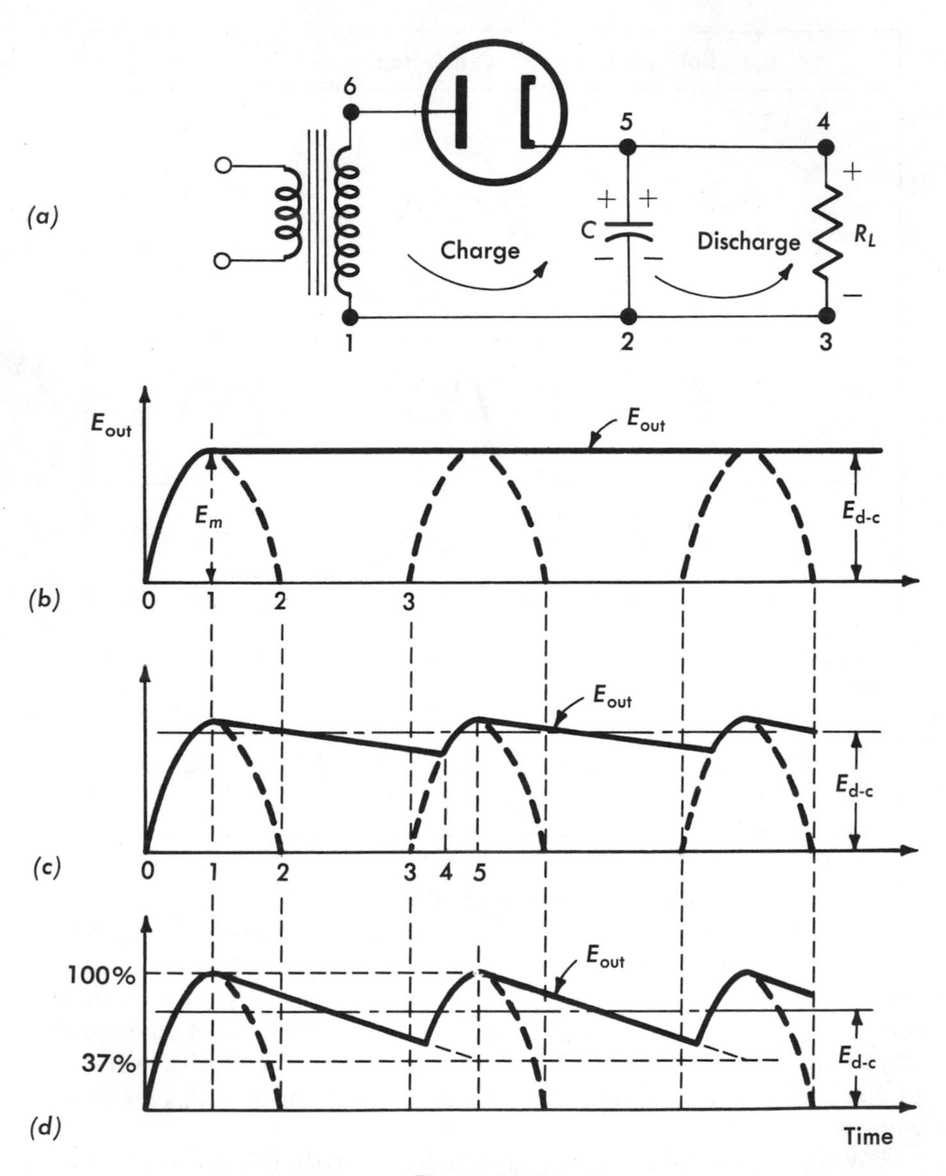

Figure 22-14
A capacitor-type filter.

current when the circuit is turned on. It is also uneconomical to make use of extremely large capacitors.

Hence, we find that an *R-C* pi-section filter is often used, as seen in Figure 22-15. C_1 has much the same circuit action as explained above;

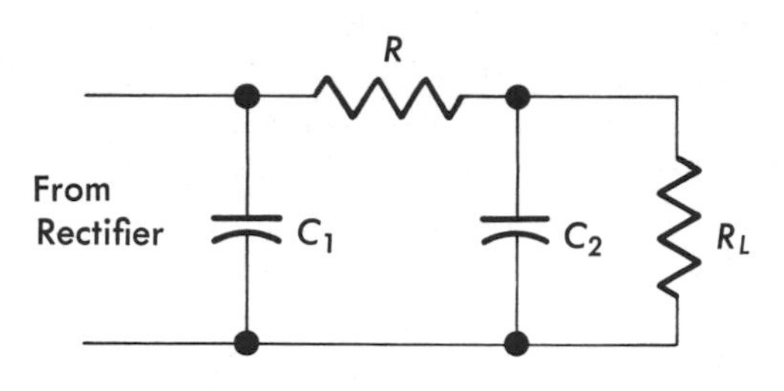

Figure 22-15
A pi-section RC filter.

however, R now adds to R_L in the time constant of the circuit. Note that R and C_2 form a voltage divider. This divider has much different ratios for a-c and d-c; C_2 is an open circuit for d-c, but is a low reactance for a-c. Thus, the ripple voltage is attenuated to a much greater extent than the d-c component. Attenuation of the d-c component is proportional to the IR drop across R. Hence, the pi-section RC filter is efficient at light loads, but is inefficient at heavy loads.

It is of interest to consider a practical example of the pi-section RC filter shown in Figure 22-15. The cathode-ray tube in a certain oscilloscope requires 840 volts at 0.26 ma. This is a low-current demand, which can be provided most economically by an RC filter. Capacitors (particularly high-voltage capacitors) are much more costly than resistors; it is therefore advantageous to choose as high a value as possible for R in Figure 22-15. The highest practical resistance value depends on power-transformer costs; the higher the value of R, the greater is the IR drop. This IR drop must be met by use of increased input voltage to the filter.

In this example, it was decided that an IR drop of 260 volts across R represented a good design compromise. In other words, an output of 840 volts plus an IR drop of 260 volts requires that 1100 volts be applied to the input end of the filter. The ripple waveform varies at a rate of 60 cycles per sec. Of course, the time constant of RC_2 must be much greater than 1/60 sec to obtain good filtering. A time constant of 0.1 sec was selected. The R and C values are then calculated as follows: Since $R = E/I$, the value of R in Figure 22-15 is 260/0.00026, or 1 megohm. Next, the time constant of RC_2 is given by $RC_2 = 0.1$, or $C_2 = 0.1/1{,}000{,}000 = 0.1$ μf. C_1 is assigned the same value in the pi section.

C_1 must withstand 1100 volts and C_2 must withstand 840 volts in this example. A working-voltage rating of 1200 volts is adequate. Finally, note the power dissipated by R. $W = I^2R = (0.26 \times 10^{-3}) \times 10^6$ or 0.07 watt, approximately. Hence, a power rating of ⅛ watt is ample for R. In summary, C_1 and C_2 are assigned a value of 0.1 μf each, at 1200 working volts.

R is assigned a value of 1 megohm at a rated power dissipation of 1/8 watt.

When a power-supply filter must provide substantial current, a pi-section *LC* configuration is commonly used, as shown in Figure 22-16. If the inductor is wound with wire of suitably large diameter, its d-c resistance is low and little d-c voltage is dropped. Yet, the inductive reactance opposes the flow of a-c (ripple current). L and C_2 then form a very effective voltage divider for this application. We know that an iron core will saturate unless its cross-section is ample. If the core saturates, the inductor has less reactance. Hence, good filtering action at high-current demand entails the use of an inductor with an appropriately large core.

Let us consider a practical example such as a power-supply filter for a three-tube high-fidelity audio amplifier. The current demand is approximately 90 ma, which can be efficiently filtered with a pi-section *LC* configuration as depicted in Figure 22-16. A full-wave rectifier is used; hence, the ripple waveform varies at a 120-cycle rate. It is advantageous to use full-wave rectification because the ripple frequency is double (compared with a half-wave rectifier), which permits use of smaller component values in the filter. With reference to Figure 22-16, the circuit designer specified a value of 20 μf each for C_1 and C_2, and a value of 5 henrys for L. Note that the reactance of 20 μf at 120 cycles is approximately 65 ohms, and that the reactance of 5 henrys at 120 cycles is approximately 3800 ohms.

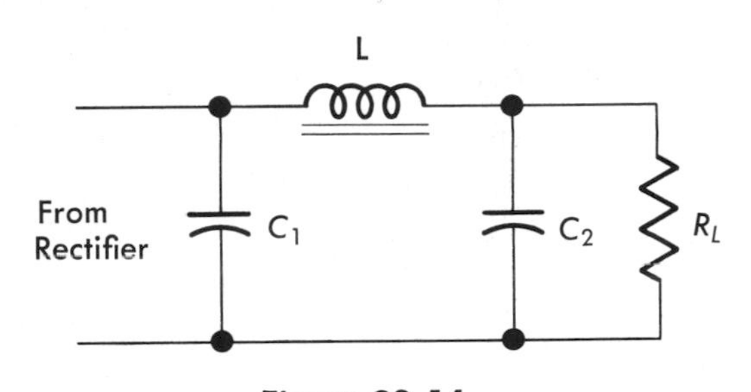

Figure 22-16
A pi-section *LC* power-supply filter.

22.5 TROUBLESHOOTING FILTER CIRCUITS

We have seen that there are two general classes of filters used in electronic equipment. One class is designed to have a specified frequency characteristic; the other class is designed to pass d-c only. Accordingly, a defect in a filter such as depicted in Figure 22-8 becomes apparent as nonuniform output over the pass band, usually accompanied by an incorrect cutoff frequency. Considerable time can be saved by checking the terminating resistor R first. The mechanical design of filter units often places the resistor in a comparatively exposed position where it is more subject to damage than the inductors or capacitors. However, if the resistor is found to have rated value and is making good electrical connection to the circuit, the inductors and capacitors must next be investigated.

Capacitors are apt to fail more often than inductors. A capacitor may become leaky or short-circuited; in some cases, it may open completely. It is easy to check a low-pass LC filter for capacitor leakage. We disconnect R temporarily (Figure 22-8), and apply an ohmmeter or megohmmeter across the input terminals of the filter. Any reading other than infinity indicates the presence of a leaky capacitor. In turn, each capacitor must be disconnected and tested for leakage. The defective capacitor must be replaced with a new capacitor which has a value within the tolerance specified for the filter. Otherwise, the replacement capacitor will detune the filter more or less. A tolerance of ± 5 percent is typically specified for this type of filter.

If the capacitors are not leaky or shorted, they must next be tested for an open-circuit. This test requires that each capacitor be disconnected in turn and checked on a capacitance bridge. In case the capacitors are not leaky, shorted, or open, suspicion is directed next to the inductors. Visual inspection may disclose corrosion between turns, or mechanical damage. However, if there is no visible defect, each inductor must be disconnected in turn and checked on an impedance bridge. A defective inductor must be replaced with a new inductor which has a value within the tolerance specified for the filter. For example, a tolerance of ± 5 percent is typically specified.

We know that inductors are not ideal. Thus, an inductor has distributed capacitance. In turn, the characteristics of an ideal filter are not fully realized in practice. Thus, the cutoff frequency of a low-pass filter might be higher than indicated by simple theory, due to distributed capacitance of the inductors. Hence, it can be important to replace a filter inductor with a coil which not only has the specified inductance value, but also has the same value of distributed capacitance as the original inductor. This is simply another way of saying that the self-resonant frequency of the replacement should be the same as that of the original.

Next, let us consider the power-supply filter depicted in Figure 22-16. This type of filter commonly utilizes electrolytic capacitors. We know that electrolytic capacitors are shorter lived than paper, mica, or ceramic capacitors; hence, they are prime suspects when a power-supply filter becomes defective. As explained in previous chapters, a suspected electrolytic capacitor should be disconnected from its circuit and checked on a capacitor bridge for capacitance value, leakage, and power-factor value. Sometimes a technician simply discards a suspected electrolytic capacitor without testing it, and substitutes a new capacitor.

Short-circuited electrolytic capacitors sometimes cause damage to other components. For example, if C_2 (Figure 22-16) is short-circuited, the winding on L might burn open. Even if the winding does not open, the heat that is generated can char insulation and cause shorted turns or shorted layers. Such internal short-circuits reduce the inductance value and consume a-c power, and the inductor will run hot. A suspected inductor can be checked on an impedance bridge for inductance value and Q. Note that an ohmmeter check of the winding resistance is not conclusive, because a few shorted turns do not change the resistance value substantially. On the other hand, the shorted turns will consume a large amount of a-c power. Hence, it is good practice to check suspected inductors on an impedance bridge.

We have seen that power supplies may utilize either vacuum diodes or semiconductor diodes. Vacuum diodes gradually lose emission in service, and the voltage drop across the tube becomes excessive. In turn, the output voltage from the filter becomes subnormal. If a vacuum diode is suspected to have low emission, it is either checked on a tube tester, or a substitution test is made. Vacuum diodes can become damaged if a leaky filter capacitor demands excessive current. The plate of the tube becomes red-hot, and gas may be liberated inside the tube which permits an arc to form between filament (or cathode) and plate. If a rectifier tube is observed to be seriously overheated, do not plug a new tube into the socket until the cause of excessive current demand has been corrected.

Power supplies also utilize selenium, germanium, or silicon diodes. If a selenium rectifier is overloaded, it becomes damaged and produces a poisonous vapor that smells like rotten eggs. The chief figure of merit for a semiconductor diode is its front-to-back ratio. An ohmmeter test of front-to-back ratio for a power-type semiconductor diode is not very informative. The ohmmeter does not apply sufficient voltage to provide a useful test. Test instruments designed to check power-type semiconductor diodes under typical working conditions are used by some technicians. Other technicians merely make a substitution test of a suspected diode. Power supplies for television receivers must supply normal output voltage with an acceptably low ripple level. Hence, the power supply for a TV receiver is often checked at the onset with an oscilloscope, to observe the ripple amplitude.

SUMMARY OF FUNDAMENTAL CONCEPTS

A filter is a reactive network which provides an output that is a function of frequency.

Band-pass filters transmit a certain range of frequencies, but attenuate or reject frequencies that are outside the pass band.

A basic band-pass filter has two cutoff frequencies at which output attenuation starts.

The cutoff frequency defines the point on the filter characteristic at which output attenuation starts.

Filter sections can be cascaded to obtain rapid attenuation past the cutoff frequency.

Power-supply filters are low-pass networks with a cutoff frequency close to d-c (zero frequency).

Low-pass filters transmit low frequencies, but attenuate or reject high frequencies.

High-pass filters transmit high frequencies, but attenuate or reject low frequencies.

LCR filter networks can provide a uniform transmission characteristic over the pass range.

Most basic filters comprise *T* or pi sections of pure reactances, terminated by a suitable value of resistance.

A uniform transmission characteristic entails uniquely related values of reactance and resistance.

QUESTIONS

1) An example of a circuit which can be regarded as a filter is:
(*a*) a resistive voltage divider. (*b*) a capacitive voltage divider. (*c*) an *RC* coupling circuit. (*d*) a transistor.
2) A pi-section low-pass filter has a uniform output over its pass band because:
(*a*) its inductive reactance is equal to its capacitive reactance. (*b*) the pi section is terminated with a suitable value of resistance. (*c*) it has a constant-*k* configuration. (*d*) the generator has a d-c component.
3) A *T*-section low-pass filter has reactive components which comprise:
(*a*) two capacitors and one inductor. (*b*) three inductors. (*c*) three capacitors. (*d*) two inductors and one capacitor.
4) The *L* and *C* values in a low-pass pi-section filter are related to the terminating resistance and cutoff frequency by the equation:
(*a*) $L = R/(\pi f_c)$; $C = 1/(2\pi f_c R)$. (*b*) $f_c = 1/(2\pi\sqrt{LC})$. (*c*) $Q = (2\pi fL)/R$. (*d*) $k = (2\pi fL)/(2\pi fC)$.
5) The inductors in a low-pass *T*-section filter must be:
(*a*) tightly coupled. (*b*) tuned to zero frequency. (*c*) nonresonant at any frequency. (*d*) free from any magnetic coupling.
6) When identical pi sections are cascaded:
(*a*) the filter output is increased. (*b*) drop-off is more abrupt past the cutoff frequency. (*c*) drop-off is more gradual past the cutoff frequency. (*d*) the inductors operate as capacitors.
7) The source resistance for a constant-*k* filter should be:
(*a*) zero. (*b*) infinite. (*c*) equal to the terminating resistance. (*d*) equal to f_c.
8) A power-supply filter is:
(*a*) a special-purpose high-pass filter. (*b*) a special-purpose low-pass filter. (*c*) not used in electronic equipment. (*d*) the same as a constant-*k* filter.
9) The ripple factor is equal to:
(*a*) the rms value of the input voltage. (*b*) the average value of the input voltage. (*c*) the rms value of the output voltage. (*d*) the rms value of the a-c components divided by the average value in the output waveform.
10) The percentage ripple is equal to:
(*a*) the ripple factor multiplied by 100. (*b*) the rms value of the ripple components. (*c*) the average value of the output waveform. (*d*) the output voltage divided by the input voltage, multiplied by 100.

PROBLEMS

1) A coupling circuit (Figure 22-1) comprises a 0.25-μf capacitor and a 1-megohm resistor. If the a-c source applies 117 volts at 60 cycles, calculate the voltage across R. (Assume that the voltmeter does not load the circuit.)
2) If the circuit depicted in Figure 22-2 comprises a 0.1-henry inductor and a 50-ohm resistor, calculate the voltage across R when the source applies 117 volts at 60 cycles.
3) You are asked to design a low-pass pi-section filter with a cutoff frequency of 1 mc. The pi section will be driven from a source with an internal resistance of 75 ohms, and will be terminated with a 75-ohm resistor. What values of L and C will you specify?
4) A T-section low-pass filter is to be designed to operate from a source resistance of 1000 ohms, and with a terminating resistance of 1000 ohms. The cutoff frequency is 3 mc. What values of L and C will you specify?
5) It is desired to suppress all frequencies above 200 mc with a low-pass pi-section filter. The source resistance is 300 ohms, and the terminating resistance is 300 ohms. What values of L and C will you specify?
6) A high-pass pi-section filter is desired to suppress frequencies below 550 kc. The filter operates from a source resistance of 75 ohms, and terminates in 75 ohms. What values of L and C will you specify?
7) If a constant-k filter utilizes 0.19-mh inductors and 1000-pf capacitors, what is the value of k?
8) A high-pass T-section filter is desired to suppress frequencies below 550 kc. The filter operates from a source resistance of 75 ohms, and terminates in 75 ohms. What values of L and C will you specify?
9) What is the average value of the half-sine output from a half-wave rectifier?
10) What is the average value of the half-sine output from a full-wave rectifier?
11) The transformer in Figure 22-14 has a step-up ratio of 3-to-1. If R_L is disconnected, what voltage will be measured across C, if the primary of the transformer is energized by a 117-volt 60-cycle line?
12) An rms voltmeter connected across the output terminals of a filter measures 1 volt for the a-c components. A d-c voltmeter measures 50 volts. What is the ripple factor? What is the percent ripple?

23

NETWORK THEOREMS

23.1 THE SUPERPOSITION THEOREM

We have solved electric circuits in various ways, by application of Ohm's law, Kirchhoff's voltage law, and Kirchhoff's current law. Although we did not realize it, we often made a basic assumption that each component current of a total current may be considered by itself, and that the total current is then found by adding the component currents. For example, consider the resistive circuit depicted in Figure 23-1. There is a total current I_T flowing through resistor R_3. This total current has two component currents; one component current is I_1, which is produced by the voltage source E_1, the other is I_2, which is produced by the voltage source E_2. Currents I_1 and I_2 oppose each other; hence,

$$I_T = I_1 - I_2 \tag{23.1}$$

Since I_1 and I_2 flow in opposite directions, we can call I_1 positive, and call I_2 negative. Then, I_T is given by the sum of I_1 and I_2

$$I_T = I_1 + (-I_2) \tag{23.2}$$

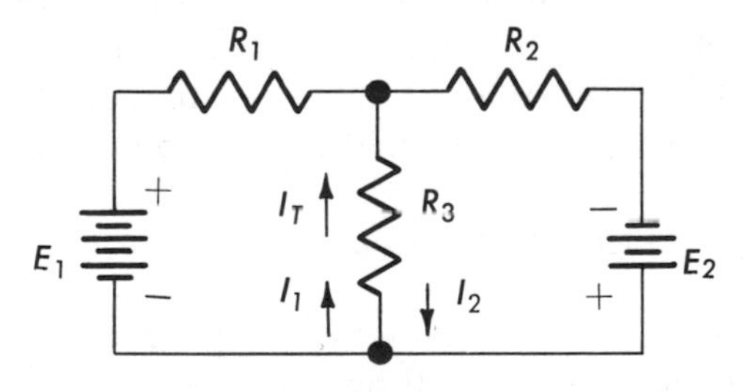

Figure 23-1
Total current I_T is the difference between currents I_1 and I_2.

This is all very elementary. What we wish to recognize now is that we can solve the circuit first for I_1, then for I_2, and finally calculate I_T by means of Equation (23.2). To proceed with this method of solution, let us first replace E_2 with a short-circuit. We can do so without changing the resistance relations, because E_2 has zero internal resistance as represented in

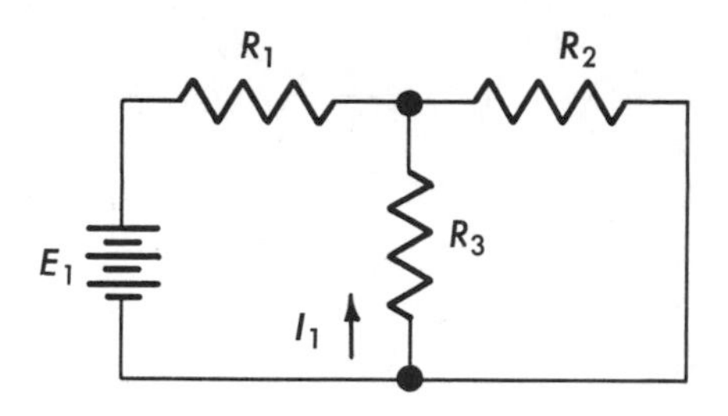

Figure 23-2
E_2 has been replaced by its internal resistance (zero).

Figure 23-1. Thus, we obtain the simplified configuration depicted in Figure 23-2, and it is now easy to calculate I_1.

The configuration in Figure 23-2 is a simple series-parallel circuit. We have learned in previous chapters how to apply Kirchhoff's current law and Ohm's law to calculate I_1; hence, it is unnecessary to repeat this procedure. Instead, let us proceed to observe how I_2 is calculated. With reference to Figure 23-1, we replace E_1 by its internal resistance, which is zero in this example. We can then replace E_1 with a short-circuit, as depicted in Figure 23-3. We apply Kirchhoff's current law and Ohm's law to calculate I_2 and subtract I_2 from I_1 to find I_T in Figure 23-1. It is clear that we can calculate each component current as if the other were not present, and then combine component currents to find the total current.

This understanding can be stated in a general form which applies to a-c circuits as well as to d-c circuits, and to configurations which contain any number of voltage sources and any number of impedances. This statement is called the *superposition theorem: In any configuration consisting of linear impedances, the current flowing at any point is the algebraic sum of the currents which would flow if each generator were considered separately, all other generators being replaced at this time by impedances equal to their internal impedances.*

This is a general statement of the principles illustrated in Figures 23-1, 23-2, and 23-3. It is evident that we could replace R_1, R_2, and R_3 by capacitors, and replace E_1 and E_2 by a-c generators. We could replace R_1, R_2, and R_3 by inductors; however, we must use air-core inductors, because iron-core inductors are nonlinear. The superposition theorem cannot be applied to nonlinear circuits. We could replace R_1 by a capacitor, R_2 by an air-core inductor, and let R_3 remain a resistor. Moreover, we could connect another series-parallel circuit across R_2 in Figure 23-1. We can also connect another parallel circuit, or another series-parallel circuit

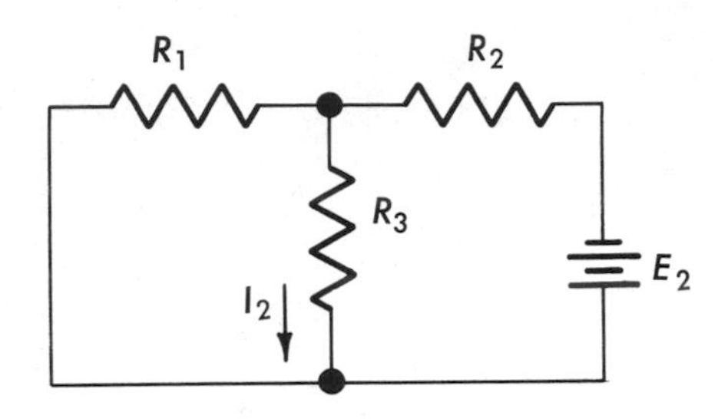

Figure 23-3
E_1 has been replaced by its internal resistance (zero).

across E_1, and solve the elaborated network by means of the superposition theorem.

23.2 MESH ANALYSIS

Mesh analysis is a small extension of the superposition theorem and is merely another way (and often an easier way) of applying Kirchhoff's laws and Ohm's law to networks. It is used to great advantage when we solve networks with many series-parallel sections; however, let us consider mesh analysis for the simple circuit depicted in Figure 23-4. Here we have a battery E connected to a circuit comprising resistors R_1, R_2, and R_3. This circuit has two loops; the first loop is the closed circuit that includes E and R_1, the second loop is the closed circuit that includes R_1, R_2, and R_3.

We know from Kirchhoff's voltage law that the algebraic sum of all the voltages around a closed circuit is equal to zero. The voltage drops across the resistors are caused by current flow. Hence, let us indicate the two component currents in this network as i_1 and i_2. It is obvious that these currents flow clockwise in Figure 23-4. Now, if we were considering a complicated network, it is quite possible that the direction of current flow would not be obvious. We would then *assign* an arbitrary direction of current flow. Then, if we should discover that the value of current flow which we calculate is negative, we would know that we had assigned an incorrect direction to the current flow—we would retain the value we calculated, but we would understand that the current actually flows in the opposite direction to that which was assumed.

Now, let us use the technique of mesh analysis to solve the circuit depicted in Figure 23-4. First, we write the algebraic sum of the voltage drops around the first loop, or mesh. Observe that both i_1 and i_2 flow through R_1. Furthermore, we have assigned directions of current flow which make i_2 oppose i_1. In other words, if we say that i_1 is positive, then

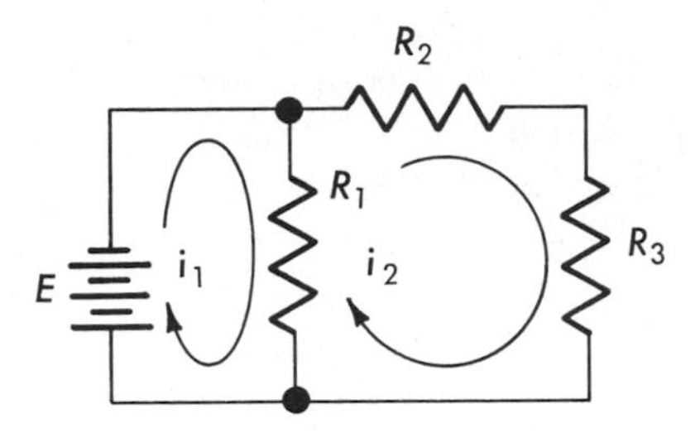

Figure 23-4
We assign currents i_1 and i_2 to the loops, or meshes, of the circuit.

we must say that i_2 is negative. Hence, the voltage drop across R_1 is equal to $i_1R_1 - i_2R_1$. Observe, that in accordance with Kirchhoff's voltage law, the algebraic sum of E and the drop across R_1 must be zero; or,

$$E = i_1R_1 - i_2R_1 \tag{23.3}$$

Next, we write the algebraic sum of the voltage drops around the second mesh in Figure 23-4. As before, note that both i_1 and i_2 flow through R_1. The voltage drop across R_1 is equal to $i_1R_1 - i_2R_1$. In accordance with Kirchhoff's voltage law, the algebraic sum of the voltage drops around the second mesh must be zero; or,

$$0 = i_2R_1 - i_1R_1 + i_2R_2 + i_2R_3 \tag{23.4}$$

Equations (23.3) and (23.4) are simultaneous equations. You have learned how to solve simultaneous equations in your algebra courses. Equation (23.3) can be rearranged

$$i_1 = \frac{E + i_2R_1}{R_1} \tag{23.5}$$

If we then substitute this value for i_1 given by Equation (23.5) into Equation (23.4), we calculate that

$$i_2 = \frac{E}{R_2 + R_3} \tag{23.6}$$

This is obvious, since E is applied across R_2 and R_3 in series; but, if we were solving a complicated network, the value of a current would be far from obvious. Equation (23.6) permits us to calculate the value of i_2. Next, if we substitute this value for i_2 into Equation (23.5), we obtain the value of i_1

$$i_1 = E\left(\frac{1}{R_1} + \frac{1}{R_2 + R_3}\right) \tag{23.7}$$

Again, this value for i_1 stated by Equation (23.7) is obvious from inspection of the circuit in Figure 23-4. But the important point is that current values are far from obvious in complicated networks, and that we must fall back on a detailed mesh analysis to calculate the current values. Note that after we have solved a circuit for its component current values, the various voltage drops follow directly from Ohm's law, $E = IR$; the circuit is then completely solved. If more than one current flows through a resistor, we must, of course, take both currents into account. For example, both i_1 and i_2 flow through R_1 in Figure 23-4. Hence, the voltage drop across R_1 is given by

$$V = (i_1 - i_2)R_1 \tag{23.8}$$

where V is the voltage drop across R_1 in Figure 23-4.

Now, i_1 is expressed by Equation (23.7), and i_2 is expressed by Equation (23.6). If we substitute these expressions into Equation (23.8), we find that

$$V = E\left(1 + \frac{R_1}{R_2 + R_3} - \frac{R_1}{R_2 + R_3}\right) \tag{23.9}$$

or,

$$V = E \tag{23.10}$$

which is entirely obvious by inspection of Figure 23-4. The validity of mesh analysis would be impossible to establish by inspection of a complicated network. It has been instructive to consider a simple network, because we can check each step of our calculation by inspection. Therefore, we can now apply our new technique to complicated networks, where mesh analysis is indispensable.

23.3 RECIPROCITY THEOREM

Although the reciprocity theorem is quite simple, it is perhaps unexpected. This theorem states: *In any system of linear impedances, if a voltage E is applied between any two terminals, and the current flow I is measured in any branch, their ratio will be equal to the ratio obtained when the positions of E and I are interchanged.*

Let us see how the reciprocity theorem is applied to the simple network depicted in Figure 23-5. The voltage is first applied at E, and the current flow is measured at A. We observe that

$$I_2 = I_1\left(\frac{R_3}{R_2 + R_3}\right) \tag{23.11}$$

$$I_1 = \frac{E}{R_1 + \dfrac{R_2 R_3}{R_2 + R_3}} \tag{23.12}$$

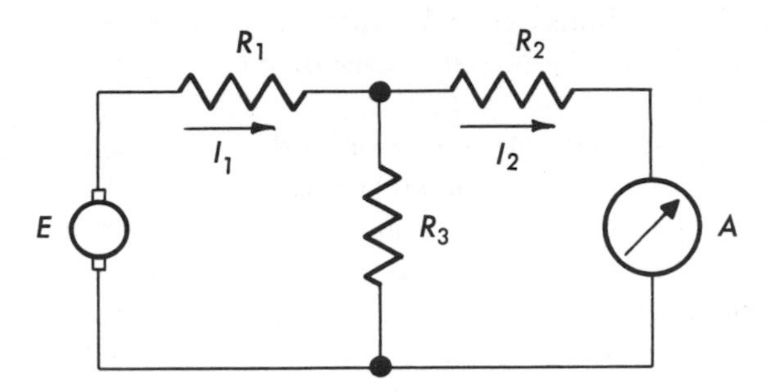

Figure 23-5
If the generator E is interchanged with the ammeter A, the same current flow is indicated.

or,

$$\frac{E}{I_2} = \frac{R_1R_2 + R_2R_3 + R_1R_3}{R_3} \tag{23.13}$$

So far, this is a simple application of Ohm's law and Kirchhoff's law. Now, if we interchange E and A in Figure 23-5, we perceive that this is the same as interchanging R_1 and R_2 in Equation (23.13). But this does not change the value of E/I_2. Thus, the validity of the reciprocity theorem has been demonstrated for one example, Figure 23-5. Next, we need to convince ourselves that the reciprocity theorem is valid for any network. To do so, note that *any network can be reduced to an equivalent* T *section.* This network reduction is not derived in this book; however, you will learn how to make this derivation in your advanced studies of electricity.

Evidently, if any network can be reduced to an equivalent T section, the reciprocity theorem must be valid for any network. The only restrictions are that the resistances (or impedances) must be linear, and that they must not be devices such as rectifiers, which block current flow in one direction; that is, the resistances (or impedances) must be *bilateral* and conduct current equally in either direction. Note that the resistances depicted in Figures 23-4 and 23-5 can be coils or capacitors, and that the d-c voltage sources may be a-c voltage sources. We have considered d-c situations only in our analyses merely in the interest of simplicity.

The reciprocity theorem is very useful, because it shows that any circuit consisting of linear bilateral resistances (or impedances) always operates in the same manner from input to output, or from output to input. It is essential to observe in Figure 23-5 that the generator and the ammeter are assumed to have zero internal resistances (or zero internal impedances). Our analysis is based upon this assumption. Suppose that the generator and the ammeter do *not* have zero internal resistance. In such case, it is evident that the reciprocity theorem is still valid, provided that the generator has the same value of internal resistance as the ammeter. In this case, R_1 combines with the internal resistance of the generator, and R_2 combines with the internal resistance of the ammeter; the analysis is basically unchanged.

Again, suppose that the generator and the ammeter in Figure 23-5 have unequal internal resistances. We cannot merely interchange the generator with the ammeter, and obtain the same current reading. The reciprocity theorem evidently holds true only if we leave the internal resistances unchanged, which introduces the following limitation. The generator must be replaced with an ammeter that has the same internal resistance as the generator; the ammeter must be replaced with a generator that has the same internal resistance as the ammeter. In practice, this particular situation usually means that the reciprocity theorem cannot be conveniently applied. Hence, you must evaluate the internal resistances of the generator and ammeter (if significant), before you apply the reciprocity theorem.

23.4 THEVENIN'S THEOREM

There is another interesting theorem which is almost obvious for simple networks, and which is very helpful in analysis of complicated networks. This theorem is usually called Thevenin's theorem, and it states: *The current in any impedance Z, connected to two terminals of a network, is the same current that would flow if Z were connected to an ideal generator, which applies a voltage equal to the open-circuit voltage of the two network terminals, and which has an internal impedance equal to the impedance of the network, looking back from the two network terminals, when all generators are replaced by their internal impedances.*

Let us consider Thevenin's theorem for the simple circuit depicted in Figure 23-6. We are aware of the fact that *any* network can be reduced to an equivalent T section. First, measure the open-circuit voltage at terminals 1 and 2, then connect a resistance R across the terminals. How much current flows through R? To answer this question by means of Thevenin's theorem, we will measure the resistance of the T section with the generator stopped (or replaced by a short-circuit in this example, since the generator is assumed to have zero internal impedance). Let us call this measured (or calculated) value R_T. Then, the current flowing through R in Figure 23-6 is the same as the current that would flow if R were connected to a generator that has an emf equal to the open-circuit voltage, and an internal resistance equal to R_T.

Note that the generator in Figure 23-6(d) is not the same generator as in Figure 23-6(b); the latter has no internal resistance, and its voltage is not specified. On the other hand, the generator in Figure 23-6(d) has an

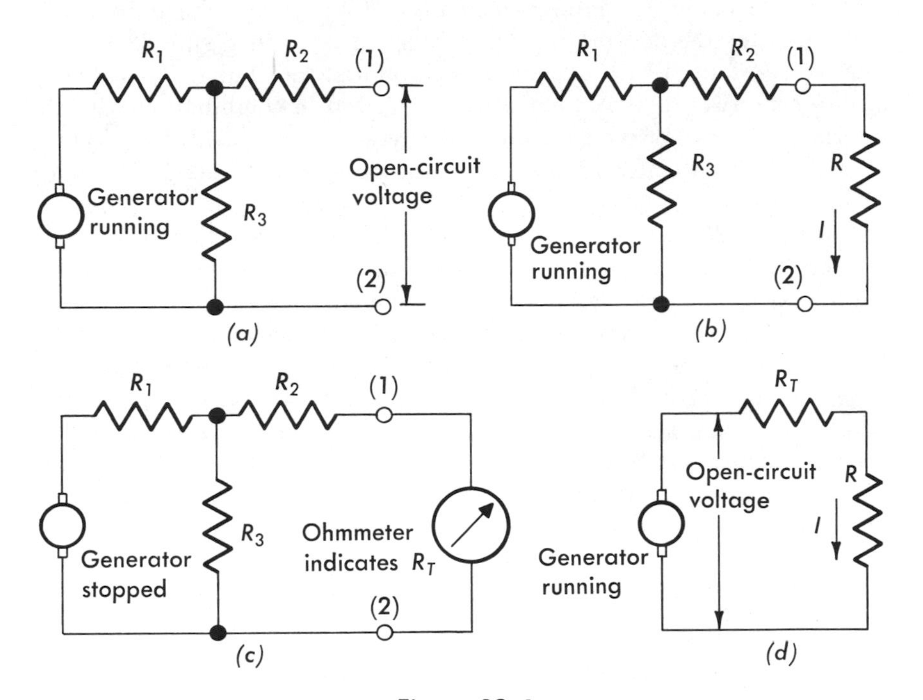

Figure 23-6

(*a*) An open-circuit voltage appears between terminals (1) and (2). (*b*) When a resistance R is connected between terminals (1) and (2), a current (I) flows. (*c*) An ohmmeter measures the resistance between terminals (1) and (2). (*d*) The current I is the same as the current I in Figure 23-6(*b*).

internal resistance equal to R_T, and its emf is equal to the open-circuit voltage measured in Figure 23-6(*a*). What is the value of R_T? A simple calculation will show that

$$R_T = \frac{R_1R_2 + R_2R_3 + R_1R_3}{R_1 + R_3} \tag{23.14}$$

Although this discussion of Thevenin's theorem has been made in terms of resistances, it is evident that it applies in the same manner to reactances or impedances energized by an a-c source. Suppose that there is more than one generator in a complicated network to be analyzed by means of Thevenin's theorem. Then, we can invoke the superposition theorem, and consider the resulting currents one by one. Accordingly, combination of the superposition theorem and Thevenin's theorem provides a powerful tool for analysis of complicated networks. Finally, let us observe the situation in which the generator in Figure 23-6(*a*) has significant internal resistance. However, this does not change the mode of analysis. We first measure the open-circuit voltage between the terminals (1) and (2). When the network resistance is measured as in Figure 23-6(*c*), the internal resistance of the generator is accounted for. Then, R_T in Figure 23-6(*d*) comprises the resistance of the *T* section in combination with the internal resistance of the generator. The new generator in Figure 23-6(*d*), of course, has an emf that is equal to the open-circuit voltage in Figure 23-6(*a*).

We should observe that Thevenin's theorem denotes only the current flowing through *R* in Figures 23-6(*b*) and 23-6(*d*); in other words, the theorem does not imply that the power consumption in the generator of Figure 23-6(*b*) is the same as the power consumption in the generator of Figure 23-6(*d*). This fact is quite obvious in the example–recall that the generator in Figure 23-6(*b*) was assigned zero internal resistance. But, the generator in Figure 23-6(*d*) has an internal resistance R_T. In turn, the first generator has zero internal power consumption, while the second generator has a finite power consumption. Therefore, we must limit our application of Thevenin's theorem to consideration of load currents.

23.5 MAXIMUM POWER TRANSFER THEOREM

At this point, it is interesting to recall the maximum power transfer theorem which was explained in Chapter 4: *Maximum power is transferred from a generator to a load when the load resistance is equal to the internal resistance of the generator.*

Now, we shall make a simple extension of the maximum power transfer theorem to a-c circuits. Our theorem will now be stated: *Maximum power is transferred from a generator to a load when the load impedance is the conjugate of the internal impedance of the generator.*

In Figure 23-7, we have a generator which has an internal impedance comprising inductor *L* and resistor R_1. This internal impedance has a value equal to $R_1 + jX_L$. The load impedance comprises R_2 and *C*, which has a value equal to $R_2 - jX_C$. If *L* and *C* were out of the circuit, we know that maximum power would be transferred when R_2 is made equal to R_1. If we then add inductor *L*, its reactance will reduce the current through the load. Or, if we remove *L* and include *C*, the reactance of *C* will reduce the current through the load. However, suppose we include both *L* and *C*, and assign a value to *C*, making the circuit series resonant. Obviously, maximum power transfer now occurs as if *L* and *C* were not present.

We say that *C* and R_2 have an impedance which is the conjugate of the impedance of *L* and R_1 when R_2 is equal to R_1, and *C* resonates with *L* at the operating frequency. We can formulate conjugate impedances as follows:

$$\begin{matrix} R + jX \\ R - jX \end{matrix} \qquad (23.15)$$

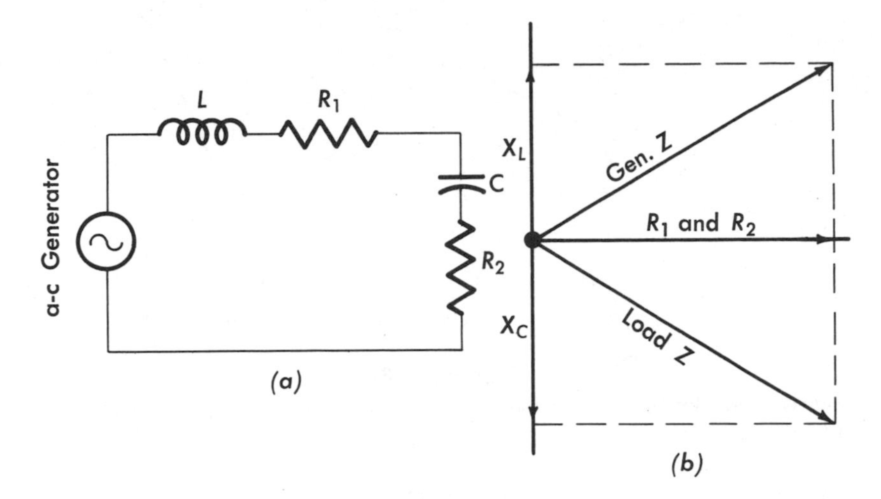

Figure 23-7
(a) Maximum power is transferred when R_2 equals R_1, and C resonates with L at the operating frequency. (b) X_L cancels X_C when the load impedance is the conjugate of the generator's internal impedance.

Conjugate impedances have equal resistance values, and have equal and opposite reactance values.

Next, let us consider a very practical situation, in which the generator has an inductive internal impedance, and the load also has an inductive impedance. We may be able to adjust the magnitude of the load impedance, but not the sign of its reactance. In other words, our practical situation does not permit us to make the load capacitive. Now we ask, under this limitation, what value of load impedance will provide maximum power transfer? Since the derivation is somewhat involved, let us merely state the condition for maximum power transfer: *When the magnitude of the load impedance may be varied, but not its phase angle, maximum power will be transferred when the absolute magnitude of the load impedance is equal to the absolute magnitude of the generator's internal impedance.*

The term *absolute magnitude* means the number of ohms, without regard to phase angle. In Figure 23-8, we have a load impedance with an absolute magnitude equal to the absolute magnitude of the generator's internal impedance. The two impedances have different phase angles. However, we are operating under the limitation that the inductance of the load cannot be changed; only its magnitude can be changed by adjustment of R. Under this limitation, maximum power is transferred, because the absolute magnitudes of the impedances are equal. Of course, if we were

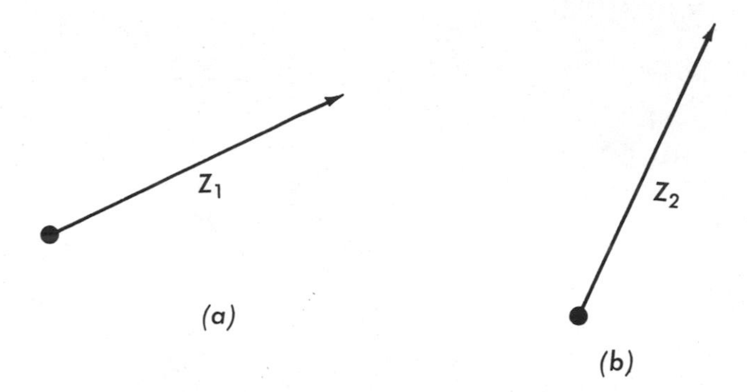

Figure 23-8
These two impedances are equal in absolute magnitude, but they have different phase angles. (*a*) Internal impedance of generator. (*b*) Impedance of load.

permitted to make the phase angle of the load the conjugate of the generator's internal impedance, power transfer would be at its maximum possible value.

Most generators of the rotating machinery type have an inductive internal impedance. Most motors also present an inductive load. However, there is one exception. A synchronous motor presents a capacitive load. Hence, a shop may employ synchronous motors in addition to induction motors. If the synchronous motors are arranged to draw an appropriate value of leading current, the total current demand will be in phase with the line voltage, and the power factor of the system will be unity. Public utilities are pleased when systems operate at unity power factor, because efficiency is then maximum and electricity can be supplied by the utility at lower cost. Why is efficiency maximized when the power factor is unity? It is because no reactive current is then present in the supply line. Reactive current merely surges back and forth, and does no useful work. Instead, the reactive current merely produces additional I^2R loss as heat in the resistance of the line.

Norton's theorem is the constant-current form of Thevénin's theorem. Norton's theorem states: The current in any impedance Z_R, connected to two terminals of a network, is the same as if Z_R were connected to a constant-current generator whose current is equal to the current flow through the two terminals when these terminals are short-circuited, the constant-current generator being in shunt with an impedance equal to the impedance of the network looking back from the two terminals.

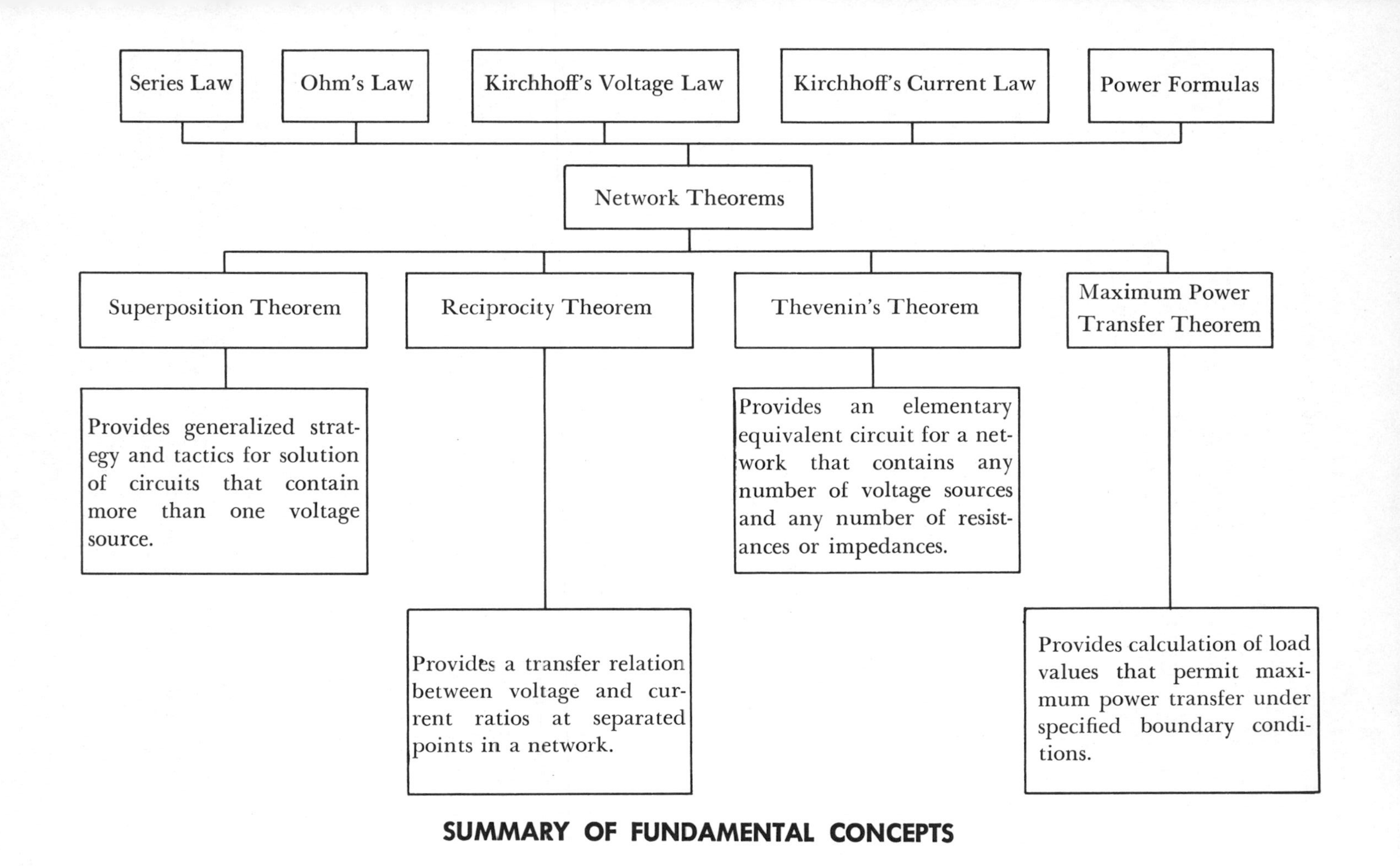
Series Law
Ohm's Law
Kirchhoff's Voltage Law
Kirchhoff's Current Law
Power Formulas
Network Theorems
Superposition Theorem
Reciprocity Theorem
Thevenin's Theorem
Maximum Power Transfer Theorem
Provides generalized strategy and tactics for solution of circuits that contain more than one voltage source.
Provides a transfer relation between voltage and current ratios at separated points in a network.
Provides an elementary equivalent circuit for a network that contains any number of voltage sources and any number of resistances or impedances.
Provides calculation of load values that permit maximum power transfer under specified boundary conditions.

SUMMARY OF FUNDAMENTAL CONCEPTS

QUESTIONS

1) The superposition theorem states that:
(*a*) maximum power is transferred when impedances are equal. (*b*) the sum of the voltages around any closed circuit is zero. (*c*) a total current may be calculated by computing the algebraic sum of its component currents, provided the configuration consists of linear impedances. (*d*) any voltage source may be replaced by an open-circuit.
2) Mesh analysis is used to:
(*a*) calculate the permeability of an iron sample. (*b*) calculate the currents and voltage drops in complicated networks. (*c*) correct the heat loss in a load resistor. (*d*) match a series circuit to a parallel circuit.
3) The reciprocity theorem states that
(*a*) action and reaction are equal and opposite. (*b*) a generator and an ammeter may be interchanged in any system of linear impedances, and the E/I ratio remains unchanged. (*c*) any series circuit has an equivalent parallel circuit. (*d*) the Q of an inductor is equal to the Q of the associated capacitor in a resonant circuit.
4) Thevenin's theorem permits:
(*a*) measurement of voltage with a wattmeter. (*b*) measurement of source resistance at the output terminals of any network. (*c*) calculation of the radiated field from a nonlinear inductor. (*d*) easy derivation of a simple equivalent circuit for a complicated network on the basis of a voltage measurement and a resistance measurement.
5) A pair of conjugate impedances have:
(*a*) zero internal resistance. (*b*) equal resistances, and equal phase angles. (*c*) equal resistances, and equal but opposite phase angles. (*d*) infinite internal resistance.
6) Conjugate impedances exhibit:
(*a*) series resonance. (*b*) parallel resonance. (*c*) series-parallel resonance. (*d*) double-frequency resonance.
7) If the magnitude of a load impedance may be varied, but not its phase angle, maximum power will be transferred when:
(*a*) the magnitude is zero. (*b*) the magnitude is infinite. (*c*) the magnitude is equal to the power factor. (*d*) the absolute magnitude of the load impedance is equal to the absolute magnitude of the generator's internal impedance.
8) The superposition theorem cannot be applied to circuits which have:
(*a*) linear impedances. (*b*) nonlinear impedances. (*c*) linear inductances. (*d*) linear resistances.

9) Mesh analysis procedures apply to:
(*a*) d-c circuits only. (*b*) a-c circuits only. (*c*) either a-c circuits or to d-c circuits. (*d*) neither a-c circuits nor d-c circuits.
10) If the direction of current flow is incorrectly assigned in a mesh analysis, the calculated value of the current will be:
(*a*) negative. (*b*) positive. (*c*) imaginary. (*d*) zero.

PROBLEMS

1) With reference to Figure 23-1, calculate the value of I_T if $E_1 = 6$ volts, $E_2 = 3$ volts, $R_1 = 4$ ohms, $R_2 = 6$ ohms, and $R_3 = 8$ ohms.
2) If the polarity of E_1 is reversed in Problem 1, what is the value of I_T?
3) If the polarity of E_1 is reversed in Problem 1, and its value changed to 3 volts, what is the value of I_T?
4) If the value of I_2 is 1 amp in Figure 23-5, the generator and ammeter are interchanged, and the generator speed is increased to double its terminal voltage, what is the current value indicated by the ammeter?
5) With reference to Figure 23-6, the open-circuit voltage between terminals (1) and (2) measures 50 volts. When the generator is stopped, an ohmmeter measures 100 ohms between terminals (1) and (2). If you start the generator and connect a 10-ohm resistance between terminals (1) and (2), what is the value of current flow through the 10-ohm resistance?
6) If $R_1 = 10$ ohms, $R_2 = 20$ ohms, and $R_3 = 30$ ohms in Figure 23-6(*a*), what is the corresponding value of R_T in Figure 23-6(*d*)?
7) If the generator in Figure 23-7 has an internal impedance of $10 + j5$, what value of impedance must be provided by C and R_2 to obtain maximum power transfer?
8) If the generator in Figure 23-7 has an internal impedance of $10 + j5$, and the reactance of C is fixed at a value of $-j2$, what value of R_2 will you choose to obtain maximum power transfer?
9) Calculate the value of the power factor in Problem 8.
10) Suppose that C in Problem 8 is replaced by an inductor which has a fixed value of $j3$. What value of R_2 will you choose to obtain maximum power transfer?

REVIEW SUMMARY

Chapters 16 through 23 have been concerned with laws of electricity and electronics, and with basic devices. The following review summary presents the fundamental principles with which you should now be familiar.

1. Transformers are designed to step voltage, current, or impedance up or down, to pass a chosen band of frequencies, and to provide d-c isolation from input to output.

2. The general power-transformer equation states that in the ideal situation, the product of primary voltage and current is equal to the product of secondary voltage and current.

3. Voltage step-up or step-down in an ideal power transformer is directly proportional to the turns ratio of the secondary to the primary winding.

4. Current step-up or step-down in an ideal power transformer is inversely proportional to the turns ratio of the secondary to the primary winding.

5. Impedance step-up or step-down in an ideal power transformer is directly proportional to the square of the turns ratio of the secondary to the primary winding.

6. Power input is equal to power output in an ideal power transformer.

7. The primary of a power transformer is wound with a sufficient number of turns to provide substantial reactance (negligible no-load current demand) at the chosen frequency of operation.

8. A shell-type core provides minimum leakage reactance in a power transformer.

9. Cores fabricated from conducting substances (such as transformer iron) are laminated to provide minimum eddy-current loss.

10. Good transformer iron has a hysteresis curve which encloses only a small area.

11. Core cross-section must be sufficiently large to avoid magnetic saturation at maximum rated power output.

12. Tuned transformers have high leakage reactance and are used to pass a chosen range of frequencies.

13. Secondary loading broadens the pass band of a tuned transformer.

14. Fleming's left-hand rule for motor action states that if your forefinger points in the direction of magnetic flux, and your middle finger points in the direction of conventional current flow, your thumb then points in the direction of force exerted on the conductor.

15. The force in pounds exerted on a conductor is equal to $8.85BIL/10^{-8}$, where B is the flux density in lines per square inch, L is the length in inches of the conductor in the field, and I is the current flow in amperes.

16. Torque is the product of force by the radius through which the force acts.

17. A conductor that moves in a magnetic field in response to current flow generates a counter emf which opposes the applied voltage.

18. An ideal motor provides an output in horsepower which is equal to the product of current flow by counter emf, divided by 746.

19. The d'Arsonval meter movement operates on the motor principle.

20. Direct-current voltmeters utilize a movement connected in series with a multiplier resistor.

21. Direct-current voltmeters are rated for sensitivity in terms of ohms-per-volt.

22. Direct-current current meters comprise a movement connected in parallel with a shunt resistor.

23. An ohmmeter comprises a movement, resistive network, and an internal battery.

24. Alternating-current voltmeters are similar to d-c voltmeters except that an instrument rectifier is connected in series with the movement.

25. Electrodynamometer instruments indicate real power values regardless of the input waveform.

26. Vacuum tubes utilize electron flow in "empty" space; electrons are commonly launched into space by thermal emission, termed the Edison effect.

27. Diode vacuum tubes comprise a cathode and a plate. The Fleming valve was the first application of the Edison effect in high-frequency rectification.

28. Triode vacuum tubes comprise a diode construction with a control grid inserted between cathode and plate. A triode operates as an amplifier.

29. Tetrode vacuum tubes comprise a triode construction with an electrostatic shield (screen grid) inserted between control grid and plate.

30. Pentode vacuum tubes comprise a tetrode construction with a suppressor grid inserted between screen grid and plate.

31. Gas-filled tubes contain neon, nitrogen, argon, or mercury vapor, and are used as electronic switches, rectifiers, or voltage regulators.

32. Phototubes utilize photo-emissive cathodes; a phototube changes light energy into electrical energy.

33. Semiconductor devices generally employ junction action which entails electron and hole flow with respect to a potential gradient.

34. A semiconductor diode operates as a rectifier.

35. Tunnel diodes have a negative-resistance characteristic and operate as amplifiers.

36. Basic transistors have two junctions and operate as amplifiers.

37. Transistors are utilized in common-base, common-emitter, and common-collector configurations.

38. The basic parameter of a transistor is its α or β value.

39. Semiconductor photodiodes and phototransistors are analogous to phototubes.

40. Filters are generally classified into low-pass, high-pass, and band-pass types.

41. A filter has a flat pass characteristic if it comprises specified relations among L, C, and R values.

42. Power-supply filters are low-pass networks which have a cutoff frequency close to d-c (zero frequency).

43. The superposition theorem states that the current flow produced by generators in a linear network can be found by considering the generators separately and taking the algebraic sum of the separate currents.

44. Mesh analysis provides useful strategy in solution of complex networks.

45. The reciprocity theorem states that in any system of linear impedances, if a voltage E is applied between any two terminals, and the current flow I is measured in any branch, their ratio will be equal to the ratio obtained when the positions of E and I are interchanged.

46. Thevenin's theorem states that the current in any impedance Z, connected to two terminals of a network, is the same current which would flow if Z were connected to an ideal generator which applies a voltage equal to the open-circuit voltage of the two network terminals, and which has an internal impedance equal to the impedance of the network, looking back from the two network terminals, when all generators are replaced by their internal impedances.

APPENDIX I

APPLIED MATHEMATICS

Prehistoric man had little language and less mathematics. Our recorded history of mathematics starts with the Ahmes papyrus, written about 2000 B.C. It states a few simple laws of measurement, and is titled *Directions for Obtaining the Knowledge of All Dark Things.* Applied mathematics, particularly surveying, is stressed by Ahmes. This is an exceedingly interesting circumstance, since it proves that applied mathematics precedes pure mathematics.

What is mathematics? Most authorities define mathematics as a science, or as an art and science, based on counting. We must not suppose that human beings are the only creatures who can count. If a dog has a small litter, she knows immediately whether one of her pups may be missing. Jackdaws have been trained to count up to three or four. Chimpanzees can be taught the most basic elements of arithmetic. It has been found that Australian aborigines can count up to three. Beyond three, all numbers are simply classified by them as "the many."

Mathematics is an *exact* science. For example, we say that two plus two equals four *exactly*. We laugh if someone suggests that two and two are approximately four. However, in everyday life, it is impossible to find separate objects that are identical or equal in *every* respect. This "1" which I write is *exactly* equal to this next "1" which I write. The separate "1's" are exactly equal simply by *definition*. It is not so in the physical domain. If you attempt to find two oranges that are *exactly* similar in *every* respect, you shall find it impossible. Accordingly, we can count oranges only by disregarding their individual differences. This is the most basic distinction between pure mathematics and applied mathematics.

Until we stop to think, we do not clearly realize what we are doing when we count. If we count oranges, we are setting up a one-to-one correspondence between "1's" in the domain of pure mathematics, and separate oranges that are only approximately the same in all respects. Thus, in the physical domain, one plus one equals *approximately* two in a very important sense. Until we abstract an ideal concept from the physical situation, we are quite unable to count physical objects at all, and to set up a one-to-one correspondence which translates back and forth between the domains of pure mathematics and physics.

WHY WE COUNT LIKE HUMAN BEINGS

We use the decimal system when we count because we have ten fingers. Scientists thus far have been unable to explain why we have five fingers on each hand which are arranged in mirror symmetry. It is a

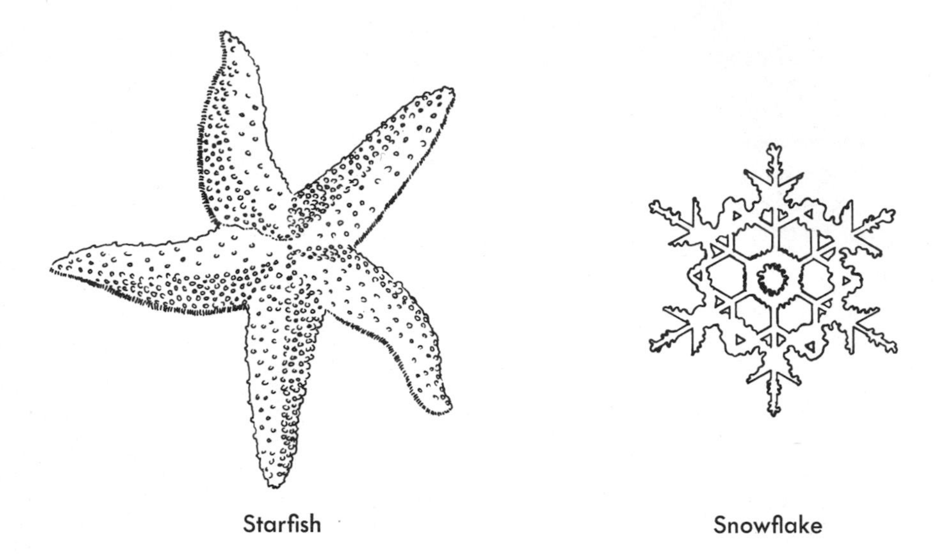

Figure A1
Symmetrical five-membered and six-membered organic and inorganic structures.

curious fact that protoplasm (living substance) has evolved into symmetrical five-membered organs. Figure A1 illustrates the five-membered structure of a starfish and the six-membered structure of a snowflake. It is impossible to find any inorganic structure that has a symmetrical five-membered configuration.

Historically, counting operations developed in the framework of applied mathematics. Thus, our antediluvian ancestors made the assumption that fingers are identical or equal in every respect when they discovered how to count. If you have gone to a school which teaches the new math, you know that Roman notation symbolizes the fingers. Figure A2 depicts how the Roman system of notation symbolizes the first three fingers. This is a primitive example of applied mathematics. Since the fingers are assumed to be identical in every respect, it is just as logical to let "I" symbolize the little finger, and to count from right to left.

Although the I's can be repeated indefinitely, a large collection becomes confusing and cannot be easily read. Hence, the Romans developed simplified symbols for "four" and "five." Their symbol "V" stands for all five fingers, as illustrated in Figure A3. In turn, the Roman numeral "IV" symbolizes the finger *before* V, when counting from left to right. Note that the concept of subtraction is also implicit in the symbol "IV," since it denotes five less one. The Roman symbol "VI" symbolizes a finger

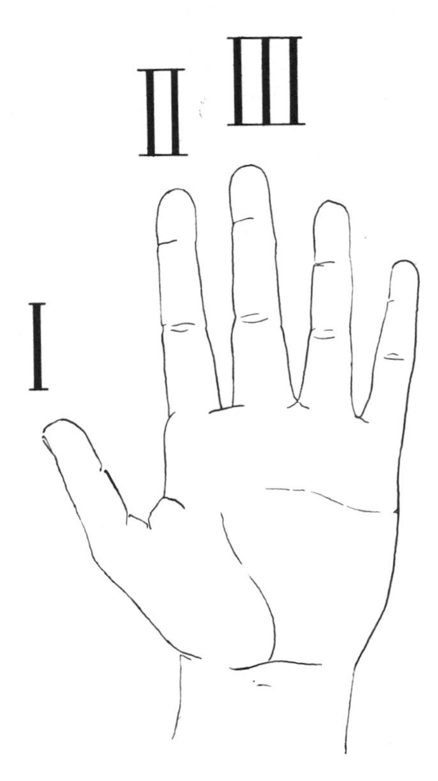

Figure A2
Origin of the first three Roman numerals.

after "V" (on the next hand), and implies the concept of addition, since it denotes one more than five.

Similarly, VII and VIII identify successive fingers. The Roman symbol "X" is a *shorthand* symbol for all the fingers on both hands, as shown in Figure A4. In turn, "IX" denotes the finger *before* the last finger on the second hand. Their symbol "XI" denotes the finger *after* the last, on still another hand, or starting over again on the first hand. We are very familiar with symbols such as V because they are used on clock dials, in chapter headings, and on architectural facades. An earlier and more complex symbol for all the fingers on one hand is seen in Figure A5. This ancient symbolization is still used today in tally procedures.

What is the origin of the Roman symbol "L"? This is illustrated in Figure A6. It appears that the Romans achieved this shorthand by letting each finger stand for all the fingers on both hands. Thus, the symbol L probably represented a "handful of tens." The origin of other Roman

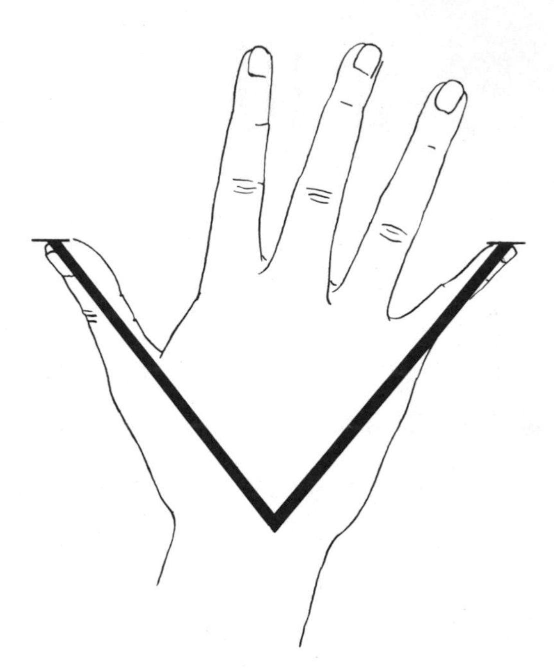

Figure A3
Origin of the Roman numeral V.

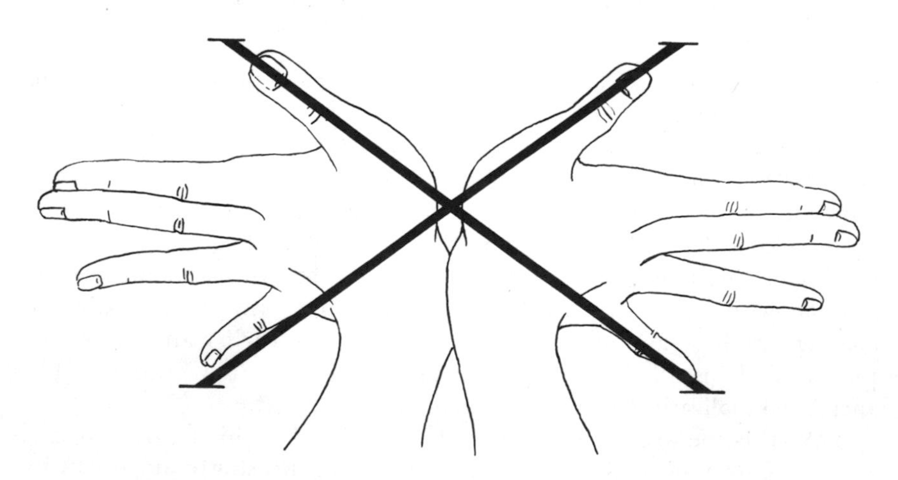

Figure A4
Origin of the Roman numeral X.

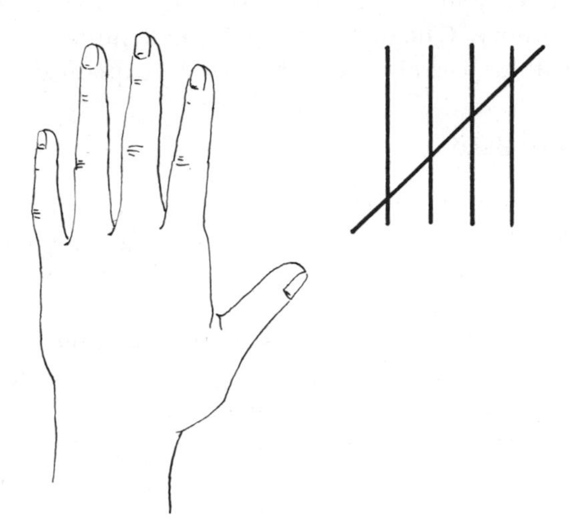

Figure A5
An ancient symbolic representation of a hand.

Figure A6
Representation of a "handful of tens."

symbols such as "C" and "M" is more doubtful, and is largely lost in the mists of early history. Calculation with Roman numerals is almost forbiddingly difficult for several reasons that will be explained.

THE DISCOVERY OF ZERO

Roman thought was extremely objective, and this preoccupation with tangible objects prevented them from conceiving of a symbol for "no fingers," or *zero*. Somewhat later in recorded history, Persia, Arabia, and India developed civilizations which discoursed of counting operations in deeply subjective form. These ancients were preoccupied with the inner vision, and their thought was basically abstract. After pure mathematics was better distinguished from applied mathematics, the discovery of zero was imminent. Subsequently, the concept of zero was applied also to physical situations.

Our particular form of decimal notation, which expresses numbers through powers of ten, thus comprising nine digits and zero, was invented in India. One major achievement of the Hindus was the concept of zero, a cipher corresponding to the metaphysical nothing, or naught. Mathematically, zero is defined by the equations:

$$A + 0 = A \tag{A1.1}$$

$$A \times 0 = 0 \tag{A1.2}$$

Calculation with the Hindu-Arabic notation is easy, and as we know, many problems in arithmetic can be solved mentally without the aid of pencil and paper. The essential Hindu-Arabic concepts are those of

$$\begin{cases} \text{Position} \\ \text{Zero} \\ \text{Addition} \end{cases}$$

For example, 425 denotes four hundreds, plus two tens, plus five units. It is most interesting to trace the development of Hindu-Arabic numerals. Figure A7 illustrates the highlights of the most probable steps, as disclosed by classical scholars. The first step was to make collections of units more recognizable at a glance. Thereby, it became easy to read any numerical symbol rapidly and easily.

It is a curious circumstance that "sloppy writing" of the scribes contributed to modern notation. Rapid writing of symbols resulted in leaving diagonal strokes between units, so that the symbol could be written without lifting pen from paper. Furthermore, upright strokes in some symbols were changed into horizontal strokes—the original symbol was evidently turned over on its side. The symbols then evolved into our present-day forms. Note that the original symbol for zero was a dot. This was eventually enlarged into a circle, to have the same height as its fellow symbols.

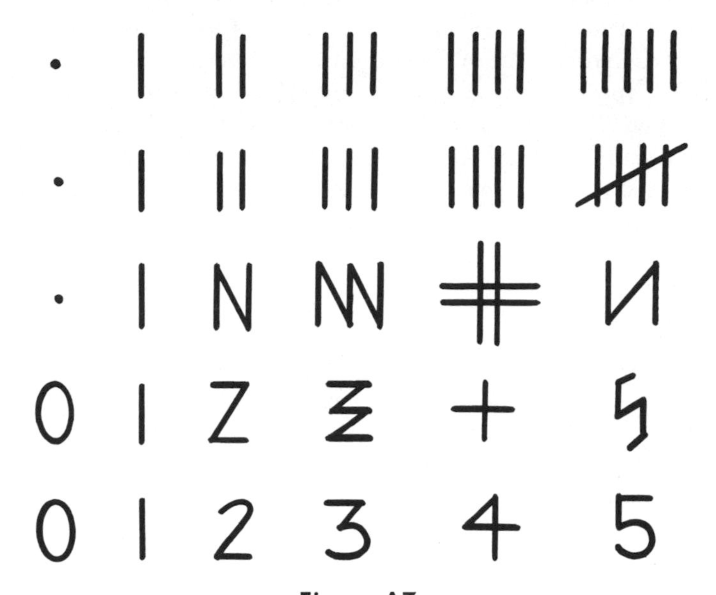

Figure A7

Some basic steps in development of Hindu-Arabic numerals.

Invention of the symbol for zero was an outstanding achievement. The concept of *position,* as in expression of "425," ranked next in importance. It perhaps comes as a surprise to learn that *decimal* notation, which expresses numbers through powers of ten, is of no great significance—it is merely a historical accident in our cultural tradition. The Hindu-Arabic system, which comprises nine digits followed by "10," is based simply on the circumstance that human beings have ten fingers. But we also have ten toes, which leads to the *vigesimal* system of counting. We shall find that the vigesimal system is practically as useful as the decimal system. Again, electronic computers have neither fingers nor toes; a computer must count "on" and "off" in the immensely important *binary* system.

Finger-and-Toe Arithmetic

The Mayas, like the Eskimos, counted on both fingers and toes. Hence, the all-but-forgotten Mayan civilization introduced a series of nineteen digits followed by the first digit and zero. This is called the *vigesimal* system. Our "20" was represented by a symbol similar to "I0." The unit "I" occupies the position which represents *twenty units* plus no units. Clearly, it is merely a historical accident that we inherited the decimal system instead of the vigesimal system. On the other hand, the Western world did not inherit the binary system—it was invented by an English mathematician and logician named George Boole.

It must not be supposed that the vigesimal system is difficult to use. In fact, it is almost as easy to solve problems with the vigesimal system as with the decimal system. We are merely exposed to the decimal system from early childhood, and have it ingrained in subconscious thought processes. Eskimos find our decimal system difficult and confusing on first acquaintance. It is always difficult to speak other than mother-languages fluently. Yet, with persistence, we may learn Latin, French, and the vigesimal system of mathematical language. One is no more difficult than another.

The Past Lives On

Vestiges of the past are found in mathematical language; we still use Roman numerals on clock dials, in chapter headings, and to denote dates on architectural facades. Our time measure retains certain features of the Greek *sexagesimal* system, based on powers of sixty. Thus, we assign 60 min to 1 hour, and 60 sec to 1 min. The Greeks had little application for still smaller units of time, and hence, our own civilization has provided them. Curiously, we have provided this subdivision decimally, into milliseconds and microseconds. However, we are quite used to our hybrid system of time subdivision.

It would seem very confusing if we were to subdivide the hour into 100 min and the minute into 100 sec. Yet, this would be entirely consistent in our structure of mathematical language. Our angular measure also retains certain features of the Greek sexagesimal system. Thus, we assign 360 degrees to a complete circle; we define 1 degree as 60 min; we define 1 min as 60 sec. What is the origin of the sexagesimal system? It is evidently based on the ancient belief that a year comprises 360 days.

Yet, our time measure and angular measure retains only certain features of the Greek sexagesimal system. The Greeks used letters, as did the Romans, to denote numerals. Their thought was deeply subjective; however, the Greeks failed to conceive of a symbol for zero. They honored geometry far above arithmetic, although the Greeks did occupy themselves with the theory of numbers. It is probable that their primary concern with geometry veered them away from the concept of the metaphysical nothing, or naught. In the language of modern mathematics, we do well to quote Samuel Beckett, who observed in *Malone Dies* that nothing is more real than nothing.

The Binary System

Modern electronic computers (see Figure A8) perform addition and subtraction in the binary system. This system employs one digit and zero. The essential ideas are those of position, zero, and addition, as in the

Figure A8
Modern electronic computers. (Courtesy of IBM.)

decimal system. Circuit-switching operations are best adapted to the use of one digit and zero. Figure A9 illustrates how zero, one, two, three, and four are represented in the binary system. Note the following comparison:

Binary	*Decimal*
0	0
1	1
10	2
11	3
100	4

The base of the binary system is 2. Note in Figure A9 that zero is represented by 0×2^2 plus 0×2^1 plus 0×2^0. Next, one is represented by 0×2^2 plus 0×2^1 plus 1×2^0. Two is represented by 0×2^2 plus 1×2^1 plus 0×2^0; three is represented by 0×2^2 plus 1×2^1 plus 1×2^0. Finally, four is represented by 1×2^2 plus 0×2^1 plus 0×2^0. The binary system is not well suited to ordinary calculation because even small numbers have many positions occupied. For example, the decimal number 4 occupies three positions (and is written as 100) in the binary system. Engineers and computer programmers must necessarily become very adept in binary-system calculation.

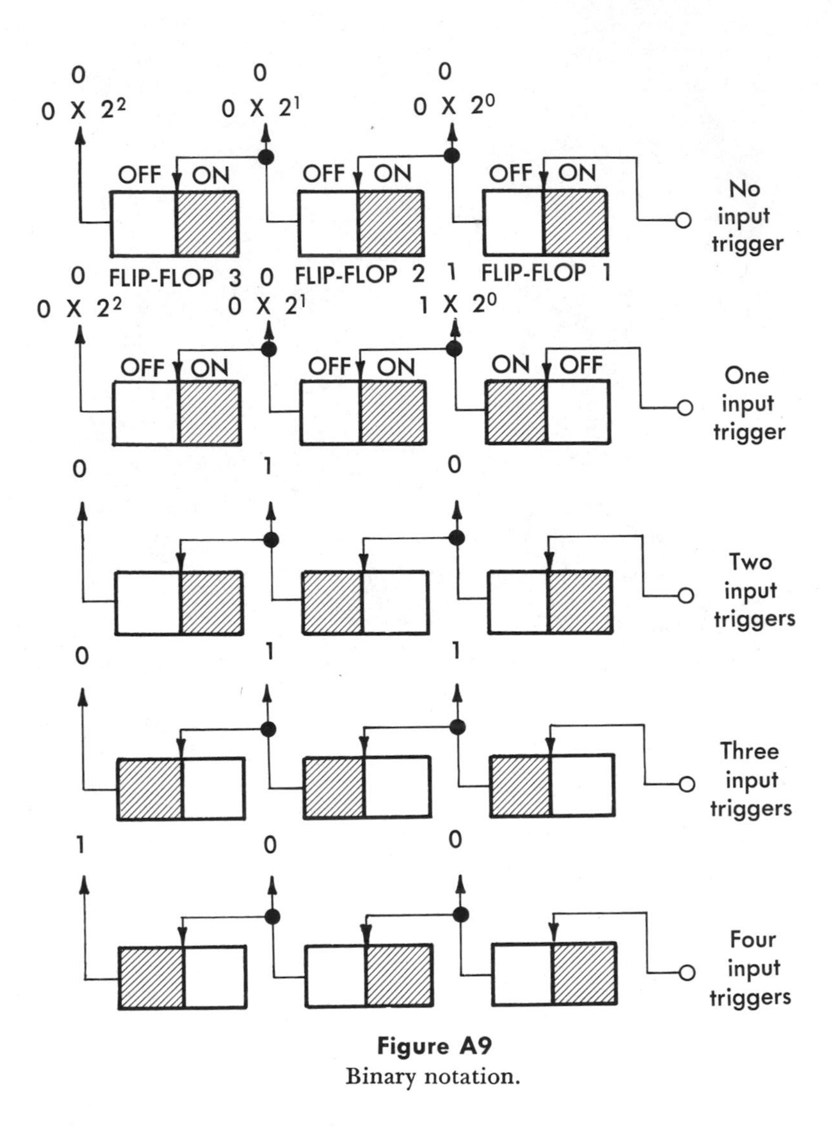

Figure A9
Binary notation.

Application of Mathematics

Absolute precision exists only in the domain of mathematics. Thus, the so-called exact sciences are at base no more exact than their *correspondences* which may be found with the domain of mathematics. Our descriptions of physical situations are no more exact than our precision of measurement. In the domain of mathematics, everything is perfect. In the domain of physics, nothing is perfect. In turn, it is not surprising to find that mathematical formulas often fit physical situations poorly, and that the formulas we use may yield absurd answers. We call manifestly absurd answers nonphysical solutions, and reject them out-of-hand. In some instances, we are puzzled. We cannot determine whether a mathematical answer may or may not describe a characteristic of the physical situation. Careful investigation may show that the answer does indeed describe a physical characteristic that was overlooked at the outset. On the other hand, the answer may be found merely absurd.

Furthermore, an equation such as $I = E/R$ implies no boundary limits. Application requires assignment of certain limits. For example, we know that if a metal is cooled to the vicinity of absolute zero, Ohm's law does not apply as stated. Infinitely large voltages and currents are not attainable in practice, although the equation imposes no such limits. Hence, an equation really tells us only how to calculate a result within boundary limits that must be empirically determined.

Thus, when we apply mathematics to physical objects and situations, we attempt to discuss the real world in terms of the ideal world of mathematics. Suppose that we are given the cross-sectional area of a circular conductor, and are required to calculate its radius. In the language of mathematics, the area of a circle is related to its radius by the formula:

$$A = \pi r^2 \tag{A1.3}$$

or,

$$r = \pm\sqrt{A/\pi} \tag{A1.4}$$

In turn, if the area of the circle is equal to pi sq in., the formula states that its radius is equal to +1 in. or −1 in. We observe that the answer of −1 in. is absurd, and reject it as nonphysical. But this answer arose because the mathematical language is more general than the physical situation; that is, conductors with negative radius (radius less than zero) do not exist in the physical domain. However, mathematical language includes both positive and negative numbers. We next ask whether there are situations in the everyday world which are discussed mathematically in terms of negative numbers. We soon find that there are, indeed, many such situations.

The ancients developed mathematics with negative numbers in order to calculate debts. If you overdraw your bank account by $100, then your account is represented as −$100. If you go twice as deeply in debt, your bank account becomes 2 × (−$100) = −$200. On the other hand, suppose you go twice as much out of debt. Your bank account becomes −2 × (−$100) = +$200. Note that you have subtracted from your debt, instead of adding to it. Hence, it is easy to see that the multiplication of two negative numbers is necessarily and logically a positive number. This is the significance of the negative answer in Equation (A1.4). The square of a negative radius would indeed correspond to a positive area, if the negative radius should have physical existence.

We see that the debt concept involves a reference point of zero. Now, let us consider a physical situation in which we reject the positive answer and retain the negative answer. For example, there are two temperatures below freezing (0°C), one of which is 1° higher than the other, and wherein the product of the two temperatures is 600. What are the temperatures? This problem is stated mathematically

$$T(T+1) = 600 \qquad \textbf{(A1.5)}$$

or,

$$T^2 + T - 600 = 0 \qquad \textbf{(A1.6)}$$

This formula states that T is equal to $-25°$, or to $+24°$. We conclude that the positive answer is not possible under the conditions of our problem. Hence, we retain the negative answer, and the temperatures sought are $-25°$ and $-24°$. Observe how similar this temperature problem is to a debt problem.

Mathematics does not predict anything; however, a seemingly absurd answer might point out a physical characteristic that had been overlooked at the outset. For example, consider the L pad depicted in Figure A10.

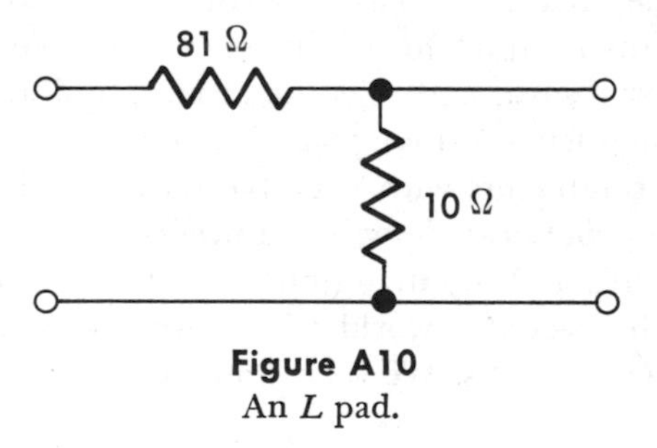

Figure A10
An L pad.

What is its characteristic resistance? There are at least two ways of finding this value. The customary method is to terminate the pad with the unknown, and solve for R_{in}, as indicated in Figure A11. This is a simple series-parallel circuit, leading to the quadratic equation

$$R_{in} = \frac{81 \pm \sqrt{6561 + 3240}}{2} \qquad \textbf{(A1.7)}$$

We find that $R_{in} = 90$ ohms, or -9 ohms. Let us be careful before we

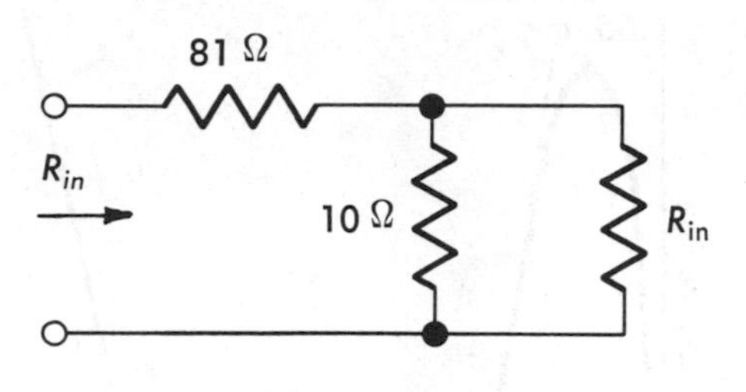

Figure A11
The value of R_{in} is sought.

reject the negative answer. It reminds us that negative resistance is a real physical parameter, although we had perhaps overlooked this fact. If the L section is terminated by a negative-resistance source with a value of −9 ohms, the input resistance to the section becomes −9 ohms. However, there is a *boundary condition* in Figure A12. The circuit will be stable only if the load line intersects the resistance characteristic at *one* point, as depicted in Figure A12. The slope of the load line is determined

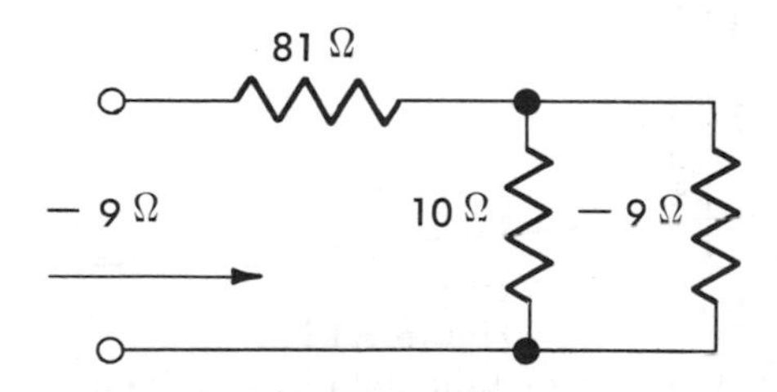

Figure A12
Negative resistance is exhibited across the input terminals.

by the value of positive resistance shunting the −9 ohms in Figure A13. Hence, stability will exist only if the absolute value of the positive resistance is less than the absolute value of the negative resistance (−9 ohms). Obviously, the configuration in Figure A12 does not meet this requirement—the absolute value of 10 ohms is greater than that of −9 ohms. Hence, the circuit is unstable and cannot operate in the manner implied by the mathematical language.

Next, let us introduce a new boundary condition. Referring to Figure A14, we have connected a battery across the input terminals of the L section. The battery has practically zero internal resistance. Hence, the

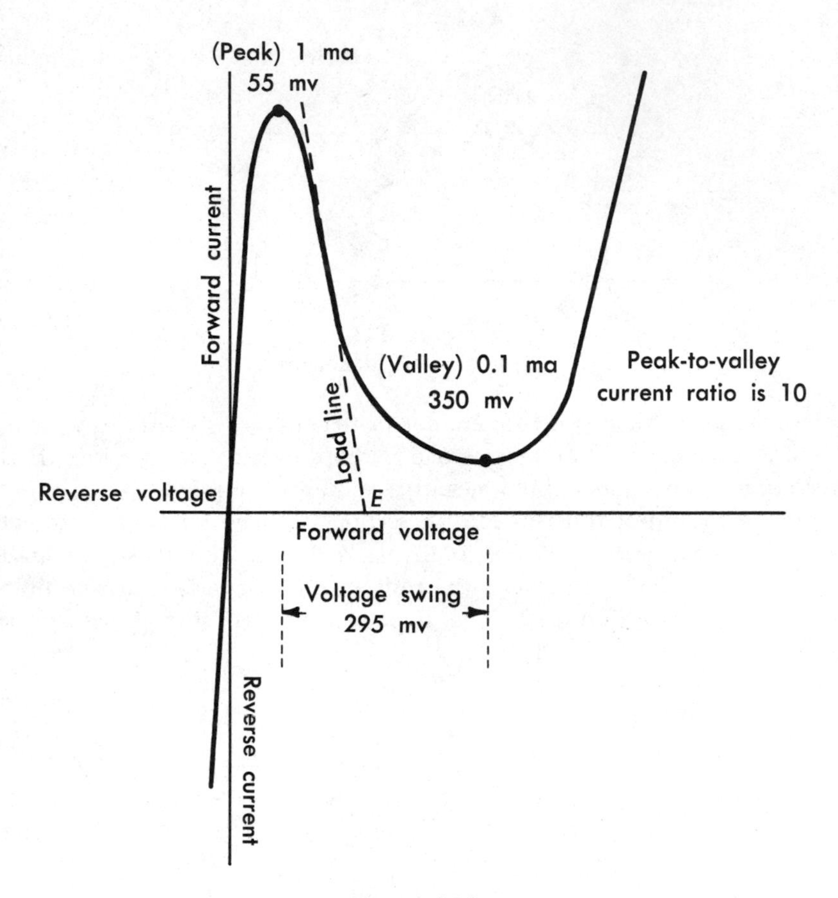

Figure A13
Illustration of the stability condition.

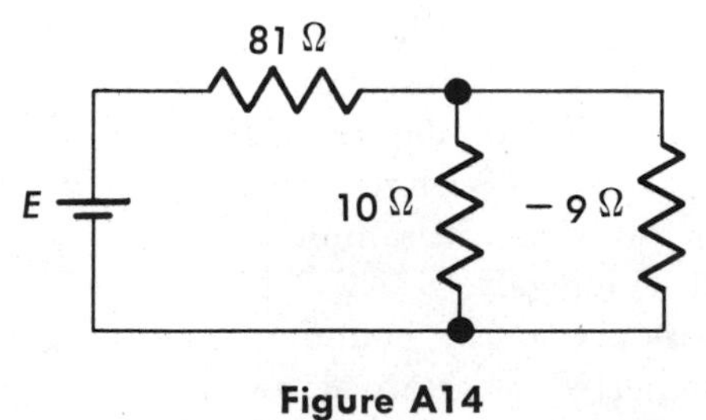

Figure A14
A stable configuration.

−9 ohm resistance is shunted by a positive resistance of 8.9+ ohms. This value fulfills the stability requirement. Hence, the circuit is stable and operates in the manner implied by the mathematical language. But mathematics did not actually predict anything at all. All that mathematics has done is to tell us how to calculate results within the limits of known boundary conditions. The Greeks supposed that all the facts of the real world could be deduced from pure mathematics. Today, we dismiss this concept as completely unfounded and undemonstrated.

There is usually more than one mathematical approach to a problem. Let us see how another approach to the characteristic resistance of a ladder network affords a positive answer only. Consider Figure A15(*a*).

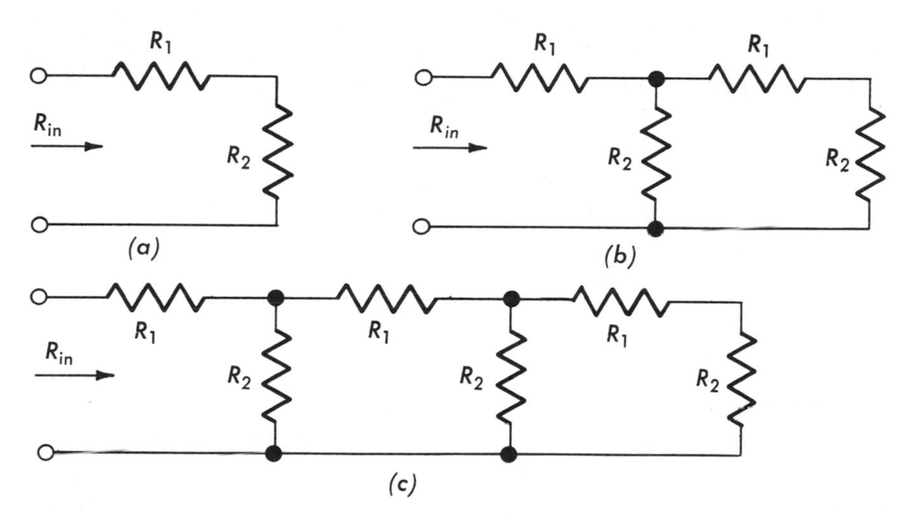

Figure A15
Ladder networks can be analyzed by continued fractions.

The input resistance R_{in} is obviously equal to $R_1 + R_2$. If we continue adding similar *L* sections, we know that we will approach the value of the characteristic resistance as a limit. Calculation of the input resistance can be made by the use of continued fractions. It is accomplished as follows: With reference to Figure A15(*b*), we note that $R_1 + R_2$ is in shunt to R_2 of the first section. Now, let us express the input resistance to Figure A15(*b*) in terms of the reciprocal of the reciprocals, as we have previously learned.

$$R_{\text{in}} = R_1 + \cfrac{1}{\cfrac{1}{R_2} + \cfrac{1}{R_1 + R_2}} \tag{A1.8}$$

This equation contains only positive resistance values; it cannot give a negative-resistance answer. Next, let us add another L section at the input end of the ladder, as shown in Figure A15(c). The value for R_{in} in Equation (A1.8) will then be reduced by an amount imposed by the resistance in shunt to R_2 in the first section of Figure A15(c). Again, we express the input resistance R_{in} in terms of the reciprocal of the reciprocals:

$$R_{in} = R_1 + \cfrac{1}{\cfrac{1}{R_2} + \cfrac{1}{R_1 + \cfrac{1}{\cfrac{1}{R_2} + \cfrac{1}{R_1 + R_2}}}} \tag{A1.9}$$

Note that this is a *continued fraction*. Its terms in the denominator are repeated again and again, as far out as we choose to carry the calculation. We approach closer and closer to the value of the characteristic resistance for an infinite ladder. The method is comparatively cumbersome, but it illustrates a basic point of applied mathematics: some forms of mathematical language are less general than others. Thus, the attack by means of continued fractions is less general than the attack by quadratic equations, because continued fractions do not provide a negative answer (which is nevertheless physically real within certain boundary conditions).

Curve Fitting by Power Series

When a series of measurements are made, they may be presented in the form of a graph. For example, if we measure the current flowing through a semiconductor diode at various applied voltages, the values plot as a curve. The curve may be used to obtain *graphical solutions* of circuit action, as exemplified in Figure A16. However, it is usually desired to find a formula, if possible, that fits the curve with good accuracy. A widely used method employs the *power series*. A basic understanding of the power series can be obtained from the curves shown in Figure A17. Note that $y = x$ plots as a straight line; $y = x^2$ is a graph that curves upward; $y = x^3$ curves upward more rapidly.

Suppose that the measured data plot as almost a straight line, but that the graph follows a slight upward curvature. Evidently, its formula can be approximated by

$$y = x + kx^2 \tag{A1.10}$$

Clearly, if $k = 0$, the graph becomes a straight line. However, if a small value is assigned to k, the graph will then curve upward slightly. A greater value of k makes the graph curve upward more rapidly. In some

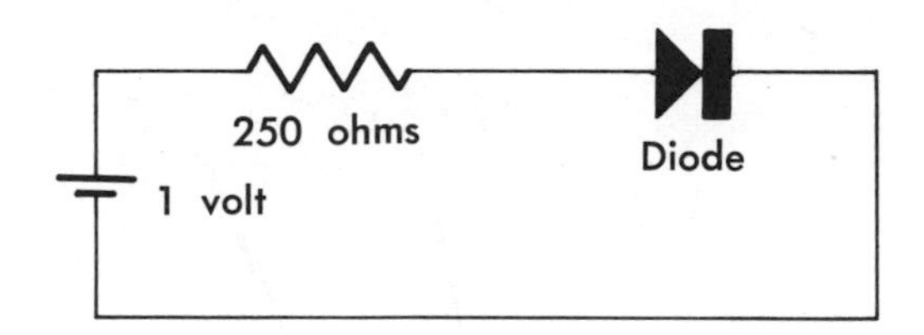

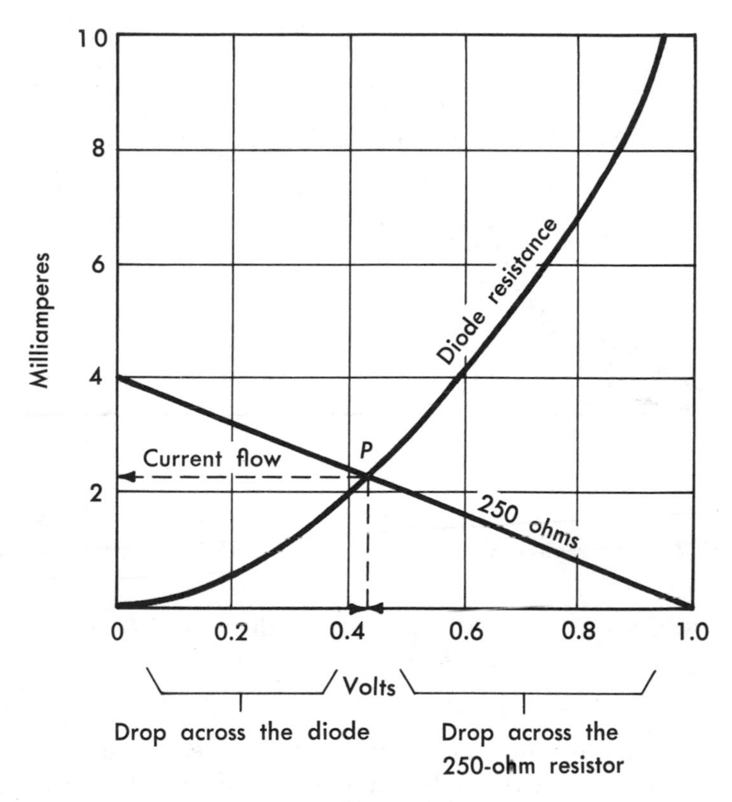

Figure A16

Graphical solution of current value and voltage drops in a diode circuit.

cases, selection of a suitable value for k results in an acceptable "fit." However, if a further fitting is necessary, a cubic term can be added

$$y = x + kx^2 + nx^3 \tag{A1.11}$$

When a suitable value is selected for n, it may be possible to obtain a closer fit than before. A practical example is found in the increase in

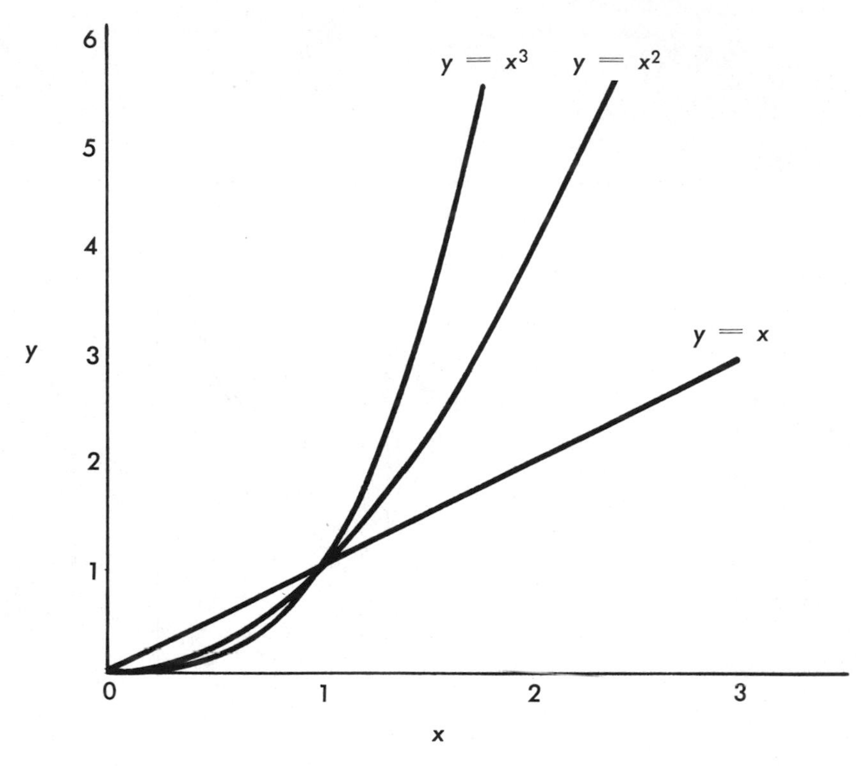

Figure A17
Graphs of $y = x$, $y = x^2$, and $y = x^3$.

length of a wire when heated. If the length of the wire is L_0 at 0°C, its length L_t at a temperature t is given by

$$L_t = L_0\,(1 + at + bt^2 + ct^3) \qquad \textbf{(A1.12)}$$

where a, b, and c are constants, and t is the centigrade temperature.

Again, we recall that the emf of a Weston normal cell varies with temperature according to the formula:

$$E_t = 1.0183\,[1 - 0.0000406(t - 20) - 0.00000095(t - 20)^2] \qquad \textbf{(A1.13)}$$

This is another example of curve fitting by means of a power series. When curvature is gradual, a power series is well adapted to its formulation. But if a curve has a fairly sharp bend, it may be difficult or impossible to formulate the curve satisfactorily with a power series. In this case, two approaches are possible. First, graphical solutions may be used; a very simple example of a graphical solution is depicted in Figure A16. Second, suitable limits may be chosen along the curve within which it can be

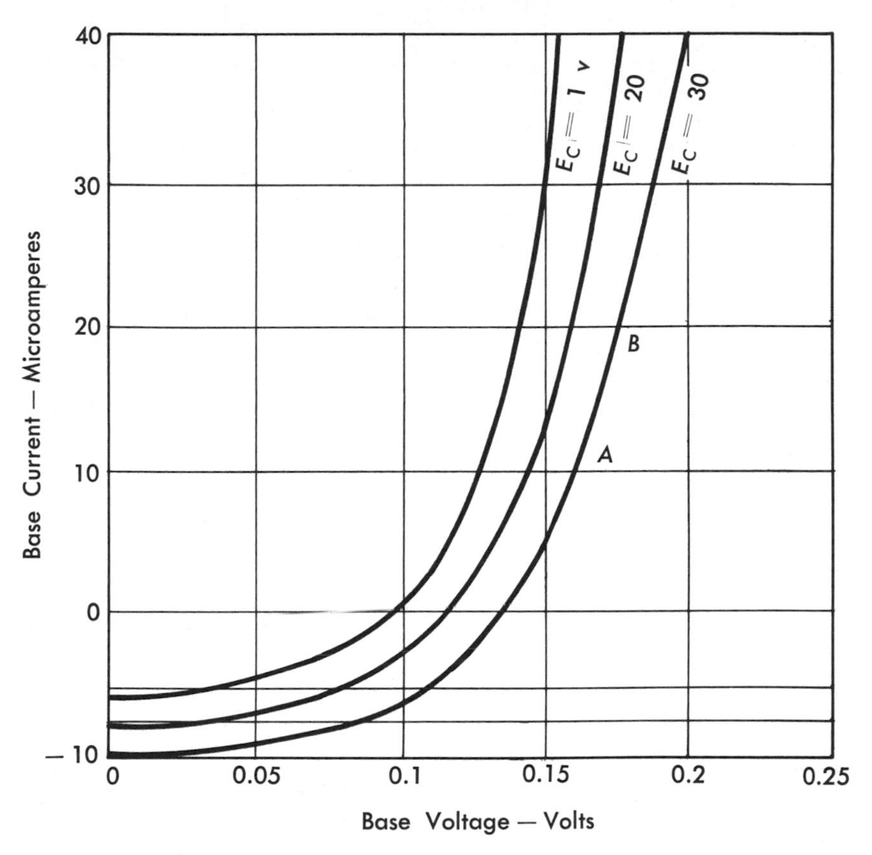

Figure A18
Base current versus base voltage for a typical transistor.

assumed that the graph is linear. For example, the excursion from *A* to *B* in Figure A18 can be assumed linear within a small error.

In still other situations, such as a nonlinear resistance connected in series with a reactance, graphical solution becomes forbiddingly difficult, and assumptions of linearity may represent only a very rough approximation. The engineer first assumes linearity in his attack, in order to obtain a rough answer. Then, he connects an experimental circuit using the values obtained in his calculations. Departures from the desired response are noted, which usually permit assignment of more precise parameters in the calculations. In turn, the experimental circuit is modified using the values obtained from the second calculation. This hybrid analytical and experimental procedure may be repeated several times until the desired response is satisfactorily approximated.

APPENDIX II

RESISTANCE

RMA Preferred Values

Commercial tolerances on resistance values are 5, 10, and 20 percent. RMA preferred values are nominal resistance values that avoid duplication of stock within each tolerance range. The nominal resistance values tabulated below can be multiplied or divided by any power of 10.

TOLERANCE

5%	10%	20%
10	10	10
11		
12	12	
13		
15	15	15
16		
18	18	
20		
22	22	22
24		
27	27	
30		
33	33	33
36		
39	39	39
43		
47	47	47
51		
56	56	
62		
68	68	68
75		
82	82	
91		
100	100	100

RESISTOR COLOR CODES

Three chief color codes are in use to indicate resistance values and tolerances of small resistors. The color-band system is preferred by most manufacturers. Code data depicted below are supplied through the courtesy of Precision Apparatus Co.

RESISTOR CODES (RESISTANCE GIVEN IN OHMS)

Color	Digit	Multiplier	Tolerance
Black	0	1	±20%
Brown	1	10	±1%
Red	2	100	±2%
Orange	3	1000	±3%*
Yellow	4	10000	GMV*
Green	5	100000	±5% (RETMA Alternate)
Blue	6	1000000	±6%*
Violet	7	10000000	±12½%*
Gray	8	.01 (RETMA Alternate)	±30%*
White	9	.1 (RETMA Alternate)	±10% (RETMA Alternate)
Gold		.1 (JAN and RETMA Pref.)	±5% (JAN and RETMA Pref.)
Silver		.01 (JAN and RETMA Pref.)	±10% (JAN and RETMA Pref.)
No color			±20%*

* GMV = guaranteed minimum value, or −0 + 100% tolerance.
±3, 6, 12½, and 30% are ASA 40, 20, 10, and 5 step tolerances.

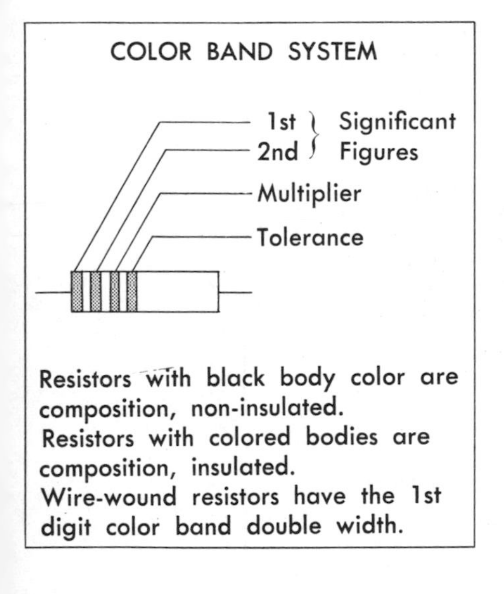

COLOR BAND SYSTEM
1st
2nd
Significant
Figures
Multiplier
Tolerance
Resistors with black body color are composition, non-insulated.
Resistors with colored bodies are composition, insulated.
Wire-wound resistors have the 1st digit color band double width.

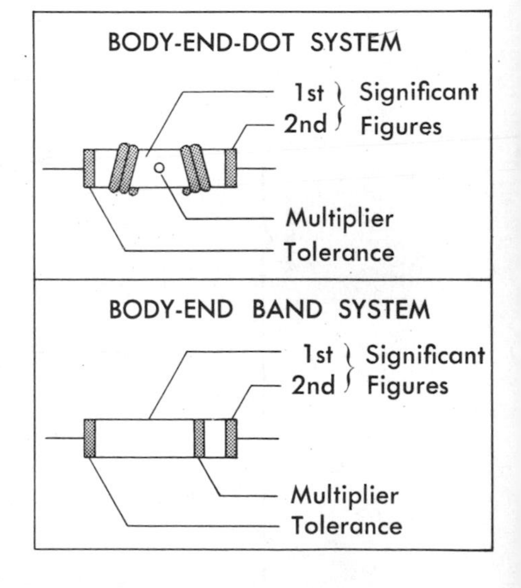

APPENDIX III

DIODE IDENTIFICATION

Various markings and case shapes are used to identify the anode and cathode terminals of semiconductor diodes. The anode terminal corresponds to the plate of a vacuum tube, and the cathode terminal corresponds to the cathode of a vacuum tube. Identification data depicted below are supplied through the courtesy of the Heath Co.

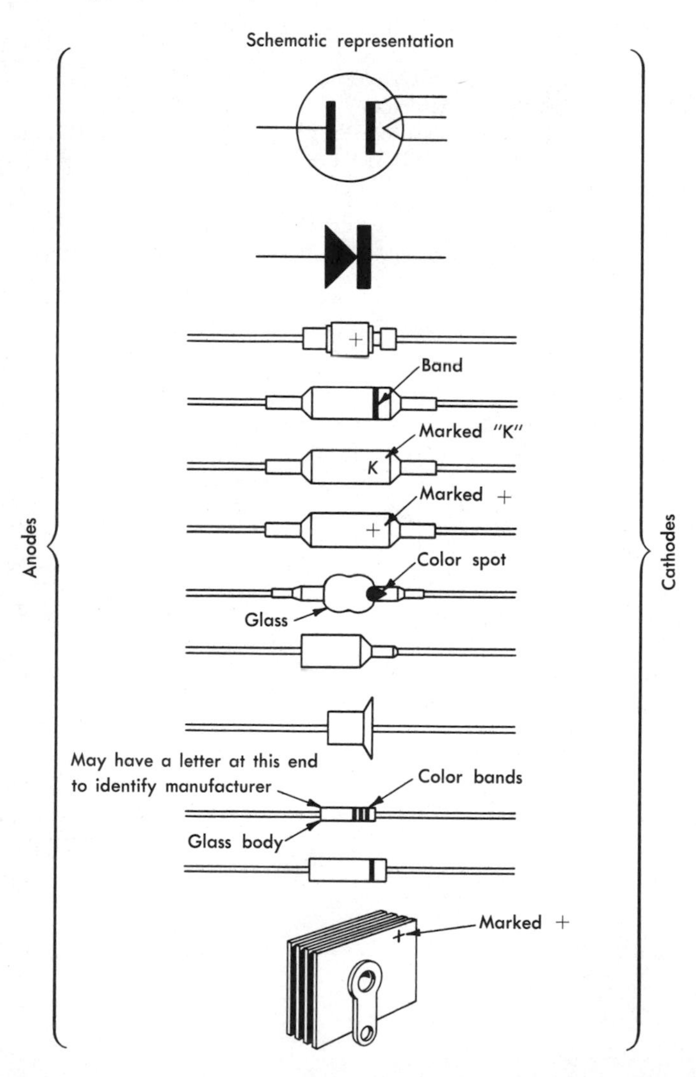

APPENDIX IV

CAPACITOR COLOR CODES

Capacitance values, tolerances, and temperature coefficients are indicated by the color codes depicted below. These data are supplied through the courtesy of the Precision Apparatus Co.

CERAMIC CAPACITOR CODES (CAPACITANCE GIVEN IN MMF)

			Tolerance			Extended range temp. coeff.	
Color	*Digit*	*Multiplier*	*10 mmf or less*	*Over 10 mmf*	*Temperature Coefficient PPM/°C*	*Significant Figure*	*Multiplier*
Black	0	1	±2.0 mmf	±20%	0(NPO)	0.0	−1
Brown	1	10	±0.1 mmf	±1%	−33(N033)		−10
Red	2	100		±2%	−75(N075)	1.0	−100
Orange	3	1000		±2.5%	−150(N150)	1.5	−1000
Yellow	4	10000			−220(N220)	2.2	−10000
Green	5		±0.5 mmf	±5%	−330(N330)	3.3	+1
Blue	6				−470(N470)	4.7	+10
Violet	7				−750(N750)	7.5	+100
Gray	8	.01	±0.25 mmf		+30(P030)		+1000
White	9	.1	±1.0 mmf	±10%	General purpose		+10000
Silver					Bypass & coupling		
Gold					+100(P100) (Jan)		

Ceramic capacitor voltage ratings are standard 500 volts, for some manufacturers, 1000 volts for other manufacturers, unless otherwise specified.

MOLDED PAPER CAPACITOR CODES (CAPACITANCE GIVEN IN MMF)

Color	*Digit*	*Multiplier*	*Tolerance*
Black	0	1	20%
Brown	1	10	
Red	2	100	
Orange	3	1000	
Yellow	4	10000	
Green	5	100000	5%
Blue	6	1000000	
Violet	7		
Gray	8		
White	9		10%
Gold			5%
Silver			10%
No color			20%

	Tolerance	
JAN Letter	*10 mmf or less*	*Over 10 mmf*
C	±0.25 mmf	
D	±0.5 mmf	
F	±1.0 mmf	±1%
G	±2.0 mmf	±2%
J		±5%
K		±10%
M		±20%

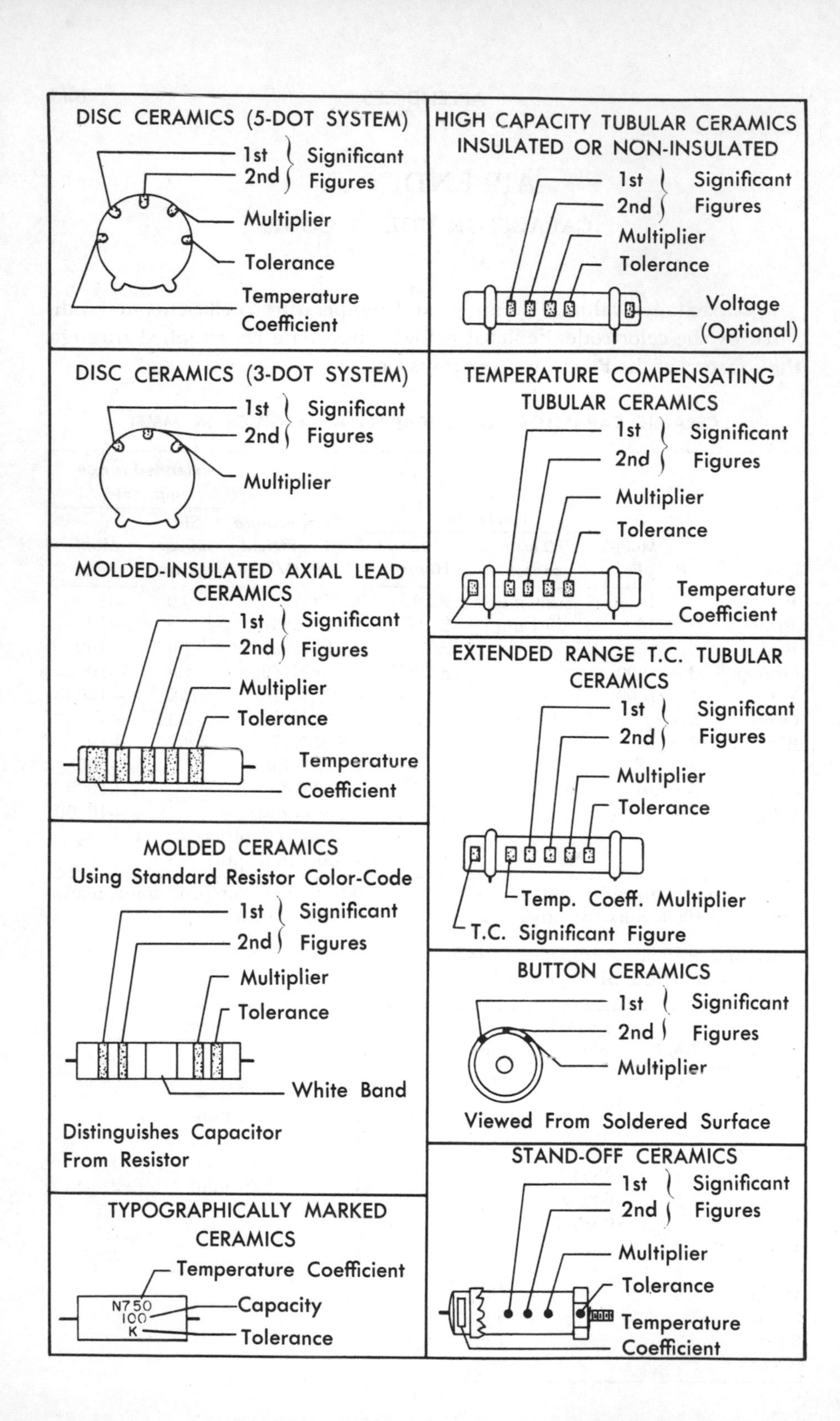

DISC CERAMICS (5-DOT SYSTEM)
1st
2nd
Significant Figures
Multiplier
Tolerance
Temperature Coefficient
HIGH CAPACITY TUBULAR CERAMICS INSULATED OR NON-INSULATED
1st
2nd
Significant Figures
Multiplier
Tolerance
Voltage (Optional)
DISC CERAMICS (3-DOT SYSTEM)
1st
2nd
Significant Figures
Multiplier
TEMPERATURE COMPENSATING TUBULAR CERAMICS
1st
2nd
Significant Figures
Multiplier
Tolerance
Temperature Coefficient
MOLDED-INSULATED AXIAL LEAD CERAMICS
1st
2nd
Significant Figures
Multiplier
Tolerance
Temperature Coefficient
EXTENDED RANGE T.C. TUBULAR CERAMICS
1st
2nd
Significant Figures
Multiplier
Tolerance
Temp. Coeff. Multiplier
T.C. Significant Figure
MOLDED CERAMICS
Using Standard Resistor Color-Code
1st
2nd
Significant Figures
Multiplier
Tolerance
White Band
Distinguishes Capacitor From Resistor
BUTTON CERAMICS
1st
2nd
Significant Figures
Multiplier
Viewed From Soldered Surface
TYPOGRAPHICALLY MARKED CERAMICS
Temperature Coefficient
N750
100
K
Capacity
Tolerance
STAND-OFF CERAMICS
1st
2nd
Significant Figures
Multiplier
Tolerance
Temperature Coefficient

FEED-THRU CERAMICS

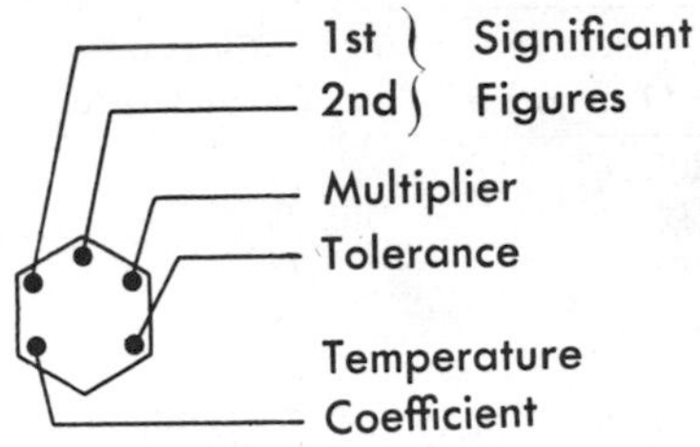

1st } Significant
2nd } Figures
Multiplier
Tolerance
Temperature
Coefficient

CURRENT STANDARD JAN AND RETMA CODE

White (RETMA) Black (JAN)
1st } Significant
2nd } Figures
Multiplier
Tolerance
Class Or Characteristic

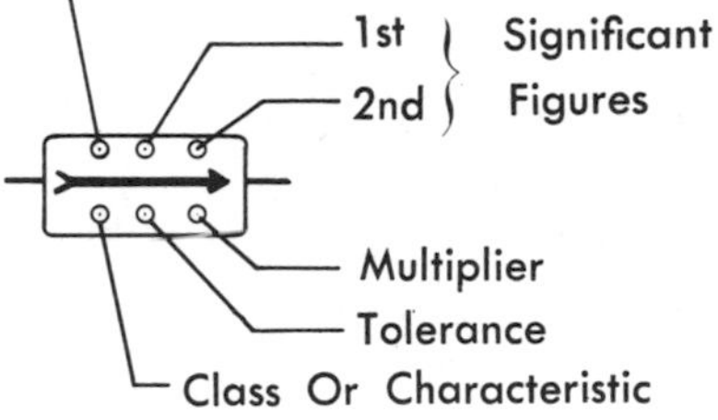

BUTTON SILVER MICA

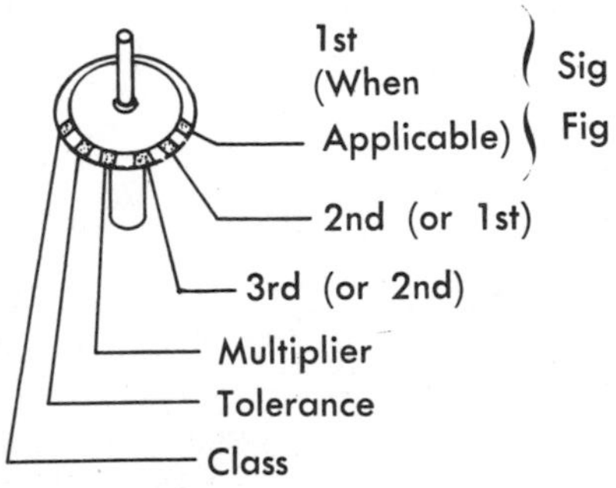

1st (When Applicable) } Sig Fig
2nd (or 1st)
3rd (or 2nd)
Multiplier
Tolerance
Class

MOLDED PAPER CAPACITOR CODES

(Capacity Given in MMF)

MOLDED PAPER TUBULAR

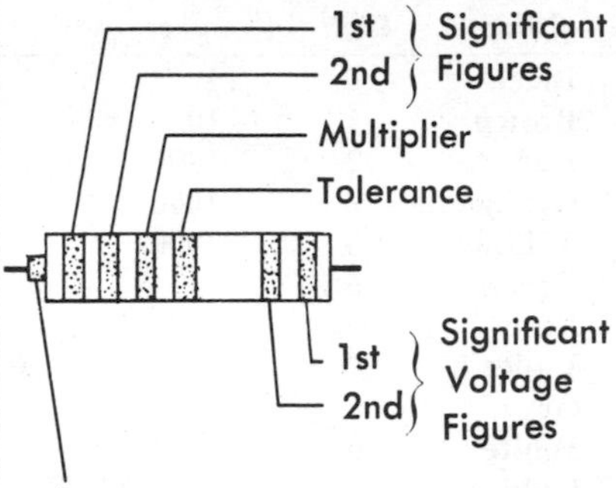

1st } Significant
2nd } Figures
Multiplier
Tolerance
1st } Significant
2nd } Voltage Figures

Indicates outer Foil. May Be On Either End. May Also Be Indicated By Other Methods Such As Typographical Marking Or Black Stripe

Add Two Zeros to Significant Voltage Figures. One Band Indicates Voltage Ratings Under 1000 Volts

MOLDED FLAT PAPER CAPACITORS (COMMERCIAL CODE)

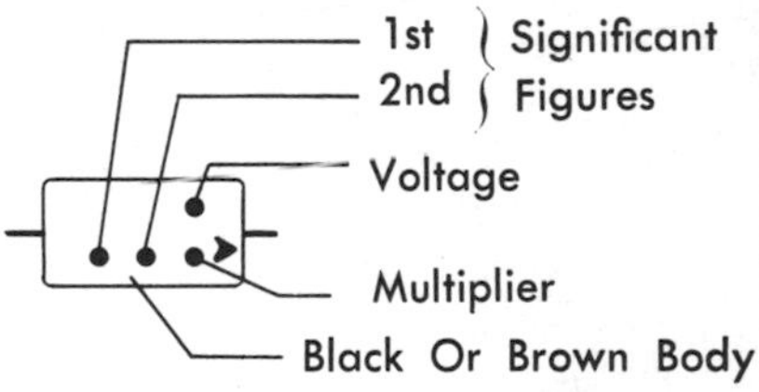

1st } Significant
2nd } Figures
Voltage
Multiplier
Black Or Brown Body

MOLDED FLAT PAPER CAPACITORS (JAN CODE)

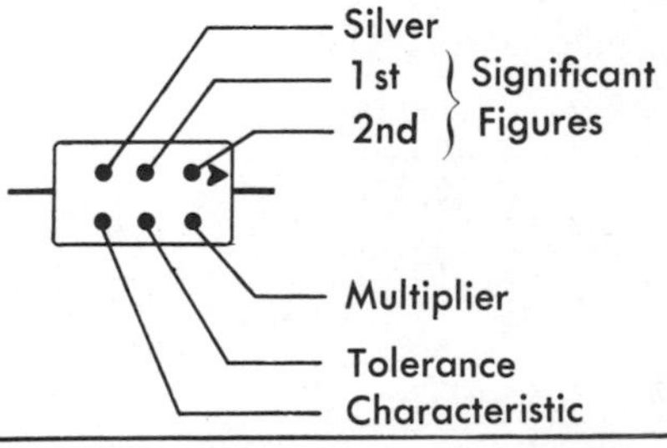

Silver
1st } Significant
2nd } Figures
Multiplier
Tolerance
Characteristic

MOLDED MICA CAPACITOR CODES (CAPACITANCE GIVEN IN MMF)

Color	Digit	Multi-plier	*Tolerance	Class or Characteristic
Black	0	1	20%	A
Brown	1	10	1%	B
Red	2	100	2%	C
Orange	3	1000	3%	D
Yellow	4	10000		E
Green	5		5% (RETMA)	F (JAN)
Blue	6			G (JAN)
Violet	7			
Gray	8			I (RETMA)
White	9			J (RETMA)
Gold		.1	5% (JAN)	
Silver		.01	10%	

Class or characteristic denotes specifications of design involving Q factors, temperature coefficients, and production test requirements.

All axial lead mica capacitors have a voltage rating of 300, 500, or 1000 volts.

* or ± 1.0 mmf whichever is greater.

APPENDIX V

INTERNATIONAL MORSE CODE

Electronic communication is accomplished telegraphically with the International Morse Code. Code symbols for the alphabet and numerals are tabulated below. This tabulation is incomplete, and interested readers are referred to the *Radio Amateur's Handbook*, published by the American Radio Relay League.

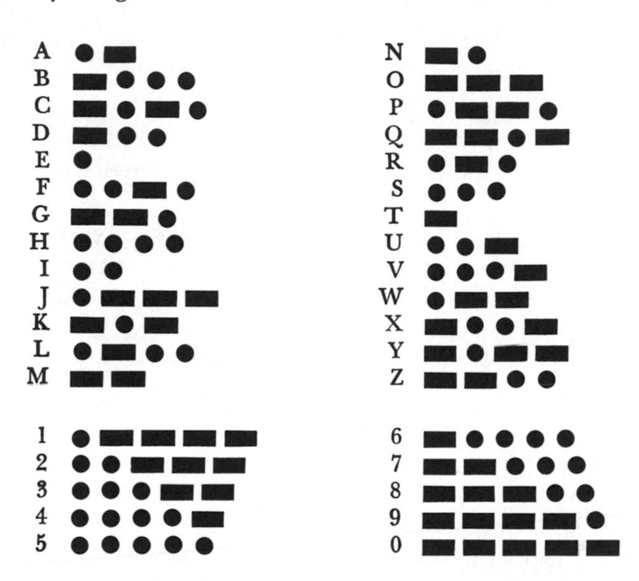

APPENDIX VI

GREEK ALPHABET

Greek letters are widely used in electronics technology to denote various physical concepts. Upper-case and lower-case Greek letters are given below, with their names.

Letters	*Names*	*Letters*	*Names*	*Letters*	*Names*
Α α	Alpha	Ι ι	Iota	Ρ ρ	Rho
Β β	Beta	Κ κ	Kappa	Σ σ ς	Sigma
Γ γ	Gamma	Λ λ	Lambda	Τ τ	Tau
Δ δ	Delta	Μ μ	Mu	Υ υ	Upsilon
Ε ϵ	Epsilon	Ν ν	Nu	Φ ϕ	Phi
Ζ ζ	Zeta	Ξ ξ	Xi	Χ χ	Chi
Η η	Eta	Ο ο	Omicron	Ψ ψ	Psi
Θ θ	Theta	Π π	Pi	Ω ω	Omega

APPENDIX VII

GOOD SOLDERING PRACTICE

Although solder joints are not difficult to make, certain precautions must be observed. The following good practices are explained through the courtesy of Precision Apparatus Co.

Soldering Iron

The soldering iron transfers the correct amount of heat to a junction or terminal so that the solder will flow smoothly, producing a good mechanical and electrical bond. Soldering irons can be grouped into the barrel types, the gun and trigger heat types, and the pencil types. The choice of soldering iron is a personal one and is usually based on previous experience.

The barrel type is the most common of the three types. The tip of this iron can be changed to match the soldering operation. For the soldering required in the construction of this kit a small diameter tip is the best. A wattage rating of 50 to 125 watts, which is the most widely used in radio and television work, is more than adequate.

Copper Tips

The copper soldering tip requires a certain amount of upkeep because of corrosion and pitting. The corrosion is a black scale (Cupric oxide) that is produced when copper is heated in the presence of air. The pitting is caused by the copper in the tip alloying with the solder.

The oxide coating or scale can be brushed or scraped from the tip. This scale occupies a larger area than the metallic copper. When the tip is left in the barrel of an iron for a long time, this oxide will form and will cause the tip to bind in the barrel. The tip should be removed periodically and cleaned.

Pitted copper soldering tips can be remedied only by removing some of the metal. This is accomplished by filing or grinding the pitted area until a smooth, clean surface is exposed. The tip is then heated to the temperature at which the solder begins to melt. Solder is then rubbed over the cleaned surface until it adheres and spreads over all the cleaned area.

Sometimes the copper oxidizes rapidly and prevents easy tinning. When this occurs, a piece of steel wool should be used to wipe the surface. A heavy piece of cloth can also be used to clean the iron.

Soldering

The actual process of soldering is more than just sticking some solder to a piece of metal. The metal to be soldered should be heated with the soldering iron; then the rosin core solder is applied. The solder should actually *flow* across the metal surface.

Keep in mind that solder will not flow smoothly into a connection unless the joint itself has been heated enough to melt the solder. Unless this is done, "cold" solder or "high resistance" joints often result. Note that "cold"-solder joints have a "dull" and "grainy" appearance. A good solder connection will present a smooth and "shiny" appearance. Other causes of cold-solder joints are poor mechanical connections; melting drops of solder on the joint with the iron; leads and wires not sufficiently cleaned of dirt, wax, and corrosion; and moving leads before the solder has "set" or hardened. When in doubt as to the condition of a joint, it may be tested by moving the leads slightly and observing whether they are loose. Loose leads indicate a cold connection. When correcting a cold-solder condition, always apply new solder. As a rule, simply reheating the joint will not do the job.

To obtain a good solder connection follow the directions given below carefully:

1. Hold the iron against the terminal to heat the metals being joined. A small amount of solder may be placed on the tip of the iron to aid in heat transfer. Do not load the tip with solder—it will just roll off into the equipment.

2. When the temperature of the junction reaches the melting point of the solder, the solder on the iron will begin to flow away from the iron and into the junction. Apply more solder at this time. The amount depends upon the size of the junction. Apply only enough solder to make a good electrical and mechanical bond. Do not cover the wires and terminals with excessive amounts of solder.

3. The iron should be left on the junction only until the solder has flowed to all of the surfaces. A large soldering iron will quickly "sweat" the solder into the junction. A smaller iron will require a little more time. Do not try to rub the solder into the terminal; instead, hold the iron in one place. If the terminal does not solder completely, it may be necessary to move the iron to another point. When soldering to the leads of transistors, special care must be used in the soldering process to prevent damage to the transistor. The transistor can easily be protected by "heat sinking" before soldering. One method of heat sinking is done by holding the transistor lead firmly with long-nose pliers between the transistor body and the solder point (as far away from the body of the transistor as possible). The pliers then conduct away the heat preventing overheating of the transistor body.

APPENDIX VIII

TELEVISION CHANNELS AND FREQUENCIES

Channel	Frequency Limits (mc)	Channel	Frequency Limits (mc)
2	54–60	43	644–650
3	60–66	44	650–656
4	66–72	45	656–662
5	76–82	46	662–668
6	82–88	47	668–674
7	174–180	48	674–680
8	180–186	49	680–686
9	186–192	50	686–692
10	192–198	51	692–698
11	198–204	52	698–704
12	204–210	53	704–710
13	210–216	54	710–716
14	470–476	55	716–722
15	476–482	56	722–728
16	482–488	57	728–734
17	488–494	58	734–740
18	494–500	59	740–746
19	500–506	60	746–752
20	506–512	61	752–758
21	512–518	62	758–764
22	518–524	63	764–770
23	524–530	64	770–776
24	530–536	65	776–782
25	536–542	66	782–788
26	542–548	67	788–794
27	548–554	68	794–800
28	554–560	69	800–806
29	560–566	70	806–812
30	566–572	71	812–818
31	572–578	72	818–824
32	578–584	73	824–830
33	584–590	74	830–836
34	590–596	75	836–842
35	596–602	76	842–848
36	602–608	77	848–854
37	608–614	78	854–860
38	614–620	79	860–866
39	620–626	80	866–872
40	626–632	81	872–878
41	632–638	82	878–884
42	638–644	83	884–890

APPENDIX IX

NATURAL TRIGONOMETRIC FUNCTIONS

Degrees	Radians	Sine	Tangent	Cotangent	Cosine		
0	0	0	0	———	1.0000	1.5708	**90**
1	.0175	.0175	.0175	57.290	.9998	1.5533	89
2	.0349	.0349	.0349	28.636	.9994	1.5359	88
3	.0524	.0523	.0524	19.081	.9986	1.5184	87
4	.0698	.0698	.0699	14.301	.9976	1.5010	86
5	.0873	.0872	.0875	11.430	.9962	1.4835	**85**
6	.1047	.1045	.1051	9.5144	.9945	1.4661	84
7	.1222	.1219	.1228	8.1443	.9925	1.4486	83
8	.1396	.1392	.1405	7.1154	.9903	1.4312	82
9	.1571	.1564	.1584	6.3138	.9877	1.4137	81
10	.1745	.1736	.1763	5.6713	.9848	1.3963	**80**
11	.1920	.1908	.1944	5.1446	.9816	1.3788	79
12	.2094	.2079	.2126	4.7046	.9781	1.3614	78
13	.2269	.2250	.2309	4.3315	.9744	1.3439	77
14	.2443	.2419	.2493	4.0108	.9703	1.3265	76
15	.2618	.2588	.2679	3.7321	.9659	1.3090	**75**
16	.2793	.2756	.2867	3.4874	.9613	1.2915	74
17	.2967	.2924	.3057	3.2709	.9563	1.2741	73
18	.3142	.3090	.3249	3.0777	.9511	1.2566	72
19	.3316	.3256	.3443	2.9042	.9455	1.2392	71
20	.3491	.3420	.3640	2.7475	.9397	1.2217	**70**
21	.3665	.3584	.3839	2.6051	.9336	1.2043	69
22	.3840	.3746	.4040	2.4751	.9272	1.1868	68
23	.4014	.3907	.4245	2.3559	.9205	1.1694	67
24	.4189	.4067	.4452	2.2460	.9135	1.1519	66
25	.4363	.4226	.4663	2.1445	.9063	1.1345	**65**
26	.4538	.4384	.4877	2.0503	.8988	1.1170	64
27	.4712	.4540	.5095	1.9626	.8910	1.0996	63
28	.4887	.4695	.5317	1.8807	.8829	1.0821	62
29	.5061	.4848	.5543	1.8040	.8746	1.0647	61
30	.5236	.5000	.5774	1.7321	.8660	1.0472	**60**
31	.5411	.5150	.6009	1.6643	.8572	1.0297	59
32	.5585	.5299	.6249	1.6003	.8480	1.0123	58
33	.5760	.5446	.6494	1.5399	.8387	.9948	57
34	.5934	.5592	.6745	1.4826	.8290	.9774	56
35	.6109	.5736	.7002	1.4281	.8192	.9599	**55**
36	.6283	.5878	.7265	1.3764	.8090	.9425	54
37	.6458	.6018	.7536	1.3270	.7986	.9250	53
38	.6632	.6157	.7813	1.2799	.7880	.9076	52
39	.6807	.6293	.8098	1.2349	.7771	.8901	51
40	.6981	.6428	.8391	1.1918	.7660	.8727	**50**
41	.7156	.6561	.8693	1.1504	.7547	.8552	49
42	.7330	.6691	.9004	1.1106	.7431	.8378	48
43	.7505	.6820	.9325	1.0724	.7314	.8203	47
44	.7679	.6947	.9657	1.0355	.7193	.8029	46
45	.7854	.7071	1.0000	1.0000	.7071	.7854	**45**
		Cosine	Cotangent	Tangent	Sine	Radians	Degrees

TRIGONOMETRIC FORMULAS

Solution of circuit problems often requires the use of trigonometric formulas. The most-often used formulas are given below:

Sums of Angles

$\sin(X + Y) = \sin X \cos Y + \cos X \sin Y$
$\sin(X - Y) = \sin X \cos Y - \cos X \sin Y$
$\cos(X + Y) = \cos X \cos Y - \sin X \sin Y$
$\cos(X - Y) = \cos X \cos Y + \sin X \sin Y$

Sums of Functions

$$\sin X + \sin Y = 2 \sin \frac{X+Y}{2} \cos \frac{X-Y}{2}$$

$$\sin X - \sin Y = 2 \cos \frac{X+Y}{2} \sin \frac{X-Y}{2}$$

$$\cos X + \cos Y = 2 \cos \frac{X+Y}{2} \cos \frac{X-Y}{2}$$

$$\cos X - \cos Y = -2 \sin \frac{X+Y}{2} \sin \frac{X-Y}{2}$$

Functions of Multiple Angles

$\sin 2X = 2 \sin X \cos X$
$\cos 2X = \cos^2 X - \sin^2 X = 2\cos^2 X - 1 = 1 - 2\sin^2 X$

DEGREES TO RADIANS

Most a-c circuit problems utilize radian measure. The tabulation below gives the number of radians corresponding to an angle expressed in degrees, minutes, or seconds.

DEGREES, MINUTES, AND SECONDS TO RADIANS

°	Radians	°	Radians	°	Radians	′	Radians	″	Radians
0	0.000 000	60	1.047 198	120	2.094 395	0	0.000 000	0	0.000 000
1	0.017 453	61	1.064 651	121	2.111 848	1	0.000 291	1	0.000 005
2	0.034 907	62	1.082 104	122	2.129 302	2	0.000 582	2	0.000 010
3	0.052 360	63	1.099 557	123	2.146 755	3	0.000 873	3	0.000 014
4	0.069 813	64	1.117 011	124	2.164 208	4	0.001 164	4	0.000 019
5	0.087 266	65	1.134 464	125	2.181 662	5	0.001 454	5	0.000 024
6	0.104 720	66	1.151 917	126	2.199 115	6	0.001 745	6	0.000 029
7	0.122 173	67	1.169 371	127	2.216 568	7	0.002 036	7	0.000 034
8	0.139 626	68	1.186 824	128	2.234 021	8	0.002 327	8	0.000 039
9	0.157 080	69	1.204 277	129	2.251 475	9	0.002 618	9	0.000 044
10	0.174 533	70	1.221 730	130	2.268 928	10	0.002 909	10	0.000 048
11	0.191 986	71	1.239 184	131	2.286 381	11	0.003 200	11	0.000 053
12	0.209 439	72	1.256 637	132	2.303 835	12	0.003 491	12	0.000 058
13	0.226 893	73	1.274 090	133	2.321 288	13	0.003 781	13	0.000 063
14	0.244 346	74	1.291 544	134	2.338 741	14	0.004 072	14	0.000 068
15	0.261 799	75	1.308 997	135	2.356 194	15	0.004 363	15	0.000 073
16	0.279 253	76	1.326 450	136	2.373 648	16	0.004 654	16	0.000 074
17	0.296 706	77	1.343 903	137	2.391 101	17	0.004 945	17	0.000 082
18	0.314 159	78	1.361 357	138	2.408 554	18	0.005 236	18	0.000 087
19	0.331 613	79	1.378 810	139	2.426 008	19	0.005 527	19	0.000 092
20	0.349 066	80	1.396 263	140	2.443 461	20	0.005 818	20	0.000 097
21	0.366 519	81	1.413 717	141	2.460 914	21	0.006 109	21	0.000 102
22	0.383 972	82	1.431 170	142	2.478 367	22	0.006 399	22	0.000 107
23	0.401 426	83	1.448 623	143	2.495 821	23	0.006 690	23	0.000 111
24	0.418 879	84	1.466 077	144	2.513 274	24	0.006 981	24	0.000 116
25	0.436 332	85	1.483 530	145	2.530 727	25	0.007 272	25	0.000 121
26	0.453 786	86	1.500 983	146	2.548 188	26	0.007 563	26	0.000 126
27	0.471 239	87	1.518 436	147	2.565 634	27	0.007 854	27	0.000 131
28	0.488 692	88	1.535 890	148	2.583 087	28	0.008 145	28	0.000 136
29	0.506 145	89	1.553 343	149	2.600 547	29	0.008 436	29	0.000 141
30	0.523 599	90	1.570 796	150	2.617 994	30	0.008 727	30	0.000 145
31	0.541 052	91	1.588 250	151	2.635 447	31	0.009 017	31	0.000 150
32	0.558 505	92	1.605 703	152	2.652 900	32	0.009 308	32	0.000 155
33	0.575 959	93	1.623 156	153	2.670 354	33	0.009 599	33	0.000 160
34	0.593 412	94	1.640 609	154	2.687 807	34	0.009 890	34	0.000 165
35	0.610 865	95	1.658 063	155	2.705 260	35	0.010 181	35	0.000 170
36	0.628 318	96	1.675 516	156	2.722 714	36	0.010 472	36	0.000 174
37	0.645 772	97	1.692 969	157	2.740 167	37	0.010 763	37	0.000 179
38	0.663 225	98	1.710 423	158	2.757 620	38	0.011 054	38	0.000 184
39	0.680 678	99	1.727 876	159	2.775 073	39	0.011 345	39	0.000 189
40	0.698 132	100	1.745 329	160	2.792 527	40	0.011 635	40	0.000 194
41	0.715 585	101	1.762 782	161	2.809 980	41	0.011 926	41	0.000 199
42	0.733 038	102	1.780 236	162	2.827 433	42	0.012 217	42	0.000 204
43	0.750 492	103	1.797 689	163	2.844 887	43	0.012 508	43	0.000 208
44	0.767 945	104	1.815 142	164	2.862 340	44	0.012 799	44	0.000 213
45	0.785 398	105	1.832 596	165	2.879 793	45	0.013 090	45	0.000 218
46	0.802 851	106	1.850 049	166	2.897 247	46	0.013 381	46	0.000 223
47	0.820 305	107	1.867 502	167	2.914 700	47	0.013 672	47	0.000 228
48	0.837 758	108	1.884 956	168	2.932 153	48	0.013 963	48	0.000 233
49	0.855 211	109	1.902 409	169	2.949 606	49	0.014 253	49	0.000 238
50	0.872 665	110	1.919 862	170	2.967 060	50	0.014 544	50	0.000 242
51	0.890 118	111	1.937 315	171	2.984 513	51	0.014 835	51	0.000 247
52	0.907 571	112	1.954 769	172	3.001 966	52	0.015 126	52	0.000 252
53	0.925 024	113	1.972 222	173	3.019 420	53	0.015 417	53	0.000 257
54	0.942 478	114	1.989 675	174	3.036 873	54	0.015 708	54	0.000 262
55	0.959 931	115	2.007 129	175	3.054 326	55	0.015 999	55	0.000 267
56	0.977 384	116	2.024 582	176	3.071 779	56	0.016 290	56	0.000 271
57	0.994 838	117	2.042 035	177	3.089 233	57	0.016 581	57	0.000 276
58	1.012 291	118	2.059 488	178	3.106 686	58	0.016 871	58	0.000 281
59	1.029 744	119	2.076 942	179	3.124 139	59	0.017 162	59	0.000 286
60	1.047 198	120	2.094 395	180	3.141 593	60	0.017 453	60	0.000 291

APPENDIX X

FOUR-PLACE LOGARITHMS

n	0	1	2	3	4	5	6	7	8	9
10	0000	0043	0086	0128	0170	0212	0253	0294	0334	0374
11	0414	0453	0492	0531	0569	0607	0645	0682	0719	0755
12	0792	0828	0864	0899	0934	0969	1004	1038	1072	1106
13	1139	1173	1206	1239	1271	1303	1335	1367	1399	1430
14	1461	1492	1523	1553	1584	1614	1644	1673	1703	1732
15	1761	1790	1818	1847	1875	1903	1931	1959	1987	2014
16	2041	2068	2095	2122	2148	2175	2201	2227	2253	2279
17	2304	2330	2355	2380	2405	2430	2455	2480	2504	2529
18	2553	2577	2601	2625	2648	2672	2695	2718	2742	2765
19	2788	2810	2833	2856	2878	2900	2923	2945	2967	2989
20	3010	3032	3054	3075	3096	3118	3139	3160	3181	3201
21	3222	3243	3263	3284	3304	3324	3345	3365	3385	3404
22	3424	3444	3464	3483	3502	3522	3541	3560	3579	3598
23	3617	3636	3655	3674	3692	3711	3729	3747	3766	3784
24	3802	3820	3838	3856	3874	3892	3909	3927	3945	3962
25	3979	3997	4014	4031	4048	4065	4082	4099	4116	4133
26	4150	4166	4183	4200	4216	4232	4249	4265	4281	4298
27	4314	4330	4346	4362	4378	4393	4409	4425	4440	4456
28	4472	4487	4502	4518	4533	4548	4564	4579	4594	4609
29	4624	4639	4654	4669	4683	4698	4713	4728	4742	4757
30	4771	4786	4800	4814	4829	4843	4857	4871	4886	4900
31	4914	4928	4942	4955	4969	4983	4997	5011	5024	5038
32	5051	5065	5079	5092	5105	5119	5132	5145	5159	5172
33	5185	5198	5211	5224	5237	5250	5263	5276	5289	5302
34	5315	5328	5340	5353	5366	5378	5391	5403	5416	5428
35	5441	5453	5465	5478	5490	5502	5514	5527	5539	5551
36	5563	5575	5587	5599	5611	5623	5635	5647	5658	5670
37	5682	5694	5705	5717	5729	5740	5752	5763	5775	5786
38	5798	5809	5821	5832	5843	5855	5866	5877	5888	5899
39	5911	5922	5933	5944	5955	5966	5977	5988	5999	6010
40	6021	6031	6042	6053	6064	6075	6085	6096	6107	6117
41	6128	6138	6149	6160	6170	6180	6191	6201	6212	6222
42	6232	6243	6253	6263	6274	6284	6294	6304	6314	6325
43	6335	6345	6355	6365	6375	6385	6395	6405	6415	6425
44	6435	6444	6454	6464	6474	6484	6493	6503	6513	6522
45	6532	6542	6551	6561	6571	6580	6590	6599	6609	6618
46	6628	6637	6646	6656	6665	6675	6684	6693	6702	6712
47	6721	6730	6739	6749	6758	6767	6776	6785	6794	6803
48	6812	6821	6830	6839	6848	6857	6866	6875	6884	6893
49	6902	6911	6920	6928	6937	6946	6955	6964	6972	6981
50	6990	6998	7007	7016	7024	7033	7042	7050	7059	7067
51	7076	7084	7093	7101	7110	7118	7126	7135	7143	7152
52	7160	7168	7177	7185	7193	7202	7210	7218	7226	7235
53	7243	7251	7259	7267	7275	7284	7292	7300	7308	7316
54	7324	7332	7340	7348	7356	7364	7372	7380	7388	7396

FOUR-PLACE LOGARITHMS (*Continued*)

n	0	1	2	3	4	5	6	7	8	9
55	7404	7412	7419	7427	7435	7443	7451	7459	7466	7474
56	7482	7490	7497	7505	7513	7520	7528	7536	7543	7551
57	7559	7566	7574	7582	7589	7597	7604	7612	7619	7627
58	7634	7642	7649	7657	7664	7672	7679	7686	7694	7701
59	7709	7716	7723	7731	7738	7745	7752	7760	7767	7774
60	7782	7789	7796	7803	7810	7818	7825	7832	7839	7846
61	7853	7860	7868	7875	7882	7889	7896	7903	7910	7917
62	7924	7931	7938	7945	7952	7959	7966	7973	7980	7987
63	7993	8000	8007	8014	8021	8028	8035	8041	8048	8055
64	8062	8069	8075	8082	8089	8096	8102	8109	8116	8122
65	8129	8136	8142	8149	8156	8162	8169	8176	8182	8189
66	8195	8202	8209	8215	8222	8228	8235	8241	8248	8254
67	8261	8267	8274	8280	8287	8293	8299	8306	8312	8319
68	8325	8331	8338	8344	8351	8357	8363	8370	8376	8382
69	8388	8395	8401	8407	8414	8420	8426	8432	8439	8445
70	8451	8457	8463	8470	8476	8482	8488	8494	8500	8506
71	8513	8519	8525	8531	8537	8543	8549	8555	8561	8567
72	8573	8579	8585	8591	8597	8603	8609	8615	8621	8627
73	8633	8639	8645	8651	8657	8663	8669	8675	8681	8686
74	8692	8698	8704	8710	8716	8722	8727	8733	8739	8745
75	8751	8756	8762	8768	8774	8779	8785	8791	8797	8802
76	8808	8814	8820	8825	8831	8837	8842	8848	8854	8859
77	8865	8871	8876	8882	8887	8893	8899	8904	8910	8915
78	8921	8927	8932	8938	8943	8949	8954	8960	8965	8971
79	8976	8982	8987	8993	8998	9004	9009	9015	9020	9025
80	9031	9036	9042	9047	9053	9058	9063	9069	9074	9079
81	9085	9090	9096	9101	9106	9112	9117	9122	9128	9133
82	9138	9143	9149	9154	9159	9165	9170	9175	9180	9186
83	9191	9196	9201	9206	9212	9217	9222	9227	9232	9238
84	9243	9248	9253	9258	9263	9269	9274	9279	9284	9289
85	9294	9299	9304	9309	9315	9320	9325	9330	9335	9340
86	9345	9350	9355	9360	9365	9370	9375	9380	9385	9390
87	9395	9400	9405	9410	9415	9420	9425	9430	9435	9440
88	9445	9450	9455	9460	9465	9469	9474	9479	9484	9489
89	9494	9499	9504	9509	9513	9518	9523	9528	9533	9538
90	9542	9547	9552	9557	9562	9566	9571	9576	9581	9586
91	9590	9595	9600	9605	9609	9614	9619	9624	9628	9633
92	9638	9643	9647	9652	9657	9661	9666	9671	9675	9680
93	9685	9689	9694	9699	9703	9708	9713	9717	9722	9727
94	9731	9736	9741	9745	9750	9754	9759	9763	9768	9773
95	9777	9782	9786	9791	9795	9800	9805	9809	9814	9818
96	9823	9827	9832	9836	9841	9845	9850	9854	9859	9863
97	9868	9872	9877	9881	9886	9890	9894	9899	9903	9908
98	9912	9917	9921	9926	9930	9934	9939	9943	9948	9952
99	9956	9961	9965	9969	9974	9978	9983	9987	9991	9996

APPENDIX XI

TABLE OF SQUARE ROOTS AND SQUARES

n	n^2	$\sqrt{n}$	n	n^2	$\sqrt{n}$
			50	2500	7.0711
1	1	1.0000	51	2601	7.1414
2	4	1.4142	52	2704	7.2111
3	9	1.7321	53	2809	7.2801
4	16	2.0000	54	2916	7.3485
5	25	2.2361	55	3025	7.4162
6	36	2.4495	56	3136	7.4833
7	49	2.6458	57	3249	7.5498
8	64	2.8284	58	3364	7.6158
9	81	3.0000	59	3481	7.6811
10	100	3.1623	**60**	3600	7.7460
11	121	3.3166	61	3721	7.8102
12	144	3.4641	62	3844	7.8740
13	169	3.6056	63	3969	7.9373
14	196	3.7417	64	4096	8.0000
15	225	3.8730	65	4225	8.0623
16	256	4.0000	66	4356	8.1240
17	289	4.1231	67	4489	8.1854
18	324	4.2426	68	4624	8.2462
19	361	4.3589	69	4761	8.3066
20	400	4.4721	**70**	4900	8.3666
21	441	4.5826	71	5041	8.4261
22	484	4.6904	72	5184	8.4853
23	529	4.7958	73	5329	8.5440
24	576	4.8990	74	5476	8.6023
25	625	5.0000	75	5625	8.6603
26	676	5.0990	76	5776	8.7178
27	729	5.1962	77	5929	8.7750
28	784	5.2915	78	6084	8.8318
29	841	5.3852	79	6241	8.8882
30	900	5.4772	**80**	6400	8.9443
31	961	5.5678	81	6561	9.0000
32	1024	5.6569	82	6724	9.0554
33	1089	5.7446	83	6889	9.1104
34	1156	5.8310	84	7056	9.1652
35	1225	5.9161	85	7225	9.2195
36	1296	6.0000	86	7396	9.2736
37	1369	6.0828	87	7569	9.3274
38	1444	6.1644	88	7744	9.3808
39	1521	6.2450	89	7921	9.4340
40	1600	6.3246	**90**	8100	9.4868
41	1681	6.4031	91	8281	9.5394
42	1764	6.4807	92	8464	9.5917
43	1849	6.5574	93	8649	9.6437
44	1936	6.6332	94	8836	9.6954
45	2025	6.7082	95	9025	9.7468
46	2116	6.7823	96	9216	9.7980
47	2209	6.8557	97	9409	9.8489
48	2304	6.9282	98	9604	9.8995
49	2401	7.0000	99	9801	9.9499
50	2500	7.0711	**100**	10,000	10.0000

APPENDIX XII

TYPICAL POWER RATINGS OF ELECTRICAL AND ELECTRONIC DEVICES

Device	*Power rating (watts)*	*Device*	*Power rating (watts)*
Television Receiver	300	Coffee Maker	1000
Radio Receiver	100	Hand Iron	1000
Electric Clock	2	Ironer	1650
Ultra-violet Lamp	385	Floor Lamp	300
Electric Fan	100	Vacuum Cleaner	125
Portable Electric Heater	1000	Electric Skillet	1100
Record-changer	75	Mixer	100
Electric Blanket	200	Toaster	1100
Heating Pad	60	Broiler	1500
Electric Shaver	12	Waffle Iron	1000
Sewing Machine	75	Washer	700
Refrigerator	150	Baker	900

APPENDIX XIII

ANALYSIS OF COMPLEX WAVEFORMS

Pure sine waves are seldom encountered in audio-frequency equipment. An audio oscillator supplies a pure sine waveform. On the other hand, piano, cello, or trombone tones are complex waveforms, as depicted in Figure A19. It is not obvious that these complex waveforms can be built up from a number of sine waves. However, this fact was deduced in the ninteenth century by the mathematician Fourier. Fourier's theorem states that any complex wave can be synthesized from a number of sine waves that have specified amplitudes and phases, and that these sine waves are in harmonic relationship. These harmonic components of a complex wave can be picked out individually by tuned filters, and their physical aspect thereby demonstrated experimentally.

The square wave (Figure A20), is a basic complex waveform. The diagram depicts a partial synthesis of the square wave from its fundamental *A*, third harmonic *B*, fifth harmonic *D*, and seventh harmonic *F*. An ideal square wave would have an infinite number of successive harmonics, all of which are odd harmonics. The fundamental and all harmonics are in phase; they all pass through zero with the fundamental sine wave. The synthesized square wave also passes through zero with the fundamental

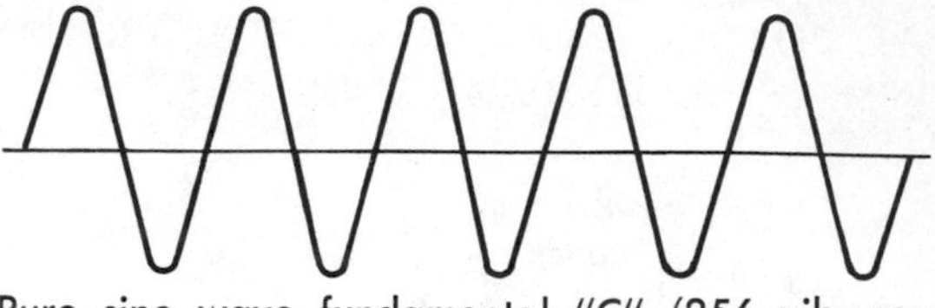

Pure sine wave fundamental "C" (256 vib. sec.)

Piano "C" (256 vib. sec.)

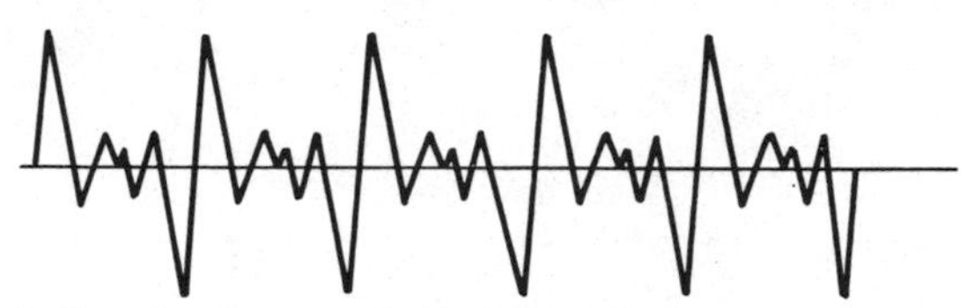

Cello pipe organ "C" (256 vib. sec.)

Trombone Organ Pipe "C" (256 vib. sec.)

Figure A19

Complex waveforms of piano, cello, and trombone tones.

sine wave. It is shown in advanced mathematics that the equation of an ideal square wave may be written

$$e = \frac{4E}{\pi}\left(\sin \omega t + \frac{1}{3}\sin 3\omega t + \frac{1}{5}\sin 5\omega t + \ldots\right)$$

where e is the instantaneous amplitude of the square wave, and E is the peak amplitude of the square wave.

Thus, the amplitude of the fundamental is greater than the amplitude of the square wave by the ratio $4/\pi$. The third harmonic has an amplitude that is one-third of the fundamental amplitude, the fifth har-

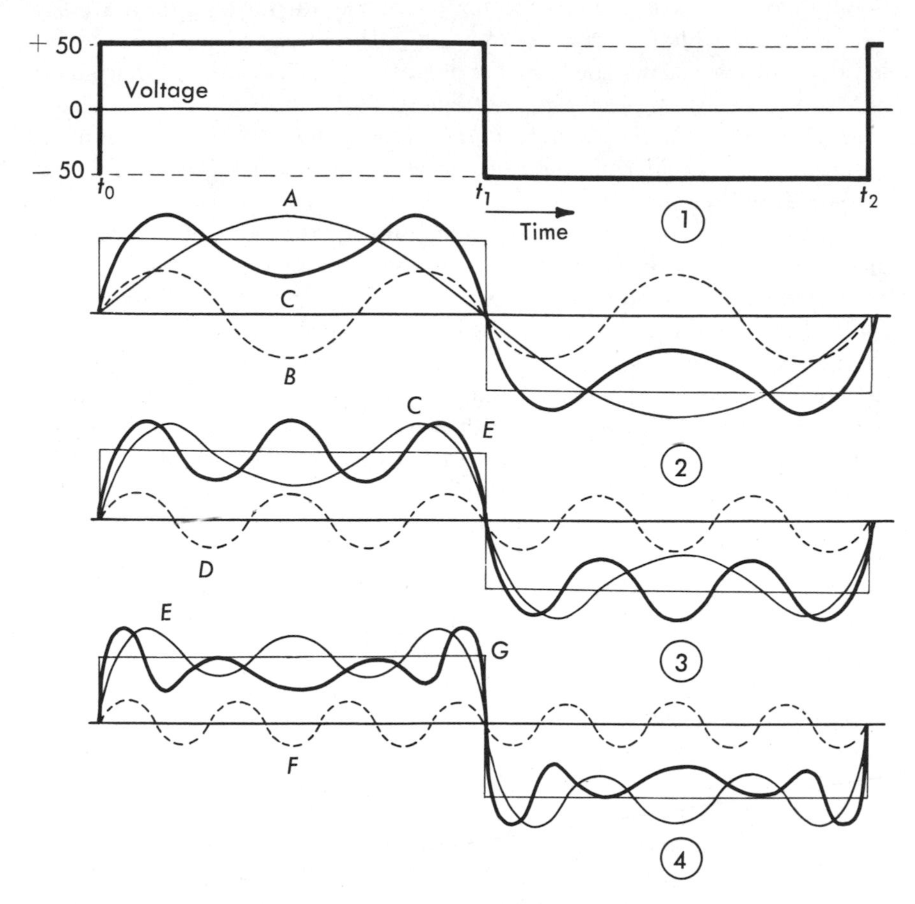

Figure A20
Composition of symmetrical square waves.

monic has one-fifth the amplitude of the fundamental, the seventh harmonic has one-seventh the amplitude of the fundamental, and so on. In theory, an infinite series of harmonics is required to synthesize an ideal square wave. However, about twenty harmonics suffice to form a reasonable facsimile of a square wave.

The Fourier series must be applied with due caution in practical situations, because conclusions are completely valid only for an infinite series of harmonics. In practice, circuits do not have infinite bandwidth. Hence, absurd conclusions can result. For example, if a square wave is passed through a circuit which rejects all harmonics higher than the twentieth, the Fourier series *seems* to state that the output waveform will have a wavy contour along top and bottom (see Figure A20). On the other hand, we observe that the top and bottom of the output waveform are flat. The conclusion that a wavy contour would be obtained is simply a consequence of associating the terms of an infinite series with the harmonics of a finite spectrum. *There are not enough harmonics in the finite spectrum to exhaust the terms of the infinite series.* Hence, our conclusion was absurd. Other basic considerations in applied mathematics are briefly explained in Appendix I.

This is an exceedingly troublesome point for the student who does not distinguish clearly between concepts in the domain of pure mathematics and concepts in the domain of physical reality. What is the source of the contradiction? The answer is that we did *not* apply a *series of sine waves* to the oscilloscope. Instead, we actually applied a d-c voltage that is switched on and off at a certain rate. A transient response is observed on the oscilloscope screen that has satisfactory correspondence with a certain *differential equation.* As you will learn in your advanced mathematics courses, the solution to this differential equation yields a reproduced square wave with finite rise time, and with flat top and bottom excursions.

It was previously noted that various branches of pure mathematics can be invoked to discuss a particular physical situation in the language of size. One branch of mathematics may have good correspondence with the physical situation, while another branch of mathematics may have only partial and unsatisfactory correspondence. The basic distinction between application of a Fourier series and application of the calculus to a reproduced square waveform is that the former is a description of the *synthesis* of a square wave from sine waves, while the latter is a description of oscilloscope *amplifier response* to a suddenly applied d-c voltage.

Instead of coming to grips with fundamental concepts, the beginner is apt to beg the question by vague assertions such as "the higher harmonics in a Fourier series contribute comparatively little to a waveform." The good student does not beg the question. Instead, he attacks the question resolutely on the basis of fundamental concepts. When he writes an equation, he asks "what does this equation state?" If the equation does not describe the physical situation satisfactorily, he seeks another equation to meet the need.

APPENDIX XIV

PRACTICAL UNITS, ELECTROSTATIC UNITS, AND ELECTROMAGNETIC UNITS

Electricians work with practical units designated as volts, amperes, ohms, and watts. Those electricians who are concerned with power-factor correction may also work with the practical units of henrys and farads.

However, engineers work with both practical units, and with other systems. Two of these systems are called the *electrostatic* system and the *electromagnetic* system. Electrostatic (ESU) units are utilized in the electrostatic system. Electromagnetic (EMU) units are used in the electromagnetic system. Physicists work extensively with ESU and EMU values; they seldom use the practical system. It makes no difference what system of units we use in equations, provided that we are *consistent* throughout.

It is easy to convert values from one system of units to another by employing suitable conversion factors. The relations between practical, electrostatic, and electromagnetic units are listed below:

Practical Unit	*Electrostatic Unit*	*Electromagnetic Unit*
Volt	1 ESU = 300 volts	1 EMU = 10^{-8} volt
Ampere	1 ESU = $\frac{1}{3} \times 10^{-9}$ amp	1 EMU = 10 amp
Ohm	1 ESU = 9×10^{11} ohms	1 EMU = 10^{-9} ohm
Coulomb	1 ESU = $\frac{1}{3} \times 10^{-9}$ coulomb	1 EMU = 10 coulombs
Farad	1 ESU = $\frac{1}{9} \times 10^{-11}$ farad	1 EMU = 10^{9} farads
Henry	1 ESU = 9×10^{11} henrys	1 EMU = 10^{-9} henry

HERTZ

On October 14, 1965, the IEEE Standards Coordinating Committee No. 14 on Quantities and Units adopted the term *hertz* for the unit of frequency. This name had been adopted earlier by the National Bureau of Standards, and before that by the International Committee on Weights and Measures and by the International Electrotechnical Commission. In adopting the term hertz, the IEEE Committee observed that this term is preferred because of the widespread use of "cycle" alone as a unit of frequency. "Cycle per second" is, of course, technically correct, but the use of "cycle" in place of "cycle per second" is declared incorrect.

APPENDIX XV

CALCULATION WITH SLIDE RULES

A slide rule is an analog computing device, which speeds up the solution of problems in multiplication, division, squares, square roots, cubes, and cube roots. Many slide rules also provide scales of trigonometric functions and logarithms. Specialized slide rules provide scales for calculation of resonant frequencies, capacitive and inductive reactance, quality factor (Q), dissipation factor (D), and various other functions. We will find that a generalized slide rule can perform the same calculations provided by a specialized slide rule. However, a problem in resonant frequency, for instance, can be solved with one setting of a specialized slide rule. If you solve the same problem on a generalized slide rule, you must first multiply L by C, take the square root of the product, multiply the product by 2π, and finally take the reciprocal of this value.

Since a slide rule is not a digital device, but an analog computer, its answers are limited in accuracy. Typical slide rules provide answers which are accurate to about 0.5 percent, which suffices for most engineering problems. We will also find that a slide rule does not show the actual place of decimals to which a number belongs. For example, if you read the answer "6" on a scale, this answer might denote 6, 0.6, 0.06, 0.006, 60, 600, 6000, and so forth. We determine the position of the decimal point by a rough calculation with round figures. Thus, if 215 is multiplied by 109, the answer appears as 234. Since 100 times 200 is 20,000, our final answer is evidently 23,400.

Slide-rule scales are identified by letters. Observe the scales C and D on your slide rule. These basic scales give the clearest idea of the way in which the scales are subdivided. Once you have become familiar with the graduation of these two scales, it will be easy to understand the other scales. The simplest slide rules have A, B, C, and D scales printed in black. More elaborate slide rules often have additional scales marked in red, which run in the opposite direction (reciprocally) from right to left. The red markings serve to remind the user that the scale values increase from right to left.

Let us now look at the basic scales C and D. The reading and setting exercises are carried out by means of the long cursor line or the index-1 (beginning of the scale) or index-10 (end of scale). Note that a few slide rules are provided with a magnifying glass over the long cursor line, to facilitate scale readings. Observe Figure A21. This is a section of the graduation range from 1 to 2 on scale C or scale D. From guide-number 1 to guide-number 1.1, we see that there are 10 subdivisions. Here, an accurate reading can be made to 3 places (that is, at 1-0-1). Next, by *halving* the space between two graduation marks, we can read 4 figures to fairly

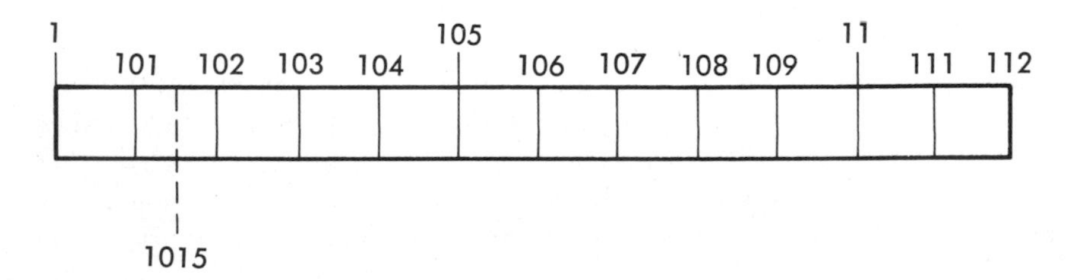

Figure A21

Figures A21 to A27 are through the courtesy of Eugene Dietzgen Co.

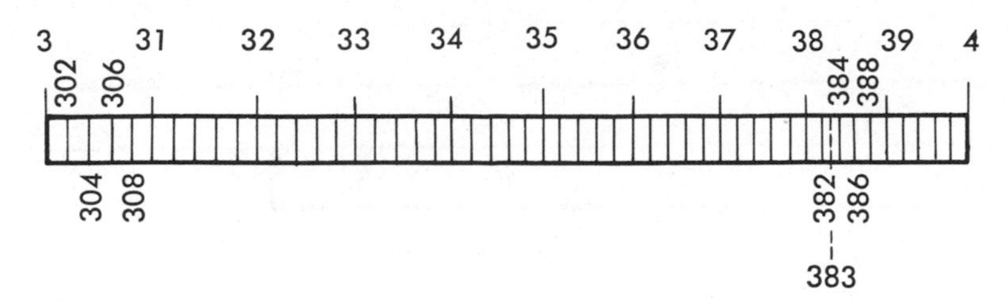

Figure A22

high accuracy. Thus, the dotted line in Figure A21 shows the location of 1-0-1-5 on the scale.

Figure A22 is a section of the graduation range from 2 to 4 on scale *C* or scale *D*. From guide-number 3 to guide-number 4 there are 10 subdivisions of 5 intervals each. An accurate reading can be made to 3 places (that is, 3-8-2). If an intermediate space is halved, as shown by the dotted line, we will read 383 halfway between 382 and 384. Evidently, the popular notion that slide-rule scales are difficult to read has no basis in practice. Let us take another example. Figure A23 depicts a section of the graduation range from 4 to 10 on scale *C* or scale *D*. From guide-number 8 to 9, and 9 to 10, we see that there are 10 subdivisions in each case, with 2 intervals in each subdivision. An accurate reading can be made to 3 places. By halving an intermediate space, it is even possible to make a fairly accurate reading to 4 places. Thus, the dotted line depicts 9075 halfway between 9050 and 9100.

Basically, a slide rule comprises logarithmic scales, which are marked with corresponding antilogarithms. In turn, when we perform a multiplication, for example, we use logarithms. It is much faster to use logarithms graphically than to calculate from tables of logarithms. Multiplication is chiefly carried out with the *C* and *D* scales. Suppose we wish to

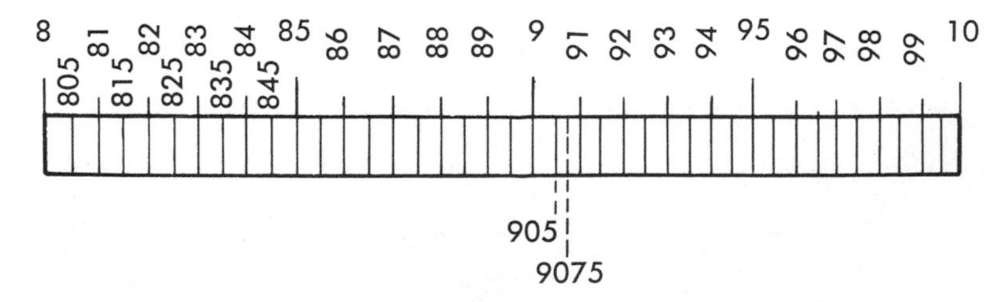

Figure A23

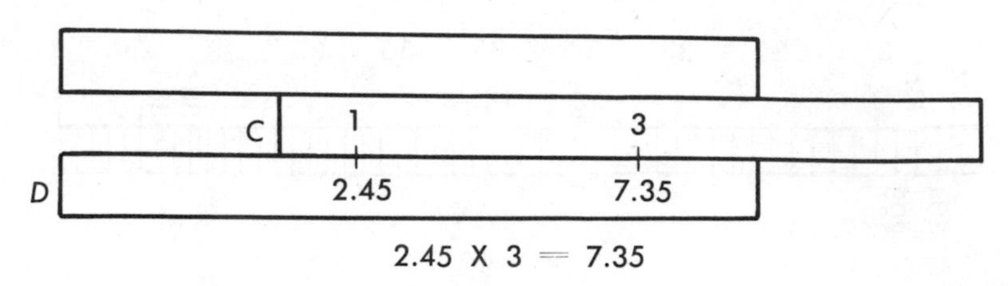

Figure A24

multiply 2.45 by 3. Of course, this is a very simple calculation which can be done mentally. However, let us see how we read the answer, 7.35, from the slide-rule scales. Figure A24 shows the required procedure. Set the 1 on the *C* scale above 2.45 on the *D* scale. We simply locate 245 on the *D* scale, since the decimal point is not explicit, but "understood." Now, it will be helpful to move the cursor line into position on 3 of the *C* scale. Read the product, 7.35 (actually 735) underneath the cursor line on the *D* scale. The decimal point must be placed mentally.

Now, consider a problem which is very difficult to do mentally. Let us multiply 2.04 by 3.18. Place the 1 on the *C* scale above 2.04 on the *D* scale. If you choose, "fix" the answer point by placing the cursor line on 3.18 of the *C* scale, and read 6.48 on the *D* scale below the cursor line. As you gain experience, you may read the answer without the aid of the cursor. Next, let us multiply 11.45 by 4.22. Place the 1 on the *C* scale above 11.45 on the *D* scale. Slide the cursor line over 4.22 on the *C* scale, and read 48.35 on the *D* scale. This answer requires careful setting and reading; otherwise, we might conclude that the answer is 48.4, or 48.3.

You will find sometimes that the foregoing multiplication procedure results in a reading which is off the *D* scale to the right. In this case, we use the right-hand 1 on the *C* scale. For example, suppose 7.5 is to be multiplied by 4.8. We merely set the right-hand 1 on the *C* scale over 7.5 on the *D* scale, as shown in Figure A25. Then the answer, 36, appears on

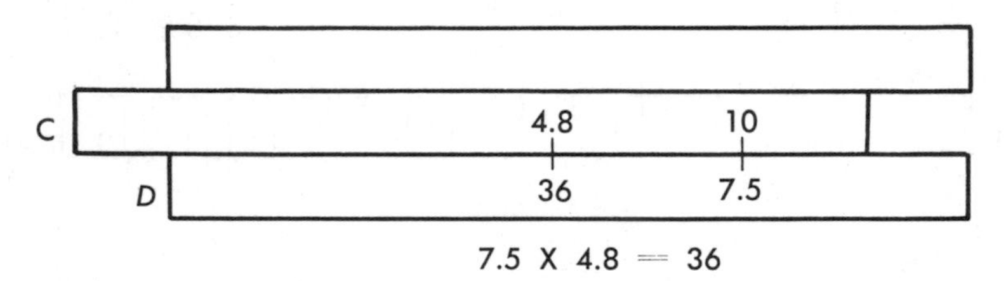

Figure A25

the D scale below 4.8 on the C scale. Technically, this operation is called *pushing the slide through*. Verify on your slide rule that $4.63 \times 3.17 = 14.67$, and that $0.694 \times 0.484 = 0.336$.

Division is the opposite of multiplication. Thus, we use the cursor line over the numerator on the D scale, and move the denominator on the C scale under the cursor line. The answer then appears on the D scale under 1 of the C scale, regardless of whether the left-hand 1 or the right-hand 1 of the C scale is in position to indicate the answer. For example, let us divide 9.85 by 2.5. The procedure is illustrated in Figure A26. First, bring the cursor line into position on the numerator, 9.85 on the D scale. Then, slide the numerator, 2.5 on the C scale, under the cursor line. Under the left-hand 1 of the C scale, we read 3.94 on the D scale, which is the answer

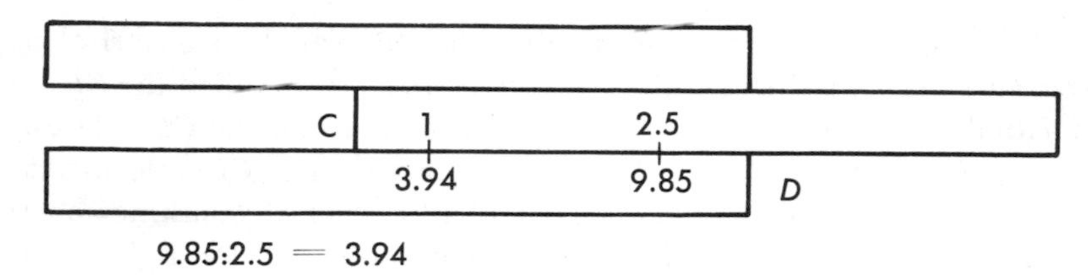

Figure A26

to the problem. Verify on your slide rule that $970/26.8 = 36.2$, and that $68/258 = 0.264$.

Now that we know how to multiply and divide with a slide rule, consider the best procedure for combined multiplication and division. This type of problem is common in electricity and electronics work. For example, let us solve

$$\frac{13.8 \times 24.5 \times 3.75}{17.6 \times 29.6 \times 4.96}$$

Always start with a division, and then alternate with multiplication and division. No readings need be taken of intermediate results. First, use the cursor line to place 1-3-8 on the D scale under 1-7-6 on the C scale. This is a division, but we do not read the answer (which is somewhat less than 8 on the D scale). Instead, we proceed to multiply by moving the cursor line to 2-4-5 on the C scale. Again, we do not read the answer (approximately 1-9 on the D scale). Instead, we divide by 29.6; we leave the cursor line in its position, and bring 2-9-6 on the C scale beneath the cursor line. Do not read the answer (approximately 6-5 on the D scale); instead, multiply by 3.75; move the cursor line to 3-7-5 on the C scale. Do not read the answer (which is somewhat greater than 2-4 on the *D* scale). Instead, make the final division by 4.96; slide 4-9-6 on the *C* scale beneath the cursor line. Then, read the final answer 4-9-1 on the *D* scale below the right-hand 1 of the *C* scale. The decimal point is placed to give 0.491 as explained previously.

Evidently, the accuracy of the final answer can be no better than your precision of settings. How close did you come to the correct answer? If you made an appreciable error, repeat your calculation. Next, verify that

$$\frac{38.9 \times 1.374 \times 16.3}{141.2 \times 2.14} = 2.883$$

and that

$$\frac{1.89 \times 7.68 \times 8.76}{0.723 \times 4.76} = 39.96$$

As we know, reciprocals must often be calculated in electrical and electronics work. Most slide rules have a reciprocal scale called the *CI* scale. It facilitates calculation of reciprocals. The intervals on the *CI* scale correspond to those on the *C* and *D* scale, except that the *CI* scale increases from right to left. To remind the user of this reversal, markings on the *CI* scale are printed in red. Let us see how it is used. If, for a given number a, the reciprocal $1/a$ is required, we slide the cursor line to the value of a, on either the *C* or the *CI* scale. Then, we read the reciprocal of a on either the *CI* or *C* scale, respectively. For example, let us take the reciprocal of 8. We may slide the cursor line to 8 on the *CI* scale. Then, we will read 0.125 below on the *C* scale.

We find that multiplication can be carried out with the *D* and *CI* scales, because division by a reciprocal is the same thing as multiplication. This method of multiplication is popular with many slide-rule users. For example, let us multiply 0.66 by 20.25. We proceed as with division; that is, slide the cursor line over 0.66 on the *D* scale, and then slide the *CI* scale to bring 20.25 under the cursor line. The answer, 13.37, now appears on the *D* scale under the 1 on the left-hand end of the *CI* scale.

The following example shows how simply you can calculate products with a number of factors. Let us multiply $0.66 \times 20.25 \times 2.38$. With reference to Figure A27, multiply the first two factors as shown; this was described above. The 1 on the *C* scale is at 13.37 on the *D* scale (an intermediate result in the present problem). We have the first setting required for multiplication by the next factor. Consequently, we now bring the cursor line into position over 2.38 on the *C* scale. The result, underneath on the *D* scale, is 31.8. Of course, this result could be followed, if desired, by a further muliplication. We would simply bring the next factor, on the *CI* scale, into position beneath the cursor line, and read the answer on

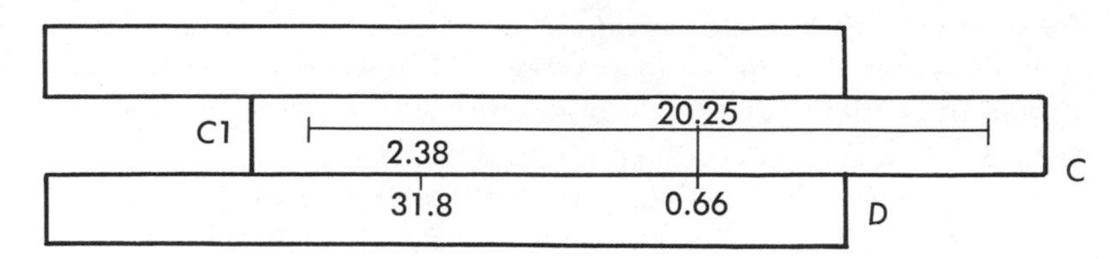

Figure A27

the D scale under 1 of the C scale. Thus, we make use of both methods of multiplication which we have learned, when the product of a number of factors is to be calculated.

Combined multiplication and division is also widely encountered in electrical and electronics work. For example, consider the problem

$$\frac{36.4}{3.2 \times 4.6}$$

This calculation can be made advantageously with the CI scale. We divide first. Move the cursor line over 3-6-4 on the D scale. Then slide 3.2 on the C scale under the cursor line. The intermediate result is 11.37 on the D scale below 1 on the C scale. Thus, we already have the first setting for the subsequent multiplication by 1/4.6. The cursor line is now brought into position above 4.6 on the CI scale, and the answer, 2.472, is read on the D scale under the cursor line.

Now, consider the A and B scales. These are basically used in combination with the C and D scales to find squares and square roots. You can use the A scale with the D scale, or the B scale with the C scale, whichever is more convenient. Slide the cursor line to 3 on the C scale. You then read 3^2, or 9, on the B scale under the cursor line. Of course, if you start with 9 on the B scale, you read the square root of 9, or 3, on the C scale. Again, slide the cursor to 9 on the C scale.You then read 9^2, or 81, on the B scale under the cursor line. Of course, if you start with 81 on the B scale, you read the square root of 81, or 9, on the C scale. Observe carefully that we take the square root of 9 to the left of center on the B scale; on the other hand, we take the square root of 90 to the right of center on the B scale. If you forget where the decimal point is in the number, the root that you read may be incorrect.

Many slide rules have a K scale, which is used to calculate cubes and cube roots of numbers. To cube a number, we use the D and K scales. Simply set the cursor line over the number on the D scale, and read its cube on the K scale under the cursor line. Of course, if you start with the number on the K scale, you read the cube root of the number on the D

scale. Note that the K scale has three identical groups of intervals, just as the A scale has two identical groups of intervals. Before you take the cube root of a number, start at the decimal point and separate the number into groups of three digits to the right and to the left of the decimal point. You will then have a first group which might comprise, one, two, or three numbers. This determines whether you will use the first, second, or third group on the K scale.

For example, 7854.23 has one digit in the first group. Therefore, we set the cursor line over this number in the left third of the K scale. We read the cube root of 7854.23 on the D scale. Again suppose that we wish to find the cube root of 78,542.3. This number has two digits in the first group. Hence, we set the cursor line over this number in the second third of the K scale, and read the answer on the D scale. Finally, suppose that we wish to find the cube root of 785,423. This number has three digits in the first group. Thus, we set the cursor line over this number in the last third of the K scale, and read cube root on the D scale. Thus, we must keep decimal points in mind when calculating cube roots, just as when we calculate square roots.

A slide rule that has A, B, C, and D scales is called a *Mannheim rule*. Engineering slide rules also have CI and K scales, as explained previously. The more elaborate engineering rules also have S and T scales for calculation of sines, cosines, tangents, and cotangents. These scales are marked with both black numbers and red numbers. The S scale, when the black figures are read, provides in conjunction with the D scale, a table of sines. The S scale, when the red figures are read, provides in conjunction with the D scale, a table of cosines. Similarly, the black and red figures on the T scale provide in conjunction with the D scale a table of tangents and of cotangents. Very elaborate engineering slide rules provide additional mathematical functions that are beyond the scope of this text.

Let us briefly review the facilities provided by specialized slide rules, as illustrated in Figure A28. This rule has scales on both sides. Figure A28 shows the side that is used to solve resonant-frequency problems. Six scales are provided, identified as a, b, c, d, e, and f. The a scale is calibrated in microfarads, the b scale in henrys, the c scale in cycles per second, the d scale in micro-microfarads, the e scale in millihenrys, and the f scale in megacycles.

Suppose that in the design of a filter section, it is desired to resonate a 0.13-henry inductance at a frequency of 1500 cycles per sec. To find the required capacitance value, set 1500 cps on scale c opposite the arrow; then, opposite 0.13 henry on scale b you will read 0.087 microfarad on scale a. Next, let us consider another practical problem. In a high-frequency oscillator, the tank circuit consists of a 35-micro-microfarad capacitor and a 1.5-microhenry coil. We are to find the frequency of oscillation. Note that

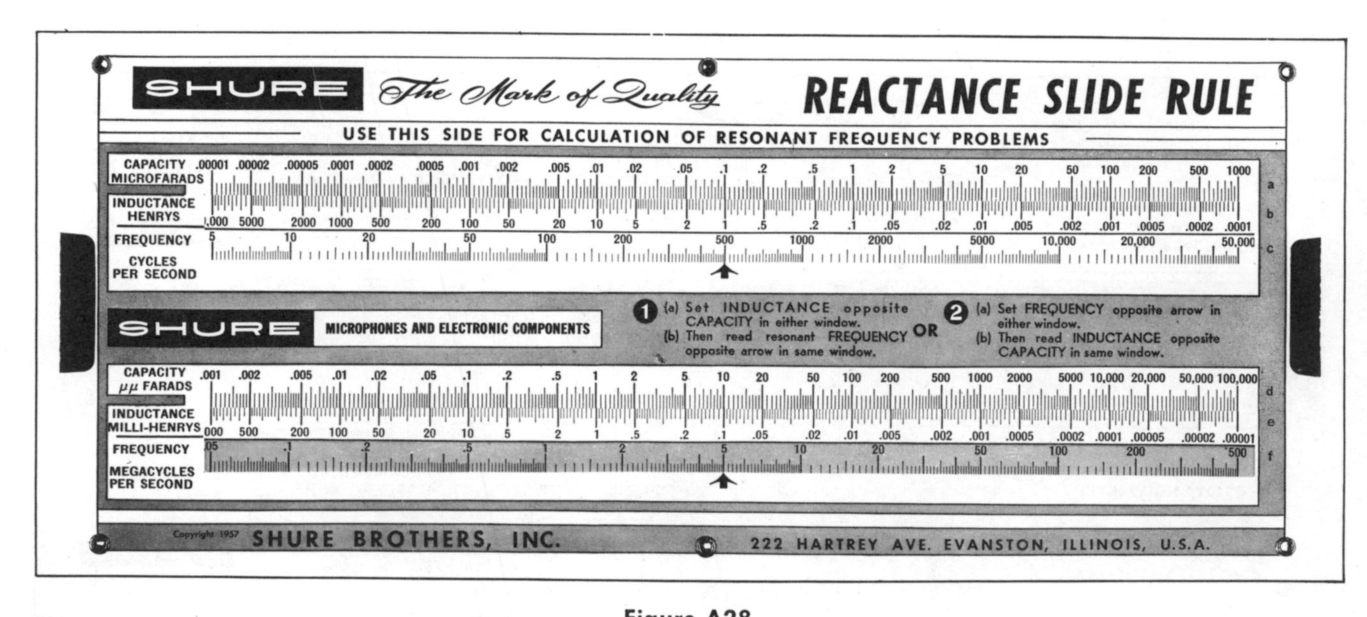

Figure A28

A specialized reactance slide rule. (Courtesy of Shure Brothers, Inc.)

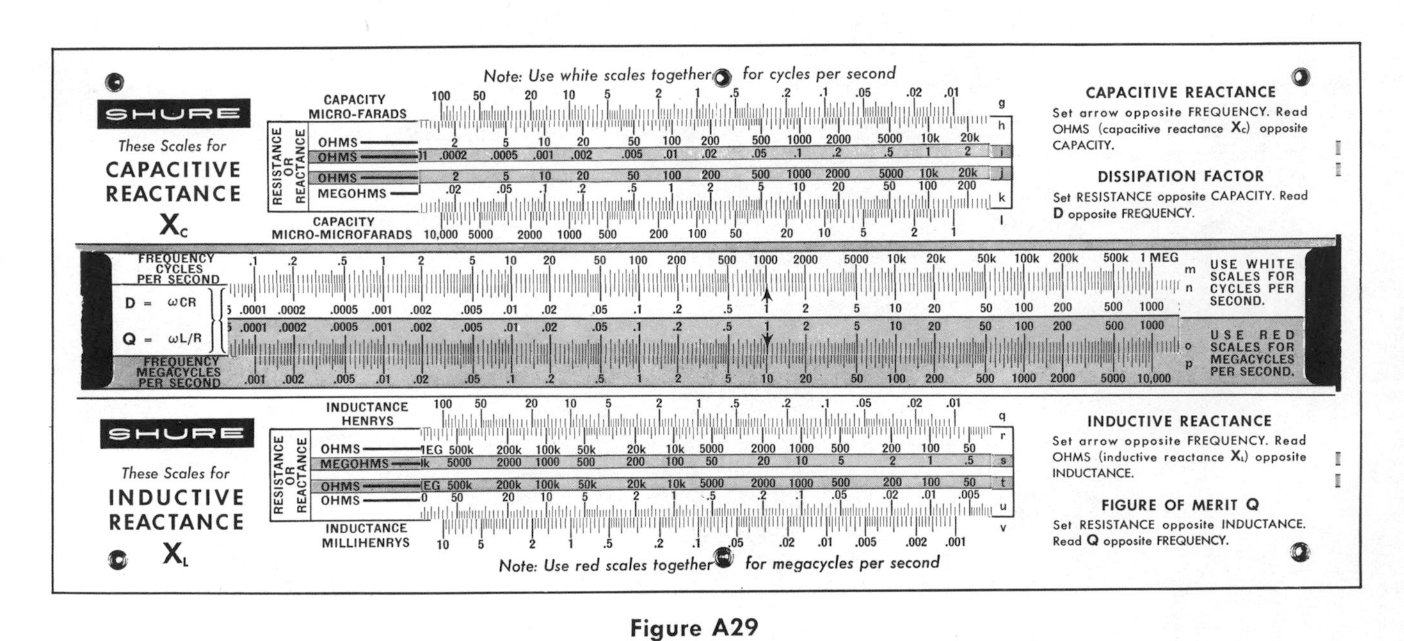

Figure A29

Reverse side of the slide rule illustrated in Figure A28. (Courtesy of Shure Brothers, Inc.)

1.5 microhenrys equals 0.0015 millihenrys. Set 0.0015 on scale *e* to 35 micro-microfarads on scale *d*. Read 22 mc at the arrow on scale *f*.

The other side of the reactance slide rule is illustrated in Figure A29. It has six scales that are identified as *g, h, i, j, k, l, m, n, o, p, q, r, s, t, u,* and *v*. Scale *g* is calibrated in microfarads. Scales *h* through *k* are calibrated in ohms or megohms. Scale *l* is calibrated in micro-microfarads. Scale *q* is calibrated in henrys. Scales *r* through *u* are calibrated in ohms or megohms. Scale *v* is calibrated in millihenrys.

Let us consider a practical example of inductance calculation. In the design of a grid transformer for a microphone with 35 ohms output impedance, find the inductance value for the primary of a transformer, if the primary reactance is to equal the microphone impedance at 50 cps. In other words, X_L is assigned a value of 35 ohms at 50 cps. Set the arrow on scale *n* to 50 cps on scale *m*. Opposite 35 ohms on scale *r*, read 0.11 henry on scale *q*. Here is another practical problem: Determine the value of a bypass capacitor for a 2500-ohm cathode resistor in an amplifier which is to have a substantially flat response down to 30 cps. Assume that the reactance of the capacitor must be equal to 0.1 the value of the resistance. In other words, $X_c = 250$ ohms. Set the arrow on scale *n* to 30 cps on scale *m*. Opposite 250 ohms on scale *h*, read 21 microfarads on scale *g*.

This type of specialized slide rule also provides readings of *Q* on the *n* and *o* scale, and *D* (dissipation factor) values also on the *n* and *o* scale. Recall that $Q = X_L/R$. Similarly, $D = R/X_C$, or $D = \omega CR$. It is evident that a specialized slide rule is more convenient than a generalized slide rule for solution of problems within specific areas. Fewer manipulations are required, and the scales are easier to read because they are calibrated in electrical values.

BIBLIOGRAPHY

Aerovox Research Worker, Aerovox Corp., New Bedford, Massachusetts, February–March 1956, vol. 26.

Assembly and Operating Manual B-10, Paco Electronics Co., Inc., Long Island, New York, pp. 2–5.

Basic Electricity, U. S. Bureau of Naval Personnel, Washington, D. C., Dover Publications, 1960.

Basic Electricity, Howard W. Sams & Co., Inc., Indianapolis, Indiana, 1959.

Basic Electronics, U. S. Bureau of Naval Personnel, Washington, D. C., Dover Publications, 1963.

Basic Theory and Applications of Electron Tubes, U. S. Departments of the Army and Air Force, Washington, D. C., 1962.

Belevitch, V., "Summary of the History of Circuit Theory," *Proc. I.R.E.,* vol. 50, p. 848, May 1962.

Bleaney, B. I., *Electricity and Magnetism,* Oxford University Press, New York, 1957, pp. 66–72.

Butterfield, Herbert, *et al., A Short History of Science: A Symposium,* Doubleday & Company, Inc., Garden City, New York, 1959.

Capacitor, Cornell-Dubilier Electric Corp., South Plainfield, New Jersey, April, 1958; March–April, 1960.

"Charles Proteus Steinmetz," *IEEE Spectrum,* vol. 2, pp. 82–95, April 1965.

"Clip-on DC Milliammeter, Probes; Electronic Test Instruments," *Hewlett-Packard Catalog No. 25,* 1965, p. 136.

Cobine, J. D., "The Development of Gas Discharge Tubes," *Proc. I.R.E.,* vol. 50, p. 970, May 1962.

Conwell, E. M., "Properties of Silicon and Germanium," *Proc. I.R.E.,* vol. 46, p. 1281, June 1958.

Crombie, A. C., "Helmholtz," *Scientific American,* vol. 198, p. 94, March 1958.

Crow, Leonard R., *Learning Electricity and Electronics Experimentally,* Universal Scientific Co., Inc., 1949, pp. 189–194.

"Current, Voltage, and Power Relations in Series Circuits," *Radar Circuit Analysis,* Department of the Air Force, AF Manual 52-8, 1960, pp. 2.10–2.12.

Dantzig, Tobias, *Number, The Language of Science,* The Macmillan Co., New York, 1954.

"D-C Voltage Measurement," *Instruction Manual, Model 360,* B&K Manufacturing Co., Chicago, 1962, pp. 5–8.

"D-C Voltage Measurements," *Operator's Manual, Volt-Ohm-Milliammeter 260,* Simpson Electric Co., Chicago, 1964, pp. 11–14.

"Direct-Current Circuits," *Radar Electronic Fundamentals,* Bureau of Ships, Navy Department, T.O.16-1-195, 1944, pp. 7–13.

DeFrance, J. J., *General Electronics Circuits,* Holt, Rinehart and Winston, Inc., New York, 1963.

De Ville, Eric, *Electricity,* Penguin Books, Ltd., Harmondsworth, Middlesex, England, 1955.

DuBridge, Lee A., "Science—The Endless Adventure," *Bulletin of the Atomic Scientists,* vol. 13, p. 74, March 1957.

Dull, Charles E., H. Clark Metcalfe, and John E. Williams, "Resistances in Series-parallel Combinations—Simple Networks," *Modern Physics,* Holt, Rinehart and Winston, Inc., New York, 1960, pp. 432–434.

Easteal, E. R., "Making the Most of Technical Periodicals," *Radio, Electronics and Communications,* vol. 19, p. 32, October 1, 1964.

"Electric Circuits," *Encyclopedia Americana,* vol. 10, p. 74, 1964.

"Electrical Quantities," *Radar Circuit Analysis,* Department of the Air Force, 1960, pp. 2.5–2.6.

"Electricity, Conduction of," *Encyclopedia Britannica,* pp. 192–209, 1964.

"Electricity, Direct-Current Circuits," *Encyclopedia Britannica,* p. 137, 1964.

"Electricity, Interpreting the Law of Circuits," *Compton's Pictured Encylopedia,* vol. 4, pp. 223–224, 1946.

Escoffery, C. A., *First Principles of Semiconductors,* International Rectifier Corporation Engineering Handbook, 1961, pp. 7–24.

Eves, Howard, and Carroll V. Newsom, *An Introduction to the Foundations and Fundamental Concepts of Mathematics,* Holt, Rinehart and Winston, Inc., New York, 1957.

Feinberg, G., and H. Goldhaber, "Conservation Laws," *Scientific American,* vol. 209, p. 36, October 1963.

Ford, Kenneth W., "Magnetic Monopoles," *Scientific American,* vol. 209, p. 122, December 1963.

Gardner, Eugene, *et al.,* "Mesons Produced by the Cyclotron," *Science,* vol. 3, p. 191, February 24, 1950.

Ghirardi, A. A., and J. E. Dines, *Radio and Television Receiver Circuitry and Operation,* Holt, Rinehart and Winston, Inc., New York, 1965.

Gilfillan, S. C., "Who Invented It?", *Scientific Monthly,* vol. 25, p. 529, December 1927.

Gregg, R. Q., H. E. Hammond, and R. H. Frost, "Precision of Measurements," *A Manual of Electrical Measurements,* Addison-Wesley Press, Inc., Reading, Massachusetts, 1950.

Hawkes, H. E., W. A. Luby, and F. C. Touton, "Theory of Quadratic

Equations," *Second Course In Algebra,* The Athenaeum Press, New York, 1918, pp. 168–176.

Herrington, Donald, and Stanley Meacham, *Handbook of Electronic Tables and Formulas,* Howard W. Sams & Co., Inc., Indianapolis, Indiana, 1964, pp. 52–58.

Hirst, A. W., *Electricity and Magnetism,* Blackie & Son, Ltd., London, 1959, pp. 70–75.

Hodgman, Charles D., "Dimensional Formulae," *Handbook of Chemistry and Physics,* Chemical Rubber Publishing Co., 28th ed., 1944, p. 2231.

"I.R.E. Standards on Letter Symbols," *Proc. I.R.E.,* vol. 45, p. 1140, August 1957.

"I.R.E. Standards on Solid-State Devices; Definition of Superconductive Electronic Terms," *Proc. I.R.E.,* vol. 50, p. 451, April 1962.

Keller, A. C., "Relays and Switches," *Proc. I.R.E.,* vol. 50, p. 932, May 1962.

"Kirchhoff's Current Law," *Basic Electricity,* Howard W. Sams & Co., Inc., Indianapolis, Indiana, 1959, pp. 24–26.

"Leclanché Dry Batteries," *"Eveready" Battery Applications and Engineering Data,* Union Carbide Co., pp. 15–19.

Lindsay, R. B., "Concept of Energy in Mechanics," *Scientific Monthly,* vol. 85, p. 188, October 1957.

Lissman, H. W., "Electric Location by Fishes," *Scientific American,* vol. 208, p. 50, March 1953.

Marsten, Jesse, "Resistors, A Survey of the Evolution of the Field," *Proc. I.R.E.,* vol. 50, p. 920, May 1962.

Matthias, B. T., "Superconductivity," *Scientific American,* vol. 197, p. 92, November 1957.

Maxwell, E., and Myron Strongin, "Filamentary Structure in Superconductors," *Physical Review Letters,* vol. 10, p. 212, March 15, 1963.

McNish, A. G., "The Basis of Our Measuring System," *Proc. I.R.E.,* vol. 47, p. 636, May 1959.

"Measuring D-C Volts," *Instruction Manual, Model 630,* Triplett Electrical Instrument Co., pp. 6–7.

"Nobel Prize in Physics," *Physics Today,* vol. 10, p. 16, January 1957.

Orr, William, "Resistors in Series Parallel," *The Radio Handbook, Editors and Engineers,* pp. 26–30, 1959.

"Papyrology," *Encyclopedia Britannica,* vol. 17, p. 242, 1964.

"Parallel Circuit," *Radio Technician 3C,* Bureau of Naval Personnel, 1943, pp. 3–6.

"Parallel Circuits," *Radar Electronic Fundamentals,* Bureau of Ships, 1944, pp. 9–10.

Petritz, Richard L., "Contributions of Materials Technology to Semiconductor Devices," *Proc. I.R.E.,* vol. 50, p. 1025, May 1962.

Podolsky, Leon, "Capacitors," *Proc. I.R.E.,* vol. 50, p. 924, May 1962.

Principles of Electricity Applied to Telephone and Telegraph Work, 1953, American Telephone and Telegraph Co., pp. 5–12.

Quantum Electronics Issue, *Proc. I.R.E.,* vol. 51, January 1963.

Quinn, A. K., "Parallel Resistance Shortcut," *Electronics World,* vol. 66, p. 84, December 1961.

"Resistance," *The Radio Amateur's Handbook,* American Radio Relay League, 1965, pp. 18–20.

Risse, Joseph A., *Know Your VOM-VTVM,* Howard W. Sams & Co., Inc., Indianapolis, Indiana, 1963, pp. 70–71.

Rosenthal, Evelyn B., *Understanding the New Mathematics,* Fawcett Publications, Inc., Greenwich, Connecticut, 1965.

Salpeter, J. E., "On the Nature of the Electron," *IEEE Spectrum,* vol. 2, p. 171, March 1965; vol. 2, p. 96, April 1965.

Schroeder, Henry, *History of Electric Light,* Smithsonian Institution, vol. 76, pp. 1–43, August 15, 1943.

Segall, B., "Fermi Surface of Aluminum," *Physical Review,* vol. 131, p. 121, July 1, 1963.

"Series-Parallel Combination," *Elementary Mathematics and Electricity,* Naval Training Schools, TAM-747, pp. 9–14.

Silsbee, F. B., "The Ampere," *Proc. I.R.E.,* vol. 47, p. 643, May 1959.

Steinmetz, Carl Heinrich, *Alternating Current Phenomena,* The W. J. Johnston Co., New York, 1897.

Still, Alfred, *Soul of Amber,* Murray-Hill Books, Inc., New York, 1945.

Still, Alfred, *Soul of Lodestone,* Murray-Hill Books, Inc., New York, 1946.

Stone, Marshall, "The Revolution in Mathematics," *The American Mathematical Monthly,* vol. 68, p. 715, October 1961.

Sutton, Graham, ed., *The World Around Us,* Collier Books, New York.

Teasdale, H., and E. C. Walton, *Electro-Technology for National Certificate,* The English Universities Press Ltd., 1947, pp. 47–48, 84–86.

"The New Type 1432 Decade Resistors," *General Radio Experimenter,* vol. 26, June 1951.

Transistor Issue, *Proc. I.R.E.,* vol. 46, June 1958.

Transistors, Introduction to Electronics, United States Bureau of Naval Personnel, 1963, p. 63.

"Units, Constants, and Conversion Factors," *Reference Data for Engineers,* 3rd ed., Federal Telephone and Radio Corp., 1949, pp. 22–27.

Wannier, Gregory H., "The Nature of Solids," *Scientific American,* vol. 187, p. 39, December 1952.

Whitmore, Charles E., "The Language of Science," *Scientific Monthly,* vol. 80, p. 185, March 1955.

"Wiring Materials," *Electrical Wiring,* Departments of the Army and the Air Force, TM5-760, 1957, pp. 15–30.

ANSWERS TO QUESTIONS

CHAPTER 1

1) *c* 3) *c* 5) *d* 7) *b* 9) *b*
2) *d* 4) *a* 6) *a* 8) *d* 10) *a*

CHAPTER 2

1) *c* 3) *d* 5) *a* 7) *d* 9) *c*
2) *b* 4) *a* 6) *a* 8) *c* 10) *c*

CHAPTER 3

1) *d* 3) *a* 5) *b* 7) *b* 9) *b*
2) *d* 4) *c* 6) *d* 8) *c* 10) *c*

CHAPTER 4

1) *d* 3) *b* 5) *c* 7) *d* 9) *c*
2) *b* 4) *a* 6) *a* 8) *c* 10) *a*

CHAPTER 5

1) *a* 3) *b* 5) *a* 7) *c* 9) *b*
2) *a* 4) *d* 6) *b* 8) *c* 10) *d*

CHAPTER 6

1) *c* 3) *b* 5) *d* 7) *b* 9) *c*
2) *d* 4) *a* 6) *c* 8) *a* 10) *d*

CHAPTER 7

1) *c* 3) *d* 5) *d* 7) *c* 9) *a*
2) *a* 4) *a* 6) *d* 8) *c* 10) *c*

CHAPTER 8

1) *c* 3) *b* 5) *d* 7) *b* 9) *d*
2) *d* 4) *c* 6) *d* 8) *d* 10) *d*

CHAPTER 9

1) *a* 3) *b* 5) *d* 7) *b* 9) *d*
2) *b* 4) *b* 6) *d* 8) *c* 10) *b*

CHAPTER 10

1) *b* 3) *a* 5) *d* 7) *c* 9) *b*
2) *a* 4) *d* 6) *d* 8) *a* 10) *d*

CHAPTER 11

1) *b* 3) *b* 5) *d* 7) *b* 9) *a*
2) *d* 4) *c* 6) *c* 8) *d* 10) *b*

CHAPTER 12

1) *d* 3) *b* 5) *b* 7) *d* 9) *d*
2) *c* 4) *a* 6) *b* 8) *a* 10) *c*

CHAPTER 13

1) *c* 3) *a* 5) *a* 7) *d* 9) *d*
2) *d* 4) *d* 6) *c* 8) *b* 10) *c*

CHAPTER 14

1) *c* 3) *d* 5) *b* 7) *b* 9) *a*
2) *b* 4) *c* 6) *c* 8) *b* 10) *a*

CHAPTER 15

1) *b* 3) *c* 5) *c* 7) *c* 9) *d*
2) *a* 4) *a* 6) *b* 8) *a* 10) *d*

CHAPTER 16

1) *b* 3) *d* 5) *a* 7) *d* 9) *c*
2) *a* 4) *d* 6) *a* 8) *b* 10) *a*

CHAPTER 17

1) *c* 3) *d* 5) *a* 7) *c* 9) *a*
2) *a* 4) *c* 6) *d* 8) *c* 10) *c*

CHAPTER 18

1) *c* 3) *c* 5) *d* 7) *c* 9) *a*
2) *a* 4) *b* 6) *d* 8) *d* 10) *b*

CHAPTER 19

1) *d* 3) *d* 5) *a* 7) *a* 9) *b*
2) *c* 4) *b* 6) *b* 8) *d* 10) *a*

CHAPTER 20

1) *b* 3) *c* 5) *b* 7) *d* 9) *a*
2) *a* 4) *c* 6) *a* 8) *b* 10) *c*

CHAPTER 21

1) *b* 3) *a* 5) *a* 7) *c* 9) *c*
2) *c* 4) *d* 6) *b* 8) *b* 10) *b*

CHAPTER 22

1) *c* 3) *d* 5) *d* 7) *c* 9) *d*
2) *b* 4) *a* 6) *b* 8) *b* 10) *a*

CHAPTER 23

1) *c* 3) *b* 5) *c* 7) *d* 9) *c*
2) *b* 4) *d* 6) *a* 8) *b* 10) *a*

ANSWERS TO PROBLEMS

CHAPTER 1

1) $f/2$.
2) $f/25$.
3) 2 units.
4) ¼ unit.
5) 5 ohms.
6) 15 volts.
7) 28.3×10^{27} electrons.
8) 13,750 volts.
9) 2 farads.
10) 2200 lbs, approx.
11) 80 electrons.
12) 7.65×10^{-5} in./sec, approx.
13) ⅙ amp.
14) 0.102 amp, approx.
15) 4.42 ft-lb, approx.
16) 186 miles, approx.
17) 4.7×10^{-8} cm, approx.
18) 6.24×10^{19} electrons.

CHAPTER 2

1) 1.017790 volts.
2) 5.9×10^{7} meters/sec, approx.
3) 2.2×10^{-15} ft-lb, approx.
4) 1 amp.
5) 0.24 calorie.
6) 1000 mhos.
7) 3 HP.
8) 585 watts per sec.
9) 4680 watt-hours.
10) 136.89 ohms.
11) 13,750 watt-hours.
12) 585 watts.
13) 150 candles.
14) 0.001 microfarad.
15) 60×10^{-6} mc.
16) 1500 mv.
17) 1 microwatt.
18) 1 microvolt.

CHAPTER 3

1) 0.274 ohms, approx.
2) 100 cm.
3) 1.05 watts per sec, approx.
4) No. 18 is closest.
5) 66.2 mils, approx.
6) No. 12 is closest.
7) 12,950 sq m.
8) 11 microamps.
9) Twice as many.
10) 7.1×10^{12} holes, approx.
11) The current is halved.
12) The resistivity is theoretically unchanged.
13) 12,500 volts versus 500 volts.
14) 0.182 in., approx.

CHAPTER 4

1) 2.1 ohms.
2) 10 ohms.
3) I = 1 amp; $R_1 = 2$ ohms; $R_2 = 4$ ohms.
4) 1 ohm.
5) 0.25 ohm.
6) 48,000 ohms; 2000 ohms.
7) 180 ohms.
8) 12 ohms; 4 ohms; 8 ohms.
9) 4 ohms.
10) 7.5 ohms, approx.
11) 1 ohm; 100 watts.
12) 3 ohms, approx.
13) 228 ohms, approx.
14) 0.01 ohm, approx.
15) 444 ohms; 27.75 watts.
16) 135 ohms.

CHAPTER 5

1) 6.67 amp, approx.
2) 11 amps.
3) 3.13 amp, approx.
4) 0.033 ohm, approx.
5) 2 ohms.
6) 0.0658 amp, approx.
7) 0.488 amp; 0.325 amp; 0.163 amp, approx.

8) 9.50 amps, approx.
9) 0.263 amp, approx.
10) 0.085 amp, approx.
11) 1.59 amps.
12) 2.4 amps.
13) 1.5 watts.
14) 1.3 ohms, approx.
15) Infinity.

CHAPTER 6

1) 188.1 volts, approx.
2) 50 volts.
3) 9000 ohms, or −900 ohms.
4) $I_T = 1$ amp; $R_2 = 3$ ohms; $V_1 = 38.1$ volts; $I_3 = 0.7$ amp; $R_3 = 1.286$ ohms, approx; $V_p = 0.9$ volt.
5) 39 watts.
6) $P_{R_1} = 38.1$ watts; $P_{R_2} = 0.27$ watt; $P_{R_3} = 0.629$ watt.
7) 0.342 volt, approx.
8) 125 ohms.
9) $I = 7E/300$ amp.
10) R_4 most; R_2 least.
11) 4.24 volts.
12) 4.5 ohms.
13) 6.75 volts; 0.368 volt.
14) 0.642 watt; 0.020 watt.
15) 56.3%; 3%.

CHAPTER 7

1) ¾ dyne.
2) 9 dynes.
3) 4.999998+ dynes.
4) 1000 amp-turns per meter.
5) 2000 amp-turns per meter.
6) 100 amp-turns.
7) 100 amp-turns.
8) 10,000 lines/m^2.
9) 20×10^7 lines/m^2.
10) 1000 amp-turns.
11) 10,000 lines/m^2.
12) 100 amp-turns; 1000 amp-turns.
13) 2 watts.
14) 1000 lines/cm^2.

CHAPTER 8

1) 5 lines.
2) 5000 amp-turns.
3) 5.55×10^{-2} lb.
4) 44.4 lb, approx.
5) 0.250 lb, approx.
6) 155 gauss.
7) 6.3 oersteds.
8) 2.10 oersteds.
9) 31.5 gilberts.
10) 10 kilolines.
11) 10,000.
12) 0.5 rel^{-1}.
13) 0.1875 rel.
14) 0.5/gauss $\times 10^4$.
15) 6.45×10^4 lines/$in.^2$.

CHAPTER 9

1) 1 volt.
2) 1 amp.
3) 1.356 ft-lb/sec, approx.
4) 100 amps.
5) 50 amps.
6) 0.335 HP, approx.
7) 74.5 volts, approx.
8) 60 watts.
9) 120 cycles per sec.
10) 7.07 volts.
11) 28.24 volts, approx.
12) 58.5 watts, approx.
13) 248.2 watts, approx.
14) No difference.
15) 100 cycles per sec.
16) 377 radians/sec, approx.

CHAPTER 10

1) 1.5×10^{-4} coulombs.
2) 6 volts.
3) 6 volts.
4) 18 volts.

5) 1 sec.
6) 2640 ohms, approx.
7) 44 ma, approx.
8) Zero.
9) 1.4 volts, approx.
10) 100 amps.
11) 10×10^{-12} sec.
12) 120 amp.
13) 44 ma, approx.
14) 22 ma, approx.
15) 1.29 VARS, approx.

CHAPTER 11

1) 100 mh.
2) 10^8 flux linkages.
3) 0.05 joule.
4) 0.1 microsec.
5) 0.1 microsec.
6) 0.1 microsec.
7) 7.14×10^{-13} joule, approx.
8) 2×10^{-26} joule, approx.
9) 0.31 amp, approx.
10) 1.86 ma, approx.
11) 1 microsec.
12) 25 hy, approx.
13) 12.5 joules, approx.
14) Zero.
15) 6 volts.

CHAPTER 12

1) 106.7 ohms; $106.7 < 20.7°$ ohms.
2) $1.095 < -20.7°$ amp; $2.190 < -20.7°$ amp.
3) $E_R = 109.5 < -20.7°$; $E_L = 41.3 < 69.3°$; $E_R = 219 < -20.7°$; $E_L = 82.6 < 69.3°$
4) 10 ma, approx.
5) 92 mc/sec, approx.
6) 44 ma, approx.
7) 1 mfd, approx.
8) 4540 ohms, approx.
9) 0.048 watt; 2.19 watts; 1.29 VARS, approx.
10) 1.5 watts.
11) 0.75, approx.
12) 0.75, approx.
13) $R = 41.4$ ohms; 642 μfarad, approx.
14) 26.5 millisec, approx.
15) 0.087 watt-sec, approx.
16) 0.087 watt-sec, approx.

CHAPTER 13

1) 27.38 watts, approx.
2) $L = 2.28$ hy; $R = 62.3$ ohms; $W = 27.38$ watts, approx.
3) 1.25 VARS.
4) $R = 9.23$ ohms; $C = 11.5$ μf; $P = 1.25$ VARS, approx.
5) 10 VARS.
6) 691 micromhos.
7) 3.92 millimhos.
8) $R = 97.6$ ohms; $C = 2.48$ μf, approx.
9) 0.986; same value.
10) The inductance value becomes 0.25 hy.
11) The capacitance value becomes 0.2 μf.
12) $0.0117 - j\,0.0441$; $P = 1.389$ watts.
13) 6844.5 ohms; $0.017 - j\,0.0441$ ma, approx.
14) 0.530, approx.

CHAPTER 14

1) $f = 1$ mc, approx.
2) 99.9 approx.
3) 10 kc, approx.
4) 1 mc; 49.9; 20 kc, approx.
5) 5 watts; 5 watts.
6) $-j$ 1000 volts.
7) 20 kc.
8) 1.76 μf; 754 ohms, approx.
9) 2.88 watts, approx.
10) 1.44 watts, approx.
11) 0.867 mc.
12) 0.276 cycles.

13) 0.999 mc.
14) An infinite sequence.
15) Imaginary.

CHAPTER 15

1) 0.71 mc, approx.
2) 0.949 mc, approx.
3) 1.02 mc, approx.
4) 1; 14.1 ma, approx.
5) unity.
6) 991 ohms, approx.
7) 0.71 mc.
8) 20 mv, approx.
9) 0.5, approx.
10) 0.181 volt.
11) 4 volts, approx.
12) 56.3 mw, approx.
13) 31.9 mw, approx.
14) 707 ohms; 0.7, approx.

CHAPTER 16

1) 58.5 volts.
2) 234 volts.
3) 250 ohms.
4) The ratio is always unity.
5) Tap at 0.316 the total number of turns.
6) $P = 2.5$ mw.
7) 1170 amps.
8) 83.3 percent, approx.
9) 66.6 to 1.
10) 1 to 66.6, approx.
11) 173 mh, approx.
12) Zero.
13) 1 mh.
14) 0.0103 percent, approx.
15) 1.96 volts, approx.

CHAPTER 17

1) 2000 dynes.
2) 0.00177 lb.
3) 0.0045 lb, approx.
4) 788 dynes, approx.
5) 5 lb-ft.
6) 3.42 kw, approx.
7) 217.8 volts.
8) 40 watts, approx.
9) 82.9 percent, approx.
10) 0.46 HP, approx.
11) 3.05 HP, approx.
12) 3600 rpm.
13) Speed = 656 rpm; efficiency = 77.5 percent; torque = 25 lb-ft, approx.
14) Speed = 810 rpm; efficiency = 82.5 percent; torque = 116 lb-ft, approx.
15) 100 rpm.

CHAPTER 18

1) 5 microwatts.
2) 58,000 ohms.
3) Zero ohms.
4) 599.998 megohms.
5) 0.001 ohm, from a practical standpoint.
6) 10 watts.
7) 1.36 volts, approx.
8) 100 megohms.
9) ± 5 volts; 112 to 122 volts.
10) ± 1 volt; 0.5 to 2.5 volts.
11) To half of full scale.
12) To ⅔ of full scale.
13) 3000 ohms.
14) 350 microamps.
15) 750 ohms.

CHAPTER 19

1) 52.7 volts, approx.
2) 31.2 volts, approx.
3) 3 volts.
4) 2 percent.
5) 4 percent.
6) 10 db.
7) 20 db.
8) 10–1; 100–1.
9) 152.1 watts, approx.

10) 175.5 watts.
11) Zero.
12) No difference.
13) 1.73 watts, approx.
14) 60 watts.

CHAPTER 20

1) 10.
2) 5.
3) No change.
4) 10,000 ohms.
5) Infinite.
6) 1000 micromhos.
7) 500 microamps.
8) 10,000 ohms.
9) 10,000 ohms.
10) 1 watt.
11) 20 watts.
12) 6.67 ma, approx.
13) −2 volts.
14) −4 volts.

CHAPTER 21

1) 20 micro-microcoulombs.
2) 10–1.
3) 250 mv.
4) −40 ohms.
5) 50 mw.
6) 1 ma.
7) 0.97.
8) 100.
9) 19.
10) 0.497.
11) 20 mw.
12) 140 microwatts.
13) 0.99, approx.
14) 99 percent.

CHAPTER 22

1) 115.8 volts, approx.
2) 66.7 volts, approx.
3) 23.8 μh; 0.0021 μf, approx.
4) 53.1 μh; 106.1 $\mu\mu$f, approx.
5) 0.477 μh; 2.66 $\mu\mu$f, approx.
6) 21.7 μh; 0.0019 μf, approx.
7) 190,000.
8) 10.85 μh; 0.0038 μf, approx.
9) 0.318 of peak.
10) 0.634 of peak.
11) 491.4 volts.
12) 0.02; 2 percent.

CHAPTER 23

1) 3/13 amp.
2) 6/13 amp.
3) 15/52 amp.
4) 2 amps.
5) 5/11 amp.
6) 27.5 ohms.
7) $10 - j5$ ohms.
8) 11 ohms.
9) 0.988, approx.
10) 10.71 ohms, approx.

INDEX